cm
4
5
6
7
8
9
10
11
12
13
14
15
16
17
18
19
20
21
22
23

Trees of Southern Africa

KEITH COATES PALGRAVE

Trees of Southern Africa

in association with
R B DRUMMOND
Keeper of the National Herbarium Salisbury

Edited by
Dr E J MOLL

Photography by
PAUL and MEG COATES PALGRAVE

Tree drawings by
TERRY DUGGAN

C. Struik Publishers
Cape Town

C Struik (Pty) Ltd, Oswald Pirow Street, Foreshore, Cape Town
First edition 1977
Second Impression 1981
Third, updated impression 1983
Copyright © Keith Coates Palgrave

ISBN 0 86977 081 0

Design by Wim Reinders
Leaf drawings by Margo L Branch
Lithographic reproduction by Unifoto (Pty) Limited Cape Town
Photoset by McManus Bros (Pty) Limited Cape Town
Printed and bound by Tien Wah Press (Pte) Ltd.

Frontispiece: *Breonadia microcephala.* Matumi

AUTHOR'S NOTE
All the photographs in this book were taken by Paul and Meg Coates Palgrave, with the exception of the following:

Keith Cooper: *Xymalos monospora* (bark)
J. M. J. Dumoulin: *Schotia afra*
E. J. Moll: *Cunonia capensis, Mackaya bella, Podalyria calyptrata, Podocarpus latifolius* (strobilus), *Raphia australis, Rhizophora mucronata.*
Keith Coates Palgrave: *Alsophila dregei, Atalaya alata, Buxus natalensis, Cassipourea gummiflua, Combretum paniculatum, Cryptocarya wyliei, Englerodaphne pilosa, Erythrina humeana, Gerrardina foliosa, Harungana madagascariensis, Loxostylis alata, Millettia grandis, Mimusops caffra, Oxyanthus pyriformis, Pappea capensis, Portulacaria afra, Rhigozum zambesiacum, Urera tenax, Voacanga thouarsii*
D. C. H. Plowes: *Welwitschia mirabilis*

Frean, J. M.
Funke, Erich and Minnie
Gawith, Toby
Gettliffe, R.
Gluckman, De Beer, Margoles Partnership
Godlonton, Christopher
Goodwin, M. G. N.
Gordon, Huntley Herbert
Graaff, J. de V.
Graham, A. W.
Grainger, Col D. H. (O. B. E., K.St.J,
    F. R. G. S.)
Gubbins Library, Univ. of Witwatersrand
Hall, Jimmie
Hall, M. M.
Hartley, David
Hatty, Miss Karen
Hill, L. J.
Hill, Richard
Hillstead, W. R. S.
Higgs, Joan
Hofmeyr, Dr J. M.
Hojem, Lesley Margaret
Hosken, F. W.
Houston, Douglas
Hunt Botanical Library, Pittsburgh, U.S.A.
Hutton, J. M. and G. I.
Hyde, M. J.
Jeffery, R. G.
Jex, W. F. C.
Johnson, Dennis
Johnstone, A. H.
Johnstone, Carole and Peter
Joubert, Dr J. M. L.
Joubert, Y. E.
Kassier, Prof. W. E.
Keynes, Quentin
Kroon, Wendy
Kynnersley-Browne, Mrs R. S.
Lamont Smith, D.
Lee, Derek
Leibel, Miss W. A.
Le May, B. C.
Ley, Joyce J.
Lightfoot, Chris
Line, John
Lombard, Jurie and Beverley
Louw, J. A.
Lyons, Eliot
Lyttelton Manor High School
MacGregor, Dr J. M.
Marchand, B. C. J.
Marnie, Miss H. M.
McCay, P. W.
McGregor, Mrs L. C.
McIntosh A. R. D. (Pty) Limited
Maras, William
Mellish, Francis
Mentz, Miss E. G.
Michell, Andrew
Middelmann, H. W.
Miller, V. S.
Missouri Botanical Garden Library
Moore, A. F.
Morrison, Angus

Mullins, Mrs D. M.
Murray, Miss C. K.
Natal Parks, Game and Fish Preservation
    Board
Nagel, Mrs Hildegard
Nathan, Chief Justice and Mrs C. J. M.
National Archives of Rhodesia
Neethling, Dr P. G. S.
Nicholson, Reginald Merriman
Nixon, Miss K. M.
Noel, Mrs J. N.
Nolte, Carel A.
O'Brien, Sidney Martin
Patz, Dr and Mrs I. N.
Pauw, Mrs Lesnè A.
Pellatt, Thomas M.
Pepler, David
Pickard, F.
Pitchford, Sigrid Johanna
Ploger, Rosemarie
Potgieter, Zim and Joan
Press, Sydney
Prevôst, M. J.
Pringle, V. L.
Reilly, Ted and Liz
Renny, A. T.
Reynolds, Mrs G. W.
Rissik, G. A.
Rissik, Ulrich
Robarts, W. E.
Robin, G. F.
Robson, T. R.
Savage, Inez Doreen
Scheepers, Jack
Scott-Barnes, Ian
Sinclair, Colin and family
Sinclair, Mr and Mrs J. M.
Slogrove, A. E.
Stead, Mr and Mrs W. H.
Stekhoven, Ann and Jan
Stretton, Sandy
Struik, Mrs J. W.
Teare, Dr A. J.
Testi, E. E.
Thöle, Lyle F.
Thompson, Miss M. F.
Tilney, M. F.
Townsend, Trevor
Traill, J. C.
Van der Schijff, Prof. H. P.,
    Universiteit Pretoria
Van Zyl, H. S.
Venter, Jacomina Susanna
Von Puttkamer, Eric C. I.
Wasserfall, Molly
Weinberg, Mr and Mrs P.
Wentzel, Durandt
Whytock, I. Y. S.
Williamson, Mary
Wilson, A. A. T.
Wilson, Derric Harmen
Witney, Peter
Woolcock, Michael Walter
Zway, Mr and Mrs S. D.

Contents

Acknowledgements

In writing a book such as this encouragement, assistance, and advice have been received from many people. I offer most sincere thanks to the Director, and his staff, of the Botanical Research Institute in Pretoria, South Africa, and to the Officer-in-Charge, and his staff, of the National Herbarium in Salisbury, Rhodesia; in both cases every facility was placed at my disposal. I would also like to express my gratitude for the invaluable help and encouragement received from Dr L. E. Codd of the Botanical Research Institute, Pretoria; Dr J. P. Rourke, Curator of the Compton Herbarium, Cape Town; and Mr R. B. Drummond, Keeper of the National Herbarium, Salisbury, who, besides all his other help, finally checked the manuscript. However, it must be made clear that these people are in no way responsible for any errors in this book and only I can answer for those that remain.

For their outstanding contribution to this book I would like to thank most particularly Meg and Paul Coates Palgrave who worked untiringly on the project; their help and enthusiasm have been immeasurable. Their daughter and son, Shirley and Tony, have also been of tremendous help in the preparation of this book and together with their father drew all the fruits other than those of the *Acacia* pods.

The production of this book would have been impossible without the willing and often outstanding help from all the many people in the field, both in South Africa and in Rhodesia. To list all these people individually would be a mammoth task and to attempt to single out a few, a most invidious exercise. Simply let it be said that our most grateful thanks go out to all these people; without their help this undertaking would have been impossible.

I owe a special word of thanks to Mrs Sally Milne who typed the greater part of the manuscript with remarkable skill and accuracy and to Mrs Dorothy Gilbert-Green who completed the task with equal efficiency. My thanks are also due to Mrs Phillida Simons who worked through the text checking consistency and style, and to Olive Anderson who drew the fruits of all the indigenous species of *Acacia*.

Finally I would like to thank the many people who read through the text and offered their helpful comments:

Prof. E. A. C. L. E. Schelpe; Drs L. E. Codd, R. A. Dyer, K. D. Gordon-Gray,
D. J. B. Killick, O. A. Leistner, J. H. Ross, J. P. Rourke, H. R. Tölken,
A. van der Walt, I. C. Verdoorn, Mrs B. Jeppe and Messrs P. C. V. du Toit,
E. G. H. Oliver, R. G. Strey, J. V. van Greuning and F. White.

Keith Coates Palgrave 1977

I would like to express my gratitude to those who responded to my request in providing information included in this revision, in particular Messrs M.A.N. Müller, of the Windhoek Herbarium, and A.A. Gubb, of the McGregor Museum in Kimberley. I hope in future revisions to further refine the text so that, ultimately, it will be perfect.

Eugene Moll 1981

Introduction

This book describes and illustrates all the indigenous and many of the naturalised, non-indigenous species of trees at present known to occur in South Africa, Rhodesia, South West Africa, Botswana, Lesotho, Swaziland and Moçambique south of the Zambezi River. The first, and perhaps the most contentious question that arises is, 'What is a tree?' This is a very difficult, indeed impossible question to answer for 'a tree' is a popular concept and not a scientific entity. Authors have had to draw up their own criteria which can be applied when deciding which species to include and which to omit. There are, of course, the obvious 'trees' – tall specimens with comparatively large boles; it is the borderline cases which present the problems. In this book the widest interpretation has been given to the term 'tree', for it is the author's opinion that a low-growing plant, say 1 m in height but with a comparatively massive stem 30 cm or more in diameter, is just as much a tree as a plant 5 to 8 m tall but with many rather slender stems, each perhaps not more than 5 to 7 cm across. The evidence of any reputable collector who has recorded a specimen as a 'tree', even once, has been accepted. It would seem to be far wiser to include a few species which, strictly, should not be there than to omit one which a reader would expect to find in the book. The language has been kept as simple as possible and should be fairly easily understood by the layman; the use of botanical terms has been reduced to the minimum and those that are unavoidable are explained in the illustrated glossary.

Keys

All keys must be considered only as guides, for probably no key has yet been produced that will guarantee success. Botanical classification is based on the structure of the reproductive organs, i.e. the flowers and fruits, but to use these characters in a key requires not only a microscope but also detailed botanical knowledge and training. In this book these details have been avoided and every effort has been made to limit the characters used to those which can be seen easily, only occasionally resorting to a 10× or 20× lens. As a result considerable problems arose when attempting to separate closely related genera and species.

In the introductory key vegetative characters have been used almost exclusively and in only a few instances has it been necessary to refer to fruits; recourse has not been made to flowers. In the other keys throughout the book leaf characters and geographical distribution have been used in the first instance but often reference to flower and fruit characters has been unavoidable. Flowers have a comparatively short life and, although fruits may persist for considerably longer – sometimes into the next season – or old fruits may be found under the tree, they, too, are often unavailable for study at any one time; even the leaves are frequently absent at certain times of the year. All this is regrettable and it will probably require a little patience on the part of the reader to assemble all the facts required for identification.

Although flowering and fruiting times are given in the text, this does not imply that flowers or fruits will always be found over the whole of these periods. The first date given is the earliest when flowers or fruits have been recorded; the later time being the last record. The actual time of flowering or fruiting varies, not only with habitat and from year to year, but from tree to tree depending on climatic conditions, rainfall, genetic variation and many other factors.

Classification and plant names

The basic unit of classification in the plant kingdom is the *species*, and no two species are exactly alike. Those which show a marked resemblance to one another are then grouped together into a *genus* and similar genera are then placed together in a *family*.

The only definitive names for plants are those accepted and governed by *The International Rules of Botanical Nomenclature*. This system aims at eliminating any confusion which might arise and indeed has arisen in the past. The oldest name is the valid one, and this often means various name-changes – confusing to the layman but of vital importance to the professional. The name of each species is made up of two parts – the name of the genus to which the plant belongs, followed by the specific name which is that of the actual species. For example, four different tree ferns occur in southern Africa and because they show marked affinities with one another they are all placed in the genus *Alsophila*. Each entity is then given its own specific name which clearly establishes it as a separate species – the common tree fern thus becomes *Alsophila dregei* and the others *Alsophila capensis*, *Alsophila manniana* and *Alsophila thomsonii*. Finally, to complete the picture and also to provide information important to the botanist, the name of the author – the person who first named the plant – is given next, although this is frequently abbreviated. Thus the full designation of the common tree fern becomes *Alsophila dregei* (Kunze) Tryon. In this case Kunze was the first person to describe the plant and he placed it in the genus *Cyathea*, calling it *Cyathea dregei*. Since then – very recently in fact – Tryon decided that it was better placed in the genus *Alsophila* but credit is still given to Kunze by placing his name in brackets.

In this book the method of stating the author's names, or their abbreviations, follows the suggestions set out in a draft *Index of Authors and Authors Abbreviations* recently distributed by the Royal Botanic Gardens, Kew; in many cases, therefore, these will not conform exactly with the citations used in either *Flora of Southern Africa* or *Flora Zambesiaca*. In this list a fair number of names are now spelt out in full (for example, E. G. Baker in place of Bak. f.) and it is felt that this would be more meaningful to, and also add interest for, the layman.

The first time a plant is referred to in writing, the entire name is spelt out, but references to it which follow immediately, or references to other species in the same genus, are given the initial letter only of the genus, followed by the specific name in full. Thus *Alsophila dregei* would become *A. dregei*, and *A. capensis* would refer to *Alsophila capensis*.

Within some species there may be further subdivisions into subspecies (subsp.) and/or varieties (var.). Subspecies are populations that show some differences from the original type but are not sufficiently different to justify a new species. Varieties are not as clearly defined as subspecies nor are they necessarily distinctly separate either ecologically or geographically, yet they do occur sufficiently frequently to rule out the possibility of being a chance freak or mutation. Some authors carry the fragmentation of the species even further into forms, but this has not been followed in the present work as it seems to be of doubtful value. In this book I have occasionally referred to two species as a single entity. My reason for doing so is that from the outward appearance of the two species it is very difficult to separate them unless one is an expert. My treatment here is for convenience and does not constitute a taxonomic judgement.

Synonyms

In some instances, immediately under the name of the tree, there will be found another name or names, in italics and in square brackets.. This is a *synonym* – a name which was applied to this tree in the past but which has now been superseded. These synonyms have been included to facilitate cross-reference between this book and other fairly recent publications on trees.

The arrangement used in this book

When working with thousands of plants it is obviously highly desirable to have them classified in some sort of sequence. Various workers have produced arrangements of the families and genera of plants placing them, in their opinion, in a natural or evolutionary order starting from the most primitive and leading to the most advanced. Opinions obviously differ as to the correct order. Two of the earlier systems of classification which are still widely used today are those of Bentham and Hooker, and Engler and Prantl. The *Flora Zambesiaca* follows the order suggested by Bentham and Hooker while the *Flora of Southern Africa* follows that of Engler and Prantl, nevertheless in this sphere work still progresses and new ideas have been published only recently. Any arrangement of this kind is primarily a matter of convenience and it is of little account which one is used. However, as the National Herbaria in Pretoria and in Salisbury are both arranged according to the system of Engler and Prantl it seems convenient and logical that this should also be followed with the families and genera in the present book. Within each genus the species are arranged alphabetically.

Tree numbers

The numbers from both the South African *National List of Trees,* and the Rhodesian *List of Trees, Shrubs and Woody Climbers* have been given for each species appearing on those lists; only the numbers officially recognised by the authors of these works have been used. If a species does not occur in one of the countries this absence is indicated by a dash; if a species does occur but has not been given a number on either one or the other, or both, of the lists, then a blank has been left. Should a number be allocated in the future the reader will be able to fill it in. It is strongly recommended that all interested persons should purchase a copy of each of these works, which are available from booksellers and are very inexpensive, for they contain not only the list in numerical order but also in alphabetical order which makes for easy cross-reference. Details of these works are:
The National List of Trees by B. de Winter & F. Von Breitenbach (J. L. van Schaik Bpk, Pretoria). *A List of Trees, Shrubs and Woody Climbers Indigenous or Naturalised in Rhodesia* by R. B. Drummond (as separate from *Kirkia* Vol. 10, Part 1, 1975: The Department of Printing and Stationery, Salisbury).

Exotic species

Exotic or non-indigenous species which are known to have become naturalised in one or more areas are mentioned and marked with an asterisk*. However, as far as these are concerned, it is very difficult to get a full picture of their prevalence and distribution as many collectors, on encountering them in the field, recognise them for what they are and so pass them by. Non-indigenous species are therefore seldom collected and official records remain incomplete.

Illustrations

(a) The leaf drawings
These drawings show each leaf in outline, the petiole (leaf-stalk), and how this joins the stem; the most important features are the general shape, the base, margin, apex and **13**

venation. The drawings are not to scale as large leaves have been reduced to fit into the allocated space. Small leaves have never been enlarged and in most cases a number of leaves have been drawn and some of the stem is also included. It was felt that little would be accomplished by giving scales, either figuratively or graphically, as these are always difficult to interpret. However, the description is always placed close to the drawing and a quick reference to it will give the exact size of the leaves and their degree of difference. It can be appreciated that in an area as vast and as diverse as that covered by this book, the variations within even a single species can be considerable. In preparing these leaf drawings care was taken in each case to select a good average leaf with characters which occurred most frequently over its range.

(b) Photographs
The drawings in the composite colour illustrations aim to give a valuable field impression of the tree, with close-up detail provided by natural material superimposed over it – a process devised specifically for this work. There are also close-up illustrations of flowers or fruits and habit illustrations when these are considered to be preferable. Black and white photographs have been used when it was felt that colour would serve no useful purpose.

The distribution maps

Each indigenous species is accompanied by a distribution map. These were prepared from official records lodged in the herbaria in Pretoria, Cape Town, Grahamstown, Durban and Salisbury. In only a very few cases have verbal accounts been accepted. There is no doubt that, perhaps in many instances, readers will have personal knowledge of a species occurring outside the area shown on the map; this can only mean that no collection has been made from that locality.It is earnestly suggested that in all such cases material should be collected and sent to the nearest herbarium for only in this way can an accurate picture of the distribution of the species be built up. On these maps the shading represents broad areas where collections have been correctly reported and recorded. Also, two types of arrows have been used: *(a)* a long arrow, always coming in from the sea and pin-pointing some isolated locality which might otherwise pass unnoticed; and *(b)* a short arrow placed in one of the northern countries – Angola, Zambia, Malawi and, occasionally, Moçambique north of the Zambezi River; these arrows indicate merely that the species is known to occur in that country. The direction of the arrow is also significant as it indicates that the species may have originated in the south and spread northwards, or that it seems more likely to have had its origins in central, west or north tropical Africa and has spread southwards.

Medicinal and poisonous uses of trees

To simple people the world over, folklore, superstition and fear of the unknown are part of everyday life and this is no different in Africa. To the rural African peoples, medicine means far more than the drug to cure a disease; it means also the poison to kill an enemy, the charm carried to ensure a safe journey, or witchcraft and magic with their influences, both good and evil. Some of the healing properties ascribed to parts of trees have been proven, as it has been that others are poisonous to a greater or lesser extent. However, it is certain that much of the healing and many of the cures claimed are due to faith, either in the doctor or in the reputation of the 'medicine'. Sometimes the use made of a particular part of a tree is associated with a certain property of that tree; for instance, one with milky latex might be used to increase lactation, either in domestic animals or in humans.

Even with the advance of western medicine and the establishment of dispensaries and clinics in rural areas, many African herbalists and witchdoctors continue to flourish, having set themselves up in peaceful opposition to their modern counterparts, or even in a complementary capacity, and drawing their custom from people impatient with the slow treatment they receive in the hospitals. Witchdoctors frequently interweave their medical treatments with magic – and this certainly is not confined to Africa.

The various medical uses of trees which are described in this book have been culled from many sources; it must be emphasised that no claims are made as to their effectiveness. There is no doubt that some of these medicines are very harmful and idle experimentation could prove dangerous.

Conservation and protection

Most of the countries in southern Africa have legislated against the indiscriminate removal or destruction of the natural flora.

In all the provinces of South Africa and in South West Africa the following general regulations apply, as pertaining to trees:

1. No person may pick a *protected* plant without a permit from the Administrator.
2. No person may pick any *indigenous* plant without the written permission of the owner of the land.
3. No person may pick any *indigenous* plant within 100 m of a public road without a permit issued by the Administrator.
4. No person may pick any *indigenous* plant in a nature reserve or in a game reserve unless he is the holder of a permit issued by the Administrator.
5. No person may convey any *protected* plant without either a permit issued by the Administrator or a document indicating that such plant was received from a person legally entitled to sell or donate such a plant.
6. No person may buy a *protected* plant except from a person lawfully selling it.
7. No person may receive as a gift a *protected* plant except from a person lawfully donating it.
8. A *protected* plant received as a gift must be accompanied by a document giving details as to the circumstances under which it was collected.
9. No person may export from the Territory any *protected* (in the Cape, any *indigenous*) plant unless he is the holder of a permit issued by the Administrator.

In addition Government Notice No. 5242 in the Government Gazette of 6 August 1976 includes a list of trees now given full State protection in South Africa. These protected trees are indicated in the text of this book.

In Rhodesia the new Parks and Wildlife Act was introduced in1975. This lays down that the conservation of flora (and fauna) on private land, apart from specially protected areas, now becomes the responsibility of the landowner and local conservation committees. In addition, the more sought-after species have been given extra protection and are listed in a special schedule; any species concerned in this book have been indicated in the text. Provision has been made for the issue of permits to collect these plants for scientific or other purposes, while permission to collect other species lies with the owner of the land, or, in the case of public land, with a designated official.

Common names

Botanical names are often difficult to grasp and remember and so common names have been included in this book. Previously some trees had many names, others had none, and often the same common name had been given to a number of different species. **15**

To dispel much of the confusion that has arisen, every tree in this book has been given an English common name, both for South Africa and Rhodesia. In addition all species that appeared in the recently revised *National List of Trees* have been given the Afrikaans common name from that list.

After considerable thought and discussion it was decided to omit all African vernacular names. Over the area covered by this book the number of languages and dialects is so vast that the list of names becomes unmanageable. Furthermore the task of checking all these in their own areas would be near impossible.

The common names that appear in this book have been drawn from two sources: an unpublished list by Paul and Meg Coates Palgrave, who have made a study of the subject, and the *National List of Trees* by Dr B. de Winter and F. von Breitenbach.

RECENT NAME CHANGES AND ADDITIONS

● Where a straight name change is involved the page number refers to the position of the previously known name, and usually this is then shown in italics as a synonym, in square brackets below the new name.

● Where a species has been added the page number refers to the place in the text where this would slot in.

● Where the addition of subspecies or varieties only is involved, the page number refers to the name of the main species.

CYATHEACEAE

p.41. Change to: CYATHEA Smith
[*ALSOPHILA* R. Br.]

p.41. Change to: **Cyathea capensis** (L.f.) Smith
[*Alsophila capensis* (L.f.) J. Smith]

p.41. Change to: **Cyathea dregei** Kunze
[*Alsophila dregei* (Kunze) Tryon]

p.42. Change to: **Cyathea manniana** Hook.
[*Alsophila manniana* (Hook.) Tryon]

p.43. Change to: **Cyathea thomsonii** Baker
[*Alsophila thomsonii* (Baker) Tryon]

MORACEAE

FICUS L.

This partial revision of the genus *Ficus* is based on recent works by Dr. C. C. Berg and Dr. J. V. van Greuning; their kind permission to use these name changes is acknowledged.

p.114. Change to: **Ficus abutilifolia** (Miq.) Miq.
[*F. soldanella* Warb.; *F. picta* T. R. Sim]

p.114. Change to: **Ficus bubu** Warb.
[*F. sp. no. 1* sensu Palgrave *Trees of Southern Africa*]
See note on p.114 under **Ficus sansibarica**

p.107. Change to: **Ficus lingua** Warb. ex De Wild. & Durand
[*F. depauperata* T. R. Sim]

p.118. Change to: **Ficus lutea** Vahl
[*F. vogelii* (Miq.) Miq.; *F. quibeba* Welw. ex Ficalho; *F. nekbudu* Warb.]

p.112. Add: **Ficus pygmaea** Welw. ex Hiern
Botswana, Caprivi Strip

p.119. Change to: **Ficus platyphylla** Delile
[*F. zambesiaca* Hutch.]

p.105. Change to: **Ficus sur** Forsk.
[*F. capensis* Thunb.; *F. mallotocarpa* Warb.]

p.110. Change to: **Ficus thonningii** Blume
[*F. burkei* (Miq.) Miq.; *F. petersii* Warb.; *F. rhodesiaca* Warb. ex Mildbr. & Burret]
In *Trees of Southern Africa, Ficus thonningii* was placed temporarily in a loose complex with *F. natalensis*. It is now separated away from the latter species, and the following brief pointers may help to identify the two spieces:

natalensis	thonningii
Leaf obovate, widest above the middle, tapering to the base	Leaf elliptic with more or less parallel sides, base square to narrowly lobed
Apex rounded to almost square	Apex tapering to abruptly tapering or acuminate

Leaf size varies considerably but leaves generally smaller, about 2,5 × 5,5 cm	Leaf size varies considerably but leaves generally larger, about 3 to 4 × 6,5 to 9 cm
Petiole shorter, up to 2 cm long	Petiole longer, up to 4 cm long

p.162.
            Add: After **NYCTAGINACEAE**
MESEMBRYANTHEMACEAE
STOEBERIA Dinter & Schwantes
Stoeberia beetzii (Dinter) Dinter & Schwantes   (S.A. no: 103,3)
— var. *arborescens* Friedr.

ROSACEAE
p. 210.   Add: **Cliffortia strobilifera** Murray   (S.A. no: 145,3)

LEGUMINOSAE
MIMOSOIDEAE
p.222.   **Albizia tanganyicensis** E. G. Baker
      Add: — subsp. *tanganyicensis* (the only subspecies to occur south of the Zambezi River)
p.248.   **Acacia reficiens** Wawra
para. 2, line 4, insert: only the typical subspecies, subsp. *reficiens* occurs south of the Cunene River.

PAPILIONOIDEAE
p.304.   Add: **Wiborgia mucronata** (L.f.) Druce   (S.A. no: 225,2)
p.304.   Add: 12A ASPALATHUS L.
              Aspalathus biedouwensis Dahlgr.   (S.A. no: 225,3)
p.306.   Add::   **Indigofera frutescens** L.   (S.A. no: 225,5)
p.308.   Add: **Psoralea aphylla** L.   (S.A. no: 225,8)

RUTACEAE
p.351.   Add: **Teclea rogersii** Mendonça   (Zimb. no: 400)

EUPHORBIACEAE
p.399. Change to: **Phyllanthus ovalifolius** Forsk.
              [*P. guineensis* Pax]
p.404.   Add: **Drypetes reticulata** Pax   (Zimb. no: 461/1)
              South Africa, Zimbabwe, Moçambique
p.417.   Add: **Croton madandensis** S. Moore   (Zimb. no: 479/1)
p.419.   Under **Croton scheffleri** Pax
      Delete: [*C. madandensis* S. Moore]

ANACARDIACEAE
p. 461. Change to: **Lannea schweinfurthii** (Engl.) Engl.
              [*L. stuhlmannii* (Engl.) Engl.; *L. stuhlmannii* (Engl.) Engl. var. *tomentosa* Dunkley]
p.461.   Add:: — var. *stuhlmannii* (Engl.) Kokwaro
              — var. *tomentosa* (Dunkley) Kokwaro
p.468. Change to: **Ozoroa insignis** Delile   (Zimb. no: 545)
              [*O. reticulata* (E. G. Baker) R. & A. Fernandes] p.471
      Add: — subsp. *reticulata* (E. G. Baker) Gillett
p.491.   Add: **Rhus vulgaris** Meikle   (Zimb. no: 560/1)
              Zimbabwe, Moçambique

OCHNACEAE
p.604.   Add::   **Ochna cyanophylla** N.K.B. Robson

p.608.   Under **Ochna schweinfurthiana** F. Hoffm.
          Delete: [*O. cyanophylla* N.K.B. Robson]

FLACOURTIACEAE
p.631.   **Homalium abdessammedii** Aschers. & Schweinf.
          Add;   — subsp. *abdessammedii* (Moçambique)
                          — subsp. *wildemannianum* (Gilg) Wild (Botswana, Zimbabwe, Caprivi Strip)

RHIZOPHORACEAE
p.657.   Add::   **Cassipourea euryoides** Alston   (Zimb. no: 762)
                          Zimbabwe east and south, Moçambique
p.657. Change to: **Cassipourea malosana** (Baker) Alston   (Zimb. no: 762/1)
                          [*C. congoensis* auct. non DC.; *C. gerrardii* (Schinz) Alston]
p.659. Change to: **Cassipourea gossweileri** Excell   (Zimb. no: 764)
                          [*C. sp. no. 1* sensu Palgrave *Trees of Southern Africa*]

COMBRETACEAE
p.665.   Add: **Combretum coriifolium** Engl. & Diels   (Zimb. no: 768/1)
                          Zimbabwe east, Moçambique
p.666. Change to: **Combretum schumannii** Engl.
                          [*C. engleri* Schinz]
p.670.   Add: **Combretum microphyllum** Klotzsch
                          This species is now separated away from *C. paniculatum* Vent. p.673
p.673.   **Combretum paniculatum** Vent.
          Delete: [*C. microphyllum* Klotzsch]
p.674.   Delete: Reference to subspecies
p.680.   **Terminalia brachystemma** Welw.
          Add.   — subsp. *brachystemma* (the only subspecies to occur south of the Zambezi River)

MYRTACEAE
p.692.   **Syzygium masukuense** (Baker) R.E. Fries
          Add: — subsp. *masukuense* (Zimbabwe central, Moçambique)
                          — subsp. *pachyphyllum* F. White. A tree of higher altitudes (Zimbabwe east, Moçambique)
p.693.   Add: **Syzygium owariense** (Beauv.) Benth.   (Zimb. no: 804)
                          Zimbabwe east, Moçambique
p.694.   Add: **Heteropyxis dehniae** Suesseng.
                          This species has now been separated away from **H. natalensis**
                          Heteropyxis natalensis Harvey
          Delete: [*H. dehniae* Suesseng.]
                          These two species can be separated on distribution:
                          H. dehniae — northern Transvaal, Zimbabwe, Moçambique
                          H. natalensis — Transvaal, Natal, Swaziland, Moçambique

MELASTOMATACEAE
p.696.   **Memecylon sansibaricum** Taub.
          Add: — var. *buchananii* (Gilg) A. & R. Fernandes (includes all the material south of the Zambezi River)

ARALIACEAE
p.700.   Add: **Cussonia arenicola** Strey   (S.A. no: 565,3)

APIACEAE
p.707. Change to: **Heteromorpha trifoliata** (Wendl.) Ecklon & Zeyher
                          [*H. arborescens* auct.]

SAPOTACEAE

p.733.   Add: **Manilkara nicholsonii** Van Wyk
                              Natal, Transkei

EBENACEAE

p.736. Change to: **Euclea crispa** (Thunb.) Sonder ex Gürke
                              [*E. linearis* Zeyher ex Hiern] p.738
            Add: — subsp. *crispa*
                              — subsp. *linearis* (Zeyher ex Hiern) F. White

p.738.   **Euclea natalensis** A. DC.
            Add: — subsp. *natalensis* (From Moçambique to the Cape)
                              — subsp. *acutifolia* F. White (Zimbabwe)
                              — subsp. *angustifolia* F. White (Zimbabwe, Transvaal)
                              — subsp. *obovata* F. White (Moçambique)
                              — subsp. *rotundifolia* F. White (Moçambique, Natal)

p.739. Change to: **Euclea racemosa** Murray
                              [*E. schimperi* (A.DC.) Dandy] p.740
            Add: — subsp. *schimperi* (A.DC.) F. White

p.743.   **Diospyros abyssinica** (Hiern) F. White
            Add: — subsp. *abyssinica* (the only subspecies involved south of the
                              Zambezi River)

p.748.   **Diospyros lycioides** Desf.
            Add: — subsp. *lycioides*
                              — subsp. *guerkei* (Kuntze) De Winter
                              — subsp. *sericea* (Bernh.) De Winter

p.753.   **Diospyros usambarensis** F. White
            Add: —subsp. *usambarensis* (the only subspecies involved in this area)

OLEACEAE

p.759.   Add: **Olea chimanimani** Kupicha   (Zimb. no: 869/1)
                              Zimbabwe east

SALVADORACEAE

p.762.   **Salvadora persica** L.
            Add: — var. *persica*
                              — var. *pubescens* Brenan

APOCYNACEAE

p.782.   **Carissa bispinosa** (L.) Desf. ex Brenan
      Change to: — subsp. *bispinosa* (previously var. *bispinosa*)
                              — subsp. *zambesiensis* Kupicha (previously var. *acuminata* (E.
                              Meyer) Codd)

p.789. Change to: 8 CALLICHILIA Stapf
                              [*EPHIPPIOCARPA* Markgraf]

p.789. Change to: **Callichilia orientalis** S. Moore
                              [*Ephippiocarpa orientalis* (S. Moore) Markgraf]

p.798.   Add: 20 PLEIOCERAS Baillon
                              Pleioceras orientale Vollesen
                              Moçambique, just south of the Zambezi River

BORAGINACEAE

p.802. Change to: **Ehretia obtusifolia** Hochst. ex DC.
                              [*E. amoena* Klotzsch; *E. coerulea* Gürke]

SOLANACEAE

p.820. Change to: **Lycium oxycarpum** Dunal   (S.A. no: 669,1 — taking
                                                                                      the place of *L. austrinum* Miers)

RUBIACEAE

p.848.   Add: **Tarenna nigrescens** (J.D. Hook.) Hiern
Moçambique, Swaziland

p.849   **Tarenna pavettoides** (Harvey) T.R. Sim
          Add: —subsp. *pavettoides* (Maputo, Natal, Transkei)
                   —subsp. *affinis* (K. Schum.) Bridson (Moçambique, Zimbabwe)

p.850.   Add: **Tarenna supra-axillaris** (Hemsley) Bremek. (S.A. no. 686,1; Zimb.
no: 1064/1)
[*T. barbertonensis* (Bremek.) Bremek.]
—subsp. *supra-axillaris* (Moçambique, Zimababwe)
—subsp. *barbertonensis* (Bremek.) Bridson (Transvaal, Natal)

p.851. Change to: 10 CATUNAREGAM Wolf. (was part of *Xeromphis*)
          Add: **Catunaregam spinosa** (Thunb.) Tirvengadum
— subsp. *spinosa*
[*Xeromphis obovata* (Hochst.) Keay; *Randia kraussii* Harvey; *R. dumetorum* auct. non (Retz.) Lam.]
— subsp. *taylori* (S. Moore) Verdc.
[*Randia vestita* S. Moore]

p.852.   Add: 10A CODDIA Verdc. (was part of *Xeromphis*)
Change to: **Coddia rudis** (E. Meyer ex Harvey) Verdc.
[*Xeromphis rudis* (E. Meyer ex Harvey) Codd; *Randia rudis* E. Meyer ex Harvey]

p.856.   **Gardenia resiniflua** Hiern
          Add: — subsp. *resiniflua* (all the material of tree size south of the Zambizi River)

p.862.   **Oxyanthus pyriformis** (Hochst.) Skeels
          Add: — subsp. *pyriformis* (all the material of tree size south of the Zambezi River)

p.862.   **Oxyanthus speciosus** DC.
          Add: — subsp. *gerrardii* (Sonder) Bridson (Transvaal excluding northern Transvaal, Natal, Swaziland, Transkei): Fruits small, ellipsoidal, 1,7 to 2,8 (3,5) cm long.
— subsp. *stenocarpus* (K. Schum.) Bridson (northern Transvaal, Zimbabwe, Moçambique): Fruits larger, spindle-shaped, 3 to 6,3 cm long.

p.864.   Add: **Tricalysia acocantheroides** K. Schum. (Zimb. no: 1083)
Zimbabwe

p.864. Change to: **Tricalysia junodii** (Schinz) Brenan   (Zimb. no: 1087)
[*T. allenii* (Stapf) Brenan; *T. allenii* var. *kirkii* (J.D. Hook.) Brenan; *T. allenii* var. *australis* (Schweik.) Brenan]
          Add: — var. *junodii* (Maputo, Transvaal, Natal)
— var. *kirkii* (J.D. Hook.) Robbrecht (eastern Transvaal, Zimbabwe, Moçambique, Botswana, Caprivi Strip)

p.865. Change to: **Tricalysia ruandensis** Bremek.
[*T. congesta* auct.]

p.868.   **Sericanthe andongensis** (Hiern) Robbrecht
          Add: — var. *andongensis* (South Africa, Zimbabwe, Moçambique)
— var. *mollis* Robbrecht (Zimbabwe, Moçambique)

p.868.   Add: **Sericanthe odoratissima** (K. Schum.) Robbrecht   (Zimb. no: 1089/1)
— var. *ulugurensis* Robbrecht (Zimbabwe)
(A forest species, as opposed to *S. andongensis* which is a species of open woodland, stream banks and rocky areas)

p.869   **Heinsia crinita** (Afzel.) G. Taylor
          Add: — subsp. *parviflora* (K. Schum. & Krause) Verdc. (includes all the material south of the Zambezi River)

p.879   Add: **Canthium bibracteatum** (Baker) Hiern   (Zimb. no: 1102/1)
Zimbabwe, Moçambique

p.893   Change to: **Pavetta comostyla** S. Moore
[*P. angolensis* sensu Palgrave *Trees of Southern Africa; P. inyangensis* Bremek.; *P. johnstonii* sensu Palgrave *Trees of Southern Africa*]
p.895

      Add: — var. *comostyla* (Zimbabwe)
— var. *inyangensis* (Bremek.) Bridson (Zimbabwe)

p.894.   **Pavetta gardeniifolia** Hochst. ex A. Rich.

      Add: — var. *gardeniifolia* (South Africa, Zimbabwe, Botswana, Moçambique)
— var. *subtomentosa* K. Schum. (South Africa, Zimbabwe, Botswana)

p.899   **Psychotria capensis** (Ecklon) Vatke

      Add: — var. *capensis* (South Africa, Zimbabwe, Moçambique)

ASTERACEAE (Nom. altern. **Compositae**)

p.904.   Add: **Vernonia kreismannii** Welw. ex Hiern   (Zimb. no: 1146/1)
Zimbabwe, Moçambique

p.904. Change to: **Vernonia hymenolepsis** A. Rich.
[*V. leucocalyx* sensu Palgrave *Trees of Southern Africa*]
— subsp. *meridionalis* Wild (the only subspecies to occur south of the Zambezi river)

p.905. Change to: **Vernonia subuligera** O. Hoffm.
[*V. stipulacea* Klatt; *V. ampla* Hoffm.]

LIST OF HERBARIA

Alexander McGregor Memorial Museum Herbarium, P.O. Box 316, Kimberley 8300
Bolus Herbarium, University of Cape Town, Private Bag Rondebosch, Cape 7700
Botanical Research Institute, Private Bag X101, Pretoria 0001
Botanical Research Unit, Herbarium of the Albany Museum, P.O. Box 101,
Grahamstown 6140
Botanical Research Unit, Natal Herbarium, Botanic Gardens Road, Durban 4001
Botanical Research Unit, P.O. Box 471, Stellenbosch 7600
Compton Herbarium, Kirstenbosch, Private Bag X7, Claremont, Cape 7735
National Herbarium, P.O. Box 8100, Causeway, Salisbury, Rhodesia
National Museum of Rhodesia, 8th Avenue, Bulawayo, Rhodesia
Port Elizabeth Museum, Humewood, Port Elizabeth 6001
South West Africa Herbarium, Private Bag 13184, Windhoek 9100

How to use this book

The entire book should be regarded essentially as a key for every part of it contributes towards the identification of the trees of southern Africa. At the outset, the illustrated introductory key, or guide, to the families should enable the reader to arrive at the relevant section, although it may require a little trial and error investigation to ascertain the actual family concerned, for these are frequently keyed out in groups.

Having determined this, a key to the genera will be found under each family, and under each genus there is yet a further key which will run down the actual species.

Reference should then be made to the distribution map which is, in itself, a valuable aid to identification, and to the line drawing of the habit, or leaves and/or fruit which can be used for rapid comparison with the specimen in hand.

Each species is described simply and concisely; all the relevant information is given so that full identification is possible.

The colour illustrations provide a very reasonable coverage of the families represented and reference to them will also be a valuable guide. They have been placed together in one section for easy and rapid reference.

The black and white photographs, which appear in the text, also illustrate important diagnostic features.

Readers are strongly advised to study the Introduction which has been kept as short as possible, for this explains most of the features in the book and gives the reasons for treating them in this way. Without this information the readers might be puzzled or confused as to what is intended or implied.

LIST OF HERBARIA

Alexander McGregor Memorial Museum Herbarium, P.O. Box 316, Kimberley 8300
Bolus Herbarium, University of Cape Town, Private Bag Rondebosch, Cape 7700
Botanical Research Institute, Private Bag X101, Pretoria 0001
Botanical Research Unit, Herbarium of the Albany Museum, P.O. Box 101, Grahamstown 6140
Botanical Research Unit, Natal Herbarium, Botanic Gardens Road, Durban 4001
Botanical Research Unit, P.O. Box 471, Stellenbosch 7600
Compton Herbarium, Kirstenbosch, Private Bag X7, Claremont, Cape 7735
National Herbarium, P.O. Box 8100, Causeway, Salisbury, Rhodesia
National Museum of Rhodesia, 8th Avenue, Bulawayo, Rhodesia
Port Elizabeth Museum, Humewood, Port Elizabeth 6001
South West Africa Herbarium, Private Bag 13184, Windhoek 9100

Terminalia sericea. Silver terminalia

General guide to the Families

How to use this key

A key to the families is given on pages 20 and 21. This has been compiled to assist you in finding your way into the book.

To select the correct group, compare your specimen leaf with the thumbnail description given on page 20. Once you have recognised the group to which your leaf belongs – see page 21 – then turn to the page on which that group is described. Take for example a protea leaf which fits the description given on page 20: 'leaves simple, alternate, margins not entire.' Directly opposite is the group number, in this case group 4 page 30. Now turn to page 30 and work through the key until you find the likely family or families. From here turn to the family – in the case of protea, page 122 – and from there you will be able to consult the generic key and check against the relevant leaf drawings, map and descriptions for final identification. (For further information see 'How to use this book', page 17.)

There will inevitably be difficulties with keying out certain species for many are extremely difficult to identify except under a microscope. When unable to identify a tree you may send a pressed and labelled specimen to your local herbarium for identification. The addresses of these herbaria are given on page 17.

Key to groups

Trees that are distinctive and easily recognised by their character and habit, usually unbranched or only sparingly branched; leaves large, usually in distinct terminal clusters

Mature leaves very small or scale-like, usually 2 to 3 mm long but up to 5 mm, usually tightly adpressed; or very slender and needle-like then up to 2 × 0,2 cm;

or

Mature leaves usually absent except in the most active growing season when small leaves are produced for a short time, especially on very young shoots

Leaves simple, alternate, margins entire. Some species have undulating margins which appear superficially to be serrate, but close examination will reveal that the margins are in fact entire

Leaves simple, alternate, margins not entire

Leaves simple, in fascicles (clusters) on short, even dwarfed lateral shoots, or crowded at the ends of branches

Leaves simple, whorled, margins entire or not entire

Leaves simple, opposite or sub-opposite, margins not entire

Leaves simple, opposite or sub-opposite, margins entire

Leaves compound, with two leaflets, or tri-foliolate, or digitately or bi-digitately compound (i.e. more than 3 leaflets arising from the same point at the end of the petiole); margins entire or not entire

Leaves pinnately or bi-pinnately compound; margins entire or not entire

Leaves simple

Leaves compound

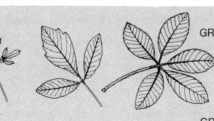

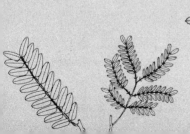

GROUP 1

Trees that are distinctive and easily recognised by their character and habit, usually unbranched or only sparingly branched; leaves large, usually in distinct terminal clusters

Tree ferns
Fronds 3-pinnate, the margins of the fronds scalloped; fronds expanding like an un-coiling spring (circinnate vernation) .... **Cyatheaceae** (p. 41)

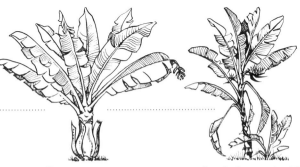

Trees banana-like
Leaves simple, very large, often ragged and wind-torn ....

Musaceae (p. 87)   **Strelitziaceae** (p. 88)

Leaves compound
   CYCADS: leaves pinnate, hard, rigid, leathery, spine-tipped, often with the margins spinescent; midrib absent; reproductive organs large, usually terminal cones; flowers not produced .... **Cycadaceae** (p. 44)
Zamiaceae (p. 44)

   PALMS: leaves pinnate (feather-shaped) or palmate (fan-shaped); leaflets leathery but pliable, folded along a prominent midrib; lightly spine-tipped; reproductive organs in flowers, developing into fruits ....

Arecaceae (p. 65)

Leaves simple

Strap-shaped, produced in terminal rosettes, not succulent; leaf margins without prickles
.... **Agavaceae** (p. 86)

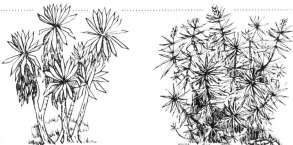

Strap-shaped, spirally arranged and terminally clustered, not succulent; leaf margins
with prickles .... **Pandanaceae** (p. 65)

WELWITSCHIA
Strange desert plants along the coastal strip
north of Walvis Bay, South West Africa; with a
massive dwarf stem usually less than 1 m
high, with two opposite persistent leaves
which may be 2 m or more in length, split and
torn by wind to form a tangled mass .... **Welwitschiaceae** (p. 61)

BAMBOOS
Stems hard, shiny; leaves grass-like .... **Poaceae** (p. 62)

ALOES
Leaves simple, succulent, terminally clustered, often with a spinescent margin. Trees often unbranched or only sparsely
branched ....

Liliaceae (p. 72)

GROUP 2

Leaves simple, in fascicles (clusters) on short, even dwarfed, lateral shoots, or crowded at the ends of the branches

1   Leaves fascicled or clustered 2

Leaves crowded at the ends of the branches 11

2   Leaf margins entire 3

Leaf margins lobed,
     scalloped or toothed 10

3   Branches thick, succulent, creamy white; leaves very small, fleshy, almost cylindric in scattered clusters on black, almost pustular protuberances .... **Portulacaceae** (p. 162)
Branches not thick and succulent, not creamy white with black raised patches 4

4   Plants with milky latex .... **Montiniaceae** (p. 203) **Euphorbiaceae** (p. 390)
Plants without milky latex 5

5   Fruits winged .... **Combretaceae**
(p. 660)
Polygalaceae
(p. 387)

Fruits not winged 6

6   Fruits in a characteristic thistle-like head; each very small fruit with a tuft of hairs...........................
.... **Compositae** (p. 901)
Fruits not produced in thistle-like heads 7

7   Fruits fleshy, indehiscent 8
Fruits dehiscent, splitting into two or more sections 9

8   Fruits small, up to 10 mm long .... **Capparaceae** (p. 181) **Erythroxylaceae** (p. 334)
     Euphorbiaceae (p. 390) **Anacardiaceae** (p. 456) **Rhamnaceae** (p. 549) **Boraginaceae** (p. 798)
     Solanaceae (p. 819)
Fruits larger than 10 mm, may be 1,5 to 3 cm long or more .... **Olacaceae** (p. 157)
     Capparaceae (p. 181) **Linaceae** (p. 333) **Celastraceae** (p. 493)

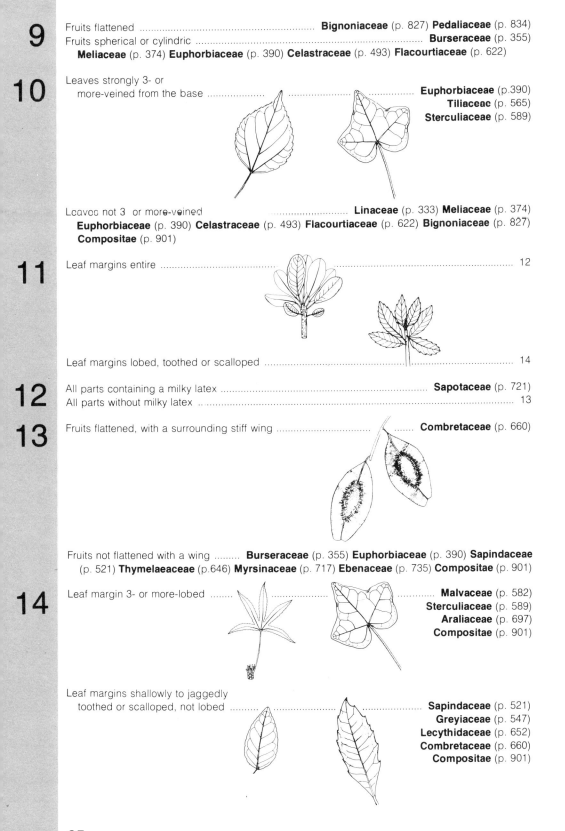

9 Fruits flattened .... **Bignoniaceae** (p. 827) **Pedaliaceae** (p. 834)
Fruits spherical or cylindric .... **Burseraceae** (p. 355)
    Meliaceae (p. 374) **Euphorbiaceae** (p. 390) **Celastraceae** (p. 493) **Flacourtiaceae** (p. 622)

10 Leaves strongly 3- or
more-veined from the base .... **Euphorbiaceae** (p.390)
                                        Tiliaceae (p. 565)
                                  Sterculiaceae (p. 589)

Leaves not 3 or more-veined .... **Linaceae** (p. 333) **Meliaceae** (p. 374)
    Euphorbiaceae (p. 390) **Celastraceae** (p. 493) **Flacourtiaceae** (p. 622) **Bignoniaceae** (p. 827)
    Compositae (p. 901)

11 Leaf margins entire 12

Leaf margins lobed, toothed or scalloped 14

12 All parts containing a milky latex .... **Sapotaceae** (p. 721)
All parts without milky latex 13

13 Fruits flattened, with a surrounding stiff wing .... **Combretaceae** (p. 660)

Fruits not flattened with a wing .... **Burseraceae** (p. 355) **Euphorbiaceae** (p. 390) **Sapindaceae**
    (p. 521) **Thymelaeaceae** (p.646) **Myrsinaceae** (p. 717) **Ebenaceae** (p. 735) **Compositae** (p. 901)

14 Leaf margin 3- or more-lobed .... **Malvaceae** (p. 582)
                                   Sterculiaceae (p. 589)
                                        Araliaceae (p. 697)
                                       Compositae (p. 901)

Leaf margins shallowly to jaggedly
toothed or scalloped, not lobed .... **Sapindaceae** (p. 521)
                                       Greyiaceae (p. 547)
                                Lecythidaceae (p. 652)
                                Combretaceae (p. 660)
                                   Compositae (p. 901)

GROUP 3

Leaves simple, alternate, margins entire. Some species have undulating margins which appear superficially to be serrate, but close examination will reveal that the margins are in fact entire.

1 Leaves with a single midrib and without lateral veins .... **Podocarpaceae** (p. 55)
Leaves with 1 or more main veins and lateral veins present 2

2 Leaves with 3 or more veins from the base 3

Leaves with a single midrib and lateral veins arising from it 8

3 Leaves with a deep apical notch giving a characteristic 'butterfly wing' appearance .... **Leguminosae** – Subfam.(p. 214)
Caesalpinioideae (p. 262)

Leaves not 'butterfly wing' in appearance 4

4 Fruits winged or keeled .... **Tiliaceae** (p. 565) **Sterculiaceae** (p. 589)
Fruits not winged or keeled; fleshy and indehiscent or splitting when mature 5

5 Fruits splitting when mature .... **Euphorbiaceae** (p. 390) **Sterculiaceae** (p. 589)
Fruits fleshy, not splitting when mature 6

6 Base of the leaf oblique .... **Ulmaceae** (p. 95)

Base of the leaf not markedly oblique 7

7 If the leaf is crackled (i.e. bent backwards and forwards) the surface lifts and a little milky latex exudes onto the surface .... **Flacourtiaceae** (p. 622)
Leaf surface does not become milky if the leaf is bent backwards and forwards ....
.... **Piperaceae** (p. 90) **Lauraceae** (p. 175) **Alangiaceae** (p. 709)

8 Most parts exuding a milky latex or copious watery sap 9
Without milky latex or copious watery sap 10

26

9 Branchlets marked with clear stipular scars .... **Moraceae** (p. 99)

Stipules not leaving clear scars .... **Ulmaceae** (p. 95) **Montiniaceae** (p. 203) **Euphorbiaceae** (p. 390) **Sapotaceae** (p. 721) **Apocynaceae** (p. 779)

10 Fruits with wings or with much enlarged and persistent calyx lobes, which may be petal-like, round the base 11

Fruits without wings or persistent enlarged calyx lobes 13

11 Leaves with a pair of conspicuous gland-like structures, extra-floral nectaries, at the junction of the blade and the petiole; fruits with 5 membranous petal-like persistent sepals .... **Dipterocarpaceae** (p. 615)
Leaves without conspicuous extra-floral nectaries 12

12 Fruits with one or 2 membranous wings, or a wing which almost encircles the fruit .... **Malpighiaceae** (p. 386) **Polygalaceae** (p. 387) **Euphorbiaceae** (p. 390) **Sapindaceae** (p. 521)
Fruits with much enlarged persistent sepals round the base; these may be brightly coloured and petal-like .... **Ochnaceae** (p. 600) **Ebenaceae** (p. 735)

13 Fruit a pod, usually splitting on maturity; flowers characteristically pea-shaped .... **Leguminosae** – subfam. **Papilionoideae** (p. 292)

Fruits not a pod 14

14 Fruits splitting at maturity 15
Fruits fleshy, leathery or woody, not splitting at maturity 20

15 Leaf petiole with a characteristic swelling or small glands near the base of the blade .... **Euphorbiaceae** (p. 390) **Sterculiaceae** (p. 589)
Leaf petiole without a swelling 16

16 Fruits more than 1,5 cm long when mature .... **Annonaceae** (p. 164) **Euphorbiaceae** (p. 390) **Celastraceae** (p. 493) **Flacourtiaceae** (p. 622)
Fruits less than 1,5 cm long when mature 17

17 Leaves conspicuously gland-dotted and crushed leaves and twigs strongly aromatic, often smelling of lavender .... **Myrtaceae** (p. 687)
Leaves and twigs not strongly aromatic when crushed 18

27

18   Leaves dark green but a characteristic brilliant green when viewed against the sunlight; the seeds coated with a bright red, sticky, slow-drying resin .... **Pittosporaceae** (p. 203)

Leaves not conspicuously brilliant green when viewed against sunlight 19

19   Leaves not more than 1,3 cm wide .... **Polygalaceae** (p. 387) **Euphorbiaceae** (p. 390) **Celastraceae** (p. 493)

Leaves more than 1,3 cm wide .... **Hamamelidaceae** (p. 206) **Euphorbiaceae** (p. 390) **Celastraceae** (p. 493) **Sapindaceae** (p. 521) **Flacourtiaceae** (p. 622) **Myrsinaceae** (p. 717)

20   Leaves without a petiole which is usually masked by a decurrent leaf base 21

Leaves with distinct petioles 23

21   When the leaf is crackled (i. e. bent backwards and forwards), the leaf surface lifts and some milky latex oozes out .... **Flacourtiaceae** (p. 622)

The leaf surface does not become milky when crackled 22

22   The bark is very tough and strips into string-like, or rope-like sections ..... **Thymelaeaceae** (p. 646)

The bark not stripping .... **Proteaceae** (p. 122) **Boraginaceae** (p. 798) **Solanaceae** (p. 819) **Compositae** (p. 901)

23   Fruits and flowers in catkin-like spikes 24

Fruits and flowers not in catkin-like spikes 25

24   Fruits small, fleshy .... **Euphorbiaceae** (p. 390)

Fruits small nutlets, densely hairy, dart-like, with the long dry remains of the old style forming a 'tail' .... **Proteaceae** (p. 122)

25   Flower heads or fruiting heads either daisy-like or thistle-like .... **Compositae** (p. 901)

Flower heads and fruiting heads not daisy-like or thistle-like 26

26   Fruits large, more than 2,5 cm long or broad .... **Annonaceae** (p. 164) **Capparaceae** (p. 181) **Brexiaceae** (p. 202) **Chrysobalanaceae** (p. 211) **Euphorbiaceae** (p. 390) **Canellaceae** (p. 618) **Flacourtiaceae** (p. 622)

Fruits small, up to 2,5 cm long or broad 27

28

27 Fruits black, flattened, berry-like with a scarlet fleshy lateral appendage, thus giving the sharply two
coloured fruit a kidney shape .... **Icacinaceae** (p. 519)
Fruits not sharply two coloured with the scarlet appendage 28

28 Leaves and/or branchlets aromatic when crushed .... **Myricaceae** (p. 93)
Annonaceae (p. 164) **Lauraceae** (p. 175) **Myrsinaceae** (p. 717)
Leaves and branchlets not aromatic 29

29 Leaves with more or less well defined net-veining
at least on the under surface .... **Capparaceae** (p. 181)
Polygalaceae (p. 387)
Euphorbiaceae (p. 390)
Anacardiaceae (p. 456)
Celastraceae (p. 493)
Flacourtiaceae (p. 622)
Boraginaceae (p. 798)

Leaves without well defined net-veining 30

30 Leaves with conspicuously parallel lateral veins
at almost right angles to mid-vein .... **Anacardiaceae** (p. 456)

Leaves with lateral veins not conspicuously parallel 31

31 Leaves with more or less dense hairs, either short or long and shaggy on one or both surfaces of the leaf,
at least when young 32
Leaves without hairs or with only sparse hairs 33

32 Fruits up to 10 mm long or broad when mature .. **Euphorbiaceae** (p. 390) **Anacardiaceae** (p. 456)
Flacourtiaceae (p. 622) **Myrsinaceae** (p. 717) **Ebenaceae** (p. 735) **Solanaceae** (p. 819)
Fruits more than 10 mm long or broad when mature .... **Olacaceae** (p. 157)
Annonaceae (p. 164) **Capparaceae** (p. 181) **Euphorbiaceae** (p. 390) **Celastraceae** (p. 493)
Flacourtiaceae (p. 622) **Cornaceae** (p. 709)

33 Fruits up to 10 mm long or broad when mature .... **Ebenaceae** (p. 735) **Aquifoliaceae** (p. 492)
Dichapetalaceae (p. 389) **Erythroxylaceae** (p. 334) **Myrsinaceae** (p. 717) **Anacardiaceae** (p. 456)
Celastraceae (p. 493) **Flacourtiaceae** (p. 622)
Fruits more than 10 mm long or broad when mature 34

34 Leaf base oblique .... **Ulmaceae** (p. 95)
Leaf base not markedly oblique 35

35 Leaf when rolled backwards and forwards exudes a slight milky latex as the surface cracks ....
.... **Flacourtiaceae** (p. 622)
Leaf does not exude latex as the cuticle cracks .... **Santalaceae** (p. 156)
Olacaceae (p. 157) **Annonaceae** (p. 164) **Capparaceae** (p. 181) **Linaceae** (p. 333) **Celastraceae** (p. 493) **Rhamnaceae** (p. 549)

GROUP 4

Leaves simple, alternate, margins not entire.

1 Leaves and branchlets covered with stinging hairs .... **Urticaceae** (p. 120)
Leaves and branchlets without stinging hairs 2

2 Leaves and/or stems with a milky latex or copious watery sap .... **Moraceae** (p. 99)
Hernandiaceae (p. 181) **Euphorbiaceae** (p. 390) **Vitaceae** (p. 560) **Passifloraceae** (p. 642)
Leaves and stems without milky latex or copious watery sap 3

3 Leaves 3-, 5- or more-veined from the base 4

Leaves with a single midrib and lateral veins arising from it 6

4 Leaf margin strongly lobed .... **Hernandiaceae** (p. 181)
Vitaceae (p. 560) **Malvaceae** (p. 582) **Sterculiaceae** (p. 589) **Araliaceae** (p. 697)
Leaf margin not strongly lobed 5

5 Leaf surface cracks to allow droplets of milky latex to exude when rolled backwards and forwards
.... **Flacourtiaceae** (p. 622)
Leaf surface does not exude a milky latex .... **Euphorbiaceae** (p. 390)
Greyiaceae (p. 547) **Rhamnaceae** (p. 549) **Tiliaceae** (p. 565)

6 Leaves with from 3 to 10 large teeth apically .... **Proteaceae** (p. 122)

Leaves with teeth covering at least one third of the margin 7

7 Leaves strongly aromatic when crushed .... **Myricaceae** (p. 93) **Myrsinaceae** (p. 717)
Leaves not aromatic 8

8 Fruits with much enlarged, persistent, petal-like,
brightly coloured sepals; the fruits produced
on a much swollen receptacle .... **Ochnaceae** (p. 600)

Fruits without enlarged, petal-like sepals 9

9 Leaf petiole with a conspicuous swelling just
below the blade .... **Euphorbiaceae** (p. 390)
Sterculiaceae (p. 589)

Petiole without a conspicuous swelling 10

10 Leaves with more or less dense hairs, which may be short and velvety or long and shaggy, covering one
or both sides of the blade at least when young 11
Leaves without hairs, or with very sparse hairs on the blade, any hairs present being confined to the
petiole and main veins 13

11 Leaves with dense woolly hairs below and usually
with prickles on the petiole which often extend up
onto the midrib .... **Solanaceae** (p. 819)

Leaves without prickles on the petiole or midrib 12

12 Trees confined to riverbanks and islands in the larger rivers, and to vleis .... **Salicaceae** (p. 91)
Trees not confined to the immediate proximity of water .... **Ulmaceae** (p. 95)
Euphorbiaceae (p. 390) **Celastraceae** (p. 493) **Sapindaceae** (p. 521) **Flacourtiaceae** (p. 622)
Myrsinaceae (p. 717) **Boraginaceae** (p. 798) **Compositae** (p. 901)

13 Leaves without a petiole blade almost triangular, the
broad base clasping the stem .... **Rosaceae** (p. 207)

Leaves with a petiole, although this may be short 14

14 Trees confined to river banks, islands in larger rivers and to vleis .... **Salicaceae** (p. 91)
Trees not confined to river banks 15

15 Leaves comparatively narrow, about two and a half times as long as broad or narrower ....
Euphorbiaceae (p. 390) **Aquifoliaceae** (p. 492) **Celastraceae** (p. 493) **Rhamnaceae** (p. 549)
Violaceae (p. 618) **Flacourtiaceae** (p. 622) **Ericaceae** (p. 711) **Boraginaceae** (p. 798) **Compositae**
(p. 901)
Leaves comparatively broad, less than two and a half times as long as broad ... **Ulmaceae** (p. 95)
Iteaceae (p. 202) **Euphorbiaceae** (p. 390) **Celastraceae** (p. 493) **Sapindaceae** (p. 521) **Violaceae**
(p. 618) **Flacourtiaceae** (p. 622) **Myrsinaceae** (p. 717)

GROUP 5

Leaves simple whorled; margins entire or not entire.

1   Leaf margins toothed or scalloped .... **Proteaceae** (p. 122)
                   Loganiaceae (p. 763)
                   Verbenaceae (p. 804)
                  Scrophulariaceae (p. 822)

     Leaf margins entire 2

2   Leaves and/or stems with milky latex .... **Apocynaceae** (p. 779)
     All parts without milky latex 3

3   Confined to a small area of arid mountains in the Clanwilliam district .... **Euphorbiaceae** (p. 390)
     Not confined to the Clanwilliam district 4

4   Leaves without lateral veins .... **Podocarpaceae** (p. 55)
     Leaves with lateral veins 5

5   Interpetiolar stipules, which may be conspicuous, are present, although
       they may fall early .... **Rhizophoraceae** (p. 652) **Rubiaceae** (p. 838)
     Stipules, if present, not interpetiolar 6

6   Fruits with 2 to 5 wings .... **Combretaceae** (p. 660)

     Fruits without wings 7

7   Lateral veins many, parallel, usually unbranched, running almost
       to the thickened margin .... **Anacardiaceae** (p. 456)
     Lateral veins not conspicuously parallel .... **Ebenaceae** (p. 735) **Loganiaceae** (p. 763)
       Verbenaceae (p. 804) **Scrophulariaceae** (p. 822)

GROUP 6

Leaves simple opposite or sub-opposite, margins not entire.

1 Leaves and/or stems with milky latex,
or fleshy with copious watery sap .... **Euphorbiaceae** (p. 390) **Apocynaceae** (p. 779)
Leaves and stems without milky latex, or copious watery sap 2

2 Fruits paired, or markedly lobed. .... **Verbenaceae** (p. 804)
Fruits single, not paired 3

3 The pair of leaves usually of unequal size, one leaf being large, up to 14 × 10 cm, while its opposite
leaf is usually considerably smaller ....**Euphorbiaceae** (p. 390)

The pair of leaves usually of equal size 4

4 The leaves with a very characteristic 'quilted' appearance,
caused by the conspicuous veining .... **Trimeniaceae** (p. 174)
Leaves without a very characteristic 'quilted' appearance 5

5 Leaves markedly succulent, occasionally entire, but usually with spine-tipped teeth; often with a dense
covering of cobweb-like hairs, flowers large, yellow and daisy-like ... . **Compositae** (p. 901)

Leaves not markedly succulent; without cobweb-like hairs; flowers not daisy-like and yellow 6

6 Leaves with the lateral veins on the under sur-
face very conspicuously looping .... **Flacourtiaceae** (p. 622)

Lateral veins on the undersurface not conspicuously looping 7

7 Leaves with dense hairs, either short or long, on either upper or lower or both surfaces ....
.... **Celastraceae** (p. 493) **Rhizophoraceae** (p. 652) **Cornaceae** (p. 709)
Boraginaceae (p. 798) **Verbenaceae** (p. 804)**Lamiaceae** (p. 818)
Leaves without hairs, or with sparse hairs, or hairs confined to the petiole and main veins only ....
Celastraceae (p. 493) **Icacinaceae** (p. 519) **Rhamnaceae** p. 549) **Rhizophoraceae** (p. 652)
Loganiaceae (p. 763) **Verbenaceae** (p. 804) **Scrophulariaceae** (p. 822) **Acanthaceae** (p. 836)

33

GROUP 7

Leaves pinnately or bi-pinnately compound; margins entire or not entire.

1   Leaves twice-compound, or twice-pinnate (i.e. secondary axes, the pinnae, arise from the rachis, and the leaflets are produced on these pinnae) .... **Moringaceae** (p. 199)
Leguminosae – subfam.
Mimosoideae (p. 214)
Caesalpinioideae (p. 262)
Sapindaceae (p. 521)

Leaves once-compound, or once-pinnate (i.e. with the leaflets arising from a single common axis, the rachis) 2

2   Crushed leaves and/or branchlets aromatic .... **Leguminosae** – subfam. **Papilionoideae** (p. 292)
Rutaceae (p. 339) **Burseraceae** (p. 355) **Apiaceae** (p. 707)
Leaves and branchlets not aromatic 3

3   Leaves very large, up to almost 1 m in length; 9 to 13 pairs of leaflets plus a terminal leaflet, the leaflets large, up to 16 × 8 cm, the under surface densely covered with creamy rusty hairs; the stem characteristically unbranched for more than half its length, then comparatively few clean branches with the leaves crowded at the tips .... **Araliaceae** (p. 697)
Leaves not very large as above; trees not characteristically shaped as described above 4

4   Apical leaf bud enclosed by two large paddle-shaped stipules which are distinctive, and when young contain a little thick, white creamy substance .... **Cunoniaceae** (p. 204)

Stipules, if present, are not distinctively paddle-shaped, nor having the other characters described above 5

5   Leaves with petiole and/or rachis winged .... **Simaroubaceae** (p. 353)
Burseraceae (p. 355)
Meliaceae (p. 374)
Anacardiaceae (p. 456)
Sapindaceae (p. 521)
Melianthaceae (p. 543)
Oleaceae (p. 754)

Petiole and rachis not winged 6

6   Leaves with 16 to 32 or more pairs of leaflets .... **Connaraceae** (p. 213) **Leguminosae** – subfam.
Caesalpinioideae (p. 262) **Simaroubaceae** (p. 353) **Sapindaceae** (p. 521) **Anacardiaceae** (p. 456)
Leaves with less than 12 pairs of leaflets 7

34

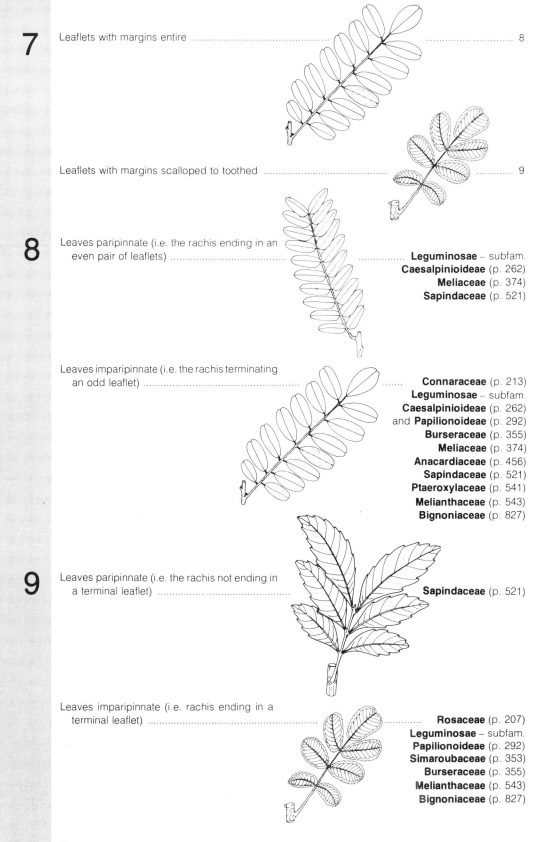

7   Leaflets with margins entire 8

Leaflets with margins scalloped to toothed 9

8   Leaves paripinnate (i.e. the rachis ending in an
even pair of leaflets) .... **Leguminosae** – subfam.
Caesalpinioideae (p. 262)
Meliaceae (p. 374)
Sapindaceae (p. 521)

Leaves imparipinnate (i.e. the rachis terminating
an odd leaflet) .... **Connaraceae** (p. 213)
Leguminosae – subfam.
Caesalpinioideae (p. 262)
and **Papilionoideae** (p. 292)
Burseraceae (p. 355)
Meliaceae (p. 374)
Anacardiaceae (p. 456)
Sapindaceae (p. 521)
Ptaeroxylaceae (p. 541)
Melianthaceae (p. 543)
Bignoniaceae (p. 827)

9   Leaves paripinnate (i.e. the rachis not ending in
a terminal leaflet) ....
Sapindaceae (p. 521)

Leaves imparipinnate (i.e. rachis ending in a
terminal leaflet) .... **Rosaceae** (p. 207)
Leguminosae – subfam.
Papilionoideae (p. 292)
Simaroubaceae (p. 353)
Burseraceae (p. 355)
Melianthaceae (p. 543)
Bignoniaceae (p. 827)

GROUP 8

Mature leaves very small or scale-like, usually 2 to 3 mm long but up to 5 mm, usually tightly adpressed or very slender and needle-like, then up to 2 × 0,2 cm 1

or Mature leaves usually absent except in the most active growing season when small leaves are produced for a short time, especially on very young shoots 8

1 Reproductive organs in the form of cones, usually woody; male cones 3 to 4 mm long, female cones up to 2,5 cm in diameter (in *Juniperus* the female cones become fleshy, berry-like and blue-black when mature) .... **Pinaceae** (p. 58)
Cupressaceae (p. 59)
Reproductive organs in the form of flowers producing small fruits 2

2 Fruits producing 5 papery, petal-like wings, in all about 7 mm in diameter .... **Chenopodiaceae** (p. 160)
Fruits without wings 3

3 Fruits about 6 mm long .... **Rhamnaceae** (p. 549) **Compositae** (p. 901)
Fruits 2 mm long or less 4

4 Leaf margins tightly rolled under .... **Ericaceae** (p. 711)
Leaf margins not tightly rolled under 5

5 Bark very tough and strips off like string or rope .... **Thymelaeaceae** (p. 646)
Bark not stripping like rope 6

6 Leaves pinnately compound, but needle-like .... **Proteaceae** (p. 122)
Leaves simple or tri-foliolate 7

7 Leaves simple .... **Tamaricaceae** (p. 617) **Compositae** (p. 901)
Leaves tri-foliolate .... **Rosaceae** (p. 207)

8 Plants with a milky latex .... **Euphorbiaceae** (p. 390)
Plants without a milky latex .... **Capparaceae** (p. 181)

GROUP 9

Leaves compound with two leaflets, or tri-foliolate, or digitately or bi-digitately compound (i.e. more than 3 leaflets arising from the same point at the end of the petiole); margins entire or not entire.

1 Leaves with a single pair of leaflets (i.e. two leaflets) .... **Leguminosae** – subfam. **Caesalpinioideae** (p. 262)
Balanitaceae (p. 337)
Sapindaceae (p. 521)

Leaves with more than two leaflets 2

2 Leaves with 3 leaflets, i.e. tri-foliolate 3

Leaves with more than 3 leaflets, all arising from the same point on the petiole 7

3 Leaflets very narrow to needle-like .... **Proteaceae** (p. 122)
Rosaceae (p. 207) **Leguminosae** – subfam. **Papilionoideae** (p. 292)
Leaflets not very narrow to needle-like 4

4 Leaves aromatic when crushed .... **Rutaceae** (p. 339)
Burseraceae (p. 355) **Anacardiaceae** (p. 456) **Apiaceae** (p. 707)

N. B. Caution: if the plant has fruits and flowers forming large heads near the ends of the branches and the fruits are small, flattened and encircled by a bright red papery wing, this plant is probably *Smodingium argutum,* and should not be handled; see p. 465 for details and distribution map.

Leaves not aromatic when crushed 5

5 Petiole and/or rachis conspicuously winged .... **Meliaceae** (p. 374)
Anacardiaceae (p. 456)

Neither petiole nor rachis winged 6

6 Leaflet margins entire ..... **Capparaceae** (p. 181) **Leguminosae** – subfam. **Papilionoideae** (p. 292)
Burseraceae (p. 355) **Anacardiaceae** (p. 456) **Sapindaceae** (p. 521) **Vitaceae** (p. 560)
Bignoniaceae (p. 827)
Leaflet margins scalloped to toothed .... **Cunoniaceae** (p. 204)
Burseraceae (p. 355) **Anacardiaceae** (p. 456) **Sapindaceae** (p. 521) **Vitaceae** (p. 560)

7 Stem and branches exude copious watery sap, or a milky latex or gum .... **Moraceae** (p. 99)
Euphorbiaceae (p. 390)
Stem and branches do not exude copious watery sap or a white gum .... **Capparaceae** (p. 181)
Anacardiaceae (p. 456) **Vitaceae** (p. 560) **Bombacaceae** (p. 587)**Sterculiaceae** (p. 589)
Passifloraceae (p. 642) **Araliaceae** (p. 697) **Verbenaceae** (p. 804)

GROUP 10

Leaves simple, opposite or sub-opposite, margin entire.

1
Leaves without lateral veins .... **Podocarpaceae** (p. 55)
Leaves with lateral veins 2

2
Leaves with dense hairs, either short or long on either upper or lower or both surfaces
when mature.. 3
Leaves without hairs or with only sparse hairs 7

3
Stipules large, distinctive and persisting long enough to be distinctive 4
Stipules small, inconspicuous, usually falling early, or absent 5

4
Stipules up to 2,5 to 1 cm, at first ensheathing
the leaf bud, later opening out to stand side
by side, like a pair of wings, silvery on the
outside, reddish brown within .... **Euphorbiaceae** (p. 390)

Stipules green, large and leaf-like .... **Loganiaceae** (p. 763) **Rubiaceae** (p. 838)

5
Fruits conspicuously 2- to 5-winged .... **Combretaceae** (p. 660)

Fruits not winged 6

6
Leaves with distinct to conspicuous parallel
veining or net-veining .... **Anacardiaceae** (p. 456)
Celastraceae (p. 493)
Clusiaceae (p. 610)
Loganiaceae (p. 763)
Boraginaceae (p. 798)
Rubiaceae (p. 838)

Leaves without distinct parallel veining or net-veining .... **Hamamelidaceae** (p. 206)
Celastraceae (p. 493) **Thymelaeaceae** (p. 646) **Rhizophoraceae** (p. 652) **Ebenaceae** (p. 735)
Salvadoraceae (p. 761) **Apocynaceae** (p. 779) **Verbenaceae** (p. 804) **Acanthaceae** (p. 836)
Rubiaceae (p. 838)

7
Constituents of mangrove swamps .... **Sonneratiaceae** (p. 651) **Rhizophoraceae** (p. 652)
Combretaceae (p 660) **Verbenaceae** (p. 804)
Not constituents of mangrove swamps 8

38

8 Leaves very large, up to 95 × 35 cm or more and crowded at the ends of the branches; branches arise high up in characteristic fashion, all from nearly the same point .... **Loganiaceae** (p. 763)
Leaves not exceptionally large as described above 9

9 Fruits with 4 to 5 wings .... **Combretaceae** (p. 660)
Fruits without wings 10

10 Leaves strongly or rather obscurely 3-veined
from the base .... **Melastomataceae** (p. 695)
Loganiaceae (p. 763)

Leaves not 3-veined from the base, having a midrib with lateral veins arising from it 11

11 Leaves with fine to conspicuous parallel veining
or net-veining 12

Leaves without parallel veining or net-veining 16

12 Leaves aromatic when crushed, with pellucid gland dots .... **Rutaceae** (p. 339)
Leaves not aromatic 13

13 Stems and branchlets with yellow to orange sap .... **Clusiaceae** (p. 610)
Stems and branchlets without yellow to orange sap 14

14 Bark of branchlets very tough, stripping into rope-like or
string-like lengths .... **Portulacaceae** (p. 162) **Thymelaeaceae** (p. 646)
Bark of branchlets not conspicuously tough and fibrous 15

15 Trees with occasional conspicuous bright red to
yellow leaves among the green .... **Anacardiaceae** (p. 456)
Trees without scattered red to yellow leaves .... **Lauraceae** (p. 175) **Hamamelidaceae** (p. 206)
Celastraceae (p. 493) **Rhamnaceae** (p. 549) **Oliniaceae** (p. 643) **Lythraceae** (p. 650) **Rubiaceae**
(p. 838)

16 Plants armed with strong spines, straight or hooked .... **Nyctaginaceae** (p. 162)
Rhamnaceae (p. 549) **Salvadoraceae** (p. 761) **Rubiaceae** (p. 838)
Plants unarmed 17

17 Bark containing a conspicuous red pigment immediately beneath the outer bark **Celastraceae** (p. 493)
Bark without red pigment 18

18 The mature fruit with 3 conspicuous, large woody horns ....
Without stipules .... **Buxaceae** (p. 454)
Fruits with persistent calyx which might be mistaken for such horns; characteristic stipules present
placed between the leaf petioles on either side of the stem .... **Rubiaceae** (p. 838)
Fruits without large, conspicuous woody horns 19

19 The crushed leaves with an unpleasant foetid smell .... **Verbenaceae** (p. 804)
The crushed leaves without an unpleasant smell 20

20 The leaves with a conspicuous gland which ter-
minates the midrib before it reaches the apex .... **Lythraceae** (p. 650)

The leaves without the conspicuous gland, and the midrib terminating in the apex 21

21 Bark of stem and branchlets tough, fibrous, stripping and difficult to break **Thymelaeaceae** (p. 646)
Bark not particularly tough and fibrous 22

22 Petiole short and running down the stem forming ridges down the stem .... **Santalaceae** (p. 156)
Petiole not forming ridges down the stem 23

23 Leaves thick and fleshy; stems brittle to succulent or semi-succulent .... **Portulacaceae** (p. 162)
Crassulaceae (p. 199)
Leaves and stems not thick and fleshy 24

24 Leaves without petioles or very nearly so, or the
petiole obscured by the decurrent leaf base: .... **Clusiaceae** (p. 610)
stipules, if present, not as described below. **Myrtaceae** (p. 687)
Scrophulariaceae (p. 822)

Leaves with characteristic stipules placed between the leaves on either side of the stem ....
.... **Rubiaceae** (p. 838)
Leaves with well defined petioles, though they may be short 25

25 Fruits indehiscent, fleshy to thinly fleshy, occasionally rather hard-shelled:
Leaves with characteristic stipules placed between the petioles on either side of the stem
.... **Rubiaceae** (p. 838)
Stipules, if present, not characteristic as above .... **Celastraceae** (p. 493)
Icacinaceae (p. 519) **Myrtaceae** (p. 687) **Cornaceae** (p. 709) **Ebenaceae** (p. 735) **Oleaceae** (p. 754)
Salvadoraceae (p. 761) **Apocynaceae** (p. 779)
Fruits dehiscent, thinly woody to woody capsules, or paired mericarps:
Leaves with characteristic stipules placed between the petioles on either side of the stem
.... **Rubiaceae** (p. 838)
Stipules, if present, not characteristic as above .... **Celastraceae** (p. 493)
Rhizophoraceae (p. 652) **Oleaceae** (p. 754) **Apocynaceae** (p. 779) **Scrophulariaceae** (p. 822)
Acanthaceae (p. 836)

Pteridophyta *(The ferns and closely related plants)*

CYATHEACEAE *(The tree fern family)*

ALSOPHILA R. Br.

Stems: usually straight, covered with brown scales and old persistent leaf bases. **Leaves (fronds):** large, arching, compound, 3-pinnate, produced in a crown at apex of the stem. Spores are produced in sori, positioned along the veins on the under surface of the leaflets.
All species are protected in South Africa.

Key to the tree species (all very similar in general appearance):
1 Stem, stipe and rachis (leaf stems) sharply spiny .... **A. manniana**
  Stem and leaves not spiny 2
2 Basal leaflets at the extreme base of leaf modified into a tangled mass of fine hair-like structures,
    resembling fibrous roots (aphlebia); margins of leaflets finely toothed .... **A. capensis**
  Aphlebia absent; margins of leaflets entire 3
3 Under surface of leaflets smooth, or with sparse, loose, rusty, hair-like scales which readily fall off,
    visible under hand lens only .... **A. dregei**
  Very similar to above species, but under surface of leaflets always has pale, stiff, twisted hairs
    along the veins, visible with hand lens only .... **A. thomsonii**

Alsophila capensis (L.f.) J. Smith
[*Hemitelia capensis* (L.f.) Kaulf; *Cyathea capensis* (L.f.) Smith]
S.A. no: 2   Forest tree fern. Bosboomvaring
Rhod. no: 1   Forest tree fern

Height: up to 5 m; found in moist evergreen forests, usually above 1 370 m, although at lower altitudes around Knysna in the high, wet forests. **Leaves:** large, up to 3 m; stalks smooth; leaflets have finely toothed margins; the lowermost leaflets are modified to form conspicuous tangled masses of green, later brown hair-like structures, called *aphlebia*.
The tree is said to transplant badly and will not tolerate drying winds, sunshine, frost or any degree of drought.

Alsophila dregei (Kunze) Tryon
[*Cyathea dregei* Kunze]
S.A. no: 1   Common tree fern. Gewone boomvaring
Rhod. no: 2   Common tree fern

41

A forested ravine with the common tree fern, Alsophila dregei, *and in the foreground* Ensete ventricosum, *the Wild banana (page 88)*

Height: usually 3 to 5 m, but may reach 7 m; found on forest margins, wooded kloofs and along streams on grassy mountainsides. **Leaves:** 2 to 3 m long, stalks smooth, aphlebia absent, leaflet margins entire.

This is the most common and widespread of the tree ferns.

Alsophila manniana (Hook.) Tryon
[*Cyathea deckenii* Kuhn; *C. manniana* Hook.]
S.A. no: —
Rhod. no: 3   Spiny tree fern

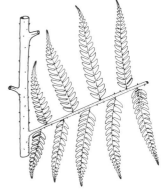

Height: 6 m; slender, tending to lean over and even becoming prostrate, when upright shoots are produced from the recumbent stem; lateral prop stems are sometimes formed; found in wet, shaded places in forests. **Stem:** dark and spiny. **Leaves:** 2 to 3 m long leaf bases and stalks armed with sharp prickles; this feature sets it apart from the other species.

Alsophila thomsonii (Baker) Tryon
[*Cyathea zambesiaca* Baker; *C. thomsonii* Baker]
S.A. no: —
Rhod. no: 4   Thomson's tree fern

 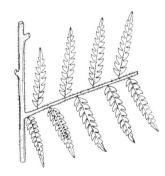

Height: up to 3 m; slender; found in forests and along shaded stream banks. This species closely resembles *C. dregei* but for the pale, twisted hairs on under surface of leaflets.

Spermatophyta *(The seed-bearing plants)*

Gymnospermae *(The cone-bearing plants)*

Cycadales *(The cycad order)*

This is an ancient order of plants which flourished between 300 and 200 million years ago; those which exist today represent only a remnant of this once dominant group for the cycads are now a dying race. However, the fact that they have survived some 200 million years indicates how immensely resilient and successful they have been.

At present three families are recognised within the cycads:
1. Stangeriaceae, which has only one genus and a single species, is endemic to South Africa, and occurs from the eastern Cape to Zululand; this low-growing, fern-like plant with firm leathery leaves has never been known to reach tree proportions.

2. Cycadaceae, which has only one genus, *Cycas,* and species ranging from Australia to Japan, China and India; one species occurs in the Malagasy Republic and on the east coast of tropical Africa and islands in the Indian Ocean.

3. Zamiaceae, which includes some eight genera ranging from Mexico to Australia and southern Africa. In southern Africa only one genus, *Encephalartos,* occurs.

The poisonous properties and also the food value of cycads
Cycad seeds are large with a fleshy outer layer and an inner kernel. The fleshy layer is often edible, but the kernel may be poisonous; the seeds of *Encephalartos longifolius* (Jacq.) Lehm. have been known to cause the death of cattle but, despite this, many of the seeds are eaten by baboons, monkeys, rodents and birds. It is difficult to distinguish the poisonous from the non-poisonous so it would be as well to avoid eating the seeds of all species.

43

CYCADACEAE/ZAMIACEAE

The pith within the stems of almost all cycads yields a high quality starch very similar to that produced from the rhizomes of *Maranta arundinacea* L., the arrowroot. This is a pure, nutritious starch recommended for infants and invalids and also used in high quality confectionery. Carl Thunberg was the first to record its use by the African people. Between 1772 and 1779 he collected the first specimens of *Encephalartos longifolius*, which he called the *bread tree*, and he described how the trunks were split open to remove the pith which was then wrapped in an animal skin and buried underground to partly ferment. The resulting fibrous mass was then ground to a flour, made into a dough with water, shaped into small loaves and baked under the glowing coals of a fire. Probably all the species could be – and were – used in a similar fashion.

Most species produce so-called *root tubercles* from the secondary roots. These are odd structures resembling clusters of fungi and occurring just at ground level. They have been found to contain an alga and a bacterium and it is possible that these may assist the cycad by fixing atmospheric nitrogen.

Key to the tree genera of cycads (this key cuts across two families):
Leaflets with a midrib, female cone a terminal head of loose, densely woolly scale leaves; not found south of the Zambezi delta .... **1. Cycas**

Leaflets with many parallel veins; female cones compact, scales fitting tightly together .... **2. Encephalartos**

CYCADACEAE

1. CYCAS L.

Cycas thouarsii Gaudich.
S.A. no: —
Rhod. no: —   African cycas

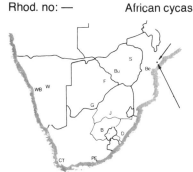

Height: up to 10 m; usually unbranched; found in hot, humid areas fringing forest or in open woodland, not further south than the Zambezi delta. **Leaves:** 1 to 3 m long upright at first, pendant later; the leaflets are long and slender, up to 30 × 1 cm, with a conspicuous yellowish midrib and no secondary veins; margin entire, apex spine-tipped; lowermost leaflets reduced to short spines. **Cones:** male and female on separate trees; male cones yellowish-orange, up to 60 × 20 cm, with close wedge-shaped scales; female cones consist of loose, spirally arranged scales, covered with dense creamy-grey woolly hairs; the outer margins of the scales are irregularly toothed and scalloped and each bears 2 to 5 pairs of ovules. **Seeds:** almost spherical, 6 × 5 cm, brick-red in colour; they develop only if fertilized, in contrast to *Encephalartos*.

The plant has a long tap-root which will not regenerate if damaged and the plant will not survive unless given the hot, humid conditions of its natural environment.

ZAMIACEAE

2. ENCEPHALARTOS Lehm.

Plants dioecious. **Stem:** usually unbranched, occasionally branched from the base, usually aerial and covered with alternating series of woolly bracts and dry, hard, persistent leaf bases, but in some species the stem is subterranean. **Leaves:** large, up to 3,5 m, arising spirally at stem apex forming a crown, each leaf lasting 2 years or more; pinnate; leaflets spine-tipped, hard, thickly leathery, margins entire, toothed or lobed on one or both margins; sometimes the lowermost leaflets are reduced to a series of spines; veins parallel, numerous, with no defined midrib. **Cones:** 1 to 5, sometimes more, shortly stalked, on or round the stem apex; the male cones usually smaller than the female, sub-cylindric, the scales densely packed in many spiral rows, with the tip of each scale forming a thickened, down-curving beak; pollen is produced in densely packed pollen sacs on the under surface of the scale leaves; the female cones usually larger and broader than the male, scales densely packed, each bearing only 2 naked ovules on upper surface, the tip of the scale forming a shield-like head. **Seeds:** large, red, yellow or brown, fleshy; development is slow but the seeds will develop fully whether fertile or not (cf. seeds of *Cycas*).

In addition to the 23 tree species included here, there are 10 further species which have their stems underground and only the crown of leaves showing above the soil's surface.

Note: the cycads are a slowly dying group and therefore, as the author sees it, the species remaining today must represent only a few of those that were most successful in the past, and therefore these last survivors should be static and well-founded. It is also the author's opinion that too many species have been created, in southern Africa at least. It is not unusual for the situation to arise where supposedly different, but very closely related, species are found on adjacent hills or in neighbouring river valleys, these being the *only* areas where they are said to occur, and often there is no apparent natural barrier which could account for the separate development of these small populations. The differences between them are frequently so slight that geographical distribution plays a large part in their determination. It is suggested that there is room for considerable combining of species and that the true picture today is one of a comparatively few species showing fairly considerable variation as a result of geographical, climatic and other conditions. All species of cycads are protected in South Africa and Rhodesia.

Key to the tree species of *Encephalartos:*

A. CAPE

1 South, central and eastern regions; not in Transkei 2
  Eastern Cape and Transkei 4
2 Bathurst and Albany districts only; leaflet margins with 2 to 3 teeth on lower margin, with one large tooth near the apex, giving a 'forked tongue' appearance .... **E. latifrons**
  West of Albany only 3
3 Leaf bases swollen with a conspicuous red-brown collar; leaflets narrow, 12 to 18 × 1,5 to 2 cm; cones solitary, dark red, with fine black hairs .... **E. lehmannii**
  Leaf bases not conspicuously swollen or red-collared; leaflets up to 20 × 4 cm; cones 1 to 2 together, greenish-brown, with reddish flattened hairs .... **E. longifolius**
4 Leaves 2 m or more in length 5
  Leaves under 2 m in length 6
5 Lowermost leaflets not reduced to a series of spines: Bushmans River eastwards to Transkei .... **E. altensteinii**
  Lowermost leaflets reduced to a series of spines; from eastern Transkei eastwards to north Natal .... **E. natalensis**
6 Leaflets very narrow, margins tightly rolled under, thus making the leaflets needle-like; Flagstaff east and north to the slopes of the Drakensberg .... **E. ghellinckii**
  Leaflets not very narrow and needle-like, margins not rolled under 7
7 Leaflets 1 to 1,4 cm broad; in catchment area of the Kei River only .... **E. princeps**
  Leaflets more slender than above, not more than 7 mm broad; Uitenhage to Kokstad .... **E. friderici-guilielmi**

B. NATAL

1 Leaves up to 1 m in length; leaflets very narrow and tightly rolled under giving a needle-like appearance; upper slopes of the Drakensberg only .... **E. ghellinckii**
  Leaves 1 m or more in length 2

2 Leaves arching, bow-shaped, producing an umbrella canopy; only known specimen from Ngoye forest in Zululand, now considered to be extinct in the wild .... **E. woodii**
  Leaves spreading, not arching or bow-shaped 3
3 Lowermost leaflets reduced to form numerous spines; median leaflets narrower than those of next species, here not more than 2,5 cm in width; Lebombo mountains north of the Pongola River .... **E. lebomboensis**
  Lowermost leaflets reduced to form fewer spines; median leaflets broader than the above species, up to 4,5 cm in width; widespread in Natal, but not north of the Pongola River .. **E. natalensis**

C. TRANSVAAL

1 Northern area; exceptionally large cycad up to 13 m in height; leaves up to 2,5 m long, leaflet margins with a number of small teeth; Soutpansberg and Letaba .... **E. transvenosus**
  Central, eastern and southern areas 2
2 Central area; on isolated mountains in the Witbank, Pietersburg and Middelburg districts and on the Waterberg range; stems 3 to 4 m in length, often reclining with age; margins of leaflets without teeth, or with 1 to 2 small teeth .... **E. eugene-maraisii**
  Eastern and southern areas 3
3 Leaves 1,5 m or more in length 4
  Leaves less than 1,5 m in length 5
4 On stony cliffs and in rocky gorges of the Lebombo mountains and adjacent areas in Swaziland only .... **E. lebomboensis**
  In low forest and mountain bush, only in the mountains near Barberton and immediately adjacent areas in Swaziland; rare .... **E. paucidentatus**
5 Cones densely woolly 6
  Cones not densely woolly, although they may be finely velvety 7
6 Cones densely grey woolly; stems short, seldom more than 1 m in length; found only in the catchment area of the Olifants River .... **E. lanatus**
  Cones densely brown woolly; stems up to 3 m in length; found only in the mountains on the border between the Transvaal and Swaziland in the area round Piggs Peak and Havelock **E. heenanii**
7 Lowermost leaflets not reduced to spines .... **E. laevifolius**
  Lowermost leaflets reduced to 2 to 6 spines .... **E. inopinus**

D. RHODESIA and MOÇAMBIQUE

North-east, east and south of Rhodesia and adjacent areas in Moçambique. Stems up to 2,5 m in height .... **E. manikensis**
(and including under this the closely related species *E. chimanimaniensis*, *E. concinnus*, *E. munchii*, and *E. pterogonus*)

Encephalartos altensteinii Lehm.
S.A. no: 3   Eastern Cape cycad. Oos-Kaapse broodboom
Rhod. no: —

Encephalartos altensteinii, *the Eastern Cape cycad, in characteristic country.*

Height: up to 4 m, occasionally 7 m; this is a coastal species occurring in low forest or on rocky hillsides. **Leaves:** large, up to 3,5 m in length, among the largest found in the cycads; leaflets up to 15 × 2,5 cm with 2 to 5 teeth along both margins; the lowermost leaflets are not reduced to spines. **Cones:** in groups of 2 to 5 yellowish-green when mature; male cones 50 × 12 cm; female cones 55 × 28 cm. **Seeds:** oval, about 2,3 cm long, scarlet.

This species is very similar to *E. natalensis* and also to *E. lebomboensis*.

Encephalartos eugene-maraisii Verdoorn
S.A. no: 3,1   Waterberg cycad. Waterbergbroodboom
Rhod. no: —

Height: up to 4 m; old specimens tending to sprawl and recline; infrequent on isolated mountains. **Leaves:** rather short, up to 1,3 m; leaflets bluish-green, 15 to 20 × 1,3 to 1,5 cm, margin entire, or with 1 to 2 small teeth on the lower margin; the lowermost leaflets are not reduced to spines. **Cones:** 1 to 3 together, dark brown when mature; male cones 20 to 40 × 6 to 8 cm; female cones 30 to 50 × 16 to 20 cm. **Seeds:** about 4 × 3 cm, amber-coloured, sometimes tinged with red.

This cycad was found by the naturalist, author and poet Eugène Marais, but details of its locality died   **47** with him. It was due to the efforts of his niece, Dr Inez Verdoorn, that these trees were found again and she named the species after its original discoverer, Eugène Marais.

Encephalartos friderici-guilielmi Lehm.
S.A. no: 4　White-haired cycad. Withaarbroodboom
Rhod. no: —

Height: up to 4 m; stem conspicuously stout, up to 60 cm in diameter; occurring on mountainsides and rocky hill slopes. **Leaves:** up to 1 m only, under surface loosely, whitish woolly, losing these hairs later; leaflets long and narrow, up to 17 × 0,7 cm, closely spaced and overlapping, margin entire, the lowermost leaflets are not reduced to spines. **Cones:** 3 to 10 together, densely woolly, yellowish-grey to brownish in colour; male cones 20 to 30 × 6 to 7 cm; female cones 20 to 30 × 15 to 17 cm. **Seeds:** about 3 × 2 cm, yellow to orange.

This is closely related to *E. cycadifolius* (Jacq.) Lehm., a species with an underground stem; apart from this character, these two are easily confused.

Encephalartos ghellinckii Lehm.
S.A. no: 5　Drakensberg cycad. Drakensbergbroodboom
Rhod. no: —

Height: only up to 3 m, with an open brown woolly crown, the old specimens often leaning over; occurring in mountains from 700 m upwards. **Leaves:** only up to 1 m; leaflets up to 14 × 0,4 cm, conspicuously tightly rolled under, making them almost needle-like; densely greyish woolly when young, losing most of these hairs later; the lowermost leaflets are not reduced to spines. **Cones:** 2 to 5 together, densely woolly; male cones 25 × 7 cm; female cones 22 × 14 cm. **Seeds:** about 2,5 × 2,5 cm, golden yellow.

The fine leaflets could lead to some confusion with *Cycas revoluta* Thunb., a Japanese species, which is seen quite frequently in gardens, but the female cones of the latter are characteristic and closely resemble those of *Cycas thouarsii*.

Encephalartos heenanii R. A. Dyer
S.A. no: 14,1　Woolly cycad. Wollerige broodboom
Rhod. no: —

Height: up to 3 m with the stem more or less clothed with woolly hairs; occurring in mountainous areas among rocks in sheltered ravines, at altitudes of 1 800 m. **Leaves:** 1 to 1,3 m long, slightly

curved upwards; leaflets pale silver-green, when young densely covered with brownish woolly hairs some of which persist to maturity; oblong-lanceolate, 12 to 15 × 1,5 cm; spine-tipped, margin entire, rarely with a few small teeth, inclined to roll upwards; the lowermost leaflets are not reduced to spines. **Cones:** 1 to 3, usually produced laterally, stalked, densely covered with shaggy brown woolly hairs, sub-cylindric, up to 30 × 17 cm, male and female cones similar in size and shape but the female cone heavier.

This is the most recent of the species of *Encephalartos* to be found and was described and named only in 1972. It is closely related to *E. paucidentatus* Stapf & Burtt Davy, which occurs in the same area. The differences between the two species are that in the latter species the male and female cones are clearly distinct in size and shape; it is taller, reaching 6 m in height, the leaflets are dark glossy green, the plants are generally almost without hairs although the crown may be more or less woolly when young, and the leaves, 2 m or more in length, are straight and spreading. In *E. heenanii,* on the other hand, the male and female cones are almost indistinguishable externally, the plant is lower growing not exceeding 3 m in height, the leaflets are grey-green, the leaves, only 1 to 1,3 m in length, tend to curve upwards giving a somewhat basin-shaped crown, and all parts of the plant are densely brown woolly.

Encephalartos inopinus R. A. Dyer
S.A. no: 5,1   Lydenburg cycad. Lydenburgse broodboom
Rhod. no: —

Height: up to 3 m; freely branched from base and frequently reclining; occurring in a very limited area in hot dry valleys. **Leaves:** only up to 1,2 m; swollen leaf bases densely covered with brown woolly hairs, smooth later; leaflets bluish-green with a marked whitish bloom when young, especially on the under surface; 14 to 21 × 0,8 to 1,3 cm, margin entire or with 1 to 2 very small teeth; the lowermost leaflets are abruptly modified to form 2 to 6 pairs of short spines. **Cones:** 2 to 4 together; the immature male cone only is known and measures 8 to 10 × 4 cm; the female cones and mature male cones have not been recorded. The diagnostic characters are said to be the slightly sickle-shaped leaflets and the lower leaflets which point backwards.

Encephalartos laevifolius Stapf & Burtt Davy
S.A. no: 6   Kaapsehoop cycad. Kaapsehoopse broodboom
Rhod. no: —

Height: up to 3 m; robust; found on mountain slopes. **Leaves:** up to 1 m only; leaflets with a greyish bloom when young, up to 12 × 7 cm, margins entire; the lowermost leaflets are not reduced to spines. **49**

Cones: with short, fine grey hairs, not woolly; male cones 30 to 40 × 10 cm; female cones shorter, 20 to 30 × 10 to 13 cm. **Seeds:** about 2,7 × 2,3 cm, orange in colour.

Encephalartos lanatus Stapf & Burtt Davy
S.A. no: 5,2   Olifants River cycad. Olifantsrivierbroodboom
Rhod. no: —

Height: up to 1 m only; occurring in sheltered places in valleys along the upper reaches of the Olifants River. **Leaves:** up to 1 m only; leaflets bluish-green when young, green later; 10 to 13 × 6 to 8 cm, overlapping, margin entire; the lowermost leaflets are not reduced to spines. **Cones:** 1 to 4, cream to grey and densely woolly; male cones 25 to 30 × 5 to 6 cm; female cones 25 to 35 × 12 to 15 cm. **Seeds:** up to 3 × 2,5 cm, yellow in colour.

Encephalartos latifrons Lehm.
S.A. no: 7   Albany cycad. Albanybroodboom
Rhod. no: —

Height: up to 3 m; often branched; occurring in scrub bush and on rocky outcrops. **Leaves:** up to 1,5 m; the leaflets are finely velvety when young, losing these hairs later, large 10 to 15 × 4 to 6 cm, overlapping, upper margin entire, the lower margin with 2 to 3 large teeth; the lowermost leaflets are occasionally reduced to spines. **Cones:** large, 1 to 3 together, dark green to bluish-green; male cones 30 to 50 × 8 to 17 cm; female cones up to 60 × 25 cm. **Seeds:** about 5 × 2,5 cm, red in colour.

This closely resembles *E. arenarius* R. A. Dyer, a species with an underground stem; apart from this character these two can be confused.

Encephalartos lebomboensis Verdoorn
S.A. no: 8   Lebombo cycad. Lebombobroodboom
Rhod. no: —

Height: up to 4 m; occurring in a comparatively confined area on cliffs and in rocky river gorges. **Leaves:** 1 to 2 m long, forming a dense crown; the leaflets are rather narrow, 12 to 17 × 1 to 2,5 cm, 1 to 4 teeth on both margins; the lowermost leaflets are reduced to spines. **Cones:** yellow or salmon-pink 1 to 3 together; male cones up to 45 × 13 cm; female cones up to 45 × 22 cm. **Seeds:** about 4 × 2,2 cm, scarlet in colour.

When the Jozini Dam across the Pongola River was under construction, several thousand specimens of this cycad were doomed to destruction by the rising waters. However, *Operation Wild Flower* was organised and the plants were rescued and floated across the river to safety. They were then distributed to botanic gardens and some were offered to interested members of the public.

This cycad can be confused with *E. natalensis*, but *E. lebomboensis* is said not to occur south of the Pongola River, while *E. natalensis* is said not to occur north of the Umfolozi River. Both these species are closely related to *E. altensteinii*.

Encephalartos lehmannii Lehm.
S.A. no: 8,1   Karoo cycad. Karoobroodboom
Rhod. no: —

Height: 1,5 to 3 m, often branched from base and frequently reclining; occurring on dry, stony hillsides in karroid scrub. **Leaves:** up to 1,5 m, the swollen leaf bases having a conspicuous red-brown collar; leaflets blue-grey, rather narrow, 12 to 18 × 1,5 to 2 cm, margin entire or with 1 to 2 very small teeth on the lower margin; the lowermost leaflets may be reduced to 1 pair of spines. **Cones:** solitary, dark red with fine black hairs; male cones 25 to 35 × 8 to 10 cm; female cones 30 to 50 × 15 to 23 cm. **Seeds:** about 5 × 2 cm, red in colour.

This species closely resembles *E. princeps* R. A. Dyer, *E. trispinosus* (Hook.) R. A. Dyer and *E. horridus* (Jacq.) Lehm., the latter two not reaching tree size. Apart from this character, they are difficult to separate.

51

ZAMIACEAE

Encephalartos longifolius (Jacq.) Lehm.
S.A. no: 9   Suurberg cycad. Suurbergbroodboom
Rhod. no: —

 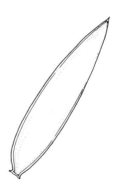

Height: up to 3 m, stem thickset; may be locally common on exposed mountain slopes well inland.
Leaves: up to 1,75 m; leaflets dark green with a grey bloom, up to 20 × 4 cm, margin entire or with 1 to 3 teeth on the lower margin; the lowermost leaflets may be reduced to spines. **Cones:** 1 to 2 together, greenish-brown with reddish flattened hairs; male cones 40 to 60 × 14 to 20 cm; female cones about 60 × 40 cm. **Seeds:** about 5 × 2,5 cm, red in colour.
These cones are among the largest in the genus, a female cone weighting up to 35 kg. This species is closely related to *E. altensteinii,* which, however, is fairly well confined to areas of coastal bush.

Encephalartos manikensis (Gilliland) Gilliland
[including in this complex the closely related *E. chimanimaniensis* R. A. Dyer & Verdoorn (Rhod. no: 5), *E. concinnus* R. A. Dyer & Verdoorn (Rhod. no: 6), *E. munchii* R. A. Dyer & Verdoorn, and *E. pterogonus* R. A. Dyer & Verdoorn]
S.A. no: —
Rhod. no: 5,6 and 7   Rhodesian cycad

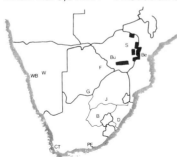 

Height: 1,5 to 2,5 m; occurring on mountainsides and granite hills. **Leaves:** 1 to 2 m long; the leaflets may have a temporary greyish bloom, 15 to 20 × 2 to 3 cm, with 2 to 4 teeth along both margins; the lowermost leaflets are reduced to spines. **Cones:** 1 to 4 together; male cones 25 to 65 × 8 to 15 cm, the scales may or may not gape wide; female cones 30 to 50 × 20 to 25 cm. **Seeds:** about 4,5 × 2,5 cm, orange to red in colour.
The presence of 5 separate species endemic to so confined an area would seem to be unlikely. In the author's opinion it is probable that 2 species are involved: typical *E. manikensis,* in which the scales on the male cones do not gape open, and a second species in which these scales do gape open. However, insufficient fertile material was available to make any firm decision on this matter. The distribution map treats all these species as one.

Encephalartos natalensis R. A. Dyer & Verdoorn
S.A. no: 10   Natal cycad. Natalbroodboom
Rhod. no: —

Height: 3 to 4 m, occasionally up to 6,5 m and often branched from the base; occurring on krantzes and in rocky valleys, sometimes fringing forests and always some distance inland from the coast.

Leaves: large, reaching 3,5 m in length; leaflets 16 to 23 × 2 to 4,5 cm, margin entire or with 1 to 5 teeth on one or both margins; the lowermost leaflets are reduced to several spines. **Cones:** 2 to 3 together, dark green with a thin covering of brownish wool; male cones up to 45 × 10 cm; female cones up to 50 × 25 cm. **Seeds:** 5 × 2 cm, scarlet in colour.

A group of these cycads grows in a kloof in the park at Monteseel, near the Valley of a Thousand Hills in Natal. The largest tree stands about 6 m high and the age of its rootstock has been estimated at about 1 000 years, while that of its stem and branches at probably more than 250 years. This specimen was declared a scientific monument in 1951.

This species closely resembles *E. altensteinii,* but is reported to hold to inland hills, while *E. altensteinii* is a coastal species.

Encephalartos paucidentatus Stapf & Burtt Davy
S.A. no: 11   Barberton cycad. Barbertonse broodboom
Rhod. no: —

Height: up to 6 m; a rare species of low forest and mountain bush. **Leaves:** 1 to 2 m in length; leaflets 15 to 25 × 2 to 3 cm, widely spaced, margins entire or with 1 to 3 small teeth; the lowermost leaflets may be reduced to a few spines. **Cones:** 2 to 3 together, golden-yellow; male cones up to 60 × 15 cm; female cones: the size and shape have not been recorded. **Seeds:** about 4 × 2,5 cm, red in colour.

Encephalartos princeps R. A. Dyer
S.A. no: 12   Kei cycad. Keibroodboom
Rhod. no: —

53

ZAMIACEAE

Height: up to 3 m, occasionally 5 m, usually branched and frequently leaning over or reclining when old; occurring on cliffs and rocky outcrops in karroid scrub. **Leaves:** 1 to 1,3 m only; leaflets up to 15 × 1,3 cm, overlapping, margin entire or with a few teeth on the lower margin; the lowermost leaflets are not reduced to spines. **Cones:** 2 to 4 together, dull green; male cones 16 to 26 × 8 to 10 cm; female cones about 30 to 20 cm. **Seeds:** about 4,5 × 2 cm, red in colour.

The close relationship between this species and *E. lehmannii* is discussed under the latter species.

Encephalartos transvenosus Stapf & Burtt Davy
S.A. no: 13   Modjadji cycad. Modjadjibroodboom
Rhod. no: —

A very large cycad, usually 5 to 8 m, occasionally reaching 13 m; occurring in forests and on hillsides. **Leaves:** up to 2,5 m in length; leaflets 10 to 20 × 2 to 3,5 cm, with 2 to 5 small teeth along upper margin, and 1 to 3 along the lower; the lowermost leaflets are reduced to several spines. **Cones:** 2 to 4 together; male cones up to 40 × 15 cm; the female cones are massive, up to 80 × 30 cm, and weighing up to 37 kg. **Seeds:** about 5 × 2,5 cm, scarlet in colour.

This is perhaps the most famous of the southern African cycads and one of the largest in the world. The trees form natural forests on the mountainsides in the Modjadji location near Duiwelskloof in the north-eastern Transvaal where they have been strictly protected by succeeding generations of Rain Queens who are the hereditary rulers of the people in this area. There is little doubt that royal protection has played a part in the establishment of this unique cycad forest which was proclaimed a National Monument in 1936, for here the plants must be numbered in their thousands. They also occur on the Soutpansberg mountains.

Encephalartos woodii Sander   Illust. 1
S.A. no: 14   Wood's cycad. Wood-se-broodboom
Rhod. no: —

Height: up to 6 m; apparently a forest species which must now be considered extinct in its natural state. **Leaves:** up to 2,5 m, forming a dense umbrella-like canopy; leaflets up to 20 × 5 cm; margins toothed in young leaves, entire when mature; the lowermost leaflets are reduced to spines. **Cones:** only the male cones are known and these are bright orange-yellow and unusually large, 40 to 90 cm × 15 to 20 cm. **Seeds:** not known.

In 1895 Medley Wood, Curator of the Durban Botanic Gardens, found this single male cycad growing in the Ngoye forest in Zululand; the plant was 4-stemmed from the base with a few small off-shoots.

As the years passed and no further specimens of this species were found, Medley Wood arranged for part of the original tree to be collected and for some of the material to be planted in Durban and some sent overseas. Years later, part of the remaining plant was found to have been mutilated, and finally, in 1916, to prevent the last remaining stem from being annihilated by fire or the local peoples, it was removed and sent to Pretoria. So ended the only known wild specimen of *E. woodii*. However, the material collected has thrived, particularly that in Durban, where fine specimens can be seen.

PODOCARPACEAE *(The yellowwood family)*

PODOCARPUS L'Hérit. ex Pers.

Evergreen trees. **Leaves:** alternate, sub-opposite, whorled or spiralled. **Male cones:** catkin-like, axillary. **Female cones:** scales greatly reduced and fused together with the cone axis to form a receptacle which may remain woody or become swollen and fleshy (recently the term *podocarpum* has been applied to this unusual structure); ovules, completely exposed and only slightly protected by a false aril, the epimatium, are produced on the receptacle; 1 or more ovules may abort so that 1 to 2 seeds are finally produced. **Seeds:** ellipsoidal to globose, the false aril forming a leathery or fleshy covering.

All species of *Podocarpus* are protected in South Africa.

Key to the species of *Podocarpus:*
1 Branchlets usually less than 1,5 mm in diameter near the apex, often square in section and deeply ridged; leaves twisted at the base so that the leaf lies vertically. Seeds produced on scaly or leafy branchlets which do not form a swollen receptacle. From Swellendam eastwards to the Transvaal; also on the Chimanimani mountains in Moçambique .... **P. falcatus**
  Branchlets usually more than 1,5 mm in diameter near the apex, often with shallow grooves or slight ridges; the leaves not twisted so that they lie horizontally; seeds produced on receptacles which become more or less swollen and sometimes fleshy when mature, borne on stalks with no scales or leaves 2
2 Leaves usually longer than 8 cm, up to 17 cm, more or less pendulous, gradually tapering to a narrow apex; receptacle only slightly swollen, never fleshy or brightly coloured ....
  .... **P. henkelii**
  Leaves usually shorter than 8 cm 3
3 Leaves usually wider than 5 mm; receptacle swollen and turning bright red or purplish. Cape Peninsula eastwards through Natal to the Transvaal, eastern Rhodesia and adjacent areas in Moçambique .... **P. latifolius**
  Leaves usually only 4 to 5 mm wide; receptacle swollen and turning bright red or purplish. Western Cape only .... **P. elongatus**

Podocarpus elongatus (Ait.) L'Hérit. ex Pers.
S.A. no: 15 Breede River yellowwood. Breëriviergeelhout
Rhod. no: —

PODOCARPACEAE

The smallest of the southern African species, usually only spreading shrubs to small rounded trees 3 to 6 m high as they are particularly susceptible to damage by fire, but when protected they can develop into fine trees; confined to the winter-rainfall areas of the western Cape, favouring sandy soils, often along rivers and streams but also on exposed mountainsides where they remain small and stunted, often becoming almost prostrate. **Bark:** grey to brown, longitudinally peeling in narrow strips. **Leaves:** crowded towards the ends of the branchlets, narrowly elliptic, grey-green, 4 to 6 × 0,3 to 0,5 cm, sometimes larger; tapering to both apex and base; margin entire, slightly rolled under; petiole short. **Cones:** male cones axillary, about 2,5 × 0,3 cm; female receptacle 2-lobed, swollen, crimson red, about 10 × 10 mm (January to May). **Seeds:** 1 to 2 on each receptacle, maturing rapidly to a dark blue-green, oval, 7 to 10 mm long.

This species could be confused with *P. latifolius* where their ranges overlap, but *P. elongatus* has, on its leaves, scattered stomata or pores which lie in grooves visible to the naked eye; the stomata themselves can be seen with a hand lens.

Podocarpus falcatus (Thunb.) R. Br. ex Mirb.
[*P. gracillimus* Stapf]
S.A. no: 16   Outeniqua yellowwood. Outeniekwageelhout
Rhod. no: —

A medium to large tree reaching 20 to 60 m in the high, moist forests of the southern Cape, but lower-growing under drier conditions; it also occurs in wooded ravines, patches of mountain forest and in coastal swamp forest. **Bark:** thin, rather smooth, greyish-brown to dark brown. **Leaves:** small, dark green, often with a greyish bloom, sometimes slightly sickle-shaped, or falcate (the specific name refers to this), hard, leathery, narrow, 3 to 5 × 0,3 to 0,5 cm; apex sharply pointed; tapering to the base; margin entire; petiole short. **Cones:** male cones axillary, small, about 10 × 3 mm; in the female structure no fleshy receptacle is formed and usually one seed only is produced at the end of a woody stalk which is only slightly expanded at the apex (September to May). **Seeds:** large, fleshy, almost spherical, about 1,5 cm in diameter, turning a deep yellow colour and taking a full year to develop, so that seeds at some stage of development may be found on the tree throughout the year.

The bark of Podocarpus falcatus, *the Outeniqua yellowwood, flaking in irregular pieces.*

There is considerable evidence that *P. falcatus* may be conspecific with the tropical species *P. gracilior* Pilger; however, the author lacked personal knowledge of the latter and no move towards a combination has been made. Should this prove to be necessary, then *P. falcatus* would stand as the earlier name. This is the well-known 'Big Tree' of the Knysna forest. The wood is valuable: the straight stems were used for the topmasts and yards of ships and the timber is highly esteemed in boat building today. Its rate of growth is average and it is gaining in popularity as a garden subject.

Podocarpus henkelii Stapf
S.A. no: 17   Henkel's yellowwood. Henkel-se-geelhout
Rhod. no: —

 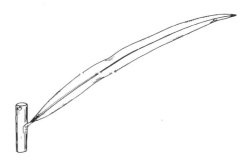

A fine, large tree up to 20 m or more in height; occurring in moist, evergreen mountain forests and, less commonly, in coastal forests. **Bark:** yellowish-grey, brown or dark grey; in large specimens the bark is longitudinally fissured and peels in long, narrow strips, exposing the reddish-brown under-bark. **Leaves:** dark green, shiny, long and slender, up to 17 × 1 cm, drooping; gradually tapering to a narrow apex and base; margin entire and finely and tightly rolled under. **Cones:** male cones rather large, about 3 × 0,4 cm; in female cones the receptacle is not well developed and remains greenish (September to January). **Seeds:** large, oval, up to 2,5 × 2 cm, olive-green in colour.
There is considerable evidence that *P. henkelii* may be conspecific with the tropical east African species *P. ensiculus* Melville; however, the author lacked personal knowledge of the latter and no move towards combining the two has been made. Should this prove to be necessary, then *P. henkelii* would stand as the earlier name. The seed germinates easily, but the trees are rather slow-growing; nevertheless they are gaining popularity as garden subjects. The species also yields a fine timber with a wide range of uses.
Dr John Henkel was formerly Conservator of Forests for Natal and Zululand and at one time Chief of the Division of Forestry in Rhodesia. He was the author of *A Field Book of the Woody Plants of Natal and Zululand*, published in 1934, a work which is still frequently referred to.

Podocarpus latifolius (Thunb.) R. Br. ex Mirb.   Illust. 2 and 3
[*P. thunbergii* Hook.; *P. milanjianus* Rendle]
S.A. no: 18   Real yellowwood. Opregte geelhout
Rhod. no: 8   Yellowwood

 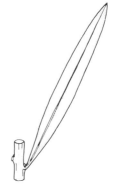

The bark of the real yellowwood, Podocarpus latifolius, *flaking in narrow vertical strips.*

A large tree, 20 to 30 m in height; occurring in evergreen forests and patches of mountain forest and also on exposed mountainsides when it is low-growing and stunted, barely exceeding 2 m in height. **Bark:** yellowish-brown, greyish-brown to dark brown and peeling in narrow vertical flakes. **Leaves:** thick, tough, dark green, narrowly elliptic, 6 to 15× 0,5 to 1,3 cm; apex broadly tapering and finally sharp-tipped; narrowly tapering to the base; margin entire, rolled under; petiole short. **Cones:** male cones axillary, pinkish, large, up to 5 × 0,5 cm; female receptacle conical, fleshy, bright red, about 10 mm long (July to September). **Seeds:** 1 to 2 seeds are produced, large, fleshy, oval, 1 to 1,5 cm, maturing rapidly and ripening from December to February.

The receptacles and seeds are very showy and striking when a tree is bearing heavily. This is the most common and most widespread of the species. The trees yield a fine timber of a uniform pale yellow colour, which seasons and saws well, works easily and takes a good finish. It has been used more than any other indigenous timber and most of the beautiful floors in the fine old Cape homesteads were made of this wood. These trees are slow-growing but are worthwhile garden subjects; like all the species of *Podocarpus* they will stand several degrees of frost.

*PINACEAE *(The pine family)*

*PINUS L.

There are no indigenous members of this family in southern Africa, but many species of *Pinus* have been introduced for their valuable soft wood. Most of these species remain in their plantations, the regeneration from seedlings being confined to these limited areas. However, two species are now seriously competing with the indigenous vegetation in various areas. *Pinus patula* Schlecht. & Cham., the patula pine (Rhod. no: 9), introduced from east-central Mexico, is now invading the natural forests in parts of the eastern Transvaal and eastern Rhodesia. *Pinus pinaster* Ait., the cluster pine, introduced from the Mediterranean countries and Europe, is now seriously threatening the natural flora in the south and south-western Cape. Other escapes, limited to the south and south-western Cape, that may cause serious problems in the future are *P. canariensis* Sm., *P. halipensis* Mill. and *P. radiata* D. Don.

58

CUPRESSACEAE *(The cypress family)*

All the species of the two genera occurring in southern Africa contain an aromatic resin which makes them particularly susceptible to fire; even a mild fire causes these trees almost to explode into flame and, once alight, they frequently burn to death.

Key to the genera:
Mature female cone hard, woody and dehiscent; mature leaves 2 mm or more in length, tightly pressed against the stem giving the branchlets a smooth appearance .... **1. Widdringtonia**

Mature female cone fleshy and berry-like; mature leaves less than 2 mm long, not tightly pressed against the stem so the branchlets have a rough appearance .... **2. Juniperus**

1. WIDDRINGTONIA Endl.

Evergreen shrubs or trees; wood fragrant. **Leaves:** juvenile leaves needle-like, spirally arranged; adult leaves scale-like, pressed tightly against the branchlets, opposite decussate or alternate. **Cones:** sexes separate but on the same tree. Male cones small, more or less 4 mm long, terminal on short lateral branchlets. Female cones woody, 1,3 to 2,5 cm in diameter, solitary or in clusters on elongated shoots; scales few, usually 4 of equal size, rarely 5 to 6, arranged in a whorl, the scales opening to allow pollination and then later closing again; each scale terminates in a thick, woody, smooth to warty face, or valve, and each has several ovules at the base. **Seeds:** ovoid with a papery wing. All the species of *Widdringtonia* are protected in South Africa.

Key to the tree species of *Widdringtonia:*
1 Valves (or faces) of the female cones smooth, wrinkled or only slightly warty; adult leaves on branchlets narrowly oblong. Fairly widespread in mountain areas .... **W. nodiflora**
Valves conspicuously rough and warty; adult leaves on branchlets ovate 2
2 Seeds oval, 3-cornered; wing comparatively small; in the Cedarberg mountains, Clanwilliam district only .... **W. cedarbergensis**
Seeds rather flattened with a conspicuous wing; Willowmore district only ...... **W. schwarzii**

Widdringtonia cedarbergensis Marsh
S.A. no: 19   Clanwilliam cedar. Clanwilliamseder
Rhod. no: —

SEED

A rare tree usually 5 to 7 m, but in protected places up to 20 m, in height, the old trees being spreading, gnarled and massive; occurring singly or in scattered groups on rocky outcrops and mountain tops. **Bark:** reddish-grey, thin, fibrous and flaking. **Leaves:** juvenile leaves up to 2 × 0,2 cm; adult leaves up to 4 mm long. **Cones:** male cones very small, only up to 2 mm long; female cones almost spherical, up to 2,5 cm in diameter, with 4 scales, each with woody, rough, warty faces, dark brown; they may be found on the tree at various stages of development throughout the year. **Seeds:** ovoid, narrowly winged.
This species is very similar to *W. schwarzii,* but the 2 species can be separated on their geographical distribution. The wood is beautiful, light yellow to whitish; it works well, takes a fine polish and is borer-proof. The pews, doors and carved altar in the Anglican church, and the appointments in the

59

CUPRESSACEAE

Courthouse, both in Clanwilliam, show this wood at its best. In past years this species was almost annihilated by woodcutters and veld fires, but today an active planting scheme is in progress and future generations may see these fine trees re-established.

Widdringtonia nodiflora (L.) Powrie   Illust. 4
[*W. whytei* Rendle; *W. cupressoides* auct.]
S.A. no: 20   Mountain cedar. Bergsipres
Rhod. no: 10   Mountain cedar

SEED

Most often a scrubby bush or small tree 4 to 6 m in height, but in a few remote areas in the eastern mountains of Rhodesia much larger specimens are still found; occurring at high altitudes on mountain-sides, among rocks and in gullies. **Bark:** brown to grey, thinly vertically fissured and flaking in long narrow strips revealing reddish underbark. **Leaves:** juvenile leaves needle-like, fresh green, spirally arranged, up to 2 cm long; adult leaves scale-like, about 2 mm long, dark green. **Cones:** male cones small, 2 to 4 mm long, terminal; female cones globose, 1,5 to 2 cm in diameter, dark brown, scales 4, with the scale surfaces wrinkled and with a few protuberances; the cones ripen about March, but cones in varying stages of development may be found throughout the year. **Seeds:** dark brown to blackish with a conspicuous reddish wing.

The name *cedar* is applied loosely to a number of trees with this characteristically fragrant wood, several of which, including *Widdringtonia,* yield a pleasantly aromatic oil. The timber is very durable out-of-doors and makes hard wearing roofing shingles that weather to an attractive silver-grey. The wood has a natural satiny sheen and makes fine furniture and panelling. Unfortunately, south of the Zambezi, there are very few sizable trees left today, although beautiful kists made in the late 19th century by the pioneers in the Melsetter district are evidence that large trees grew at that time. Now only a few good specimens remain in all but inaccessible places. An exceptionally fine tree is illustrated in the habit drawing (Illust. 4). On Mount Mlanje in Malawi such specimens are normal and this is considered one of the most important timber trees in that country. Replanting and re-afforestation schemes have been encouraging although long-term projects, but such schemes have met with little success in South Africa or Rhodesia.

Widdringtonia schwarzii (Marloth) Mast.
[*Callitris schwarzii* Marloth]
S.A. no: 21   Willowmore cedar. Baviaanskloofseder
Rhod. no: —

SEED

A large tree 17 to 30 m in height, and some fine old specimens reaching 40 m can still be found; occurring only in the low-rainfall areas of the Baviaanskloof and Kouga mountains, in rocky ravines about 900 m. **Bark:** reddish-grey, thin, fibrous, flaking. **Leaves:** juvenile leaves up to 2 cm long, needle-like; adult leaves 3 to 4 mm long, opposite decussate. **Cones:** male cones very small, about 2 mm long on short lateral branches; female cones almost globose, about 2 cm in diameter, dark brown, the four scales having rough and warty faces; cones in varying stages of development can be found on the trees throughout the year. **Seeds:** somewhat flattened with a conspicuous wing.

The occurrence of these trees tells the same sad story – all accessible specimens have been burnt or cut out and lost. Trees of any substantial size are now confined to remote rocky ravines and can be seen only with the greatest effort and determination. The similarity of *W. schwarzii* to *W. cedarbergensis* is discussed under the latter species; it also shows some affinities with *W. nodiflora* and is intermediate in many respects between the two.

2 JUNIPERUS L.

Juniperus procera Hochst. ex Endl.
S.A. no: —
Rhod. no: 11   African pencil-cedar

A medium to tall tree 10 to 20 m in height, but growing to 40 m in countries to the north; occurring in evergreen mountain forests between 1 500 m and 3 000 m. **Bark:** reddish-brown, thin, flaking. **Leaves:** juvenile leaves needle-like, spreading; adult leaves very small, scale-like, leaf bases pressed tightly against branchlets, but apices spreading slightly giving a roughish appearance. **Cones:** male cones small, about 3 mm long, narrowly oval, with about 10 rounded, opposite, chunky scales, irregularly overlapping; female cones with 6 to 8 fleshy scales which become swollen and fuse together at maturity so that the ripe female cone has all the appearances of a fleshy, juicy, berry-like fruit, blue-black in colour, about 6 mm in diameter, ripening in October. **Seeds:** about 1 to 2 mature seeds produced, about 5 mm long, brown, woody.

The fruits of a common European species, *J. communis* L., were once used to flavour gin, liqueurs and cordials, but today cheaper substitutes are used. The wood is hard, durable, termite-proof and faintly scented; it is pale reddish in colour, attractive, fine-grained and takes a good finish. It is an important timber tree in Kenya. In Rhodesia only a single specimen is known in its wild state at the present time; it is a specially protected plant.

WELWITSCHIACEAE *(The welwitschia family)*

This family contains only a single genus and a single species.

WELWITSCHIA J. D. Hook.

Welwitschia mirabilis J. D. Hook.   Illust. 5
[*W. bainesii* (J. D. Hook.) Carriere]
S.A. no: 21,1 Welwitschia, Wonderplant
Rhod. no:—

61

A dwarf but massive tree driven underground by the rigours of the desert climate; the largest specimens have a stem 1,5 m in diameter rising 2 m above the ground, with 2 to 3 m below the ground before the very large tap-root starts; occurring in gravelly soils along dry watercourses in desert regions, even surviving in the deep, loose sand of the desert itself. **Stem:** the crown is flattened or saucer-shaped, dark brown, hard, woody, warty and cracked, most often forming a rock-like hump just protruding above ground-level, like a large, inverted elephant's foot (see Illust. 5); around the rim of this flattened apex there are 2 semicircular grooves (occasionally 3) from which the leaves grow. **Leaves:** the plant produces only 2 true leaves throughout its lifetime; these are persistent, continually growing outwards from the base, and can be compared with tough, leathery paste as it is slowly squeezed from a gigantic tube. At the same time the ends are constantly blackened and worn away by the desert sun and searing winds, while the whole leaf blade is torn into long thong-like shreds, resulting in a great tangled mass lying on the ground; the leaves may reach 3 m in length, while the width varies with the size of the stem, each leaf being rather less than half the circumference of the apex. **Flowers:** sexes separate; while still in the form of cones, in many ways these flowers represent a bridge between the cone-bearing plants and the flowering plants: here stamens are produced in the male cones, while, in the female cones, the ovules are still naked, though now partly protected by two enveloping scale-like segments and a style-like structure is also present; the cones, on branched structures round the rim of the stem apex, may be quite brightly coloured, the male cones salmon-pink, the female cones greenish-yellow banded with reddish-brown. **Seeds:** winged.

The first collections of these plants, made separately by Baines and Welwitsch in 1860, caused some confusion at Kew Gardens and two generic names were created, *Tumboa* and *Welwitschia,* and also two specific names, *bainesii* and *mirabilis*. Since then the generic name *Welwitschia* has been conserved, but controversy over the validity of one or the other of the specific names has continued to the present day.

These plants are certainly among the oldest in the world, for recent tests using the carbon-14 dating technique established the age of an average specimen to be between 500 and 600 years and, by comparison, the age of a large, old specimen has been estimated to be 2 000 years or more.

Angiospermae *(The flowering plants)*

Monocotyledons

POACEAE (Nom. altern. **Gramineae**) *(The grass family)*

Key to the genera of 'tree grasses' or bamboos:
1 Stems solid, or thick-walled with only a narrow central cavity; veins in the leaves not forming a conspicuous tessellate (square-marked) pattern on the surface .... **3. Oxytenanthera**

Stems with a substantial central cavity; if thick-walled, then veins in the leaves forming a more or less conspicuous pattern of small squares (tessellate) 2

2 Stamens 3; leaves conspicuously tessellate .... **1. Arundinaria**

   Stamens 6; leaves obscurely tessellate 3

3 Stamen filaments joined; flower heads conspicuously spherical, spiky ..... **3. Oxytenanthera**

   Stamen filaments free; flower heads cup-shaped; veining on leaf surfaces very obscure
   .... **2. Oreobambos**

1. ARUNDINARIA Michx.

Arundinaria tessellata (Nees) Munro
S.A. no: Southern mountain bamboo
Rhod. no: —

Height: 3 to 4 m, in dense, leafy clumps; occurring on the margins of high altitude forest, along streams and among rocks on mountain tops. **Leaves:** at the base of the plant rather small, almost sheath-like, about 3 to 5 × 0,6 to 1 cm in dense clusters, near the stem apex larger, up to 12 cm long; margins harsh, minutely spiny; veins on the leaf surface marking out conspicuous small squares (tessellate – a feature to which the specific name refers). **Flowers:** bisexual, enclosed in a series of specialised bracts; stamens only 3; ovary smooth or hairy, styles 3, joined at the base. **Grain:** ovate to oblong.
The flowering seems to be sporadic, and the plants do not flower annually.

2. OREOBAMBOS K. Schum.

Oreobambos buchwaldii K. Schum.
S.A. no: —
Rhod. no: 12   Northern mountain bamboo

63

Height: 2,5 to 7 m, in dense clumps; only recently collected on one mountain in Rhodesia, but known habitats in east and central Africa are clearings in evergreen forest, in swamp forest and along mountain streams. **Stems:** sheaths first with fine appressed hairs. **Leaves:** pale green to bluish-green, smooth, lanceolate to oblong, 10 to 35 × 2,5 to 6 cm; square patterned veining on leaf surface even less distinct than on *Oxytenanthera*. **Flowers:** bisexual, enclosed in specialised bracts forming loose, cup-shaped heads; stamens 6, free; ovary with silky hairs at apex. **Grain:** crustaceous with a tuft of silky hairs on apex.

Flowers have not been recorded from Rhodesia, but in Tanzania populations are said to flower annually.

A large clump of bamboo, covering almost 0,2 hectares, grows near Sibasa in the northern Transvaal and features in the rites and practices of the Venda people who, observing custom and the strictest taboos, fashion reed flutes from the stems. Each pipe produces only one single note and as a result the music created by the combined orchestra consists of the most complex interplay of instruments, each sounding its solitary note at precisely the right moment. This clump of bamboo is the only one of the species known to occur in South Africa; the plant has never been known to flower so positive identification has not been possible. It does not seem to be satisfactorily placed under *Oxytenanthera*, but a new possibility has been provided by the recent discovery of *Oreobambos buchwaldii* in Rhodesia at a locality far closer to the Transvaal than the nearest known colony of *Oxytenanthera*.

3. OXYTENANTHERA Munro

Oxytenanthera abyssinica (A. Rich.) Munro
S.A. no: —
Rhod. no: 13   Wild bamboo

Height: 7 m, or more, in dense clumps; occurring along river banks, in damp places on wooded hillsides, often associated with termite mounds. **Stems:** arching slightly near the tips; sheaths covered with short, dark brown, bristly hairs, easily rubbed off and irritating to the hands. **Leaves:** bluish-green, narrowly lanceolate, 5 to 25 × 1 to 3 cm, tapering to a spine-tipped apex; sometimes the veins on the leaf surface may form a pattern of small squares, but usually these are obscure and ill-defined. **Flowers:** in 1- to 4-flowered spikes, the upper flowers bisexual, the lower flowers sterile; stamens 6, joined at base; ovary without hairs, styles 3, and hollow (this feature is unique). **Grain:** narrowly tapering to both ends and crowned with the persistent bases of the styles.

64   There is considerable evidence that each plant flowers only once in its lifetime and then dies.

PANDANACEAE *(The pandanus family)*

PANDANUS L.

Pandanus livingstonianus Rendle
S.A. no: —
Rhod. no: —   Screw-pine

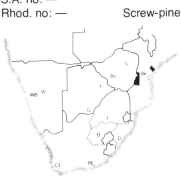

Trees up to 13 m, rather palm-like, the leaves and fruits making it strongly reminiscent of a tree pineapple; occurring along river banks at low altitudes. **Stem:** pale brown, raised above the ground on many sturdy stilt roots; the stem and roots are spiny. **Leaves:** dark, shiny, olive-green above, paler bluish-green below, hard, rigid, strap-like, 1 m or more in length, arising from the apex of stems in 3 spiralling ranks (hence the common name); margins with sharp, hooked, backward-facing prickles. **Flowers:** sexes separate; male flowers in dense branched spikes, 15 to 20 cm long, creamy-white, with conspicuous, large spathe-like bracts; female flowers in short, more compact spikes, green or cream (October). **Fruits:** small, fleshy, crowded along a common axis, producing a cone-like structure about 12 × 7 cm resembling a miniature pineapple.

It has been suggested that the population in the Musapa Gap, Chimanimani mountains (almost on the Rhodesian border) and adjacent areas in Moçambique constitutes a separate species. However, this material needs very careful comparison with the specimens of *P. livingstonianus* from the areas around the Zambezi delta as they appear to be difficult to separate.

ARECACEAE (nom. altern. **Palmae**) *(The palm family)*

Palms are widespread throughout the tropics and subtropics and are remarkably constant in their general pattern – a smooth slender stem with a crown of graceful leaves; it is not common for the stem to develop branches. In southern Africa there are five genera and seven species occurring naturally, although many have been introduced and cultivated.

Key to the genera:
1 Leaves fan-shaped 2

  Leaves pinnate or feather-shaped 3

2 Leaves, including the petiole, or stalk, 3 to 4 m long; fruits large, 12 to 18 cm in diameter .... **3. Borassus**

  Leaves, including the petiole, 1,5 to 2 m long; fruits small, 4 to 5 cm in diameter **2. Hyphaene**

3 Leaves very large, up to 18 m in length; fruits with conspicuous, thick, overlapping scales .... **4. Raphia**

  Leaves 3 to 4 m in length; fruits without scales 4

4 Lower leaflets reduced to spines; male and female flowers on different trees; fruits oblong, fleshy, 1 to 1,5 cm long .... **1. Phoenix**

  Lower leaflets not reduced to spines; male and female flowers on the same tree; fruits round, fibrous, 2 cm in diameter .... **5. Jubaeopsis**   **65**

The wild date palm, Phoenix reclinata, *showing its reclining habit.*

1. PHOENIX L.

Phoenix reclinata Jacq.
S.A. no: 22   Wild date palm. Wildedadelboom
Rhod. no: 14   Wild date palm

Height: usually 3 to 6 m but reaching 10 m, often several-stemmed from the base, the old stems often leaning far over, curving upwards again near the apex, producing a very characteristic appearance; occurring along river banks in low-lying open grassland, and in the Okavango delta where they are often associated with termite mounds. **Leaves:** pinnate, or feather-shaped, 3 to 4 m long, the lowermost leaflets being reduced to spines. **Flowers:** sexes separate, on different trees. Male flowers: calyx cup-shaped; petals 3; stamens 6, joined at base; ovary vestigial; forming large showy sprays and producing clouds of dust-like pollen. Female flowers globose, insignificant; calyx as in male; petals 3, rounded; ovary with 3 free carpels; 6 vestigial stamens; forming short, branched heads among leaf bases (August to October). **Fruits:** oval, 1 to 1,5 cm long, green becoming bright orange when mature, thinly fleshy, edible, sweet when ripe, but astringent when green (February to April).

66

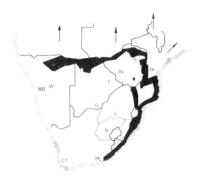

The fruits resemble those of the commercial date palm, *P. dactylifera* L. but are smaller and lack the thick flesh. Some specimens of this true date palm grow near a spring in the Fish River Canyon in South West Africa; these are not indigenous, but are said to have grown from seeds thrown away by escaped German prisoners of war during World War I. In *P. reclinata* there is an increased flow of sap to the flower heads just before the flowering season and this is tapped from the flower stalk (spadix) by local Africans who make an intoxicating drink from the liquid. These palms adapt to a wide range of conditions; they grow readily from seed, transplant easily and make decorative garden plants.

2. HYPHAENE Gaertn.

Large palm trees often 5 to 7 m, but sometimes up to 15 m, in height, single to several-stemmed, with a slight swelling about half way up the stem; occurring in open sandy country, not normally along river banks. **Leaves:** fan-shaped, grey-green, 1,5 to 2 m long including the petiole, which is armed with sharp recurved thorns; the bases of the leaflets are asymmetric. **Flowers:** sexes separate on different trees. Male flowers: calyx 3-lobed, the lobes overlapping; petals ovate, concave, overlapping, joined at base forming a short tube; stamens 6; ovary 0; the male flowers are short-lived and are produced in fairly short, tangled spikes among leaf bases. The female flowers are larger than the male and shortly stalked; sepals ovate, overlapping, slightly shorter than petals; ovary subglobose, stamens 0; produced in large, branched sprays developing into heavy branched trusses of fruits (September to October). **Fruit:** almost spherical or pear shaped 4 to 5 cm in diameter, orange-red to dark brown, a thin layer of sweet-tasting, ginger-flavoured, spongy, fibrous pulp surrounds the seed; within the seed the endosperm is white and bony, resembling vegetable ivory. The fruits are produced in large quantities, up to 2 000 per tree, each taking two years to mature and up to two further years to fall, so they may be seen on the tree all the year round. Elephants and baboons eat this fruit and are therefore possibly the agents for its dispersal. When young, it produces a little milk similar to that of the coconut and this is relished by the indigenous peoples of Botswana and South West Africa.

These palms are widely exploited as a source of wine and unfortunately many are killed as a result. Local people tap the tree near the growing-tip but afterwards the sap hardens as it dries to from a crust over the wound and this must be cut back before a further supply can be obtained. After three or four weeks of tapping and cutting back the growing-tip will have been entirely removed and the stem inevitably dies.

The wine itself is sweet and only slightly intoxicating, and though about 60 to 70 litres may be obtained from the average tree, this relatively innocuous liquor can be distilled to form a highly potent spirit, about two litres of which are obtained from every 20 litres of wine.

The hard white kernels of the seeds, closely resembling the commercial *vegetable ivory* of South America, are too small to be of any economic importance though they are often used to make ornaments, trinkets or curios.

This is a difficult palm to cultivate: the seeds do not germinate easily and the plants are very slow-growing. Furthermore, the massive tap-roots make it almost impossible to transplant the trees once they are established and for these reasons they are rarely seen in gardens.

Two species are apparently involved in southern Africa but they are very similar and are separable only on the shape of the fruit:

67

ARECACEAE

Fruits with a distinctly narrow base, pear shaped; often a coastal species .... **H. natalensis**
Fruits round or slightly oval, base not narrowed; an inland species, Botswana, Caprivi Strip, etc.
.... **H. benguellensis**

However, palms of this type are widespread in Moçambique, and also along the Limpopo valley eastwards from the Shashi River, but as fruiting material has not been available, it has not been possible to place them in one or the other of the species. These populations have been omitted from both the distribution maps.

Hyphaene benguellensis Welw.
S.A. no: 24   Real fan palm. Opregte waaierpalm
Rhod. no: 15   Northern ilala palm

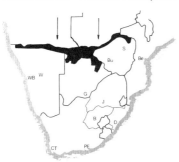 

For differences between this and *H. natalensis,* see the key. All the material occurring south of the Zambezi is placed in var. *ventricosa* (Kirk) Furtado.

Hyphaene natalensis Kunze
[*H. crinita* auct.]
S.A. no: 23   Ilala palm. Lalapalm
Rhod. no: 16   Southern ilala palm

For differences between this and *H. benguellensis,* see the key.

Hyphaene natalensis,
with its fan-shaped leaves.

3. BORASSUS L.

Borassus aethiopum Mart.
S.A. no: 25   Borassus palm. Borassuspalm
Rhod. no: 17   Borassus palm

Height: up to 20 m, straight bole, with a strange swelling about half way up which is seen also in tall specimens of *Hyphaene;* occurring at low altitudes along rivers and in coastal woodland, in sandy, well-drained soil. **Leaves:** very large, fan-shaped, bluish-green, up to 4 m long, including petiole which is armed with sharp black thorns; the leaflets are symmetric at the base. **Flowers:** sexes separate on different trees. Male flowers in spikes; sepals 3; petals 3; stamens 6; ovary vestigial; produced in branched heads up to 2 m long. Female flowers larger than the male, globose; sepals overlapping; petals inrolled; 6 vestigial stamens; ovary globose, stigmas 3; produced in large branched heads up to 3 m long. **Fruits:** large, 12 to 18 cm in diameter, orange-brown, with three large seeds (cf. *Hyphaene* with one seed) embedded in an edible fibrous pulp.

The borassus palm is very slow-growing: it may be as much as ten or 12 years before the stem develops, while flowering possibly does not occur until the tree is 30 or 40 years old and as much as 7 m in height. This late flowering may be linked with the swelling on the trunk which would develop at about the same stage.

Like that of *Hyphaene,* the sap is used to make wine and though the fruit-pulp is edible it is not much relished. In East Africa, however, the fruit is often eaten as are the young plants, the stems of which yield a type of starch. In Mocambique this tree serves yet another purpose, for here people use the trunk for making their dugout canoes.

There is a plaque on the road between Tzaneen and Leydsdorp in the northern Transvaal which marks the spot where a well-known specimen of borassus palm once stood. It was believed that within the swelling on its trunk the spirit of Magoeba, last chief of the Batlou tribe, was entrapped after he had been brutally murdered by the Swazis at the end of the last century. Only when the palm died were the local people satisfied that Magoeba's spirit had at last been released, though by that time his tribe was virtually extinct. This plant is protected in South Africa and Rhodesia.

There has been considerable controversy as to whether the Transvaal specimens are indigenous or introduced but reference to the distribution map will show that their natural occurrence here is quite acceptable.

4. RAPHIA Beauv.

Stem absent or comparatively short, up to 10 m, but the vast arching leaves, each up to 18 m long, can give a substantive height of 28 m; this is essentially a palm of swamp areas. **Leaves:** very large, pinnate, or feather-shaped, up to 18 m long, which means that they are the longest leaves in the plant kingdom. **Flowers:** sexes separate, both sexes being produced in a huge, branched, plume-like structure, up to 3 m long and taking 2 to 3 years to develop. Male flowers: calyx and petals tubular; stamens 6 to 16; ovary 0. Female flowers: calyx and corolla similar to the male; ovary ovoid and 3-chambered; stamens 0. **Fruits:** oblong, about 9 cm long, with conspicuous overlapping scales, shiny, polished-looking and golden-brown, 1-seeded.

These massive and impressive palms are comparatively short-lived, for after 25 to 35 years they flower, set fruit, then the tree starts to wither and eventually it falls prey to the first high wind, which sends it crashing down, scattering seeds over a wide area.

69

ARECACEAE

Key to the two species:

Flower head upright, carried vertically above the crown of leaves; southern Moçambique and extreme northern Zululand .... **R. australis**

Flower head starts erect, but later bends over and hangs down below the leaves; north and east of Rhodesia, adjacent areas in Moçambique and northwards .... **R. farinifera**

Raphia australis Oberm. & Strey   Illust. 6
S.A. no: 26   Kosi palm. Kosipalm
Rhod. no: —

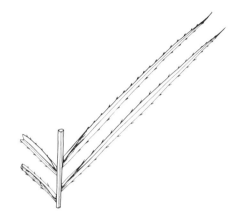

These palms occur naturally in southern Moçambique and, in Zululand, only round Kosi Bay. Just after the turn of the century a magistrate planted a grove of these trees at Mtunzini and later, their spread in this area was encouraged by an official employed in malarial control who, in the course of his work, planted seeds wherever he thought the situation suitable. They all prospered, and today many raffia palms are to be seen in the Mtunzini area, although the original specimens have almost certainly all flowered, fruited and died. The grove near the railway station – the site of the original plantings – has been declared a scientific monument and the Mtunzini population, although originally introduced and now escaped, has been included on the distribution map. The giant petioles are buoyant and in Moçambique Africans use them to make outriggers for their canoes.

Raphia farinifera (Gaertn.) Hylander
[*R. ruffia* (Jacq.) Mart.]
S.A. no: —
Rhod. no: 18   Raffia palm

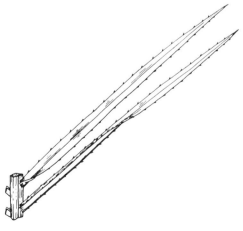

It is possible that the isolated colonies of these trees in Rhodesia and in Moçambique may be relics of a once much wider population. The stands at the north end of the Great Dyke in Rhodesia have been declared a Botanical Reserve and have given the name 'Palm Block' to the farming district in that area. Craftsmen have made use of the great petioles and midribs of the species of *Raphia* to fashion unique and beautiful furniture. This tree is protected in Rhodesia.

70

The raffia palm. The leaves, up to 18 m long, are the largest in the plant kingdom.

5. JUBAEOPSIS Becc.

Jubaeopsis caffra Becc.

S.A. no: 27   Pondo coconut. Pondokokospalm
Rhod. no: —

Height: seldom more than 5 m, although some specimens can reach 8 m; always multi-stemmed from the base; occurring only in Pondoland, lining the northern banks of two rivers – the Mtentu and Msikaba. **Leaves:** pinnate, or feather-shaped, 3 to 4 m long, very similar to the leaves of *Phoenix reclinata,* but without the spines on the leaf stem, which are conspicuous in the latter species. **Flowers:** about 1 cm in diameter; male and female flowers are separate but on the same tree in zigzag-branched sprays, or panicles, among the leaves. Male flowers on the upper parts of the branches; sepals free, small, triangular; petals larger, ovate, leathery; stamens 8 to 16, slightly shorter than the petals; ovary vestigial. Female flowers on the lower parts of the branches; sepals broadly overlapping; petals overlapping; stamens vestigial; ovary ovoid. **Fruits:** almost spherical, about 2 cm in diameter, resembling a miniature coconut with its fibrous coating and hard centre or endocarp. A small quantity of milk and a white 'meat' are produced by the fruits which, in smell and taste, closely resemble little coconuts and are greatly relished by children, even though each one is scarcely **71**

a mouthful. Graceful miniature palms can be propagated from the seed which is in great demand in America. Indeed, the plants have become so popular there that almost certainly more specimens are now growing in the United States than in South Africa where they are protected.

LILIACEAE *(The lily family)*

ALOE L.

Plants more or less succulent, herbaceous, shrubby to tree-like, unbranched or occasionally branched. **Leaves:** long, narrow, fleshy, the base clasping the stem; margins with or without teeth, veining parallel, arising as a closely packed head at the apex of the stem. **Flowers:** in spikes, unbranched or branched, terminal or lateral; bisexual, sepals and petals alike and petalloid forming the perianth; perianth parts 6, tubular, brightly coloured from cream to yellow through to orange and red; stamens 6 in 2 whorls; ovary ovate, 6-grooved, style thread-like. There are approximately 150 species of *Aloe* in southern Africa; of these only a few develop a conspicuous stem of any size and can therefore be considered as trees. These larger *Aloes* are of two distinct types: those with a main stem and conspicuous branches and therefore truly tree-like, and those with a single upright stem, most often unbranched, and which may be called the *pedestal* form.

Many of the species of *Aloe* hybridize readily with one another and hybrids are frequently found in their natural state. This can certainly create complications when trying to identify material.

Key to the species of 'tree' *Aloe,* including the pedestal forms:

A. NORTHERN and NORTH-WESTERN CAPE, including SOUTH WEST AFRICA, BOTSWANA, and areas in NAMAQUALAND as far south as Clanwilliam and Calvinia

1 Stout, several to many stemmed trees or bushes, 2 to 9 m in height 2
  Single stemmed, unbranched, or with two short branches, usually up to 2 m in height 4
2 Main stem very short, barely reaching 60 cm in length, multi-branched, the whole plant forming a spreading, bushy mass, 2 to 3 m high; flowers bright yellow .... **A. ramosissima**
  Stem large, up to 3 m in height, main branches heavy and ascending, reaching a total of 5 to 9 m in height 3
3 Branches spreading forming a dense rounded crown; tree very thickset, seldom more than 5 m in height; leaves, spreading to upright in rather sparse rosettes, bluish-green to yellow-green; flower heads upright, borne above the leaf rosette; flowers bright yellow (June/July); widespread in the north-western Cape and well into South West Africa .... **A. dichotoma**
  Branches upright rather than spreading, generally more slender and taller than the previous species, up to 10 m in height; leaves grey-green to brownish, curving over and drooping downwards, not upright; flower heads hanging down, produced below the leaf rosette; flowers yellow (October), very limited distribution in inaccessible areas of the Richtersveld and only just entering South West Africa .... **A. pillansii**
4 South West Africa, Botswana, northern Transvaal and Rhodesia and Moçambique only, not recorded from further south; pedestal aloe, unbranched; leaves erect; flower heads branched, flowers bright red (January to August, mainly March) .... **A. littoralis**
  Namaqualand only, from Orange River in the north to Vanrhynsdorp in the south; leaves erect; flower heads branched, flowers orange-red (June/July) .... **A. khamiesensis**
  Vanrhynsdorp, Clanwilliam to Calvinia only; leaves spreading to upstanding; flowers in single spikes, unbranched, remarkably long, up to 2 m; flowers bicoloured, buds rose-pink, open flowers creamy-white (December) .... **A. comosa**

B. SOUTH-WESTERN CAPE

Confined to a mountainous area from Elandskloof to the Franschhoek mountains; plants 3 to 5 m high, many-branched; leaves very distinctive, grey-green with minutely toothed margins, arranged, not in rosettes, but in upstanding fans at the ends of the branches; flowers scarlet (August/October) .... **A. plicatilis**

C. CENTRAL CAPE, KAROO REGIONS, SOUTHERN and EASTERN CAPE, ORANGE FREE STATE and LESOTHO

1 Plants always many-branched; leaf rosettes out on the ends of the branches 2
  Plants single-stemmed, pedestal forms; if branched then shortly so and limited to 2 to 5 branches; leaf rosettes forming a dense cluster 3
2 Large tree 10 to 18 m in height, with heavy branches; leaves dark green, long and narrow, in dense rosettes .... **A. bainesii**
  Spreading bush to small tree, 2 to 3 m high, occasionally reaching 4 m, branches slender, naked, the old dry leaf remains persisting only just below the rosette; leaves bluish to greyish-green .... **A. arborescens**
3 Single-stemmed, bearded with dry leaf remains over upper half only, lower half of the stem bare .... **A. pluridens**
  Single-stemmed, the whole stem bearded with dry leaf remains to ground level, or nearly so 4
4 Leaf surfaces smooth, without spines; flower head a single spike, unbranched, thickset, about 30 × 12 cm, producing a tricoloured effect, the buds red, the open flowers greenish-white and the protruding stamens brownish-orange .... **A. speciosa**
  Leaf surfaces with few to many spines 5
5 Leaves strongly upstanding, even the lowermost leaves curving upwards; surfaces of the leaves usually with many strong spines; flower head branched; individual spikes long and slender 50 to 80 × 9 to 12 cm; flowers scarlet; widespread in the southern and eastern Cape and just entering the Orange Free State, Lesotho and Natal .... **A. ferox**
  Leaves spreading, uppermost ones almost horizontal, lower ones hanging straight down; flower heads branched, individual spikes long and slender, 40 to 60 × 10 to 12 cm; flower buds dull red, open flowers yellow-orange; confined to a small area roughly in the triangle between Humansdorp, Bedford and Port Alfred .... **A. africana**
  Leaves deeply U-shaped, curving over and downwards, giving a drooping effect; flower head branched, individual spikes short and squat, 25 × 10 to 12 cm; buds greenish-orange, open flowers lemon-yellow; confined to a strictly coastal belt in Natal, only just entering the Cape .... **A. thraskii**

D. NATAL, SWAZILAND and extreme southern areas of MOÇAMBIQUE

1 Plants always distinctly branched, mature plants more than 2 m 2
  Plants typically pedestal form; if branched, then branches are short and somewhat obscure (one species may be branched but it then forms a sprawling mass less than 2 m high) 3
2 Large tree, 10 to 18 m in height; branches massive; old dry leaves not persistent; leaves dark green; flower heads branched; individual spikes 20 to 30 × 8 to 10 cm; flowers rose-pink (occasionally orange) .... **A. bainesii**
  Bush to small tree, 2 to 4 m; branches slender; old dry leaves persisting only just below the leaf rosette; leaves blue-green or grey-green; flower heads usually unbranched, spike squat, 20 to 30 × 10 to 12 cm; flowers coral-pink to scarlet .... **A. arborescens**
3 Leaves pale green, edged with pinkish-white teeth .... **A. pluridens**
  Leaves dull green, grey-green or reddish, edged with red to reddish-brown teeth 4
4 Upper and lower surfaces of leaves never with spines 5
  Lower leaf surface, or both surfaces, with a few to many spines, along the median line or scattered 6
5 True pedestal aloe, unbranched, 3 to 6 m, occasionally 7 m in height; stem bearded with old dry leaves over the upper one-third only; flower head branched .... **A. rupestris**
  A short pedestal aloe, up to 2 m in height, the stem bearded with old dry leaves, or may be branched when it forms a low, sprawling bush (this latter is usually the form seen in Natal); flower heads unbranched, simple spikes .... **A. sessiliflora**
6 Leaves conspicuously U-shaped, curving over and drooping downwards .... **A. thraskii**
  Leaves not conspicuously U-shaped and not drooping downwards 7
7 Flower heads branched; individual spikes conspicuously horizontal .... **A. marlothii**
  Flower heads branched; individual spikes upright, not horizontal 8

8 Flower spikes short and compact, about 25 cm long; flowers bicoloured, buds red, open flowers yellow .... **A. spectabilis**
 Flower spikes long, 50 to 80 cm, uniform red or scarlet 9
9 From eastern Cape northwards and only just entering the south of Natal; 3 inner perianth lobes (or petals) tipped with brown .... **A. ferox**
 A plant of Natal only just entering the Cape; the three inner perianth lobes (or petals) tipped with white .... **A. candelabrum**

E. TRANSVAAL

1 Plants always distinctly branched, with the branches rebranching 2
 Plants typically pedestal form; if branched the branches are short and rather obscure, producing little more than a cluster of leaf rosettes (one species may be many branched but it then forms a low, sprawling mass less than 2 m high) 4
2 Large tree, 10 to 18 m in height; branches massive; old dry leaves not conspicuous; leaves dark green; flower heads branched; flower spikes short, about 25 × 8 to 10 cm, rose-pink (occasionally orange) .... **A. bainesii**
 Bushes or small trees up to 4 m in height; leaves bluish-green; flower heads unbranched simple spikes 3
3 Branches slender, numerous, generally bare, the old, dry leaves persisting just below the leaf rosette only; flower spikes short and squat, 20 to 30 × 10 to 12 cm, usually coral-pink to scarlet; nectar not obvious .... **A. arborescens**
 Branches thickset, short, not numerous (seldom more than 20); branches densely bearded with old dry leaves for most of their length; flower spikes very long and snake-like, up to 1 m long; flowers reddish-brown, producing copious dark coloured nectar .... **A. castanea**
4 Stems bearded with old dry leaves only over the upper half 5
 Stems bearded with old dry leaves over more than half their length or to ground level 6
5 Flower heads branched, spikes conspicuously horizontal; spikes 30 to 50 cm long; the purplish buds and orange-red flowers are arranged along the upper side of the spike; the section of the stamens protruding from the mouth of the flower are coloured a dark purplish-black ....
 .... **A. marlothii**
 Flower heads branched, spikes upright, not horizontal; flower spikes very short, almost spherical, about 8 to 10 cm long and broad, strikingly bicoloured with the buds red, the open flowers yellow; stamens yellow to orange .... **A. angelica**
6 Flower heads branched 7
 Flower heads unbranched, simple spikes 8
7 Stems bearded with old dry leaves for about three-quarters of their length, the lower quarter often bare; leaves spreading and curving downwards .... **A. excelsa**
 Stems completely bearded with old leaves to ground level; leaves upright .... **A. littoralis**
8 Leaves curving over and downwards, the leaf tips even touching the main stem, bright green with a reddish border; flower spikes long and slender, strikingly bicoloured with the buds green and the open flowers yellow .... **A. aloöides**
 Leaves spreading or upright, not curving over and down; flower spikes not bicoloured green/yellow
 9
9 In frost-free, hot, hilly areas; leaves spreading, leaf rosette open .... **A. sessiliflora**
 In high mountain areas, on mountain tops, frequently in the mistbelt; leaves upright, tending to curve inwards, leaf rosette compact .... **A. dolomitica**

F. RHODESIA and MOÇAMBIQUE

1 Plants distinctly branched, branches slender, forming a many-branched bush or small tree, 2 to 3 m high .... **A. arborescens**
 Plants single-stemmed, pedestal form 2
2 Plants confined strictly to the Chimanimani mountains; stem bearded with old dry leaves over the upper half only .... **A. munchii**
 Plants not confined to the Chimanimani mountains; stems bearded for more than half their length   3

3 Flower heads unbranched, up to 5 single spikes per rosette .... **A. sessiliflora**
  Flower heads branched 4
4 Stems bearded with old dry leaves for about three-quarters of their length, the lower quarter often
  bare; leaves spreading and curving downwards .... **A. excelsa**
  Stems completely bearded with old dry leaves to ground level; leaves upright .... **A. littoralis**

Aloe africana Miller
S.A. no: 28,2   Uitenhage aloe. Uitenhaagsaalwyn
Rhod. no: —

Height: up to 4 m, unbranched, with stem densely bearded with old dry leaves; occurring in dense bush. **Leaves:** dull green, edged with strong reddish teeth and a few reddish spines over the upper surface. **Flowers:** in branched heads, two to three heads per rosette, flower spikes 40 to 60 cm long, buds dull red, open flowers with an up-turned tube yellow-orange (July/August).

Aloe aloöides (H. Bolus) Van Druten
[*A recurvifolia* Groenewald]
S.A. no: 28,3   Graskop aloe. Graskopaalwyn
Rhod. no: —

Height: 1 to 2 m, unbranched, with the stem bearded with old dry leaves for three-quarters of its length; occurring on rocky, mainly dolomite outcrops and ledges in the high mountains of the eastern Transvaal. **Leaves:** long and narrow, upper surface channelled, margins reddish with reddish teeth curved forward; the leaves curving over and down so that the tips touch the stem. **Flowers:** heads unbranched, simple spikes, 3 to 5 per rosette, long and sinuous up to 80 cm long, bicoloured, the buds green, the open flowers cup-shaped rather than tubular, bright yellow (August).

Aloe angelica Pole Evans
S.A. no: 28,4   Wylliespoort aloe. Wylliespoortaalwyn
Rhod. no: —

Height: 3 to 4 m, stem usually single, occasionally branched, especially when growing in exposed places, stems bearded with old dry leaves over their upper half only; occurring on the northern faces of the Soutpansberg mountains, on rocky slopes and in patches of dense bush. **Leaves:** green with a reddish-brown tinge, edged with strong reddish teeth, surfaces smooth, the leaves curved over and down. **Flowers:** heads branched, one per rosette; the spikes very short, almost spherical, about 8 to

75

LILIACEAE

10 cm long and broad, strikingly bicoloured, the buds red, the open flowers yellow (May/June). These plants do not cultivate well, but if cultivation is attempted the plant is best grown where the stems are well protected from both cold and heat.

Aloe arborescens Miller   Illust. 7
S.A. no: 28,1   Krantz aloe. Kransaalwyn
Rhod. no: 19   Mountain bush aloe

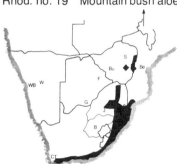

Height: usually 2 to 3 m (rarely 4 m), a many-branched bush or small tree, branches slender, the old dry leaves persisting just below the leaf rosette only; occurring mainly in high, hilly or mountainous areas, but over its great range it has adapted to many different habitats. **Leaves:** rather small and narrow, bluish or greyish-green, with conspicuous pale teeth along the margins. **Flowers:** usually in unbranched, simple triangular-shaped spikes, 2 to 4 per rosette; flower spikes rather short and compact, 20 to 30 cm × 10 to 12 cm, coral-pink to bright orange-red (May/June).

In the eastern Cape and Transkei this plant is frequently used for hedges; this is shown in the photograph.

A pulp produced from the leaves has proved effective in treating X-ray burns. This is a specially protected plant in Rhodesia.

Aloe bainesii Dyer
S.A. no: 28   Tree aloe. Boomaalwyn
Rhod. no: —

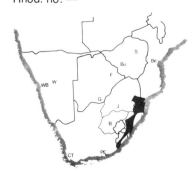

76

True trees, a group of Aloe bainesii.

Height: a true tree, 10 to 18 m, with massive branches forming a well rounded crown, this is the largest of all the species of *Aloe;* over its fairly extensive range it is found in its natural state in dense bush, forested ravines and rugged mountainsides, all with a high annual rainfall. **Leaves:** long and narrow, up to 90 × 9 cm, arching over and downwards; dull, dark green with a pale margin with white, brown-tipped teeth. **Flowers:** flower heads are branched and upright; flower spikes short, 20 to 30 × 8 to 10 cm, rose-pink to orange, tipped with green (June).
These plants strike readily from cuttings and grow well in cultivation.

Aloe candelabrum Berger
S.A. no: 28,5   Candelabra aloe. Kandelaaraalwyn
Rhod. no: —

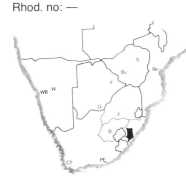

Height: 2 to 4 m, single stemmed, densely bearded with old dry leaves; occurring in thornveld and patches of bush in hilly areas in central Natal. **Leaves:** gracefully arching, dull green, forming a large rosette, leaf edges reddish with small reddish teeth; the lower surface may be spiny. **Flowers:** flower head widely branched, 1 per rosette, with up to 12 long, erect flower spikes; flowers scarlet, rose-pink or orange, with the 3 inner perianth lobes (or petals) tipped with white (cf. *A. ferox* in which they are brown).
The Zulus burn the dry leaves and use the ash as snuff.

Aloe castanea Schönl.
S.A. no: 28,6   Cat's-tail aloe. Katstertaalwyn
Rhod. no: —

Height: 3 to 4 m, branched, often from near the base, and then rebranching with thickset branches which are densely bearded; the main stem is usually bare; occurring on wooded hill slopes and in open   **77**

LILIACEAE

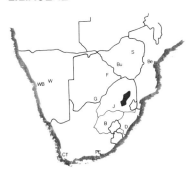

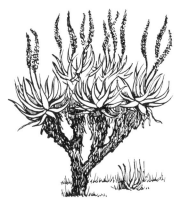

hilly grassland. **Leaves:** form a dense rosette, bluish-green edged with a fine brownish-red line and small reddish teeth. **Flowers:** flower heads unbranched simple spikes, very long and snake-like, up to 1 m long, up to 5 rising from each rosette; flowers cup-shaped rather than tubular, reddish-brown, producing copious dark-coloured nectar (July/August).

This species can grow well in gardens but it should be given a warm, sheltered position. The ash produced by burning the dry leaves is used by Africans to keep weevils from their grain.

Aloe comosa Marloth & Berger
S.A. no: 28,7   Clanwilliam aloe. Clanwilliamaalwyn
Rhod. no: —

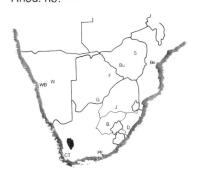

Height: up to 2 m, single stemmed, bearded with the old dry leaves; occurring in a very restricted area, in hot, dry river valleys and on rocky, stony hill slopes. **Leaves:** large, broad, 65 × 12 cm, spreading to upstanding, blue-green tinged with brownish-pink; margin pale pink with small reddish-brown teeth. **Flowers:** flower heads unbranched simple spikes, very long, up to 2,5 m in length, 3 to 5 rising from each rosette, strikingly bicoloured, the buds dull pink, the open flowers pinkish-ivory (December); there are distinctive hairy bracts between the young flowers (specific name refers to these).

These plants do not thrive under cold conditions.

Aloe dichotoma Masson   Illust. 8
S.A. no: 29   Quiver tree. Kokerboom
Rhod. no: —

Height: usually 3 to 5 m, occasionally reaching 7 m; this is a thickset and massive aloe with the stem up to 1 m or more in diameter at ground-level but tapering above this and branching and rebranching from approximately half way up (the specific name refers to the type of branching); occurring in the dry desert and semi-desert areas, on and among rocky hills, where they are a conspicuous feature of the landscape. **Bark:** smooth, occasionally flaking and frequently folded like melting wax, ochreous; the bark on the branches is pearly-grey. **Leaves:** smallish, about 35 × 5 cm, bluish-green or yellowish-green to brownish with a very narrow yellowish-brown margin and fine yellowish-brown teeth which almost completely disappear on old leaves; the leaves form rather sparse rosettes, in a fairly dense, rounded, compact crown. **Flowers:** flower heads branched; flower spikes rather short, about 30 cm long, canary-yellow, upright above the leaf rosette (June to July) (cf. *A. pillansii*).

It was Simon van der Stel who, in 1685, first recorded this fascinating and distinctive tree. He noticed, too, that Bushmen skilfully fashioned quivers for their arrows from the soft branches, and this custom gave rise to the name *kokerboom,* or *quiver tree,* by which it has been known ever since. Landmarks in their blistering, stony desert country, these trees frequently drew comment from early travellers and explorers, and to this day are among the best known species in Africa and of unfailing interest to tourists. Swarms of birds and locusts are attracted to their copious nectar, and baboons tear the flowers apart for the sake of the sweet liquor, often stripping a tree of its blossom within a very short time. *A. dichotoma* is a protected plant in South Africa and, as can be expected, it does not survive well in cold or damp areas.

Aloe dolomitica Groenewald
S.A. no: 29,1   Wolkberg aloe. Wolkbergaalwyn
Rhod. no: —

Height: up to 2,5 m, stem unbranched and heavily bearded with old dry leaves which are broad at the top of the stem, tapering to a narrow base, giving the appearance of a shaggy spinning top; occurring on high mountain slopes and on rocky dolomite formations, in the mist-belt above 1 500 m. **Leaves:** curved upwards and inwards, thick, dark green with reddish-brown margins bearing pungent teeth. **Flowers:** flower head an unbranched simple spike, several arising from the one rosette; the flowers, cup-shaped rather than tubular, are yellow or greenish-yellow (July to August).

These plants require an alkaline soil to succeed under garden conditions.

Aloe excelsa Berger
S.A. no: 28,8   Zimbabwe aloe. Zimbabwe-aalwyn
Rhod. no: 20   Excelsa

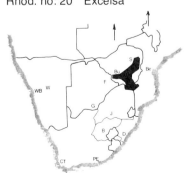

79

LILIACEAE

Height: 2 to 4 m, the single stem densely bearded with old dry leaves, but not quite to ground-level, the lowermost section being bare; occurring in warm areas, in wooded grassland, and very frequently on rocky outcrops and among rocks on koppies and hills. **Leaves:** dark green, large, spreading, the lower ones drooping; margin reddish-brown with pungent teeth and there may be odd spines on the lower leaf surface, particularly near the apex. **Flowers:** flower heads branched; flowers orange to dark crimson-red (July to August).

Dr Reynolds described this as 'a noble plant'; it is not difficult to germinate from seed and does well in cultivation unless growth is attempted in frost areas.

Aloe ferox Miller   Illust. 9
S.A. no: 29,2   Bitter aloe. Bitteraalwyn
Rhod. no: —

Height: 2 to 3 m, may be up to 5 m, the single stem densely bearded with old dry leaves; occurring in bush scrub and on open hill slopes, but over its wide range, both climatic conditions and its habitats vary considerably. **Leaves:** form a rather compact rosette, dull green edged with stout brownish-red teeth; the leaf surfaces may be smooth but usually have a few, and often many, scattered spines (the specific name meaning 'fierce' refers to this). **Flowers:** flower heads branched, one per rosette; flowers in long, dense, erect spikes, unicoloured scarlet, although occasionally white forms occur (May to October); the tips of the inner perianth lobes (or petals) are brown (cf. *A. candelabrum*, which are white-tipped); the flowers produce copious nectar.

Of all the aloes, *A. ferox* was probably the first to be illustrated for it features at least twice in Bushman paintings on the rock walls of caves. Its fleshy leaves have several practical uses: in times of drought and famine farmers have used them to provide fodder for their stock; they are said to make an excellent jam which resembles the traditional Cape preserve, watermelon konfyt, and the drug, *Cape aloes*, which is obtained from them is an effective laxative. The leaves are often dried and burnt to repel insects, and the stockades of *A. ferox* which are planted round cattle kraals, form a characteristic and attractive feature of rural areas.

Aloe khamiesensis Pillans
S.A. no: 29,3   Namaqua aloe. Namakwa-aalwyn
Rhod. no: —

Height: 1 to 2,5 m, single-stemmed, or separating into two branches from about the middle, densely bearded with old dry leaves; occurring in the dry, hot, stony mountains. **Leaves:** spreading and curved up then outwards forming a rather open rosette; dull green, smallish, about 40 × 8 cm, with a few scattered white spots; margin reddish-brown armed with sharp teeth. **Flowers:** flower heads large, branched, upright; flowers in dense pointed spikes, orange-red tipped with green (June to July). These plants do not tolerate a change in environment.

Aloe littoralis Baker
[*A. rubrolutea* Schinz]
S.A. no: 29,4   Mopane aloe. Mopanie-aalwyn
Rhod. no: 21   Mopane aloe

Height: up to 3,5 m, the single stem densely bearded with old dry leaves over its entire length (cf. *A. excelsa);* occurring in flat lowveld woodland, mopane woodland and extending into *Brachystegia* woodland. **Leaves:** erect, not hanging downwards (cf. *A. excelsa),* greyish-green, the margins armed with sharp light brown teeth which arise from small white spots. **Flowers:** flower heads branched; flowers in dense pointed spikes, rose-red, the tips of the perianth lobes (petals) turning yellowish (January to August, depending upon its locality).
This species responds well in cultivation but requires an alkaline and well-drained soil. This is a specially protected plant in Rhodesia.

Aloe marlothii Berger   Illust. 10
S.A. no: 29,5   Flat-flowered aloe. Bergaalwyn
Rhod. no: —

Height: 2 to 4 m, the single stem bearded with old dry leaves for half its length; widespread and conspicuous, in warm valleys and hill slopes, among rocks and in bush. **Leaves:** form a dense rosette; dull grey-green, edged with reddish-brown teeth and with scattered reddish spines over the surfaces. **Flowers:** flower heads branched, 1 per rosette; the flower spikes are carried horizontally, which is very characteristic, with purplish buds and orange flowers with purple stamens clustered along the upper side of the branches (June to August); the flowers produce copious nectar. In the Barberton area there is a distinct bi-coloured form (pinkish-red and cream), and in the Utrecht district flower colour is frequently a deep scarlet.
Africans burn the dried leaves and mix the ash with snuff. A decoction of the leaf is used to treat roundworm, and Zulu women rub the bitter leaf-pulp and juice on to their breasts to hasten the weaning of their babies.

81

LILIACEAE

Aloe munchii Christian
S.A. no: —
Rhod. no: 22   Large Chimanimani aloe

Height: a slender aloe 2 to 3 m tall, occasionally growing to 5 m, a few old dry leaves persisting near the leaf rosette but the stem mainly bare; it may be very shortly branched near the apex to form two leaf rosettes; strictly confined to the Chimanimani mountains. **Leaves:** dull greyish-green, the margin reddish tinged with very small pale teeth. **Flowers:** flower heads branched, sometimes 2 heads per leaf rosette; flowers orange-scarlet (July).

This is a specially protected plant in Rhodesia.

Aloe pillansii L. Guthrie
S.A. no: 30   Bastard quiver tree. Basterkokerboom
Rhod. no: —

Height: up to 10 m, resembling *A. dichotoma* but with fewer branches, taller, and the branches more ascending; strictly confined to a very small intensely hot and arid area in the Richtersveld and just across the Orange river. **Bark:** pale, smooth, tending to flake in shield-like sections. **Leaves:** tend to droop downwards. **Flowers:** heads branched, but arise from below the leaf rosette and so hang downwards; flowers also bright yellow (October) (cf. *A. dichotoma*).

This aloe does not thrive out of its natural environment. It is a protected plant in South Africa.

Aloe plicatilis (L.) Miller   Illust. 11
S.A. no: 29,6   Fan aloe. Waaieraalwyn
Rhod. no: —

Height: 3 to 5 m, with a short thick stem, grey to dark grey, and numerous branches, the old dry leaves not persisting; occurring on rocky mountain slopes. **Leaves:** these are unique, being dull grey-green, flat, strap-shaped, small (about 30 × 4 cm), not arranged in a rosette but in an upstanding, flat fan (the specific name, meaning 'pleated', refers to this); margins almost smooth, or with minute teeth along the edge for about the upper third of the leaf length. **Flowers:** flower head an unbranched simple spike, short, 15 to 25 cm long, 1 only per head of leaves; flowers uniform scarlet (August to October).

This aloe can respond well in cultivation but its natural environment should always be remembered: it requires cool, high humidity and an acid well-drained soil.

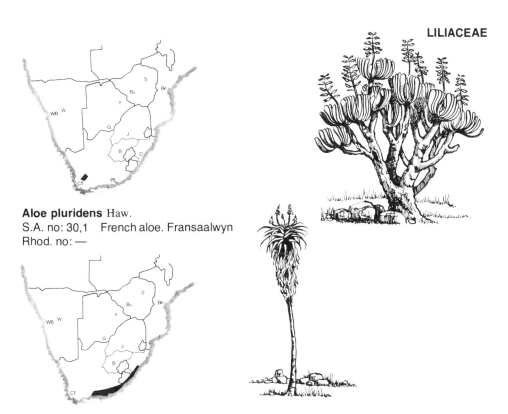

Aloe pluridens Haw.
S.A. no: 30,1   French aloe. Fransaalwyn
Rhod. no: —

Height: 2 to 5 m, unmistakably a pedestal aloe which may develop a few very short vertical branches near the apex giving a cluster of leaf rosettes, with the branches and stem bearded with old leaf remains over the upper half only; occurring in dry scrub and coastal bush. **Leaves:** spreading outwards and downwards, the lower leaves distinctly drooping; pale green to yellowish-green with a pale marginal line and edged with pinkish-white teeth (the specific name refers to its many teeth). **Flowers:** flower heads 4-branched, about 3 per leaf rosette; flowers salmon-pink to strawberry-pink (May). This plant grows successfully in cultivation if the stem is well protected from the hot rays of the sun and from cold winds.

Aloe ramosissima Pillans
S.A. no: 30,2   Maiden's quiver tree. Nooienskokerboom
Rhod. no: —

Height: 2 to 3 m, with a very short, squat main stem, often barely 60 cm long, then branching and rebranching to form a spreading, bushy mass, though more sparse and upright specimens do occur (the specific name refers to the very many branches); the stem and branches are golden-brown and shiny; occurring in areas of extreme heat and drought, on desert mountainsides and in arid ravines and valleys. **Leaves:** small and narrow 15 to 20 × 2,2 cm, curved upwards in small rosettes, bluish-green, grey-green or yellowish-green with a brown tinge, with a yellowish marginal line armed with very

83

small teeth. **Flowers:** flower heads 2-branched, 1 per leaf rosette; flower spikes short, 12 to 15 cm long, flowers yellow (June), very similar to those of *A. dichotoma*.

This species does not adapt well to cultivation outside its own desert environment. It is a protected plant in South Africa.

Aloe rupestris Baker
S.A. no: 30,3 Bottlebrush aloe. Borselaalwyn
Rhod. no: —

Height: 3 to 6 m, occasionally 7 m, the single stem bearded with old dry leaves over the upper one-third only; a plant of hot hill slopes and valleys (the specific name means 'of the rocks'). **Leaves:** curving upwards then outwards in dense rosettes, dull green with a thin reddish marginal line bearing stout reddish teeth. **Flowers:** flower heads branched and re-branched to produce up to 18 spikes per rosette; flower spikes short, about 20 to 25 cm long, producing a tricoloured effect, the buds orange-yellow tipped with green, while the young open flowers are lemon-yellow, the older and lower flowers are brownish-orange (September).

This aloe responds quite well to cultivation if given an alkaline soil and a warm, sunny, sheltered situation. In addition the bare lower part of the stem should be well protected from both heat and cold.

Aloe sessiliflora Pole Evans
S.A. no: 30,4 Lebombo aloe. Lebombo-aalwyn
Rhod. no: 23 Gazaland aloe

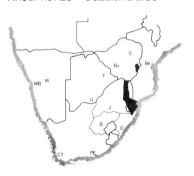

Height: 1 to 1,5 m, to a maximum height of 2 m; it may be upright and single-stemmed when the stems are fully bearded (this form occurs mainly in the Transvaal), or it may develop numerous branches, in which case it forms a low, sprawling mass barely more than 1 m in height (this form occurs mainly in Swaziland and Zululand); occurring on rocky outcrops and hill sides and in bush. **Leaves:** form dense rosettes, green to reddish with a reddish marginal line bearing small reddish teeth; in exposed dry areas the leaves become conspicuously red. **Flowers:** flower heads unbranched, simple spikes, up to five per rosette, 30 to 40 cm long; flowers cup-shaped rather than tubular, yellow (August).

This species can be difficult to cultivate and should be given a warm, sheltered place, with
84 well-drained soil. It is a specially protected plant in Rhodesia.

Aloe speciosa Baker
S.A. no: 30,5   Tilt-head aloe. Slaphoringaalwyn
Rhod. no: —

Typically a pedestal aloe, 3 to 6 m, but it may develop a few branches which tend to produce a dense cluster of leaf rosettes, the branches and stem are bearded with old dry leaves over the upper three-quarters of the length; found in hot dry areas, rocky outcrops, hill sides and valleys. **Leaves:** long and slender, 60 to 70 × 7 to 9 cm, curved, forming a dense spiralled rosette, dull bluish-green, often tinged with red, with a very fine pale red marginal line bearing small pale red teeth. **Flowers:** flower heads unbranched, simple spikes, up to 4 per rosette; flower spikes short and thickset, about 30 × 12 cm; buds red, open flowers greenish-white, and the protruding stamens brownish-orange, producing a tricoloured effect (August/September). (The specific name, meaning 'showy', refers to this.)
This aloe is frost-tender but responds well in cultivation if given a warm situation.

Aloe spectabilis Reynolds
S.A. no: 30,6   Natal aloe. Natalaalwyn
Rhod. no: —

Height: 2 to 4 m, the single stem densely bearded with old dry leaves; occurring in river valleys and on hill slopes. **Leaves:** curving upwards, dull green, often reddish tinged with a reddish-brown marginal line bearing stout teeth. **Flowers:** flower heads branched, up to 3 per rosette; peduncles dark brown or black, buds orange-red, open flowers golden-yellow (July). This species can be distinguished from *A. ferox* as it has shorter spikes, a more dense rosette of leaves, and the tips of the inner perianth lobes are purplish-black and not brown (or white as in *A. candelabrum*).
This aloe grows well in cultivation.

Aloe thraskii Baker
S.A. no: 30,7   Dune aloe. Strandaalwyn
Rhod. no: —

Height: 1 to 2 m, occasionally reaching 4 m, the single stem heavily bearded with old dry leaves; occurring in a narrow coastal belt seldom more than a few hundred metres from the sea, in low dune scrub. **Leaves:** deeply U-shaped, curving over and downwards giving a generally drooping effect to the large rosette, dull green to grey-green with a thin reddish marginal line bearing small reddish teeth;

85

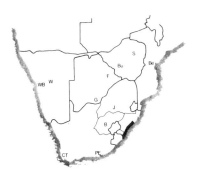

the lower leaf surface may be dotted with scattered spines. **Flowers:** flower heads branched, up to 4 per rosette; flower spikes short and squat, about 25 × 12 cm, buds greenish-orange, open flowers lemon-yellow to pale orange and green-tipped (late May to early July).

This species does not thrive away from the sea air and spray, but near the coast it does well if cultivated in a situation where the stem is shaded.

AGAVACEAE *(The agave and sisal family)*

DRACAENA Vand. ex L.

Trees or shrubs, stems simple or branched. **Leaves:** leathery and rigid, or soft and sub-fleshy, strap-shaped. **Flowers:** inflorescence a panicle; perianth 6-lobed, divided half way down or almost to base; stamens inserted high up on perianth segments; ovary ovoid, sessile. **Fruit:** a globose berry.

Key to the species of *Dracaena:*
1 Leaves 16 to 25 × 1 to 2 cm .... **D. reflexa**
  Leaves over 30 × 2 cm 2
2 In South Africa: eastern Cape, Transvaal and Natal; a many-branched tree ..... **D. hookerana**
  In eastern mountains of Rhodesia and adjacent areas in Moçambique; not in South Africa; a sparsely branched tree .... **D. steudneri**

Dracaena hookerana C. Koch
S.A. no: 30,9   Large-leaved dragon tree. Grootblaardrakeboom
Rhod. no: —

Height: 2 to 4 m, a softly woody shrub to a dichotomously branched small tree; occurring over a wide range of habitats from shady places in the dry, sour bushveld, through dune forest undergrowth to mountain forests. **Bark:** pale grey, smooth but marked by leaf scars. **Leaves:** large, leathery, strap-like, up to 60 × 8 cm, dark green, shiny, in rosettes at the ends of the branches. **Flowers:** white to yellowish-green in large, loose panicles, up to 1 m in length, terminal or axillary with 2 heads per branch; petals up to 2 cm long, slender, sweetly smelling, opening at night (November to February). **Fruit:** berry-like, 2-lobed, up to 2 cm in diameter with thick stalks, turning red when mature (February to April).

Dracaena reflexa Lam.   Illust. 12
[*D. usambarensis* Engl.]
S.A. no: 30,8   Small-leaved dragon tree. Kleinblaardrakeboom
Rhod. no: 29   Small-leaved dragon tree

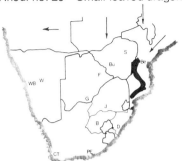 

Height: usually 3 to 5 m, but can reach 12 m, a much-branched small tree; occurring on the edges of and in moist evergreen forest, swamp forest and dune forest. **Bark:** whitish, smooth, inclined to develop a papery peel; the branches are marked with leaf scars. **Leaves:** narrow, 16 to 25 × 1 to 2 cm, dark green, shiny, tending to be in rosettes at the ends of the branches. **Flowers:** cream in colour, attractive, in loose spikes, or branched panicles, terminal, up to 25 cm long; the flowers close during the day and open at night when they give off a sweet scent (September to October). **Fruit:** berry-like, fleshy, about 2 to 2,5 cm in diameter, bright red and conspicuous when mature (October to November).
All the material south of the Zambezi is assigned to var. *nitens* (Welw. ex Baker) Baker.

Dracaena steudneri Engl.
S.A. no: —
Rhod. no: 30   Northern large-leaved dragon tree

Height: up to 12 m, frequently a single-stemmed, rather palm-like tree which may develop a few branches; occurring at the margin of and in evergreen forest. **Bark:** pale grey-brown, smooth but marked with leaf scars. **Leaves:** large, up to 80 × 10 cm, shiny green, in rosettes at the ends of the branches. **Flowers:** dull white to yellowish-green in large terminal sprays or heads, up to 1 m long; opening at night only, sweet smelling (August). **Fruit:** berry-like, spherical, about 1 cm in diameter, green turning red and finally black when mature; in large, yellow, branched terminal heads (October to December).
These handsome plants are widely cultivated, in Rhodesia at least, and are useful landscaping subjects. They root easily from cuttings.

MUSACEAE (*The banana family*)

The vegetative appearance of members of the genus *Ensete* is very similar to that of the species of *Strelitzia* which fall in the following family. These plants can easily be confused in the field and the following key is given as a guide, although it cuts across two families:

Leaves with short petioles, or petiole almost absent, midrib pink; flowers in massive, pendulous, racemes, the flowers protected by large, saucer-shaped, maroon bracts; the fruits resembling 'hands' of small bananas .... **Ensete**

Leaves with long petioles up to 2 m in length; midrib pale yellowish-green; flowers single or in a group, all with the well-known 'crane-flower' shape; fruit a small, woody capsule .... **Strelitzia**

ENSETE Bruce ex Horan.

Ensete ventricosum (Welw.) E. E. Cheesman   [Photograph page 42]
[*E. edule* Horan.]
S.A. no: 31   Wild banana. Afrikaanse wildepiesang
Rhod. no: 33   Wild banana

Height: A large, fleshy tree 6 to 12 m with a head of banana-like leaves; occurring in patches of high rainfall forest, in forested ravines and along streams. **Stem:** made up of old leaf bases. **Leaves:** large, banana-like, spirally arranged, fresh green, 2 to 5 m long × 1 m wide, midrib rose-pink, petiole almost absent, the leaf base running on to the stem. **Flowers:** in massive, pendulous, spikes 2 to 3 m long; petals 1, stamens 5, ovary 3-chambered, the flowers protected by large, maroon-coloured, spathe-like bracts (October to November). **Fruits:** indehiscent and leathery, resembling a 'hand' of small bananas, but instead of the soft, delectable flesh, there is a packed mass of hard seeds, like dried peas in size and appearance (December to March).

Despite their disappointing fruit, these trees are used as a staple food-crop in some mountainous areas of the south and south east of Ethiopia; a meal is prepared from the pulp in the stems and rootstock, and the residue is made into a fibre used for cordage and sacking.

STRELITZIACEAE *(The strelitzia family)*

STRELITZIA Dryander

Fleshy, banana-like plants, low-growing or tree-like. **Leaves:** large, oblong petioles up to 2 m long, arranged in two vertical ranks. **Flowers:** large conspicuous, 1 or several in the axil of a leathery bract, the flower arises from a maroon-coloured, boat-shaped spathe; there are 6 perianth parts, the 3 sepals cream or white (or orange in the small species) and upstanding like the crest of a bird; of the 3 petals, the lower 2 touch to form a unique arrowhead-shaped structure, almost beak-like, usually coloured blue but it may be white, with a channel down the centre in which lie the 5 long, very thin stamens, and the hair-like style; the third petal is a small frilled structure, scarcely contributing towards the striking appearance of the whole flower. **Fruits:** a 3-lobed, woody capsule; seeds with an orange, woolly aril.

The small species, about 0,5 to 0,7 m high, with the bright orange sepals, is *S. reginae* Banks, the 'crane flower' of nurserymen.

The 3 tree species are vegetatively very similar and difficult to separate; the differences lie in the flowers and in the geographical distribution of the plants.

Key to the tree species of *Strelitzia:*

A. From EASTERN CAPE through NATAL and ZULULAND into MOÇAMBIQUE to the eastern mountains of RHODESIA

Flower heads compound; several flowers in the spathe, then a second complete spathe and flowers arising out of the first, a third rising out of the second, and even a fourth and a fifth, each one rising out of the preceding one, producing a 'multi-storey' structure; petals blue (very rarely white), with deeply sagittate lobes .... **S. nicolai**

B. TRANSVAAL, north and east SWAZILAND

Flower heads simple; several flowers arising from a single spathe; petals blue with distinct sagittate lobes .... **S. caudata**

C. CAPE, confined to a small area from George to Humansdorp

Flower heads simple; several flowers per spathe; petals white, not blue, and lobes rounded not sagittate .... **S. alba**

Strelitzia alba (L.f.) Skeels
[*S. augusta* C. H. Wright, pro parte]
S.A. no: 32   White strelitzia. Kaapse wildepiesang
Rhod. no: —

Height: up to 10 m; occurring in evergreen forest. **Leaves:** large, up to 2 m × 0,6 m, usually split into ribbons by the wind. **Flowers:** all the petals and sepals are white lacking the blue present in the other species; the flowers may be found on the tree at almost any time but mainly from July to December. **Fruit:** a 3-lobed woody capsule; the seeds with a yellowish woolly aril. Confined to the forests of the southern Cape (October to February, but may be found at almost any time of the year).

Strelitzia caudata R. A. Dyer
S.A. no: 33   Transvaal strelitzia. Transvaalse wildepiesang
Rhod. no: —

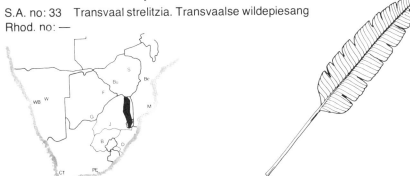

Very similar in size and general appearance to *S. alba,* but the petals are blue to mauve (not white as in *S. alba),* and the group of flowers are produced in a single spathe, not a tiered structure as in *S. nicolai.* Confined to the forests of the Transvaal and Swaziland.

89

Strelitzia nicolai Regel & Koern.   Illust. 13
S.A. no: 34   Natal strelitzia. Natalse wildepiesang
Rhod. no: 34   Wild strelitzia

Very similar in general appearance to the preceding species, the difference lying in the extraordinary multiple structure of the flowers with 1 spathe after another rising out of the preceding one, up to a total of about 5, each spathe with its group of flowers, being at right angles to those below and above it, so that a column with 5 layers of flowers results. A slimy mucilage produced within the spathe assists the very tightly packed flowers to emerge. **Fruit:** a 3-lobed woody capsule 5 to 7 cm long; the woolly aril on the seed is bright orange, so that it has the appearance of a small black face with a brilliant orange furry cap above it.

Dicotyledons

CASUARINACEAE *(The beefwood family)*

*CASUARINA Adans.

*Casuarina equisetifolia J. R. & G. Forster

The casuarina was introduced into southern Africa from the Far East and Australia. It has been planted widely in Africa and has been used to stabilise shifting sand at the coast. In certain areas it has escaped and, at least in parts of coastal Natal and Moçambique, it has now become naturalised but is not yet considered a pest plant.

PIPERACEAE *(The pepper family)*

PIPER L.

Piper capense L.f.
S.A. no: Wild pepper
Rhod. no: 35   Wild pepper

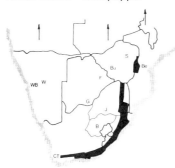

A soft-wooded, straggling shrub, or occasionally a small tree up to 4 m in height which can develop a well-rounded crown; occurring in moist, shady places, in forests and along streams. **Bark:** light brown and corky, the stem and branches having conspicuously thickened nodes which give them a jointed appearance. **Leaves:** simple, alternate, often with a leaf-opposed short lateral shoot which may give a false impression of an opposite leaf, ovate, 7 to 15 cm long and almost as broad, dark green and glossy above, paler below with conspicuous veining, thinly textured with a rather 'quilted' appearance; apex tapering and frequently attenuate; base shallowly lobed, sometimes somewhat asymmetric; margin entire; petiole 2 to 4 cm long; stipules leaf-like and joined to the petiole although they soon fall. **Flowers:** small, pure white, in dense, cylindric spikes up to 8 cm long, at the end of short lateral branches; without calyx or petals; stamens 2 to 4 per flower, giving the spike its white appearance (August to February). **Fruit:** a small berry, broadly oval to almost spherical, densely clustered along the axis forming a spike about 8 cm long, green at first turning black when ripe (October to June).

This is a large genus widely distributed throughout the warm regions of the world. Some of the species are of economic importance: both black and white pepper are obtained from *P. nigrum* L. and betel pepper from *P. betle* L., while *P. cubebe* L.f. provides cubebs. In the past pepper was obtained from *P. capense* but this is probably no longer the case; the berries have a spicy taste and smell and Swynnerton recorded that they imparted a good flavour to soups and stews.

SALICACEAE *(The willow family)*

*POPULUS L.

*Populus canescens (Aiton) J. E. Smith

The grey poplar (Rhod. no: 37), originally from Europe and Asia, was introduced into southern Africa and has now escaped and become naturalised locally, especially in vleis and in river valleys.

SALIX L.

Trees or shrubs. **Leaves:** often small and narrow, entire or serrate. **Flowers:** in spikes, or catkins. Sexes separate: perianth parts (sepals and petals) absent. Male flowers: stamens 2 to 3 to many. Female flowers: ovary with or without a stalk, style often very short; ovules 4 to 8. **Fruit:** a capsule, 2-valved. Seeds woolly.

The tough, elastic wood of *S. alba* is used for cricket bats.

Key to species of *Salix:*
1 In Natal, Transvaal and northwards .... **S. subserrata**
  A more southerly distribution (see maps) 2
2 Leaves fresh green, paler below, not conspicuously hairy .... **S. mucronata**
  Leaves densely silvery silky; in the Cedarberg mountains and closely adjacent areas only ......
  .... **S. hirsuta**

*Salix babylonica L.

The weeping willow, or *huilwilgeboom,* was introduced from Europe, but originally came from central and southern China; it is planted extensively in southern Africa (Rhod. no: 38) along rivers and round dams, and has now escaped and become naturalised, at least in Natal and in parts of Rhodesia.

Salix hirsuta Thunb.
S.A. no: Silver willow
Rhod. no: —

This species closely resembles *S. mucronata,* except that in *S. hirsuta* the leaves, especially when young, are covered with dense, silvery silky hairs. This is certainly very distinctive and in a wind the leaves have a silvery sheen not unlike that of the silver tree, *Leucadendron argenteum.* It occurs only along stream banks in the Cedarberg mountains and the adjacent areas of Algeria and the Biedouw valley. This could be a local variant of *S. mucronata.*

91

SALICACEAE

Salix mucronata Thunb.
[*S. gariepina* Burch.; *S. capensis* Thunb.]
S.A. no: 36,1   Cape willow. Kaapse wilger
Rhod. no: —

A bush or tree up to 12 m; in the larger specimens the branches have a tendency to droop; occurring along stream and river banks, in a wide range of habitats. **Bark:** rough, brown, deeply vertically fissured and scaling in narrow flakes. **Leaves:** simple, alternate, lanceolate, 2,5 to 12 × 0,6 to 2 cm, with or without fine hairs, clear green, paler below; tapering to base and apex; margin entire or finely serrate; petiole short. **Flowers:** small, in short spikes; sexes separate. Male spikes coloured yellowish by the stamens, dense, about 1,5 to 2 × 0,5 cm. Female spikes about 2 × 1 cm, more open than those of the male, the flowers small, greenish, urn-shaped (September to October). **Fruit:** a small capsule, splitting to release the tufted, woolly seeds which are wind-distributed but do not remain viable for long.

The wood is light and soft and, in areas where these are almost the only trees, they have been put to a wide range of uses. Farmers used to travel many miles to collect logs for their rafters and Africans make bowls and mortars for grinding their maize from the wood. The leaves, although rather bitter, are a valuable fodder and an excellent fowl food; they are widely used for this purpose and also as a natural remedy for fevers and rheumatism. The trees are easily propagated from cuttings or truncheons. This species is very similar to *S. subserrata* and could well prove to be inseparable.

Salix subserrata Willd.   Illust. 14
[*S. safsaf* Forsk. ex Trauty.; *S. wilmsii* Seemen; *S. woodii* Seemen]
S.A. no: 36,2   Safsaf willow. Safsafwilger
Rhod. no: 39   Wild willow

Height: seldom exceeds 7 m and the trees are frequently distorted, becoming almost prostrate by the force of flood waters; occurring along river and stream banks and on islands, in places likely to become inundated for at least part of the year. **Bark:** dark brown and deeply longitudinally fissured. **Leaves:** simple, alternate or scattered, narrowly lanceolate, 5 to 12 × 0,8 to 1,5 cm, dark green above, pale to almost silvery-grey below; very fine hairs may be present on the petiole and veins but these are generally absent; narrowly tapering to apex and base; margin finely serrate; petiole short. **Flowers:** small, rather inconspicuous, in short spikes. Male spikes dense, 2 to 5 cm long, coloured yellowish by the stamens. Female spikes shorter, broader and less dense than those of the male; the

flowers small, greenish, urn-shaped (August to September, but may have a second flowering season from March to April). **Fruit:** a small capsule, splitting to release the tufted, woolly seeds which are wind dispersed (January to April, and again in June and July). In years past a group of these trees was believed to indicate that the ground was hard and that the river at that point could be forded safely either on horseback or with a wagon. This tree is frequently associated with African folk-medicine and superstition. Certain peoples make a decoction of the roots with which they treat headaches and fevers; the bark is used by the Sotho to soothe and heal burns and by the Ndebele to cure urinary complaints in males. Twigs from the wild willow are believed to have the power to ward off storms, but to be effective they must first be coated with a special mixture which has the fat of a black goat as one of its main ingredients. Then one stick is thrust into the thatch to protect the hut from lightning, and another is pointed towards the threatening thunder-clouds, presumably in the hope that they will change direction. These sticks are also used to kindle fire by friction in the time-honoured manner.

S. wilmsii and *S. woodii* are both placed in synonomy here; no firm distinguishing characters could be found and *S. subserrata* is seen as being very widely distributed and stretching in an unbroken line from the Nile lands, through Kenya, Uganda, Zaire, Rwanda, Burundi, Zambia and Rhodesia to the Transvaal and Natal. It has already been pointed out that this species, *S. mucronata* and *S. hirsuta* are very similar, and certainly the differences between them are far from being clear-cut.

MYRICACEAE *(The waxberry family)*

MYRICA L.

Shrubs or trees, often aromatic. **Leaves:** simple, alternate, entire or variously indented. **Inflorescence:** a spike. **Flowers:** sexes separate, on different trees or on the same tree; perianth (sepals and petals) 0. Male flowers with 2 to many stamens, (often 4 to 6), short filaments and a vestigial ovary. Female flowers with vestigial stamens, the ovary without a stalk, stigmas 2. **Fruit:** a small drupe, spherical or oval, often waxy.

Key to the tree species of *Myrica:*
1 Leaf bases broadly tapering to rounded; leaves 3 to 7 cm long, rarely with conspicuous gland-dots
 .... **M. pilulifera**
 Leaf bases narrowly tapering 2
2 Leaves small and conspicuously narrow, usually about 3 cm long and less than 7 mm wide;
 endemic to Inyanga mountains .... **M. microbracteata**
 Leaves larger, not conspicuously narrow, usually more than 5 × 1 cm 3
3 Leaves usually conspicuously net-veined, or reticulate, not usually conspicuously gland-dotted.
 Western and south-western Cape only .... **M. integra**
 Leaves not conspicuously reticulate, usually conspicuously gland-dotted .... **M. serrata**

Myrica integra (A. Chev.) Killick
[*M. conifera* N. L. Burm. var. *integra* A. Chev.]

S.A. no: 38,1 Bastard lance-leaf waxberry. Bastersmalblaarwasbessie
Rhod. no: —

A shrub or small tree up to 3 m; often occurring in hilly or mountainous places, usually along the rocky banks of streams or rivers and confined to one small area only. **Bark:** grey to blackish. **Leaves:** **93**

slender, lanceolate 2,5 to 7,5 × 0,3 to 1,3 cm, leathery, with conspicuous net-veining; tapering to apex; narrowly tapering to base; margin entire, occasionally finely toothed; petioles very short. **Flowers:** small, in short, axillary spikes; the sexes are separate and on different trees (usually March and April, although some plants may flower in September). **Fruit:** very small, about 3 mm in diameter, spherical, warty with a layer of white wax over the surface (October).

Myrica microbracteata Weimarck
S.A. no: —
Rhod. no: 40   Inyanga waxberry

Usually a shrub, but may become a small tree reaching 3,5 m in height; occurring in mountainous areas, among rocks and along stream banks. This species is endemic to the Inyanga mountains in the east of Rhodesia. **Bark:** dark grey. **Leaves:** small, conspicuously narrow, linear to narrowly lanceolate, frequently only 2,5 × 0,3 cm, but occasionally may reach 4 × 0,7 cm; narrowly tapering to base and apex; margin conspicuously, often deeply, toothed; petiole short. **Flowers:** in short dense axillary spikes. Sexes separate but on the same tree; male spikes about 10 × 3 mm, reddish with yellow anthers; female spikes 1 to 3 cm long, greenish (July to October). **Fruit:** small, berry-like, about 3 mm in diameter (October to December).

Myrica pilulifera Rendle
S.A. no: 37   Broad-leaved waxberry. Breëblaarwasbessie
Rhod. no: 41   Broad-leaved waxberry

Usually a small tree 3 to 4 m high, but specimens growing under very favourable conditions can reach 10 to 12 m; occurring in mountainous places, among rocks, along streams, on grassy slopes and fringing forests. **Bark:** dark grey-brown to almost black, thin and rather smooth. **Leaves:** young leaves hairy, losing many of these hairs later, oval to ovate up to 11 × 4 cm, but usually much smaller, about 7 × 2,8 cm, yellowish-green, leathery; apex and base broadly tapering to almost rounded; margin variable, from almost entire to jaggedly toothed; petiole short, hairy. **Flowers:** sexes separate, on the same tree or on separate trees; flowers in short spikes; male spikes rusty-red, female spikes yellowish-green; the female spikes are usually longer than the male spikes (July to September). **Fruit:** small, almost spherical, dark brown to black when ripe, with a waxy outer layer (October to November).

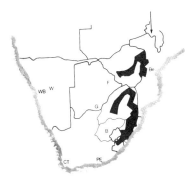

Myrica serrata Lam. Illust. 15
[*M. conifera* auct. non N. L. Burm.]
S.A. no: 38   Lance-leaf waxberry. Smalblaarwasbessie
Rhod. no: 42   Lance-leaved waxberry

Sometimes a shrub, but usually a small tree 3 to 4 m high, although under favourable conditions it can reach 10 m; locally common along stream banks, in forests, swamp forests and on coastal flats. **Bark:** grey to brownish and rough, but pale grey and smoothish when young. **Leaves:** narrowly elliptic, usually about 10 × 2 cm, but sometimes up to 15 × 2,5 cm, young leaves markedly yellow, mature leaves yellowish-green, conspicuously golden gland-dotted, aromatic; tapering to base and apex; margin more or less conspicuously serrate; petiole short. **Flowers:** small, in short spikes; male spike short and squat, rusty-red, with whitish-yellow anthers; female spike longer, more slender and green (August to September). **Fruits:** small, spherical, about 5 mm in diameter, bluish-black when ripe, with a waxy coating (October).

The fruits of this tree, and also its stems and leaves, produce oil: that of the fruits is pure and greenish-yellow in colour while the oil produced by the stems and leaves has an aromatic smell fleetingly reminiscent of *Eucalyptus*. Traditionally, branches used to be immersed in boiling water and a substance known as *berry wax* skimmed off as it rose to the surface. In fact, this was not a wax at all but a true fat rich in fatty acids, only 9% of which were saturated. The Sotho people eat the fruits of this tree, but when the leaves are chewed an intense burning at the back of the throat and nose and a severe headache result – unpleasant conditions which persist for several hours.

ULMACEAE *(The elm family)*

Key to the tree genera:
1 Branches spinescent; stipules large, ensheathing the leaf buds; leaves with a marked bristle tip
.... **3. Chaetacme**

Branches without spines; stipules not joined over leaf buds; leaf apex without a bristle tip .....
.... 2   **95**

2 Leaves with the margin completely and finely serrate; flowers very shortly stalked, almost sessile, in short, dense, axillary cymes, or clusters .... **2. Trema**

Leaves with margins entire or with lower half or one-third of the margin entire, and the coarse serrations confined to the upper half or two-thirds of the margin; flowers with distinct stalks, or pedicels, up to 1,8 cm long; in small clusters or solitary .... **1. Celtis**

1. CELTIS L.

Shrubs or trees. **Leaves:** simple alternate, stipulate, the stipules falling early. **Flowers:** on stalks up to 1,8 cm long, solitary, or in small, axillary clusters; bisexual, or sexes separate on the same tree; floral parts in fours to fives, the stamens opposite the perianth segments; ovary sub-globose, stigmas sessile, stout and spreading.

Key to the tree species of *Celtis:*
1 Leaf apex very long and slender, drawn out into a conspicuous drip-tip which accounts for almost one-third of the total length of the leaf; margins usually entire, but a few obscure teeth may be present along the upper half (notably in coppice leaves and shade leaves); not very conspicuously 3-veined from the base; fruit top-shaped, about 10 mm long .... **C. gomphophylla**
  Leaf apex may be attenuate but not extremely long and slender 2
2 Leaf margins finely and regularly serrate along the upper half; leaves up to 10 × 5 cm, conspicuously 3-veined from the base, apex abruptly attenuate; fruits small, almost spherical, about 4 mm in diameter .... **C. africana**
  Leaf margins with coarse, more or less rounded, irregular teeth along the upper half; apex shortly and abruptly attenuate; fruits urn-shaped, about 1,2 cm long .... **C. mildbraedii**

Celtis africana N. L. Burm.   Illust. 16
[*C. kraussiana* Bernh.]
S.A. no: 39   White stinkwood. Witstinkhout
Rhod. no: 43   Common celtis

Occasionally small and shrubby, but usually a fine spreading tree about 12 m high, sometimes reaching a height of 30 m when in forests; away from the coastal belt it is nearly always deciduous, standing stark in winter and conspicuous with its pale trunk and branches; occurring in a very wide range of habitats, from the coast to 2 100 m, from rocky outcrops to evergreen forests, usually, however, associated with higher rainfall or moister places. **Bark:** pale grey to almost whitish, smooth. **Leaves:** ovate, 1,5 to 10 × 1 to 5 cm, from very sparsely to densely hairy, mature leaves dark green, young leaves pale fresh green, conspicuously 3-veined from the base; apex shortly and abruptly attenuate; base rounded or lobed, oblique; margin finely and regularly serrate over the upper half or two-thirds; petiole short. **Flowers:** sexes separate but on the same tree, small, greenish, inconspicuous, the male flowers in dense clusters at the base of new green branchlets, the female flowers solitary or in small groups of 2 to 3 in the leaf axils (August to October). **Fruits:** small, about 6 mm in diameter, ovoid, yellow or brownish when ripe on slender stalks about 1,3 cm long (October to December).

96   The wood, which is white to yellowish in colour, is of medium hardness, but because it is tough and strong it is difficult to work. Nevertheless, since it takes quite a good polish it would be suitable for domestic purposes – indeed, Africans use it widely to fashion a variety of household articles.

From its unpleasant smell when freshly cut, this tree has been called white stinkwood – an unfortunate name since it leads to confusion with the true stinkwood, *Ocotea bullata*. In actual fact, the two are not related in any way, nor has the wood of *Celtis africana* any commercial value. This is an excellent tree for large gardens and it is also very suitable in parks and along streets. The seed germinates well when fresh and, if given good soil and plenty of water, the plant can grow 1 to 2 m per year. It is fairly drought resistant and can withstand a certain amount of frost; some strains appear to be more frost resistant than others. *C. africana* is protected in the Orange Free State and in the Black homelands. Vegetatively, this tree may be confused with *Trema orientalis*.

Celtis gomphophylla Baker
[*C. dioica* S. Moore; *C. durandii* Engl.]
S.A. no: 40   Bastard white stinkwood. Basterwitstinkhout
Rhod. no: 44   Forest celtis

A large tree reaching at least 25 m in height; occurring in evergreen forests. **Bark:** grey, smooth, with the trunk often fluted. **Leaves:** ovate to oblong, 8 to 19 × 2,5 to 9 cm, dark green, minutely and stiffly hairy, giving the leaf a roughish feel; apex conspicuously attenuate forming a long, slender drip-tip which accounts for almost one-third of the leaf length; base rounded and broadly tapering, oblique; margin usually entire or with a few obscure teeth along the upper half; petiole short. **Flowers:** very small, greenish, inconspicuous, in small clusters; sexes are separate but on the same tree (July to October). **Fruit:** top-shaped, about 10 × 6 mm, yellow when ripe (December to March).

The leaves resemble those of *C. africana,* but are generally larger with the very pronounced drip-tip; the base is less asymmetric and the three veins at the base are somewhat obscure, while they are prominent in *C. africana*. The wood has an unpleasant smell, described by various collectors as 'foetid and persistent' and 'a vile smell'; this is noticeable from the decaying wood of fallen trees in the forest. It is said that Africans hang pieces of bark in their huts to guard against snakes, and certainly trees are sometimes found with strips of the bark torn away. This tree is protected in South Africa.

Celtis mildbraedii Engl.   Illust. 17
[*C. franksiae* N. E. Brown]
S.A. no: 41   Natal white stinkwood. Natalse witstinkhout
Rhod. no: 45   Red-fruited celtis

ULMACEAE

A large tree reaching a height of 30 m; uncommon, in isolated patches of forest. This species reaches the southernmost limit of its range in southern Africa. **Bark:** light brown, fairly smooth; the trunk is well buttressed in large specimens and, together with the branches, may carry fairly conspicuous whitish lenticellate dots. **Leaves:** oblong, 5 to 17 × 2 to 7 cm, stiff, shiny green, obscurely 3-veined from the base; apex shortly and abruptly attenuate; base rounded to broadly tapering, oblique; margin entire over the lower half, with coarse, rounded and irregular teeth over the upper half, inclined to be wavy; petiole short. **Flowers:** small, inconspicuous, greenish, in small axillary clusters; bisexual, or with the sexes separate but on the same tree (September to October). **Fruits:** small, urn-shaped, up to 1,2 cm long, red, fleshy when ripe, tipped with the shrivelled, rather contorted remains of the stigmas (October to November). This tree is protected in South Africa.

2. TREMA Lour.

Trema orientalis (L.) Blume
[*Celtis orientalis* L.; *Trema guineensis* (Schumacher & Thonn.) Ficalho]
S.A. no: 42   Pigeonwood. Hophout
Rhod. no: 46   Pigeonwood

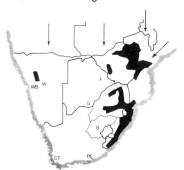

A shrub or medium sized tree reaching 13 m; occurring in a variety of habitats, usually in moist soils, on forest margins, along watercourses, often a constituent of the riverine fringe thicket, also in ravines and valleys and even along dry, sandy river-beds; in the drier habitats its size diminishes. **Bark:** smooth, light grey on both the trunk and branches. **Leaves:** ovate, 4 to 20 × 2,5 to 5 cm, glossy, bright green above, dull paler green below, rather tough, 3-veined from the oblique base, the veins depressed above, more or less prominent below, but not as conspicuous as those in *Celtis africana;* apex tapering; base rounded to lobed; margin finely and regularly serrate along the entire length (cf. *Celtis africana*; see key to the genera); petiole short. Stipules present, but they fall very early. **Flowers:** small, yellowish-green, inconspicuous; sexes separate but on the same tree; all floral parts usually in fives, the ovary almost without a stalk and with a fringe of hairs round the base. The flowers are produced in dense axillary clusters, or cymes, about 10 mm in diameter (flowering usually lasts for about 3 months, the main season being December to February, but flowers may be found for several months before or after this time). **Fruit:** small, round, 4 to 6 mm in diameter, on very short stalks; the fruit becomes dark purple and finally black when ripe; the first fruits ripen while the last of the flowers are still on the tree (January to June).

This is a common pioneer tree, and was one of the first to become established on disturbed soils. Seeds germinate readily and growth is rapid so specimens of *T. orientalis* are widely planted for the reclamation of soils. The wood is light pinkish in colour and has little commercial value. It has been used for fruit boxes but, when tested for the manufacture of matches, was found to be unsuitable.

3. CHAETACME Planchon

Chaetacme aristata Planchon
[*C. nitida* Planchon & Harvey; *C. serrata* Engl.]
S.A. no: 43   Thorny elm. Doringolm
Rhod. no: 47   Thorny elm

A vigorous shrub with a tendency to scramble, or a tree with a dense canopy reaching 13 m or more, often branching low down; occurring along streams in wooded grassland, in riverine fringe thicket, in

wooded ravines and near the coast, often in scrub and forest. **Bark:** pale grey; the bole is often fluted and, together with the branches, may be armed with spines. Sharp, tough spines, often paired, also arise on either side of the leaves, particularly coppice leaves. **Leaves:** elliptic to ovate, up to 9 × 5 cm, dark green, thick and rather leathery not always conspicuously oblique at the base; apex broadly tapering to rounded, notched, with a conspicuous hair-like bristle (up to 7 mm) at the tip; margins usually entire occasionally sharply serrate especially on young specimens or coppice leaves; petiole 5 to 10 mm long, petiole and branchlets velvety. Stipules conspicuous, joined to form a sheath over the young leaf bud; the stipules fall early. **Flowers:** small, greenish; sexes separate, but on the same tree. All floral parts in fives. Male flowers in small dense axillary clusters, or cymes. Female flowers solitary, with the stigmas long and densely hairy (October to December). **Fruit:** globose, about 1,5 cm in diameter, yellow when ripe, tipped with the remains of the long, slender stigmas (January to September).

The wood is heavy, yellowish in colour, and very hard and tough; it is difficult to chop and so frequently survives when other trees fall. The timber has no commercial value.

MORACEAE *(The fig and mulberry family)*

All the genera are characterised by the much enlarged and swollen receptacles (bearing the flowers and the fruits). The receptacle may either grow up as a fleshy central column on which the flowers and fruits are produced, as in the mulberry (in these cases, the fruits themselves may become enveloped by the persistent perianth segments which may become fleshy, as in the mulberry and in *Myrianthus),* or it may grow out, up and over, so forming a hollow sphere inside which the flowers and fruits are produced, a small pore being left open at the apex, as in the figs. The copious sap, often milky, is also characteristic.

Key to the genera:

1 Leaves compound, very large, completely divided to give 5 to 7 leaflets, all arising from the tip of the petiole; leaflets up to 36 cm long .... **6. Myrianthus**

  Leaves simple 2

2 Spiny shrub or small tree .... **2. Cardiogyne**

  Shrubs or trees without spines 3

3 Flowers on the inside of a hollow, almost closed receptacle, opening only by a small apical pore 4

  Flowers on the outside of an enlarged receptacle 5

4 Mouth at the apex of receptacle partially closed over by very small bracts; stamens and styles never protrude from the mouth .... **5. Ficus**

  Mouth at the apex completely open, bracts absent; stamens and styles protrude from the mouth, the stamens forming a conspicuous white brush-like head often partly concealing the containing receptacle .... **4. Trilepisium**   **99**

MORACEAE

5 Leaves oblong-elliptic to broadly ovate; the lateral veins arise from a well-defined midrib
.... **3. Chlorophora**

Leaves ovate, strongly 3-veined from the base .... **1. Morus**

1. MORUS L.

*Morus alba L.

The mulberry, or moerbei (Rhod. no: 48), introduced from Asia and fairly widely planted in southern Africa, is now known to have escaped and become naturalised in areas around Salisbury and along the Busi River in Moçambique.

Morus mesozygia Stapf
[*Celtis lactea* T.R. Sim; *Morus lactea* (T. R. Sim) Mildbr.]
S.A. no: 44   African mulberry. Afrikaanse moerbei
Rhod. no: —

A large tree reaching 20 to 30 m in height; a common canopy tree in inland evergreen forest, coastal forest and dune forest. **Bark:** light grey to brown, characteristically mottled with paler patches and longitudinally fissured; milky latex present. **Leaves:** simple, ovate, 7 to 15 × 4 to 8 cm, much resembling those of the cultivated mulberry but larger, light to darkish green, with sparse rough hairs, conspicuously 3-veined from the base; apex abruptly attenuate forming a long, slender drip-tip; base rounded, square to lobed; margin roughly toothed; petiolate. Stipules present but they fall early. **Flowers:** sexes separate, either on the same tree or on different trees. All floral parts in fours. Male flowers in short creamy-white, axillary spikes; the stamens are bent double in the bud and as they are released they straighten suddenly with an audible 'click', throwing out a visible puff of pollen. Female flowers several, in compact, axillary heads, the long, hair-like styles being conspicuous; the perianth completely envelops the ovary (October to November). **Fruit:** actually a very small nutlet, but completely surrounded by the persistent, fleshy, reddish to purplish-black perianth lobes; much resembling the cultivated mulberry, but smaller (October to December).
The wood is light coloured, yellow darkening to brown; it is hard and handsome. The field observations by Ian Garland on the pollen ejection from the flowers are acknowledged. This is a protected plant in South Africa.

2. CARDIOGYNE Bur.

Cardiogyne africana Bur.
[*Maclura africana* (Bur.) Corner]
S.A.no: —
Rhod. no: 49   Cardiogyne

A spiny shrub, often scrambling, or a small tree up to 8 m; occurring in hot, dry, low-lying areas and on coastal dunes. **Bark:** creamy-brown with white or yellowish latex; lateral branchlets spine-tipped. **Leaves:** simple, alternate, elliptic, 3 to 9 × 2 to 4 cm, dark green, without hairs; apex broadly tapering to rounded, and notched; base broadly tapering to square; margin entire, slightly rolled under; petiolate. **Flowers:** sexes separate on separate trees, white, sweetly scented, in small, dense, almost spherical, heads, about 1,5 cm in diameter. All floral parts in fours. Male flowers have the stamens

bent double in the bud and so the pollen is probably ejected as in *Morus mesozygia*. Female flowers with the perianth completely enveloping the ovary (March to May). **Fruit:** a head of small nutlets, each surrounded by the persistent perianth parts, now thick and fleshy and forming an agreeable pulp, each fruit separate but densely packed together, grey shaded orange in colour, reminiscent of a mulberry in appearance (August to October).

Africans use the roots and leaves to treat snake-bite.

3. CHLOROPHORA Gaudich.

Chlorophora excelsa (Welw.) Benth. & J. D. Hook.
S.A. no: —
Rhod. no: 50   Mvule

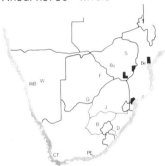 

A large tree reaching 50 m in height; occurring in low altitude evergreen forest. **Bark:** pale whitish-grey, roughish and scaly, the bole with irregular buttresses; sap slightly milky. **Leaves:** simple, alternate, large, oblong to broadly ovate, 12 to 18 × 6,5 to 9,5 cm, thinly textured, without hairs to roughly hairy and rather scabrous, green above, finely velvety and paler below, the old leaves often becoming a bright yellow; apex rounded, finally abruptly and shortly attenuate; base lobed; margin entire, wavy; petiolate. Stipules present but fall early. **Flowers:** in spikes; sexes separate on separate trees. All floral parts in fours. Male spikes long and slender, 6 to 14 × 0,5 cm; flowers white, the stamens bent double in the bud and so possibly ejecting pollen as in *Morus mesozygia;* anthers yellow. Female spikes short and thickset, 2 to 3 × 1 cm; flowers greenish; the perianth lobes enveloping the ovary (September and October). **Fruit:** a small nutlet, surrounded by the fleshy perianth lobes, clustered closely together forming a mulberry-like structure (October to December); dispersed by birds and bats.

The wood is an attractive brown colour which darkens on exposure and with oiling. Under the name *mvule,* it is in great demand in East Africa as a general purpose timber especially in building. Although it is heavy, it is also used for furniture.

MORACEAE

4. TRILEPISIUM Thouars
Trilepisium madagascariense DC.
[*Bosqueia phoberos* Baillon]
S.A. no: 45   Bastard fig. Bastervy
Rhod. no: 51   False fig

Large trees reaching 20 m in height; occurring in riverine forest fringes and in patches of evergreen forest. **Bark:** grey, smooth; milky latex present. **Leaves:** simple, alternate, elliptic, 7 to 14 × 3 to 6,5 cm, very dark green and glossy, leathery; apex broadly tapering to rounded, finally abruptly attenuate forming a narrow tip about 1,5 cm long; base broadly tapering to rounded; margin entire, rolled under; veins looping to form a sub-marginal vein; petiolate. Stipules present around the petiole, but soon falling. **Flowers:** sexes separate, but both inserted inside the same bell-shaped, or urn-shaped receptacle; the receptacle, about 1,5 cm long, somewhat resembles a fig, but has a wide opening at the apex. Male flowers many, perianth absent, stamens long, creamy-white to mauvish, protruding from the apical mouth and forming a puff about 10 mm in diameter which might almost hide the receptacle. Female flowers solitary and embedded in the fleshy receptacle, perianth absent, style 2- to 3-lobed (September to October). **Fruit:** a nut, embedded within the fleshy receptacle, the whole structure rather fig-like, ellipsoidal, and about 2 cm long (September to November). This is a protected plant in South Africa.

5. FICUS L.

A large and taxonomically difficult genus. Shrubs, trees or, rarely, climbers. **Leaves:** alternate, simple; stipules frequently conspicuous, enveloping the leaf bud, but usually falling as soon as the leaves unfold, leaving a conspicuous, characteristic scar. **Receptacles** (the *figs*) growing out, up and over to form a hollow fleshy sphere, with or without a stalk, solitary, in pairs or in heavy clusters (panicles or fascicles); the apical pore is loosely closed over by minute bracts which may or may not be visible from the outside. **Flowers:** sexes separate, produced inside the hollow receptacle. Male flowers: perianth 2- to 6-lobed, overlapping, membraneous; stamens usually 1 to 2; ovary absent or vestigial. Female flowers: perianth lobes usually fewer and narrower than those in the male; stamens absent; ovary obliquely ellipsoidal or ovoid, style usually lateral. **Fruit:** a very small nut.
All the indigenous figs are edible, if somewhat insipid. They are smaller and drier than the cultivated species, *Ficus carica* L., and lack its juicy flavour.
The figs are destinctive and by referring to their position on the tree, two main groups can be seen:
(a) Trees with large figs, 1,5 cm or more in diameter, produced on the stem or main branches in small groups of 2 to 3, or in large heavy branched clusters.
(b) Trees with smaller, or small figs, produced in the axils of the leaves on the terminal branchlets.

The trees may also be grouped according to their growth form and habit:
(a) Some species start growth in the fork of the branches of a host tree, the seeds being dropped by birds or other animals. The seeds germinate and send down long aerial roots which twine round the host until they reach the ground when they become the true roots while the aerial sections become the stem of the new tree, thickening and strengthening until they slowly strangle the host tree to death. These species can be called the *strangler figs*.

(b) Other species tend to grow on rocky outcrops. Their roots creep, tightly pressed, against the bare rock-faces, squeezing their way into almost imperceptible crevices and cracks until even great boulders are split apart. These can be called the *rock-splitting figs*.

(c) Many species grow as ordinary trees or shrubs, and even those which tend to be stranglers or rock-splitters can grow as normal trees if the seed happens to germinate in open land.

Key to the tree species of *Ficus:*

1 The tips of the branches, young shoots, the under surface of the leaves and petioles densely clothed with long, tawny-gold, shaggy, silky hairs .... **F. glumosa**
  Young parts and leaves not densely clothed with long, shaggy hairs, though they may be finely hairy, or velvety 2
2 Leaf surfaces rather harshly hairy to very rough and sandpapery 3
  Leaf surfaces not conspicuously harsh to the touch 7
3 Leaves elliptic to broadly elliptic 4
  Leaves almost circular 5
4 Stems and branches conspicuously yellowish .... **F. sycomorus**
  Stems whitish, grey or greenish-grey 6
5 Leaves small, conspicuously kidney-shaped, seldom more than 5 cm long .... **F. tettensis**
  Leaves large, 5 to 17 cm long .... **F. sycomorus**
6 Figs large, pear-shaped, 2,5 to 3 × 2 cm, narrowly tapering to the base, produced among the leaves .... **F. capreifolia**
  Figs small, about 1 cm in diameter, spherical, produced among the leaves ... **F. exasperata**
7 Figs produced on the trunk or low down on the main branches 8
  Figs produced among the leaves, or occasionally on the main branches, but not low down . 12
8 Figs produced in large branched appendages, leaves serrate .... **F. capensis**
  Figs in small groups, usually 2 to 3, on short stalks arising together 9
9 Figs large, up to 2 to 5 cm in diameter 10
  Figs smaller, 1 to 1,8 cm in diameter 11
10 Leaves conspicuously heart-shaped, tapering to apex, base more or less lobed ..... **F. polita**
  Leaves narrowly oblong, sides parallel, apex abruptly attenuate into a short narrow tip .... **F. sansibarica**
11 In this area found in South West Africa, Botswana and Rhodesia...................... **F. fischeri**
  Does not occur in South West Africa, Botswana or Rhodesia; found only in Zululand and Moçambique south of the Zambezi River .... **F. tremula**
12 Base of the leaves tapering 13
  Base of the leaves rounded, square or lobed 21
13 Leaf apex more or less truncate or squared off 14
  Leaf apex not at all truncate 15
14 Leaf apex more or less squared but still slightly rounded ....**F. natalensis**
  Leaf apex extremely truncate, squared off and even slightly concave .... **F. craterostoma**
15 Conspicuously small leaves, not more than 4,5 cm long; so far known only from the Manica e Sofala province of Moçambique .... **F. depauperata**
  Leaves not conspicuously small, average longer than 4,5 cm 16
16 Figs large, up to 2,5 cm in diameter, with a conspicuous 'nipple', up to 5 mm long, round the pore .... **F. kirkii**
  Figs small, 1 to 1,3 cm in diameter, apical pore may be slightly raised, but without a conspicuous nipple, 5 mm long 17
17 Found in the western and north-western Cape and South West Africa 18
  Does not occur in the western or north-western Cape 19
18 A small tree, associated with rocks; whitish smooth stem and roots flattened and plastered over the rock-faces and in cracks .... **F. ilicina**
  A large, densely leafy, rounded tree, not associated with rocks, frequently a strangler .... **F. natalensis**
19 A large, rounded, dark green, densely leafy tree; massive main branches, frequently with adventitious roots descending from them, often a strangler .... **F. natalensis**
  A small tree, usually up to 5 m, if taller then slender; never large and spreading 20 **103**

20 Leaves thickly leathery, lateral veins many, stipules about 10 mm long, reddish-brown, falling early .... **F. verruculosa**

Leaves thinly papery, lateral veins about 5 pairs, stipules large, conspicuous, up to 3 cm long, falling early .... **F. burtt-davyi**

21 Leaves strongly 3- to 5-veined from the base .... **F. vallis-choudae**

Leaves with a strong midrib, not markedly 3- to 5-veined from the base 22

22 Leaves very large, usually more than 15 cm long, frequently 30 cm long or more 23

Leaves usually 15 cm or less in length 24

23 Very large forest tree up to 25 m high; veins in the leaves and petiole pale-coloured; figs up to 2 cm in diameter, crowded near the tips of the branches .... **F. vogelii**

Also a forest tree but often a shrub and seldom more than 12 m high; the main branches spreading, almost parallel with the ground, with many stilt-roots dropping from them **F. trichopoda**

24 Leaf base extremely lobed, almost forming 2 semicircles overlapping each other; in the north of Rhodesia along the Zambezi River only .... **F. zambesiaca**

Leaf bases may be lobed, but not extremely so and the lobes not overlapping 25

25 Figs large, up to 2,5 cm in diameter, in leaf axils .... **F. soldanella**

Figs not more than 1,3 to 1,5 cm in diameter 26

26 Found in the western and north-western Cape and South West Africa 27

Not in the western, north-western Cape or South West Africa 28

27 Leaves rather small, heart-shaped, up to 7 × 3,5 cm; from the western and north-western Cape right through South West Africa and northwards .... **F. cordata**

Leaves rather large, oblong, up to 15 × 8 cm; in the north-west of South West Africa only .... **F. glumosa**

28 Figs conspicuously small, 5 to 7 mm in diameter 29

Figs about 8 to 13 mm in diameter 31

29 Leaves usually more than 10 cm long .... **F. stuhlmannii**

Leaves usually less than 10 cm long 30

30 Very young stems, petioles and leaf surfaces velvety .... **F. nigropunctata**

Stems, petioles and leaves without hairs .... **F. salicifolia**

31 Leaves thickly leathery; frequently a small shrub, even a suffrutex; most often associated with water .... **F. verruculosa**

Leaves thinly textured, shrub to large tree, not always associated with water 32

32 Lateral veins 5 on each side of the midrib; a small tree, straggler or even climber .. **F. burtt-davyi**

Lateral veins 8 to 9 on each side of the midrib; a medium to large tree .... **F. ingens**

Ficus burtt-davyi Hutch.

S.A. no: 49   Veld fig. Veldvy
Rhod. no: —

A shrub, climber, or small tree up to about 5 m, occasionally taller; occurring in forest, dune forest and swamp forest and also on coastal sand dunes where it may form a low-growing dense cover no more than 1 m high. **Bark:** pale whitish-grey, smooth, young branches velvety. **Leaves:** elliptic to narrowly obovate, 1,3 to 10 × 0,8 to 7,6 cm, glossy green, thinly textured, without hairs; more or less conspicuously net-veined below; apex broadly tapering to rounded; base tapering; margin entire; petiolate. Large reddish-brown stipules, about 3 cm long, ensheathing the young leaves, distinctive, but they fall early. **Figs:** usually paired, axillary, among the leaves, small, about 10 mm in diameter, green mottled white, turning yellowish when ripe (August to March).

Ficus capensis Thunb.   Illust. 18 (now *F. sur*, see 'Name changes' sheet)
[*F. mallotocarpa* Warb.]
S.A. no: 50   Cape fig. Kaapse vy
Rhod. no: 52   Cape fig

A large, spreading tree, usually about 12 m high, but reaching 25 to 30 m in some areas; occurring in forests and in open wooded grassland. **Bark:** grey, rather smooth; milky latex present. **Leaves:** ovate to broadly elliptic, up to 23 × 12,8 cm, green, sometimes grey-green, the young emergent leaves being a conspicuous and beautiful red; apex very broadly tapering to rounded; base square to slightly lobed; margin almost entire but usually with irregular scalloped serrations, wavy; petiolate, the petioles holding the reddish colour for some time. Stipules papery, about 10 mm long, falling very early. **Figs:** produced in large, heavy, branched clusters, or fascicles, on the stem and low on the main branches; figs large, 3 to 4 cm in diameter, becoming red mottled with cream or pink (September to March).

The wood of the Cape fig is light and soft and though it is of little actual commercial value it has a number of practical uses. Africans sometimes make drums from it; in the days of wagons it provided effective brake-blocks, and sticks from the tree produced fire by friction. The figs have a sweet if somewhat insipid flavour but they can be used for jam if apples or other suitable fruits are added – and provided they are not unpleasantly full of insects, as is often the case.

Several African folk-remedies make use of the Cape fig: burns and septic conjunctivitis are treated with an application of its latex and an infusion from its leaves and bark is administered to cows if their milk-production is considered inadequate. Indeed, widely separated tribes ascribe considerable magical powers to the Cape fig, particularly in East Africa where, through many generations, certain trees have been regarded as sacred shrines and symbolic of *Earth* and *Forest,* the two great divinities of productivity. Sacrifices, usually of goats, are made at these trees to appease ancestral spirits, to bring rain, to relieve famine and to ensure a rich harvest. The heavily clustered fruits suggest fecundity and are used in a variety of ways to promote both human fertility and an abundance of crops. Moreover, to eat the first fruits is believed to safeguard the welfare of the tribe itself and of the entire area in which it lives.

These are good shade trees and will grow fairly easily from truncheons, although seed is difficult to germinate. Their surface roots are a nuisance in a small garden, but if space and water are available they make fine subjects.

Ficus capreifolia Delile
S.A. no: 50,1   Sandpaper fig. Skurwevy
Rhod. no: 53   Riverine sandpaper fig

Often a shrub, but may form a small, slender tree up to 7 m; occurring in swamps, and frequently forming tangled thickets along river banks and on sandy islands in the larger rivers. **Bark:** pale whitish and smooth, the branches often long and whip-like. **Leaves:** elliptic, up to 11 × 4,5 cm, dark green, with the surface very rough and scabrid resembling sandpaper; apex tapering; base narrowly rounded or slightly lobed; margin entire, frequently toothed; petiolate. **Figs:** pear-shaped, up to 3 × 2 cm, green to yellowish when ripe, borne singly on fairly long slender stalks in the axils of the leaves (September to February).

The very harsh leaves are used by the Africans as sandpaper in the preparation of hides and also in finishing the wood of their bows.

105

MORACEAE

Ficus cordata Thunb.
[*F. cordata* Thunb. var. *marlothii* Warb.]
S.A. no: 51   Namaqua fig. Namakwavy
Rhod. no: —

Usually a medium sized tree, about 10 m in height and rather slender, but old specimens can be up to 20 m, with a wide spread; characteristically associated with rocks where its pale roots flattened against the rock-faces are distinctive; common in the dry, stony deserts of the north-western Cape. **Bark:** pale grey and rather smooth. **Leaves:** ovate, or heart-shaped, rather small, usually about 7 × 3,5 cm, although they may be larger, dark green; apex drawn out into a long, slender point; base may be square but usually lobed, or cordate (the specific name refers to this); margin entire; net-veining fairly conspicuous on both surfaces; petiolate. **Figs:** about 7 to 12 mm in diameter, paired in the axils of the leaves; finely velvety and brown to purplish when ripe (September to February).

In the Heerenlogement Cave near Clanwilliam in the western Cape there is a famous specimen of *F. cordata* which was first described by the French naturalist, François le Vaillant in 1783. At that time it was already of considerable size and must therefore now be more than 200 years old. Early travellers and explorers, some now famous in South African history, often sought shelter in the cave and left their names beautifully and painstakingly inscribed upon the walls. Among these are the signatures of pioneer botanists C. P. Thunberg (1743-1828) and C. L. P. Zeyher (1799-1858).

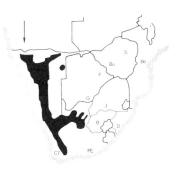

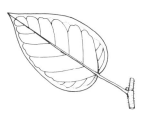

Ficus cordata, *the Namaqua fig,*
flattening itself
against the rocks at Augrabies Falls.

Ficus craterostoma Warb.
S.A. no: 52   Rare forest fig. Bosvy
Rhod. no: 57/2   Rare forest fig

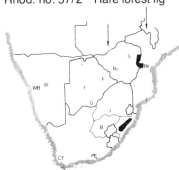
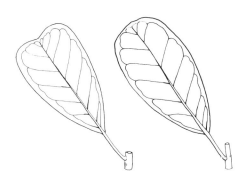

A rare tree, usually small to medium sized, reaching 12 m in height; occurring in swamp forest and in deep, heavily wooded mountain ravines; it can become a strangler; this species reaches the southern limit of its range in Natal. **Bark:** grey, smoothish. **Leaves:** very characteristic, narrowly triangular-truncate, usually about 7 × 3 cm, but reaching 8,5 × 5 cm; thinly leathery, without hairs; apex remarkably truncate, the squared-off end even concave; base narrowly tapering; margin entire; petiolate. **Figs:** small, 7 to 10 mm in diameter, without hairs, in the axils of the leaves (September to December, but the time is variable).

Confusion can arise between these leaves and those of the truncated form of *F. natalensis,* but the apex of the latter is slightly rounded while the apex of *F. craterostoma* is slightly to fairly markedly concave. The author, having examined the South African specimens, is satisfied that typical *F. craterostoma* does occur in Zululand, although it is a rare tree, as it is in all areas south of the Zambezi River.

Ficus depauperata T. R. Sim (Now *F. lingua*, see 'Name changes' sheet)
S.A. no: —
Rhod. no: —   Small-fruited fig

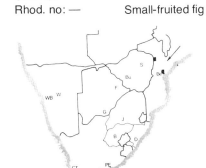
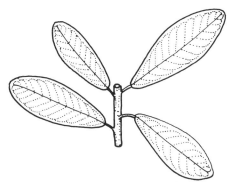

A strangler usually 6 to 12 m high, but may be larger, even up to 20 m; occurring in evergreen forest, but nowhere common. **Bark:** whitish; branchlets very slender and twiggy. **Leaves:** conspicuously small, narrowly obovate, up to 4,5 × 1,3 cm, dull green, thinly textured, without hairs; apex broadly tapering to rounded and slightly notched; tapering to base; margin entire; petioles short. **Figs:** very small, 5 mm or less in diameter, stalked, in pairs in the axils of the leaves (September to March).

Ficus exasperata Vahl
S.A. no: —
Rhod. no: 54   Forest sandpaper fig

Often about 10 m high, but usually a large tree up to 20 m; occurring in evergreen forest where it is often a strangler. **Bark:** pale grey-green, smooth; in the large specimens the stem becomes fluted or buttressed. **Leaves:** broadly elliptic, 7 to 15 × 3 to 8,5 cm, both surfaces extremely rough and sandpapery (the specific name refers to this); apex broadly tapering, finally abruptly attenuate; base

107

rounded to square, margin entire but inclined to be finely scalloped, wavy; petiole long, slender, up to 6 cm. **Figs:** small, about 10 mm in diameter, also harsh to the touch, singly or in pairs in the axils of the leaves, green becoming pink to red when ripe (probably about October).

The trunk, when slashed, exudes a clear amber latex.

The extremely rough nature of the leaves has led to their use, wherever the tree occurs, as a substitute for sandpaper in finishing wood surfaces, and also for scarifying furred tongues and inflamed throats. In these cases, a leaf is wrapped round a finger and then rubbed against the affected area until bleeding occurs. In central Africa the leaves have a further use: they are shaken in water and the liquid, which is said to be analgesic, is applied to infected eyes. Scrapings of the bark are used to scratch all parts of the body as a stimulant and tonic.

Ficus fischeri Warb. ex Mildbr. & Burret
[*F. kiloneura* Hornby]
S.A. no: 68   Savanna fig. Savannevy
Rhod. no: 59

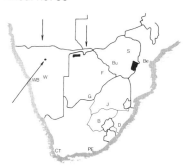

A large strangler up to 15 m high; occurring in riverine forest. **Bark:** grey, rather smooth; the branches are often festooned with tangled masses of aerial rootlets. **Leaves:** large, ovate, 10 to 17 × 7 to 11 cm, thinly papery; apex broadly tapering, finally abruptly and shortly attenuate; base shallowly lobed; margin entire, wavy; petiole up to 9 cm long. **Figs:** up to 1,8 cm in diameter, almost spherical, in clusters, or fascicles, on the main trunk and possibly on the main branches (January to June).

Ficus glumosa (Miq.) Delile
[*F. sonderi* Miq.; *F. rehmannii* Warb.; *F. montana* T. R. Sim]
S.A. no: 52,1   African rock fig, Afrikaanse rotsvy
Rhod. no: 63   African rock fig

This may be a small to medium sized tree, 5 to 10 m tall or may become a large tree reaching 13 m; occurring on rocky outcrops when it can become a rock splitter, along dry watercourses or in open

country frequently in valleys where it reaches its greatest size. **Bark:** pale grey to grey, smoothish to slightly rough, branchlets finely hairy to hairy and may be marked with large leaf scars. **Leaves:** oval to oblong, 5 to 15 × 1,8 to 9 cm, green or greyish-green, the young leaves, young branchlets and petioles frequently with long, tawny, golden to greyish silky hairs giving a shaggy appearance to the young shoots, or these may be almost absent, mature leaves usually smooth above with the lower surface finely hairy and may have scattered long hairs; apex broadly tapering to rounded; base rounded to shallowly lobed; margin entire; petiole comparatively short. Stipules present, pinkish-brown, conspicuous, sometimes falling early. **Figs:** small, less than 10 mm in diameter on the specimens in northern South West Africa, or larger, 10 to 14 mm in diameter on the specimens elsewhere in southern Africa, in pairs in the leaf axils and often clustered at the ends of the branches (January to June).

Ficus glumosa, *the african rock fig, its roots splitting open crevices in the rocks.*

MORACEAE

Ficus ilicina Sonder ex Miq.
[*Ficus guerichiana* Engl.]
S.A. no: 53   Laurel fig. Louriervy
Rhod. no: —

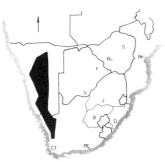 

A small tree, about 5 m in height; occurring in rocky places, its white stem and roots flattened and plastered over the rocks being very characteristic. **Bark:** whitish-grey and smooth. **Leaves:** oblong to oblanceolate 2,5 to 10 × 1,5 to 5 cm, dark green; apex narrowly rounded; base broadly tapering; margin entire; petiole short and thick. **Figs:** small, about 10 mm in diameter, solitary or in pairs in the leaf axils.

This species grows in the same areas as *F. cordata* and the two could be confused; however, while the latter species is upright in habit and up to 10 m or more in height, *F. ilicina* is low-growing and spreads over the rocks, rarely exceeding 5 m in height.

Ficus ingens (Miq.) Miq.
S.A. no: 55   Red-leaved rock fig. Rooiblaarrotsvy
Rhod. no: 55   Red-leaved rock fig

Variable in height and in habit, from a small to medium sized tree up to 13 m or more, the larger specimens tending to be straggling; occurring on rocky outcrops, stony hillsides, in riverine fringes and in thick woodland; round the Witwatersrand it is a sub-shrub clinging flatly to north and north-west-facing rock-faces. **Bark:** grey to yellowish-grey, rather smooth. **Leaves:** ovate to oblong, 6 to 15 × 3 to 10 cm, pale green, thinly textured, the new flush of young leaves being strikingly bronze-red; apex broadly tapering to almost rounded; base square to slightly lobed; margin entire; petiole slender, about 10 mm long. **Figs:** about 1 to 1,3 cm in diameter, in the axils of the leaves, dull red when ripe (June to December).

The smaller leaved forms of this could be confused with some forms of *F. natalensis*, but in that species the base of the leaves is narrowly tapered, while here the leaf base is square to cordate; also *F. natalensis* is usually evergreen. The leaves could also be confused with those of *F. salicifolia*, but again those of *F. salicifolia* are usually narrowed to the base; it is always a tree and its figs are smaller than those of *F. ingens*. Theoretically, it could be confused with *F. cordata*, but the two are clearly geographically distinct. The name *ingens* is a misnomer, for very large specimens are extremely rare; one such giant, which grows in the Boshoek area of the western Transvaal, was re-discovered by Eve Palmer, and it is thought to be the original 'inhabited tree' of Robert Moffat.

110

Ficus kirkii Hutch.
S.A. no: —
Rhod. no: 56   Crown-fruited fig

An enormous strangler reaching heights of 30 to 40 m; occurring in evergreen forests; here the species reaches the southern limit of its range. **Bark:** very pale grey, smooth; the tips of the very young branches are smooth and greenish-purple with prominent leaf scars. **Leaves:** large, elliptic to obovate, up to 17 × 7,5 cm, thick, dark glossy-green above, paler below; apex rounded, occasionally obscurely pointed; tapering to base; margin entire, inclined to be wavy; petiole about 2 cm long, stout. **Figs:** about 2 cm in diameter, inclined to be warty, crowned with a most conspicuous nipple-like neck, about 5 mm long around the apical pore, green tinged with purple, solitary in the leaf axils (September to June).

Ficus natalensis Hochst. Illust. 19
F. thonningii now comes out of this complex, see 'Name changes' sheet
S.A. no: 57   Common wild fig. Gewone wildevy
Rhod. no: 57   Wild fig

Very variable in size and habit from a small to medium sized tree, up to almost 20 m in height and densely leafy, often a strangler; occurring in a variety of habitats. **Bark:** grey, smoothish, often with thin aerial roots hanging down from the branches. **Leaves:** very variable, narrowly oblong to narrowly obovate, sometimes tending towards truncate, generally rather small, 2,5 to 9 × 2 to 5 cm, dark green; apex broadly tapering to narrowly rounded to almost truncate; tapering to the base; margin entire; petiole up to 2 cm long. **Figs:** small, about 1 cm in diameter, smooth or hairy, stalked or sessile, solitary or paired in the axils of the leaves (March to January).

Ficus nigropunctata Warb. ex Mildbr. & Burret
S.A. no: —
Rhod. no: 58   Velvet fig

A shrub or small tree, occasionally reaching 6 m; a strangler, but frequently associated with rocky outcrops in mixed woodland. **Leaves:** oblong-elliptic, 4 to 10 × 2,5 to 4 cm, slightly shiny green   **111**

Ficus natalensis, *the common wild fig, strangling its host tree.*

above, dull below; apex broadly tapering; base rounded to slightly lobed; margin entire; fairly conspicuous net-veining below; petiole up to 2 cm long; branchlets, petioles and the under surface of the leaves are finely velvety. **Figs:** small, about 7 mm in diameter, solitary or in pairs in the leaf axils, but also found on the young branches and may develop on the main stem also; yellowish with red markings when ripe (November to July).

Ficus polita Vahl
[*F. bizanae* Hutch. & Burtt Davy]
S.A. no: 59   Wild rubber fig. Wilderubbervy
Rhod. no:—

A large tree, 10 to 16 m tall; occurring in evergreen forest, coastal forest and dune forest, here reaching the southernmost limit of its range. **Bark:** light brown to grey-brown, flaking in small sections; the stem is inclined to be buttressed. **Leaves:** broadly ovate, 6 to 15 × 4 to 10 cm, dark green glossy above, light green below; apex shortly attenuate; base more or less rounded to lobed; margin entire; petiole slender. **Figs:** 1,5 to 3 cm in diameter, shortly stalked, typically in pairs, either on the branches or on the trunk, but tending to be confined to the branches in large, old specimens; green and rather warty (September to June).

This species can be confused with *F. sansibarica,* but the latter species has typically oblong leaves, with parallel sides and with a very shortly and bluntly attenuate apex.

Ficus salicifolia Vahl
[*Ficus pretoriae* Burtt Davy]
S.A. no: 60   Wonderboom fig. Wonderboomvy
Rhod. no: 60   Wonderboom fig

A spreading, medium sized tree, its height seldom exceeding 9 m; occurring in kloofs along watercourses, on rocky outcrops and rocky hillsides and also in open woodland. **Bark:** dark grey and rough, but in young trees paler grey and smoothish. **Leaves:** elliptic, usually about 7 × 3,5 cm, clear green, thickly leathery, clearly visible net-veining on the under surface; the sides are almost parallel; apex broadly tapering to almost rounded; base square or slightly lobed; margin entire; petiolate. **Figs:** small, about 5 to 8 mm in diameter, massed along the branchlets in the leaf axils; white turning yellowish-pink when ripe (August to May).

The huge and famous *Wonderboom* near Pretoria is an extraordinary phenomenon; its spreading, lax branches have drooped down and where they have touched the ground, they have rooted and a new tree has grown up. This process has continued, and is continuing, resulting in a huge complex tree, or trees now covering a vast area. By means of carbon-dating, the original tree has been calculated as being about 1 000 years old. This remarkable system of natural layering is not typical of this species; in fact, one of the other rare known examples is a giant specimen of *Ficus ingens,* thought to be Moffat's 'inhabited tree', in the western Transvaal.

The Wonderboom Fig, Ficus salicifolia, *showing the branches touching down, rooting and growing into new trees.*

Ficus sansibarica Warb.

[*F. brachylepis* Welw. ex Hiern; *F. delagoensis* T. R. Sim; *F. gossweileri* Hutch.]
S.A. no: 47   Zanzibar fig. Zanzibarvy
Rhod. no: 61   Large-fruited fig

Often about 10 m in height, but it can become an enormous strangler 20 to 40 m in height; occurring in low altitude woodland and forest. **Bark:** light grey, smoothish, although uneven, lumpy or folded. **Leaves:** oblong, 2,5 to 21 × 2 to 9 cm, sides almost parallel; apex rounded, finally abruptly and shortly attenuate; base rounded, square or slightly lobed; margin entire; petiole slender. **Figs:** large, up to 5 cm in diameter on conspicuous stalks; borne in groups of 2, occasionally 3, on the main stem and on the main branches; green, but may turn reddish when mature, bitter to taste (October to February).

See also *F. polita* for similarities.

A large forest species of *Ficus* occurs in low altitude evergreen forest in the extreme south-east of Rhodesia and a nearly adjacent area in Moçambique (*Ficus sp. no: 1;* Rhod. no: 70). This tree reaches 30 m in height and can develop stilt-roots. It appears to be allied to *F. sansibarica*, but the leaves are oval rather than oblong; the only figs seen were about 1,5 cm in diameter and appear to be produced, in stalked pairs, on second year branches. It has also been visually recorded from Zululand.

Ficus soldanella Warb. (now *F. abutilifolia*, see 'Name changes' sheet)
[*F. picta* T. R. Sim]
S.A. no: 63   Large-leaved rock fig. Grootblaarrotsvy
Rhod. no: 62   Large-leaved rock fig

 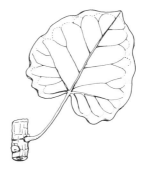

A shrub to small tree up to 8 m, occasionally higher; occurring along stream banks, and scrambling over rocks, frequently growing out of cracks and crevices; essentially a rock-splitter. **Bark:** pale whitish-grey, or yellowish-grey, rather smooth; the trunk is often twisted. **Leaves:** very large, almost round, often wider than long 6 to 16 × 8 to 25 cm, completely without hairs, dark green, with pale yellowish or reddish veins; apex rounded, finally abruptly and shortly attenuate; base deeply lobed; margin entire, may be wavy; petiole up to 14 cm long. **Figs:** 1,5 to 2,5 cm in diameter, with stalks up to 10 mm long, or without stalks, borne singly or in small groups of 2 to 5 in the axils of the leaves; green mottled white, with the apical pore somewhat raised (August to February, or may be even later).

Ficus stuhlmannii Warb.
S.A. no: 65   Lowveld fig. Laeveldvy
Rhod. no: 64   Lowveld fig

A medium sized strangler up to 10 m, with a dense, well-formed crown, able to grow as a normal tree as well, but this is probably unusual; occurring in mixed woodland at low altitudes and sometimes fringing forests. **Bark:** pale whitish-grey; the stem noticeably ribbed and fluted. **Leaves:** oblong, 9 to 18 × 4 to 8 cm, leathery, dark green and conspicuous, under surface very markedly net-veined and velvety; apex rounded, finally abruptly and bluntly attenuate; base square to shallowly lobed; margin entire; petioles short and thick, 2 to 4 cm long. The tree is deciduous for a brief time only. **Figs:** small, **115**

MORACEAE

usually less than 10 mm in length but may reach 2 cm long, oval, borne in pairs, or singly, in the leaf axils, velvety, green with a reddish tinge when mature and speckled (February to October). Despite its apparently wide distribution, this species is seldom common.

Ficus sycomorus L.
[*F. gnaphalocarpa* (Miq.) A. Rich.; *F. damarensis* Engl.]
S.A. no: 66   Sycamore fig. Sycomorusvy
Rhod. no: 65   Sycamore fig

A medium to large tree, 5 to 25 m, fine and spreading; frequently occurring along river banks, forming a distinctive part of the riverine thicket; also in mixed woodland. **Bark:** distinctive yellow, or greenish-yellow, occasionally creamy-brown, smooth; the stem may develop buttresses in the very large specimens. **Leaves:** large, broadly oblong to almost circular, 5 to 17 × 3,5 to 15 cm, dark green, rough and harsh to the touch; apex broadly tapering to almost rounded; base rounded to lobed; margin entire, sometimes toothed, occasionally sinuate; petioles short, about 2 to 3 cm in length. Stipules are oblong, hairy and fall very early. **Figs:** quite large, up to 3 cm in diameter, in heavy, branched masses on the trunk and main branches, yellowish to reddish when ripe (July to December mainly, but some figs can be found at most times of the year).

These figs have a good flavour and, according to Eve Palmer, the Tonga women dry them after which they acquire a rather sultana-like taste. Although the fruits are often insect-infested, they are eaten by birds and animals as are the leaves which have a high nutritional value. An infusion of the bark and the latex is used for the treatment of chest and glandular complaints, diarrhoea and inflamed throats. When considered together, the yellow bark and the harsh, rough leaves are diagnostic features.

Ficus tettensis Hutch.
[*F. smutsii* Verdoorn]
S.A. no: 62   Small-leaved rock fig. Kleinblaarrotsvy
Rhod. no: 66   Small-leaved rock fig

 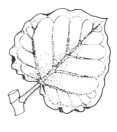

A small rock-splitter, sturdy, reaching 5 to 7 m in height; occurring in and on rocks and boulders, often in apparently impossible situations, its roots seeming to be remote from the soil. **Bark:** white to very pale grey, the stem and roots often plastered over the rock-faces. **Leaves:** distinctive, small, kidney-shaped, 2 to 5 (occasionally 9) cm long, and as wide as they are long, or even wider, densely and rather harshly velvety, the under surface pale grey-green; apex very broadly tapering to rounded;

116

base lobed; margin entire, wavy; petioles up to 2,5 cm long. Stipules large, up to 3 × 1 cm, pale brown, falling early. **Figs:** small, up to 10 mm in diameter, hairy, singly or in pairs in the leaf axils (April to December).

Ficus tremula Warb.
S.A. no: 67   Quiver-leaf fig. Trilblaarvy
Rhod. no: —

A small tree, up to 10 m, often a strangler; occurring in coastal forests. **Bark:** pale grey, smooth, mottled. **Leaves:** oval to ovate, 3 to 7 × 1 to 3 cm, without hairs, dark shiny green above, paler below; apex narrowly attenuate; base rounded or slightly lobed; margin entire; petiole conspicuously long and slender, up to 4 cm in length, almost half the length of the leaf. **Figs:** inclined to be oval, 1 to 1,4 cm long, without hairs, in clusters, or fascicled, on dwarf lateral shoots from the old main branches (October to November).
South of the Zambezi, this species is known so far from two isolated areas only. The long, slender petioles cause the leaves to tremble in the wind.

Ficus trichopoda Baker
[*F. hippopotami* Gerstn.]
S.A. no: 54   Swamp fig. Moerasvy
Rhod. no: —

A shrub or tree to 12 m; occurring in coastal and swamp forests where it may be raised on stilt-roots dropped down from the main horizontal branches. **Bark:** grey-brown or grey-green, smooth. **Leaves:** very large, oval to ovate, commonly 15 × 12 cm, but reaching 30 × 23 cm, bright green, glossy with almost white veins which may be tinged with pink; the young leaves are red; apex broadly tapering, abruptly and bluntly pointed; base square to slightly lobed; margin entire; petiole thick and reddish-coloured. Stipules large, red, ensheathing the leaf buds, later falling. **Figs:** up to 2,5 cm in diameter, ripening to red mottled with pinkish-white, paired on stalks 10 mm long, in the axils of the leaves (September to March).
This species resembles *F. vogelii* but the latter has sessile figs and has 5 to 6 pairs of veins in the leaves instead of 8 as in *F. trichopoda*.
In Zululand the distribution of these trees is roughly the same as that of the hippopotamus and the Zulus use the name, *umVu*, or *umVubu*, for both the tree and the animal. The Rev. Jacob Gerstner followed this lead when naming the tree *F. hippopotami*, a name which is now, unfortunately, in synonymy.

117

MORACEAE

Ficus vallis-choudae Delile
S.A. no: —
Rhod. no: 66/1   Haroni fig

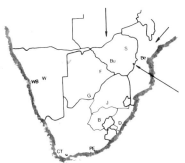 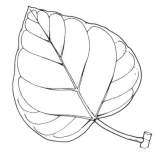

A medium to large tree 10 to 16 m in height; occurring in riverine forest. **Bark:** dark brownish. **Leaves:** heart-shaped to almost circular, 11 to 20 × 9 to 17 cm, thickly textured when fresh but drying thin and parchment-like, dark green above, paler below; strongly 3-veined from the base, the veins being prominent on both surfaces; fine hairs may be present on the under surface and sometimes along the veins on both surfaces; apex broadly tapering to rounded; base shallowly lobed; margin generally entire, but often rather sinuate; petiole brownish, frequently 9 to 15 cm long, but may be shorter. Stipules quite large, up to 2 × 1 cm, but falling early. **Figs:** up to 4 cm in diameter, greenish, softly velvety, solitary on stalks 1 to 1,5 cm long, in the axils of leaves on current year's growth (September to December).

Ficus verruculosa Warb.
S.A. no: 67,1   Water fig. Watervy
Rhod. no: 67   Water fig

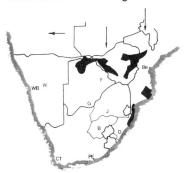 

A shrub or a weak-stemmed, sparsely-branched tree reaching 8 to 12 m; fairly widespread in gallery forest, in grassland, always near water, and as a pioneer in swamp forest where it often forms low, dense creeping clumps; in the Okavango delta it forms thickets on some of the islands. **Bark:** grey. **Leaves:** oblong, 5 to 15 × 2,5 to 7,5 cm, very thick, leathery, without hairs, glossy green above, the under surface paler and sometimes speckled with small, warty encrustations (the specific name refers to this); apex very broadly tapering to rounded; base tapering to rounded or slightly lobed; margin entire and rolled under; petiole short and thick. Stipules about 10 mm long, reddish-brown, falling early. **Figs:** 1 to 1,3 cm in diameter, the apical pore slightly raised; paired in the leaf axils, bright red when mature (January to August).

Ficus vogelii (Miq.) Miq. (now *F. lutea*, see 'Name changes' sheet)
[*F. quibeba* Welw. ex Ficalho; *F. nekbudu* Warb.]
S.A. no: 61   Giant-leaved fig. Reuseblaarvy
Rhod. no: 68   Giant-leaved fig

A large, spreading tree, reaching 25 m; occurring in forest and riverine fringe forest. **Bark:** grey, the bole is usually short and often buttressed, with the branches widely spreading. **Leaves:** very large,

crowded at the ends of the branches, elliptic, up to 38 × 20,5 cm, shiny green with the veins pale coloured; apex rounded, finally abruptly, shortly and bluntly pointed; base rounded to lobed; margin entire; petiole thick, up to 15 cm long. **Figs:** up to 2 cm in diameter, often smaller, 1 to 2 per leaf axil, tightly crowded at the tips of the branchlets (apparently June to October).

In Moçambique the Africans make a cloth from the bark. Truncheons strike easily and grow fast under favourable warm, moist conditions.

Ficus zambesiaca Hutch. (now *F. platyphylla*, see 'Name changes' sheet)
S.A. no: —
Rhod. no: 69   Zambezi fig

A large spreading tree up to 18 m with a spread of 35 m; occurring in low-lying deciduous woodland; it may be a rock-splitter. **Bark:** grey, smooth. **Leaves:** elliptic, 7,5 to 20 × 3,5 to 8,5 cm, finely velvety above and below; apex tapering to rounded; base markedly lobed, almost forming two overlapping semicircles; margin entire; petiolate. **Figs:** up to 2,5 cm in diameter, velvety, on slender stalks, in the axils of the leaves (September to November).

6. MYRIANTHUS Beauv.

Myrianthus holstii Engl.
S.A. no: —
Rhod. no: 71   Myrianthus

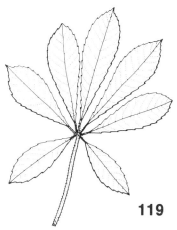

119

Usually a medium sized tree 7 to 10 m, but it can reach 17 m in height; occurring in evergreen forest; the tree may be carried on stilt-roots. **Bark:** greyish to brownish, rather smooth, containing much watery sap. **Leaves:** alternate, distinctive, very large, digitately compound, completely divided into 5 to 7 large leaflets; leaflets oblong-elliptic to oblanceolate, up to 36 × 12,5 cm, but usually smaller, upper surface dark green and without hairs, the lower surface again distinctive, being very pale greyish-green with the veining very conspicuous; tapering to base and apex; margin finely and regularly serrate; petiolules short and thick; petiole long. **Flowers:** sexes separate, on separate trees; male flowers in thick, staghorn-like heads (paniculate cymes) about 6 × 6 cm, the thick branches of the head densely covered with very small greenish flowers, all floral parts 4, the orange-coloured anthers on the stamens being conspicuous; female flowers as for the male but without the stamens, in a round, yellow head about 2 cm in diameter (September to December). **Fruit:** Smallish, round, up to 4 cm in diameter, with closely fitting 'plates' resembling a custard apple, or a miniature pineapple, bright yellow when ripe (March to June).

This is a most conspicuous forest tree, the large leaves falling with an audible 'plop' and carpeting the forest floor as they lie there rotting slowly. They often get caught up by fronds and branches before reaching the ground and so festoon the surrounding undershrubs in an untidy fashion.

URTICACEAE *(The nettle family)*

Key to the genera:
1 Leaves, branches and even stems may be armed with stinging hairs 2

All parts without stinging hairs; the under surface of the leaves conspicuously white and woolly .... **3. Pouzolzia**

2 In South West Africa and north to Angola only .... **2. Obetia**

Not in South West Africa; in Cape, Natal and Transvaal and Rhodesia .... **1. Urera**

1. URERA Gaudich.

Shrubs or trees often with or without stinging hairs, lianes often without stinging hairs. **Leaves:** simple, alternate, petiolate, stipulate. **Flowers:** in axillary cymes or panicles; sexes separate on separate trees, or occasionally on the same tree. Male flowers with a vestigial ovary. Female flowers without stamens. **Fruit:** a nut, enclosed by the persistent perianth lobes.

Key to the tree species of *Urera:*
All parts more or less densely armed with stinging hairs; leaf margins toothed; shrub to small, stocky tree; most frequently found on rocky hills .... **U. tenax**
Stems smooth; under surface of the leaves and flower heads may have sparse stinging hairs; leaf margins entire; a shrub, frequently climbing, or a small tree; found in forests ....
.... **U. cameroonensis**

Urera cameroonensis Wedd.
[*U. woodii* N. E. Brown]
S.A. no: 71,1   Climbing nettle. Rankbrandnetel
Rhod. no: 72   Climbing nettle

A soft, scrambling shrub, which may become a small tree, about 3 m in height, most often a canopy climber in evergreen forest, dune forest and at forest margins. **Bark:** brown to greenish. **Leaves:** oval, heart-shaped to almost round, about 12 × 6 cm, with microscopic, pale glandular patches on the upper surface of the leaf giving it a 'textured' appearance, strongly 3-veined from the base; the under surface of the leaf may carry sparse stinging hairs, especially along the veins; apex rounded, then abruptly attenuate forming a long, slender tip; base broadly tapering to slightly lobed; margin entire, wavy; petiolate. **Flowers:** sexes separate, on separate plants; small, greenish-white, in short, branched sprays (panicles) in the leaf axils; the stalks in the flower head may carry sparse stinging hairs (December to March). **Fruit:** small nuts surrounded by the persistent perianth lobes (January to April).

This species climbs by means of very distinctive 'attachment roots' in bunches, which cling on to nearby trees or dig into pockets of soil.

Urera tenax N. E. Biown
S.A. no: 71   Tree nettle. Bergbrandnetel
Rhod. no: 74   Tree nettle

Commonly a large, softly woody or fibrous, deciduous shrub or small tree 2 to 7 m in height; occurring in hot, dry areas, among rocks and on rocky koppies and hillsides, quite often near water. **Bark:** bronzy-brown or pinkish-brown, smooth, branches and even the main stem beset with stinging hairs. **Leaves:** round to heart-shaped, usually 7 to 10 cm long and wide but may be up to 16 × 17 cm, green, rather fleshy, all parts covered with stinging hairs; apex broadly tapering, finally shortly pointed; base quite deeply lobed; margin deeply and jaggedly toothed; petioles 4 to 14 cm long. **Flowers:** small, greenish-yellow to whitish, in short, branched axillary heads, produced before the leaves, and densely covered with stinging hairs (August to September). **Fruit:** small, ovoid, to rather flattened, about 2 to 3 mm in diameter and clustered into spikes; also covered with stinging hairs (October to November).

The hairs cause an intense, burning irritation and the skin may blister as a result. The bark yields a fibre which can be made into a tough, pale-coloured cord or rope.

2. OBETIA Gaudich.

Obetia carruthersiana Rendle
S.A. no: 69   Angola nettle. Angolabrandnetel
Rhod. no: —

A small tree up to 7 m, with stout stems and branches; occurring on stony hills and mountainsides. **Bark:** pinkish, smooth; with bright red twigs at the ends of the branches. **Leaves:** very similar in size

The stinging hairs of Urera tenax, *the tree nettle.*

and shape to those of *Urera tenax*, and also clothed with stinging hairs; petiole 4 to 9 cm long; stipules conspicuous, large, reddish-brown, which may persist or may fall fairly early. **Flowers:** very small, greenish-yellow, in much-branched, wispy heads, produced before the leaves; sexes separate (September). **Fruit:** a small oval nut, partly enveloped by the 4 papery perianth parts (October to November).

3. POUZOLZIA Gaudich.

Pouzolzia hypoleuca Wedd.   Illust. 20
S.A. no: 70   Soap nettle. Seepnetel
Rhod. no: 76   Snuggle-leaf

Commonly a many-stemmed shrub, but it may become a small tree reaching about 4 m in height; occurring in open woodland, in wooded ravines, in riverine thicket and sheltered among boulders on rocky koppies. **Bark:** darkish red-brown, smooth; the branchlets are velvety. **Leaves:** simple, alternate, ovate, 2,5 to 10 × 1,3 to 7,5 cm, dark green and rather rough above, the lower surface being almost silvery-white and woolly (the specific name refers to this), clearly 3-veined from the base; apex tapering; base rounded or lobed; margin entire; petiolate. **Flowers:** very small, greenish-white, in small, dense, axillary clusters; sexes separate, but on the same tree, the male flower with 4 to 5 stamens and perianth lobes, the latter being joined in the female flower to form a tube which is persistent (November to December). **Fruit:** a very small nut, the ovary barely increasing in size; enclosed in the papery, persistent perianth tube (December to February).

The bark is stripped by Africans for fibre. It amuses children to fashion cups, bowls, baskets or hats from the leaves which can be made to stick together, top surface to bottom surface.

PROTEACEAE *(The protea family)*

All species are protected plants in South Africa.

Key to genera (Exotics marked*):
1 Leaves in whorls of 4 to 6; fruits almond-shaped, up to 4,5 cm long, and densely velvety
.... **1. Brabejum**

122   Leaves alternate 2

1. BRABEJUM L.

Brabejum stellatifolium L.   Illust. 21
S.A. no: 72   Wild almond. Wilde-amandel
Rhod. no: —

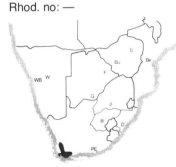
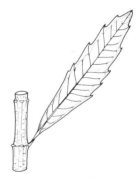

A large shrub or tree up to 8 m with spreading branches; occurring in sheltered valleys and along streams. **Bark:** pale greyish-brown, rather smooth. **Leaves:** simple, long, narrowly obovate, up to 16 × 2,5 cm, yellowish-green, arranged in whorls of 4 to 6 (giving the 'star' appearance referred to in the specific name), finely velvety or without hairs, fine net-veining fairly conspicuous, especially on the under surface; tapering to apex and base; margin irregularly and roughly toothed, with the teeth often sharp-tipped; young leaves rusty-golden in colour; petiole 1 to 1,5 cm long. **Flowers:** with rusty, velvety bracts which fall when the flower opens; flowers numerous, small, about 5 mm long, white, sweetly scented, in spikes up to 8 cm long in the axils of the upper leaves; bisexual or occasionally single sexed by abortion, both on the same tree; perianth parts 4, separating to the base when the flower opens (December to January). **Fruit:** almond-shaped, up to 4,5 × 3 cm, densely covered with rusty-brown or chocolate-brown velvety hairs; the very young fruits, when about 5 to 10 mm long, are a beautiful magenta or lilac-purple colour, later turning the typical brown (fruits mature February to May).

This tree was extensively established at the Cape in the very early days of its history. In 1660 Jan van Riebeeck planted *Brabejum stellatifolium* round the small settlement at the foot of Table Mountain to form a hedge, hoping that it would become so thick that 'no cattle or sheep will be able to be driven through it' and eventually protect the handful of Dutch farmers against marauding Hottentots. Fragments of van Riebeeck's hedge may still be seen and those sections within the National Botanic Gardens at Kirstenbosch and on Wynberg Hill have been proclaimed a National Monument.

123

Not to be confused with this 'wild almond' is 'Livingstone's tree' near Kuruman in the northern Cape. Outside Robert Moffat's original house and church, stands the remains of a tree, now only a stump, and a plaque which reads: 'Under this almond tree David Livingstone proposed to Mary Moffat. They were married in this church, 9th January 1845.' The roots of this old tree have sent up suckers which indicate that it was a European almond, or true almond, *Prunus amygdalus* Batsch.

Illust. 21 shows the young magenta fruits, the mature brown fruits, old flower spikes and the leaves of *Brabejum stellatifolium*.

2. MIMETES Salisb.

Shrubs or spreading, bushy trees. **Leaves:** simple, alternate, entire to 3-dentate, densely appressed long, silky hairs. **Flowers:** in clusters of 3 to 12, in the axils of the terminal leaves (these involucral leaves are often brightly coloured); bisexual; perianth tube very small or absent; stamens 4, short, fleshy, hairy; ovary hairy. **Fruit:** ovoid more or less without hairs.

Key to the species of *Mimetes:*

Leaves broadly elliptic, 2 to 2,5 cm wide, covered with very conspicuous long, appressed silvery hairs .... **M. argenteus**
Leaves narrowly elliptic, up to 1,5 cm wide, covered with silky hairs, but not silvery .... **M. fimbriifolius**

Mimetes argenteus Salisb. ex J. Knight
S.A. no: 72,1   Silver bottlebrush. Vaalstompie
Rhod. no: —

A large shrub, sometimes tree-like, up to 4 m in height; occurring in damp, cool, peaty places, in *fynbos* on south-facing slopes above 1 000 m. **Bark:** grey-brown. **Leaves:** broadly elliptic, up to 6 × 2 to 2,5 cm, with silvery appressed hairs, especially near the ends of the branches. **Flowers:** among the leaves at the tips of the branches; the leaves bearing the groups of flowers in their axils are larger and coloured pink, edged with green and clothed with the silvery appressed hairs; the perianth is also pink; the flowers are produced in small groups of 6 to 12, and each group has pink bracts round the base; the whole effect is unusual and attractive (May to July). **Fruit:** a small, smooth nut, remaining embedded in the remains of the flower at the base of the leaves (probably June to August).

Mimetes fimbriifolius Salisb. ex J. Knight
[*M. hartogii* R. Br.]
S.A. no: 72,2   Fringed bottlebrush. Manhaarstompie
Rhod. no: —

A sturdy, rather gnarled small tree, low-growing, spreading and dense, up to about 5 m; endemic to the extreme south-western Cape on rocky hill slopes above 300 m, frequent round Cape Point, but also on the Cape flats. **Bark:** grey-brown. **Leaves:** narrowly elliptic, about 7 × 1,5 cm, thick, leathery, densely crowded near the ends of the branches, clothed with dense appressed hairs which are not silvery; apex generally rounded with 2 shallow, rather obscure teeth, 1 on each side very close to the apex; base slightly tapering; margin entire, except for the apical teeth, fringed with silvery-white hairs (the specific name refers to this); petiole absent. **Flowers:** bisexual, in the axils of the upper

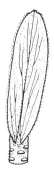

leaves which are often brownish to reddish; the groups of 6 to 12 small, greenish-yellow flowers are surrounded by reddish hairy bracts, but the whole structure is almost hidden by the leaves with only the tips of the flowers protruding (September to April, but mainly January and February). **Fruit:** a small nut remaining at the base of the leaves, and developing after the flower has faded (possibly February to April).

3. FAUREA Harvey

Shrubs or trees. **Leaves:** simple, alternate, petiolate. **Flowers:** bisexual, in catkin-like spikes; perianth tubular with a club-shaped limb; stamens 4, filaments very short and attached to the perianth limb; ovary with long silky hairs, style persistent. **Fruit:** a small nut with the long silky hairs and persistent style lending buoyancy for wind dispersal.

Key to the tree species of *Faurea:*
1 Flower spikes striking red; confined to the eastern mountains of Rhodesia and adjacent Moçambique .... **F. forficuliflora**
  Flower spikes white, cream or pink 2
2 Confined to the high altitude, mist-belt forest fringes in the eastern Transvaal and Swaziland
  .... **F. galpinii**
  Not high altitude species 3
3 Leaves, especially petioles and the under surface, also flower buds, densely velvety   **F. speciosa**
  Leaves, petioles and flower buds without hairs, or only very finely velvety 4
4 Bark dark grey to almost black; more often a species of open woodland, or in bushveld clumps on hillsides, only occasionally associated with forest; widespread in Rhodesia and the Transvaal, less so in Natal .... **F. saligna**
  Bark grey; a forest tree confined to several very localized and confined areas **F. macnaughtonii**

Faurea forficuliflora Baker
[*F. racemosa* Farmar]
S.A. no: —
Rhod. no: 77   Manica beechwood

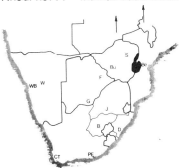

PROTEACEAE

A large tree, under favourable conditions reaching 25 m in height; occurring in and fringing mountain forests. **Leaves:** tough and glossy green, closely resembling those of *F. saligna* in size and shape (see under the latter species); young leaves red. **Flowers:** forming a sturdy spike 15 to 25 cm long, very showy, red to bright crimson in colour (mainly March and April). **Fruit:** a small nut, short, hairy, winged (June onwards, and may still be on the tree in January).

Faurea galpinii Phillips
S.A. no: 73   Bush beechwood. Bosboekenhout
Rhod. no: —

A shrub or small tree up to 10 m high, either erect or much-branched with a spreading crown; confined to high altitude, mist-belt areas, fringing forests, on mountain slopes and on exposed misty ridges. **Bark:** dark, rough. **Leaves:** lanceolate, up to 10 × 2,5 cm; tapering to base and apex; margin entire; petiole about 10 cm long, petiole and young twigs reddish. **Flowers:** usually in short spikes, about 8 to 10 cm long, but they can be up to 18 cm long, greenish-white, finely velvety (October to January): **Fruit:** small nutlets clothed with long, hoary, whitish hairs, with persistent styles, and still in the spike form of the flower (November to April).

This species resembles *F. saligna*, but *F. galpinii* has somewhat broader leaves; it grows at higher altitudes, each flower is shortly stalked (the flowers of *F. saligna* have no stalks) and it is confined to the mountains of the eastern Transvaal and Swaziland, while *F. saligna* is much more widespread.

Faurea macnaughtonii Phillips
[*F. natalensis* Phillips]
S.A. no: 74   Terblans. Terblans
Rhod. no: —

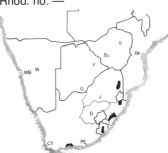

A tall evergreen tree up to 20 m in height; found in forests and on forest margins. **Bark:** thick, grey, shortly longitudinally furrowed. **Leaves:** narrowly elliptic in young trees, variable in older trees, often shorter, broadly elliptic to obovate, midrib conspicuous, up to 12 × 2,5 to 3 cm; tapering to base and apex; margin entire, wavy; petiole about 10 mm long. **Flowers:** in strong, robust spikes, up to 16 × 3 cm, white or pale pink, sweet-smelling (December to February). **Fruit:** a small brown nutlet, covered with long whitish to yellowish hairs and tipped with the long persistent style (February onwards to June).

The wood is characteristically sweet-smelling; it is hard, heavy, dark brown and beautifully grained. The distribution is strange – small, isolated areas, widely separated, from the Transvaal to Knysna in the southern Cape; it is said to occur also in Tanzania and in the Malagasy Republic.

Faurea saligna Harvey   Illust. 22
S.A. no: 75   Beechwood. Transvaalboekenhout
Rhod. no: 78   Beechwood

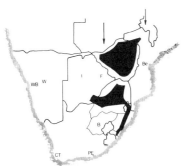

Usually a small to medium sized tree 7 to 10 m in height, slender and graceful, but in Natal it reaches 20 m in height, when it can be confused with *F. macnaughtonii;* occurring in lower to medium altitude open woodland and on stony hillsides, sometimes along river banks. **Bark:** dark greyish-brown to almost black, rough and deeply longitudinally fissured. **Leaves:** long, narrow, drooping, 6,5 to 12,5 × 1,3 to 2 cm, sometimes somewhat sickle-shaped, shiny, fresh green to yellowish-green, turning red in autumn, young leaves pink; tapering to base and apex; margin entire, wavy; petiole up to 2 cm long, pink in clour. **Flowers:** in rather slender spikes, 12 to 15 × 2 to 3 cm, greenish, to creamy-white, honey-scented (August to February). **Fruit:** a small nutlet, with long hairs and the slender persistent style (October to April).

A first field impression is that the tree resembles *Rhus lancea* but closer inspection will reveal the absence of the 3-foliate leaf typical of this plant. The presence of *F. saligna* is associated in South Africa with sourveld, and it is reported that while it can withstand moderate burning it will not survive fierce grass fires. The wood is pale yellowish to red in colour; it is beautifully figured, polishes well, makes excellent furniture and is a valuable general purpose timber. A red' dye may be obtained by soaking it in water.

It seems likely that a second subspecies is involved in Rhodesia (subsp. no: 1): this is the *Faurea saligna* subsp. *B* of White, in *Forest Flora of Northern Rhodesia;* it is very similar to the typical subspecies, but frequently grows near rivers, often has a more spreading habit and has leaves which are appreciably wider.

Faurea speciosa (Welw.) Welw.   Illust. 23
S.A. no: 76   Broad-leaved beechwood. Breëblaarboekenhout
Rhod. no: 79   Broad-leaved beechwood

Usually a small, leafy tree 4 to 7 m in height; found in mixed deciduous woodland, on low open hills and in hilly grassland. **Bark:** dark grey and deeply longitudinally furrowed. **Leaves:** oblong to elliptic, up to 7 to 17 × 2,5 to 6 cm, thick, glossy green above, paler and dull below, almost without hairs when old but velvety when young, veining distinct and pale coloured on both surfaces, especially below; tapering to base and apex; margin entire, wavy; petiole short and thick. **Flowers:** in robust spikes up to 25 × 3 to 4 cm, cream to pink (March to September). **Fruit:** a small nut, with long hairs and a slender, persistent style (June onwards).

127

PROTEACEAE

An extract of the roots is used to treat diarrhoea, and also ear infections. The leaves of this tree develop beautiful fiery autumn colours; at this stage it is easily confused with *Combretum fragrans* which can have a very similar habit and also produces splendid red leaves in autumn.

4. PROTEA L.

Shrubs or small trees. **Leaves:** simple, alternate, entire, usually thickly leathery. **Flowers:** many, in a broad flattened head on a widely expanded receptacle; the heads of flowers are surrounded by protective, and often decorative, shield-like bracts; heads solitary, rarely in groups of 2 to 3; individual flowers bisexual, perianth tubular, dividing for about half its length into 2 sections and may be extended into awn-like structures; stamens joined to the perianth lobe; ovary with long dense hairs, style persistent, slender. **Fruit:** a small nut, about 10 × 4 mm, densely hairy and tipped with the persistent style.

Proteas, on the whole, respond well in cultivation; they must be given a sandy, acid, well-drained soil. Unfortunately, attempts in Rhodesia to grow the splendid Cape winter-rainfall species have met with little success.

Key to the tree species of *Protea:*

A. EXTREME SOUTH-WESTERN and SOUTHERN CAPE, reaching just east of Port Elizabeth:

1 Flower heads large, either more than 10 cm long, or 10 to 20 cm in diameter 2
  Flower heads medium to small, usually 5 to 7 cm long, or 3 to 7 cm in diameter 7
2 Inner bracts and perianth awns with conspicuous, long white to black beards . **P. magnifica**
  Inner bracts and perianth awns not bearded, but may have rather short hairs 3
3 Bracts green, finely fringed with white hairs .... **P. coronata**
  Bracts coloured, not green 4
4 Flower heads shorter than the leaves and partly hidden by them 5
  Flower heads longer than the leaves, not hidden 6
5 Growing on dry, arid, interior mountain ranges .... **P. lorifolia**
  Always growing near the sea; southern Cape .... **P. susannae**
6 Flower heads opening wide; leaves whitish-green .... **P. eximia**
  Flower heads partially opening; leaves bluish-green, green or yellowish-green .... **P. repens**
7 Flower heads small, usually 3 to 5 cm in diameter 8
  Flower heads medium, usually 5 to 10 cm in diameter 12
8 Open flower heads soon look ragged and untidy .... **P. lanceolata**
  Open flower heads do not soon look ragged and untidy 9
9 Styles with very conspicuous club-like stigmas; midrib often reddish .... **P. mundii**
  Styles not club-tipped 10
10 In the flower heads the upper bracts densely black-bearded .... **P. lepidocarpodendron**
  Bracts not black-bearded 11
11 Strictly coastal, confined to limestone hills and ridges very close to the sea .. **P. obtusifolia**
  On inland mountain ranges, not close to the sea .... **P. punctata**
12 Inner bracts black-bearded .... **P. neriifolia**
  Inner bracts not black-bearded 13
13 Leaves conspicuously narrow, not more than 1,2 cm wide .... **P. rupicola**
  Leaves wider than 1,2 cm 14
14 Leaves conspicuously blue-green .... **P. nitida**
  Leaves green, not blue-green 15
15 Buds conspicuously long and slender, candle-like .... **P. aurea**
  Buds compact, oval or elliptic 16
16 Uppermost bracts curved back forming a very conspicuous lip .... **P. subvestita**
  Uppermost bracts not recurved .... **P. lacticolor**

B. HOT DRY AREAS OF WESTERN CAPE, not further south than Ceres:

1 Leaves conspicuously narrow, less than 10 mm wide .... **P. repens**
  Leaves usually more than 10 mm wide 2

2 Bracts tipped with conspicuous black hairs, or black-bearded 3
  Bracts not tipped with black hairs 5
3 Leaves oblong, up to 10 × 3 cm, dark green, apex narrowly tapering; flowers yellow to pink, the
  perianth produced into 2 purple-black-bearded awns; flower heads 10 cm or more in diameter
  .... **P. magnifica**
  Leaves lanceolate or narrowly so, grey-green, apex broadly tapering; flowers white or pink to
  yellow, the perianth not produced into conspicuous awns 4
4 In hot, low-rainfall, mountainous areas; flower heads up to 15 × 10 cm, flowers salmon-pink, the
  central mass yellow .... **P. laurifolia**
  In damp ground on mountain slopes; flower heads up to 10 × 6 cm, flowers cream ....
  .... **P. lepidocarpodendron**
5 Flower heads up to 10 cm in diameter .... **P. nitida**
  Flower heads about 5 cm in diameter 6
6 Flowers white; locally abundant on inland mountains of the southern Cape .... **P. punctata**
  Flowers greenish-yellow, in low-rainfall, dry, stony mountains in the western Cape only
  .... **P. glabra**

C. EASTERN CAPE, NATAL, and the extreme SOUTHERN MOCAMBIQUE:

1 Flower heads often produced in groups of 2 to 4 at the ends of branches .... **P. welwitschii**
  Flower heads solitary 2
2 Flower heads large, usually about 10 cm in diameter, or slightly more .... **P. roupelliae**
  Flower heads smaller, 5 to 8 cm in diameter, rarely up to 10 cm in diameter 3
3 Leaf midrib pink to red .... **P. caffra**
  Leaf midrib green or pale yellow 4
4 Extending no further south than Zululand .... **P. gaguedi**
  Extending no further north than the extreme south of Natal .... **P. subvestita**

D. TRANSVAAL and SWAZILAND:

1 Flower heads in groups of 2 to 4 at ends of branches .... **P. welwitschii**
  Flower heads solitary 2
2 Flower heads large, more than 10 cm in diameter 3
  Flower heads smaller, less than 10 cm in diameter 5
3 Leaves unusually large, 12 to 24 × 3 to 6 cm, oblong, fleshy, apex rounded, notched
  .... **P. comptonii**
  Leaves usually less than 15 cm long, apex not rounded or notched 4
4 Leaves oblong; flowering December to March............. .... **P. caffra**
  Leaves linear-lanceolate; flowering April to June .... **P. roupelliae**
5 Leaves usually more than 2 cm broad 6
  Leaves usually less than 2 cm broad 8
6 Flower heads with a distinct, robust stalk, or stipe up to 3 cm long .... **P. laetans**
  Flower heads without a distinct stalk, or stipe 7
7 At high altitudes above 1 800 m, on rocky, quartzite outcrops .... **P. rubripilosa**
  Below 1 800 m, in warmer areas, frequently at the transition between highveld and lowveld
  .... **P. gaguedi**
8 Flower head on a distinct, robust, woody stalk, or stipe .... **P. laetans**
  Flower head without a pronounced stipe 9
9 Extremely restricted distribution, one hill near Barberton only; flowering June and July
  .... **P. curvata**
  More widespread; flowering November to February .... **P. caffra**

PROTEACEAE

E. RHODESIA and adjacent areas in MOÇAMBIQUE:

1 Flower heads in groups of 2 to 4 at ends of branches .... **P. welwitschii**
  Flower heads usually solitary 2
2 Petiole pronounced, formed partly by the excessively narrowly tapering base .... **P. petiolaris**
  Petiole short or absent 3
3 On mountain slopes and mountain grassland; confined strictly to the eastern mountains of Rhodesia
  and adjacent Moçambique; flowers usually pink to red.................................... **P. caffra**
  More widespread, flowers usually white, although they may be tinged with pink 4
4 Leaves narrow, generally less than 3 cm broad .... **P. gaguedi**
  Leaves generally broader than 3 cm .... **P. angolensis**

Protea angolensis Welw.
S.A. no: —
Rhod. no: 80   Northern protea

A small, straggling tree up to 3 m; found in open wooded grassland. **Bark:** black and fissured.
Leaves: oblanceolate to elliptic, 10 to 16 × 2 to 8 cm, light green to bluish-green; apex tapering to
rounded; base tapering; margin entire; petiole absent. **Flower heads:** up to 10 cm in diameter, bracts
pale green sometimes flushed with red near the tips; flowers generally white, sometimes tinged with
rose-pink (April to July). **Fruit:** a nut, densely hairy (June and July).
There are two varieties of this species: the typical variety, var. *angolensis,* is a dwarf plant, growing
only 50 cm high; the tree is var. *divaricata* (Engl. & Gilg) Beard.

Protea aurea (N. L. Burm.) Rourke Illust. 26
[*P. longiflora* Lam.; *Leucadendron aureum* N. L. Burm.]
S.A. no: 90,3   Long-bud protea. Langknopsuikerbos
Rhod. no: —

A shrub or small, bushy tree up to 5 m in height; occurring in dense *fynbos* on lower south-facing
mountain slopes, often in cool, moist positions. **Bark:** greyish or brownish; young branchlets reddish.
Leaves: elliptic to oblong, up to 10 × 2 to 3 cm, dark green, finely hairy when young, losing these
hairs later; apex tapering, finally sharp-tipped; base slightly lobed, clasping the stem; margin entire,

130

pink translucent; petiole absent. **Flower heads:** about 10 cm long × 6 cm in diameter; bracts silvery-green edged with brown, flowers white, but occasionally an attractive pink form is found; the unopened bud is the most distinctive feature of this species, being conspicuously long and slender, like a green candle; also the freshly open flower is a very typical shuttlecock shape, but later it opens more fully as the bracts curve back and the flower head then looks untidy (October to February). **Fruit:** a hairy nutlet (soon after the flowering).

These plants respond well in cultivation.

Protea caffra Meissner

[*P. gazensis* Beard; *P. multibracteata* Phillips; *P. rhodantha* J. D. Hook.; *P. peglerae* Phillips; *P. natalensis* Phillips; *P. baurii* Phillips; *P. flanaganii* Phillips]

S.A. no: 87   Highveld protea

Rhod. no: 83   Manica protea

A small gnarled tree seldom exceeding 7 m in height; occurring on dry rocky ridges, on hill and mountain slopes, in mountain grassland and, at high altitudes in the mistbelt, in moist rather sheltered places. **Bark:** grey to black, fissured and sometimes warty. **Leaves:** 8 to 20 × 0,8 to 5 cm, the larger leaves at higher altitudes, narrowly oblong, narrowly elliptic to elliptic, occasionally slightly sickle-shaped, green to light green, stiff, crowded towards the ends of the branches, midrib yellowish to reddish; apex broadly tapering to rounded; base tapering; margin entire; petiole absent. **Flower heads:** 5 to 10 cm, occasionally up to 12 cm, in diameter, outer bracts whitish, greenish to brownish, inner bracts pinkish white to red. (November to March) **Fruit:** a hairy nutlet (forming shortly after the flowers).

This is an attractive little tree when the flowers are fresh, but the old heads remain on the tree for some time and give it an unkempt appearance. This was the protea which was depicted on the old South African 3d and 6d pieces.

This species could be confused with *P. gaguedi* which has smaller leaves and the flower buds are definitely longer and broader.

Protea comptonii Beard

S.A. no: 88   Barberton mountain protea. Barbertonse bergsuikerbos

Rhod. no: —

PROTEACEAE

A short trunked, gnarled tree up to 5 m high; with a very limited distribution, occurring on steep rocky mountain slopes. **Bark:** very thick, corky and longitudinally fissured. **Leaves:** unusually large, oblong, 12 to 24 × 3 to 6 cm, crowded at the ends of the branchlets, thick, dark green, fleshy, midrib coloured red to yellow on the upper surface; apex rounded and slightly notched; base tapering; margin entire and translucent red; petiole absent. **Flower heads:** large, 10 to 15 cm in diameter, opening very wide; bracts pale green with a shiny, waxy covering; flowers white, or pinkish (May to July). **Fruit:** a hairy nutlet (developing shortly after the flowers).

Protea coronata Lam.
[*P. macrocephala* Thunb. *P. incompta* R. Br.]
S.A. no: 91,1   Green protea. Groenhofiesuikerbos
Rhod. no: —

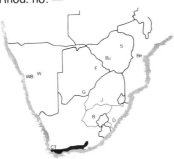
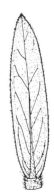

An erect, slender shrub or small tree reaching 4 m; locally common on open plains and mountain slopes along the coastal belt from sea level to about 500 m; it is now common only in the eastern and western limits of its range. **Bark:** grey-brown; young branches softly velvety, later losing these hairs. **Leaves:** tightly clustered along the stems, elliptic, up to 10 × 2,5 cm, green or greyish-green, young leaves densely clothed with silky hairs producing a silvery effect, older leaves without hairs; apex tapering, ultimately sharp-tipped; base variable, usually lobed and clasping the stem; margin entire; petiole absent. **Flower heads:** inconspicuous but distinctive, up to 13 cm long and opening only slightly, with the white flowers only just protruding from the mouth; bracts green with a fine fringe of whitish hairs; the flower heads are often almost hidden by the foliage leaves (main season from April to August). **Fruit:** a hairy nutlet (following shortly after the flowers).
This species is comparatively easily cultivated.

Protea curvata N. E. Brown
S.A. no: 88,1   Barberton lowveld protea. Barbertonse laeveldsuikerbos
Rhod. no: —

A slender tree up to 6 m, with long ascending branches, distinctive in appearance and habit; this is probably the most rare of the species of *Protea,* occurring only on one small hill of talcose schist in the lowveld near Barberton. **Bark:** black, scaly and fissured. **Leaves:** long, narrow, 10 to 20 × 1 to 1,5 cm, frequently sickle-shaped, leathery, light green, the branchlets densely leafy; apex rounded; base very narrowly tapering; margin entire, translucent; petiole almost absent. **Flower heads:** 6 to 7 cm in diameter; bracts deep red, velvety over the lower half, the upper half without hairs; flowers rose-pink (June to July). **Fruit:** a nutlet, with long red to golden-brown hairs (shortly after the flowers).

Protea eximia (Salisb. ex J. Knight) Fourc.
S.A. no: 88,3   Broad-leaved protea. Breëblaarsuikerbos
Rhod. no: —

A dense shrub or small bushy tree up to 3 m; occurring in a variety of habitats, from arid mountain slopes in the Swartberg, to moist, peaty slopes in the Langeberg, forming dense stands in certain areas. **Bark:** brownish-grey. **Leaves:** elliptic, up to 10 × 3 to 5 cm, whitish-green, stongly curved upwards and densely sheathing the upright branchlets; apex rounded; base lobed, clasping the stem; margin entire, often pink-edged; petiole absent. **Flower heads:** large, handsome, up to 12 cm in diameter; bracts pink, orange to red; flowers pink, woolly, the central flowers in the head with long, dark purple hairs on the awns, so producing a dark patch in the centre (mainly September to October, but sporadically throughout the year); paler and less attractive forms do occur. **Fruit:** a hairy nutlet (a short time after flowering).

Protea gaguedi J. F. Gmelin   Illust. 25
[*P. abyssinica* Willd.]
S.A. no: 89   African protea. Afrikaanse suikerbos
Rhod. no: 82   African protea

A small, gnarled tree usually 3 to 4 m in height, but reaching 8 m under favourable conditions; occurring in warmer areas, often on rocky ground, and in the Transvaal frequently holding to the transition area between highveld and lowveld; it is widely distributed and so occupies widely varying habitats. **Bark:** pale brown, flaky; the young stems are often densely hairy. **Leaves:** lanceolate, 9 to 18 × 1,5 to 3 cm, light green with the midrib yellowish; tapering to base and apex; margin entire; petiole absent or very short. **Flower heads:** very variable in size, 4 to 10 cm in diameter; bracts pale green, sometimes rose-tinted, with dense silvery hairs; flowers densely hairy, white or tinged with pink. Flowering time very variable over its range; in South Africa usually about June to July; in Rhodesia often October to November. **Fruit:** a hairy nutlet (shortly after the flowering).
The similarities and differences between this species and *P. caffra* are given under the latter species.

133

PROTEACEAE

Protea glabra Thunb.
S.A. no: 89,1   Clanwilliam protea. Kaiingsuikerbos
Rhod. no: —

A large shrub or small bushy tree, reaching 5 m in height; occurring on dry, stony mountain slopes, on rocky outcrops and among boulders at high altitudes in the low rainfall areas fringing the Karoo. **Bark:** grey. **Leaves:** elliptic to oblanceolate, up to 10 × 2,5 cm, but usually rather smaller, leathery, veining very obscure; apex broadly tapering to rounded; base tapering; margin entire; petiole extremely short or absent. **Flower heads:** not spectacular, small, about 5 cm in diameter; the bracts rusty-brown, shorter than the flowers; the flowers greenish-yellow and sweetly scented, which is unusual in this genus (August to September). **Fruit:** a hairy nutlet; develops only a few weeks after flowering and is shed very rapidly (October to November).

Protea lacticolor Salisb.
S.A. no: 90   Hottentot white protea. Hottentotwitsuikerbos
Rhod. no: —

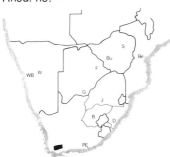

A small, spreading tree up to 4 m; occurring among rocks in mountainous places. **Bark:** grey, smooth. **Leaves:** densely crowded into rosettes at the ends of the branches; elliptic to oval, about 8 × 2,2 to 3,5 cm, dark green, thick, leathery; apex very broadly tapering; base tapering to almost rounded; margin entire; petiole absent. **Flower heads:** rather small, up to 7 cm in diameter and they do not open wide; bracts small, greenish to pinkish; flowers creamy-white or tinged with red (January to April). **Fruit:** a hairy nutlet (following on after the flowers).
This species is very similar to *P. subvestita*, the differences being noted under *P. subvestita*.

Protea laetans L. E. Davidson
S.A. no: 90,4   Blyde protea. Blydesuikerbos
Rhod. no: —

A small slender tree up to 5 m in height; occurring on grassy rocky hillsides in the Blyde River Canyon Reserve in the eastern Transvaal. **Bark:** grey, cracking into rectangles; the short trunk bears long ascending branches; young branches pink to yellow but rapidly become grey. **Leaves:** twisted through 90°, narrowly oblanceolate, 10 to 19 × 1,5 to 3 cm, but usually about 10 to 14 × 1,5 to 1,7 cm, slightly sickle-shaped, leathery, grey-green, without hairs; midrib reddish near the base, yellow near the apex, conspicuous on both surfaces; apex tapering to slightly rounded; base narrowly tapering;

134

margin entire, pale yellow and translucent; petiole absent. **Flower heads:** 8 to 10 × 8 to 10 cm, with a distinct, stout and woody stalk, or stipe, up to 3 cm long, terminal on the branchlets. Bracts carmine, flowers creamy-white shading to pink (March to November, but mainly May). **Fruit:** a hairy nutlet (following on after the flowers).

Protea lanceolata E. Meyer ex Meissner
S.A. no: 90,1   Lance-leaf protea. Smalblaarsuikerbos
Rhod. no: —

A shrub to small tree up to 3 m; locally common on sandy flats and in coastal scrub, never more than 24 km from the sea. **Bark:** grey-brown. **Leaves:** narrowly elliptic to narrowly obovate, up to 7 × 1,3 cm; apex broadly tapering; base narrowly tapering; margin entire; petiole absent. **Flower heads:** small, rather sparse, about 3 cm in diameter; bracts comparatively few, whitish-green with odd brownish hairs; flowers sparse, white also with occasional brownish hairs; at first the flower head has a rather attractive spidery appearance, but very soon it seems to fall apart, becoming ragged and untidy (May to July). **Fruit:** a hairy nutlet (August onwards).

Protea laurifolia Thunb.
S.A. no: 90,2   Laurel protea. Louriersuikerbos
Rhod. no: —

Often a large, rather lax bush, but it can form a sturdy tree up to 6 m; conspicuous on dry mountain slopes and plateaux, in hot, low-rainfall, mountainous areas. **Bark:** grey. **Leaves:** oblanceolate, up to **135**

15 × 4 cm, typically grey-bluish-green, veining more or less distinct; apex broadly tapering, finally abruptly sharp-tipped; base narrowly tapering and running into the petiole; margin entire, thickened; petiole obscure due to the decurrent leaf base, very short, 5 to 7 mm or almost absent. **Flower heads:** very attractive, up to 15 cm long × 10 cm in diameter; bracts silvery-pink tipped with a tuft of black hairs, or of grey and white woolly hairs often with an intermingling of black; flowers salmon-pink, the central mass being yellow (June to August, but sporadically for months before and after this period). **Fruit:** a hairy nutlet (developing soon after the flowers fade).

This species is very similar to *P. neriifolia,* but both are clearly geographically distinct. The specific name is pronounced exactly like *P. lorifolia* and the two are easily confused but *laurifolia* means 'laurel-leaved', while *lorifolia* means 'strap-leaved'.

Protea lepidocarpodendron (L.) L.

S.A. no: 90,5   Black-bearded protea. Swartbaardsuikerbos
Rhod. no: —

Usually a shrub, occasionally assuming the proportions of a small tree; occurring on mountain slopes, in damp ground, subdominant on scree slopes, sometimes forming dense stands. **Bark:** grey. **Leaves:** narrowly elliptic, to linear lanceolate, leathery, grey-green; apex broadly tapering; base narrowly tapering; margin entire, pink translucent; petiole absent. **Flower heads:** distinctive, up to 10 × 6 cm, lower bracts brown, upper bracts greenish-cream, densely black-bearded often fringed with white; flowers cream; the flower heads are numerous but they are frequently obscured by the leaves which extend beyond the tip of the flower (April to August). **Fruit:** a hairy nutlet (following shortly after the flowering).

This species can be distinguished from the other black-bearded proteas by its contrasting colours of brown, cream and black, with no pink or red.

Protea lorifolia (Salisb. ex J. Knight) Fourc.

S.A. no: 91   Strap-leaved protea. Riemblaarsuikerbos
Rhod. no: —

Frequently a bush 1 to 2 m high, but it can grow into a small loosely spreading tree about 3 to 4 m; occurring on dry, arid, inland mountain ranges where fairly drastic extremes of temperature are experienced. **Bark:** grey and rough; in younger trees grey and smooth with rough, dark circular markings. **Leaves:** long, narrow, 10 to 22 × 2 to 4 cm, green, leathery, velvety when young; midrib and lateral veins yellow; apex rounded, often shallowly notched; base tapering; margin entire, edged

136

with a reddish-brown rim; petiole absent. **Flower heads:** about 10 cm in diameter; colour variable, bracts olive-yellow and brown-edged with the flowers dull yellow; or the bracts cream to pink with silvery hairs, and pink flowers; the perianth awns are bearded with reddish-purple hairs; the latter form is very striking, but the flowers are often hidden by the leaves (May to August). **Fruit:** a hairy nutlet (soon after flowering).

The specific name sounds identical to *laurifolia;* the meanings of the two names are given under *P. laurifolia.*

Protea magnifica Andr.

[*P. barbigera* Meissner]
S.A. no: 86,1   Bearded protea. Baardsuikerbos
Rhod. no: —

Usually a shrub about 1,5 to 2 m high, but it can attain heights of 3,5 m if left unburnt; occurring in rocky mountains, mainly above 1 000 m. **Bark:** dark brown to grey. **Leaves:** oblong, up to 10 × 3 cm, leathery, dark green; tapering to base and apex; margin entire, thickened, cartilaginous; petiole very short or absent. **Flower heads:** large, up to 12 cm or more in diameter, floral bracts yellow, pink or red, with fine silky hairs, and with conspicuous white to pinkish woolly tips which resemble candy floss; each flower is up to 6 cm long, yellow to pink, with the perianth produced into two awns, each tipped with a blackish-purple beard (June to November). **Fruit:** a small hairy nut (developing shortly after the flowers).

This is one of the most splendid of the proteas and it is proving successful in cultivation if given the correct treatment.

Protea mundii Klotzsch

S.A. no: 93   White protea. Witsuikerbos
Rhod. no: —

A shrub 3 to 4 m in height, but 8 m is not uncommon and exceptional specimens even reach 13 m; occurring on mountain slopes, in ravines and along streams where it is locally common and can form dense stands; it is a pioneer at evergreen forest margins. **Bark:** dark grey-brown. **Leaves:** elliptic to oval or narrowly obovate, up to 11 × 2,5 to 4 cm, young leaves velvety, the older leaves may have long hairs near the base, otherwise without hairs, pale green, distinctly veined, with the midrib often reddish; apex broadly tapering to narrowly rounded; base tapering; margin entire; petiole absent. **Flower head:** rather small but standing well clear of the leaves, up to 7,5 cm long and 5 cm in

137

diameter, not opening wide; bracts usually silky green with a deep thick fringe of white hairs; flowers white and the styles are tipped with a conspicuous club-like stigma, so that the top of the flower is like a forest of pins; an attractive form with pink bracts sometimes occurs (April to September). **Fruit:** a hairy nutlet (shortly after flowering).

This is the conspicuous pale-coloured protea seen in numbers over Prince Alfred's Pass and the Montagu Pass.

Protea neriifolia R. Br. Illust. 27
S.A. no: 93,1   Oleander-leaved protea. Blousuikerbos
Rhod. no: —

Often widespreading bushes 1 to 2 m high, but also more tree-like at 3 to 4 m and occasionally even taller; occurring in a wide variety of situations from the coast up to the mountainsides, very often on gravelly hills; it can form immensely dense stands, sometimes excluding almost all other plants over small areas. **Bark:** dark grey with pale markings. **Leaves:** densely crowded along the branches, narrowly elliptic, up to 15 × 2 cm, hard, leathery, yellowish or olive-green, occasionally bluish-green without hairs, but occasionally white woolly at the base, midrib yellow; apex tapering, finally sharp-tipped; base gradually tapering; margin entire; petiole absent. **Flower heads:** 12 × 7,5 cm, but usually rather less than 10 cm long; bracts deep pink with black beards, or occasionally white beards; flowers pink, the central section pink or often purplish (April to September). **Fruit:** a hairy nutlet (shortly after the flowering)

This species could be confused with *P. laurifolia* but the two species are geographically distinct. The leaves of *P. neriifolia* resemble those of *Nerium*, the oleander, and the specific name refers to this.

Protea nitida Mill. Illust. 24
[*P. arborea* Houtt. *P. grandiflora* Thunb.]
S.A. no: 86   Waboom. Waboom
Rhod. no: —

A small tree reaching about 7 m in height; occurring from sea level to 2 000 m in very rough terrain, on rocky mountain slopes. **Bark:** dark brown, flaking in small squares to reveal paler patches beneath. **Leaves:** narrowly oblong to obovate, up to 15 × 5 cm, but usually smaller, grey-green to blue-green, thick, leathery, stiff; apex broadly tapering or rounded; tapering to the base; margin entire; petiole absent. **Flower heads:** up to 10 cm in diameter but usually less, the general impression being white;

138

bracts yellowish-green; flowers white or creamy (March to July). **Fruit:** a small hairy nut (May to August, or later).

Burchell recorded that the 'waboom' or 'wagon tree' was so named because it provided wood for making the felloes of wagon wheels. The early Cape botanist, C. W. L. Pappe (1803-1862), noted that if the crushed leaves were mixed with a saturated solution of iron in water 'a tolerably good ink' was produced, and Eve Palmer records that the Voortrekker leader, Louis Trichardt, probably wrote with this ink in his famous journals. The wood which is reddish in colour and has an attractive grain is a functional general purpose timber, while the astringent bark has been used for tanning hides and for an infusion for treating diarrhoea.

Protea obtusifolia Buek ex Meissner
S.A. no: 94   Bredasdorp protea. Bredasdorpsuikerbos
Rhod. no: —

A large rounded shrub about 3 m high, it may develop into a tree at about 3,5 m, with a spread of 5 m and a stem up to 30 cm in diameter; strictly coastal, always occurring very close to the sea, on limestone hills and ridges. **Bark:** dark brown or grey. **Leaves:** elliptic, up to 11 × 4 cm, leathery, without hairs and with the veining distinct; apex rounded (the specific name refers to this); base tapering; margin entire; petiole obscure. **Flower heads:** rather small, up to 9 cm long and 3 cm in diameter, not opening widely; bracts cream, pink to red, sometimes brown-tipped; flowers white or pink (April to August, but sporadically as late as December). **Fruit:** a hairy nutlet (shortly after the flowering).

Hybrids between this species and *P. susannae* can be found which grow into good sized trees.

Protea petiolaris (Engl. ex Hiern) Baker
S.A. no: —
Rhod. no: 84   Sickle-leaved protea

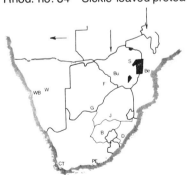

A straggling tree up to 6 m; occurring in higher altitude *Brachystegia* woodland or high mountain grassland in wet and rocky places. **Bark:** black and fissured. **Leaves:** crowded at the ends of the branchlets; broadly lanceolate, 10 to 16 × 1 to 3 cm, dull green, markedly sickle-shaped, limply drooping; apex broadly tapering to almost rounded; base excessively narrowed; margin entire, translucent; petiole probably absent, although the extremely narrow tapering of the leaf base gives the impression of quite a long petiole (the specific name refers to this). **Flower heads:** about 10 cm in

139

diameter; bracts green to red; flowers white or pink (almost throughout the year). **Fruit:** a hairy nutlet (almost at any time of the year).

Protea punctata Meissner
S.A. no: 94,1   Water white sugarbush. Waterwitsuikerbos
Rhod. no: —

A stout shrub or small tree, 2 to 3 m tall; locally abundant on north-facing slopes and hillsides of inland mountain ranges. **Bark:** grey to brownish; branchlets with dense yellowish to reddish hairs. **Leaves:** oval to broadly oval, up to 7 × 2,5 to 3 cm, dull bluish-green, the young leaves with long hairs, the mature leaves losing most of these; apex broadly tapering to rounded; base broadly tapering; margin entire; petiole absent. **Flower heads:** small, up to 5 cm in diameter; bracts silvery-white, tinged with pink or green with brown tips; flowers white with brownish styles (December to May). **Fruit:** a nutlet with reddish-brown hairs (August to October).

Protea repens (L.) L.   Illust. 28
[*P. mellifera* Thunb.]
S.A. no: 94,2   Sugarbush. Opregtesuikerbos
Rhod. no: —

A shrub about 2,5 m high, or a small tree up to 5 m; occurring from sea level to 2 000 m, growing in a wide variety of habitats; often exterminated by farming when the lower altitude arable areas are cleared; one of the best-known of all the proteas, and a primary succession plant on fire-ravaged land. **Bark:** greyish to brown. **Leaves:** clustered near the ends of the branches; narrowly elliptic, sometimes almost linear, up to 13 × 0,8 to 1,3 cm, without hairs, bluish-green, green or yellowish; apex bluntly tapering; base narrowly tapering; margin entire, yellowish to pinkish translucent; petiole absent. **Flower heads:** slender, 10 to 13 cm in length and about 7,5 cm in diameter, never opening very wide; the colour is very variable; bracts deep pink; the flowers varying from pure white to delicate rose-pink to deep pink; frequently populations in different localities have their own colour variants and often their own flowering times (ranging roughly from December to June). **Fruit:** a nutlet with golden-brown hairs (very variable, often about August to December).

The common name *suikerbos,* or *sugarbush,* was first applied to this species as the plentiful nectar was collected from the flowers and boiled down to form a thick syrup – used to treat coughs – and finally sugar. *Protea repens* appears as a floral emblem on the South African coat-of-arms.

140

Protea roupelliae Meissner   Illust. 29
S.A. no: 96   Silver protea. Silwersuikerbos
Rhod. no: —

A small gnarled tree up to 5 m, usually with a neat crown and spreading branches; occurring on grassy hills and mountain slopes where it often forms small patches of open *Protea* woodland. **Bark:** dark grey, rough, deeply fissured and cracked. **Leaves:** closely set in rosettes at the ends of the branches; variable in shape, usually linear-lanceolate, 6 to 16 × 1,5 to 4,5 cm, dark green and leathery, young leaves hairy, these hairs being lost later, midrib more or less prominent on both surfaces; apex tapering; base very narrowly tapering, almost forming a petiole; margin entire; petiole absent, but the narrowly decurrent leaf base gives the impression of a petiole. **Flower heads:** large, 8 to 12 cm in diameter, frequently almost hidden by the leaves; the colour is variable over its great range; at its best the bracts are silky, the outer brownish through silvery-pink to the deep rose-pink of the inner bracts, and the flowers are deep red, but the heads are frequently much paler and less spectacular (April to June). **Fruit:** a hairy nutlet (following shortly after the flowering).
At its most colourful, this is one of the most noteworthy of the summer-rainfall *Proteas*.

Protea rubropilosa Beard
S.A. no: 97   Transvaal mountain protea. Transvaalse bergsuikerbos
Rhod. no: —

A gnarled tree with spreading branches, commonly about 5 m tall, but reaching 8 m on occasions; occurring on rugged quartzite outcrops in the mountain mistbelts. **Bark:** very dark and flaking. **Leaves:** produced on last season's wood; obovate, up to 15 × 5 cm, dark green, without hairs, rather glossy, midrib red and prominent on both surfaces; apex rounded; base slightly narrowed; margin entire, translucent; petiole absent. **Flower heads:** very beautiful, 8 to 10 cm in diameter; bracts rose-pink, with dense long, rusty hairs outside, and long, tawny hairs inside giving a remarkable and beautiful metallic bronze sheen (the specific name refers to these long, reddish, silky hairs); flowers white with rosy-red veins (August to October). **Fruit:** a hairy nutlet (following shortly after the flowering).

141

PROTEACEAE

Protea rupicola Mund ex Meissner
[*P. dykei* Phillips]
S.A. no: 88,2   Krantz protea. Kranssuikerbos
Rhod. no: —

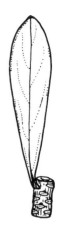

A sturdy, gnarled and twisted small tree, 3 to 4 m in height; occurring on krantzes and crags, always on the summits of very high mountain peaks in windswept situations. **Bark:** dark grey to almost black. **Leaves:** lanceolate, up to 6 × 1,2 cm, greyish-green, without hairs, leathery, all veins submerged; apex broadly tapering to rounded; base tapering; margin entire, conspicuously reddish, translucent; petiole absent. **Flower heads:** about 7 cm in diameter; bracts and flowers brownish to rose-pink, the flowers curving inwards, and the styles bright red tipped with yellow (October). **Fruit:** a nutlet with red-brown hairs (following shortly after the flowering).

Protea subvestita N. E. Brown
S.A. no: 98   Lipped protea. Lippeblomsuikerbos
Rhod. no: —

A high mountain species, seldom below 1 800 m. This species is very like *P. lacticolor*. The main differences are that in *P. subvestita:*
(a) the young branches are much more densely covered with woolly hairs;
(b) the young leaves are covered with densely woolly hairs; these hairs are later shed;
(c) the flower heads are shorter, about 5 cm long instead of 7 cm;
(d) the most distinctive feature lies with the inner bracts, the tips of which curve back, forming a lip.

Protea susannae Phillips
S.A. no: 98,1   Stinkleaf protea. Stinkblaarsuikerbos
Rhod. no: —

A shrub, or occasionally a small tree, reaching 4 m or a little more; frequently occurring among limestone ridges close to the sea. **Bark:** grey to brownish; young stems sometimes a marked reddish colour and hairy. **Leaves:** lanceolate, up to 13 × 1 to 2 cm, almost without hairs, brownish-green,

midrib red; apex broadly tapering; base tapering; margin entire; petiole absent or very short. **Flower heads:** about 10 cm or more in diameter; bracts pinkish-brown; flowers pink; styles white, stigmas red; the flowers are partly hidden by the leaves (May to October). **Fruit:** a hairy nutlet (shortly after the flowering).

The crushed or bruised leaves have a characteristic and unpleasant smell. This is also noticeable in hybrids between this species and other *Protea* species, e.g. *P. obtusifolia*.

Protea welwitschii Engl.

[*P. melliodora* Engl. & Gilg]
S.A. no: 98,2   Honey-scented protea. Vaalsuikerbos
Rhod. no: 85   Honey-scented protea

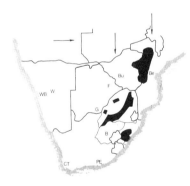 

A low shrub 1 to 2 m high or a small tree up to 3,5 m; occurring on stony outcrops and on sandy flats in deciduous woodland. **Bark:** grey to greyish-brown. **Leaves:** all along the branches; elliptic, up to 15 × 3,5 cm, brownish-green, densely hairy when young losing almost all the hairs later, leathery; apex rounded; base tapering; margin entire; petiole absent. **Flower heads:** this has the unusual habit of producing 2 to 4 heads together at the ends of the branches; each head is rather small, 4 to 6 cm in diameter; bracts pale yellowish, to tawny-pink or brown; flowers creamy-white, very hairy, tinged with brown (December to May). **Fruit:** a hairy nutlet (shortly after the flowering).

The specimens occurring in South Africa are low-growing shrubs, only occasionally reaching 3 m in height (Transvaal), and can seldom be classed as trees. The species as a whole is very susceptible to fire-damage, which probably accounts for the low-growing habit of many of the plants.

143

Protea Gaguedi

5. LEUCOSPERMUM R. Br.

Shrubs or small trees, often multi-stemmed from the base. **Leaves:** simple, alternate, entire or with a few apical teeth. **Inflorescences:** axillary, occasionally terminal, typically spherical, solitary or in groups of 2 to 4 (or more, up to 10); involucral bracts usually rather small, inconspicuous (cf. *Protea*, where the bracts are large and often showy). **Flowers:** perianth a tube, with the 3 upper lobes joined to form a sheath containing the anthers, the lower lobe separating away and dividing for three-quarters of the length of the tube, but remaining joined at the base; stamens without a filament, the anthers joined to the perianth lobes, the pollen presenter cylindric, club-shaped or cone-shaped; ovary very small, hardly more than a slight swelling at the base of the style, styles long and conspicuous giving the well-known 'pincushion' appearance. **Fruit:** a small nut up to 8 mm long, brownish, and remaining embedded in the dry remains of the flower and simply falling to the ground 6 weeks to 2 months after the flower opens, when it is often carried away by field mice and so lost.

These are the well-known 'pincushions', many of them rivalling the proteas in their beauty. On the Chimanimani mountains there is one species which is a small shrub 1 to 2 m in height, *L. saxosum* S. Moore (Rhod. no: 86); the flowers are beautifully coloured butter-yellow and orange-red; fairly recently this was found also on the northern end of the Drakensberg in the eastern Transvaal.

In South Africa out of some 47 species most are shrubs, and only six can be said to reach tree size.

Key to the tree species of *Leucospermum:*
1 In the hot, arid desert mountains of the western Cape, round Vanrhynsdorp as far south as
   Koudeberg and Wupperthal 2
   Not in the arid mountain areas above 4
2 Flower heads 8 to 10 cm in diameter; flowers sharply bent backwards and downwards in a very
   distinctive fashion (see Illust. 31) .... **L. reflexum**
   Flowers upright, in typical pincushion (cf. Illust. 30) 3
3 Flower heads about 7 cm in diameter; pale carmine, with the styles orange to crimson
   .... **L. praemorsum**
   Flower heads small, about 3,5 cm in diameter; deep yellow .... **L. rodolentum**
4 Bark grey to brown, rough, with warty protuberances; from Caledon eastwards to Transkei
   .... **L. cuneiforme**
   Bark without warty protuberances; not further east than Mossel Bay 5
5 Branches crooked and characteristically interlocking; flowers yellow .. **L. conocarpodendron**
   Branches more or less straight, not interlocking; flowers orange to crimson ..... **L. patersonii**

Leucospermum conocarpodendron (L.) Buek   Illust. 30
[*Leucadendron conocarpodendron* L.]
S.A. no: 84 and 84,1   Tree pincushions. Kreupelhout
Rhod. no: —

145

PROTEACEAE

A shrub or small tree 3 to 5 m in height; occurring in a variety of habitats from coastal dunes to mountain slopes, from sea level to about 200 m, in some places becoming dominant and forming dense stands; the frequent fires which sweep these areas have caused many of these trees to develop rounded, umbrella-shaped crowns. **Bark:** thick, reddish-grey, dark grey to almost black, almost smooth, marked only with leaf scars, or, in fire-tortured specimens, deeply vertically and longitudinally fissured, forming rough, rectangular segments; the branches are very characteristically crooked and interlocking *(kreupelhout);* the young flowering branches are covered with long hairs. **Leaves:** oblong to obovate, 6 to 11,5 × 2,5 to 5 cm, deep green, with or without fine, greyish, short hairs; apex rounded, except for 3 to 10 teeth just below the apex, and sometimes fringed with hairs; base tapering; margin entire, except for the apical teeth which may be reddish; petiole absent. **Flower heads:** up to 9 cm in diameter, solitary or in groups of 2 to 3; flowers large, up to 5 cm long, butter-yellow, styles up to 5,5 cm long; the whole head very showy (August to January). **Fruit:** typical of the genus (shortly after the flowering).

The species is divided into two subspecies:
(a) subsp. *conocarpodendron:* leaves greyish with dense shaggy, finely crisped hairs; very restricted distribution, endemic to the Cape Peninsula, and only from the eastern slopes of Devil's Peak, along the northern and western slopes of Table Mountain to Llandudno. It favours well-drained soils.
(b) subsp. *viridum* Rourke: leaves deep green and without hairs, although the margins may be fringed; much wider distribution, and occupying a range of habitats, from compacted coastal sand dunes to stony mountain slopes.

A decoction of the bark is a powerful astringent and it was once considered to be excellent for tanning hides. The flowers are in great demand and at one time the Cape Town flower-sellers, trying to 'gild the lily', dyed the beautiful flowers red!

Leucospermum cuneiforme (N. L. Burm.) Rourke
[Leucadendron cuneiforme N. L. Burm.]
S.A. no: 84,2   Common pincushions. Gewone luisiesbos
Rhod. no: —

A shrub with many stems arising from a stout underground rootstock, but if undisturbed, and if left unburnt in a sheltered place, it will grow into a small tree up to 3 m, with one main stem; occurring in a wide range of habitats, from winter-rainfall ericoid scrub to subtropical coastal dune forest in Transkei, from the fringes of the Karoo to the margins of temperate evergreen forest, and from sea level to 1 000 m; this is the most wide-ranging species in this genus. **Bark:** grey to brown and rough, with warty protuberances and pustules; this is definitive. **Leaves:** narrowly to broadly oblanceolate, 4,5 to 11 × 0,6 to 3 cm, leathery; apex broadly tapering to flattened, toothed; tapering to base; margin entire except for 3 to 10 teeth immediately below the apex; petiole absent. **Flower heads:** ovoid, 5 to 9 cm in diameter, usually solitary, but occasionally in groups of 2 to 3; flowering branchlets covered with dense brownish, crisped hairs; flowers up to 4 cm long, yellow aging to orange and red, conspicuous and showy (mainly August to February, but sporadically at any time of the year). **Fruit:** typical of the genus (shortly after flowering).

The fruits, smooth and light coloured, somewhat resemble ticks and this gave rise to the common name *luisiesboom,* which is applied loosely to several of the species in this genus.

Leucospermum patersonii Phillips
S.A. no: 85   Bastard pincushions. Basterkreupelhout
Rhod. no: —

A large rounded shrub to small tree up to 5 m tall; confined to the coastal belt and growing on limestone hills close to the sea from Cape Agulhas to Stanford, with an outlying population at Kleinmond; it used to occur round Hermanus but it seems that it has now been exterminated in this area. **Bark:** greyish-brown; stem and main branches stout, the smaller branchlets with dense woolly brownish-grey hairs. **Leaves:** broadly oblong, 5 to 9 × 3 to 5 cm, without hairs; conspicuously broad for this genus; closely ranked and overlapping up the stem; apex rounded; base lobed to conspicuously so, almost forming two overlapping semicircles; margin entire, except for 3 to 8 large teeth immediately below the apex; petiole absent. **Flower heads:** up to 9 cm in diameter, usually solitary but may be in groups of 2 to 3, upstanding; flowers up to 3 cm long, yellow, orange or crimson; styles bright red in the upper part; these flower heads are conspicuous and showy but may be partly hidden by the leaves (August to December). **Fruit:** typical of the genus (shortly after flowering).

Leucospermum praemorsum (Meissner) Phillips
S.A. no: 85,1   Nardouw pincushions. Nardouwluisiesbos
Rhod. no: —

Large shrubs or small trees up to 5 m in height; occurring on very dry, arid mountainsides and among rocks. **Bark:** grey, smooth. **Leaves:** oblong to oblanceolate, 7 to 8 × 1,5 to 2,5 cm, crowded towards the ends of the branchlets; apex abruptly squared-off (truncate), toothed; base narrowly tapering; margin entire, except for the 3 to 5 teeth below the apex, or as part of the apex; petiole distinct, probably 1 to 2 cm long, although it is difficult to determine precisely because of the decurrent leaf base, which is unusual in this genus; the petiole and the lower section of the leaf are covered with long, whitish, cobweb-like hairs. **Flower heads:** about 7 cm in diameter, rather obscured by the foliage leaves; the bracts below the flower head, usually somewhat obscure in the other species, are here up to 2 cm long, narrow, hairy and very loosely arranged; flowers up to 3 cm long, pale carmine when fresh, becoming deep crimson; the styles are almost 6 cm long and orange in colour (July to December, but sporadically at most times of the year). **Fruit:** typical of the genus (shortly after flowering).

This is an attractive, distinctive and interesting species, with several characters which separate it from other members of the genus; the squared-off leaf apex (the specific name meaning 'bitten, or chewed off' refers to this), the distinct petiole, and the large, loosely arranged bracts below the flower heads, **147**

PROTEACEAE

all make it easy to identify. Owing to the very dry, arid conditions existing in the mountains where these trees grow, (e.g. the Gifberg and Nardouwberg), a fire hazard as such does not arise as there is simply not enough vegetation to burn well, so many of these plants become sizeable trees with stem diameters of up to 30 cm.

Leucospermum reflexum Buek ex Meissner   Illust. 31
S.A. no: Rocket pincushions
Rhod. no: —

A large rounded shrub or small tree 4 to 5 m in height, with a single stem at the base; found in hot, dry, arid mountain *fynbos,* only between 900 m and 1 800 m, but always near moisture, along stream beds or in seepage areas. **Bark:** grey, smooth; the flowering branches are conspicuously hairy. **Leaves:** distinctly small, elliptic to oblanceolate, 2 to 5 × 0,5 to 1,3 cm, pointing upwards, closely ranked along the stem and covered with fine grey hairs; apex may be broadly tapering to rounded, but usually with 2 to 3 teeth; base tapering; margin entire, except for the apical teeth; petiole absent. **Flower heads:** very distinctive; 8 to 10 cm in diameter; flowers up to 5 cm long, sharply bent backwards and downwards, deep orange to crimson (August to January). **Fruit:** typical of the genus (soon after flowering).
The small, grey leaves and the deflexed flowers are definitive characters.

Leucospermum rodolentum (Salisb. ex J. Knight) Rourke
[*Leucadendron rodolentum* Salisb. ex J. Knight; *Leucospermum candicans* (Andr.) Sweet]
S.A. no: 83   Sandveld pincushions. Sandveldluisiesbos
Rhod. no: —

A large, rounded bush with the branches reaching down to the ground and obscuring the stem; common throughout the sandveld of the western Cape. **Bark:** grey, smooth. **Leaves:** elliptic-oblong, up to 6,5 × 1,5 cm, greyish-green, covered with very fine, crisped hairs; apex square, rounded or with 3 to 6 blunt teeth; base tapering; margin entire, apart from the apical teeth; petiole absent. **Flower heads:** small, only about 3,5 cm in diameter, solitary, or 2 to 4 together at the ends of the flowering branches; flowers up to 2,5 cm long, deep yellow; each flower has a small, carmine-coloured bracteole at the base, but the overall colour remains yellow (August to October, but may be found either earlier or later). Fruit: typical of the genus (shortly after flowering).

148 The common name, 'rose-centered leucospermum', was that applied in England and Europe when plants were grown first in 1802, probably from seed gathered by Masson. This is therefore the revival of an antique name.

6. LEUCADENDRON R. Br.

Shrubs or trees. **Leaves:** simple, alternate, entire, leathery. **Flowers:** sexes separate on separate trees, in solitary lateral and terminal heads. All floral parts in fours. Male heads loose, spherical, not cone-like; perianth joined in the lower section, 4-lobed near the mouth; stamens without filaments, the anthers joined to the perianth; ovary vestigial. Female flowers in cone-like heads formed by overlapping bracts; perianth parts joined or overlapping in the lower section, 4 -lobed near the mouth; stamens vestigial; ovary very small. **Fruit:** a small nut, usually with some mechanism for wind dispersal. The leaves immediately below the flower heads (the involucral leaves) are often brightly coloured and attractive, sometimes almost petal-like.

Key to the tree species of *Leucadendron:*

1 Leaves with conspicuous dense, silver, silky hairs .... **L. argenteum**
  Leaves without silver silky hairs 2
2 Mature leaves usually more than 10 mm broad 3
  Mature leaves usually less than 10 mm broad 5
3 Confined to the Cape Peninsula .... **L. strobilinum**
  Not occurring in the Cape Peninsula 4
4 Leaves broadly obovate, up to 5 × 2 cm, green, flowers with an unpleasant foetid smell.......
  .... **L. discolor**
  Leaves narrower, oblanceolate, up to 5,7 × 1,5 cm, greyish-green, flowers with a sweet smell
  .... **L. pubescens**
5 Leaves needle-like .... **L. nobile**
  Leaves less than 10 mm wide, but not needle-like 6
6 Bracts at the base of the flower head hairy .... **L. conicum**
  Bracts without hairs, or very sparsely hairy 7
7 Western Cape, Clanwilliam, Calvinia, but not south of Piketberg .... **L. procerum**
  Not Western Cape, occurring in South Western Cape and Southern Cape 8
8 Bark light greyish-brown; slender shrub or tree with ascending branches, characteristically forming
  hedge-like screens along stream banks .... **L. salicifolium**
  Bark brown or reddish-brown; not given to forming screen-like growths 9
9 Leaf tipped with short, blunt, sharp, firm bristle .... **L. eucalyptifolium**
  Leaf tipped with reddish, hair-like, soft bristle .... **L. coniferum**

N.B. *L. ericifolium* R. Br. is not included in the key as it is now considered to be extinct; it is, however, described in the body of the text.

Leucadendron argenteum (L.) R. Br.   Illust. 32
[*Protea argentea* L.]
S.A. no: 77   Silver tree. Silwerboom
Rhod. no: —

149

Distinctive leaf scars
on the bark of the silver tree,
Leucadendron argenteum.

Usually a small, slender, graceful tree, 5 to 7 m high, but it can reach 16 m under ideal conditions; in its natural state it is confined to one small area in the extreme south western Cape, where it is locally abundant on the eastern slopes of Table Mountain and the Vlakkenberg at altitudes between 150 m and 330 m; it is confined to heavy gravel soils derived from Malmesbury shales and granite rather than Table Mountain sandstone. In its own area it is remarkably hardy, able to withstand wind in open, dry localities and to continue to thrive despite devastating mountain fires. **Bark:** grey, smooth, with very distinctive leaf scars. **Leaves:** tending to be clustered at the ends of the branches; very distinctive, elliptic to narrowly obovate, up to 18 × 2,5 cm, densely covered with long, silky, silver hairs, giving the leaf a wonderful glistening sheen; apex narrowly tapering; base tapering; margin entire; petiole absent. **Flower heads:** sexes separate on separate trees. Male flowers in short compact heads about 4 cm long × 5 cm wide at the ends of the branches; bracts small, inconspicuous. Female flowers in cone-like heads, about 5 × 4 cm, increasing in size until finally they are about 9 × 6 cm when fully mature; the bracts are conspicuous, semicircular, silvery with a pinkish tinge and the upper margin is fringed with long silky hairs (maturing about August and September). **Fruit:** a small black nut about 4 mm in diameter, hanging by the old style from the remains of the old flower, forming a remarkable little parachute which is carried by the wind; the bracts enclosing the flowers become lax and open to release the seeds (they ripen some months after the flowers mature, but may be held on to the tree for several years before they are shed).

The extraordinary silver sheen on the leaves makes these trees among the most beautiful in the world. In summer they have a vivid silver glittering appearance which is almost like the play of light on a mirror, but this is lost in winter when they seem dull and grey in comparison. It is the changing position of the leaf-hairs that is responsible for this variation for they are raised or lowered by the basal cells beneath them which become turgid during the rainy season and flaccid when it is dry. In summer the hairs lie smooth and sleek and the foliage shimmers in the sunlight, while in winter they are raised to increase water-loss and consequently the leaves appear rough and dull. Sometimes small pictures are painted on them and they are then sold to souvenir-hunters as curios, bookmarks or ornaments; unadorned, they are much sought after to enhance floral arrangements. The wood is soft and rather spongy and has no real value.

The sheer beauty of the silver tree makes it a highly desirable garden subject and there is no reason why it should not be cultivated outside its own winter-rainfall area provided its roots are left undisturbed and it is given an airy position where the soil is acid and the drainage good. In addition, in summer-rainfall areas it requires generous watering in winter and spring. The theory that it cannot survive outside its native Cape Peninsula is fallacious for silver trees were grown in England as long ago as 1693.

Leucadendron conicum (Lam.) I. J. M. Williams
[*Protea conica* Lam.]
S.A. no: 78,1   Grey conebush. Vaaltolletjiesbos
Rhod. no: —

A shrub or small tree up to 6 m, often pyramidal in shape; occurring in mountainous areas, growing at altitudes between 300 m and 1 000 m, always in damp places, in valleys, ravines and along streams. **Bark:** dark purplish, rather smooth. **Leaves:** the leaves on the male plants tend to be smaller than those on the female plants; long and slender, narrowly oblanceolate, up to 5 × 0,6 cm, dark green; tapering to a finely pointed reddish apex; base tapering; margin entire; petiole absent. **Flower heads:** small. Male heads about 1,5 cm in diameter and greenish in colour. Female heads oval, up to 2 × 1,2 cm, maturing to a conspicuous wine-red cone up to 3,5 × 3 cm. In both sexes the bracts at the base of the flower heads are quite large and velvety, and in the female cones the floral bracts are densely hairy, almost to the point of having a fringed margin; these hairy bracts are definitive; the cones have a pleasantly fruity scent (October and November). **Fruit:** mature fruits are heart-shaped, dark brown, about 7 × 5 mm, with a small tuft of hairs round the point of attachment (December to February, but are held on to the tree for two to three years before they are shed).

Leucadendron coniferum (L.) Meissner
[*L. sabulosum* Salter]
S.A. no: 82   Dune conebush. Duinegeelbos
Rhod. no: —

A stout shrub or small many-branched tree up to 4 m in height with a conspicuous trunk; occurring from coastal flats to mountainsides, in sandy soil in positions exposed to the full sea wind. **Bark:** reddish-brown. **Leaves:** conspicuously twisted through 90°, narrowly oblanceolate, up to 5,5 × 1 cm; apex tapering to a fine point, finally tipped with a reddish-brown bristle; base tapering, twisted; margin entire; petiole absent; involucral leaves (i.e. those immediately below and around the flowering heads) yellow, colourful and attractive. **Flower heads:** male heads spherical, up to 3 × 1,8 cm, basal bracts dusky, floral bracts small; female heads silvery-green, about 3 × 1,4 cm,

151

maturing to a cone about 5 × 3 cm (August to September). **Fruit:** almost orbicular, about 10 × 9 mm, dusky coloured, broadly winged with an apical notch; the seed ripens several months after flowering but is held in the cone until it is released by veld fires when it germinates immediately.

Leucadendron discolor Phillips & Hutch.
S.A.no: 79   Red conebush. Rooitolletjiesbos
Rhod. no: —

 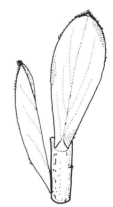

Shrubs about 2 m high, occasionally becoming tree-like and reaching about 4 m; occurring in very arid situations, in rocky or sandy valleys. **Bark:** dark, purplish, smooth. **Leaves:** obovate, up to 5 × 2 cm, rigid, leathery, distinctly veined, the leaves of the male plants being slightly smaller than those of the female plants; involucral leaves (i.e. those below and around the flower heads) colourful, yellow tinged with red; apex very broadly tapering to rounded, with a conspicuous tuft of hairs at the tip which obscures the final small bristle-tip; base tapering; margin entire, cartilaginous; petiole absent. **Flower heads:** male heads reddish, not hairy, stalked, up to 4 × 2,5 cm, with an unpleasant foetid smell; female heads about 2,5 × 1,5, maturing to 4,5 × 2,5, with small narrow bracts (September). **Fruit:** about 7 × 6 mm, winged, apex notched, (ripens in several months, but is retained in the cone for several years).
This is not a common species and is very restricted in its distribution.

Leucadendron ericifolium R. Br.
S.A. no: 80   Erica-leaved conebush. Heideblaargeelbos
Rhod. no: —

 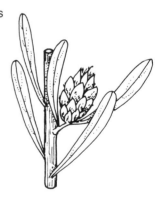

A strange and unusual species which must now be considered to be extinct. It was known only from a very small area – a narrow strip about 64 km long between Riversdale and Barrydale in the southern Cape. **Leaves:** it had two distinct leaf forms: on young plants, and low down on older plants, there were small needle-like leaves, very narrow and up to 2,7 cm long, while the upper leaves in older plants were no longer needle-like, though still narrow, and up to 4 × 0,4 cm; the leaves of female plants were rather larger than those of male plants. **Flower heads:** this species was conspicuously few-flowered; the male heads were very small, only about 7 × 3 mm, and in each only about 12 flowers developed; the female flowers were unique in this genus in that only single flowers were produced, each about 8 mm long and each subtended by a single bract about 6 mm long (July). **Fruit:** because the female flowers were produced singly, and each flower in turn produced only a single seed, few seeds were produced. The fruits were small nuts which ripened in about November and were shed

152

at once with no very effective method of dispersal. This, coupled with the fact that so few seeds were formed, probably helped to lead to the final extinction of the species.

Plants belonging to this species were collected in the early, and again in the mid 19th century, but in recent years all efforts to locate it have failed; collectors should constantly be on the lookout for this species.

Author's note: Since the fore-going description was written Dr I. Williams, in December 1975, rediscoverd a very small population of these plants. There were only about nine specimens in all, growing in a remote valley on the north slopes of the Langeberg a few kilometres east of the north end of Cloete's Pass in the Ladismith area, and subsequently another small group was found on the south slopes of the Rooiberg near Calitzdorp. So living material of this species is again known although it remains extremely rare; it could be said that it has evolved itself almost out of existence.

Leucadendron eucalyptifolium Buek ex Meissner
S.A. no: 81   Tall conebush. Grootgeelbos
Rhod. no: —

A shrub, or small, slender tree reaching 5 m, with erect branches; occurring in the coastal mountains at altitudes between 150 m and 1 600 m, favouring moist conditions; frequent at the edge of forests and along streams. **Bark:** brownish. **Leaves:** conspicuously twisted through 90°; narrow, linear-lanceolate, up to 10,5 × 0,8 cm, finely veined; apex narrowing to a sharply-tipped point; base tapering, twisted; margin entire; petiole absent; the involucral leaves (i.e. immediately below and around the flower heads) become broader at the base and conspicuously yellow. **Flower heads:** male heads up to 2,5 × 1,5 cm, with a faint, attractive scent; the basal bracts are yellow, forming a conspicuous cup round the flower head. Female heads about 2,3 × 1,2 cm developing into a silvery-green cone about 4,5 × 2 cm with a faint, fruity smell and also with the yellow basal bracts (July to October). **Fruit:** up to 7,5 × 6,5 mm, apex notched, dark brown, winged (ripens in several months but is held in the cone for some years before it is released).

Leucadendron nobile I. J. M. Williams
S.A. no: 81,1   Needle-leaved conebush. Naaldblaartolletjiesbos
Rhod. no: —

A shrub to a small tree reaching 4 to 5 m in height, it is one of the taller species; occurring on dry mountain slopes, in gravelly soils. **Bark:** pale grey, smooth; branches purplish, stout. **Leaves:** **153**

The cone-like structures of
Leucadendron nobile,
characteristic of the genus.

distinctive, needle-like, up to 6 × 0,15 cm, sharp-tipped; the leaves in the female plants are rather larger than those in male plants; in involucral leaves (i.e. below and around the flower heads) similar in shape to the foliage leaves but often becoming very pale green to ivory-coloured. **Flower heads:** male heads rather long and spike-like, up to 4 × 1 cm, green, on a bract-sheathed stalk. Female heads about 3 × 1,2 cm maturing into a narrowly oval cone up to 9 × 4 cm with many closely packed, pale edged bracts (October to March, but mainly December). **Fruit:** heart-shaped, attached by the point, dark brown and mottled, narrowly winged (ripens several months later, but is held in the cone for several years, or until the parent plant dies).

Leucadendron procerum (Salisb. ex J. Knight) I. J. M. Williams
[*L. concinnum* R. Br.]
S.A. no: 81,2   Lanky conebush. Langbeentjie
Rhod. no: —

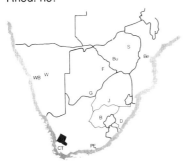

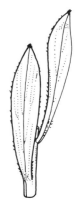

A shrub to small tree, about 3 m high; occurring on arid, stony hillsides, among rocks and on sandy flats. **Bark:** greyish-brown; young stems and branches purplish. **Leaves:** erect, oblanceolate, up to 5 × 1 cm, increasing in size towards the flower heads, green with a bluish flush, leathery, veining obscure; apex broadly tapering to almost rounded, with a conspicuous apical callus and small tuft of hairs when young; base tapering; margin entire; petiole absent; involucral leaves crowded near the flower heads, larger than the foliage leaves, pale green to ivory-coloured. **Flower heads:** male heads small, about 2,2 × 2 cm, basal bracts brownish, shortly hairy and fringed. Female head at first about 1,6 × 1,2 cm, green with brown basal bracts, developing into a reddish cone about 2,5 × 2,2 cm with the bracts rather fleshy and somewhat recurved; the flowers of both sexes produce an unpleasant foetid smell (August). **Fruit:** about 8 × 8 mm, dark brown and pitted, winged (ripens within several months but is not released from the cone for several years, or until the parent tree is damaged).

Leucadendron pubescens R. Br.

[*L. pillansii* Phillips; *L. sericocephalum* Schlechter; *L. retusum* R. Br.; *L. elatum* Buek]
S.A. no: 81,3　Silky conebush. Syhaartolletjiesbos
Rhod. no: —

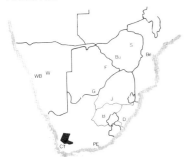 

A robust, greyish-green shrub or small tree up to 3 m in height; occurring in dry, hot low rainfall areas at altitudes from 70 m to 1 600 m, in sandy soil and on dry, rocky mountain slopes. **Bark:** brown and thinly cracked. **Leaves:** rather small and narrow, oblanceolate, up to 5,7 × 1,5 cm on female plants and about half this size on the male plants; smooth to silky haired, but not shining, the dull, grey-green colour being very noticeable; apex tapering, occasionally rounded; base tapering, twisted through 90°; margin entire; petiole absent; involucral leaves not conspicuous. **Flower heads:** male heads small, about 10 × 18 mm, the basal bracts brown-tipped and fringed with hairs, floral bracts reddish, the flowers producing a sweet smell. Female heads globose, about 2 × 2 cm, the basal bracts densely velvety and fringed with hairs, developing into a mature, globose cone about 4 cm in diameter, the bracts clothed with dense, silvery hairs (July to October). **Fruit:** broader than long, about 7 × 8 to 11 mm, brown with scattered hairs (ripening about November and the seeds are immediately released from the cone, but germinate only after the area has been swept by a grass fire).

Leucadendron salicifolium (Salisb.) I. J. M. Williams

S.A. no:　　　Stream conebush
Rhod. no: —

Usually a shrub or a small slender tree, up to 3 m in height, with a single stem at the base; found on acid soils from sea level to 1 000 m, and characteristically forming almost hedge-like screens along the banks of streams. **Bark:** light grey-brown. **Leaves:** narrow, up to 6 × 0,5 cm, fresh green, finely velvety when young, these hairs being lost later, inclined to be sickle-shaped; the base is twisted through 90°; tapering to base and apex; margin entire; petiole absent. **Flower heads:** male heads small, about 1,3 × 0,9 cm, the basal bracts light coloured. Female heads about 1,4 × 1 cm, apple-green, flowers with a fruity smell, maturing to a cone up to 3 to 4 × 2,5 to 3 cm with broad, laterally-lobed bracts (July to September). **Fruit:** small, black, pitted, with no special dispersal mechanism (they are held in the cone for several years or until the parent tree is killed by fire or some other agency, then the seeds simply fall to the ground close by).

155

Leucadendron strobilinum (L.) Druce
[*L. concolor* R. Br.]
S.A. no: 78   Rock conebush. Rotstolletjiesbos
Rhod. no: —

A shrub or small tree about 3 m high; found at altitudes above 500 m, in south-facing, damp, rocky places. **Bark:** purplish; stems short; branches with sparse hairs. **Leaves:** elliptic, 6,7 to 8 × 2 to 2,3 cm, dark green, the leaves on the female plant being rather larger than those on the male plant; apex very broadly tapering to rounded, tipped with a soft, reddish bristle; base tapering; margin entire, sometimes reddish towards the apex, edges of the leaves curved back; petiole absent; the involucral leaves (i.e. those immediately below and round the flower heads) not numerous, but tend to be more crowded round the stem apex, and become cream-coloured. **Flower heads:** male heads rather wider than long, about 2,5 × 3,5 cm, silvery when young, the bracts very small. Female heads maturing to a cone, narrowly oval, about 4 × 2,5 cm, with conspicuous bracts; the flowers have a strong smell of yeast (September to October). **Fruit:** about 8 × 6 mm, greyish-brown and winged (mature about November to January but are held in the cone until the parent tree dies).

7. *HAKEA Schrader

***Hakea tenuifolia** (Salisb.) Domin; **Hakea gibbosa** (Smith) Cav.; **Hakea suaveolens** R. Br.

The silky hakea, the rock hakea and the sweet hakea respectively, were introduced from Australia. They are rigid, tough, spiky, harsh shrubs or small trees which have escaped and are now naturalised over considerable areas from the south-western Cape to Natal where they can form inpenetrable stands which are very difficult to eradicate. Unfortunately, they are what can only be described as a pestilential invasion and all three species are proclaimed noxious weeds throughout the Republic of South Africa.

SANTALACEAE *(The sandalwood and bergbas family)*

Key to the genera:
Leaves opposite; flower heads terminal .... **1. Colpoon**

Leaves alternate; flower heads in the axils of the leaves .... **2. Osyris**

1. COLPOON Bergius

Colpoon compressum Bergius   Illust. 33
[*Osyris compressa* (Bergius) A. DC.]
S.A. no: 99   Cape sumach. Pruimbas
Rhod. no: —

A shrub or small bushy tree 3 to 5 m in height; particularly common on coastal sand dunes, but also occurring in dune bush, among rocks and on the lower slopes of mountains. **Bark:** grey, smooth. **Leaves:** simple, opposite, crowded up the stem, small, oval, up to 3,5 × 1,7 to 2,7 cm, blue-green with a grey bloom, tough; apex broadly tapering to rounded with a fine, sharp tip; base broadly tapering; margin entire, tightly rolled under; petiole short, thickset, about 2 mm long, running down on to the stem forming ridges down the stem. **Flowers:** small, yellowish-green, inconspicuous; all

floral parts in fours, the stamens attached to the base of the fleshy perianth lobes; the flowers are produced in short terminal heads or panicles (March to August or later). **Fruit:** oval, fleshy, about 1,5 × 1 cm, becoming bright, shiny red, then purplish-black when ripe (July to February).

Both bark and leaves have been used for tanning; the wood is heavy and fine grained, but because of the small size of the tree, it is suitable only for ornaments and fancy work.

2. OSYRIS L.

Osyris lanceolata Hochst. & Steudel   Illust. 34
S.A. no: 100   Transvaal sumach. Bergbas
Rhod. no: 87   Barkbush

 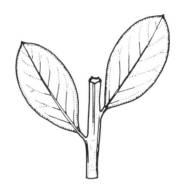

Usually a large evergreen, hardy shrub, but it may become a small tree growing up to 4 m; although never locally abundant, it is very widespread, often occurring on rocky ridges or outcrops, and on mountain slopes. This species is very similar to *Colpoon compressum,* the only obvious differences being in the leaves which are alternate, not opposite, and in the flower heads which are produced in the axils of the leaves and not terminally.

OLACACEAE *(The sour plum family)*

Key to the genera:

1 Stamens equal the number of petals .... **3. Strombosia**

   Stamens plus staminodes more numerous than the petals 2

2 Staminodes 3 to 6 in number; petals not bearded on the inner surface .... **1. Olax**

   Staminodes absent; petals bearded on the inner surface .... **2. Ximenia**

1. OLAX L.

Shrubs or trees; young branches narrowly 4-winged. **Leaves:** simple, alternate, in two ranks on either side of the green branches. **Flowers:** axillary, solitary, fascicled, or in few-flowered racemes; calyx small, cup-shaped, persistent; petals 5 to 6, overlapping; 3 to 6 fertile stamens, with 3 to 6 staminodes, both with their filaments more or less attached to the petals; ovary conical. **Fruit:** a drupe, almost enveloped by the fleshy, persistent calyx.

157

OLACACEAE

Key to the species of *Olax:*

Leaf petiole 3 to 8 mm long .... **O. dissitiflora**
Leaf petiole never longer than 2 mm .... **O. obtusifolia**

Olax dissitiflora Oliver
S.A. no: 101   Small-fruited olax. Bastersuurpruim
Rhod. no: 90   Small-fruited olax

A scrambling shrub, or a small tree reaching 5 to 7 m in height, occasionally up to 10 m, with lax, drooping branches; occurring in dense bush, sometimes along the banks of rivers and streams, in low altitude, hot areas. **Bark:** light to dark grey, rather smooth. **Leaves:** ovate to narrowly ovate, 1,5 to 5 × 0,5 to 2,5 cm, glossy green, without hairs; apex tapering to somewhat attenuate; base rounded; margin entire; petiole 3 to 8 mm, slender. **Flowers:** white, small, about 10 mm long, solitary, or in rather loose, axillary clusters, or short racemes, produced in profusion; the stalks are longer and more slender than those of the following species, giving a more open, graceful appearance (the specific name refers to this 'spacing out') (October). **Fruit:** round or oval, 7 to 9 mm long, becoming orange to red when ripe (November to January).

Olax obtusifolia De Wild.
S.A. no: —
Rhod. no: 91   Large-fruited olax

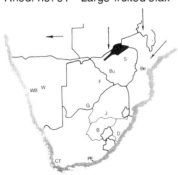
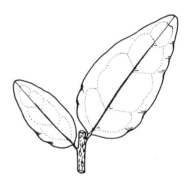

A shrub or small tree up to 6 m; not common, occurring in hot, dry types of woodland. **Bark:** light grey, finely wrinkled to rather rough; the young shoots are rust coloured. **Leaves:** ovate to elliptic, 4 to 8 × 2 to 4 cm, light dull green, thinly textured; apex broadly tapering to more or less rounded (the specific name refers to this); base rounded; margin entire; petiole very short, not more than 2 mm. **Flowers:** creamy-white, small, shortly stalked, occasionally solitary, usually in small axillary clusters and closely crowded along the branches (October to November). **Fruit:** about 2,5 cm in diameter, yellowish-orange when ripe (November to December).

2. XIMENIA L.

Shrubs or small trees, with dwarf, spinescent lateral branches. **Leaves:** simple, alternate, or fascicled. **Inflorescence:** a short axillary cyme or, rarely, solitary. **Flowers:** all floral parts usually in fours to fives; petals 3 to 5, bearded within; stamens 8 to 10 in 2 whorls. **Fruit:** a drupe.

158

Key to the species of *Ximenia:*

Generally tending to be more shrub-like, more spiny and with smaller leaves than the following species; flowers produced in small branched heads (pedunculate cymes) .... **X. americana**

Generally tending to be a small tree, less spiny and with larger leaves (see specific descriptions); flowers solitary, or fascicled (in small single stemmed groups) .... **X. caffra**

Ximenia americana L.
S.A. no: 102   Small sourplum. Kleinsuurpruim
Rhod. no: 92   Small sourplum

A shrub, or a small, bushy, spiny tree up to about 4 m in height; occurring in thornbush, sandy open woodland and on dry, stony slopes with scattered bush. **Bark:** grey, smoothish to rough. **Leaves:** oblong, 2 to 3 × 1 cm, or up to 4 × 2 cm, in the axils of straight spines, or fascicled on dwarf lateral shoots, bluish-green to grey-green, without hairs, folded upwards along the midrib; apex rounded, slightly notched; base broadly tapering or rounded; margin entire; petiolate. **Flowers:** small, greenish-white with a white bearded throat; in short, branched heads, or pendunculate cymes, in the axils of the spines (September to December). **Fruit:** oval, about 2,5 cm long, yellow to red when ripe, edible, rather sour but refreshing (December to February).

The seeds from this tree produce an oil which is used by Africans to soften leather and also as a cosmetic to rub over their bodies. The bark forms the basis of a medicine for the treatment of infant maladies while a type of beer is made from the fruits.

Ximenia caffra Sonder   Illust. 35
S.A. no: 103   Large sourplum. Grootsuurpruim
Rhod. no: 93   Large sourplum

A shrub, or more often a small tree up to 6 m; occurring over a wide range of altitudes, common in woodland and wooded grassland, also on koppies, rocky hillsides and termite mounds. **Bark:** grey to dark grey and rough on older, larger specimens. **Leaves:** elliptic, up to 6 × 2,5 cm, leathery, dark green, smooth or with rusty hairs at least when young, but losing their hairs and becoming shiny when mature, often fascicled on dwarf, lateral shoots; apex rounded, notched; base broadly tapering to rounded; margin entire, rolled under; petiole about 8 mm long. **Flowers:** small, creamy-white, clustered, or fascicled, in the axils of spines or on dwarf lateral shoots; white-bearded in the throat of the flower (September to October). **Fruit:** oval, about 2,5 cm long, bright red, edible but very sour (December to January).

159

There are two varieties involved; they are separable only in the degree of hairiness of the leaves:
var. *caffra:* the leaves remain velvety or hairy to maturity.
var. *natalensis* Sonder: the leaves are without hairs even when young.
In South Africa the two varieties can be conveniently separated on geographical grounds as well: var. *caffra* occurs in the central and northern Transvaal, while var. *natalensis* is the more southerly and easterly species, occurring from Natal through to the eastern Transvaal. However, outside South Africa the distribution of the two varieties becomes confused.
The seeds from this tree yield a good, viscous, non-drying oil which the Africans use in a variety of ways. It is used for rubbing into chapped feet and for anointing the body generally; it softens animal hides and is worked into bows and bow-strings. The fruits make a delicious, tart jelly and a decoction of the leaves soothes inflamed eyes. The Ndbele grind the roots which they then mix with cow-dung and smear on to their floors to ward off witches.

3. STROMBOSIA Blume

Strombosia scheffleri Engl.
S.A. no: —
Rhod. no: 94   Strombosia

A large tree reaching 30 m in height; occurring in evergreen mountain forest. **Bark:** dark brown, flaking to reveal pale patches; the trunk is fluted. **Leaves:** simple, alternate, oblong, 7 to 20 × 4 to 12 cm, light green, without hairs, rather shiny above; apex broadly tapering; base rounded; margin entire; petiolate. **Flowers:** clustered or fascicled, on very dwarf lateral shoots, yellowish-green, inconspicuous, about 5 mm long; all floral parts in fives; sepals joined to form a tube; stamen filaments joined to the petals (October). **Fruit:** oblong, up to 2,5 cm long with a circular depression at the apex round the remains of the persistent style; green when young (January).
The wood is hard and red in colour, and it would be a useful general purpose timber if the trees were not so rare.

CHENOPODIACEAE *(The ganna, salt bush and goosefoot family)*

SALSOLA L.

A large genus with the species closely resembling each other and very difficult to separate. **Leaves:** simple, alternate, small, fat, fleshy, scale-like, about 2 mm long and as broad, tightly packed along the branchlets. **Flowers:** very small, axillary, almost indistinguishable among the leaves; perianth 5-partite; stamens 5 or less; ovary globose. **Fruit:** enclosed in the perianth which is persistent, and grows, developing large petal-like wings; the fruits can easily be mistaken for the flowers.
All species in this genus, frequently growing in hot, arid areas, provide valuable fodder for stock and are heavily grazed.
It is difficult to produce a key to separate the two species described here; the differences are small and lie in the flowers, which themselves are most difficult to see. Suffice it to say that *S. arborea* is more tree-like with hairy branches and is found only in South West Africa; therefore all the tree-like specimens in South Africa are *S. aphylla.*

160

Salsola aphylla, *the lye ganna, with five papery, flower-like fruits, about 7 mm in diameter, towards the bottom centre and right of the illustration.*

Salsola aphylla L.f.
S.A. no: Lye ganna
Rhod. no: —

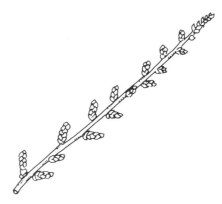

A strange plant, forming dense shrublets or small trees up to 4 m high, generally pale greyish in colour; occurring frequently in dry, arid, hot areas along dry watercourses. **Bark:** dark brown or grey, finely longitudinally flaking; they frequently develop 2 to 3 main stems, substantial in size being 8 to 12 cm in diameter which, however, split easily so that the small trees are often found sprawling sideways. **Leaves:** very small, greyish, about 2 mm long and broad, fleshy, chunky, clustered tightly along the stem giving it a knobby appearance. **Flowers:** almost invisible among the strange, minute leaves (approximately September). **Fruit:** surrounded by the persistent perianth; each of the 5 lobes develops a large papery wing thus forming 5 petal-like structures, in all about 7 mm in diameter, and looking far more like a flower – albeit membraneous and papery – than do the flowers themselves (January).

Salsola arborea C. A. Smith ex Aellen
S.A. no: 103,1   Cattle ganna. Beesganna
Rhod. no: —

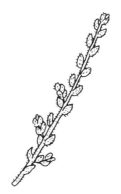

161

Dense shrublets to small trees up to 4 m; occurring on clay soils along dry watercourses or on sandy loam flats where they can become dominant.

This species so closely resembles the preceding one that attention is simply drawn, in the case of *S. arborea,* to its hairy branches and its comparatively restricted distribution.

NYCTAGINACEAE *(The bouganvillea family)*

PISONIA L.

Pisonia aculeata L.
S.A. no: Pisonia
Rhod. no: —

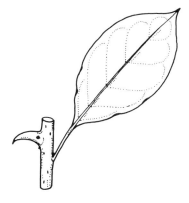

A climbing spiny shrub, a large liane, or a slender tree gaining support from the surrounding vegetation; occurring in forest, dune forest or bush, and sometimes along streams; common in the forests of Zululand and the extreme south of Moçambique. **Bark:** whitish to pale brown, and smooth, with occasional longitudinal fissures. **Leaves:** simple, opposite, broadly oval, up to 12,5 × 6,5 cm, leathery, arising on dwarf lateral shoots on either side of single spines, or between paired spines which are sharp and downward hooked; apex broadly tapering; base narrowly tapering and running into the petiole; petiole up to 3 cm long. **Flowers:** small, greenish, sweetly scented, in fairly compact branched heads, or paniculate cymes, up to 3 cm in diameter, in the axils of the leaves near the ends of the young branches. Sexes separate but on the same tree. Bracts 2 to 3, not brightly coloured. All floral parts in fives, perianth tube bell-shaped. In the male flower, stamens 5, or 10 in 2 whorls; absent in the female flower (November to March). **Fruit:** enclosed in the hardened perianth, cylindric to narrowly oblong, 2 to 2,5 × 0,2 to 0,5 cm, with 5 double rows of very conspicuous, club-tipped, sticky, glandular hairs; in loose branched heads 7 to 9 cm in diameter (January to May).

PORTULACACEAE *(The portulaca family)*

Key to the tree genera:
Leaves obovate to almost round, 1,5 to 2,5 cm long, opposite; bark smooth, reddish-brown to slate grey .... **1. Portulacaria**

Leaves small, narrow, often almost cylindric, about 5 mm long, fascicled on conspicuous, black almost pustular protuberances; bark smooth, silver-grey, branches almost creamy-white, conspicuously dotted with the black raised protuberances .... **2. Ceraria**

1. PORTULACARIA Jacq.

Portulacaria afra Jacq.   Illust. 36
S.A. no: 104   Spekboom. Spekboom
Rhod. no: —

A fleshy, softly woody shrub or small tree up to 3 to 4 m, often sprawling; occurring on dry rocky hillsides and in succulent scrub. **Bark:** green when young, becoming red-brown to slate-grey, and smooth with conspicuous leaf scars. **Leaves:** simple, opposite, almost circular, about 1,5 cm in

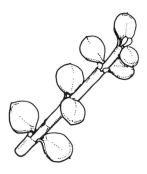

diameter, or obovate, up to 2,5 × 1,7 cm, fleshy, pale grey, pale grey-blue-green to dark green; each pair of leaves at right angles to the next along the reddish stems, apex rounded with a short, abrupt point; base tapering; margin entire; petiole very short or almost absent. **Flowers:** small, star-shaped; sepals 2; petals 5, pale pink to purplish; stamens 5 to 7. The flowers are produced in profusion, in dense sprays at the ends of the short lateral branchlets, making the tree beautiful (October to November). **Fruit:** a small capsule, about 5 mm long, 3-winged, hanging down on a thin, short stalk (November to January or later).

The leaves which are edible with a pleasantly acid flavour are eaten by African women when they have insufficient natural milk for their babies. The leaves, dried and ground, are used as snuff and the plant itself provides an excellent and valuable fodder. It is widely planted as a hedge, being quick growing, evergreen and dense, and it is becoming increasingly used to check soil erosion as it binds the soil very effectively. It is now so widely cultivated that it becomes difficult, at times, to determine whether it occurs naturally or has been planted.

2. CERARIA H. H. W. Pearson & Stephens

Ceraria namaquensis (Sonder) H. H. W. Pearson & Stephens   Illust. 37
[*Portulacaria namaquensis* Sonder]
S.A. no: 104,1   Namaqualand ceraria. Wolftoon
Rhod. no: —

A strange, waxy, fleshy deciduous small tree 2 to 5 m in height; found in the rocky deserts of the north-western Cape and southern South West Africa. **Bark:** silver-grey, to brown, the pale grey to almost creamy-white branches bearing distinctive, very reduced lateral side branches with hardly more than slightly raised black, almost pustular patches scattered all along the stems. **Leaves:** simple, very small, fleshy, narrow, often almost cylindric, up to 4 to 5 mm long, and not more than 2 mm wide, in groups, or fascicled, on the very reduced side branches. **Flowers:** small, ethereal and attractive, in short, few-flowered axillary sprays, 3 to 4 cm long, pale pink to deep pink; sexes separate but apparently on the same plant; sepals 2; petals 5, star-like. The male flower with 5 stamens, the ovary 3-angled but the stigma absent. The female flower with 5 sterile stamens, the ovary 3-angled and the stigma 2- to 3-branched (December to February). **Fruit:** very small, with a pinkish-brown wing, about 4 × 1,5 mm (January to February).

The bark is used as cordage or thongs, a custom which gave rise to the name *Hotnotsriem*. The trees seem subject to rotting, or are comparatively short-lived since, in January 1974, considerable **163**

The small leaves and very reduced side branches, looking like black pustules, are characteristic of Ceraria namaquensis.

numbers were found dead around Springbok – with the stems and branches empty within and the whole plant simply collapsed upon itself.

ANNONACEAE *(The custard apple family)*

Key to the tree genera:

1 Fruits with the carpels (sections of the ovary) joined to form a single fruit 2

   Fruits with the carpels separate, forming a cluster of apparently separate fruits 3

2 Fruits fleshy, orange when mature; petals in 2 equal whorls .... **9. Annona**
   Fruits dry and hard shelled, blackish when mature; petals in 2 unequal whorls ....
   .... **10. Monodora**

3 Flowers and fruits arising just above a leaf .... **4. Friesodielsia**

   Flowers and fruits arising opposite a leaf, or in the axils of a leaf 4

4 Flowers and fruits produced opposite the leaves 5

   Flowers and fruits axillary 7

5 Flowers and fruits on flattened, conspicuously hooked and twisted stalks ...... **8. Artabotrys**

   Flowers and fruits not produced on hooked and twisted stalks 6

6 Leaves green or greyish-green above and below; petals in 2 whorls, both overlapping ....
   .... **1. Uvaria**

   Leaves green above, blue-green below; petals in 2 whorls, abutting each other edge to edge (though the inner whorl may occasionally be overlapping) .... **5. Monanthotaxis**

7 Fruits splitting when ripe; flowers greenish .... **7. Xylopia**

   Fruits never splitting open; flowers cream to white or yellow 8

8 Carpels, or free segments, of mature fruit large, 2,5 to 5 × 2 to 3 cm; orange-scarlet when ripe
   .... **6. Hexalobus**

   Carpels of the mature fruit small, usually less than 2,3 × 1 cm; crimson to blackish-purple when ripe 9

9 Leaves with dense brownish or silvery, silky hairs on the under surface, leaf bases glandular; fruits up to 2 × 1,3 cm, crimson when ripe .... **3. Melodorum**

   Leaves with the under surfaces paler, but without silky hairs, leaf bases not glandular; fruits up to 2,5 × 1 cm, blackish-purple when ripe .... **2. Cleistochlamys**

1. UVARIA L.

Shrubs or small trees, frequently with a tendency to scramble. **Leaves:** alternate, simple. **Flowers:** solitary, or in a few-flowered cyme, terminal or leaf opposed; bisexual; sepals 3, overlapping; petals 6 in 2 whorls; stamens many; carpels many, free. **Fruit:** indehiscent.

Key to the tree species of *Uvaria:*
1 Carpels of the ripe fruit shortly cylindric, with or without very fine hairs; usually 5 to 8 in number, seldom more than 10, and rather small, about 2,5 cm long 2
   Carpels of the ripe fruit cylindric, velvety, usually more than 10 in number and larger, up to 5 cm long .... **U. lucida**
2 Leaves elliptic to oblong, up to 11 × 4 cm, apex attenuate, base running into the petiole; flowers 2,5 to 3 cm in diameter, greenish .... **U. caffra**
   Leaves ovate-lanceolate, up to 7,5 × 2,5 cm; apex not attenuate, tapering to broadly tapering; base not running into the petiole; flowers about 1,2 to 2 cm in diameter, yellow .. **U. gracilipes**

Uvaria caffra E. Meyer ex Sonder
S.A. no: 108,1   Small cluster-pear. Kleintrospeer
Rhod. no: —

A common canopy climber, scrambling shrub or occasionally a small tree; occurring in forests, at forest margins, in sand forest, thornveld and palmveld. The young branches are covered with rusty-red hairs. **Leaves:** elliptic to oblong, up to 11 × 4 cm, usually smaller, dark green, glossy above, paler below; apex broadly tapering, finally abruptly attenuate into a short narrow tip which is often slightly curled; base tapering and running into the petiole; margin entire, wavy; petiole short. **Flowers:** solitary, leaf-opposed, 2,5 to 3 cm in diameter, with 3 rusty, hairy sepals and 6 broad, greenish petals, with a central mass of many stamens (October to March). **Fruit:** apparently a cluster of 5 to 6 fruits, but which are, in fact, a single fruit, being separate carpels, or segments, of the same ovary, each one developing individually; each monocarp is about 1,5 to 2 × 1 cm, with a distinct waist and fine rusty-red hairs, becoming reddish-orange when mature (February to July).

Uvaria gracilipes N. K. B. Robson
S.A. no: —
Rhod. no: 107   Small-leaved cluster-pear

This species closely resembles *U. caffra* except that in *U. gracilipes* the leaves tend to be narrower and shorter, ovate-lanceolate to narrowly elliptic, 5 to 7,5 × 1,5 to 2,5 cm, the apex tapering to broadly tapering but not attenuate, the base not running into the petiole and with smaller flowers, 1,2 to 2 cm in diameter, which are yellow rather than green.

Uvaria lucida Benth.
[*U. virens* N. E. Brown]
S.A. no: 108,2   Large cluster-pear. Groottrospeer
Rhod. no: 108   Large cluster-pear

A forest climber, shrub or occasionally a small, evergreen tree; occurring in forests, on forest margins, in scrub forest and often in dense, almost impenetrable bush. **Bark:** grey, lenticellate, smooth; very young branches have reddish hairs, but lose these later. **Leaves:** elliptic-oblong to oblanceolate, 4 to 12 × 2 to 6 cm, leathery, rather greyish-green, with or without a few sparse hairs along the veins; the veining is prominent, especially below; apex tapering, slightly attenuate and ultimately narrowly rounded; base broadly tapering to rounded; margin entire, wavy; petiole short with rusty hairs. **Flowers:** solitary, or in 2- to 3-flowered condensed heads or cymes, terminal or leaf-opposed; individual flowers usually about 1,5 to 3 cm in diameter, fleshy, dull green to yellowish-green with a central mass of stamens (November). **Fruit:** 10-20 separate carpels, 2 to 5 × 1 to 2 cm, constricted between the seeds, dark brown to orange-brown, finely hairy (February to April). The southern African species *U. virens* has been combined with the tropical African species *U. lucida*, so all the material south of the Zambezi River now becomes *U. lucida* subsp. *virens* (N. E. Brown) Verdc.

2. CLEISTOCHLAMYS Oliver

Cleistochlamys kirkii (Benth.) Oliver
S.A. no: —
Rhod. no: 109   Purple cluster-pear

A shrub or small tree up to 9 m, often much-branched and straggling; occurring in bush and thickets in hot, dry river valleys. **Bark:** tough, pale grey to light brown and flaking. **Leaves:** alternate, in 2 rows, simple, narrowly oblong to obovate, 6 to 11 × 2 to 3,5 cm, thinly textured, dark to bright shiny green above, only slightly paler below; apex rounded, often notched; base broadly tapering to rounded; margin entire; petiole short. **Flowers:** bisexual; sepals 3; petals 6 in 2 whorls; stamens many. Flowers

166

attractive, creamy-white, about 1,2 cm in diameter with reddish-brown bracteoles below the flower; solitary, without a stalk, in the leaf axils and opening after the leaf-fall when the branches are bare (September to October). **Fruit:** up to 10 separate carpels, up to 2,5 × 1 cm, purplish-black when ripe, indehiscent, succulent (November to January).

3. MELODORUM Lour.

Melodorum gracile (Engl. & Diels) Verdc.
[*Popowia gracilis* Engl. & Diels]
S.A. no: —
Rhod. no: — Melodorum

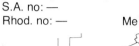

A shrub, liane or slender tree up to 12 m; occurring in open woodland and in riverine fringe forest. **Bark:** brown. **Leaves:** oblong to obovate, 5 to 12 × 2 to 5 cm, leathery, dark glossy green above, paler and bluish-green below with dense brownish or silvery, silky hairs; apex rounded and shortly attenuate; base tapering, glandular; margin entire; petiolate. **Flowers:** solitary or in cymose pairs, terminal or axillary, pendulous; sepals very small; petals greenish to dark yellow, thick. Individual flowers 1 to 2,5 cm in diameter with a central mass of stamens (September). **Fruit:** pendulous clusters of 1 to 2 (up to 19) separate monocarps, each one cylindric up to 2 × 1,3 cm, crimson when ripe (probably November onwards.)

4. FRIESODIELSIA Van Steenis

Friesodielsia obovata (Benth.) Verdc.   Illust. 38
[*Popowia obovata* (Benth.) Engl. & Diels]
S.A. no: 108   Bastard dwaba-berry. Basterdwababessie
Rhod. no: 110   Northern dwaba-berry

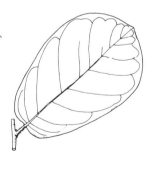

A shrub, inclined to scramble, or a small tree which may reach 7 m in height but usually considerably less; occurring in open woodland or grassland, on termite mounds, on rocky outcrops and along streams, sometimes a constituent of the riverine fringe thicket. **Bark:** grey to dark grey. **Leaves:** alternate, simple, obovate, 4,5 to 11,5 × 2,5 to 7,5 cm, clear bluish-green above, paler below, velvety when young, with or without very fine hairs when mature, veins pale and conspicuous above and below; apex rounded; base rounded or with shallow lobes; margin entire; petiole short and thickset. **Flowers:** solitary, usually produced above the leaf axil, occasionally terminal, with a   **167**

conspicuous leaf-like bracteole below the flower. Flowers bisexual; sepals 3, broadly triangular; petals 6 in 2 whorls, the outer 3 opening out flat, the inner 3 curled sharply inwards forming a central spherical shield over the stamens (see Illust. 38), rich cream, greenish-yellow to yellow in colour, thick and rather fleshy; stamens many (November to February). **Fruit:** 3 to 9 separate monocarps, each one cylindric, up to 7 cm long, constricted between the seeds, rather like a string of miniature sausages, reddish when ripe (could be found on the tree at almost any time of the year).

The fruits are edible and fleshy, with a sharp, tart taste; they are pleasant to eat when stewed.

5. MONANTHOTAXIS Baillon

Monanthotaxis caffra (Sonder) Verdc.

[*Popowia caffra* (Sonder) Benth.]

S.A. no: 107,1   Dwaba-berry. Dwababessie

Rhod. no: —

A shrub, often a liane, or a small, slender tree; occurring in evergreen forest and coastal scrub. **Bark:** greyish to brownish; branchlets slender, brown, pliant, lenticellate, with rusty hairs at first, but losing most of these later. **Leaves:** alternate, simple, oval to lanceolate, up to 10 × 4 cm, dark green above, bluish-green below and velvety to only sparsely hairy, aromatic; apex broadly tapering to rounded; base round to slightly lobed; margin entire; petiole short. **Flowers:** small, up to 1,5 cm in diameter, solitary or in small clusters, or fascicles, opposite the leaves. Individual flowers bisexual; sepals 3, not overlapping; petals 6 in 2 whorls, not overlapping, although the inner whorl occasionally does, greenish-cream to yellowish; stamens many (February to March). **Fruit:** 3 to 8 separate monocarps, each one oval, up to 8 × 6 mm, tapering down into a thickset stalk about 1,5 cm long; red when ripe (May to September).

The roots are said to smell of peppermint and the pliant young branchlets may be used to make baskets, but to many Africans the chief value of this tree lies in its magical properties. Zulus use it as a charm against nightmares; the roots are dried and smoke to prevent hysteria; the Tembu people place the wood at the gates of their kraals so that ailing cattle may jump over them and so be cured, while young hunters burn the wood and throw the ash round the carcass of their first kill so that more animals will be drawn their way.

6. HEXALOBUS A. DC.

Hexalobus monopetalus (A. Rich.) Engl. & Diels

[*H. glabrescens* Hutch. & Dalziel]

S.A. no: 106   Shakama plum. Shakamapruim

Rhod. no: 112   Shakama plum

A deciduous shrub or small tree 2 to 7 m in height, but usually about 3 to 4 m; occurring in low altitude bush and scrub, on rocky outcrops and stony hillsides; it may also fringe riverine thicket. **Bark:** dark, longitudinally fissured revealing the pale brown underbark; the young branches are conspicuous for the prominent and persistent petiole bases; the leaves, on falling, break away a short distance up the petiole, not flush with the stem, so leaving a short, hard stub, about 3 mm long. **Leaves:** alternate, simple, oblong elliptic to obovate, 3 to 11 × 1,5 to 5 cm; the under surface may or may not be covered with brownish hairs, but these always persist along the midrib; the secondary veining is obscure; apex very broadly tapering to rounded and often notched; base tapering, finally narrowly rounded; margin

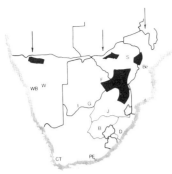

entire; petiole short, up to 4 mm. **Flowers:** solitary, axillary. The flowers are very attractive; the sepals 3, up to 6 mm long, velvety-red to brown, the buds appearing among the leaves from as early as February, but not opening until after leaf-fall; petals 6 in 2 whorls joined at the base, long, slender, up to 2,5 cm long, cream to pale yellow and crinkly, the whole flower having a spidery appearance; stamens many (October to November). **Fruit:** usually 1 but up to 3 separate monocarps, cylindric, oval, up to 3,5 cm long, finely velvety, turning scarlet when ripe, fleshy indehiscent (December to April).

Two varieties of this species occur; var. *monopetalus* being found in South Africa, Botswana and, generally, in the south of Rhodesia; var. *obovatus* Brenan, with broader leaves and prominent veining on both surfaces, occurs in the north, central and east of Rhodesia and adjacent areas in Moçambique.

The fruits are edible with quite a pleasant flavour but they are often infested with maggots. The wood is yellow in colour, finely textured and finishes well; it is attractively marked and, despite the small size of the tree, it would be suitable for ornaments.

7. XYLOPIA L.

Shrubs or trees. **Leaves:** alternate, simple. **Flowers:** bisexual, solitary or fascicled, axillary. Bracteoles 1 to 5; sepals 3, more or less united, much shorter than the petals; petals 6 in 2 whorls, long, narrow, fleshy; stamens many, often concealed by a fleshy section of the inner whorl of petals, carpels few to many. **Fruit:** a cluster of carpels, dehiscent.

Key to the tree species of *Xylopia:*
1 Carpels usually more than 10; young shoots and under surface of the leaves so finely hairy that the hairs are not visible to the naked eye .... **X. aethiopica**
   Carpels usually less than 10; young shoots and under surface of the leaves more or less densely velvety 2
2 A shrub or medium sized tree up to 9 m, of hot, dry open woodland; leaves oblong to elliptic, relatively broad; apex tending to be rounded, occasionally notched; base widely tapering to square; young shoots densely velvety .... **X. odoratissima**
   A large tree up to 30 m, of low altitude evergreen forest and riverine fringes; leaves generally narrower than the above species; apex tending to be more tapering; young shoots not so densely velvety .... **X. parviflora**

Xylopia aethiopica (Dunal) A. Rich.
S.A. no: —
Rhod. no: 113   Large red-fingers

A tall, evergreen, aromatic tree up to 30 m with a many-branched crown; occurring in evergreen forest at low altitudes. **Bark:** grey-brown, smooth or finely vertically fissured, peeling easily; the bole is sometimes thrown into buttresses. **Leaves:** oblong, elliptic to ovate, 8 to 16,5 × 2,8 to 6,5 cm, leathery, bluish-green and without hairs above, but with fine brownish hairs below; apex tapering to rounded, frequently rather abruptly attenuate to form a narrow drip-tip; base rounded to tapering and running down into the petiole; margin entire; petiole short, thickset and dark-coloured. **Flowers:** solitary or in strange, sinuous, branched spikes, or cymes, up to 5,5 × 0,4 cm, creamy-green in colour (November to December). **Fruit:** fruiting carpels 7 to 24 in number, forming dense clusters,

169

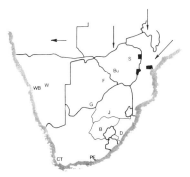

each one pod-like, up to 6 cm long, green to reddish in colour outside, red inside, succulent, splitting when ripe; seeds black, about 10 mm long with a yellow papery aril (December to February).

Xylopia odoratissima Welw. ex Oliver
S.A. no: 110   Small bitterwood. Kleinbitterhout
Rhod. no: 114·   Red-fingers

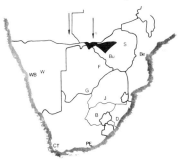
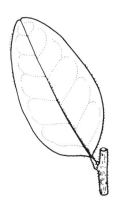

A shrub, or small to medium sized tree 2 to 9 m in height; occurring in hot, dry types of open woodland, frequently associated with Kalahari sands and also, in parts of its range, in *Brachystegia* woodland. **Bark:** light to dark grey, occasionally reddish, fissured and rough; the tree is usually many-branched, the branches reddish-brown, conspicuously dotted with lenticles; the young shoots are densely velvety. **Leaves:** variable in size and shape, but relatively broader than in the following species, oblong to elliptic, 3,5 to 10 × 1 to 5 cm, dull greyish-green above, sometimes slightly shiny, paler green and velvety below, thinly textured; apex broadly tapering to rounded, sometimes notched; base tapering, square or slightly lobed; margin entire; petiole up to 10 mm long, reddish to yellowish-brown. **Flowers:** solitary or 2 to 3 together, in the leaf axils, dull green to yellowish in colour with pale golden velvety hairs, sweetly smelling, about 2 to 2,6 cm long, pedulous on short stalks (October to December). **Fruit:** monocarps 1 to 8, up to 3 × 1 cm, often slightly constricted between the seeds, grouped together like a bunch of fingers, red in colour and splitting when ripe; seeds reddish-brown, about 10 mm long, the aril not conspicuous (the fruits remain on the tree for some time, so may be found, at practically all stages of development, almost throughout the year). The roots are aromatic and are said by certain Africans to be a 'powerful *muti*' or medicine.

This species is very similar to *X. parviflora* which follows. For practical purposes the two plants can be separated immediately on their geographical distribution and on their relative sizes; these and other differences are detailed under the latter species.

Xylopia parviflora (A. Rich.) Benth.
[*X. holtzii* Engl.]
S.A. no: 109   Tall bitterwood. Grootbitterhout
Rhod. no: 115   Forest red-fingers

A tall forest tree up to 30 m, erect, with a clean bole and a sparingly branched crown; occurring in low altitude evergreen forest and in riverine fringe forest and thicket.

170 This species is very similar to *X. odoratissima;* in practice, the two may be separate immediately on

their geographical distribution (refer to the distribution maps) and their relative sizes and ecology, *X. odoratissima* being of much smaller size, 2 to 9 m, and occurring in hot, dry types of open woodland, while *X. parviflora* reaches 30 m and inhabits evergreen forest. Furthermore, in *X. parviflora,* the leaves are comparatively narrow, narrowly oblong to narrowly elliptic, 4,5 to 11 × 1 to 4,7 cm, (compared with the oblong to elliptic leaves of *X. odoratissima,* 3,5 to 10 × 1 to 5 cm), the leaf apices tend to be more tapering and the young shoots have a sparser velvety covering.

8. ARTABOTRYS R. Br.

Shrubs with a tendency to climb, or small trees. **Leaves:** alternate, simple. **Flowers:** bisexual, solitary or in cymes, produced opposite the leaves, with very characteristic hooked, thickened stalks or peduncles. Bracts and bracteoles small; sepals 3, equalling or smaller than the petals; petals 6 in 2 whorls, free, the inner whorl usually curving over the stamens and the ovary; stamens many; ovary of up to 6 separate carpels. **Fruit:** the monocarps indehiscent and usually fleshy.

Key to the tree-like species of *Artabotrys:*
Sepals small, with sparse small hairs; petals very narrow, exposed in the bud, finely hairy; flowers only about 10 mm in diameter; leaf apex tends to be abruptly tapering; ripe fruits bright shiny red
.... **A. monteiroae**
Sepals large, with long, more or less dense hairs; petals broad, ovate, almost completely enclosed in the bud, with or without very sparse hairs; flowers about 2 cm in diameter; leaf apex tends to be rounded; ripe fruits blackish-purple .... **A. brachypetalus**

Artabotrys brachypetalus Benth.
S.A. no: 105,1   Purple hook-berry. Groothaakbessie
Rhod. no: 116   Purple hook-berry

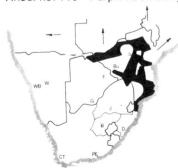

A locally common climber, shrub or low spreading tree; occurring in hot, dry, low altitude areas, along streams and in riverine fringe thicket; this is most often a strong woody climber, climbing by means of the very distinctive curling flower stalks (peduncles) which twine round the branches and twigs of neighbouring trees. **Bark:** grey, rough in larger specimens; young branches have rusty hairs which are lost later. **Leaves:** ovate to elliptic-oblong, 4,5 to 11 × 2,2 to 6,6 cm, leathery, bluish-green or glossy bright green, sometimes finely hairy above, always dull and often velvety below, net-veining visible on both surfaces; apex broadly tapering to almost rounded, often sharp-tipped; base **171**

broadly tapering to rounded; margin entire; shortly petioled. **Flowers:** solitary in the axils of bracts on remarkable, zigzag, twisted, crooked and grappling secondary stalks (peduncles), which twine round any branches they touch, often embedding themselves in the tissue of the other tree; when no other branch is close enough, these form contorted, woody bunches, the old ones becoming dry and hard; the flowers themselves are yellowish, about 2 cm in diameter, the hairy sepals bending well back, the yellowish petals rather cup-shaped, the inner whorl curving over the central mass of golden-green stamens (October to December). **Fruit:** a cluster of separate carpels, anything up to 6, but very often only 1 developing, with evidence of a further 1 or 2 which have aborted, 2,5 to 3 cm in length, elliptic, and purplish-black when ripe (September to February). Fruit-like galls are very often present and conspicuous and may be confused with the true fruits.

This species is very similar to *A. monteiroae*, and the key should be referred to for indications of differences.

The fruits said to resemble black figs, are edible; in Moçambique they are used to make an intoxicating drink.

Artabotrys monteiroae Oliver
S.A. no: Red hook-berry
Rhod. no: 117   Red hook-berry

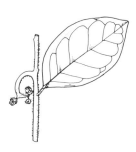

A scrambling shrub, liane or a small tree; occurring in medium altitude forest and at lower altitudes in riverine fringe forest, sand forest, lowveld bush and in swamp forest; also among rocks and boulders and on termite mounds.

This species is very similar to the preceding one, *A. brachypetalus*, and the key should be consulted for the differences.

9. ANNONA L.

Annona senegalensis Pers.
[*A. chrysophylla* Bojer]
S.A. no: 105   Wild custard-apple. Wildesuikerappel
Rhod. no: 118   Wild custard-apple

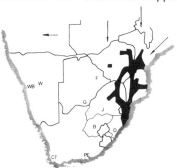

172   A shrub or small tree up to 3 to 4 m, but it may reach 8 m under very favourable conditions; favouring sandy soils, occurring along rivers, also in mixed scrub or woodland, on rocky outcrops and in swamp

The lumpy fruits and large leaves of the wild custard-apple Annona senegalensis.

forest. **Bark:** grey, smooth to roughish, with roughly circular flakes exposing paler patches of underbark; young branches with dense brown, yellow or grey hairs which are lost later. **Leaves:** alternate, simple, oval to almost circular, 6 to 18 × 2,5 to 11,5 cm, green to bluish-green, almost without hairs above, but often with brownish hairs below, net-veining green to reddish on both surfaces; apex rounded or slightly notched; base square to slightly lobed; margin entire; petiole short and thickset; the leaves are deciduous and the tree is bare for several months in the year. **Flowers:** up to 3 cm in diameter, on stalks up to 2 cm long; solitary or in groups of 2 to 4, arising above the leaf axils. One small bracteole may be present at the base of the flower; sepals 3, free, smaller than the petals; petals 6 in 2 whorls, fleshy, cream to yellow, occasionally touched with red or maroon, the inner whorl of petals curving over the stamens and the ovary; stamens many (October to December). **Fruit:** formed from many fused carpels, fleshy, lumpy, egg-shaped, about 4 cm in diameter, the covering resembling miniature crocodile scales, yellow to orange when ripe, indehiscent (December to March).

The fruit, which is edible, has a very pleasant flavour and the roots are widely used in African medicine. In Moçambique they are fed to small children to hasten weaning for they are believed to induce forgetfulness; once a baby has eaten them, it is said, it will no longer remember its mother's milk. With the same roots the Zulus treat dizziness and claim to cure madness; mixed with the roots of *Trema orientalis* they make an effective emetic. The large fruits of a low-growing species, *Annona stenophylla* Engl. & Diels, constitute a staple item in the diet of the peoples in the northern areas of Botswana and South West Africa.

10. MONODORA Dunal

Shrubs or small trees. **Leaves:** alternate, simple. **Flowers:** bisexual, solitary, axillary, or above the leaf axil or on leafless lateral shoots; sepals 3; petals 6, in 2 unequal whorls all joined at the base, the 3 petals in the outer whorl broad, flattened, spreading or bent back, the 3 in the inner whorl upright, cupped and clawed; stamens many; ovary with carpels fused. **Fruit:** a leathery, ovoid or globose, many-seeded berry with a hard, woody shell.

Key to the species of *Monodora:*
Leaves and young stems hairy; petals yellow, long, narrow and frilled .... **M. stenopetala**
Leaves and young stems without hairs; petals broad, liver coloured, maroon or wine-red ....
.... **M. junodii** **173**

ANNONACEAE/TRIMENIACEAE

Monodora junodii Engl. & Diels   Illust. 39
S.A. no: 107   Green-apple. Groenappel
Rhod. no: 119   Green-apple

A shrub or small tree occasionally reaching 7 m in height; occurring on hot, dry, rocky outcrops in woodland and in dry sand forest. **Bark:** grey, smooth. **Leaves:** oblanceolate to elliptic-oblong, 6,5 to 16 × 3 to 3,5 cm, shiny pale green, thinly textured, without hairs; apex rounded, sometimes shortly and abruptly attenuate; base tapering to rounded; margin entire; petiolate. **Flowers:** very striking and unusual (see generic description), liver-coloured, reddish-brown to wine-red, pendulous, and described by various collectors as 'orchid-like', and 'butterfly-like'; there is a short flowering period after the first good rains (September to November). **Fruit:** roundish, up to 4 cm in diameter, mottled grey-green-brown, becoming dark blackish, deeply wrinkled, even vertically ridged; a hard shell encloses many dry, brown seeds (January to March).

The seeds are strung together by African women to make necklaces. This small tree would be well worth cultivating, but it is apparently difficult to establish and it is probably tender to frost.

Monodora stenopetala Oliver
S.A. no: —
Rhod. no: —   Oval green-apple

A shrub or small tree up to 8 m; occurring in thicket and woodland. In all vegetative characters similar to the above species, except that the leaves and young stems are velvety. The flowers, however, are distinctive; the petals in the outer ring are long and very narrow, up to 5 × 0,4 cm, yellow, with a very wavy, almost frilled margin; the flower is pendulous and these petals hang downwards over the flower; the petals forming the inner whorl are short, and close over the stamens (November). The fruits are more ovoid than those of *M. junodii,* about 6 × 4 cm, and finely wrinkled.

TRIMENIACEAE

XYMALOS Baillon

Xymalos monospora (Harvey) Baillon
S.A. no: 111   Lemonwood. Lemoenhout

Rhod. no: 120   Lemonwood

The conspicuous rectangles and whorls on the bark of Xymalos monospora, *the lemonwood.*

A medium to large tree, 8 to 25 m, often poorly shaped; occurring in moist, evergreen forest, especially montane forest. **Bark:** light greyish-brown to brown, shortly flaking and most conspicuously marked with concentric rings, rectangles and whirls. **Leaves:** opposite or sub-opposite, very occasionally alternate, simple, broadly elliptic to obovate, 5 to 18 × 2 to 6,2 cm, dark green, with conspicuous midrib and veining giving the leaf a very characteristic quilted appearance, with distinct net-veining below; apex tapering, sharp-tipped; base broadly tapering; margin irregularly toothed, occasionally entire, rolled under; petiole short, thickset. **Flowers:** in short axillary spikes near the ends of the branchlets. Perianth 3- to 6-lobed, small, yellowish. Sexes separate on separate trees. Male flowers: stamens 10 to 15, ovary absent. Female flowers: stamens absent, ovary ovoid (June to October). **Fruit:** oval, about 1,5 cm long, fleshy, without hairs, red when ripe (November to May). The trees are resistant to fire and the old stumps frequently throw up coppice growth thus forming dense stands which, with their heavy foliage, exclude many other species. This is often indicative of a degraded forest. The wood is yellow and durable. The conspicuously marked bark and the 'quilted' leaves are definitive characters and either one, if not both, will serve to identify the tree with little trouble.

LAURACEAE *(The laurel and avocado pear family)*

Key to the tree genera (exotics marked*):
1 Fruits acorn-like with the receptacle enveloping the lower one third of the fruit .... **1. Ocotea**

   Fruits not acorn-like; the receptacle may not encroach up the fruit at all, or encroach only slightly, or it may completely envelop the fruit, giving the appearance of a fleshy fruit ....
   2

2 Flowers yellow-orange, in more or less conspicuous, dense, spherical heads, up to 2 cm in diameter .... **2. *Litsea**

   Flowers insignificant, greenish to creamy-white 3

3 Leaves alternate; fruit completely enveloped by the fleshy receptacle .... **4. Cryptocarya**

   Leaves opposite; receptacle not enveloping the fruit at all .... **3. Beilschmiedia** **175**

LAURACEAE

1. OCOTEA Aubl

Trees (or shrubs beyond southern Africa). **Leaves:** alternate, simple, may have pits in the axils of the veins. **Flowers:** in axillary cymes or subterminal panicles. Sexes separate on separate trees. Perianth 6- to 8-lobed. Male flowers with stamens in 3 whorls; ovary vestigial. Female flowers with an ovoid ovary; stamens vestigial. **Fruit:** ellipsoidal, half enveloped by the encroaching perianth.

Key to the species of *Ocotea:*

Lateral veins in the leaf about 6 pairs, with large blisters or pits in the axils of the lower veins
.... **O. bullata**

Lateral veins in the leaf 8 to 10 pairs, with no blisters or pits in the axils of the veins. ....
.... **O. kenyensis**

Ocotea bullata (Burch.) E. Mey.
S.A. no: 118   Stinkwood. Stinkhout
Rhod. no: —

A medium to large evergreen tree from about 8 m to 20 to 30 m; occurring in most of the high forests in South Africa; to many people the names stinkwood and Knysna are almost synonymous. **Bark:** brown and scaly when old; pale and attractively coloured when young. **Leaves:** large, oblong, 5 to 10 × 2,5 to 5 cm, aromatic, dark green, rather glossy, with conspicuous blisters or 'bubbles' on the upper surface in the axils of the veins, usually concentrated in the lower half, corresponding to finely hair-lined pits on the under surface; botanically, these are termed *bullae* and they give the tree its specific name; apex tapering, often shortly attenuate; base broadly tapering; margin entire, wavy; petiole 1,5 to 2 cm long. **Flowers:** small, pale yellowish-green in small clusters in the leaf axils near the tip of the branches (December to February, but sporadically later in the year as well). **Fruit:** obviously acorn-like, oval, about 2 cm long, the lower half or two-thirds enveloped by the cup-shaped receptacle (March to June, and may be found on the tree almost to the next flowering season).

Despite the unattractive common name of this tree – derived from the unpleasant smell of the freshly cut wood – its timber is among the most highly prized in the world. It is finely textured, naturally lustrous and beautifully coloured, from light cream, through brown to almost black and is often exquisitely figured with all these together. Ever since the earliest days of settlement in South Africa this tree has been in constant demand and even by 1812 the Knysna forest had been seriously depleted of all accessible specimens. Some time ago all felling was forbidden in order to set this matter to rights, but today, with a well organised management programme, the Department of Forestry is again removing timber. Culling is carefully controlled and the results are very encouraging. It is difficult to obtain seed for propagation as the flowers are subject to a fungal disease and the fruits to attack by maggots, but it is interesting that good viable seed can be obtained from bird droppings. Some most beautiful furniture is made from stinkwood – although today it is very expensive.

These trees have been declared protected plants in South Africa.

Ocotea kenyensis (Chiov.) Robyns & R. Wilczek
[*O. viridis* Kosterm.]
S.A. no: 119   Bastard stinkwood. Basterstinkhout

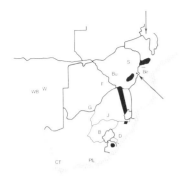 

A large tree, reaching 20 m, but frequently smaller; occurring in medium to high altitude evergreen forests. **Bark:** brownish, rough and longitudinally scaling. **Leaves:** large, elliptic, 5 to 22 × 2 to 9 cm, aromatic, leathery, deep green and glossy, with 8 to 10 pairs of lateral veins, lacking the distinctive pits, or blisters, of the previous species; apex rather attenuate; base tapering; margin entire, wavy; petiolate. **Flowers:** dull, waxy-white to yellow, browning with age, in small, lax, branched sprays at the ends of the branches (November to January). **Fruit:** again markedly acorn-like, up to 2 cm long (February to March and later).

The freshly cut wood lacks the offensive smell of stinkwood, and is said to yield a good timber. This is a protected plant in South Africa.

2. *LITSEA Lam.

*Litsea sebifera Pers.

An attractive small tree, with small heads of yellow-orange flowers, about 1 to 2 cm in diameter, on slender stalks. These plants were introduced from India and Malaysia, and have now escaped and become naturalised in the coastal areas of Natal and Zululand.

3. BEILSCHMIEDIA Nees

Beilschmiedia natalensis J. H. Ross
S.A. no: 117,1   Natal laurel. Natalkweper
Rhod. no: —

A tall evergreen tree 9 to 20 m in height, which readily coppices; sporadic in evergreen kloof forests along the Natal coast. **Bark:** brown and scaly. **Leaves:** opposite, simple, elliptic, 3,5 to 10 × 2 to 5 cm, without hairs, fresh green to dark green, usually with some leaves russet-coloured, net-veining conspicuous on both surfaces; apex tapering to almost rounded, often shortly attenuate; base tapering; margin entire; petiolate. **Flowers:** greenish-white, very small, about 2 to 3 mm in diameter, in small, axillary, branched heads about 1,5 cm in diameter. Perianth lobes 6; stamens 9 plus some sterile stamens; ovary ovoid with a short style (November). **Fruit:** fleshy, more or less spherical, 1,5 to 2 cm in diameter (probably January).

177

4. CRYPTOCARYA R. Br.

Shrubs or trees. **Leaves:** alternate, simple, may be 3-veined from the base. **Flowers:** bisexual; perianth parts 6 in 2 whorls; receptacle persistent, growing up and over until it completely envelops the ovary; stamens in 4 whorls, the innermost whorl sterile. Flowers produced in subterminal or axillary panicles. **Fruit:** completely enveloped by the persistent and growing receptacle which may become hard or fleshy.

Key to the tree species of *Cryptocarya:*

1 Leaves long and narrow, linear-lanceolate, up to 11 × 1,2 cm; confined to the western Cape, from Vanrhynsdorp to Stellenbosch .... **C. angustifolia**
  Leaves not linear-lanceolate, always comparatively broader; not extending further west than the eastern Cape 2
2 Leaves prominently 3-veined near the base, with several alternate lateral veins arising from the midrib .... **C. latifolia**
  Leaves not 3-veined near the base, or obscurely so 3
3 In the northern and eastern Transvaal, Rhodesia and northwards only, in montane evergreen forest .... **C. liebertiana**
  From the eastern Cape to Zululand and into the south and south-eastern Transvaal only 4
4 Flower stalks and outer perianth lobes with sparse, pale creamy hairs; in woodland, riverine forest and at forest margins .... **C. woodii**
  Flower stalks and outer perianth lobes with dense rusty hairs 5
5 Flowers in more or less dense, many-flowered heads; leaves, twigs and bark with a distinct camphor smell .... **C. myrtifolia**
  Flowers solitary, or in sparse, few-flowered heads; vegetative parts without a camphor smell .. .. **C. wyliei**

Cryptocarya angustifolia E. Meyer ex Meissner
S.A. no: 112   Blue laurel. Bloulourier
Rhod. no: —

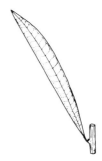

A bushy shrub or small tree about 3 m tall; occurring in the river valleys of the south-western Cape. The branchlets and leaf buds are covered with yellow hairs. **Leaves:** long and narrow, linear lanceolate, up to 11 × 1,2 cm, without hairs, the veining very conspicuous on the upper surface, the lateral veins at right angles to the midrib and all more or less parallel to each other, the under surface being finely net-veined; tapering to base and apex; margin entire; petiole about 10 mm long. **Flowers:** small, in shortly branched, narrow, axillary sprays, about 2,5 cm long (November). **Fruit:** narrowly oval, about 2 to 2,3 × 1 cm, turning purplish when ripe (March to July).

Cryptocarya latifolia Sonder
S.A. no: 113   Broad-leaved laurel. Breëblaarkweper
Rhod. no: —

A large tree up to 20 m; occurring in evergreen forests. **Bark:** grey-brown to light brown, rather smooth with fine vertical fissures and occasional horizontal ridges. **Leaves:** broadly oval or ovate (the

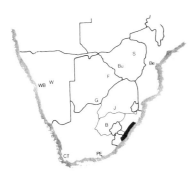 

specific name refers to the broad leaves), 5 to 10 × 2 to 4 cm, leathery, dark green and finely velvety above, greenish or cinnamon-brown below, later becoming dull, bluish-green, the hairs remaining only on the veins; 3-veined almost from the base, but the midrib branching nearer the apex; apex broadly tapering, rounded or notched; base tapering; margin entire, wavy, possibly occasionally obscurely toothed; petiole short. **Flowers:** small, about 1,2 cm in diameter, in long, slender, branched sprays rather spidery in appearance; stalks and sepals have fine cinnamon hairs, petals white and slender (September to November). **Fruit:** spherical, about 2 cm in diameter, becoming black when ripe after it is shed (January to March).

The wood is white and soft. The Zulus grind the bark, mix it with crocodile fat and use this ointment to treat chest complaints.

Cryptocarya liebertiana Engl.
S.A. no: 114   Wild quince. Wildekweper
Rhod. no: 121   Wild quince

A tall tree up to 25 m; occurring in mountain evergreen forest. **Bark:** grey to grey-brown, roughish, sometimes with conspicuous transverse bands. **Leaves:** oval to oblong, 6 to 10 × 3 to 4 cm, faintly aromatic, dark green glossy above, bluish-green below, midrib densely hairy when young; apex broadly tapering; base tapering; margin entire, wavy; petiole short. **Flowers:** small, greenish, inconspicuous, in short, branched, lax, axillary heads about 4 cm long near the ends of the branchlets (December to February). **Fruit:** about 2 cm in diameter, plum-red to purple when ripe (March to May).

The wood is light-coloured, hard and tough. This is an ornamental tree.

Cryptocarya myrtifolia Stapf
S.A. no: 115   Camphor laurel. Mirtekweper
Rhod. no: —

A medium to tall tree 10 to 20 m; occurring in evergreen forest. **Bark:** brown, smooth; young branchlets velvety. **Leaves:** smallish, variable in shape, lanceolate to broadly obovate, up to 5 × 1,5 to 2,5 cm, green above, bluish below; apex broadly tapering, sometimes abruptly and shortly attenuate; base tapering; margin entire; petiolate. **Flowers:** very small, cream-coloured, in small, branched, axillary clusters; the buds and flower stalks are covered with tawny hairs (January to

179

February). **Fruit:** small, round, about 1,2 cm in diameter, reddish when ripe (June to September). The leaves, twigs and bark have a distinct smell of camphor.

Cryptocarya woodii Engl.
[*C. acuminata* Schinz ex T. R. Sim]
S.A. no: 116   Cape laurel. Kaapse kweper
Rhod. no: —

A small to medium sized tree, 5 to 10 m, occasionally reaching 15 to 20 m in height; occurring in woodland, on forest margins and in forest in river valleys. **Bark:** grey, smoothish. **Leaves:** smallish, ovate to broadly ovate, 1,5 to 8 × 1,5 to 4, mid-green and silky textured, aromatic; apex tapering to rounded, often abruptly attenuate; base tapering; margin entire; petiolate. **Flowers:** very small, greenish-white, in short, insignificant, axillary, branched heads (October to December). **Fruit:** 1,5 to 2 cm in diameter, dark purplish-black when ripe (November to May).
The wood is brown, close-grained and hard.

Cryptocarya wyliei Stapf   Illust. 40
[*C. sutherlandii* Stapf]
S.A. no: 117   Red-haired laurel. Rooikweper
Rhod. no: —

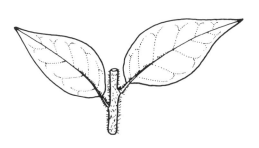

A shrub to small tree 3 to 4 m in height; occurring in coastal bush, on forest margins and in riverine fringe forest and thicket. **Bark:** greyish; the tips of the branches and leaf buds are covered with rusty hairs. **Leaves:** small, ovate, about 3 × 1,7 cm, green above, bluish below with rusty-coloured hairs along the veins and over the under surface in young leaves; apex tapering; base broadly tapering to rounded, often asymmetric; margin entire, rolled under; petiole short. **Flowers:** very small, white, insignificant, solitary or in short axillary spikes; the buds and flower stalks are rusty-velvety (December to January). **Fruit:** about 1,3 cm in diameter, bright red when ripe (February to April). The fruits are edible with a pleasant taste and are good to eat when stewed or made into a jam.

HERNANDIACEAE

GYROCARPUS Jacq.

Gyrocarpus americanus Jacq.   Illust. 41
S.A. no: 120   Propeller tree. Helikopterboom
Rhod. no: 122   Propeller tree

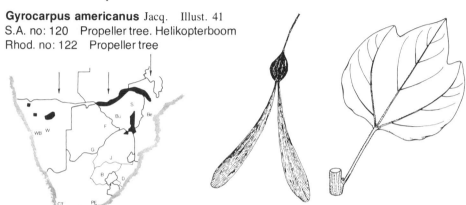

A deciduous tree, usually 9 to 15 m tall, branching well above the ground; occurring in hot, dry, low altitude areas, on rocky ridges or stony hillsides. **Bark:** smooth grey, bleaching on the sunny side to almost silver-white; somewhat flaking in older specimens. **Leaves:** alternate or scattered, simple; almost circular in general outline, the mature leaves about 10 × 10 cm, usually 3-lobed, the lobes becoming more pronounced in older leaves, with three marked yellowish veins from the base, occasionally 5-veined; leaves dark green, paler and greyish below, turning golden-yellow just before leaf-fall, softly textured, very finely velvety above and below; apex of the lobes broadly tapering; base tapering; margin entire; petiole long and slender, up to 8 cm long. **Flowers:** bisexual or separate sexes in the same flower head; flowers small, yellow to yellowish-green, in dense heads, or racemose cymes, which mature when the trees are leafless. The flower heads are made up of many male flowers with a few bisexual, or female, flowers (March to May). **Fruit:** a hard, woody nut, pale brown with marked veining (only visible when the epidermis has decayed), and terminating in 2 long, thin wings. The fruits are wind-dispersed, the wings spinning the fruit in the air, helicopter-wise, as it planes to the ground (July to September).
The flowers smell unpleasantly of cat urine. The bark contains alkaloids, one of which belongs to the group of ganglionic blocking agents, and could prove useful in the treatment of heart ailments. The plant can exude a white latex which has been used to produce rubber and the wood is white, soft and without value. The seeds germinate readily; the plants are fast-growing, but are probably frost-prone.

CAPPARACEAE *(The caper family)*

Key to the tree genera:

1 Androgynophore elongate, longer than the sepals 2

 Androgynophore short, shorter than the sepals 3

2 Leaves simple; in the flower, the upper and lower sepals overlapping the lateral ones; fruits cylindric .... **6. Cadaba**

 Leaves 3-foliolate; in the flower, the upper and lower sepals do not overlap the lateral ones; fruits globose .... **3. Cladostemon**   **181**

CAPPARACEAE

3 Calyx splitting transversely; fruits with 8 to 10 longitudinal ribs .... **8. Thilachium**

Calyx not splitting transversely; fruits not ribbed 4

4 Sepals joined to form a tube 5

Sepals joined at the base only, otherwise free 7

5 Leaves simple or 3-foliolate; receptacle cylindric or funnel-shaped, almost equalling the androgynophore in length; disc absent; petals, if present, not more than 7 mm long . **7. Maerua**

Leaves 3- to 5-foliolate; receptacle not cylindric or funnel-shaped 6

6 Disc cup-shaped with a thickened rim; petals 4, large, white, long and narrow, up to 3 cm long; flowers in rather few-flowered terminal or axillary spikes on the young branches   **1. Ritchiea**

Disc absent; petals absent; flower in abbreviated spikes on the old wood ..... **2. Bachmannia**

7 Branches usually spiny; sepals broad, overlapping; petals 4 .... **4. Capparis**

Branches never spiny, though frequently rigid and spiky; sepals narrow, abutting edge to edge, petals usually absent (small petals present only in one species) .... **5. Boscia**

1. RITCHIEA R. Br. ex G. Don

Ritchiea albersii Gilg
S.A. no: —
Rhod. no: 123   Ritchiea

A small tree up to 5 m in height; occurring in forest margins and patches up to an altitude of 1 700 m. This is a rare tree, here reaching the southernmost limit of its range. **Bark:** grey, smooth. **Leaves:** alternate, digitately compound with 3 to 5 leaflets, more often with 5; leaflets elliptic, 8 to 15 × 3 to 6,5 cm, glossy deep green; apex tapering with a marked, soft, hair-like tip; base tapering; margin entire; petiolules of the leaflets short, petiole long and slender, up to 10 cm in length. **Flowers:** receptacle cup-shaped; sepals up to 2,5 × 1,2 cm, not overlapping; petals long, narrow, white, up to 4,5 × 0,5 cm; stamens many, long and slender, up to 4 cm long; stamens and ovary shortly joined at the base. Flowers in short, terminal or axillary, 3- to 10-flowered spikes (probably January to February). **Fruit:** ellipsoidal, up to 4,5 × 2,5 cm, brown, smooth, finally splitting by 4 valves (June).

2. BACHMANNIA Pax

Bachmannia woodii (Oliver) Gilg
S.A. no: 121   Four-finger bush. Viervingerbos
Rhod. no: —

A shrub, with a tendency to climb, or a small tree up to 3 m; occurring in areas of evergreen forest near the coast. **Bark:** pale brown, often with conspicuous lenticels. **Leaves:** alternate, digitately compound with 3 to 5 leaflets, more often 3-foliolate (occasionally with one leaflet, the others aborted); leaflets elliptic to narrowly ovate, 6 to 15 × 2 to 8 cm, leathery, lateral veins prominent on the under surface and looping well before the margin; apex tapering to almost round, usually mucronate; base

182

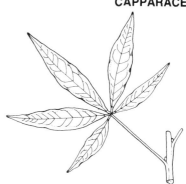

tapering; margin entire; petiolule of leaflet very short, petiole slender, up to 10 cm long. **Flowers:** quite conspicuous, pink to mauve, in abbreviated spikes of 2 to 6 flowers on the old wood. Calyx bell-shaped, 1 to 1,5 cm long; petals absent; stamens 13 to 18 on a short androphore; ovary on a long, slender gynophore (April to September). **Fruit:** oval, about 3 × 1,2 cm, pointed, rough, with 4 to 6 longitudinal sutures, on a jointed stalk about 2,5 cm long (September to May).
The plant is deep-rooted with numerous bulbous swellings along the roots.

3. CLADOSTEMON A. Braun & Vatke

Cladostemon kirkii (Oliver) Pax & Gilg
S.A. no: 131   Three-finger bush. Drievingerbos
Rhod. no: 124   Three-finger bush

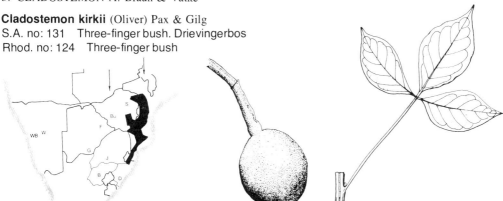

A shrub or small tree, seldom taller than 6 m; occurring in low altitude open woodland, bush, scrub or sand forest. **Bark:** yellowish-grey, thinly horizontally fissured. **Leaves:** alternate, compound, digitately 3-foliolate, with the petiole and petiolules articulated at the base; leaflets ovate to obovate, 4 to 15 × 2 to 7 cm, shiny green, thinly textured; tapering to base and apex; margin wavy; petiolule of leaflets short, petiole 5 to 20 cm long, slender. **Flowers:** very striking and attractive, in lax, terminal or axillary branched sprays, or corymbose racemes. All floral parts in fours, the upper 2 petals large, up to 6 × 3 cm, clawed and crimped, white aging to yellow, the lower 2 markedly smaller; stamens 5 to 8, united to form an androphore which, together with the gynophore, produces the most remarkable structure up to 15 cm long, hanging out of the flower and ultimately branching into the separate stamens and the style (September to November). **Fruit:** also strange and conspicuous, round, 7 to 8 cm in diameter, light brown, with the surface textured like shark's skin, on a long jointed stalk up to 15 cm long, which is sharply bent at right angles, giving the whole structure a hatchet-like appearance (June to October).

4. CAPPARIS L.

Shrubs, often scrambling, or small trees. **Leaves:** alternate, simple, with stipular spines. **Flowers:** in terminal or axillary racemose panicles, or corymbs; sepals 4, broad; petals 4, oblong, not clawed; stamens 6 to many, free; ovary on a gynophore. **Fruit:** a spherical to cylindric berry.

183

CAPPARACEAE

Key to the tree species of *Capparis:*
Sepals thickly hairy; gynophore always more than 2 cm long; fruit always more than 2 cm in diameter
.... **C. tomentosa**
Sepals with hairs or with a very finely fringed margin, never thickly hairy; gynophore never more than
2 cm long; fruit never more than 2 cm in diameter .... **C. sepiaria**

Capparis sepiaria L.
[*C. laurifolia* Gilg & A. Benn.; *C. citrifolia* Lam.; *C. subglabra* (Oliver) Gilg & A. Benn.]
S.A. no: 130   Wild caper-bush. Wildekapperbos
Rhod. no: 127   Wild caper-bush

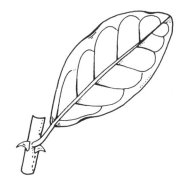

Usually a spiny scrambler, sometimes a dense shrub with long, arching branches, or it may become a
small tree reaching 6 m in height; occurring in evergreen forest or dry bushveld. **Leaves:** lanceolate to
oblong, 2 to 7 × 1 to 3 cm, with or without hairs; apex abruptly tapering to rounded, sometimes
notched; base rounded or square; margin entire, rolled under; petiole rather short and thick; stipules
modified to form 2 sharp, downward hooked thorns flanking each leaf, broad based, short but vicious.
Flowers: white, cream to mauve, about 1 to 1,6 cm in diameter, in terminal, open-flowered clusters
(October to November). **Fruit:** almost spherical, 0,6 to 1,5 cm in diameter, becoming orange and
finally purplish-black, soft and fleshy (April to May).
Two varieties of this species are recognised:
Young branches with long rather upright hairs; flowers at the ends of the main branchlets; sepals 5 to
6 mm long with hair-fringed margins .... var. *citrifolia* (Lam.) Tölken
Young branches with long hairs lying flat; flowers at the ends of short, lateral branchlets; sepals 3 to
4 mm long, margins without the fringe of hairs .... var. *subglabra* (Oliver) DeWolf

Capparis tomentosa Lam.
S.A. no: 130,1   Woolly caper-bush. Wollerige kapperbos
Rhod. no: 128   Woolly caper-bush

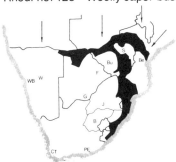

Often a spiny scrambler, or a small tree, but in northern Botswana and South West Africa it grows into
a good sized tree, up to 10 m, well-branched and densely leafy; over its very wide range it occurs in a
variety of habitats: on mountain slopes, in evergreen forest, in coastal forest, in open woodland and in
hot, dry thornveld frequently on termite mounds. All the young parts are densely velvety (the specific
name refers to this) and coloured green to yellowish. **Leaves:** oblong to broadly elliptic, 3,5 to 8 × 1,5
184 to 2,5 cm, light green to greyish-green, soft and velvety, sometimes rusty-coloured, with stipules

modified to form two sharp, downward hooked thorns flanking each leaf, broad-based, short but vicious; apex rounded or notched, with a soft hair-like tip; base broadly tapering to rounded; margin entire, rolled under; petiole up to 10 mm long, densely velvety. **Flowers:** up to 3,5 cm in diameter, yellowish-green, scented, the central mass of stamens white or pinkish and up to 3,5 cm long; showy when in full flower (August to November). **Fruit:** rather pendulous on a stout stalk (gynophore), round, up to 3,5 cm in diameter, pink to bright orange when ripe, with a semi-transparent bluish-grey flesh surrounding and strongly adhering to the brown seeds; the fruits may be produced in profusion (December to March).

The leaves are said to provide palatable grazing for cattle but they have also been reported to be poisonous. This is one of the best-known trees among African peoples for its supposed magico-medicinal properties and has the reputation of curing a variety of complaints ranging from coughs and colds to barrenness and impotence. Moreover, if a stick is coated with a paste made from the powdered root and other ingredients and pointed towards storm clouds, it is believed to act as a safeguard against floods. The Venda make a ritual remedy for pneumonia by combining parts of this tree with dried hyaena and antelope blood and mixing the concoction together with ox fat. *C. tomentosa* is a protected plant in South Africa.

5. BOSCIA Lam.

Shrubs or trees. **Leaves:** alternate or fascicled. **Flowers:** in terminal or axillary, panicles, racemes or cymes, sometimes fascicled; sepals 4, fleshy, almost free; petals absent (except in one species); stamens 5 to 22, almost free, on a very short androphore; ovary, ovoid on a very short gynophore. **Fruit:** a berry.

Key to the tree species of *Boscia:*

1 Leaves and young branches densely hairy with star-shaped hairs; only in the extreme north-west of South West Africa .... **B. tomentosa**
   Leaves and young branches, if hairy then with simple, unbranched hairs 2
2 Leaves densely hairy on the under surface only, upper surface without hairs . **B. angustifolia**
   Leaves either without hairs, or more or less hairy on both surfaces, at least when young 3
3 In eastern Cape and Karoo only, not extending further north than Graaff-Reinet; flowers with small, white petals .... **B. oleoides**
   Not in the eastern Cape; flowers without petals 4
4 Leaves usually more than 5 cm long 5
   Leaves small, usually less than 5 cm long 6
5 Leaves long and narrow, usually 7 to 15 cm by about 1,5 to 2 cm, seldom wider; bark darkish grey and rather rough; not extending further south than the north, centre and east of Rhodesia, and adjacent areas of Moçambique .... **B. salicifolia**
   Leaves comparatively broad, 4 to 7 × 1,5 to 4,5 cm; bark pale grey-brown; much more widespread (see distribution map) .... **B. mossambicensis**
6 Fruits without hairs; leaves 1,5 to 8 × 0,4 to 2 cm, same colour above and below, veining obscure .... **B. albitrunca**
   Fruits with hairs; leaves paler below than above, or, if the same colour, then very small, either 10 mm long or less, or less than 4 mm wide 7
7 Gynophore (the stalk below the ovary) about twice the length of the ovary and style; in north-western South West Africa and northwards only .... **B. microphylla**
   Gynophore about the same length as the ovary and style; widespread in South West Africa and northern Cape .... **B. foetida**

Boscia albitrunca (Burch.) Gilg & Benedict
[*B. transvaalensis* Pestal.]
S.A. no: 122   Shepherd's tree. Witgat
Rhod. no: 130   Shepherd's tree

A stocky tree up to 7 m, rarely a shrub, stiffly branched with a well-rounded crown; widespread in dry, open woodland and bushveld, often associated with termite mounds. **Bark:** smooth, conspicuously whitish-grey or yellowish; trunk stout. **Leaves:** usually arising in groups of 2 to 4 on very

185

CAPPARACEAE

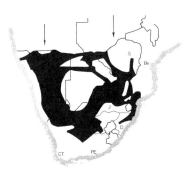

reduced, hard, spiky side shoots, rarely alternate, oblanceolate to elliptic, 1,5 to 8 × 0,4 to 2 cm, leathery, rigid, grey-green to green above and below, secondary veins scarcely visible; usually evergreen; apex rounded or abruptly attenuate often bristle-tipped; base tapering; margin entire; shortly petiolate. **Flowers:** small, petals absent, with a dense, central mass of yellowish stamens, with a sweet, heavy scent; flowers produced in very short dense clusters on the dwarfed side-shoots (August to October, or after rain). **Fruit:** round, yellowish, smooth, without hairs, about 10 mm in diameter (October to December).

In the arid areas where this species often grows it might well be called 'the tree of life' since it affords sustenance to both man and animals. The leaves provide a very nourishing fodder for game and also for livestock which browse regularly on the tree; in times of drought when food is critically short farmers often remove the branches to feed their cattle and sheep and in South West Africa they partially cut through the trunk so that it may be bent down and the leaves brought within reach of grazing animals. New shoots soon spring up from the severed area providing a further food-source, though the milk of cows feeding upon the leaves may be tainted. The roots also have their uses: people of all races dry, roast and then grind them to make a passable substitute for coffee or chicory, or else pound them to obtain a white meal for 'porridge'. In Botswana the old trunks are hollow and hold rain

The white stem of Boscia albitrunca, *the shepherd's tree, with* Croton gratissimus, *the lavender croton (page 416) in the foreground.*

water which is tapped out by Bushmen, while the flower buds, when pickled, may be used in place of capers.

The wood is heavy and tough, but is suitable only for household utensils. A cold infusion of the leaves is applied as a lotion to the inflamed eyes of cattle, and a decoction of the roots provides a treatment for haemorrhoids. These trees feature also in the folklore and superstitions of many African peoples: in some areas it is believed that the wood must never be burnt as this results in the cows' producing only bull calves. It is also said that if the fruits wither before the millet crop is ripe the harvest will be a failure. Many African peoples hold these trees in such deep regard that their destruction is forbidden. The seed germinates easily, but growth from then on appears to be unpredictable. This tree is protected in the Orange Free State and in some districts of the northern Cape.

Boscia angustifolia A. Rich.   Illust. 42

[*B. corymbosa* Gilg]
S.A. no: 122,1   Rough-leaved shepherd's tree. Skurweblaarwitgat
Rhod. no: 131   Rough-leaved boscia

A small, evergreen tree up to 8 m; occurring in dry types of woodland, it is often associated with termite mounds. **Bark:** pale grey; the bole often deeply and sinuously fluted. **Leaves:** alternate, or in groups of 2 to 4 on very dwarf lateral shoots, elliptic to oblanceolate, 2 to 7 × 0,7 to 2 cm, leathery, darkish green above, much paler and grey-green or bluish-green below, finely hairy above, but losing most of the hairs at maturity, finely but densely hairy below; apex rounded to broadly tapering, tipped with a hard, sharp short spine; base tapering; margin entire; petiolate. **Flowers:** small, sweet-smelling; petals absent, stamens short, cream to yellow; in short, terminal, crowded heads, or compound corymbs (sporadically throughout the year). **Fruit:** spherical, about 10 mm in diameter, yellow to almost black, with the seeds embedded in a sticky pulp (at almost any time of the year). All the plants in southern Africa belong to *B. angustifolia* A. Rich. var. *corymbosa* (Gilg) DeWolf; the typical variety occurs in north Africa. When not in flower or fruit, these trees could easily be confused with *B. mossambicensis* Klotzsch, but the leaves of the former are much more hairy on both surfaces and are narrower, being not more then 2 cm wide, while those of *B. mossambicensis* can reach 4,5 cm in width.

Boscia foetida Schinz (with 4 subspecies)

[*B. rehmanniana* Pestal.; *B. kalachariensis* Pestal.; *B. filipes* Gilg; *Capparis albitrunca* var. *parvifolia* T. R. Sim; *B. longipedicellata* Gilg]
S.A. no: 124, 124,1 and 127   Smelly shepherd's tree. Stinkwitgat
Rhod. no: 132   Smelly boscia

A large shrub or small dense tree, with sharply angular, spiky branches; occurring in dry bushveld and semi-desert areas, often on rocky outcrops. **Bark:** pale grey to grey, smooth. **Leaves:** very small to small, in small tight fascicles densely clustered along the branches, oblanceolate to obovate, from less than 1 cm long to 3,5 cm long (the larger leaves are found in subsp. *longipedicellata*), leathery, green to greyish-green above and below, or paler below, with or without hairs; apex broadly tapering to rounded, notched; base tapering; margin entire; very shortly petiolate. **Flowers:** small, inconspicuous, greenish, in tight, short clusters along the stems; the gynophore equalling the ovary and style in length (August to September). **Fruit:** spherical, about 10 mm in diameter, yellowish, velvety (February to April). The flowers and the freshly cut wood have an intense and very unpleasant smell (the specific name refers to this).

187

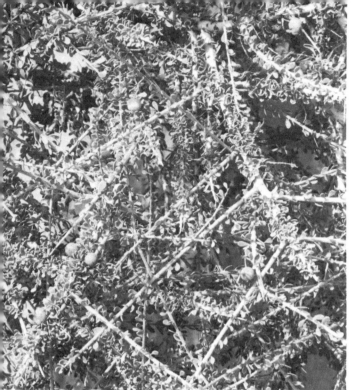

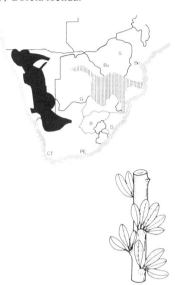

The leaves, fruits and tangled branches of the smelly-shepherd's tree, Boscia foetida.

The *foetida* complex comprises 4 very closely related plants (3 of them trees) now placed at subspecific level, and separated almost solely on their geographical distribution and the number of stamens in the flower:

(a) In South West Africa and neighbouring areas of the north and north-western Cape; leaves extremely small, same colour above and below, and the plants almost always branching from the base; number of stamens 11 to 15; the photograph on this page shows the branches, leaves and fruits (S.A. no: 124) (refer to the black area on the map) .... subsp. *foetida*

(b) In central Natal; this has the largest leaves, 1 to 3,5 cm long (it could be confused with *B. albitrunca,* but the former has hairy fruits and the leaves are markedly paler below); it invariably has a single pale stem up to at least 1 m; stamens 11 to 15; the flower stalks are notably longer and slender (S.A. no: 124.1) (cf. photograph) (refer to the horizontal lines on the map) .... subsp. *longipedicellata* (Gilg) Tölken

(c) From the extreme north-east of Natal northwards (refer to the vertical lines on the map); leaves usually small, not exceeding 1,3 cm in length; usually single-stemmed for at least 1 m; stamens 5 to 7 (S.A. no: 127) (cf. photograph) .... subsp. *rehmanniana* (Pestal.) Tölken

N.B. The fourth subspecies *minima* Tölken, is a small shrublet from the western Transvaal and the Mafeking area of the northern Cape.

Boscia microphylla Oliver
S.A. no: 125   Kaoko shepherd's tree. Kaokowitgat
Rhod. no: —

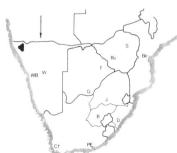

Usually a shrub or a small tree, with a very restricted distribution; occurring on rocky mountain slopes. This can be confused with *B. foetida* subsp. *foetida,* but the leaves of *foetida* turn yellow-green as they dry, while those of *microphylla* turn blue-green, and the gynophore is about twice the length of the ovary and style. It can also be confused with *Maerua parvifolia* and if flowers and fruits are not available only microscopic examination of the internal leaf structure can separate the 2 species; however, *M. parvifolia* is usually a small, lax shrub.

Boscia mossambicensis Klotzsch
[*B. welwitschii* Gilg]
S.A. no: 126   Broad-leaved shepherd's tree. Breëblaarwitgat
Rhod. no: 134   Broad-leaved boscia

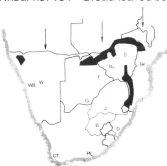 

A much-branched, robust, shrub or small tree reaching 6 m in height; occurring in the dry, hot types of woodland at lower altitudes. **Bark:** grey-brown; the young branches yellowish. **Leaves:** alternate or fascicled; oblong, comparatively large and broad, 4 to 7 × 1,5 to 4,5 cm, leathery, brittle, dark green above, paler below; apex broadly tapering to rounded, tipped with a fine bristle; base tapering; margin entire; petiolate. **Flowers:** in groups of up to 20 at the ends of the branches; petals absent, the central mass of white stamens about 3,5 cm in diameter (April to June). **Fruit:** spherical, up to 2 cm in diameter, yellowish to red when mature (June to September).

Boscia oleoides (Burch. ex DC.) Tölken
[*Capparis oleoides* Burch. ex DC.]
S.A. no: 128   Bastard shepherd's tree. Basterwitgat
Rhod. no: —

This small tree closely resembles *B. albitrunca,* but it has a more southerly distribution and the flowers have small white petals; it is the only species of *Boscia* dealt with here which possesses petals.

Boscia salicifolia Oliver
S.A. no: —
Rhod. no: 135   Willow-leaved boscia

A small to medium sized deciduous tree, occasionally reaching 15 m in height; occurring frequently on termite mounds in *Brachystegia* and dry types of woodland. **Bark:** dark grey, rough and flaky. **Leaves:** alternate, not in groups of 2 or more, long and narrow, 7 to 15 × 1,5 to 2,5 cm, dull green,

189

leathery, finely hairy above, but losing most of these hairs on maturity, while remaining finely hairy below; apex tapering, occasionally broadly so, bristle-tipped; base tapering; margin entire; petiolate. **Flowers:** petals absent; stamens 4 to 16, yellowish-green, about 7 mm long (August to October). **Fruit:** round, up to 2 cm in diameter, smooth, yellow when ripe (October to January).

Boscia tomentosa Tölken
[*B. polyantha* auct.]
S.A. no: 127,1   Hairy shepherd's tree. Harige witgat
Rhod. no: —

Usually shrubs, rarely trees, up to 6 m in height; occurring in a very restricted area in South West Africa. **Bark:** stem and branches white. **Leaves:** alternate, not in groups, broadly ovate or elliptic up to 4 cm long, stiff, fleshy, with long dense hairs which, when viewed under a 10× lens can be seen to be star-shaped; apex rounded, notched; base broadly tapering; margin entire; petiolate. **Flowers:** greenish-white, in dense, branched terminal heads (May to July). **Fruit:** not seen.

6. CADABA Forsk.

Shrubs or small trees; branches may be spine-tipped. **Leaves:** alternate or fascicled, simple, sometimes rudimentary. **Flowers:** solitary or fascicled, axillary or terminal, in leafless corymbs; sepals 4 in 2 whorls, lobes overlapping; petals 2 to 4 or absent; stamens 5 to 8, fused to form an androphore; ovary cylindric, stigma sessile. **Fruit:** long, cylindric, indehiscent or tardily dehiscent.

Key to the tree species of *Cadaba:*
1 Leaves absent except on very young shoots .... **C. aphylla**
   Leaves always present 2
2 Flowers in large, showy, terminal sprays, up to 15 cm long .... **C. kirkii**
   Flowers solitary, often clustered on dwarf, lateral shoots 3
3 Young stems, leaves and all parts without hairs, or with very short hairs .... **C. natalensis**
   Young stems, leaves, etc., with grey, hoary hairs 4
4 Fruits more than 3 cm long; Transvaal, Botswana, Rhodesia and Moçambique   **C. termitaria**
   Fruits less than 3 cm long; South West Africa only .... **C. schroeppelii**

Cadaba aphylla (Thunb.) Wild
[*Cleome aphylla* Thunb.]
S.A. no: 129   Leafless cadaba. Swartstorm
Rhod. no: 137   Leafless cadaba

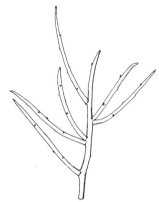

A shrub or a small tree 2 to 3 m high, often forming a tangled bush; occurring in dry bushveld, scrub and semi-desert, often associated with limestone formations. **Bark:** brownish. **Leaves:** develop only in seedlings and occasionally on very young branches, when they are about 10 × 2 mm; the branches themselves are dark green often with a purplish bloom; the tips of the branches are inclined to be spinescent. **Flowers:** 2 to 3 cm in diameter, petals absent; the sepals are yellowish, orange to reddish-purple, and the stamens red in colour; usually produced in short, flat-topped heads, axillary, on short lateral shoots (August to December). **Fruit:** large, long and narrow, up to 9 × 0,7 cm, cylindric, slightly constricted at intervals, warty with sticky glands (possibly December).
The roots have violent purgative properties and have been reported to be poisonous.

Cadaba kirkii Oliver
S.A. no: —
Rhod. no: 138   Large-flowered cadaba

Usually a large shrub, sometimes a small tree reaching 5 m in height; occurring in low altitude dry types of woodland or in riverine fringe thicket. **Bark:** brown; young branches covered with golden, viscid glands. **Leaves:** ovate to broadly elliptic, 2,5 to 9 × 1 to 5 cm, without hairs, or both surfaces covered with fine glandular hairs, midrib prominent below and pale coloured; apex rounded, with a short, soft hair-like tip; base rounded to shallowly lobed; margin entire; petiolate. **Flowers:** up to 4 cm in diameter, sepals cream to yellowish-green; petals cream to yellow, up to 2 cm long but very narrow, barely 2 mm wide; 5 yellow stamens. The flowers are produced in many-flowered terminal heads up to 15 cm long; showy when heavily in bloom (May to September). **Fruit:** narrowly cylindric, about 6 × 0,5 cm, dark green to dark brown, sticky, splitting into 2 valves (July to November).

Cadaba natalensis Sonder
S.A. no: 129,1   Mauve cadaba. Natalwurmbos
Rhod. no: 139   Mauve cadaba

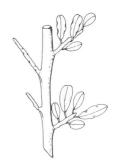

A shrub or small tree reaching 3 m in height; occurring in dry woodland, thornveld and bushveld at low altitudes. **Bark:** greyish-brown; branches stiff. **Leaves:** alternate or in tight groups on dwarf lateral branches, elliptic to obovate, 0,7 to 4,2 × 0,5 to 1,3 cm, dark green, thinly textured, may be finely hairy; apex with a needle-like point, base tapering; margin entire; petiolate. **Flowers:** solitary, on long slender stalks, produced in the leaf axils, or in clusters on dwarf lateral shoots; petals absent, but sepals petalloid, broadly ovate, about 8 mm long and broad, mauve flushed with purple or red; a slender androgynophore carries the stamens and ovary beyond the sepals (April to May). **Fruit:** narrowly cylindric, up to 5 × 0,5 cm, warty, with many seeds embedded in a scarlet powdery pulp (June to August).

Cadaba schroeppelii Suesseng.
S.A. no: Kaoko cadaba
Rhod. no: —

A large shrub reaching 3 m, many branched; occurring in the transitional zone between the inland plateau and the coastal desert belt. **Bark:** grey to reddish-brown. **Leaves:** alternate or crowded on dwarf lateral shoots, oblanceolate, 3 to 7 × 0,9 to 1,5 cm, grey to greenish-grey and densely hairy on both surfaces; apex broadly tapering; base tapering; margin entire; petiolate. **Flowers:** small, about 10 mm in diameter; petals absent. Solitary in the leaf axils, often crowded on dwarf lateral branches (October). **Fruit:** cylindric, up to 2 × 0,4 cm, on very slender stalks (December).

Cadaba termitaria N. E. Brown
S.A. no: Pink cadaba
Rhod. no: 140   Pink cadaba

A much branched shrub up to 3 m, but becoming tree-like at 5 m in height; occurring in hot, dry bushveld, or in open woodland usually at low altitudes. **Bark:** dark, blackish. **Leaves:** alternate, but often crowded on dwarf lateral shoots, elliptic to obovate, 0,7 to 2 × 0,3 to 0,7 cm, grey-green, with small whitish scales which can be seen with a 10× hand lens; apex rounded, notched, often bristle-tipped; base tapering to rounded; margin entire; shortly petiolate. **Flowers:** solitary in the leaf axils, or crowded on dwarf lateral shoots; petals absent, sepals about 8 mm long, green to pinkish (September to October). **Fruit:** cylindric, up to 9 × 0,4 cm, dark green, the seeds are embedded in an orange to scarlet powdery pulp (December onwards).

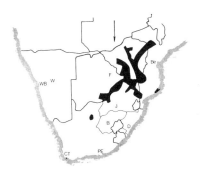 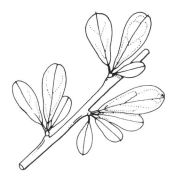

7. MAERUA Forsk.

Shrubs, scramblers or trees. **Leaves:** usually alternate, occasionally crowded on dwarf lateral shoots, simple, or digitately compound with 3 to 5 leaflets. **Flowers:** solitary or crowded on dwarf lateral shoots, axillary or in terminal racemes or corymbs; bisexual, receptacle usually cylindric; sepals 4; petals 0 to 4; stamens many, long; ovary cylindric to ellipsoidal. Androgynophore very short, seldom longer than 8 mm. **Fruit:** globose or cylindric.

Key to the tree species of *Maerua:*

1 Leaves 3- to 5-foliolate; if simple then the petiole is always jointed at the base 2
  Leaves nearly always simple, petiole not jointed 6
2 Leaflets conspicuously narrow, linear or narrowly elliptic .... **M. rosmarinoides**
  Leaflets broadly elliptic or ovate 3
3 Leaflet apex tapering to rounded; veins immersed, petals absent .... **M. cafra**
  Leaflet apex rounded, notched; veins more or less prominent; petals 4 4
4 Fruits almost spherical, up to 2,2 cm in diameter, very warty, densely and finely woolly; extending
    no further south than the northern areas of Rhodesia .... **M. prittwitzii**
  Fruits ellipsoidal or cylindric, usually larger than 2 cm, without hairs 5
5 Fruits ellipsoidal, up to 3,7 cm long, shiny and rather lumpy; mainly a coastal species of Natal and
    Moçambique, one record only from Rhodesia .... **M. nervosa**
  Fruits cylindric, up to 10 cm long, constricted between the seeds; reaching the southern limit of its
    range in the eastern areas in Rhodesia and adjacent areas in Moçambique ..... **M. triphylla**
6 Fruits globose to ellipsoidal 7
  Fruits cylindric 9
7 Leaves conspicuously narrow, less than 10 mm wide .... **M. gilgii**
  Leaves more than 10 mm wide 8
8 Flowers small, stamens barely 10 mm long; petals absent; eastern Cape and Natal to Swaziland
    only .... **M. racemulosa**
  Flowers medium to large, stamens 2 to 3 cm long; petals 4; not further south than the south of
    Rhodesia and adjacent areas in Moçambique .... **M. kirkii**
9 Leaves yellowish-green, usually finely velvety; apparently South West Africa only ....
  .... **M. schinzii**
  Leaves green, usually without hairs; widespread at low altitudes but apparently not in South West
    Africa .... **M. angolensis**

Maerua angolensis DC.   Illust. 43

S.A. no: 132   Bead-bean. Knoppiesboontjie
Rhod. no: 141   Bead-bean

A tree up to 10 m in height; occurring in low altitude wooded grassland, woodland, scrub and thickets. **Bark:** light grey or dark brown to blackish; young branches yellowish with conspicuous creamy-white lenticels. **Leaves:** simple, elliptic to lanceolate, 2,5 to 7 × 1,3 to 5,5 cm; apex rounded, occasionally notched, with a conspicuous hair-like tip; base broadly tapering to rounded; margin entire; petiole up to 3 cm long, often swollen just below the leaf. **Flowers:** solitary in the axils of the upper leaves, or in short terminal spikes, or crowded on dwarf lateral shoots. Individual flowers inconspicuous; petals absent; sepals green, up to 1,8 cm long; stamens many, long, in the characteris-   **193**

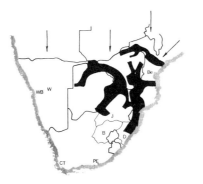

tic central mass (July to December). **Fruit:** like a long, slender, often irregularly constricted bean, 2 to 16 × 1 cm (September to February).

This species closely resembles the South West African *M. schinzii,* but they can be separated on their geographical distribution; also see note under *M. schinzii.*

Maerua cafra (DC.) Pax
S.A. no: 133   Bush-cherry. Witbos
Rhod. no: 143   Bush-cherry

194   *The bush-cherry* Maerua cafra.

A shrub or small tree which may reach 9 m in height; occurring in open woodland, in various types of forest and in dune bush. **Bark:** pale grey and mottled. **Leaves:** digitately compound, usually 3-foliolate, but may have 5 leaflets; leaflets elliptic to obovate, 2 to 7,5 × 0,6 to 3,5 cm, leathery, the median leaflet being longer than the laterals; apex tapering to rounded, notched, with a hair-like tip; base tapering; margin entire; petiolules of the leaflets very short, petiole 1 to 6 cm long. **Flowers:** in terminal corymbs (clusters) of 3 to 12, surrounded by leaves. Petals absent; sepals greenish, about 1,7 cm long; stamens many, forming a lax central mass, up to 3 cm long (August to October). **Fruit:** rounded, plum-like, with longitudinal suture lines, about 4,5 cm long (October to December). The wood is brittle and has a sickening smell when cut.

Maerua gilgii Schinz
S.A. no: 133,1   River bush-cherry. Rivierwitbos
Rhod. no: —

A scrambling shrub or a slender small tree up to 3 m; occurring in hot, arid areas of stony desert, often along river beds and dry watercourses. **Bark:** greyish. **Leaves:** simple, narrow, linear to narrowly elliptic, 5 to 12 × 0,3 to 1 cm, yellowish-green to green, without hairs, leathery; apex tapering to broadly so, or narrowly rounded, bristle-tipped; base narrowly tapering and running into the petiole; margin entire; petiolate. **Flowers:** in congested, axillary or terminal spikes of 6 to 9 flowers; petals absent, sepals green, oblong, about 10 mm long, stamens many, up to 1,2 cm long, golden-yellow (cf. Illust. 43) (August to September). **Fruit:** almost spherical, up to 1,5 cm in diameter (October to December).

Maerua kirkii (Oliver) F. White
S.A. no: —
Rhod. no: 146   Large-flowered maerua

 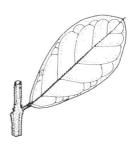

An evergreen shrub or small tree up to 5 m, which stands out when the rest of the countryside is dry, bare and brown; occurring in dry, low altitude woodland, in rocky places, and occasionally encountered above an altitude of 1 300 m penetrating *Brachystegia* woodland, but then only on termite mounds. **Leaves:** simple, oblong-obovate to oblanceolate, 4 to 12 × 2 to 5 cm, thickly leathery, brittle, shiny dark green above, dull green below with the net-veining conspicuous; apex tapering with a soft hair-like tip; base generally tapering, finally narrowly rounded to shallowly lobed; margin entire; petiole short. **Flowers:** in dense clusters at the ends of the branches. Sepals green; petals 4, **195**

CAPPARACEAE

greenish-cream; stamens many, up to 3 cm long (cf. Illust. 43) (August to October). **Fruit:** round, up to 1,7 cm in diameter, shiny red when ripe (October to January).

Maerua nervosa (Hochst.) Oliver
[*M. floribunda* T. R. Sim]
S.A. no: 136,1   Natal bush-cherry. Natalwitbos
Rhod. no: 147   Sausage-bean maerua

A shrub or small tree up to 3 m in height; mainly a coastal species, in dune scrub or forest. **Leaves:** simple or 3-foliolate, broadly elliptic, 2,5 to 6 × 1,5 to 3,5 cm, thinly textured, smooth, with prominent veins below; apex rounded, notched; base broadly tapering; margin entire; petiolate. **Flowers:** in small, axillary, branched heads of 4 to 6 flowers; sepals green, with 4 small, white petals; stamens many, up to 2 cm long (cf. Illust. 43) (July to September). **Fruit:** resembling a small, lumpy sausage, up to 3,7 × 2 cm, reddish-yellow when ripe (October to December).

Maerua prittwitzii Gilg & Benedict
[*M. rhodesiana* Wild]
S.A. no: —
Rhod. no: 149   Woolly-fruited maerua

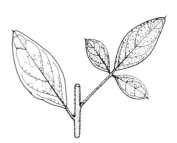

A shrub or small tree reaching 6 m in height; occurring in dry, low altitude woodland and on termite mounds in *Brachystegia* woodland. **Bark:** dark grey. **Leaves:** 3-foliolate, or the upper ones simple; leaves or leaflets broadly elliptic to ovate, 2 to 12 × 1 to 6 cm, the median leaflet about twice the length of the outer 2, greyish-green, upper surface wrinkled with deeply sunken veins, lower surface with prominent net-veining; apex very broadly tapering to rounded, with a soft, hair-like tip; base tapering to rounded; margin entire; petiole up to 4 cm long. **Flowers:** in short, dense sprays at the ends of the branches. Sepals green; petals small, white; stamens many, about 2 cm long (cf. Illust. 43) (October to December). **Fruit:** almost spherical, about 2,2 cm in diameter, pale brown, knobby with a fine woolly covering, thinly fleshy at first becoming fibrous later (January to April).

Maerua racemulosa (A. DC.) Gilg & A. Benn.
S.A. no: 134   Forest bush-cherry. Witboshout
Rhod. no: —

A slender shrub tending to scramble, or a small tree; occurring in dune forest, coastal and semi-coastal forest. **Bark:** pale grey. **Leaves:** simple (very occasionally 3-foliolate); narrowly elliptic, 5 to 12 ×

1,2 to 4 cm, thinly textured, midrib and net-veining prominent below; apex rounded, notched, with a soft, hair-like tip; base tapering; margin entire; petiolate. **Flowers:** small, in short, axillary spikes of 4 to 8 flowers; petals absent, sepals green, stamens many in the characteristic central mass (cf. Illust. 43) (May to July). **Fruit:** spherical, about 10 mm in diameter, yellow when ripe (August to October).

Maerua rosmarinoides (Sonder) Gilg & A. Benn.
S.A. no: 135   Needle-leaved bush-cherry. Naaldblaarwitbos
Rhod. no: —

Sometimes a much-branched shrub or a small tree up to 5 m in height; occurring chiefly in dry thorn, or succulent scrub usually associated with the coastal belt. **Bark:** brownish; branchlets smooth and greenish-brown. **Leaves:** usually 3-foliolate, but may have up to 5 digitate leaflets; leaflets very small, narrow and needle-like, linear, usually about $1,5 \times 0,1$ cm but may be somewhat larger; apex sharp-tipped; base tapering; margin entire, inclined to roll under; shortly petiolate. **Flowers:** in small, few-flowered terminal heads, on short side branches. Sepals green; petals 4, small, whitish; comparatively few stamens, about 10 to 12, but occasionally up to 30, about 2 cm long (September to December). **Fruit:** cylindric, with a few constrictions, about 2 cm long (January to March).

Maerua schinzii Pax
S.A. no: 136   Ringwood tree. Kringboom
Rhod. no: —

CAPPARACEAE

An erect, much-branched tree up to 7 m in height, with a dense, rounded crown; confined to South West Africa, occurring along river banks and watercourses. **Bark:** smooth whitish-grey or reddish-brown. **Leaves:** simple, elliptic, 2 to 6 × 1 to 3,5 cm, yellowish-green, usually finely velvety; apex rounded, notched, with a soft, hair-like tip; base tapering to rounded; margin entire; petiolate. **Flowers:** in terminal sprays or racemes. Sepals yellowish-green; petals absent; stamens many, forming a central mass (September to October). **Fruit:** bean-like, tightly constricted, up to 12 cm long (December to February).

This species is very closely related to *M. angolensis* and, taking into account the distribution of the 2 species, it would seem that *M. schinzii* could be reduced to subspecific level under *M. angolensis*.

Maerua triphylla A. Rich.
[*M. pubescens* (Klotzsch) Gilg]
S.A. no: —
Rhod. no: 151   Small bead-bean

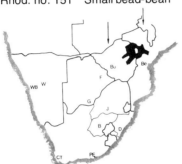

A much-branched shrub, scrambler or small tree up to 5 m in height; occurring in low altitude, dry types of woodland, and also frequently on termite mounds in *Brachystegia* woodland. **Leaves:** 3-foliolate, leaflets elliptic, 2 to 7 × 1 to 3 cm, the terminal leaflet being about twice the size of the 2 lateral leaflets; apex rounded, often notched, bristle-tipped; base broadly tapering; margin entire; petiolate. **Flowers:** in short, flat-topped heads, or corymbose racemes, axillary or terminal. Sepals green; petals 4, small, whitish; stamens comparatively few, 12 to 16, about 2 cm long (October to January). **Fruit:** cylindric, about 10 × 1 cm, pale creamy-brown, somewhat constricted between the seeds (February to June, or later).

All the Rhodesian and Moçambique material is assigned to var. *pubescens* (Klotzsch) DeWolf; the 3 other varieties do not extend as far south as this.

8. THILACHIUM Lour.

Thilachium africanum Lour.
S.A. no: 136,2   Cucumber bush. Komkommerbos
Rhod. no: 152   Cucumber bush

Shrubs or small trees up to 5 m in height; occurring in low altitude open wooded grassland, and in coastal thicket. **Bark:** pale greyish-brown; branches pale grey. **Leaves:** alternate, simple or 3-foliolate; leaves or leaflets elliptic to obovate, 3 to 10 × 1 to 4,5 cm, leathery, dark green, without

198

hairs, midrib yellowish, sunken above; lower surface paler, midrib prominent; apex rounded, notched, with a soft, hair-like tip; base tapering to rounded; margin entire, somewhat rolled under; petiole up to 6 cm long. **Flowers:** in few-flowered terminal or axillary flat-topped heads, or corymbose racemes. Petals absent; sepals splitting horizontally, the upper section separating away like a small pointed cap and remaining hinged on one side for a short time, releasing a head of many long, white to cream-coloured stamens up to 3 cm long; androgynophore present but short, about 4 mm long (August to October). **Fruit:** cylindric-oblong, up to 6 cm long, indehiscent, with about 12 very distinctive longitudinal ribs; carried on a long, slightly curved stalk (the gynophore) about 5 cm long (October to December).

MORINGACEAE *(The moringo family)*

MORINGA Adaṇs.

Moringa ovalifolia Dinter & A. Berger
S.A. no: 137   African moringo. Meelsakboom
Rhod. no: —

A conspicuous, rather succulent tree up to 7 m in height, with a strange, squat, swollen stem; occurring on dry rocky hillsides and sandy flats. **Bark:** smooth, pale whitish-grey to almost coppery and shiny. **Leaves:** alternate, compound, crowded near the ends of the branches, large, up to 60 cm long, with 4 to 7 pairs of pinnae, each bearing 2 to 7 (usually 5) pairs of opposite leaflets plus a terminal leaflet; leaflets oval to ovate, 1,3 to 2,5 × 0,7 to 1,8 cm, almost without hairs, light green; apex broadly tapering to rounded; base rounded to slightly lobed; margin entire; petiolules and petiole present. **Flowers:** attractive, up to 2 to 3 mm in diameter, with 4 to 5 white petals; the flowers are produced in large, many-flowered, branched sprays, or panicles, appearing just before or with the first young leaves (November to February). **Fruit:** podlike, flattish, 3-sided, yellowish-green to pinkish-grey, up to 40 cm long, splitting into 3 valves and releasing winged seeds (May to November).
The wood is brittle and can be snapped by a high wind. The bark, stem and roots are eaten by game and also by Africans.
M. oleifera Lam., the moringo, from India (Rhod. no: 153) is prized for its edible root which has the flavour of horse-radish; the leaves and roots are edible, too, and are said to have medicinal properties. These trees were introduced into South Africa at some early time and have been reported as escaped and naturalised in the northern Transvaal and parts of Natal; they are also cultivated in several relatively remote parts of the Zambezi valley and they may have become naturalised in these areas too.

CRASSULACEAE *(The crassula family)*

A large family, mostly succulent herbs and undershrubs, only 3 of which can be said to attain tree shape, if not size.

Key to the tree genera:
Petals free or, if joined, then at the base only, spreading; flowers small, star-like, usually in compact, clustered heads .... **2. Crassula**   **199**

CRASSULACEAE

Petals joined to form a distinct tube, often persistent, becoming thin and papery and ensheathing the fruit; flowers usually pendulous, becoming upright as the fruit matures; flowers large 2 to 3 cm long, in flat-topped heads .... **1. Cotyledon**

1. COTYLEDON L.

Cotyledon paniculata L.f.
S.A. no: 137,1   Botterboom. Botterboom
Rhod. no: —

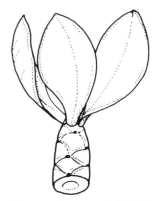

A short, very thickset, squat, succulent dwarf tree, 1 to 3 m tall; occurring on rocky hillsides and mountain slopes in dry, arid areas. **Bark:** olive-green, peeling in thin, yellow, papery sheet; branches short and thick. **Leaves:** opposite or scattered, simple, obovate, 5 to 7,6 × 2 to 5 cm, thick and fleshy, pale green to yellowish-green, shrivelling as they dry and fall, leaving a conspicuous scar; apex broadly tapering to rounded; base tapering; margin entire; petiole absent. **Flowers:** tubular; sepals 5, joined; petals 5, joined, forming a yellowish-red tube, 2 to 2,5 cm long, with yellowish lobes; stamens 10. Flowers produced in slender, branched, terminal panicles (the specific name refers to this); the flowers are pendulous but become upright as the petal-tube dries (December to January). **Fruit:** a follicle, made up of 5 separate carpels, and surrounded by the papery persistent petal-tube; upright (February to May).

The stems are soft, fleshy and brittle, and this feature gave rise to the common name. For centuries children have used the soft, slippery stems as sleds to slide down rocks and hillsides. The leaves are browsed on by stock and game, although other species in this genus are poisonous.

The botterboom, Cotyledon paniculata, *in characteristic arid country.*

2. CRASSULA L.

Fleshy herbs, shrubs or dwarf, succulent trees. **Leaves:** opposite, simple, fleshy. **Flowers:** small, all floral parts in threes to fives; petals not joined. **Fruit:** made up of 3 to 5 separate follicles.

Key to the tree species of *Crassula:*

A robust shrub or dwarf tree up to 5 m; leaves oblanceolate, comparatively narrow, apex with a distinct point; leaves grey-green, but without a waxy bloom .... **C. ovata**

A shrub or dwarf tree up to 3 m; leaves almost spherical, apex rounded, or obscurely pointed; leaves with a distinct waxy bloom .... **C. arborescens**

Crassula arborescens (Miller) Willd.
S.A. no: 137,2   Round-leaved crassula. Beestebal
Rhod. no: —

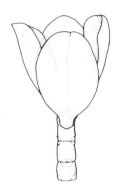

A shrub 1 to 2 m, or a small, squat, succulent tree up to 3 m in height; occurring on dry rocky hillsides in karroid scrub. **Bark:** green-grey, succulent, smooth. **Leaves:** almost round to broadly ovate, about 3 × 3 cm, thick, fleshy, with a grey, waxy bloom; apex rounded or with an obscure sharp tip; base tapering; margin entire, often reddish-rimmed; petiole absent. **Flowers:** white to pink in dense, branched, almost spherical heads (September to November). **Fruit:** small, up to 6 mm long only, with 3 to 5 separate, oval, sharply tipped follicles remaining among the dried remains of the persistent petals (November to January).

Crassula ovata (Miller) Druce
[*C. portulacea* Lam.]
S.A. no: 137,3   Narrow-leaved crassula. Kerkeibos
Rhod. no: —

In many respects this species is very similar to *C. arborescens.* The 2 species may be separated on the characters given in the key; flowering time July to August; fruits August to September.

BREXIACEAE

BREXIA Thouars

Brexia madagascariensis (Lam.) Ker-Gawl.
S.A. no: —
Rhod. no: —   Brexia

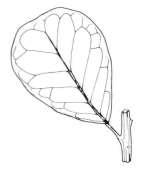

A much-branched, dense, evergreen shrub or small tree, normally only 2 to 3 m high, but occasionally up to 7 m; occurring in dense coastal bush, littoral scrub, and also at the edges of mangrove swamps, but it has no mangrove modifications such as breathing-roots or any adaptations of the seedlings; it can be found in bush and fringing forest up to 100 m above sea level. **Bark:** grey to brown, striated. **Leaves:** alternate, variable, from narrowly oblong to almost round, 3,5 to 14 cm long; thickly leathery; apex rounded, notched to deeply notched; base tapering to rounded; margin entire, slightly rolled under, often wavy, and sometimes broadly and shallowly toothed; petiole 1 to 2 cm long. **Flowers:** quite large, with 5 widely spreading petals, tending to curve backwards, up to 2 cm long, pale yellowish-green, thick and rather fleshy; 4 to 5 stamens, arising between the 5 lobes of the receptacle disc, and from each of these 5 receptacle lobes rises a short, stiff projection which may represent a sterile stamen; the flowers are produced in rather loose, branched clusters, or umbel-like cymes, in the leaf axils, sometimes on the old wood (July to October). **Fruits:** cylindric, woody, rather fibrous, more or less 9 cm long with 5 clearly defined ridges, indehiscent (October to January). The fruits are said to be edible, possibly becoming soft and rather pulpy with age. They can float in the sea for months, the seed remaining viable.

ITEACEAE

CHORISTYLIS Harvey

Choristylis rhamnoides Harvey
S.A. no: 138   Bastard dogwood. Basterblinkblaar
Rhod. no: 154   False shiny-leaf

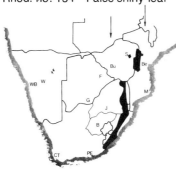

Often a shrub or scrambler with long, trailing branches, but it can become a small tree up to 3 to 4 m in height; occurring in high altitude forest and on forest margins; in the eastern Cape it can grow even in the snow-line of the higher mountains. **Leaves:** alternate, elliptic, 2 to 7,6 × 0,8 to 5 cm, shiny light green; apex tapering to rounded; base tapering to rounded; margin serrate, the teeth being glandular; petiole slender, pinkish when young. **Flowers:** small, greenish-yellow; in dense branched heads thickly clustered in the leaf axils. All floral parts in fives; sexes separate, or bisexual (August to October). **Fruit:** a leathery, 2-lobed capsule, opening by a single, small apical pore (September to May).

MONTINIACEAE

MONTINIA Thunb.

Montinia caryophyllacea Thunb.
S.A. no: 137,4   Wild clove-bush. Wildenaeltjiebos
Rhod. no: —

A shrub to small tree, generally bluish-green in colour; common on rocky hillsides in *Protea arborea* woodland, in dry scrub and along dry watercourses. **Leaves:** alternate or crowded on short, rigid, almost spinescent lateral branches; size and shape variable, from narrowly oblanceolate, 3 × 0,3 cm, to elliptic, 6 × 2,5 cm, bluish-green, rather thick; apex broadly tapering to rounded; base narrowly tapering; margin entire; petiole about 6 mm long. **Flowers:** small, white, about 6 mm in diameter. Sexes on separate trees. Floral parts in fours and fives, calyx forming a tube; petals rather fleshy. Male flowers in few-flowered terminal clusters, or corymbs. Female flowers solitary in the leaf axils (February to April, or September to October). **Fruit:** an oval, thinly woody capsule, about 2 cm long, the persistent calyx partly enveloping the lower half of the fruit: partially splitting into 2 valves (March to August; old fruits at most times of the year).
The crushed leaves have an acrid, pungent scent and the sap is milky. Cats are attracted to this plant. This is a protected tree in South West Africa.

PITTOSPORACEAE *(The pittosporum family)*

PITTOSPORUM Banks ex Solander

Pittosporum viridiflorum Sims   Illust. 44
S.A. no: 139   Pittosporum. Kasuur
Rhod. no: 155   Pittosporum

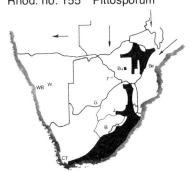

Sometimes a large shrub, but more often a tree up to 10 m high, although in the forests of Zululand it reaches 20 to 30 m; occurring over a wide range of altitudes, in deciduous woodland, scrub, in riverine fringe thicket and in evergreen forest, also on rocky outcrops. **Bark:** pale or darkish grey, smooth when young, roughish later; the stem is fluted in very large specimens. **Leaves:** alternate, scattered or whorled, very variable in size and shape, usually obovate to broadly oblanceolate, about 6 to 7 × 2 to 2,5 cm, but may be up to 11 × 4 cm, dark green or bluish-green, dull to rather glossy, but a characteristic brilliant green when caught against the sunlight; the upper surface often has the veining forming a 'square pavement' pattern, conspicuous net-veining on the lower surface; apex rounded or shortly attenuate; base tapering; margin entire; petiolate. **Flowers:** small, greenish-white to cream, sweetly scented. Flowers bisexual; all floral parts in fives; petals longer than the sepals; stamens free. Produced in terminal, branched heads, or panicles (November to December). **Fruit:** a small, creamy-brown capsule, 5 to 8 mm in diameter, splitting to release the bright red seeds which are coated with a sticky, slow-drying resin (May to September).

The bark has a sweetish smell (like liquorice, says Eve Palmer), and a bitter taste; it is reputed to have medicinal properties and is used to treat stomach complaints and also for black gall-sickness and red water in cattle. The wood is white and of little value; the seeds germinate readily, and the plants strike easily from cuttings. This is a most worthwhile garden tree.

CUNONIACEAE

Key to the tree genera:
Leaves trifoliolate. Flowers in long-stalked, branched sprays, or panicles; fruits without 'horns'; in the coastal belt from Swellendam to Port Elizabeth only .... **1. Platylophus**

Leaves pinnately compound. Flowers in dense spikes; fruits with 2 'horns'; from the south-western Cape eastwards through Natal, Zululand to the eastern Transvaal .... **2. Cunonia**

1. PLATYLOPHUS D. Don

Platylophus trifoliatus (L.f.) D. Don
S.A. no: 141 Witels. Witels
Rhod. no: —

A small to large evergreen tree reaching up to 30 m in height; occurring in forest or on stream banks. **Bark:** greyish or brownish, sparsely vertically fissured. **Leaves:** opposite, 3-foliolate; leaflets lanceolate, up to 11 × 2,5 cm, dark green above, paler below, with conspicuous net-veining; apex tapering to narrowly rounded; base narrowly tapering; margin roughly toothed, occasionally entire; petiolules absent, petiole up to 4 cm long. **Flowers:** small, white or cream, in rather dense, long-stalked, many-flowered heads, or panicles, in the leaf axils. Flowers bisexual with an urn-shaped receptacle disc; calyx tube very short, attached to the base of the ovary; petals 4 to 5, shorter than the calyx; stamens 8 to 10 (December). **Fruit:** a small russet to dark brown capsule about 10 mm long, in branched clusters among the leaves (April).

This is probably the most important honey tree in the Knysna forests and bees and other insects may be seen swarming about its profusion of flowers. The wood, which is light, durable, variable in colour and easily worked, is used for a number of different purposes. It is particularly suitable for boat keels and in Knysna it is made into furniture. Propagation is not easy as birds account for much of the seed and wild pig eat the capsules as they fall to the ground.

2. CUNONIA L.

Cunonia capensis L.

S.A. no: 140   Rooiels. Rooiels
Rhod. no: —

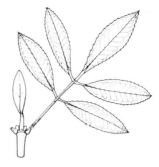

A fine evergreen tree up to 30 m; occurs on stream banks and in moist forest, being abundant in the high, wet forests and in the very wet scrub forests round Knysna; under harsher conditions it becomes shrubby. **Bark:** pale when young and rather flaky; later dark and roughish. **Leaves:** opposite, compound, usually with 3 to 5 pairs of leaflets plus 1 terminal leaflet, lanceolate to ovate, 7 to 10 × 0,8 to 5 cm, dark green, glossy and ornamental; the leaf buds are enclosed by 2 large, paddle-like stipules which are conspicuous; apex and base of leaflets tapering; margin sharply toothed; petiolate. **Flowers:** small, white to cream-coloured, in long dense spikes up to 14 cm in length, produced at the ends of the branches, showy and conspicuous. Flowers bisexual; all floral parts in fives; calyx tube short; petals oblong attached to the receptacle disc and shorter than the calyx tube; stamens 10 in 2 whorls of 5; ovary with 2 horns (March to May). **Fruit:** a 2-horned leathery capsule, brown in colour, splitting to release many minute seeds which adhere to the bills, feet and feathers of birds which are thus important dispersal agents (April to July).

The wood is pale to rich red flecked with white; it is even-grained, fairly hard, easily worked and makes attractive furniture. The trees are reasonably fire-resistant and fast growing. Seeds should be sown in light shade, not covered at all, on the surface of the soil which should be kept constantly moist for the several months they take to germinate. The young seedlings are very small and fragile but, when once established, they grow rapidly. This would make an attractive garden tree.

Flower spikes of the rooiels, Cunonia capensis.

205

HAMAMELIDACEAE *(The witch-hazel family)*

TRICHOCLADUS Pers.

Shrubs or small trees, the branches and leaves often densely hairy. **Leaves:** opposite or alternate, simple. **Flowers:** bisexual or sexes separate, in dense, spherical heads; floral parts in fours to fives; sepals joined to form a tube; petals long and narrow. **Fruit:** a 2-valved capsule, but appearing to be 4-valved at the apex.

Key to the tree species of *Trichocladus:*

1 Mature leaves without hairs or almost so; petals long, up to 2,5 cm, and comparatively broad
.... **T. grandiflorus**
  Mature leaves more or less densely hairy, especially below; petals rarely more than 10 mm long, narrow 2
2 Base of the leaf rounded to slightly lobed; branchlets and leaves usually opposite ....
.... **T. crinitus**
  Base of the leaf generally tapering towards the base; branchlets and leaves usually alternate ...
.... **T. ellipticus**

Trichocladus crinitus (Thunb.) Pers.   Illust. 45
S.A. no: 142   Black witch-hazel. Swarttowerhaselaar
Rhod. no: —

An undershrub, shrub or small tree 3 to 4 m in height; frequent in the understorey of evergreen forests, apparently not west of George. **Bark:** light grey to dark brown, smooth. **Leaves:** opposite, elliptic, 2,5 to 10 × 1,5 to 7 (occasionally larger), dark shiny green above and with dark chocolate-brown velvety hairs below, especially along the midrib but less so on the lateral veins; apex tapering; base square to slightly lobed and more or less peltate; margin entire, rather rolled under; petiole short and thickset. **Flowers:** creamy-green, yellow or orange, in small, spider-like heads; sexes separate on the same tree or on different trees (April to August). **Fruit:** a cluster of small hairy capsules, brown to red, 5 to 7 mm long (October to November).
The wood is white and very hard (the Xhosa name *iThambo* means 'a bone') but the pieces are usually too short to be of any use.

Trichocladus ellipticus Ecklon & Zeyher
S.A. no: 143   White witch-hazel. Wittowerhaselaar
Rhod. no: 156   White witch-hazel

An evergreen shrub often with a tendency to scramble, or a small, many-branched tree up to 10 m (the subsp. *malosanus* in Rhodesia and adjacent Moçambique reaches 15 m); occurring in rain forest, along streams and rivers where it is frequently dominant, and in swampy places. **Bark:** greyish-brown. **Leaves:** alternate, lanceolate to elliptic, 5 to 15 × 2,5 to 7,5 cm, usually about 7 cm long, dark green glossy above, with dense cream to rusty hairs below; apex tapering and rather attenuate; base tapering but often finally abruptly flared and narrowly lobed; margin entire; petiolate. **Flowers:** cream or yellowish-green, in rather ragged, spiky heads, axillary or terminal, about 2 cm in diameter (September to December). **Fruit:** a small, almost spherical, velvety capsule, about 6 × 5 mm, opening at the tip by 2 valves, each of which itself splits into 2 (December to February).

206

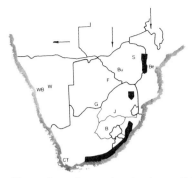

Two subspecies are involved over this range:
(a) In South Africa only, not Rhodesia; leaves smaller, narrower, with apices more attenuate .... subsp. *ellipticus*
(b) In Rhodesia and adjacent Moçambique, not in South Africa; leaves appreciably larger, broader, with the apices more rounded .... subsp. *malosanus* (Baker) Verdc.

The wood is white, hard and tough, often with a black centre; it makes an excellent firewood.

Trichocladus grandiflorus Oliver
S.A. no: 144   Green witch-hazel. Groentowerhaselaar
Rhod. no: —

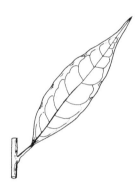

Sometimes a shrub, usually a tree up to 7 m, occasionally very large, up to 30 m; occurring on the fringe of mountain mist-belt forests, in wooded ravines and in low altitude evergreen forest. **Bark:** brown, the branchlets reddish and hairy. **Leaves:** opposite, ovate to lanceolate, 5 to 10 × 2,5 to 5 cm, glossy green above and paler below with the veining very prominent; the new leaves are covered with conspicuous reddish-brown velvety hairs, mature leaves without hairs; apex and base tapering; margin entire; petiolate. **Flowers:** handsome, almost 4 cm in diameter, in loose heads, axillary or terminal; the rather crinkly white petals are tinged with purple towards the base (December to January). **Fruit:** a small dark capsule (February to May, but might be much later).
These very attractive trees are not difficult to cultivate, but remain surprisingly little-known in gardens.

ROSACEAE *(The rose family)*

Key to the tree genera:
1 Shrubs or small trees with rigid branches; leaves often compound, leaflets usually very small, often very narrow, linear (except for *C. grandifolia*) with petioles almost absent or absent; petals absent, flowers with sexes separate .... **2. Cliffortia**

  Shrubs or trees; leaves not small and linear, petiole more or less long; flowers bisexual, petals present 2 **207**

ROSACEAE

2 Leaves compound, with silky hairs; fruit a group of small nuts included inside the old receptacle
.... **1. Leucosidea**

Leaves simple, without silky hairs; fruits fleshy, single-seeded .... **3. Prunus**

1. LEUCOSIDEA Ecklon & Zeyher

Leucosidea sericea Ecklon & Zeyher   Illust. 46
S.A. no: 145   Ouhout. Ouhout
Rhod. no: 161   Leucosidea

A greyish shrub, often straggling, or a small, much-branched tree up to 7 m; usually occurring at high altitudes along streams and in kloofs, where it forms dense stands. **Bark:** reddish-brown, characteristically flaking off in strips; the young branches are shaggy with persistent, hairy stipules. **Leaves:** alternate, compound, with 2 to 3 pairs of leaflets plus a terminal leaflet; leaflets obovate, up to 3 cm long, with the terminal leaflet and the next pair of leaflets usually larger than the lower pair; the upper surface is dark green, the lower surface greyish-green with silky hairs; apex generally rounded; base tapering; margin deeply and jaggedly toothed; petiolate. **Flowers:** small, greenish, densely clustered in shortly peduncled silky terminal sprays, or racemes; sepals 10 to 12 in 2 whorls; petals 5, obovate, greenish-yellow; stamens 10 to 12; ovary of 2 to 3 separate hairy carpels (August to December). **Fruit:** a group of small nuts enclosed in the base of the old flowers (December to January).
These plants grow easily from seed and are fast-growing and hardy; they need damp conditions. The wood is reddish-brown and soft and it makes a useful firewood. In Natal *Leucosidea* is troublesome as it invades overgrazed and disturbed areas, forming inpenetrable thickets which are best eradicated by chopping out the plants at ground level. The Zulus grind the leaves and make a paste for treating cases of ophthalmia. The common name *ouhout* may refer to the old gnarled twisted trunks, or to the fact that the wood burns slowly as if it were old and rotting. In mountainous areas the presence of these trees is taken as an indication that the streams are suitable for trout-stocking.

2. CLIFFORTIA L.

Shrubs to small trees with rigid branches. **Leaves:** alternate, petioles very short or absent; 1- to 3-foliolate often appearing simple as the 2 lateral leaflets become so reduced as to be scale-like. **Flowers:** unisexual; solitary or in pairs in the leaf axils, or forming very short, dense spikes. Male flowers: sepals 3 to 7; petals absent; stamens 3 to many; ovary absent. Female flower: sepals 3; petals absent; stamens absent; ovary surrounded by an urn-shaped receptacle. **Fruit:** a small nut.

Key to the tree species of *Cliffortia:*
1 Widespread along the Drakensberg and closely neighbouring mountains, in the mountains in the east of Rhodesia and adjacent areas of Moçambique .... **C. nitidula**
   In the western and south-western Cape only 2
2 In the western Cape, confined to mountains in the Sutherland and Calvinia districts only ....
   .... **C. arborea**
   A more southerly distribution than the preceding species; in the south-western Cape, in the Langeberg, Hottentots Holland and Franschhoek mountains only .... **C. grandifolia**

Cliffortia arborea Marloth
S.A. no: 145,1   Star cliffortia. Sterboom
Rhod. no: —

Usually a shrub or small tree 3 to 5 m in height, but able to reach 10 m in suitable sheltered positions; occurring in stony ravines and on rocky cliffs, confined to the mountains round Sutherland and Calvinia. **Bark:** grey with red flaking strips; aromatic. **Leaves:** needle-like, 1 to 2 cm long, hard and spiky, conspicuously spiralling along short, lateral branches giving the impression of tight, star-like rosettes; both simple and 3-foliolate leaves are present. **Flowers:** sepals 3; petals absent; minute bracteoles present. Male flowers solitary, without stalks, sepals up to 7 × 3 mm, stamens about 7 mm long; in the axils of the 3-foliolate leaves; female flowers sepals about 3 × 0,5 mm; produced in small groups of 5 to 8, forming a very short dense spike, in the axils of the simple leaves; both the male and the female flowers are almost lost among the strange leaves. **Fruit:** a small hard nut embedded in the dry remains of the old flowers.

It would seem likely that the common name arose from the star-like appearance of the leaf rosettes.

Cliffortia grandifolia Ecklon & Zeyher
S.A. no: 145,4   Large-leaved cliffortia. Grootblaarrysbos
Rhod. no: —

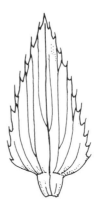

Usually a shrub, but occasionally a small tree reaching 5 m in height; occurring in forested ravines and along stream banks. **Bark:** grey, smooth and peeling. **Leaves:** broad-based, almost triangular, about 6 × 2,5 cm, shiny green on the upper surface, veining almost parallel; apex sharply pointed; base clasping the stem; margin sharply toothed; petiole absent. **Flowers:** sepals 3,2 to 3 cm long, greenish-yellow. Produced deep in the axils of the leaves almost hidden from sight and well protected by the sharp, rigid leaves and toothed margins (September to January). **Fruit:** narrowly elliptic, 1 × 0,4 cm, grey-green and vertically ribbed (March to July).

Cliffortia nitidula (Engl.) R. E. & T. C. E. Fries
S.A. no: 145,2   Common cliffortia. Sterretjierysbos
Rhod. no: 162   Common cliffortia

Most often an untidy shrub, but occasionally a small tree reaching 6 m in height; occurring in mountainous areas along stream banks, in rocky ravines, and on mountain grassland. **Bark:** brown or grey. **Leaves:** small, needle-like 3 to 10 × 1 mm, or lanceolate up to 10 × 2 mm, dark green, clustered **209**

ROSACEAE

on very short lateral branchlets, and closely packed along the slender brownish hairy branches; tapering to base and apex, petiole almost absent. **Flowers:** small, sepals 4, greenish-cream, inconspicuous, almost hidden at the base of the leafy tufts (November to April). **Fruit:** a very small oval nut about 1,5 mm long, tawny-coloured, also hidden among the leaves, ribbed and crowned with the remains of the old style (November to April).

The degree of hairiness of the leaves is very variable, South African material varying from leaves covered with long silky hairs right through to those with no hairs at all; the subsp. *pilosa* Weimarck (said to have long silky hairs, and applied to all South African material) is not upheld.

3. PRUNUS L.

Prunus africana (J. D. Hook.) Kalkman
[*Pygeum africanum* J. D. Hook.]
S.A. no: 147   Red stinkwood. Rooistinkhout
Rhod. no: 163   Bitter-almond

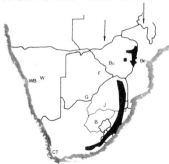

A medium to large handsome evergreen tree from 10 to 24 m in height; occurring in evergreen forests often in mountainous mist-belt areas. **Bark:** blackish-brown and rough. **Leaves:** alternate, simple, elliptic, 5 to 15 × 2 to 6 cm, smooth, dark green and glossy above, paler below, the crushed leaves having a faint smell of almonds; apex and base tapering; margin finely toothed; petiole pinkish. **Flowers:** small, white, fragrant, solitary or in branched axillary sprays 3 to 7 cm long; calyx and petals small; stamens 10 to 20 (October to May). **Fruit:** spherical, about 10 mm in diameter, pinkish-brown, intensely bitter (September to January).

The wood is close-grained, even-textured, reddish-brown in colour but as it splits and twists its use is limited. This species responds well to cultivation and makes an attractive garden shade tree.

*Prunus persica (L.) Batsch

Peach trees are encountered quite frequently, apparently growing wild. They can be seen along the main road between Aliwal North and Jamestown in the eastern Cape, having almost certainly grown from peach seeds idly tossed away by passers-by.

*Prunus serotina Ehrh.

Introduced, originally from the U.S.A., and have now escaped and become naturalised in the Chirinda Forest in the east of Rhodesia (Rhod. no: 164).

*COTONEASTER Medik.

*Cotoneaster pannosa Franchet

Originally from south-west China, this attractive shrub or small tree with red berries was introduced as an ornamental plant and has now escaped and become naturalised in some of the central areas of Rhodesia (Rhod. no: 165).

CHRYSOBALANACEAE *(The mobola family)*

Key to the tree genera:
A well-rounded, evergreen tree up to 13 m in height, of open wooded grassland: leaves oblong, usually about 7,5 cm long, apex broadly tapering, often notched; flowers small, 4 to 6 mm in diameter, in compact heads .... **1. Parinari**

A very tall tree, up to 40 m, of evergreen forests; leaves usually elliptic with a sharply attenuate drip-tip; flowers 1 to 2 cm in diameter in rather loose heads. In the east of Rhodesia in mountain forests and adjacent areas in Moçambique; not recorded from South Africa .... **2. Maranthes**

1. PARINARI Aubl.

Parinari curatellifolia Planchon ex Benth.   Illust. 47
[*P. mobola* Oliver]
S.A. no: 146   Mobola plum. Grysappel
Rhod. no: 166   Mobola plum

A large evergreen spreading tree, mushroom-shaped and usually up to 13 m in height; characteristic of sandy soils, in open deciduous woodland. **Bark:** dark grey and rough; the young shoots are densely covered with yellowish woolly hairs. **Leaves:** alternate, simple, elliptic to oblong, 3 to 8 × 2 to 4 cm, leathery, dark green above, finely velvety when young but losing these hairs later, densely hairy and greyish to yellowish below; apex broadly tapering, often notched; base square; margin entire; petiole short. **Flowers:** small, white, sweetly scented in short, branched heads, or panicles, 4 to 6 cm in diameter, in the leaf axils; the stalks and the calyces are densely covered with yellowish woolly hairs. Bisexual; sepals 5; petals 5; stamens 7 or more joined at the base into a short ring, inserted in the mouth of the receptacle; ovary 2-chambered (July to October). **Fruit:** oval to round up to 5 × 3,5 cm, russet-yellow, greyish scaly and pitted, edible (October to January).

The mobola plum is much sought after by local peoples and consequently the trees are seldom chopped down. The fruit, with its pleasant-tasting yellow flesh, has a variety of uses and forms a staple item in their diet. It may be eaten as it is or made into a porridge; a delicous syrup is prepared from it and it provides the basis of a refreshing non-alcoholic drink and also of an intoxicating liquor. An extract from the bark is used in tanning and also as a hot fomentation for the treatment of pneumonia. The light brown, hard wood is borer-proof and, although it is not durable if left exposed to weather, it has been used fairly extensively for rafters, beams, poles and benches. Unfortunately it contains silica crystals which make it difficult to work as they blunt saw-blades and other tools very rapidly. At certain times of the year the trees give off a very unpleasant smell but it is difficult to discover the cause for this.

These beautiful shady trees form a conspicuous feature of the landscape and it is easy to understand that one of them was chosen to bear the final tribute to Dr David Livingstone. After his death, on 4   **211**

CHRYSOBALANACEAE

May 1873 at Chitambo's village in central Zambia, a commemorative inscription was carved on the trunk of a fine specimen of *Parinari curatellifolia*.

The only other species of *Parinari* growing south of the Zambezi River is *Parinari capensis;* there are 2 subspecies, subsp. *capensis,* the sand apple, which is common in sandy areas and is a creeping shrub only a few centimetres in height and growing in colonies; subsp. *incohata* F. White is a dwarf shrub about 1 m high growing on the sandy plains of Zululand and Moçambique; their leaves are remarkably similar to those of *Parinari curatellifolia*.

2. MARANTHES Blume

Maranthes goetzeniana (Engl.) Prance
S.A. no: —
Rhod. no: 167   Maranthes

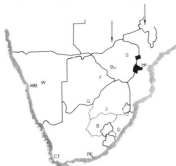

A very large tree, reaching 40 m in height; occurring in wet evergreen forest. **Bark:** grey, smooth and finely ridged. **Leaves:** alternate, simple, elliptic to oblong, 7 to 15 × 4 to 5 cm, shiny green above, dull green below; apex attenuate forming a conspicuous drip-tip; base broadly tapering to rounded; margin entire, inclined to be wavy; petiole short. **Flowers:** pale greenish to creamy-white in colour, 1 to 2 cm in diameter, in flat-topped heads (corymbs). Calyx-tube widely open-ended with 5 lobes; petals 5; stamens many, protruding well beyond the petals; the stalks and stems are finely covered with greenish velvety hairs (October). **Fruit:** oval up to 3 cm long (February).

A flowerhead of Maranthes goetzeniana

CONNARACEAE

Key to the tree genera:
Apex of the leaflets tapering, base asymmetric; apex of the fruit drawn out into a pronounced beak
.... **2. Cnestis**

Apex of the leaflets rounded, base symmetric; apex of the fruit rounded or only slightly pointed, not
beak-like .... **1. Byrsocarpus**

1. BYRSOCARPUS Schumacher

Byrsocarpus orientalis (Baillon) Baker
S.A. no: 147,2   Short-pod. Kortpeul
Rhod. no: 169   Short-pod

A shrub, often climbing, even a shrublet, but sometimes a small tree up to 6 m in height; occurring on termite mounds and in riverine thicket at low altitudes. **Bark:** grey and smooth; branches purplish-brown. **Leaves:** alternate to sub-opposite, compound, the whole leaf measuring from 9 to 20 cm long, with 8 to 16 pairs of opposite leaflets plus a terminal leaflet; leaflets elliptic or oblong, up to 4 × 1 cm, bright green above, paler below; apex and base rounded; margin entire. **Flowers:** attractive, about 2,5 cm in diameter, with 5 white to yellow petals, sweetly lemon-scented; produced in few-flowered, axillary sprays (September to November, before the new leaves). **Fruit:** an oval capsule about 2,3 cm long, red when ripe, splitting along a single ventral suture, so that the fruit wall curls back and the seed protrudes through the opening (January to February).
It is possible that this species occurs also in Natal as a single sterile specimen collected from forest in the Oribi gorge on the south coast strongly resembles the leaves of *B. orientalis*. However, flowering or fruiting material is necessary before a positive determination can be made.

2. CNESTIS Juss.

Cnestis natalensis (Hochst.) Planchon & Sonder
S.A. no: 147,1   Itch-pod. Jeukpeul
Rhod. no: 171   Itch-pod

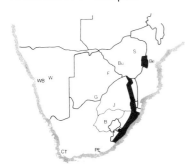

A shrub, woody liane or occasionally a small tree 3 to 4 m in height; occurring in coastal swamp and montane forests and on wooded hillsides. **Bark:** greyish. **Leaves:** alternate to sub-opposite, compound, up to 20 cm long, with 3 to 9 pairs of opposite to alternate leaflets plus 1 terminal leaflet;

213

leaflets oblong, 2 to 4 × 0,9 to 1,5 cm, dark shiny green above, pale green and may be finely velvety below, with a prominent midrib; apex broadly tapering; base of the terminal leaflet broadly tapering and symmetric but bases of the lateral leaflets often markedly asymmetric; margin entire; petiolules and petiole velvety; the leaf buds and young leaves are covered with thick rusty hairs and the new flush of young leaves is bronze. **Flowers:** small, star-like, white to cream or yellowish-green, in rather lax, branched sprays up to 4 to 5 cm long, in the axils of fallen leaves and especially on the old wood. All floral parts in fives; sepals and petals free; stamens 10 in 2 whorls; ovary densely hairy. The calyx and flower stalks covered with pale rusty velvety hairs (September to October, with the young leaves or just before the new flush). **Fruit:** a rusty-brown to orange-red hairy capsule, scimitar-shaped or broadly sickle-shaped, drawn out into a beak at the tip, more or less 2,5 cm long by 1 cm wide, with irritating hairs on the inside; the seeds are shiny blackish-brown with a yellow aril; the seed is squeezed out when the capsule splits down one side by contraction of the capsular wall (November to January).

LEGUMINOSAE *(The pod-bearing family)*

The family name *Leguminosae* is retained in the present work, in preference to the name *Fabaceae*, as there are differences of opinion as to whether the latter name should be applied to the *Leguminosae* as a whole, or only to the *Papilionoideae*.
The family is divided into three subfamilies:
- *(a)* Petals much reduced or absent; stamens many, long and conspicuous; flowers many, in distinctive, dense, fluffy, spherical or half-spherical heads, or in elongate spikes .... **Mimosoideae**
- *(b)* Petals may be absent, but usually large, and often showy; flowers more or less regular, but the back petal is often of a different shape, size and colour, which gives the flower some degree of asymmetry .... **Caesalpinioideae**
- *(c)* Flowers markedly asymmetric, with petals of three clearly different forms, producing the well-known 'pea-flower' or 'butterfly flower' .... **Papilionoideae**

MIMOSOIDEAE *(The mimosa subfamily)*

Key to the tree genera (exotic species marked*):
1 Plants armed with prickles, thorns or spines 2

  Plants unarmed (occasionally with very minute prickles) 5

2 Pods broad and flat, with a woody margin forming a rim which separates away, with the pod itself splitting transversely into 1-seeded segments .... **9. Entada**

  Pods with margins seldom separating away (if so, the pod is cylindric, not flat) and not breaking away transversely into 1-seeded segments 3

3 Spines short to long, straight or strongly curved, paired at the nodes or scattered; flowers uniformly yellow or creamy white in spherical heads or spikes .... **2. Acacia**

  Spines up to 1,5 cm long, straight or slightly curved on dwarfed side shoots or with some lateral branches terminating in a sharp point or spine 4

4 Flowers conspicuously 2-coloured, the lower portion pink (sterile), the upper portion yellow (fertile); fruit a contorted cluster of pods, indehiscent .... **3. Dichrostachys**

  Flowers creamy-white in half-spherical heads; fruit a single flat pod, dehiscent................. .... **1. Albizia**

5 Fruits bluntly 4-sided, indehiscent .... **5. Amblygonocarpus**

  Fruits flat or cylindric 6

6 The compound leaves absent, except in seedlings or in very young shoots, their place being taken by phyllodes, or flattened stems which closely resemble simple leaves .... **2. *Acacia**

  The compound leaves present 7

7 Leaf rachis with a stalked, round gland at the base of each pair of pinnae ...... **6. Newtonia**

  Leaf rachis may have pitted glands, but not stalked glands 8

8 Pinnae always 1 pair only per leaf, leaflets 4 to 6 pairs, large, up to 10 × 4 cm; the pair of pinnae form a conspicuous 'Y' at the end of the petiole .... **7. Xylia**

  Pinnae usually more than 1 pair per leaf; if only 1 pair then the leaflets not larger than 4 (occasionally 6) × 2 (occasionally 2,6) cm 9

9 Flowers usually in typical 'powder-puff' half-spherical heads; stamen filaments united basally into a tube .... **1. Albizia**

  Flowers in spikes or balls; stamen-filaments free (or may be basally joined in *Entada*) 10

10 Margin of the pod splitting away, the threads often persisting and hanging on the tree 11

  Margin of the pod not splitting away 12

11 Pods long, narrow, cylindric to subcylindric, the outer wall of the pod flaking away in almost leathery sheets, the central section eventually breaking up into unequal parts and falling away .... **8. Elephantorrhiza**

  Pods broad and flat, not flaking superficially, but the central section breaking up into 1-seeded parts that fall out of the hard woody rims .... **9. Entada**

12 Pods flattened .... **2. *Acacia**

  Pods subcylindric .... **4. *Prosopis**

1. ALBIZIA Durazz.

Shrubs or trees without spines or with some lateral branches terminating in a sharp point or spine. **Leaves:** alternate, 2-pinnate, usually with glands on the petiole and often on the rachis. **Flowers:** in characteristic half-spherical heads (a spike in 1 introduced species), solitary and terminal or in racemes. All floral parts in fives; calyx bell-shaped united at the base into a short tube; petals usually small and inconspicuous; stamens many, long and conspicuous; ovary oblong. **Fruit:** a flattened pod.

Key to the tree species of *Albizia* (exotic species marked*):
1 Flowers in spikes .... ***A. lophantha**
  Flowers in the typical half-spherical heads, or 'powder-puffs' 2
2 Leaflets small, less than 10 mm long 3
  Leaflets comparatively large, more than 10 mm long 6
3 Mature leaves and twigs without hairs .... **A. brevifolia**
  Mature leaves and twigs finely velvety 4
4 Pinnae in 15 to 35 pairs; leaflets very small and fine, in up to 45 to 50 pairs, each leaflet only 2 to 3,5 mm long and straight; petiole, rachis and leaflets with golden velvety hairs, especially when young .... **A. amara**
  Pinnae in 18 pairs or less; leaflets less than 40 pairs, each leaflet more than 3,5 mm long 5
5 Pinnae in 8 to 18 pairs, leaflets in 12 to 25 pairs, each leaflet 4 to 6 mm long and slightly sickle-shaped; young branches with pale brown velvety hairs, not silvery grey .... **A. harveyi**
  Pinnae in 2 to 7 pairs, leaflets in 6 to 14 pairs, each leaflet up to 9 mm long; young branches with silver-grey velvety hairs, not brown .... **A. forbesii**
6 Leaflets markedly and conspicuously rectangular 7
  Leaflets not so markedly rectangular 9
7 Leaflets tend to be less than 2 cm long; flowers conspicuously white, with no red .... **A. schimperana**
  Leaflets 2 cm long; flowers with showy, long, exserted staminal tubes, pink, red or green 8

8 A tree of high altitudes, above 1 000 m; all parts of the leaves and fruits almost without hairs; leaflets dark, glossy green; each leaflet with a small but distinct 'heel' at the base on the narrowed, or proximal, side; slender, lanceolate stipules at the base of the peduncle (flower stalk); bark smooth, creamy-greyish-brown. Not occurring in South Africa .... **A. gummifera**

A tree of low altitudes, usually below 1 000 m; leaf parts and fruits with yellow-brown velvety hairs, so the leaflets paler than *A. gummifera;* leaflets not 'heeled'; stipules large and shield-like at the base of the peduncle; bark roughish, shallowly crocodile-squared. Occurs both in South Africa and Rhodesia .... **A. adianthifolia**

9 Leaflets in 8 to 21 pairs 10

Leaflets in less than 8 pairs 13

10 Leaflets up to 2 × 0,8 cm 11

Leaflets 2 to 4 × 1 to 1,5 cm 12

11 Leaflets up to 1,5 × 0,5 cm, oval, apex rounded, notched. Not extending further south than the extreme north of Rhodesia .... **A. zimmermannii**

Leaflets up to 2 × 0,8 cm, apex drawn into a conspicuous, asymmetric point, or may be rounded but never notched. Not extending further south than the east of Rhodesia and adjacent areas of Moçambique .... **A. schimperana**

12 Bark pearly creamy-grey, peeling in reddish, papery flakes .... **A. tanganyicensis**

Bark grey, rough and fissured .... ***A. lebbeck**

13 Leaflet margins crisped; leaflets in 5 to 8 pairs, oblong, 2 to 2,5 cm long....... **A. suluensis**

Leaflet margins not crisped 14

14 Leaflets, especially the terminal pair, sharply narrowing to the base, producing a heart-shaped appearance, 8 to 16 mm long .... **A. petersiana**

Leaflets not sharply narrowed to the base 15

15 Leaflets smallish, 0,8 to 3,6 cm long, broadly elliptic to almost circular; rachis projecting into a short, down-bent hook .... **A. anthelmintica**

Leaflets longer than 2 cm, not broadly elliptic; rachis not forming an apical hook 16

16 Bark very smooth, pearly-grey, with a red, papery peel .... **A. tanganyicensis**

Bark without a red, papery peel, and roughish 17

17 Young branches and leaflets remaining densely hairy (often rusty-coloured) even when mature; leaflets very large for the genus, up to 5,5 cm long .... **A. versicolor**

Mature leaflets without hairs or with scattered hairs only 18

18 Leaflets conspicuously paler below .... **A. antunesiana**

Leaflets more or less uniform in colour above and below .... **A. glaberrima**

Albizia adianthifolia (Schumacher) W. F. Wight
[*A. chirindensis* (Swynnerton ex E. G. Baker) Swynnerton ex Steedman; *A. fastigiata* (E. Meyer) Oliver; *A. gummifera* auct. non (J. F. Gmelin) C. A. Smith]
S.A. no: 148   Flat-crown. Platkroon
Rhod. no: 172   Rough-bark flat-crown

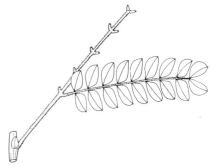

A large to very large tree, reaching 40 m in height, often with a conspicuous flat crown; occurring on forest margins, in ravines and in open forest. **Bark:** grey to yellowish-brown, roughish, crocodile-flaking. **Leaves:** 4 to 7 pairs of pinnae, each bearing 6 to 12 pairs of leaflets; leaflets most characteristically rectangular-shaped, about 2 × 0,5 to 0,8 cm, dark green, but with yellowish hairs especially below, often rusty velvety. **Flowers:** attractive, forming half-spherical heads, but larger than most of the other species, comparatively few-flowered and so more lax. Petals white, twice as long as the sepals and joined for most of their length; stamens joined to form a tube up to 5,5 cm long which protrudes from the petals, and which is tipped with red, pink or green; there are large, shield-shaped stipules at the base of the flower stalk, or peduncle (August to November). **Fruit:** a brown flattened pod with a conspicuous margin, up to 12,5 cm in length (maturing from August to October the following year).

This species is very similar to *A. gummifera* and also, to a lesser extent, to *A. schimperana;* for the differences between these species refer to paragraphs 7 and 8 of the key. The tree produces a sweet-smelling gum of somewhat inferior quality. The wood is straight-grained, works easily, is not inclined to warp and takes a good polish; it makes attractive parquet blocks for flooring. The Zulus prepare infusions, both hot and cold, from the bark and root with which they treat skin diseases such as scabies, while a cold extract from the roots alone is applied to inflamed eyes. The bark is poisonous, yet the Zulus make a 'love-charm emetic' from it and in Moçambique it provides a remedy for bronchitis. Local peoples make a sauce from the seeds and the trees themselves are valued for the shade they provide in tea plantations.

Albizia amara (Roxb.) Boiv.   Illust. 48
[*A. sericocephala* Benth.]
S.A. no: 149   Bitter albizia. Bittervalsdoring
Rhod. no: 173   Bitter albizia

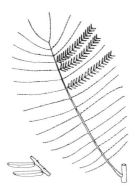

Usually a rather open, shapely tree 8 to 12 m in height; often occurring in small groups, but also singly, in woodland and wooded grassland. **Bark:** grey or brown, rather rough and fissured; young branches and leaves golden velvety. **Leaves:** 15 to 35 pairs of pinnae, each with many very small leaflets, up to 45 to 50 pairs, giving the leaves a very fine, feathery appearance; each minute leaflet is straight, up to 4 × 1 mm. **Flowers:** the characteristic half-spherical head, rather small, the stamens measuring up to 1 to 1,2 cm in length (September to October). **Fruit:** a large pod, brown to dark brown when mature, purplish when young with a conspicuous green margin (maturing from June to November the following year).

There are two subspecies involved. All the material generally encountered south of the Zambezi River is assigned to subsp. *sericocephala* (Benth.) Brenan; the typical subspecies, with fewer pinnae and leaflets, occurs mainly in India and Ceylon but spreads to the African continent being found in Kenya, Tanzania and Moçambique, just across the Zambezi River north of Sofala. The fruits are used as an emetic and also to treat coughs and malaria while the roots which contain saponin provide a substitute for soap.

Albizia anthelmintica (A. Rich.) Brongn.
[*A. umbalusiana* T. R. Sim]
S.A. no: 150   Worm-cure albizia. Wurmbasvalsdoring
Rhod. no: 174   Worm-cure albizia

A tree reaching 10 m in height, occasionally bushy and, in South Africa, smaller; in the Kruger National Park it rarely reaches 5 m in height; occurring in a variety of habitats over its very wide range. **Bark:** smooth, pale grey, reddish-grey to brown. Branchlets frequently sharply tipped or spine-tipped. **Leaves:** with 2 to 4 pairs of pinnae, each bearing 2 to 4 pairs of opposite leaflets; leaflets obovate to almost circular, up to 3,6 × 3 cm. **Flowers:** usually produced before the leaves, the white

stamens forming the half-spherical fluffy head, up to 2,5 cm long (July to September). **Fruit:** a straw-coloured pod up to 18 × 3 cm (the following September to November).

In South West Africa the bark is regarded as an anthelmintic especially against tape-worms and has for long been used in a similar way in Ethiopa and Somalia, hence the specific name. Extensive tests carried out under controlled conditions have shown that the bark is, in fact, effective against tape-worm infestation; in a powdered form it seems to be more successful than as a decoction, and treatment has produced no unpleasant side-effects. However, this should not be tried without medical advice.

Albizia antunesiana Harms   Illust. 49
S.A. no: 151   Purple-leaved albizia. Persblaarvalsdoring
Rhod. no: 175   Purple-leaved albizia

Usually a small to medium sized tree from 5 to 9 m, but it can reach 18 m in height; occurring in mixed woodland over a range of altitudes, but not frequently in the lowveld. **Bark:** smoothish, grey to brown. **Leaves:** with 1 to 3 pairs of pinnae, each with 3 to 8 pairs of rather large leaflets, ovate, 2,5 to 6 × 1 to 2,5 cm, made very distinctive by the pale under surface. **Flowers:** forming the half-spherical, fluffy heads, which are quite large, the stamens being up to 3 cm long (August to November). **Fruit:** a light brown, flat pod up to 23 cm long (April to September).

When in leaf this tree is easy to recognise by the pale under surface of the leaflets, which separates it from *A. glaberrima*. Young plants, even up to the size of saplings, sometimes have conspicuous purple leaves. In the field it can be mistaken easily for *Burkea africana* Hook., the Africans often making the same mistake, but *Albizia antunesiana* lacks the brown velvety tips to the branches which are characteristic of *B. africana*.

Albizia brevifolia Schinz
[*A. rogersii* Burtt Davy; *A. parvifolia* Burtt Davy]
S.A. no: 152   Mountain albizia. Bergvalsdoring
Rhod. no: 176   Mountain albizia

A small to medium sized tree reaching 10 m in height, but often shrub-like; occurring on dry stony hillsides. **Bark:** grey to black, narrowly fissured; young branches and leaves thinly covered with grey hairs which are lost at maturity. Branchlets frequently sharply tipped or spine-tipped. **Leaves:** usually 10 pairs of pinnae, each bearing up to 20 pairs of smallish leaflets, narrow, 3 to 8 mm long; young leaflets blue-green, mature leaflets often bluish. **Flowers:** forming the characteristic half-spherical,

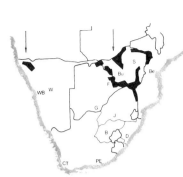

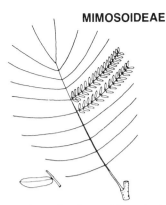

fluffy head, the stamens white to creamy-yellow and up to 1,2 cm long (October to November). **Fruit:** a brown pod up to 27 cm long, indehiscent (January to April).

This species can be confused with *A. harveyi* Fourn., but in the latter the leaflets are somewhat curved with the apex sharply pointed, while in *A. brevifolia* the leaflets are straight with the apex rounded.

Albizia forbesii Benth.

S.A. no: 154   Broad-pod albizia. Breëpeulvalsdoring
Rhod. no: 177   Broad-pod albizia

This can become a large spreading tree up to 20 m in height, often with drooping branches; occurring along streams and river banks, in thorn scrub and fringing forest. **Bark:** smooth, light grey to dark grey and roughish; young branches and leaves grey velvety. **Leaves:** with 2 to 7 pairs of pinnae, each bearing 6 to 14 pairs of small leaflets, oblong, up to 9 × 2 mm, stout-looking and closely ranked. **Flowers:** in the characteristic half-spherical fluffy heads, the stamens creamy-white, up to 1,5 cm long (November to December). **Fruit:** a russet-brown flat pod, very characteristically oblong in shape with darker transverse ridges (February to May).

This species enters Rhodesia only along the valleys of the Sabi and Nuanetsi Rivers, but with an outlying population near Marandellas. In South Africa it is not generally common, but locally forms small groups especially along river banks.

Albizia glaberrima (Schumacher & Thonn.) Benth.

S.A. no: —
Rhod. no: 178   Lowveld albizia

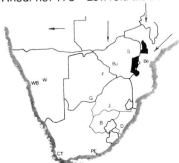

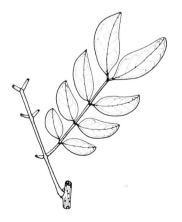

219

MIMOSOIDEAE

A large tree up to 25 m in height, with a more or less flattened crown; characteristic of low altitude mopane woodland, especially along river banks. **Leaves:** the leaflets are very similar to those of *A. antunesiana,* in fact they differ only in being not so conspicuously pale below. Confusion between the 2 species is not likely to occur in the field as *A. antunesiana* is a tree more of the medium to higher altitudes, while *A. glaberrima,* in Rhodesia, is confined almost entirely to altitudes below 1 000 m. **Flowers:** forming the half-spherical, fluffy heads; stamens small, white, up to 10 mm in length only (October to November). **Fruit:** a brown pod up to 29 cm long, narrow, about 4 cm wide (May to August).

Albizia gummifera (J. F. Gmelin) C. A. Smith   Illust. 50
S.A. no: —
Rhod. no: 179   Smooth-bark flat-crown

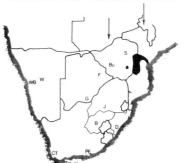
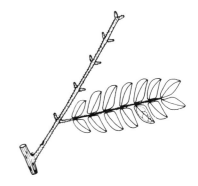

A large spreading, flat-topped tree; most frequently associated with high altitude forests. This species very closely resembles *A. adianthifolia,* so for the description and for the differences between the two, refer to that species and also to the key. All the Rhodesian material is placed in the typical variety.

Albizia harveyi Fourn.
[*A. pallida* Harvey; *A. hypoleuca* Oliver]
S.A. no: 155   Sickle-leaved albizia. Bleekblaarboom
Rhod. no: 180   Sickle-leaved albizia

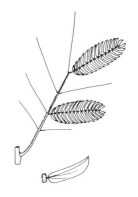

A small rather slender tree reaching 8 to 11 m in height; occurring in various types of low altitude woodland. **Bark:** grey to dark brown, rough and deeply longitudinally furrowed; young branches with pale brown velvety hairs. **Leaves:** up to 18 pairs of pinnae each bearing 12 to 24 pairs of very small narrow leaflets, 4 to 6 mm long, slightly sickle-shaped and sharply pointed; they resemble those of *A. brevifolia,* but the leaflets of the latter are straight with the apex rounded; they also resemble the leaflets of *A. amara,* but the latter are again straight and greyish velvety, while these are tawny velvety. **Flowers:** forming half-spherical white fluffy heads, comparatively large, the stamens up to 2 cm long (October to November). **Fruit:** a pod, long, narrow, 18 × 2 to 3 cm (May to August).

*Albizia lebbeck (L.) Benth.

A graceful and attractive tree introduced from tropical Asia, widely cultivated and now escaped and naturalised along the north coast of Natal. It could be confused with both *A. tanganyicensis* E. G.

Baker and *A. suluensis* Gerstner; however, it can be distinguished immediately from *A. tanganyicensis* by the bark – *A. tanganyicensis* has a beautiful red papery peeling bark, whereas the bark of *A. lebbeck* is grey and rough; *A. suluensis* has crisped margins to the leaflets and golden hairs on the calyx and the back of the petals, while *A. lebbeck* lacks both of these characteristics.

*Albizia lophantha (Willd.) Benth.

A graceful, slender tree up to 6 m in height, introduced from Western Australia and now escaped and naturalised in areas of the western Cape where it forms stands along river banks and fringing forest. It can be separated from all other likely species of *Albizia* by the flowers, which form short, dense spikes and not the characteristic half-spherical, fluffy heads.

Albizia petersiana (Bolle) Oliver

[*A. evansii* Burtt Davy]
S.A. no: 153   Many-stemmed albizia. Veelstamvalsdoring
Rhod. no: 181   Many-stemmed albizia

A medium to large tree reaching 21 m in height, usually smaller and sometimes shrubby; often showing very characteristic growth, branching freely from the base with the branches ascending at a sharp angle; the trees are deciduous and remain bare for several months in the year; occurring in low altitude open woodland on sandy soils. **Bark:** grey; young branches hairy. **Leaves:** with 2 to 4 pairs of pinnae, each bearing 2 to 5 pairs of leaflets, obovate to heart-shaped, 8 to 16 × 4 to 8 mm, sometimes inclining towards rectangular when they resemble those of *A. adianthifolia* and *A. gummifera,* the under surface of the leaflets with minute rough hairs; apex sharply tipped; base asymmetric; margin entire. **Flowers:** small, not forming the half-spherical head, the stamens being joined to form a tube with only 3 to 4 tubes per head so forming a somewhat similar structure to the flowers found in *A. gummifera/adianthifolia;* stamens white; flowers and the young leaves appear together in November. **Fruit:** pods rather narrow, 17 × 3 cm, deep reddish-purple to brown when ripe (May).
All the material south of the Zambezi River can be referred to subsp. *evansii* (Burtt Davy) Brenan; the typical subspecies with more numerous and densely velvety leaves occurs in Moçambique but only north of the Zambezi River, the leaves of *A. petersiana* subsp. *evansii* resemble those of *A. anthelmintica,* but the leaves of *A. petersiana* have minute rough hairs especially on the under surface, while those of *A. anthelmintica* are almost without hairs.

*Albizia procera (Roxb.) Benth.

A medium to large tree, introduced from tropical Asia to the eastern Rhodesian tea estates as a shade tree. It has escaped from this area and has now become naturalised along some of the rivers and also in some areas in the midlands of Natal. It has medium to large leaflets and purplish-green pods.

Albizia schimperana Oliver

S.A. no: —
Rhod. no: 183   Forest long-podded albizia

A large tree reaching 23 m in height; a mountain species, occurring in, and on the margins of mountain evergreen forest. **Bark:** smooth, pale grey or brown; young branches with brown velvety hairs. **Leaves:** with 4 to 7 pairs of pinnae, each bearing 16 to 21 pairs of leaflets, obliquely oblong, 0,7   **221**

 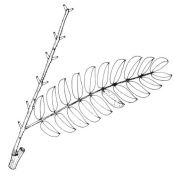

to 2 cm in length, the main vein markedly asymmetric, the apex often with a conspicuous point, sometimes rounded. **Flowers:** in rather lax heads, the stamens white, up to 1,2 cm in length (October). **Fruit:** a large brown pod up to 34 × 6 cm (March to April).

This species is very similar at first sight to *A. gummifera* or *A. adianthifolia,* but these leaves tend to be smaller and not as rectangular as are those of the other two species; also the flowers are conspicuously white and lack the long, brightly coloured staminal tubes present in *A. gummifera* and *A. adianthifolia.* In Rhodesia this species is most likely to be confused with *A. zimmermannii,* but this is not a problem in the field as *A. zimmermannii* occurs only in the north of the country and *A. schimperana* only in the east of the country.

In this species two varieties have been created, the typical var. *schimperana* and var. *amaniensis* (E. G. Baker) Brenan, the difference being that the latter has fewer leaflets which broaden towards the apex; there is considerable doubt that this is a valid separation and the var. *amaniensis* is possibly a hybrid between *A. schimperana* and *A. glaberrima.*

Albizia suluensis Gerstner
S.A. no: 156   Zulu albizia. Zoeloevalsdoring
Rhod. no: —

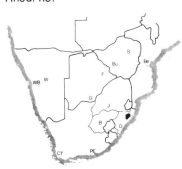 

A graceful tree with a rounded crown, from 5 to 15 m in height; it occurs in forest, wooded grassland and in riverine thicket, and is a species endemic to northern Zululand. **Bark:** grey and fissured. **Leaves:** with 2 to 4 pairs of pinnae, each bearing 5 to 9 pairs of leaflets; leaflets oblong to ovate, usually about 2,5 × 1,5 cm, dark green above, paler below; apex rounded or square sometimes abruptly attenuate; base asymmetric; margins conspicuously crisped; petiolules and petiole present. **Flowers:** calyx with golden velvety hairs; flowers forming the half-spherical, fluffy head; stamens whitish, up to 1,6 cm in length (December). **Fruit:** a light brown, slender pod, 16 × 2,6 cm (May to June).

This species could be confused with the introduced *A. lebbeck* and the differences are discussed under the latter species.

Albizia tanganyicensis E. G. Baker   Illust. 51
[*A. lebbeck* (L.) Benth. var. *australis* Burtt Davy; *A. rhodesica* Burtt Davy]
S.A. no: 157   Paperbark albizia. Papierbasvalsdoring
222   Rhod. no: 184   Paperbark albizia

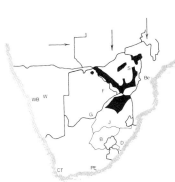 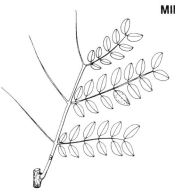

A graceful and attractive medium sized tree reaching 10 m in height, but occasionally, under ideal conditions, up to 20 m high; most frequently occurring on rocky formations, often forming groups. **Bark:** very characteristic, smooth with a thin red papery peel, revealing a beautiful pearly opalescent underbark. **Leaves:** with 2 to 6 pairs of pinnae, each bearing 5 to 13 pairs of leaflets; leaflets oblong, 1,2 to 4 × 0,7 to 1,2 cm, light green; apex tapering; base asymmetric with 1 side deeply bellied; margin entire; petiolules and petiole present, with a conspicuous gland near the base of the petiole. **Flowers:** forming half-spherical, fluffy heads; stamens creamy-white up to 3 cm long (August to October). **Fruit:** a long, flat, dark brown pod, up to 30 cm in length (the following September to December).

The beautiful brownish-red peeling bark, revealing the pearly creamy-grey underbark, separates this species from all other *Albizia* species; however, the leaves can be confused with those of the introduced species *A. lebbeck* and the differences between these two species are discussed under the latter. The wood is white, soft, light and the sawdust from it irritates the nose and throat; it has little timber value. It can be propagated from seed or from truncheons and would make a most attractive garden tree, but it is probably susceptible to frost.

Albizia versicolor Welw. ex Oliver   Illust. 52
S.A. no: 158   Poison-pod albizia. Grootblaarvalsdoring
Rhod. no: 185   Poison-pod albizia

A medium to large tree, usually about 10 m high, with a rounded, or spreading crown, but it can reach 18 m; occurs in various types of open woodland over a wide range of altitudes. **Bark:** greyish-brown and rough; young branches are hairy. **Leaves:** with 1 to 3 pairs of pinnae, each bearing 3 to 5 pairs of leaflets which are large, oblong to ovate, up to 5,5 × 3 cm. The petiole, rachis and under surface of the leaflets are clothed with coarse, dense, rusty hairs; apex rounded or very shortly pointed; base broadly tapering; margin entire; petiolules and petiole short and thick. **Flowers:** in large, half-spherical, fluffy heads, the creamy-white stamens up to 3,5 cm in length (October to November, with the young leaves). **Fruit:** a large reddish-brown to brown pod, up to 27 × 6,5 cm (September to November the following year, or later).

The seeds and, to a lesser extent, the pods of this tree have been proved to be toxic to cattle and sheep. Acute cases of poisoning frequently follow the storms and high winds that blow the young pods down from the trees. At this stage they are crimson in colour – an indication that they and the seeds are at their most poisonous and though their toxicity is reduced by about 50% as they dry and age it is never entirely lost. Death from *A. versicolor* is rapid: the stricken animal staggers; there is a wild expression

223

in its eyes, probably as a result of its extremely laboured breathing, and it may collapse in violent convulsions. In most cases that have been investigated there were signs of a frenzied struggle preceding death for the ground was scored and scraped by hooves, head and horns. Often the afflicted animals were found near watering places, indicating that large quantities of water hasten the effect of the toxic agent, and generally death occurred within 48 hours of high winds. Fortunately, of course, not all beasts will eat the pods. The toxic agent has not yet been identified and there is no known antidote; the only preventative step that can be taken is to isolate or remove the trees, or graze the stock elsewhere during the critical August to November period when the pods and seeds are young and most toxic. In Botswana the root and bark make a suitable substitute for soap, and the wood, which resembles that of *Pterocarpus angolensis*, is used for furniture, drums and mortars.

Albizia zimmermannii Harms
S.A. no: —
Rhod. no: 186   Woodland long-podded albizia

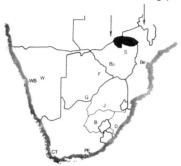
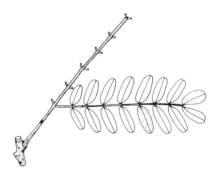

A medium sized tree reaching 15 m in height, with a flat and spreading crown; occurs in low altitude woodland. **Bark:** greyish-brown, smooth or finely fissured; young branches and the petiole and rachis of the leaves with rusty furry hairs becoming grey with age. **Leaves:** with 4 to 7 pairs of pinnae, each bearing 8 to 17 pairs of leaflets; leaflets oblong, up to 15 × 8 mm, resembling the leaflets of *A. schimperana*, the differences being discussed under the latter species. **Flowers:** rather small, forming half-spherical, fluffy heads, the white or pinkish stamens up to 1,3 cm in length (September to October). **Fruit:** a pod, up to 32 × 7 cm, crimson turning brown when mature with very conspicuous transverse raised veins; indehiscent (February to May).

2. ACACIA Wild.

Shrubs or trees with thorns or spines which may arise as modified stipules or as superficial prickles in all African species (unarmed species are all exotics, mainly introduced from Australia). **Leaves:** compound, bipinnate; leaflets often small to very small and commonly very numerous. **Flowers:** in globose heads, or in cylindric spikes. All floral parts in fours to fives; calyx cup-shaped; petals small, more or less joined, rarely free; stamens many, much longer than the sepals and petals and forming the most conspicuous part of the flower. **Fruit:** a pod, ovate, oblong or linear, straight or curved, thickly woody, leathery or thinly textured, dehiscent or indehiscent.
This is a taxonomically difficult genus.

Key to the tree species of *Acacia* (unarmed, exotic species are dealt with separately):
1 Spines straight or only slightly curved (modified stipules) 24
  Prickles strongly recurved (normal stipules usually present and non-spinescent, but fall off early)
  6
  Spines straight and hooked on the same plant (care should be taken to examine several branches)
  2
2 Some of the short recurved spines greatly swollen and inflated; flowers in white balls ....
  .... **A. luederitzii**
  Spines not inflated 3

3 Pods tightly spirally twisted and contorted; flowers in white balls .... **A. tortilis**
  Pods straight or almost straight 4
4 Pods without hairs, short, up to a maximum size of 8 × 1 cm, flat, mahogany-red. Not extending
  further south than South West Africa .... **A. reficiens**
  Pods with hairs, maximum length 13 to 15 cm, and almost always more than 1 cm wide. More
  widespread than the preceding species 5
5 Pods with conspicuous yellowish-grey woolly hairs, straight, woody, thick, like a flattened
  sausage, 4 to 15 × 1,4 to 4 cm, standing upright in a characteristic manner (but hanging down
  in 1 subspecies) .... **A. hebeclada**
  Pods grey-brown to purplish-brown with velvety hairs which may be sparse, straight, thickly
  leathery, not woody, flat, not thick, up to 13 × 2 cm, with a marked ridge round the edge
  .... **A. luederitzii**
6 Recurved prickles scattered along the stems; often climbers or shrubs, occasionally small trees
  7
  Recurved prickles in pairs, or in groups of 3, at or just below the nodes 11
7 Pinnae 1 to 9 pairs; leaflets large, up to 1,8 × 1 cm, and only 4 to 17 pairs 8
  Pinnae seldom less than 10 to 25 pairs; leaflets small and numerous to very numerous with 15 to 62
  pairs 9
8 Not extending further south than the western and northern areas of Rhodesia and adjacent areas in
  Moçambique; flowers in white spikes .... **A. eriocarpa**
  Only in Natal and the extreme south of Moçambique; flowers in white balls ....
  .... **A. kraussiana**
9 Young pods brilliant scarlet (April to July), mature pods brown, slender, up to 20 × 2,4 cm;
  flowers in creamy-white spikes; widespread .... **A. ataxacantha**
  Young pods not brilliant scarlet; flowers in white balls 10
10 Pods leathery and comparatively narrow, up to 19 × 3 cm, with conspicuous, large, smooth, oval
   domes over the seeds, almost like the rungs of a ladder along the pod, without hairs, reluctantly
   dehiscent or indehiscent; leaves clear green, without hairs; flowers in white balls (December to
   February); widespread .... **A. schweinfurthii**
   Pods leathery, narrowly oblong, up to 15 × 2,8 cm, with fine but clearly defined transverse
   veining, but without the distinctive domes of the preceding species, often finely velvety with
   many minute reddish glands; young stems and leaves yellowish-green and finely velvety, at
   least on the under surface; from Transkei, through Natal, Swaziland, just into the eastern
   Transvaal and into the extreme south of Moçambique only .... **A. brevispica**
   Pods stiffly papery, oblong, comparatively broad, up to 15 × 4 cm, without hairs, dotted with
   minute brown glands; leaves green; extreme north-east of Rhodesia and adjacent Moçambique,
   with an outlying population in central Moçambique .... **A. adenocalyx**
11 Prickles in groups of 3, the centre 1 hooked downwards, the outer 2 curved upwards .. **A. senegal**
   Prickles in pairs 12
12 Trunk with conspicuous knobby thorns, or trunk and branches with prickles 13
   Trunk without knobby thorns or prickles 16
13 Trunk with conspicuous knobby thorns on woody bosses 14
   Trunk and branches with prickles 15
14 Pinnae usually in 1 to 3 (occasionally 4) pairs, each with 1 to 2 pairs of leaflets only, large, often
   almost circular, 0,7 to 2,2 cm wide; remnant of the calyx at the base of the pod without hairs
   .... **A. nigrescens**
   Pinnae usually in more than 4 pairs (3 to 13 pairs), each with 4 or more pairs of leaflets, 0,3 to
   13 mm wide (i.e. more numerous and considerably more slender than the previous species);
   remains of the calyx at the base of the pod more or less velvety .... **A. burkei**
15 Bark pale, whitish, peeling in thick corky flakes and loose strips; pinnae in 13 to 40 pairs, each
   with 26 to 66 pairs of leaflets, 2 to 5 × 0,4 to 0,75 mm; flowers in white spikes, with pale green
   calyces .... **A. polyacantha**
   Bark brown, rough, corky, longitudinally furrowed; pinnae in 9 to 14 pairs, each with 13 to 40
   pairs of leaflets, 4 to 11 × 1 to 3 mm; flowers in slender creamy-yellow to yellow spikes with
   distinctive maroon to purple calyces .... **A. galpinii**
16 Leaflets distinctly asymmetric 17
   Leaflets symmetric or nearly so 18

225

17 Leaflets in 5 to 23 pairs, 3 to 17 × 1 to 7 mm; flowers in creamy-white spikes; occurring in a variety of types of woodland and wooded grassland; widely distributed .... **A. goetzei**
   Leaflets in about 10 pairs, each leaflet about 8 mm long; flowers in cream to yellow spikes; occurring in hot, arid, rocky and stony places; occurring in South West Africa only......... .... **A. montis-usti**
18 Leaflets usually in less than 10 pairs, each leaflet more than 2 mm wide 19
   Leaflets usually in more than 10 pairs, each leaflet less than 2 mm wide 21
19 Bushy to medium sized trees with distinctive long, whip-like branches, often upstanding, sometimes drooping; leaves in clusters, or fascicles, between the prickles, each leaf with only 1 pair of pinnae, each pinna with 6 to 8 pairs of leaflets; flowers in cream to pale yellow spikes (August to October); pods small, up to 6 × 1,8 cm, pale straw-coloured, South West Africa only .... **A. robynsiana**
   Without long, whip-like branches, pods up to more than 6 cm long 20
20 A southerly species; only in the extreme south-eastern Transvaal, Swaziland, south-western Moçambique and extreme south-east of Rhodesia; flowers in white spikes (December); pods usually 8 to 11 × 2 cm, grey-brown to reddish-brown ....
   .... **A. welwitschii** (subsp. *delagoensis)*
   A northerly species; South West Africa, Botswana, the northern areas of South Africa, fringing into Rhodesia in the extreme south, west and north, and only just south of the Zambezi River in Moçambique; flowers in white balls (September to November); pods up to 9 × 2,5 cm, pale straw-coloured, almost papery .... **A. mellifera**
21 Bark dark-coloured 22
   Bark light-coloured 23
22 A species of dry areas; South West Africa, northern Cape, northern Orange Free State and Transvaal, just into Botswana and Rhodesia; numerous prickles; 8 to 20 pairs of pinnae, petiole 0,3 to 1,3 cm long, lateral veins not visible on the under surface of leaflets; flowers in white spikes .... **A. hereroensis**
   A species of moist areas; southern Cape, through the eastern Cape, Natal, Swaziland, Transvaal, just entering Botswana and the extreme south of Moçambique; 1 of the least thorny species; not usually more than 8 pairs of pinnae (up to 38 have been recorded); petiole 1,3 to 3,5 cm long; lateral veins fairly prominent on the under surface of leaflets; flowers in creamy-white spikes .... **A. caffra**
23 Petiole 1,3 to 2,5 cm long; a very small petiolar gland may be present; glands may also be present on the leaf rachis between the pinnae .... **A. erubescens**
   Petiole 0,5 to 1,3 cm long; petiolar gland up to 2 mm long; glands on the leaf rachis absent .... **A. fleckii**
24 Leaflets with apparently finely crenulate, or scalloped, margins 25
   Margins of leaflets not crenulate or apparently so 26
25 Leaflets up to 6,5 × 2 mm with conspicuous glands making the margins appear finely crenulate, or scalloped; pods and young branches usually sticky, pods constricted between the seeds and sickle-shaped, often curled so far as to form a ring; leaves, branches and pods not grey velvety .... **A. borleae**
   Scalloped or crenulate appearance caused by the minute leaflets themselves – the pinnae could be mistaken initially for leaflets; leaflets 0,6 × 0,5 mm; leaflets not glandular; leaves, petioles, young branches and pods all densely grey velvety; pods long, slender, curved to sickle-shaped, slightly constricted, not sticky .... **A. haematoxylon**
26 Pods with a conspicuous, high-domed shield over each seed 27
   Pods without a high-domed shield over the seeds, although the position of the seeds may be seen, usually, by swellings 28
27 Pods long and slender, fleshy when young, longer than 8 cm (8 to 17 × 1 to 1,5 cm), regularly constricted between the seeds and their shields, forming a very distinctive 'string of beads' effect; seed shields warty; pods dark grey drying black; flowers in yellow balls. Widespread .... **A. nilotica**
   Pods small, oblong, up to 9 × 2 cm, the seed shield forming conspicuous nipples along the centre of the flat pods; pods partially constricted between the seeds and sometimes approaching the 'string of beads' effect, reddish-brown or grey in colour; flowers cream or white when open and pinkish-red in bud. Confined to northern South West Africa, the north and east of Botswana,

226

the extreme west and north of Rhodesia and barely crossing the Zambezi River in Moçambique
.... **A. kirkii**

28 Pods thick and woody 29
    Pods thinly textured, thinly woody or even papery 31

29 Leaflets small and numerous, pinnae 6 to 23 pairs, leaflets 14 to 45 pairs, usually about 4 to 5 ×
    1 mm; pods tardily dehiscent, straight or almost so, creamy-brown, velvety when young, but
    losing much or all of this when mature; flowers in creamy-white balls ...... **A. sieberana**
    Leaflets fewer and larger, 6 to 23 pairs, or 8 to 15 pairs 30

30 Pinnae usually in 3 to 10 pairs, seldom less than 5, leaflets in 6 to 23 pairs, 3,5 to 9 × 0,7 to 3 mm;
    pods indehiscent, bright orange to reddish-brown, not velvety, rather slender, up to 25 × 5 cm,
    very characteristically contorted, from sickle-shaped to coiled, twisted and loosely tangled;
    spines comparatively short, rarely more than 2 cm long, not inflated, flowers in creamy-white
    spikes .... **A. albida**
    Pinnae 2 to 5 pairs, leaflets 8 to 15 pairs, up to 13 × 4 mm in size; pods indehiscent, short and
    broad, up to 11 × 4,7 cm, slightly curved or sickle-shaped, finely but densely velvety,
    creamy-grey or pale grey; spines long and vicious up to 6 cm in length, frequently inflated at the
    base; flowers in bright yellow balls .... **A. erioloba**

31 Bark very distinctive greenish-yellow to yellow, smooth, becoming somewhat powdery and
    minutely flaky; flowers in yellow balls; pods indehiscent, pale brown, thin ....
    .... **A. xanthophloea**
    Bark not yellow-green or yellow 32

32 Branches red, rusty-red or even orange 33
    Branches not red or orange; branchlets may be reddish-brown 35

33 Young branchlets densely hairy, at first golden and then grey, the hairs later peeling off to reveal
    the powdery, rusty-red bark beneath; flowers in white balls .... **A. rehmanniana**
    Young branchlets not densely golden hairy at first 34

34 Pinnae usually 1 pair only (occasionally 2); leaflets only 3 to 5 pairs; South West Africa,
    Botswana, northern and eastern Transvaal and the extreme south of Rhodesia only..........
    .... **A. nebrownii**
    Pinnae 2 to 7 pairs; leaflets 8 to 20 pairs; very widespread .... **A. karroo**

35 Pods dotted with sticky glands 36
    Pods without sticky glands 38

36 Young branches densely covered with long grey hairs over the reddish-brown bark; flowers in
    yellow balls .... **A. permixta**
    Young branches not densely covered with long grey hairs 37

37 Pinnae frequently 1 pair only (occasionally 2, very seldom 3 pairs), leaflets 3 to 5 pairs, usually
    about 10 × 5 mm, widely spaced; flowers in yellow balls; pods small, about 4 × 1 cm, broadly
    sickle-shaped, flat, conspicuously dotted with dark glands .... **A. swazica**
    Pinnae usually 3 to 6 pairs (occasionally 1 pair only), leaflets usually 5 to 8 pairs (occasionally 3 or
    10 pairs), most often 5 × 2 mm in size, closely ranked and overlapping; flowers in yellow balls;
    pods small, about 6 × 1 cm, strongly sickle-shaped, more rounded than the previous species
    and conspicuously dotted with glutinous glands .... **A. exuvialis**

38 Invariably found in high altitude woodland; young trees with papery peeling bark in wads like
    pages in a book, bark of mature trees dark brown to almost black, rough; flowers in white balls
    .... **A. abyssinica**
    Not found in high altitude woodland 39

39 Branchlets finely velvety 40
    Branchlets without hairs 41

40 Branchlets, leaves and pods covered with grey, velvety hairs; flowers in white balls; pods narrow,
    up to 16 × 1,1 cm, sickle-shaped .... **A. gerrardii**
    Pods without hairs; branchlets only covered with a fine, inconspicuous, brownish down; flowers
    in white or pinkish balls; pods long and very slender, up to 18 × 0,8 cm, only slightly curved,
    deep red-brown in colour .... **A. arenaria**

41 Spines few and inconspicuous (probably the least spiny of the *Acacia* species); leaflets rather
    large, up to 11 × 4 mm, widely spaced, shiny green; flowers in yellow balls; not occurring
    further south than the central and northern areas of Rhodesia and adjacent areas in Moçambique
    .... **A. amythethophylla** **227**
    Spines many and conspicuous; not confined to the above areas 42

MIMOSOIDEAE

42 Leaves with 12 to 20 pairs of pinnae, leaflets 25 to 44 pairs; pods straight or only slightly curved; bark corky; flowers in yellow balls .... **A. davyi**
    Leaves with 2 to 9 pairs of pinnae (occasionally up to 13 pairs), leaflets 6 to 15 pairs; bark not corky 43
43 Pods straight, slightly curved or sickle-shaped, up to 19 × 3 cm; spines usually short, up to 7 mm, but may be larger; flowers in white balls .... **A. robusta**
    Pods sickle-shaped, small, up to 11 × 1 cm; spines characteristically large, up to 9 cm long, and fused together at the base, slightly inflated; flowers in white balls ...... **A. grandicornuta**

Naturalised species of *Acacia*

Over the years many species of *Acacia* have been introduced into southern Africa, frequently for commercial reasons, and among some of the most important are the wattles, once valuable for their bark extract used in tanning. Practically all these exotics can be separated from the indigenous species by their lack of thorns and spines; many have also almost entirely lost the fine, feathery leaves whose function has been taken over by green, flattened structures called *phyllodes* which resemble elliptic simple leaves. A number of the introduced species have now escaped and the trees have become naturalised, several of them now seriously endangering the natural vegetation over vast areas of the country. *Acacia melanoxylon* R. Br., the blackwood, and *A. cyclops* A. Cunn. ex G. Don, the *rooikrans*, are examples of alien *Acacias* which have invaded thousands of square kilometres in South Africa. Other exotic species mentioned in the text are *A. saligna* (Labill.) Wendl., *A. dealbata* Link, *A. decurrens* (Wendl.) Willd., *A. longifolia* (Andr.) Willd., and *A. mearnsii* De Wild.

Acacia abyssinica Hochst. ex Benth.
S.A. no: —
Rhod. no: 187   Inyanga flat-top

A grove of Acacia abyssinica, *the Inyanga flat-top.*

A large, conspicuously flat-topped tree up to 15 m in height; occurring frequently in groups in high altitude woodland and in forested mountain gullies. **Bark:** brown to nearly black and rough; young trees have very distinctive papery bark peeling off in wads, like the pages in a book; branchlets covered with grey to yellowish hairs. Stipules spinescent; the spines are very variable, short or reaching 7,2 cm in length, straight and white or ashen in colour. **Leaves:** with 15 to 51 pairs of pinnae, each bearing many very small leaflets; leaflets up to 4 × 0,75 mm; glands are present on the petiole but not on the rachis. **Flowers:** forming white balls (October to November, occasionally later). **Fruit:** a leathery pod, fairly small, 5 to 13 × 1,2 to 2,1 cm, long, narrow, straight, grey or brown (February to June).

All the material from east and southern Africa belongs to the subspecies *calophylla* Brenan; the typical subspecies is confined to Ethiopia. *A. abyssinica* is very similar to *A. rehmanniana* Schinz, but in *A. abyssinica* the young branches and branchlets do not flake as they do in *A. rehmanniana*, which is also a lower altitude species.

Acacia adenocalyx Brenan & Exell
S.A. no: —
Rhod. no: 188   Small-leaved acacia

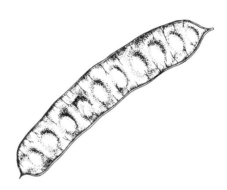

A climber, shrub or small tree up to 5 m in height; occurring in low altitude bush. **Bark:** blackish to brown; the young branches have many small brown glands. Stipules small and not spinescent; prickles are deflexed and scattered along the branches. **Leaves:** with 10 to 23 pairs of pinnae, each bearing very numerous small leaflets; leaflets linear-oblong, about 2 × 0,3 to 0,75 mm. **Flowers:** in white balls; the calyx lobes have many minute glands, but these can be seen only with a 20× lens (October). **Fruit:** a pod, stiffly papery, oblong, 6 to 15 × 1,6 to 4 cm, dotted with many minute brown glands (October to April).

Acacia albida Delile
S.A. no: 159   Ana tree. Anaboom
Rhod. no: 189   Apple-ring thorn-tree

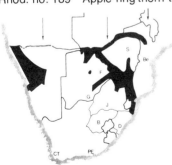

This is one of the largest species of *Acacia*, reaching 30 m in height, with spreading branches and a rounded crown; a tree of the lowveld, very widely distributed throughout Africa, occurring in woodland, in wooded grassland and in riverine fringe forest. **Bark:** rough and dark brown, or smooth and greenish-grey; the young branches are white to ashen and characteristically zigzag in shape. Stipules spinescent, straight, not large, about 2 cm long, creamy-coloured with brown tips. **Leaves:** **229**

with 3 to 10 pairs of pinnae, each bearing 6 to 23 pairs of leaflets; leaflets are quite large 3,5 to 9 × 0,7 to 3 mm, grey-green in colour. **Flowers:** in slender, creamy-white spikes 4 to 14 cm long (May to September). **Fruit:** an unusual pod, bright orange to reddish-brown in colour, thick, indehiscent, characteristically and conspicuously curled and twisted, large, up to 25 × 5 cm (September to October).

An outstanding group of these trees can be seen 15 km north-west of Potgietersrust. This group has been declared a national monument and is known as Livingstone's trees, although it is doubtful whether Dr Livingstone ever saw them. Another historic tree of this species near Pietersburg is said to have been planted by Louis Trichardt when he visited that area. The fruits are eaten eagerly by both stock and game and in South West Africa are regarded as valuable fodder for horses and cattle. The seed germinates readily if soaked in hot water and growth thereafter has been found to be fast if given favourable conditions; the trees are probably tender to frost. This is a protected plant in South Africa.

Acacia amythethophylla Steud. ex A. Rich.
[*A. macrothyrsa* Harms. *A. buchananii* Harms]
S.A. no: —
Rhod. no: 211   Large-leaved acacia

A small to medium sized tree, frequently 5 to 6 m in height, but can reach 15 m; occurring in lower to medium altitude deciduous woodland and wooded grassland. **Bark:** brown or grey, rough and fissured. Stipules spinescent, the spines being short, straight, dark, and although reaching 10 mm, they are not conspicuous, giving the tree a general appearance of being unarmed. **Leaves:** usually with 9 to 16 pairs of pinnae, each bearing 12 to 70 pairs of leaflets; leaflets comparatively large, 4 to 11 × 1 to 4 mm, rather dark green and glossy above, with a large gland at the base of the petiole. **Flowers:** in deep orange-yellow balls (January to March). **Fruit:** an oblong pod, up to 20 × 2,5 cm, but usually much shorter than this, straight, without hairs and glossy, brown to purplish-black, dehiscent (May to July).

The large leaflets and the robust panicles of deep yellow flowers make this species easy to identify, though a quick field impression can easily lead to confusion with *Peltophorum africanum* Sonder. In *Acacia amythethophylla*, however, the flowers tend to appear on the top of the tree, and this fact and the distinctive large yellow petals of *Peltophorum africanum* immediately separate the two.

Acacia arenaria Schinz
S.A. no: 186   Sand acacia. Sanddoring
Rhod. no: 190   Sand acacia

A shrub or small tree up to 9 m in height, with a short bole and branches arising from near the ground; occurring in hot dry woodland and scrub. **Bark:** grey to dark grey, flecked and banded to rough; branchlets zigzag and are covered with inconspicuous, brownish hairs. Stipules spinescent; spines slender and straight, 3,5 to 6 cm long, white in colour. **Leaves:** with 15 to 35 pairs of pinnae, each bearing 15 to 31 pairs of closely ranked leaflets, very small, 2 to 4 × 0,5 to 1 mm, greyish-green and finely velvety; glands occur between the lowest and the uppermost pairs of pinnae but no glands are present on the leaflets themselves. **Flowers:** in white or pinkish balls (December to April). **Fruit:** a long and conspicuously slender pod, up to 18 × 0,8 cm, curved to sickle-shaped, without hairs, deep red-brown, dehiscent (February to May).

230

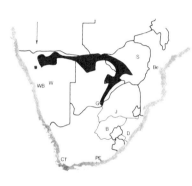

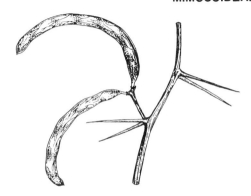

Acacia ataxacantha DC.   Illust. 53
S.A. no: 160   Flame acacia Vlamdoring
Rhod. no: 191   Flame acacia

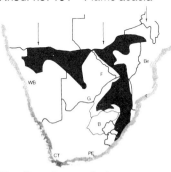

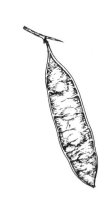

Usually a thorny climber or a straggling shrub, but it can become a small tree up to 10 m high; occurring among sand dunes, in open bush, in wooded grassland and on rocky hillsides. Stipules are not spinescent, being large, ovate or triangular and more or less shield-like, falling early; sharp hooked prickles are scattered all along the younger stems and on the leaves. **Leaves:** with 10 to 25 pairs of pinnae, each bearing 14 to 62 pairs of leaflets; leaflets small, 2 to 5 × 0,5 to 1,5 mm. **Flowers:** in creamy-white spikes up to 10 cm long (January to February). **Fruit:** the young pods (April to July) are brilliantly coloured, forming flaming red patches in the bush; the mature pods are brown, slender, 20 × 2,4 cm, straight, tapering at both ends, dehiscent (June to October).

Acacia borleae Burtt Davy
S.A. no: 160,1   Sticky acacia. Kleefdoring
Rhod. no: 192   Sticky acacia

A shrub or small, slender tree up to 5 m in height, branching from near the base; occurring in dry types of woodland, where it often forms thickets. The young branches have numerous pale to reddish, pustular glands which are sometimes sticky. Stipules spinescent; the spines white, slender, up to 5 cm long, straight, but occasionally slightly curved. **Leaves:** with 2 to 10 pairs of pinnae, each bearing 5 to 15 pairs of leaflets; leaflets 1,5 to 6,5 × 1 to 2 mm, the margins made to appear finely scalloped, or

231

crenulate, by many minute fringing glands – this is a very distinctive character. **Flowers:** in small yellow balls (November to March). **Fruit:** small, slender pods, up to 7 × 1 cm, made sticky by many glands over the surface, curved, often so far as to form a ring, markedly constricted between the seeds giving the appearance of a flattened string of beads; the surface of the mature pods is rough to the touch due to fine rough hairs (May to June).

Acacia brevispica Harms
[*A. pennata* sensu auct., pro parte, non (L.) Willd.]
S.A. no: 160,2   Prickly acacia. Dorinkiedoring
Rhod. no: —

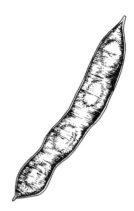

A shrub or small tree 1 to 8 m in height, often scrambling; occurring in dry types of bush and wooded grassland. Young stems yellowish-green. Hooked or horizontal prickles, arising from longitudinal pale ridges, are scattered along the branchlets. **Leaves:** with 7 to 18 pairs of pinnae, each bearing very numerous small leaflets; leaflets usually less than 1 mm wide, yellowish or olive-green, the lower surface usually finely silky. **Flowers:** in white balls (October). **Fruit:** leathery pods, 6 to 15 × 2 to 2,8 cm, narrowly oblong, more or less densely velvety with many small reddish glands and conspicuous but fine transverse veining, readily dehiscent (January to March).

All the material from southern Africa is placed in subsp. *dregeana* (Benth.) Brenan; the typical subspecies occurs in Tanzania. *A. brevispica* differs from *A. schweinfurthii* Brenan & Exell, in its olive-green leaves, the velvety under surface of the leaflets, the greyish-brown branchlets and the very readily dehiscent pods.

Acacia burkei Benth.
S.A. no: 161   Black monkey-thorn. Swartapiesdoring
Rhod. no: 193   Black monkey-thorn

One of the larger species of *Acacia*, reaching 30 m in height with a spreading or rounded crown; occurring in wooded grassland and bush. **Bark:** very variable, from almost smooth, scaly, greyish-yellow, to brownish-black and rough, with knobby thorns on the main trunk; young branchlets are densely velvety. Stipules not spinescent; the prickles occur in pairs just below the nodes, are strongly hooked downwards and are brown to blackish in colour. **Leaves:** with 3 to 13 pairs of pinnae, each bearing 4 to 19 pairs of leaflets, very variable in size, 4 to 20 × 0,3 to 13 mm. **Flowers:** in slender, white spikes; calyx lobes velvety (October to January). **Fruit:** a dark brown pod, up to 16 × 2,5 cm,

232

conspicuously veined, thinly textured, straight, irregularly constricted along its length, with the remains of the calyx at the base with velvety hairs, dehiscent (December to May).

There appear to be two forms of this species, certainly in Natal: a small-leaved form which is characteristically flat-topped and tends to favour sandier soils, and a large-leaved form which more frequently has a rounded crown and tends to favour stony and loamy soils; at the two extremes these criteria apply reasonably well, but there is considerable overlap. *A. burkei* can, in its larger leaved form, fairly closely resemble *A. nigrescens* but the leaves of the former are generally narrower and, even in their largest form, are still smaller than those of *A. nigrescens;* although the bark can develop knobby thorns these are never as large, nor as conspicuous, as those of *A. nigrescens. A. burkei* also resembles *A. welwitschii,* and the differences are discussed under the latter species.

Acacia caffra (Thunb.) Willd.   Illust. 54
S.A. no: 162   Common hook-thorn. Gewone haakdoring
Rhod. no: —

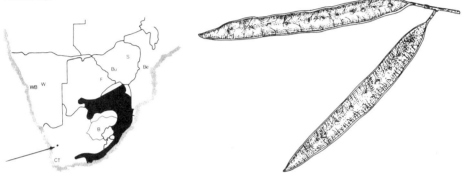

Sometimes shrubby, but usually a tree up to 12 m in height, often with a twisted trunk and a rather thin spreading crown; occurring in woodland and wooded grassland, frequently along rivers and streams. **Bark:** dark brown to black and rough, sometimes fissured and horizontally cracked forming squares. Stipules not spinescent; small, blackish, hooked or slightly hooked prickles occur in pairs just below the nodes. **Leaves:** with more than 8 pairs of pinnae, each bearing up to 57 pairs of leaflets; leaflets up to 7 × 1,5 mm, lateral veins rather prominent on the under surface; the rachis is sometimes prickly. **Flowers:** in creamy-white spikes turning yellowish with age, produced in clusters or fascicles, in the axils of the leaves (September to November). **Fruit:** a light brown to dark brown pod, up to 17 × 1,5 cm, straight or slightly curved, finely velvety to the touch (December to March).

Various mistaken identifications in the past have suggested an extended range to the north, but *A. caffra* does not occur further than indicated on the distribution map. This species resembles *A. hereroensis* but in the latter species the thorns are more developed and the flower spikes are produced singly and not in clusters. It has also been confused with *A. ataxacantha,* but *A. caffra* is never a climber; its spines are much smaller and are in pairs and not scattered along the stems. This tree would do well in a garden: it is strongly resistant to both frost and drought, is rapid-growing and very attractive. The wood is heavy, close-grained, with a light coloured sapwood and nearly black heartwood. It is not used commercially, but makes good fencing poles and provides excellent firewood. The leaves and pods are grazed by stock but have been suspected of causing poisoning. The Zulus take an infusion of the bark as an emetic for 'blood cleansing' and children are sometimes made to chew the leaves to relieve abdominal troubles. This is one of the least thorny of the *Acacia* species.

*Acacia cyclops A. Cunn.

This, the *rooikrans,* is a large shrub or small tree 3 to 5 m in height, which was also introduced from Australia and has now escaped and invaded vast areas of coastal land. From Cape Town northwards to Lamberts Bay and eastwards to Port Elizabeth it is very widespread on sandy soil, frequently forming almost pure dune scrub. *A. cyclops* has developed phyllodes which almost completely replace the compound leaves normal in African species of *Acacia.* The untidy coiled clusters of pods are characteristic.

233

MIMOSOIDEAE

Acacia davyi N. E. Brown
S.A. no: 163,1   Corky-bark acacia. Kurkdoring
Rhod. no: —

A shrub or small straggling tree, 2 to 3 m in height; occurring in bushveld and wooded grassland. **Bark:** corky, creamy to light brown. Stipules spinescent, the spines being paired, straight or slightly curved, 2 to 5 cm long. **Leaves:** with 12 to 20 pairs of pinnae (usually about 18), each bearing 25 to 44 pairs of leaflets; leaflets 5 × 1 mm, bright green, closely ranked. **Flowers:** in bright yellow balls (November to March). **Fruit:** a long narrow pod, in clusters, straight or slightly curved, up to 10 cm long, very thinly woody with thickened margins and slightly constricted between the seeds (February to August).

*Acacia dealbata Link

The silver wattle, introduced from Australia, has escaped and become naturalised in parts of Natal and areas in the east of Rhodesia (Rhod. no: 195).

*Acacia decurrens (Wendl.) Willd.

This tree was also introduced from Australia and is now naturalised in parts of Natal and areas in the east of Rhodesia (Rhod. no: 196).

Acacia eriocarpa Brenan
S.A. no: —
Rhod. no: 197   Woolly-podded acacia

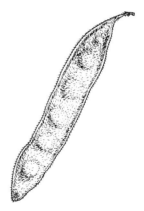

A small tree up to 6 m in height, sometimes many-stemmed from the ground and shrubby; occurring in low altitude woodland and thicket. Stipules not spinescent, broadly ovate; prickles hooked, rather slender, up to 5 mm long, scattered along the branches. **Leaves:** with 4 to 9 pairs of pinnae, each bearing 4 to 15 pairs of leaflets; leaflets closely ranked, oblong-elliptic, 7 to 18 × 3 to 9 mm. **Flowers:** in rather short, stiff, creamy-white spikes, up to 5 cm long (December to February). **Fruit:** a thinly textured pod, up to 14 × 2,4 cm, straight, with dense golden-brown matted hairs; the hairy pods are very unusual among species which have flowers in spikes (January to May).

Acacia erioloba E. Meyer   Illust. 55
[*A. giraffae* auct.plurim. non Willd.]
S.A. no: 168   Camel thorn. Kameeldoring
Rhod. no: 198   Camel thorn

Over this plant's great range, its habit varies from a small, very spiny shrub barely 2 m high, to a tree up to 16 m in height, with a wide, spreading crown. Occurring in dry woodland and arid stony or sandy areas, this is one of the major tree species of the desert regions. **Bark:** grey to blackish-brown, deeply furrowed; young branchlets shiny, reddish-brown. Stipules spinescent, the spines strongly developed, almost straight, up to 6 cm in length, often with swollen, inflated bases, whitish or brown. **Leaves:** with 2 to 5 pairs of pinnae, each bearing 8 to 15 pairs of leaflets; leaflets 4 to 13 × 1 to 4 mm; there are no glands on the petiole, but there is a small gland at the junction of each pair of pinnae, but these glands may be difficult to see. **Flowers:** in bright golden-yellow balls (July to September). **Fruit:** a much thickened, comparatively short and squat pod, up to 11 × 4,7 cm, straight or slightly curved, densely covered with creamy-grey to grey velvety hairs, indehiscent (December to March).

The thorns on these trees are among the most cruel of any produced by the *Acacia* species. Robert Moffat in his book *Missionary Labours* told the story of a lion which, in attempting to bring down a giraffe, missed its hold and fell back into the centre of a dense mass of these thorns, where it was impaled and thus doomed to a slow death. Some fine specimens of these trees can be seen along the streets of Potgietersrust and, between Potgietersrust and Nylstroom, there are two well known to travellers on the great north road. These old trees are protected as a National Monument and bear a plaque which states 'In memory of 33 Voortrekkers who were treacherously murdered by Makapan in 1854'. This party of men, women and children under the leadership of Hermanus Potgieter who was himself flayed alive while the children, it is believed, were dashed to death against the trunks of the two camel thorn trees.

The pods form an excellent fodder for stock: farmers say that animals pick them up as fast as they fall to the ground and that there is a noticeable increase in the milk-yield of cows that have eaten them. At the same time, there have been reports that at certain seasons of the year these pods are poisonous. The wood is dark red-brown and very strong; it is resistant to borers and termites and in the past has been used for mine props and wagon-building; it also makes good firewood. Camel thorns produce a good quality gum which is eaten by local peoples and also by a variety of animals. In Botswana the bark is first burnt, then ground to produce a remedy for headaches, while discharging and infected ears are treated with a powder from the dried and crushed pods. The immense value of the shade which these trees provide in desert areas cannot be over-estimated; they are slow-growing and because they develop very long tap-roots they are difficult to transplant. The widely-used common name, camel thorn, is a mistranslation from the Afrikaans *kameeldoring,* meaning 'giraffe thorn', and it was this that gave the tree the specific name previously applied to it.

It is a protected plant in South Africa.

Acacia erubescens Welw. ex Oliver
[*A. dulcis* Marloth & Engl.]
S.A. no: 164   Blue thorn. Blouhaak
Rhod. no: 199   Blue thorn

A small to medium sized tree occasionally reaching 10 m, sometimes shrubby; occurring in dry woodland and thornveld, often fringing pans and along stream banks. **Bark:** scaly or papery, peeling,

235

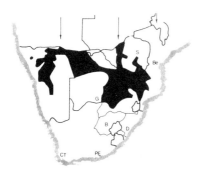

greyish-yellow or smoky-grey. Stipules not spinescent; hooked prickles up to 6 mm long, quite stout and very sharp, whitish or bluish in colour, occurring in pairs just below the nodes. **Leaves:** with 3 to 7 pairs of pinnae (usually 6), each bearing 10 to 20 pairs of leaflets (usually about 14); leaflets small, 3 to 18 × 1 to 2 mm, grey-green to blue-green; small glands may be present on the petiole and rachis. **Flowers:** in short, squat, white spikes up to 4,5 cm long, sometimes slightly tinged with pink (August to October). **Fruit:** a straight, light brown pod, up to 13 × 1,9 cm, leathery, dehiscent (September to January).

This species closely resembles *A. fleckii* Schinz, and can be separated on the following characters: in *A. erubescens* the leaf petiole measures 1,3 to 2,5 cm in length and may bear a very small gland, while the leaf rachis may also be glandular; in *A. fleckii,* the leaf petiole measures only 0,5 to 1 cm in length (never more than 1,3 cm), and bears a fairly conspicuous gland up to 2 mm long, while the leaf rachis bears no glands at all.

Acacia exuvialis Verdoorn

S.A. no: 164,1   Flaky acacia. Skilferdoring
Rhod. no: 200   Broom acacia

A densely branched and thickly spiny shrub, or a small tree reaching 4,5 m in height; occurring at low altitudes in mopane woodland, on stony hillsides often in gravelly soils. **Bark:** grey to dark grey, smooth, with a tendency to peel (the specific name refers to this); in the trees the stem branches and rebranches, producing a dense, 'broom-like' crown and the branches are often shiny glutinous in parts, having an oily appearance as a result. Stipules spinescent, the spines paired, white, straight, up to 7 cm in length, sometimes slightly inflated at the base. **Leaves:** with 1 to 6 pairs of pinnae, each bearing 3 to 6 pairs of leaflets (occasionally up to 10); leaflets oblong, 3 to 10 × 1,5 to 4,5 mm, apex rounded, often with a sharp tip; base square, asymmetric. **Flowers:** in yellow balls, on long slender stalks (October to February). **Fruit:** small, flat, glandular glutinous pods, up to 6 × 1 cm, strongly sickle-shaped, green becoming light brown or reddish-brown and conspicuously gland-dotted (February to May).

There appear to be two forms of this small tree: the typical form is a shrubby bush with peeling bark and alternate leaves which are conspicuously gland-dotted; there is a rather larger form which does not have peeling bark on the branches, and has leaves almost completely lacking glands, which arise in clusters on dwarf knobby side shoots between the spines. The latter form can be found in the Transvaal

236

outside the Kruger National Park. In Rhodesia it is seldom more than a small shrub and the peeling bark has not been observed in local specimens.

Acacia fleckii Schinz   Illust. 56
[*A. cinerea* Schinz]
S.A. no: 165   Blade thorn. Bladdoring
Rhod. no: 201   Blade thorn

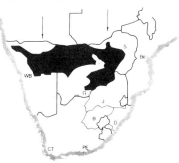

A shrub or small rounded tree up to 10 m in height; occurring on sandy soils often forming impenetrable thickets, frequently growing on sand dunes in South West Africa and Botswana. **Bark:** grey to cream and peeling in small flakes; young branches with dense grey velvety hairs, most of which are lost at maturity. Stipules not spinescent; sharply hooked prickles, strong and vicious, 5 mm or more in length, occur in pairs just below the nodes; the prickles are grey to brown or blackish in colour and broad-based. **Leaves:** with 6 to 20 pairs of crowded pinnae, each bearing 12 to 30 pairs of very small leaflets; leaflets densely ranked, greyish velvety to greyish-green, very small up to 5 × 1 mm, giving the tree an open and airy appearance; a fairly conspicuous gland, up to 2 mm long, is present on the petiole; no glands are present on the rachis. **Flowers:** in white spikes up to 6,5 cm long (November to March). **Fruit:** a straight, small pod, 6 to 12 × 1,3 to 2 cm, not thickened, pale brown or straw-coloured, without hairs, dehiscent (January to May).
This species closely resembles *A. erubescens* and the differences are discussed under the latter species.

Acacia galpinii Burtt Davy   Illust. 57
S.A. no: 166   Monkey thorn. Apiesdoring
Rhod. no: 202   Monkey thorn

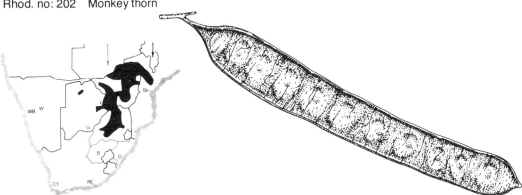

A fine, large tree up to 25 m in height; occurring in open wooded grassland often along river banks or near water. **Bark:** brown, rough, corky, longitudinally furrowed. Stipules not spinescent; stout, strong, hooked prickles, occasionally straightish, up to 10 mm in length, occurring in pairs just below the nodes, and may be found growing on the main trunk and branches as well as on the branchlets. **Leaves:** petiole and rachis often glandular; with 9 to 14 pairs of pinnae, each bearing 13 to 40 pairs of fine leaflets; leaflets oblong, without hairs, 4 to 11 × 1 to 3 mm. **Flowers:** in slender creamy-yellow

237

to yellow spikes, with red to purple calyces and petals; this last character is distinctive and unusual among species of *Acacia* (September to October). **Fruit:** a reddish to purplish-brown pod, up to 28 × 3,5 cm, straight, slightly thickened, without hairs, dehiscent (February to March).

The wood is hard, heavy and coarse-grained. It is said to make good furniture, but is difficult to work. The trees adapt well to cultivation and are reasonably fast-growing; seeds germinate readily if they are soaked in hot water. These trees are able to withstand a fair amount of frost.

Acacia gerrardii Benth.　Illust. 58
S.A. no: 167　Red thorn. Rooidoring
Rhod. no: 203　Grey-haired acacia

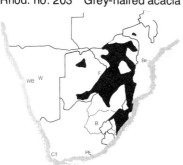
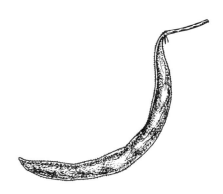

A shrub or small tree up to 8 m in height, usually with a somewhat sparse, narrow, open crown; occurring in woodland and wooded grassland. **Bark:** dark grey or reddish; it may be rough or rather smooth; the branchlets are covered with grey velvety hairs. Stipules spinescent, the spines usually being short, about 10 mm long, straight and very stout, but sometimes long, up to 5 to 6 cm; they may be slightly curved, and may have very thick almost inflated bases. **Leaves:** with 5 to 12 pairs of pinnae, each bearing 10 to 28 pairs of leaflets; leaflets 3 to 7,5 × 1 to 2 mm, margins finely hair-fringed. **Flowers:** in white balls (October to February). **Fruit:** a narrow pod, 7 to 16 × 0,6 to 1,1 cm, thin, sickle-shaped, finely grey hairy (December to May).

Only the typical variety, var. *gerrardii* occurs here.

Acacia goetzei Harms
[*A. mossambicensis* auct.]
S.A. no: —
Rhod. no: 204　Purple-pod acacia

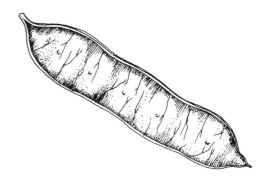

A medium to large tree, often about 15 m tall, occasionally reaching 20 m; occurring in various types of woodland and wooded grassland. **Bark:** brown or grey and rough. Stipules not spinescent; strong, downward hooked prickles on bosses, dark brown or black, occur in pairs just below the nodes. **Leaves:** with 3 to 10 pairs of pinnae, each bearing 5 to 23 pairs of leaflest; leaflets 3 to 17 × 1 to 7 mm, usually distinctly asymmetric at the base, with the apex tapering to rounded and often sharply tipped. **Flowers:** in creamy-white spikes, up to 12 cm long, rather stiff (September to November, with the leaves). **Fruit:** a straight pod, up to 18 × 3,5 cm, without hairs or nearly so, mahogany-red to purplish-brown with the surface conspicuously veined, dehiscent (December to July).

238

There are 2 subspecies involved in this area. The typical subspecies, subsp. *goetzei*, has leaflets all more than 3 mm wide, with usually only 5 to 11 pairs, and the rachis generally without prickles. The second subspecies, subsp. *microphylla* Brenan, has mature leaflets less than 3 mm wide and usually more numerous, 8 to 23 pairs, and the rachis frequently prickly. The distributions of the two subspecies overlap, but subsp. *microphylla* is less common. In extreme forms, with fewer and unusually large leaflets, this can resemble *A. nigrescens*, but typical *A. goetzei* usually has 8 to 10 pairs of leaflets which are closely ranked and measure 1,2 × 0,4 cm, so being more numerous and considerably smaller than *A. nigrescens*. *A. goetzii* also resembles *A. welwitschii*, and the differences are discussed under the latter species.

Acacia grandicornuta Gerstner
S.A. no: 168,1   Horned thorn. Horingdoring
Rhod. no: 205   Horned thorn

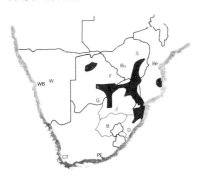

A small to medium sized, round-topped tree up to 10 m in height; occurs in low altitude dry thornveld and mopane woodland. **Bark:** black becoming deeply vertically fissured with age; young branches grey to yellowish-brown and smooth. Stipules spinescent, the spines up to 9 cm long, straight, stout to very stout, white or grey and fused across their bases. **Leaves:** arising from the hard cushion formed between the 2 spines; with 1 to 4 pairs of pinnae, each bearing 5 to 15 pairs of leaflets; leaflets 5 to 10 × 1,5 to 4 mm, smooth or finely velvety. **Flowers:** in white balls (December to January). **Fruit:** a thinly woody pod, up to 11 × 1 cm, without hairs, sickle-shaped, dehiscent (April).
This species is very similar to *A. robusta* Burch., but *A. robusta* tends to grow along river banks and around pans, while *A. grandicornuta* is to be found in drier localities; furthermore, *A. grandicornuta* has fewer pairs of pinnae, smaller leaflets and smaller, less woody pods.

Acacia haematoxylon Willd.   Illust. 59
S.A. no: 169   Grey camel thorn. Vaalkameeldoring
Rhod. no: —

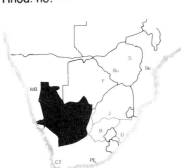
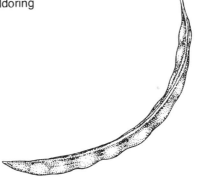

A shrub or a small tree up to 6 m in height; it is very characteristic of the desert and semi-desert areas, often occurring on deep red sandy soils. **Bark:** grey-brown; branchlets densely grey velvety. Stipules spinescent, the spines creamy-white, slender, straight, up to 6 cm. **Leaves:** with 15 to 27 pairs of pinnae, each bearing close ranks of very minute leaflets; at first sight the leaflets appear to be

239

unusually long, slender and very finely toothed, about 10 × 2 mm in size, but careful examination shows that the toothed appearance is caused, in fact, by a double row of exceedingly minute leaflets being about 0,6 × 0,5 mm in size and closely overlapping; all parts of the leaves are densely covered with fine grey hairs. **Flowers:** in yellow balls (November to January). **Fruit:** a long slender pod, up to 14 × 1,3 cm, densely grey velvety, curved, sometimes rather twisted, slightly constricted between the seeds, indehiscent (January to April).

This is a most interesting, attractive and graceful small tree. The early botanist, Burchell, referring to the soft masses of pale grey foliage, described this as 'a beautiful species of *Acacia* with a hoary complexion.' Unfortunately, it seems difficult to cultivate away from its own natural habitat. In certain areas, hybrids between this species and *A. erioloba* can be found and the cross is an interesting one: its size, general habit and pods resemble *A. erioloba,* but the leaflets are generally much smaller and are the characteristic *haematoxylon* grey.

Acacia hebeclada DC.

[*A. stolonifera* Burch.; *A. stolonifera* var. *chobiensis* O. B. Miller]
S.A. no: 170, 170,1 and 170,2   Candle acacia. Trassiedoring
Rhod. no: 206   Candle-pod acacia

A shrub to a small tree up to 7 m in height, branching from near ground level; occurring generally in hot, dry areas, often forming thickets. **Bark:** dark grey, longitudinally fissured and flaking; branchlets densely velvety with grey almost woolly hairs. Stipules spinescent; spines very variable, straight, hooked or sickle-shaped, short or long, up to 3,5 cm. **Leaves:** with 2 to 9 pairs of pinnae, each bearing 7 to 16 pairs of leaflets; leaflets 2 to 7 × 1 to 2 mm, very small and feathery; petiole and rachis covered with grey woolly hairs. **Flowers:** in creamy-white balls (July to September). **Fruit:** a hard, woody pod, 4 to 15 × 1,4 to 4 cm, straight, swollen, rather sausage-like, covered with yellowish-grey woolly hairs and with very conspicuous wrinkles and ridges spiralling round the pod; the pods stand upright and this is a very distinctive character (not conspicuous in one of the subspecies) (October to March).

There are three subspecies involved in southern Africa: the typical subsp. *hebeclada* is widespread. Subsp. *tristis* Schreiber has more slender pods which are flat, often speckled with glands, without hairs or nearly so, occasionally almost reddish-brown in colour and hanging down, not standing upright; it occurs in the north and north-west of South West Africa. Subsp. *chobiensis* (O. B. Miller) Schreiber has pods which are erect, but much broader and flatter, 3 to 5 cm wide; the leaves are hairy; it is usually a riverine species, occurring only in the north-east of South West Africa, and in Botswana in the Chobe area with a single record near Gaborones.

Acacia hereroensis Engl.

[*A. mellei* Verdoorn]
S.A. no: 171   Mountain thorn. Bergdoring
Rhod. no: 207   Red-thorned acacia

A shrub or small tree up to 10 m in height; occurring in dry woodland and wooded grassland, often on hills. **Bark:** dark, smoothish to rough, sometimes flaking away in large, thick pieces; branchlets densely velvety. Stipules not spinescent; numerous hooked prickles, 5 to 7 mm long, are paired just below the nodes. **Leaves:** with 8 to 20 pairs of pinnae, each bearing 15 to 32, occasionally up to 48,

240

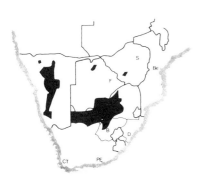

pairs of leaflets; leaflets very small, barely 2 × 0,5 mm. **Flowers:** in creamy-white, short, squat spikes (November to January, with the leaves). **Fruit:** a pod, up to 14 × 2,3 cm, straight, thin, reddish-brown, finely velvety to the touch, slightly constricted between the seeds, dehiscent (January to June).

This species is very similar to *A. caffra*, some differences being that it has a shorter leaf petiole, measuring 0,3 to 1,3 cm in length, while that of *A. caffra* measures 1,3 to 3,5 cm; the leaflets tend to stand erect while those of *A. caffra* usually droop; the spines are better developed than they are in *A. caffra*; the flower spikes are produced singly and not in clusters and the lateral veins are not visible on the under surface of the leaflets while they are fairly prominent in *A. caffra*.

Acacia karroo Hayne   Illust. 60
[*A. natalitia* E. Meyer]
S.A. no: 172   Sweet thorn. Soetdoring
Rhod. no: 208   Sweet thorn

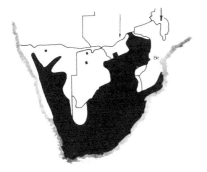

A tree up to 15 m in height, rarely shrubby; occurring over a wide range of altitudes, from coastal scrub to woodland, wooded grassland, often along rivers and streams. **Bark:** dark red-brown to blackish and rough; young branches and branchlets conspicuously rusty-red due to the outer bark peeling off to expose the red underbark. Stipules spinescent, the spines severe, white, dark-tipped, straight, stout, up to 7 cm in length very occasionally up to 17 cm. **Leaves:** with 2 to 7 pairs of pinnae, each bearing 8 to 20 pairs of leaflets; leaflets oblong, 4 to 7 × 1 to 3 mm. **Flowers:** in deep golden-yellow balls, sweetly scented, flowering several times during the summer; a tree can be a splendid sight in full flower, but after a storm the flowers become matted and spoilt by the rain and it is 10 days or more before the new blooms appear (October to February). **Fruit:** a slender very thinly woody pod, up to 16 × 1 cm, thin, sickle-shaped, slightly constricted between the seeds, without hairs, dehiscent (usually from about January onwards).

This is one of the most widespread trees in Africa, occurring in many different habitats. Despite this it shows remarkably little variation in the north, but in the Transvaal, Natal and Cape many forms are recognisable. Its presence is considered an indication of sweet veld and, since its uses are almost unlimited, it is an asset on any farm. *A. karroo* is a very good 'bee tree' as it has considerable quantities of pollen and nectar and it provides excellent fodder since the leaves, flowers and pods can all be eaten. The bark is used in tanning, imparting a red colour to the leather, and also to make an

241

infusion which is given to cattle as an antidote to poisoning by tulp (a species of *Moraea*). The inner bark makes a reliable rope much used by farmers, and the tree yields a clear, golden or red gum which is edible and suitable both for confectionery and for use as an adhesive. The massive white thorns can be an impressive sight and in certain areas Africans use them as needles. The wood is pale brown or yellow, hard and heavy. Although it is not commercially exploited today, it provides a general purpose timber suitable for furniture-making, but is somewhat subject to borer attack unless water seasoned for at least six months. This is a very adaptable species: it is easy to grow from seed provided this has been soaked in hot water; it is frost- and drought-resistant and fast-growing. In addition, it provides shade, fuel, fencing posts and even protection from wild animals! This tree is protected in the northern Cape and in the Jacobsdal district of the Orange Free State.

Acacia kirkii Oliver
S.A. no: 173   Flood-plain acacia. Vloedvlaktedoring
Rhod. no: 209   Flood-plain acacia

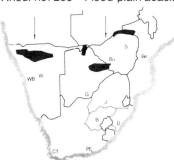

A flat-crowned tree up to 15 m in height; occurring in scrub and wooded grassland. **Bark:** green, peeling or scaly; branchlets velvety; twigs grey, brown or plum-coloured. Stipules spinescent, spines strong, straight, up to 8 cm, reddish or greyish when young, white tipped with black when mature. **Leaves:** with 6 to 14 pairs of pinnae, each bearing numerous very small leaflets; leaflets up to 5 × 1 mm, bearing no glands. **Flowers:** cream or white when open and pinkish-red in bud (July to January). **Fruit:** straight, small pods, up to 9 × 2 cm, somewhat constricted between the seeds, with a remarkable 'wart-like' projection over each seed, reddish-brown or grey in colour, indehiscent, simply breaking up on the ground (October to April).
All the southern African species are included in the typical subspecies, subsp. *kirkii;* subsp. *mildbraedii* (Harms) Brenan does not occur further south than Tanzania.

Acacia kraussiana Meissner ex Benth.
S.A. no: 173,1   Coast climbing acacia. Kusrankdoring
Rhod. no: —

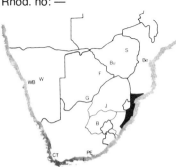
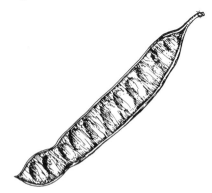

Usually a strong creeper, sometimes a shrub and occasionally a small tree up to 6 m in height; occurring in scrub and in forest. Stipules not spinescent, small hooked prickles are scattered along the stems. **Leaves:** sometimes modified to form tendrils which aid climbing or with tendrils in the leaf axils; with 1 to 6 pairs of pinnae each bearing 6 to 17 pairs of large leaflets; leaflets up to 23 × 8 mm,

242

with or without velvety hairs. **Flowers:** in creamy-white balls (October to January); the combination of round flower heads and large leaflets is definitive. **Fruit:** a flat pod, 7 to 16 × 1,5 to 2,5 cm, brown, reluctantly dehiscent or indehiscent (January to May).
This species has a superficial resemblance to *Entada spicata* (E. Meyer) Druce, but the pods of the latter are so distinctive, splitting transversely into 1-seeded segments, that confusion is not likely to arise.

*Acacia longifolia (Andr.) Willd.

The long-leaved acacia, introduced from Australia, has escaped and is now common in kloofs near Cape Town.

Acacia luederitzii Engl.
[*A. goeringii* Schinz; *A. retinens* T. R. Sim; *A. gillettiae* Burtt Davy]
S.A. no: 174 Bastard umbrella thorn. Basterhaak-en-steek and 174,1
Fat-thorned acacia. Buikdoring
Rhod. no. 210 Kalahari sand acacia

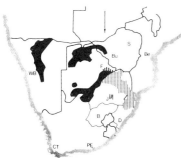
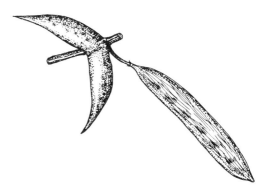

Occasionally a shrub, but usually a tree up to 12 m in height; occurring particularly on sandy soils, in dry wooded grassland, scrub and thornveld, frequently forming impenetrable thickets. **Bark:** very rough, longitudinally fissured and ridged; branchlets covered with dense grey or whitish woolly hairs, the older branches becoming purplish to dark brown-black. Stipules spinescent, the spines varying from short and hooked to long and straight, up to 7 cm in length; the spines of the var. *retinens* are remarkably swollen or inflated at the base, up to 1,5 cm in diameter and almost resembling blown-up bladders. These are the so-called 'ant galls' but it seems that there is no evidence that these structures are in fact caused by ants, although, once formed, they are frequently inhabited by a number of small insects, ants among them. The young spines are quite normal, the swelling taking place later and developing very rapidly. **Leaves:** with 2 to 9 pairs of pinnae, each bearing 10 to 26 pairs of leaflets; leaflets very small and feathery, 2 to 5 × 0,5 to 1,5 mm, narrowly oblong, with the margins finely fringed with small hairs. **Flowers:** in white balls (November to February). **Fruit:** a short pod, up to 13 × 2 cm, stiffly leathery, not woody, straight, grey-brown to purplish-brown, with a markedly thickened ridge round the edge (February to May).
There are two varieties, both of which occur in southern Africa:
In South West Africa, northern Cape, Botswana (widespread) and western Rhodesia; spines straight and hooked on the same tree, not inflated; pods generally rather larger .... var. *luederitzii*
In Natal, Swaziland and Moçambique, the Transvaal and just into Botswana; spines hooked, but become greatly inflated, making them appear straight; pods tending to be smaller ....
.... var. *retinens* (T. R. Sim) Ross & Brenan

A. luederitzii is closely related to *A. reficiens,* and the differences are discussed under the latter species.

*Acacia mearnsii De Wild.

The black wattle, introduced from Australia for the economic value of its bark, has escaped and become naturalised, now forming dense stands along river valleys in the mountains and along the coast from Cape Town to Natal, and in the eastern areas of Rhodesia (Rhod. no: 212).

243

MIMOSOIDEAE

*Acacia melanoxylon R. Br.

The blackwood, introduced and now escaped, is a large timber tree providing a fine and valuable wood if carefully managed. One of the earliest pioneers in forest clearings and spreads rapidly along rivers, it is posing a real threat to the natural forests from Cape Town to Natal and the eastern Transvaal.

Acacia mellifera (Vahl) Benth.
[*A. detinens* Burch.]
S.A. no: 176 and 176,1   Black thorn. Swarthaak
Rhod. no: 213   Hook-thorn

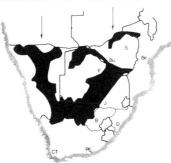 

Often a shrub, but also a small tree 5 to 8 m in height; occurring in dry bushveld. The young branches are rigid, spiky, grey-brown to purplish-black. Stipules not spinescent; prickles are dark brown or blackish, short, curved, not much more than 5 mm in length, produced in pairs just below each node. **Leaves:** with 2 to 3 pairs of pinnae, each bearing unusually few leaflets, 1 to 2 pairs, occasionally up to 4; leaflets comparatively large, 0,4 to 2,2 × 0,3 to 1,6 cm, blue-green in colour. **Flowers:** white in balls (subsp. *detinens)* or spikes (subsp. *mellifera)* usually closely packed along the rigid dark branchlets (September to November). **Fruit:** a small pod, up to 9 × 2,5 cm, straw-coloured or pale brown, thin to almost papery, straight, smooth, dehiscent (January to April).

Most of the material found in southern Africa belongs to subsp. *detinens* (Burch.) Brenan; subsp. *mellifera,* with its reddish trunk and rather larger leaflets, occurs only in the extreme north-west of South West Africa and north from there. It is a devastatingly thorny tree and although the hooked spines are not large, they are highly effective. The early botanist Burchell, after describing how he became hopelessly entangled and completely entrapped by them, wrote: 'I determined to give the tree a name which should serve to caution future travellers against allowing themselves to venture within its clutches.' He called it *Acacia detinens,* which means 'holding back' or 'detaining'. The pods, young twigs, leaves and flowers are all highly nutritious and are eagerly eaten by stock and game. The wood is widely used as fuel and the dark heartwood becomes almost black when oiled and highly polished. These trees spread very rapidly, both from seed and vegetatively – so much so that they can become a menace, forming impenetrable, tangled thickets. They are good 'bee plants'

Acacia montis-usti Merxm. & Schreiber
S.A. no: 177   Brandberg acacia. Brandbergdoring
Rhod. no: —

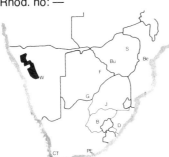 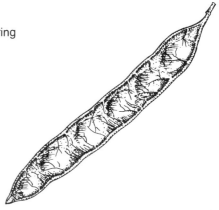

A shrub or small tree often several-stemmed from the base; occurring in hot, arid, rocky or stony places. **Bark:** in young trees it is shiny red and peeling in yellowish flakes, but it becomes dark grey and deeply fissured in older specimens; branchlets have a cinnamon-coloured papery bark. Stipules not spinescent; the strong, hooked prickles, brown to black, up to 7 mm long, are paired below the nodes. **Leaves:** with 3 to 5 pairs of pinnae, each bearing about 10 pairs of leaflets; leaflets about 8 mm long, apex rounded, with the midrib asymmetric. **Flowers:** in cream to yellow spikes (November to December). **Fruit:** an oblong pod, up to 16 × 2 cm, straight, dark red-brown and thinly woody, margin thickened (February to May).

These rather graceful trees are very conspicuous in the Brandberg valley where they may be seen by visitors; the area gives this tree its specific name which means 'burnt mountain'.

Acacia nebrownii Burtt Davy
[*A. rogersii* Burtt Davy]
S.A. no: 177,1   Water acacia. Waterdoring
Rhod. no: 214   Water acacia

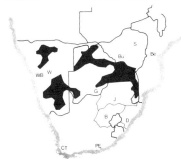

Usually a shrub, particularly in South Africa, but it can become a small tree up to 7 m in height; occurring in low altitude, dry, hot grassland and thornscrub, where it often forms thickets. Branches red-brown, sometimes even orange in colour. Stipules spinescent, the spines slender, up to 6 cm long, straight, white, slightly dark-tipped. The bushes are densely spiny. **Leaves:** short, tightly clustered along the stems, fascicled from pads between the spines; usually with only 1 pair of pinnae (occasionally 2), each bearing 3 to 5 pairs of leaflets; leaflets rather large, 2 to 8 × 1 to 5 mm; there is a gland between the pair of pinnae, and glands may also be present on the leaflets. **Flowers:** in golden-yellow balls (August to September). **Fruit:** a small pod, up to 4,7 × 1,1 cm, sickle-shaped or slightly so, without hairs, glandular glutinous, thinly textured, dehiscent (September to January). In South West Africa *A. nebrownii* is considered to be an indication of underground water.

Acacia nigrescens Oliver   Illust. 61
[*A. pallens* Rolfe; *A. mellifera* sensu Henkel *Woody Plants of Natal and Zululand*]
S.A. no: 178   Knob-thorn. Knoppiesdoring
Rhod. no: 215   Knob-thorn

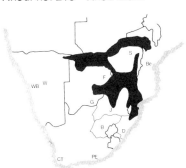
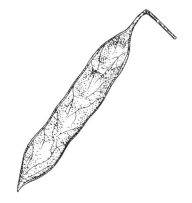

A tree up to 20 m in height, but usually 8 to 10 m, deciduous, standing bare for several months in the year; occurring in low altitude woodland and wooded grassland especially near rivers and lakes. **245**

Bark: dark brown and beset with large, conspicuous knobby prickles. Stipules not spinescent, the small, hooked, blackish prickles are paired just below the nodes. **Leaves:** with 1 to 3 (occasionally 4) pairs of pinnae, each bearing only 1 to 2 pairs of leaflets; leaflets often nearly circular, 1,5 to 2,5 × 0,7 to 2,2 cm, the largest leaflets of any species of *Acacia*, soft pale green or grey-green. **Flowers:** in white spikes, up to 10 cm long, appearing before the leaves, making the tree very conspicuous (August to November). **Fruit:** a straight pod, up to 16 × 2,5 cm, darkish brown, rather thinly textured, without hairs, dehiscent, the remains of the calyx at the base of the pod without hairs (January to June).

Old, large trees have a deeply fissured bark and fewer knobby thorns. These trees often grow in association with *rooigras, Themeda triandra* Forsk., and are generally regarded as an indication of good ranching country. They are fire- and drought-resistant but susceptible to frost. The sapwood is yellow, the heartwood dark brown, strong, tough and close-grained; it is difficult to work and saw but has been used to make furniture and also for mine props and fencing posts. It is one of the favourite woods for making *jukskeie*, used in the traditional game of that name.

Acacia nilotica (L.) Willd. ex Delile
[*A. benthamii* Rochebr.]
S.A. no: 179   Scented thorn. Lekkerruikpeul
Rhod. no: 216   Scented-pod acacia

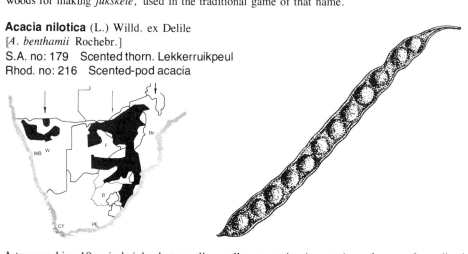

A tree reaching 10 m in height, but usually smaller; occurring in a variety of types of woodland, wooded grassland and scrub, frequently forming thickets. **Bark:** reddish-brown and smooth when young, but becoming blackish-grey and rough with age; young branches grey to brown, smooth, not peeling. Stipules spinescent, the spines long, slender, straight, up to 8 to 9 cm long, but most often about 4 to 5 cm, whitish but often reddish-brown and remaining slightly furry. **Leaves:** with 2 to 11 pairs of pinnae, each bearing 7 to 25 pairs of leaflets; leaflets small up to 7 × 1,5 mm. **Flowers:** in yellow balls (September to April). **Fruit:** a pod, 8 to 17 cm long, green and fleshy when young becoming dark when mature, and drying black; straight or slightly curved, but seldom truly sickle-shaped, somewhat constricted between the seeds, the seed shields warty and well-rounded, very like a string of beads, with or without velvety hairs, sweet-smelling, indehiscent, breaking up transversely into single-seeded segments when the fruits fall to the ground (March to September).

This species has been divided into seven subspecies in tropical Africa but only one of these occurs south of the Zambezi River; all the southern African material may be assigned to subsp. *kraussiana* (Benth.) Brenan. The wood is reddish and hard but has been used only as firewood and for fencing posts. The Voortrekkers are said to have made ink from the pods, which, as they mature, develop a fruity scent and are sought after by stock and game. The Zulus take a decoction of the bark for coughs and the trees exude a good quality gum which is edible and suitable for confectionery. These trees can form thickets and become a menace when they invade the surrounding bush to the exclusion of other natural species.

Acacia permixta Burtt Davy
S.A. no: 179,1   Hairy acacia. Slapdoring
Rhod. no: 218   Hairy acacia

Usually a shrub, but it may become a small tree up to 4 m in height; occurring on dry rocky hills and ridges in shallow gravelly soils, often in association with species of *Commiphora,* and in mopane

woodland. **Bark:** reddish-brown; young branches distinctively and densely covered with greyish hairs while the ultimate branchlets may be rusty-coloured. Stipules spinescent, the spines up to 6 cm long, whitish, straight, often slightly curved back. **Leaves:** in tight clusters, or fascicles, arising from hard cushions between the spines; with 1 to 4 pairs of pinnae, each bearing 5 to 10 pairs of leaflets; leaflets 2 to 6 × 1 to 2 mm, the apex abruptly drawn into a very conspicuous point, margins finely hair-fringed; there are glands on the rachis and possibly also along the leaflet margins. **Flowers:** in yellow balls among the leaves (December). **Fruit:** a small pod, up to 4 to 5 × 1 cm, broadly sickle-shaped, reddish-brown, leathery, conspicuously gland-dotted, containing only 2 to 3 seeds (January to April).

Acacia polyacantha Willd.   Illust. 62
[*A. campylacantha* Hochst. ex A. Rich.]
S.A. no: 180   White thorn. Witdoring
Rhod. no: 219   White thorn-tree

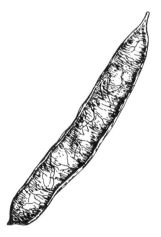

A large, handsome, deciduous tree up to 20 m in height; it most frequently occurs in wooded grassland and on alluvial soils in river valleys. **Bark:** pale, inclined to be flaky or peeling in thick corky flakes and loose strips; may have strongly hooked prickles on woody bosses which are sometimes on the trunk but more frequently on the branches. Stipules not spinescent; the rather slender hooked prickles, pale to dark brown, are produced in pairs just below each node. **Leaves:** with 13 to 40 pairs of pinnae, each bearing 26 to 66 pairs of leaflets; leaflets small, 2 to 5 × 0,4 to 0,75 mm, narrow to narrowly triangular. **Flowers:** in white spikes, up to 12 cm long, appearing with the new leaves (September to December). **Fruit:** a straight, flat pod, 7 to 18 × 1 to 2,1 cm long, brown, without hairs, tapering to both ends (March to October).

A noticeable feature of this tree is that the yellowish bark peels off in corky strips and flakes, giving the trunk a whittish appearance. In Rhodesia and Tanzania the roots have the reputation of possessing considerable magico-medicinal properties. Certain dangerous animals are believed to dislike their smell, and for this reason they are placed among the rafters of a house to ward off snakes and also in rivers at popular crossing-points as a deterrent to crocodiles. People carry them on their persons as a safeguard; they are used as a remedy for snakebite and as an infusion in which to bathe children who are restless at night.

The wood burns well, but the thorns make it very difficult to handle. All African material of this tree is placed in subsp. *campylacantha* (Hochst. ex A. Rich.) Brenan; the typical subspecies is known only from India and perhaps Sri Lanka.

247

MIMOSOIDEAE

Acacia reficiens Wawra

[*A. uncinata* Engl.]
S.A. no: 181   False umbrella thorn. Vals haak-en-steek
Rhod. no: —

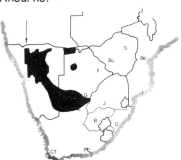

A bush or small tree up to 5 m in height; occurring on sandy and occasionally brackish soils, on mountain slopes, along dry watercourses and on stony or sandy flats. Young branches are covered with very short hairs. Stipules spinescent, the spines being hooked or straight, but more often hooked and short. **Leaves:** with 2 to 9 pairs of pinnae, each bearing 5 to 11 pairs of very small leaflets. **Flowers:** in white balls, on slender stalks, 2 to 3 cm long (January to February). **Fruit:** a short pod, 5 to 8 × 0,6 to 1 cm, mahogany-red, without hairs, thinly woody, flat, marked with fine longitudinal veins (March to June).

This species is closely related to *A. luederitzii,* but the branches are finely velvety with no long spreading hairs, and it consistently has fewer pairs of leaflets whose margins lack the fine hairy fringe. Its pods are consistently narrower, 6 to 10 mm broad, while the pods of *A. luederitzii* measure 10 to 19 mm in width. The second subsp. *misera* (Vatke) Brenan, extends no further south than Uganda.

Acacia rehmanniana Schinz

S.A. no: 182   Silky acacia. Sydoring
Rhod. no: 220   Silky acacia

A small to medium sized, flat-crowned tree up to 8 m in height, occasionally reaching 10 m; occurs in wooded grassland, along river banks and is also associated with termite mounds. The young branchlets are densely covered with golden, furry hairs which later become grey and peel off to expose the powdery rusty-red bark. Stipules spinescent, the spines straight, up to 5 cm long, white with a reddish-brown tip, remaining velvety until quite old. **Leaves:** with 15 to 44 pairs of pinnae, each bearing many pairs of leaflets; leaflets small, 1 to 3 × 0,4 to 0,7 mm, bearing no glands. **Flowers:** in white balls, grouped at the ends of the young branches (November to February). **Fruit:** a straight, flat pod, up to 14 × 2,3 cm, without hairs, greyish-brown to olive, dehiscent (March to June).

This species is sometimes confused with *A. sieberana* DC., but it can be separated by the more numerous pinnae, the much more thinly textured pods and by the way in which the flowers cluster at the ends of the branchlets.

Acacia robusta Burch.
[*A. clavigera* E. Meyer]
S.A. no: 183 and 183,1   Splendid acacia. Enkeldoring
Rhod. no: 221   Splendid acacia

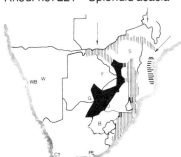

A medium sized to large, flat-crowned tree reaching 25 m in height; occurring in woodland and wooded grassland. **Bark:** grey to dark brown, sometimes smooth, but often deeply fissured. Stipules spinescent, the spines usually small, about 7 mm in length (sometimes up to 20 mm), straight, greyish in colour and sometimes semi-inflated. **Leaves:** with 2 to 6 pairs of pinnae, each bearing 10 to 25 pairs of leaflets; leaflets closely ranked, varying from 1 to 5 mm wide, dark green; petiole and the leaf rachis either without hairs or densely hairy. **Flowers:** in white balls (July to October). **Fruit:** a pod, up to 19 × 3 cm, straight or slightly sickle-shaped, grey to deep brown, not constricted between the seeds, thinly textured to thinly woody (October to February).
This species has been divided into three subspecies, all of which occur south of the Zambezi River:
    subsp. *robusta* – the leaf rachis without hairs or nearly so: usually with 2 to 4 pairs of pinnae each bearing 10 to 15 pairs of leaflets, each about 5 mm wide; pods straight or slightly curved, 2,5 to 3 cm wide. (See black area on the map.)
    subsp. *clavigera* (E. Meyer) Brenan – the leaf rachis more or less densely velvety; with 5 to 6 pairs of pinnae each bearing much smaller and more numerous leaflets, 13 to 25 pairs, each about 2 to 3 mm wide; pods much more sickle-shaped, generally narrower, 1,3 to 1,7 cm wide. (See vertical lines on the map.)
    subsp. *usambarensis* (Taub.) Brenan – the leaf rachis without hairs; pinnae and leaflets similar to subsp. *clavigera,* but leaflets 1 to 2 mm wide and pods 0,7 to 1,2 cm wide. (See horizontal lines on the map.)

Acacia robynsiana Merxm. & Schreiber
S.A. no: 184   Whip-stick acacia. Sweepstokdoring
Rhod. no: —

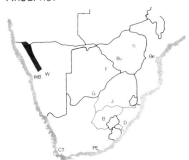

A bushy tree up to 9 m in height with long whip-like branches either upright or drooping over, often with dense or tangled growth round the base, or with the single stem up to 5 m and then drooping at the top; occurring among stony, rocky hills and mountains. Stipules not spinescent; small paired prickles are present, 2 to 3 mm in length, pale brown to grey-black, hooked, arising just below the nodes. **Leaves:** arising in clusters or tufts between the paired hooked prickles; each leaf with one pair of pinnae only, each bearing 6 to 8 pairs of leaflets; leaflets 6 to 8 × 2 to 3 mm, falling early. **Flowers:** in **249**

creamy-white to pale yellow spikes (August to October). **Fruit:** a straight pod, 3 to 6 × 1,8 cm, flat, straw-coloured to pale brown, without hairs, with a marked ridge round the edge, dehiscent (October to December).

It is said that the farmers attach their radio aerials to the straight upright branches.

*Acacia saligna (Labill.) Wendl.

[*Acacia cyanophylla* Lindl.]

This, the Port Jackson willow, was introduced from Australia. It has now escaped and become naturalised, especially near Cape Town. This species has phyllodes, resembling simple leaves, the feathery compound leaves only being seen in seedlings.

Acacia schweinfurthii Brenan & Exell

[*A. pennata* sensu auct., pro parte, non (L.) Willd.; *A. schweinfurthii* var. *sericea* Brenan & Exell]
S.A. no: 184,1   River climbing acacia. Rivierrankdoring
Rhod. no: 222   River climbing acacia

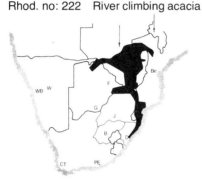

A shrub or small spreading tree, but most frequently a robust climber; occurs in riverine forest and woodland, although it is often found away from water, sometimes associated with termite mounds and frequently forming dense thickets. Stipules not spinescent; hooked prickles are scattered along the stems and rise from darkish brown vertical ribs. **Leaves:** with 9 to 17 pairs of pinnae, each bearing many, narrow leaflets; leaflets 1 to 2 mm wide, bright green, without hairs; petiole with a conspicuous gland near the base. **Flowers:** in white or pale cream balls (December to February). **Fruit:** an oblong pod, 10 to 19 × 1 to 2,9 cm, leathery; with conspicuous smooth domes over the seeds, like rungs of a ladder or a piece of corrugated iron; transverse wrinkles may be present; reluctantly dehiscent or not splitting at all (March to June).

Acacia senegal (L.) Willd.

S.A. no: 185 and 185,1   Three-thorned acacia. Driehaakdoring
Rhod. no: 223   Three-thorned acacia

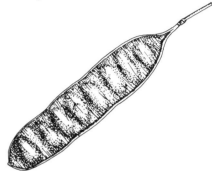

A shrub or tree 3 to 8 m in height; occurring in low altitude woodland, wooded grassland and bush. **Bark:** with a conspicuous yellow, papery peel, sometimes corky. Stipules not spinescent; prickles just below the nodes, usually in groups of 3, the middle one hooked downwards with the outer 2 curved upwards, often small, 5 mm long, but they can become formidable and grow up to 10 mm long with broad bases; the occurrence of 3 prickles in groups is unusual in this genus. **Leaves:** rather short giving the appearance of being clustered along the branchlets; with 3 to 6 pairs of pinnae (occasionally up to 12), each bearing 7 to 25 pairs of leaflets; leaflets 1 to 4 × 0,5 to 1,75 mm, finely velvety below. **Flowers:** in white, fragrant spikes, up to 10 cm long (May to August). **Fruit:** an oblong pod, usually about 8 to 10 × 2,5 to 3,5 cm (sometimes reaching 18 cm long), straight, grey-brown or light creamy-brown in colour (August to January).

Two varieties of this species extend south of the Zambezi River. The most widespread in this area is var. *rostrata* Brenan (refer to black area on the map) which is the smaller of the two; it rarely exceeds 4 m in height, often branches near the ground and has a compact, dense, flat crown; the bark has a conspicuous creamy-yellow to yellow-green papery peel; the pods are comparatively shorter and broader with a conspicuous beak at the tip. The var. *leiorachis* Brenan (refer to vertical lines on the map) is always a tree, up to 8 m in height, with a substantial stem; the bark has a conspicuous yellow papery peel; the pods are comparatively longer and narrower with the apices pointed or rounded but not forming a beak.

Acacia sieberana DC.   Illust. 63

[*A. woodii* Burtt Davy; *A. vermoesenii* De Wild.: *A. sieberana* DC. var. *vermoesenii* Keay & Brenan]
S.A. no: 187   Paperbark acacia. Papierbasdoring
Rhod. no: 224   Paperbark acacia

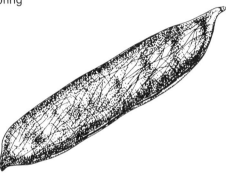

One of the most common of the flat-topped acacias, this is a large deciduous tree, widely branching and sometimes reaching 17 m in height; it can be only about 7 m in height with a comparatively immense spread; it occurs in woodland and wooded grassland, often along rivers or on flood-plains. **Bark:** light brown or greyish-yellow, inclined to be corky, sometimes peeling in papery strips and flakes. Stipules spinescent, the spines whitish, straight, up to 9 cm in length, with no swellings. **Leaves:** with 6 to 23 pairs of pinnae, each bearing 14 to 45 pairs of leaflets; leaflets narrowly oblong, 2 to 6,5 × 0,6 to 1,5 mm. **Flowers:** in white or cream balls (September to November). **Fruit:** a pod, up to 21 × 3,5 cm, without hairs to densely velvety, creamy-brown, straight or slightly curved, reluctantly dehiscent, thickened and woody (maturing from March onwards).

This species has been divided into three varieties, only one of which, var. *woodii* (Burtt Davy) Keay & Brenan, is widespread south of the Zambezi River; var. *sieberana,* the branches of which have no hairs, has been recorded from near Beira.

The wood is light, soft and of little value; it has a distinctive smell when freshly cut. The pods are eaten by game and stock, but the green fruit may sometimes be poisonous. This species is similar to *A. rehmanniana* and the differences are discussed under the latter species.

Acacia swazica Burtt Davy

S.A. no: 187,2   Swazi acacia. Swazidoring
Rhod. no: —

A slender shrub or small tree, rarely more than 2 to 3 m in height; occurring on rocky hill slopes and in barren places. Stipules spinescent, the spines paired, slender, straight, up to 2,5 cm long, brown-tipped. **Leaves:** arise in clusters from very abbreviated dwarf lateral shoots between the spines; usually with 1 pair of pinnae (occasionally 2, seldom 3), each bearing 3 to 5 pairs of leaflets; leaflets rather shiny, up to 13 × 6 mm, widely spaced, midrib conspicuous on both surfaces. **Flowers:** in bright golden-yellow balls (October to November). **Fruit:** a characteristic, small, glandular glutinous pod, about 4 × 1 cm, pale yellowish-brown to chestnut, broadly sickle-shaped and conspicuously

251

dotted with the dark sticky glands, thinly textured, with a blunt, rounded apex (December to February).

Acacia tortilis (Forsk.) Hayne   Illust. 64

[*A. heteracantha* Burch.; *A. maras* Engl.; *A. litakunensis* Burch.; *A. spirocarpoides* Engl.]
S.A. no: 188 and 188,1   Umbrella thorn. Haak-en-steek
Rhod. no: 226   Umbrella thorn

Medium to large trees, the height varying from 5 to 20 m over their extensive distribution, the smaller trees often round-crowned, the larger specimens conspicuously flat-topped; widespread in low altitude, dry areas, in a variety of types of woodland. **Bark:** grey or dark brown, fissured. Stipules spinescent, the spines very variable, sometimes sharply hooked, up to 5 mm long or straight, long, white, up to 8 cm, and often with hooked and straight spines together on the same branchlet. **Leaves:** characteristically bluish-grey-green; with 2 to 10 pairs of pinnae, each bearing 6 to 19 pairs of very small leaflets, 0,5 to 3 mm long only, closely ranked, making the tree densely leafy. **Flowers:** in white to cream, sometimes pale yellow balls (November to January). **Fruit:** a small, narrow pod, 5 to 9 mm wide, characteristically twisted and contorted, sometimes curled into a corkscrew spiral (March to June or even later).

The two types of thorns, both hooked and straight, and the tightly contorted and twisted pods make this tree easy to recognise. This species has been divided into several subspecies, two of which occur south of the Zambezi River: subsp. *heteracantha* (Burch.) Brenan, and subsp. *spirocarpa* (Hochst. ex A. Rich.) Brenan. Subsp. *spirocarpa* has more densely velvety branchlets, petiole and rachis, and its pods are about 2 mm wider than those of subsp. *heteracantha*. The leaves and pods make a very nutritious fodder, and the wood provides good fuel; otherwise the tree is of little commercial value. It is easily raised from seed and although rather slow-growing is very hardy and drought-resistant.

Acacia welwitschii Oliver

[*A. delagoensis* Harms]
S.A. no: 163   Delagoa thorn. Delagoadoring
Rhod. no: 227   Delagoa thorn

A rather crooked tree up to 12 m in height; occurring in low altitude woodland and on brackish flats. **Bark:** smooth, mottled grey-green and brown, or dark and rough. Stipules not spinescent; prickles occur in pairs just below the nodes, hooked, up to 5 mm in length, grey or blackish in colour. **Leaves:** with 2 to 4 pairs of pinnae, each bearing 3 to 8 pairs of leaflets; leaflets rather large, elliptic, 4 to 20 × 2

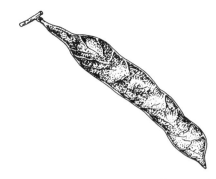

to 13 mm, apex rounded or even slightly notched, base almost symmetric. Petiole with a conspicuous gland near the base. **Flowers:** in white short, thickset spikes up to 6,5 cm long (December). **Fruit:** a flat, thin pod, usually 8 to 11 cm long, but sometimes up to 16 × 2 cm, without hairs, straight, grey-brown to reddish-brown, somewhat constricted (from about April onwards).

All the material south of the Zambezi River is assigned to subsp. *delagoensis* (Harms) Ross & Brenan; the typical subsp. *welwitschii* has longer flower spikes and occurs only in Angola. This species somewhat resembles *A. burkei,* but its leaves, petioles and branchlets are without hairs; it is also very similar to *A. goetzei* subsp. *goetzei,* but *A. welwitschii* has elliptic leaflets which are more or less symmetric at the base, and consistently narrow pods.

Acacia xanthophloea Benth.   Illust. 65
S.A. no: 189   Fever tree. Koorsboom
Rhod. no: 228   Fever tree

A medium to tall, well shaped tree, 10 to 15 m in height, but sometimes reaching 25 m; invariably growing in groups, in low-lying, swampy areas. **Bark:** very characteristic, smooth, slightly flaking, greenish-yellow to yellow, variously described by collectors as evil, pallid, leprous, sickly and sinister. Stipules spinescent, the spines white, straight, up to 7 cm in length. **Leaves:** with 4 to 7 pairs of pinnae, each bearing about 10 to 17 pairs of rather fine leaflets which fall fairly early. **Flowers:** in yellow balls (September to November). **Fruit:** a smallish pod, up to 13 × 1,4 cm, pale brown, straight, thin and rather papery, slightly but irregularly constricted between the seeds, the segments often breaking up (January onwards).

These trees growing, as they do, in low-lying swampy places, were associated with malaria, and early pioneers were sure that they were the cause of the fever; even today there are people who continue to believe that there is a link. This is not the case, and the association arises simply from the fact that the tree grows in ideal breeding grounds for the malarial mosquito. The wood is hard, heavy and a useful general purpose timber; it should be thoroughly seasoned first or it is liable to crack. In winter and early spring when the trees are standing bare, the sight of their yellow stems is unforgettable. It is these trees that were immortalised by Rudyard Kipling in his story *The Elephant's Child,* and children will remember how the Elephant's child, always travelling northwards, at last came 'to the banks of the great grey-green, greasy Limpopo River, all set about with fever trees'. They could make interesting garden subjects, but the seed is difficult to obtain.

253

3. DICHROSTACHYS (DC.) Wight & Arn.

Dichrostachys cinerea (L.) Wight & Arn.   Illust. 66
[*D. glomerata* (Forsk.) Chiov.; *D. nyassana* Taub.]
S.A. no: 190 and 190,1   Sickle bush. Sekelbos
Rhod. no: 230   Sickle bush

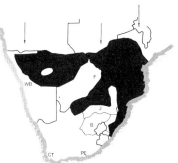

A shrub or small acacia-like tree 5 to 6 m in height; more common at low altitudes, it grows on a variety of soils in wooded grassland. It often forms secondary bush on impoverished ground and so is taken as an indication of overgrazing; under these conditions, *D. cinerea* tends to form impenetrable thickets and can be a nuisance. **Bark:** dark grey-brown, the stems often twisted and seamed and the branches intertwined, giving a thick matted appearance. Dwarf lateral shoots are modified to form short compact spines. **Leaves:** compound, paripinnate, with 4 to 13 pairs of pinnae, each carrying up to 27 pairs of leaflets; leaflets narrowly obovate to lanceolate, up to 10 × 3 mm, dark green, rather glossy above but dull below; glands are conspicuous on the petiole and on the rachis. **Flowers:** in axillary spikes, all floral parts in fives; stamens in 2 whorls of 5; the spike is clearly 2-coloured (the generic name refers to this), half the spike being formed by long, slender, pink, sterile staminodes, and the other half formed by the fertile flowers – this section forms a short, very compact yellow catkin; the whole flower spike droops and hangs upside down on the tree, so the pink sterile section is seen above the yellow fertile section. The pink colour varies considerably from almost white to mauve and bright pink, in different areas, between trees in the same area, and even on the same tree (October to January). **Fruit:** a cluster of pods, each up to 10 × 1 cm, twisted and contorted, indehiscent, falling from the tree and rotting on the ground (May to September).

Cattle and game eat the fruits with relish, and various parts of the tree feature to a certain extent in African folk-medicine. For instance, the roots are chewed and placed on the sites of snakebites and scorpion stings, and the leaves, which are believed to produce a local anaesthesia, are used for the same purpose and also as a remedy for sore eyes and toothache. The Shona name, *mupangara,* means 'tassels for the chief's hat', and is a picturesque reference to the flowers. The wood is extremely hard and durable: poles and tool handles have been made from it, but its use is limited by the small size of the tree. It is an excellent firewood, burning well but not too rapidly. This species is widespread, extending from Australia, through Burma and India to all parts of Africa; over its great range it is very variable and in an attempt to classify all the forms, the species was broken down into no less than 10 subspecies and some 11 varieties. However, several of the subspecies are of doubtful validity and the divisions at varietal level are not used in the present work. It seems possible that two of the subspecies can be recognised; subsp. *africana* Brenan & Brummitt, and subsp. *nyassana* (Taub.) Brenan; the latter tends to grow larger and has larger and less hairy leaves and leaflets. Both these subspecies occur in South Africa and in Rhodesia.

4. *PROSOPIS L.

*Prosopis glandulosa Torrey
[*P. juliflora* auct. non (Swartz) DC.; *P. chilensis* auct. non (Mol.) Schwartz]

The mesquite, imported from the south-western United States of America, has now become naturalised over considerable areas of South West Africa and there is evidence that it has spread into the northern Cape. It is an important shade tree, especially in some of the arid areas, and its pods and leaves form a valuable fodder. It would seem that two further species are also involved, *P. chilensis*

(Molina) Stuntz var. *catamarcana* Burkart and *P. pubescens* Benth., and these may be found in areas of the northern Cape.

At first sight these trees may be confused with some of the indigenous species of *Acacia,* but in *Prosopis* each flower has only 10 stamens. The genus *Prosopis* is a taxonomically difficult one and differences of opinion exist regarding the application of some of the names. The assistance and advice given by Dr J. H. Ross are acknowledged.

5. AMBLYGONOCARPUS Harms

Amblygonocarpus andongensis (Welw. ex Oliver) Exell & Torre   Illust. 67
[*A. obtusangulus* (Welw. ex Oliver) Harms]
S.A. no: 190,2   Scotsman's rattle. Skotseratel
Rhod. no: 231   Scotsman's rattle

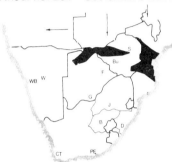 

An African genus with a single species. A large spreading tree 15 to 20 m in height; occurring in low altitude deciduous woodland – frequently mopane – often on deep Kalahari sands. **Bark:** grey, brown or black, scaling into small squares. **Leaves:** compound, twice pinnate, with 2 to 5 pairs of pinnae, each bearing 4 to 7 pairs of leaflets; leaflets rather large, oblong to ovate, up to 3 × 2 cm, apex round and notched. **Flowers:** bisexual, all floral parts in fives, stamens in 2 whorls of 5. Flowers produced in axillary, creamy-yellow spikes, solitary or paired, pendant, acacia-like; closer scrutiny reveals small petals (October). **Fruit:** a very characteristic pod, up to 17 × 3,5 cm, glossy brown, with 4 marked ridges making it more or less square in cross-section (March to July).

All parts are completely without hairs or spines. At least three specimens of these trees are well known to tourists, for two of them grow near the railway station at the Victoria Falls and a third specimen grows in the gardens of the Victoria Falls Hotel. The drawing in the illustration shows the old Victoria Falls railway station; this has since been demolished, but the trees are still there.

6. NEWTONIA Baillon

Trees, unarmed. **Leaves:** alternate, twice pinnate; pinnae opposite, often with a gland at the base, each pinna bearing few to many leaflets, opposite, obliquely elliptic or oblong to linear. **Flowers:** many, small, in slender spikes in terminal panicles. Bisexual; all floral parts in fives, stamens in 2 whorls of 5. **Fruit:** a flat pod, broadly linear, the centre section often falling away when old, leaving the thread-like rims hanging on the tree. Seeds oblong, narrowly winged.

Key to the species of *Newtonia:*

12 to 23 pairs of pinnae, each bearing 38 to 67 pairs of leaflets; a tree of high altitude, wet evergreen forest. Confined to the mountain forests in the east of Rhodesia and adjacent areas in Moçambique .... **N. buchananii**
4 to 7 pairs of pinnae, each bearing 6 to 19 pairs of leaflets; a tree of low altitude riverine fringe forest. Occurring in low-lying areas in north Natal, eastern Transvaal, Moçambique and the Sabi valley in Rhodesia .... **N. hildebrandtii**

Newtonia buchananii (Baker) Gilbert & Boutique
[*Piptadenia buchananii* Baker]
S.A. no: —
Rhod. no: 232   Forest newtonia

255

Seed

Leaves, flowers and fruit of the forest Newtonia, Newtonia buchananii.

A large to very large tree reaching 40 m in height; occurring in wet, evergreen forests, often along streams and rivers. **Bark:** light brown or greyish-brown, the stem frequently slightly buttressed at the base. All parts of the tree are unarmed. **Leaves:** compound, twice pinnate, very small and feathery, with a gland between each pair of pinnae on the rachis; with 12 to 23 pairs of pinnae, each bearing 38 to 67 pairs of leaflets; leaflets 2 to 6 × 0,5 to 1,5 mm. **Flowers:** bisexual, all floral parts in fives, with the stamens in 2 whorls of 5. Flowers are produced in axillary, white or yellow spikes, up to 19 cm long, acacia-like, but closer scrutiny reveals the presence of small petals (July to October). **Fruit:** a long, slender pod, up to 32 cm in length, splitting down one side only and opening out flat in a characteristic manner (January to June). The seeds are distinctive, up to 7,5 cm long, slender, flat, with a reddish wing round the edges.

Newtonia hildebrandtii (Vatke) Torre

[*Piptadenia hildebrandtii* Vatke; *Newtonia hildebrandtii* (Vatke) Torre var. *pubescens* Brenan]
S.A. no: 191   Lebombo wattle. Lebombowattel
Rhod. no: 233   Lowveld newtonia

Seed

A large tree reaching 25 m in height; occurring at low altitudes, often in riverine forest fringes, and associated with sandy soils. **Bark:** dark grey, cracked and flaking longitudinally. **Leaves:** compound, twice pinnate, with glands on the rachis between each pair of pinnae; with 4 to 7 pairs of pinnae, each bearing 6 to 19 pairs of leaflets, 3 to 11 × 1 to 3 mm; the leaflets are larger than those of *N. buchananii,* but there is little chance of confusion as they are isolated geographically and ecologically. **Flowers:** bisexual, all floral parts in fives, stamens in 2 whorls of 5. The flowers are produced in axillary creamy-white spikes, up to 9 cm long, forming large heads (October to November). **Fruit:** a long, slender pod, up to 30 cm, but often smaller, flat, without hairs, turning deep wine-red when maturing; the old pods are brown; the pods split down one side only opening out flat (April to September). The seeds are very conspicuous, up to 6 cm long, slender, flat and surrounded by a reddish-brown papery wing. This is a protected plant in South Africa.

7. XYLIA Benth.

Trees, unarmed. **Leaves:** compound, twice pinnate, having 1 pair of pinnae only with a conspicuous gland between them; each pinna bears few to many pairs of large leaflets. **Flowers:** in round heads with long stamens, resembling the flower heads of some species of *Albizia* at first sight. Flowers bisexual, all floral parts in fives, stamens in 2 whorls of 5. **Fruit:** a pod, oblique, thickly woody, resembling *Afzelia quanzensis* Welw., seeds flattened, without an aril.

Key to the species:
Leaflets and all young parts without hairs or nearly so; flowers without a stalk ....
.... **X. mendonçae**
Leaflets and all young parts densely velvety; flowers with a minute stalk only about 1 mm long
.... **X. torreana**

Xylia mendoncae Torre
S.A. no: —
Rhod. no: —   Smooth xylia

A small tree 4 to 7 m in height; occurring in *Brachystegia* woodland near the coast. This species very closely resembles *X. torreana* which follows, except that its leaves and all young parts are almost completely without hairs and its flowers have no stalks.

Xylia torreana Brenan
S.A. no: 192   Sand ash. Sandessenhout
Rhod. no: 234   Hairy xylia

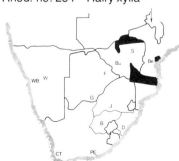

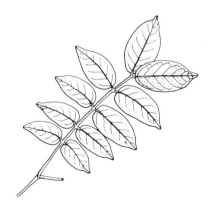

257

A small to medium sized tree, 6 to 15 m in height; occurring at low altitudes in hot, dry types of woodland. **Bark:** brown to grey, rough and flaking. **Leaves:** with 1 pair of pinnae, each pinna bearing 3 to 6 pairs of leaflets; leaflets large, narrowly elliptic to almost rounded, 2,5 to 10 × 1,3 to 5 cm, apex shortly attenuate, base square to shallowly lobed. **Flowers:** in spherical heads, up to 1,5 to 2 in diameter; stamens conspicuous, yellow, long (September to October). **Fruit:** a thickly woody pod, similar to *Afzelia quanzensis* in appearance but covered with brownish velvety hairs; the seeds lack the red aril (September to June).

8. ELEPHANTORRHIZA Benth.

Shrubs, small trees, or low bushes springing from underground rhizomes. **Leaves:** compound, 2-pinnate, each pinna bearing many pairs of small leaflets. **Flowers:** bisexual; all floral parts in fives; in axillary, spike-like racemes, solitary or in clusters. **Fruit:** a pod, more or less straight; long when mature, the outer layers peeling away and the margins separating and remaining on the trees when the sections fall out forming long, distinctive threads; the sections do not separate into 1-seeded segments as they do in the species of *Entada.*

Key to the tree species of *Elephantorrhiza:*
1 Leaflets with the midrib not central but running along the extreme inner edge of the leaflet; leaflets very fine and small; flowers normally produced with the leaves .... **E. suffruticosa**
 Leaflets with the midrib central or nearly so 2
2 Leaves with 14 to 41 pairs of pinnae; leaflet bases strongly asymmetric; flowers usually develop before the leaves; pods very long, up to 40 × 1,3 to 3 cm .... **E. goetzei**
 Leaves with 4 to 8 pairs of pinnae; leaflet bases almost symmetric; flowers usually develop with the young leaves; pods shorter and broader than in the previous species, usually about 19 × 2,5 to 4 cm, (but may reach 30 cm) .... **E. burkei**

Elephantorrhiza burkei Benth.
S.A. no: 193   Sumach bean. Basboontjie
Rhod. no: 235   Sumach elephant-root

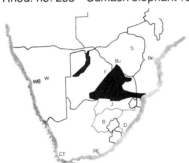

Shrubs, sometimes as low as 30 cm, or small trees up to 6 m in height; occurring on rocky hill slopes. **Bark:** dark grey to reddish. **Leaves:** acacia-like; with 4 to 8 pairs of pinnae, each bearing many leaflets; leaflets slender, sharply pointed, variable in size, 7 to 15 × 1,5 to 4 mm; base almost symmetric. **Flowers:** small, creamy-white becoming yellow, in a rather sparse spike up to 10 cm long, fragrant, appearing with the leaves (October to November). **Fruit:** a pod, up to 19 × 2,5 to 4 cm (but may reach 30 cm long), woody, reddish-brown, pendulous, splitting in a characteristic manner (March onwards).

Vegetatively this species differs only slightly from *E. elephantina* (Burch.) Skeels, and when in leaf and in flower it is not easy to tell them apart. They both grow from large underground rhizomes but the aerial parts of *E. elephantina* die back each year. *E. elephantina,* the *elandsboontjie,* is widespread in hot, dry areas of grassland and scrub, and provides food and medicine for the indigenous peoples; parts of both species have been used for tanning.

Elephantorrhiza goetzei (Harms) Harms   Illust. 68
[*E. rubescens* Gibbs; *E. elongata* Burtt Davy]
S.A. no: 192,1   Bastard sumach bean. Basterbasboontjie
Rhod. no: 236   Large-bean elephant-root

A shrub or small tree up to 7 m in height; occurring in various types of woodland and scrub, frequently associated with rocky outcrops. **Bark:** grey-brown to dark brown or red-brown. **Leaves:** acacia-like; with 14 to 41 pairs of pinnae, each bearing 20 to 48 pairs of leaflets; leaflets up to 1,2 cm long; bases strongly asymmetric. **Flowers:** small, creamy-yellow, stamens conspicuous, petals very small; flowers produced in axillary spikes appearing before the leaves (August to December). **Fruit:** a long pod, 45 × 1,3 to 3 cm, more or less cylindric, splitting in a characteristic manner, the rims remaining on the tree as long, woody threads (November to February).

In the north and west of Rhodesia subsp. *lata* Brenan & Brummitt, frequently growing as an open shrub about 2 m in height, differs from the typical subspecies, subsp. *goetzei,* in possessing only 4 to 15 pairs of pinnae, each of which bears 9 to 28 pairs of larger leaflets measuring up to 2,2 cm in length.

Elephantorrhiza suffruticosa Schinz
S.A. no: Skew-leaved sumach bean
Rhod. no: 237   Skew-leaved elephant-root

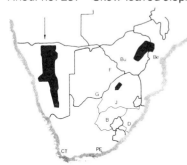

A shrub or small, several-stemmed tree up to 6 m in height; occurring in open wooded grassland often associated with species of *Acacia*. **Bark:** grey-brown to dark brown or reddish-brown; the young branches are very dark grey. **Leaves:** with 15 to 31 pairs of pinnae, each bearing 30 to 50 pairs of leaflets; leaflets linear-oblong, 5 × 0,4 to 1,2 mm; apex and base strongly asymmetric; midrib very unusual in that it is not central but runs along the extreme inner edge of each leaflet – this feature is very distinctive. **Flowers:** small, whitish to cream, in dense axillary spikes, produced with the leaves (October to November). **Fruit:** a flattened pod, 13 to 27,5 × 2 to 2,5 cm, reddish-brown, with conspicuous raised patches over the seeds (November to February).

9. ENTADA Adanson

Shrubs, lianes or trees. Prickles usually absent. Stipules very small. **Leaves:** 2-pinnate, each bearing from 1 to many pairs of leaflets. **Flowers:** forming a spike, axillary, solitary or clustered. Usually bisexual, all floral parts in fives; sepals and petals small; stamens 10 in 2 whorls, conspicuous. **Fruit:**

259

a pod, varying in size; the central section breaks transversely into 1-seeded sections that fall away from the hard, woody rims which remain on the tree for some time.

Key to the tree species of *Entada:*

1 Plants armed with scattered, recurved prickles .... **E. spicata**
  Plants unarmed 2
2 Always a substantial tree, 3 to 15 m in height, in open woodland and wooded grassland; leaflets very small, in 22 to 55 pairs .... **E. abyssinica**
  Very often a liane, or small tree, in various types of forest or woodland 3
3 Leaflets large, 2 to 6 × 1,3 to 2,6 cm, in 3 to 5 pairs; pods up to 2 m × 15 cm ....
  .... **E. pursaetha**
  Leaflets small, 0,8 to 2 × 0,2 to 0,6 cm, in 9 to 18 pairs; pods up to 17 × 3 to 4 cm ....
  .... **E. wahlbergii**

If *E. spicata, E. pursaetha* and *E. wahlbergii,* almost invariably lianes, are to be included then the following two species deserve mention:

E. chrysostachys (Benth.) Drake, a shrub or climber up to 10 m in height, found at low altitudes in riverine fringe forest and among rocks.

E. schlechteri (Harms) Harms, a forest liane in southern Moçambique, very similar to *E. spicata* in Natal; also has recurved prickles, but possesses 4 to 5 pairs of leaflets (instead of the 6 to 13 pairs of *E. spicata*) and is said to produce red flowers.

Entada abyssinica Steud. ex A. Rich.
S.A. no: —
Rhod. no: 238   Tree entada

A small to medium sized tree 3 to 15 m in height; occurring in woodland and wooded grassland. **Bark:** greyish-brown, rather smooth. **Leaves:** feathery and acacia-like with 2 to 20 pairs of pinnae, each bearing 22 to 55 pairs of leaflets; leaflets fairly long but narrow, 4 to 12 × 1 to 3 mm. **Flowers:** small, creamy-white to yellowish, in fluffy spikes up to 14 cm long, scented (November). **Fruit:** a large pod, 15 to 39 × 6 to 10 cm, flat, almost straight, breaking up in a characteristic manner (March to July).

Entada pursaetha DC.
S.A. no: Sea bean. Seeboontjie
Rhod. no: 240   Sea-bean

Usually a large forest climber or liane which can attain tree stature; occurring in low altitude, moist evergreen forest. **Bark:** grey to brown. **Leaves:** with 1 to 2 pairs of pinnae, each bearing 3 to 5 pairs of leaflets; leaflets large, oval, 2 to 6 × 1,3 to 2,6 cm; apex broadly tapering to rounded, often slightly notched; base rounded, often asymmetric; margin entire, wavy. **Flowers:** small, in fluffy, axillary spikes up to 23 cm long, creamy to pale yellow (October). **Fruit:** an enormous, flat, woody pod, up to 2 m × 15 cm, breaking up in characteristic fashion (December to April).

The huge seeds, 4 to 6 cm in diameter, are sometimes carried down the rivers and streams to the sea and may be found washed up on the beaches.

260

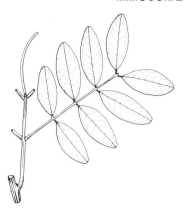

Entada spicata (E. Meyer) Druce
[*E. natalensis* Benth.]
S.A. no: Spiny splinter bean
Rhod. no: —

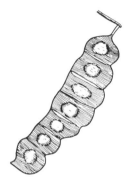

A large forest liane, sometimes sprawling on the ground, and sometimes developing on its own into a small tree up to 10 m in height; occurring frequently at forest margins while at the coast it can form dune thicket. **Bark:** light brown with pale coloured speckles and 5 straight rows of brown, recurved prickles which extend up the branchlets and are even scattered along the leaf petiole and rachis. **Leaves:** with 6 pairs of pinnae, each bearing 8 to 10 pairs of leaflets; leaflets oblong, 1,5 to 0,6 cm, dark shiny green above, paler green below; apex rounded; base asymmetric; margin entire. **Flowers:** in creamy-yellow, fluffy spikes up to 6 cm long, on slender stalks up to 2,5 cm long, in the leaf axils (December to January). **Fruit:** a thin, flat pod, up to 17 × 4 cm, but often smaller, maroon tinged with green when young, becoming pale creamy-brown tinged with red; constricted between the seeds and breaking up in a characteristic manner (November to June).

Entada wahlbergii Harvey
S.A. no: Brown-flowered splinter bean
Rhod. no: —

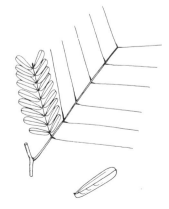

261

A slender climber or scandent shrub, occasionally becoming a self-supporting small tree; occurring in dense bush, on rocky outcrops and along dry watercourses. **Bark:** brown. **Leaves:** similar to those of *E. spicata,* with 6 pairs of pinnae, each bearing 9 to 18 pairs of leaflets; leaflets oblong, smaller and more slender than those of *E. spicata,* being 0,8 to 2 × 0,2 to 0,6 cm; base very asymmetric, one side tapering so narrowly as to touch the midrib, the other side deeply lobed; the leaves are said to be sensitive to touch. **Flowers:** in dense reddish-brown spikes, about 5 × 1,5 cm (September to November). **Fruit:** a thin, flat pod, up to 17 × 3 to 4 cm, constricted between the seeds, breaking up in a characteristic manner (December to March and even on to May).

CAESALPINIOIDEAE *(The cassia subfamily)*

Key to the genera in the subfamily:

1 Leaves simple, apex deeply notched to almost half the length of the leaf, forming 2 pronounced lobes 2

Leaves compound, with 1 pair of leaflets only; somewhat resembling the above but the division is complete, forming 2 leaflets 3

Leaves compound with more than 1 pair of leaflets 5

2 Leaves small, usually less than 2 cm long, thick, almost fleshy, often folded, dark bluish-green; petals maroon and grey tightly overlapping to form a tube. Northern and north-western Cape, and South West Africa .... **13. Adenolobus**

Leaves usually more than 2 cm long, leathery, not fleshy .... **14. Bauhinia**

3 A short, spike-like, or very small leaf-like appendage on the end of the petiole between the 2 leaflets; seeds wrinkled and folded and copiously dotted with resin glands......................... .... **4. Colophospermum**

Leaf-like appendage between the leaflets absent; seeds not gland-dotted 4

4 Pods flat, thinly woody, finely veined; flowers small, sepals up to 5 mm long; petals absent .... **3. Guibourtia**

Pods oblong- cylindric, up to 5 cm long and 3 cm in diameter, knobby and warty, thickly woody, indehiscent; flowers with 5 petals, 3 of which are large, white, up to 2 cm long .... **5. Hymenaea**

5 Leaves bipinnate (leaflets arising from 2 or more pinnae) 6

Leaves once-pinnate (i.e. leaflets arising from a single main axis) 10

6 Young shoots rusty-red to maroon, densely velvety .... **2. Burkea**

Young shoots not rusty-red to maroon; may be brown velvety 7

7 Branches and leaves armed with sharp straight or recurved spines or prickles; leaflets large, 1,2 to 4,5 cm long .... **18. Caesalpinia**

Branches and leaves without spines or prickles 8

8 Leaflets small, acacia-like, seldom more than 10 mm long; pods thinly woody to almost leathery with a wing-like margin, indehiscent... .... **20. Peltophorum**

Leaflets 2 cm or more long; pods woody, dehiscent 9

9 Leaves with 2 to 4 pairs of pinnae, leaflets 2 to 5 cm long; flowers in more or less dense spikes; pods flattened, not channelled, with 2 to 11 seeds .... **1. Erythrophleum**

Leaves with 3 to 7 pairs of pinnae, leaflets about 2 cm long; flowers in terminal panicles; pods very distinctive, oblanceolate-cylindric, narrowly tapering to the base, deeply channelled above and below; 1 to 2 seeded .... **19. Bussea**

10 Leaflets very small to minute and conspicuously widely spaced, or absent .... **17. Parkinsonia**

Leaflets clearly visible, at least 5 mm in length 11

11 Leaves imparipinnate (i.e. ending in an odd terminal leaflet) 12

Leaves paripinnate (i.e. ending in an even pair of leaflets) 14

12 Leaves with 4 to 6 pairs of leaflets plus the terminal leaflet .... **15. Dialium**

Leaves with more than 6 pairs of leaflets plus the terminal leaflet 13

13 Leaves with 11 to 28 pairs of leaflets plus the terminal leaflet; petals absent, flowers forming a semi-spherical head of orange-yellow stamens; fruit more or less spherical, 4 to 8 × 3 to 6 cm, thin-walled, fleshy, yellow when mature .... **21. Cordyla**

Leaves with 7 to 11 pairs of leaflets plus the terminal leaflet; flowers with a single, large, upstanding, conspicuous, white crinkly petal; fruit a cylindric, dry, hard, sinuous bean or pod, thick walled, dark reddish-brown when mature .... **22. Swartzia**

14 Fruits cylindric or partially compressed, leathery not woody 15

Fruits flat, woody 16

15 Fruits indehiscent, sausage-shaped, containing soft sticky pulp .... **10. Tamarindus**

Fruits partially dehiscent or indehiscent, long and slender, contents not soft and pulpy........ .... **16. Cassia**

16 Branches with thickset spines and spine-tipped dwarf lateral branches .... **8. Umtiza**

Branches not armed 17

17 Margin of the pod tending to separate away from the central section; flowers 5-partite, red to pink, with copious nectar .... **7. Schotia**

Margin of the pod not separating away 18

18 Pods do not twist into a spiral; seeds ovoid, blackish with a bright orange to red aril enveloping about one-third of the seed; flowers with a single, large, conspicuous, orange-red petal .... **11. Afzelia**

Pods dehisce exposively and immediately twist into a more of less tight spiral 19

19 Flowers large, conspicuous, with 5 mauve to pale pink, crinkly petals in a large, thickset raceme (spray) up to 30 cm long, sepals and stalks dark brown, velvety; pods brown, velvety, often showing yellowish patches where rubbed; broadest near apex, tapering to the base .... **9. Baikiaea**

Flowers not colourful and showy, greenish-white to yellowish, in spikes or branched sprays 20

20 Pods dark brown, velvety; flowers in branched heads, or panicles, about 15 to 30 cm long; not conspicuous .... **12. Julbernardia**

Pods smooth, without hairs at least when mature; flowers in small, simple or branched heads, racemes or panicles, not more than 10 cm long or broad .... **6. Brachystegia**

263

CAESALPINIOIDEAE

1. ERYTHROPHLEUM R. Br.

Trees, unarmed. **Leaves:** alternate, 2-pinnate; leaflets alternate on the rachis; glands absent. Stipules very small and falling early. **Flowers:** in panicles, each branch of which is spike-like. Bisexual, all floral parts in fives; stamens 10 in 2 whorls. **Fruit:** a woody, flattened pod, with an articulated stalk.

Key to the species of *Erythrophleum:*

1 Leaflets with apex broadly tapering to rounded; calyx lobes more or less free; pods split simultaneously down both sides; 2 to 5 seeds .... **E. africanum**
  Leaflets with apex markedly attenuate; calyx lobes distinctly joined at the base; pods split down one side at first and later, reluctantly, down the second side; 5 to 11 seeds 2
2 Stamen filaments covered with woolly hairs for almost their whole length; leaflets up to 4 × 2 cm; Swaziland and southern Moçambique .... **E. lasianthum**
  Stamen filaments without hairs; leaflets up to 5 × 2,5 cm; eastern Rhodesia, Moçambique and northwards, not in Natal .... **E. suaveolens**

Erythrophleum africanum (Welw. ex Benth.) Harms   Illust. 69
S.A. no: 194   Ordeal tree. Oordeelboom
Rhod. no: 241   Ordeal tree

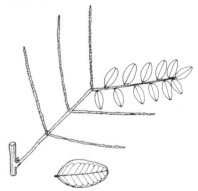

A medium to large tree 4 to 12 m in height; occurring in hot, dry, low-lying areas, associated with Kalahari sand and often a constituent of riverine thicket. **Bark:** grey to blackish and rather rough. **Leaves:** with 3 to 4 pairs of pinnae, each bearing about 10 to 17 leaflets; leaflets elliptic, 2,5 to 5 cm long, under surface finely velvety; apex broadly tapering to rounded or notched; base broadly tapering; margin entire; petiolules short; petiolate. **Flowers:** in more or less dense spikes, up to 9 cm long, cream or yellowish, often grouped together in large heads, sweetly scented; calyx lobes more or less free; petals small; stamens conspicuous (August to October). **Fruit:** a pod, up to 17 × 3 cm, brown, splitting along both sides simultaneously, each section curving backwards; 2 to 5 brown seeds (November to March).

On a quick field impression this tree resembles *Burkea africana* Hook. The roots and leaves have poisonous properties. The wood is red-brown, heavy, hard and durable; it is difficult to work but makes attractive furniture and is a useful general purpose timber. It is burnt for charcoal which is used by African iron-workers. The tree yields an amber-coloured gum similar to gum arabic.

Erythrophleum lasianthum Corbishley
[*E. guineense* G. Don var. *swazica* Burtt Davy]
S.A. no: 196   Swazi ordeal tree. Swazi-oordeelboom
Rhod. no: —

A medium to large tree, 8 to 15 m in height; with a limited distribution where it can become locally dominant in dry sand forest. This species very closely resembles *E. suaveolens* and the differences are given in the key.

The bark is poisonous and the leaves are known to have killed stock. The bark is powdered for medicinal use, although a large dose would probably prove fatal; it is ground to make snuff for the treatment of headaches and colds and to cure lung sickness in cattle.

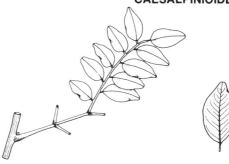

Erythrophleum suaveolens (Guillemin & Perrottet) Brenan
[*E. guineense* G. Don]
S.A. no: —
Rhod. no. 242   Forest ordeal tree

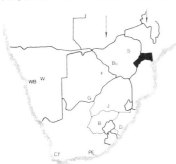

A medium to large tree reaching 20 m in height; occurring in low altitude rain forest, often along rivers. **Bark:** blackish and rough. **Leaves:** with 2 to 3 pairs of pinnae, each bearing 7 to 13 leaflets; leaflets oval to ovate, 1,9 to 5 × 1,3 to 2,5 cm, dark green and glossy; apex markedly attenuate; base asymmetric; margin entire, wavy. **Flowers:** in fluffy, cream to yellow spikes; calyx lobes distinctly joined at the base (August to November). **Fruit:** a flat pod, dark brown and leathery, 8 to 17 × 3 to 5,3 cm, splitting down one side at first, and later, reluctantly, down the other side, to release 5 to 11 seeds (March to July, but old pods can be found on the tree at most times of the year).

The wood is very hard, heavy, and is resistant to termite and fungal attack. It has been used for heavy construction, sleepers, harbour work, bridges and parquet flooring as well as in cabinet-making; there have been suggestions that this species might be grown for commercial exploitation. The roots and especially the bark contain a poisonous alkaloid, erythrophlein, a severe gastro-intestinal irritant and a cardiac depressant which causes death by heart failure. A valuable drug when administered correctly under medical supervision, it is also one of the commonest of the African poisons (known as *mwavi)* and features in the savage 'Trial by Ordeal' practices, now forbidden by law in most countries but possibly still occurring in a few isolated areas. There are many variations of this ceremony and only a brief account can be given here. A person accused of a serious crime, such as witchcraft, may be forced to submit to a Trial by Ordeal. The populace gathers round and watches as the dried bark of this tree is pounded, after which a small amount of the powder is mixed with water in a cup and given to the accused to drink. If he vomits he will live and is deemed innocent, but if he fails to do so death is almost certain to follow and he is tacitly assumed to be guilty. The unfortunate man, or woman, must remain in full view of the audience during the entire ordeal, and can only try to induce vomiting by drinking water handed to him by children.

Symptoms of the poison are giddiness, a headache and disturbed vision. In the final stages, which may occur three or four hours after taking the poison, the victim starts staggering and his legs become progressively weaker until he is no longer able to stand. At this point the onlookers usually rush in and hurl stones at the body thus crushing it. The relatives take the mangled corpse into the bush, lay it on logs and cover it with grass; no other covering is permitted and burial is not allowed. The size of the dose is a significant factor for a large overdose will almost certainly produce vomiting; the outcome of the trial, therefore, is very much in the hands of the presiding witchdoctor.

This species closely resembles *E. lasianthum*.

265

CAESALPINIOIDEAE

2. BURKEA Benth.

Burkea africana Hook.   Illust. 70
S.A. no: 197   Red syringa. Rooisering
Rhod. no: 243   Burkea

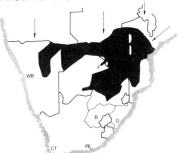 

A medium sized tree 8 to 10 m in height; occurring in various types of woodland over a wide range of altitudes and habitats, but most characteristic of the hot, low-lying areas. **Bark:** dark grey, rough and flaking. Young shoots and tips to young branches densely velvety and rusty-red to maroon; this can extend along the leaf petioles. **Leaves:** crowded at the ends of the branchlets; bipinnate, with 2 pairs of pinnae and 5 to 9 alternate leaflets per pinna; leaflets elliptic, 3 to 6 × 1,5 to 3 cm grey-green to dark green, with silvery appressed hairs when very young, losing these later; apex rounded and notched; base oblique; margin entire. **Flowers:** creamy-white, about 5 mm in diameter, produced in long, graceful, pendulous spikes, up to 24 cm long, crowded near the ends of the branchlets (September to November, often appearing before the leaves, giving the tree a showy, shaggy white appearance). **Fruit:** a thin, flat pod, about 8 × 2,5 cm, pale brown, indehiscent, hanging in conspicuous clusters from the ends of the branches (February to July, but remaining on the tree for months, frequently until after the leaves have fallen at the end of the season).

The wood is hard, heavy and tough, varying in colour from pale yellow to reddish-brown; it has an attractive lustre but is liable to borer attack if untreated. The comparatively small size of the tree provides only short lengths of timber, limiting its use to smaller pieces of furniture and parquet blocks for flooring. These trees are the hosts to a species of caterpillar which, roasted and dried, are relished by Africans who will cut down branches or whole trees to obtain this food; they call it *mukarati* which means 'the tree with caterpillars'. An extract from the bark and the pods has been used for tanning and, in Rhodesia, the Zezuru people chew the bark and apply it as a poultice to septic sores.

In the field, without flowers or fruits, these trees are often confused with *Albizia antunesiana,* even by Africans. A quick field impression can also cause confusion with *Erythrophleum africanum* but, in both cases, the velvety, rusty-red to maroon tips to the branchlets of *Burkea* are definitive.

3. GUIBOURTIA J. J. Benn. emend. J. Léonard

Unarmed, evergreen trees. **Leaves:** compound with a single pair of leaflets. Stipules small and falling early. **Flowers:** produced in small panicles. All floral parts in fours or fives; sepals white, but green-backed; petals absent; stamens 10 to 12 in 2 whorls. **Fruit:** a flat pod, finely veined, dehiscent or indehiscent, asymmetric.
(cf. *Colophospermum mopane* – see key to genera)

Key to the species:
Leaflets 3 to 10 cm long, ovate to sickle-shaped; pods small, almost circular, 2 to 3 cm long, thickly
    woody, brown to dark brown, splitting along one margin only and the single seed, about 1 cm long,
    hard, shiny red to red-brown with a yellowish aril, hangs out of the pod on a thread-like stalk.
    Occurring in western Rhodesia, Botswana, South West Africa and northwards ....
.... **G. coleosperma**
Leaflets 3 to 5 cm long, ovate, not sickle-shaped; pods larger, 4 × 3 cm, thin and flat, leathery not
    woody, pale cream-brown, indehiscent. Reaching its southern limit in western and south-eastern
    Rhodesia, north-eastern Transvaal and adjacent areas in Moçambique; not recorded from Botswana
266   or from South West Africa .... **G. conjugata**

Guibourtia coleosperma (Benth.) J. Léonard   Illust. 71
S.A. no: 199   Large false mopane. Bastermopanie
Rhod. no: 244   Large false mopane

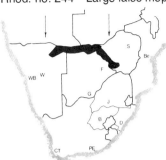

A medium sized to large evergreen tree, 6 to 20 m in height, with a fine, rounded crown; occurring in open woodland and dry forest almost confined to areas of Kalahari sand. **Bark:** smooth, cream to pinkish-cream, often with patches of dark brown to black flakes; in old, large trees the whole trunk may be dark blackish-brown, rough and flaky; young branches are conspicuously red. **Leaves:** alternate, compound with 1 pair of leaflets; leaflets ovate, curved, rather sickle-shaped, 3 to 10 × 2 to 4 cm, markedly asymmetric, without hairs, dark glossy green above, paler below, gland-dotted; apex broadly tapering to rather rounded and often abruptly attenuate; petiole short, 4 to 7 mm long. **Flowers:** small, creamy-white, star-shaped, about 10 mm in diameter, produced in profusion in rather lax terminal heads or panicles (December to March). **Fruit:** a small, thickly woody pod, almost circular, 2 to 3 cm long, brown to dark brown, eventually splitting down one side only, the valves curling back like lips to partially release the single seed, up to 10 mm in diameter, shiny red to red-brown with a yellow aril, which hangs out and down on a thread-like stalk (May to July, but extending either way by a month or more).

The wood is attractive, soft, pinkish-brown in colour and is known commercially as *machibi*. There are numerous records of the seeds and especially the arils being used as food; in Botswana and in Zambia the arils and the red skins are removed with warm water and either eaten or made into a drink which is said not only to be very nourishing but to have saved lives in times of famine. The seeds themselves are roasted under the coals of a fire then pounded and eaten as meal; this is an important staple food of the Kung Bushmen.

Guibourtia conjugata (Bolle) J. Léonard
S.A. no: 200   Small false mopane. Kleinbastermopanie
Rhod. no: 245   Small false mopane

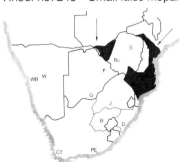

A small to medium sized tree, 7 to 9 m in height, generally smaller than the previous species; occurring in low altitude open woodland and bush, usually in deep sand, often along rivers. **Bark:** whitish-grey to brownish, smooth to flaky. **Leaves:** alternate, compound, with 1 pair of leaflets, ovate, scarcely curved, generally smaller than the previous species, 3 to 5 × 1,8 to 3,6 cm, shiny green above, paler below, gland-dotted; apex broadly tapering to rounded, markedly asymmetric; base asymmetric; margin slightly wavy; petiole 8 to 12 mm. **Flowers:** white to creamy-yellow, about 5 mm in diameter, in loose heads or panicles, smaller and shorter than those of *G. coleosperma;*

267

stamens conspicuous, giving the flowers a rather spidery appearance (November to January, but may be a month or more on either side of this). **Fruit:** a thin, flat pod, leathery not woody, almost circular, about 4 × 3 cm, pale creamy-brown, indehiscent (June to July). The pod closely resembles that of *Colophospermum mopane*, but seeds of *Guibourtia conjugata* lack the convolutions and the resin glands characteristic of the seeds of *Colophospermum mopane;* they also lack the aril possessed by the seeds of *Guibourtia coleosperma*.

The wood is hard and heavy; it is attractive in appearance being streaked with dark and medium brown; the sapwood is a pale yellowish colour. It makes good, durable fencing posts and, had it a wider distribution, it could be useful for flooring and furniture.

4. COLOPHOSPERMUM Kirk ex Benth.

Colophospermum mopane (Kirk ex Benth.) Kirk ex J. Léonard   Illust. 72
[*Copaifera mopane* Kirk ex Benth.]
S.A. no: 198   Mopane. Mopanie
Rhod. no: 246   Mopane

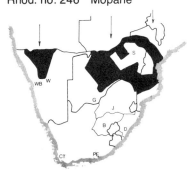 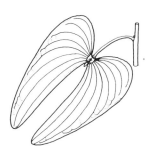

A medium to large tree 4 to 18 m in height, usually about 10 m; dominant over great areas of south tropical Africa in hot, low-lying areas, often on alluvial soils, but it tolerates alkaline and poorly drained soils better than will many other species. **Bark:** dark grey to blackish and characteristically deeply, vertically fissured and flaking in narrow strips. **Leaves:** alternate, compound, drooping, with 2 leaflets arising close together and so resembling butterfly wings; the vestigial remains of a third, terminal leaflet forms a very small appendage between the pair of leaflets; leaflets ovate, 4,5 to 10 × 1,5 to 5 cm, dotted with translucent glands; apex tapering; base markedly asymmetric and slightly lobed on 1 side; margin entire; petiole 2 to 4 cm long. **Flowers:** greenish, small, inconspicuous, in short axillary racemes, or sprays. Sepals 4, greenish; petals absent; stamens 20 to 25, hanging out of the flowers (October to March, but the flowering season can be erratic, sometimes the trees in a whole area producing no flowers for several years). **Fruit:** a flattened pod, oval or leathery not woody, indehiscent (March to June). The seeds are distinctive, flat, conspicuously convoluted, sticky, and copiously dotted with resin glands.

This is one of the principal trees of the hot, low-lying areas of south tropical Africa, reaching its southernmost limit just south of the Olifants River in the Kruger National Park in the Transvaal. The mopane is one of the most distinctive vegetation groups, often forming pure stands. These have given rise to the now accepted term 'mopane woodland' or *Colophospermum* woodland which has an atmosphere entirely of its own. The leaves of these trees hang down and during the heat of the day the leaflets move close together thus casting little shade. When conditions do not favour the development of trees, the plants can remain stunted, forming mopane scrub. The leaves provide important fodder and many animals, including cattle, browse on them eagerly and even eat the dry pods off the ground. Although these smell strongly of turpentine, fortunately neither the milk nor the meat is tainted as a result. Caterpillars of a large brownish-grey moth, *Gonimbrasia belina* – commonly known as 'mopane worms' – feed on the leaves. They are dramatically vivid in colouring and despite their somewhat alarming appearance are eagerly sought after by many Africans in whose diet they form an important ingredient since they are high in protein content. Mopane worms are roasted and, in times of plenty, are dried in which form they can be stored for months. In autumn the leaves of the mopane tree turn yellow and then brown; they are shed irregularly in the ensuing months but by the end of winter most of the trees are bare. The small, thin, flat pods are comparatively light and are to some extent dispersed by wind but mainly by adhering to the hooves or feet of passing animals. The seeds germinate easily provided they are planted while still in the pod, but seedlings are slow-growing and are susceptible to damping-off. Mopane wood is dark reddish-brown to almost black in colour; it is very durable, hard and heavy, and although it is difficult to work some beautiful pieces of furniture have been made from it. It has also been extensively used for mine props and as railway sleepers and it makes very good firewood, giving off a sweet smell and an intense heat.

5. HYMENAEA L.

Hymenaea verrucosa Gaertn.
[*Trachylobium verrucosum* Oliver; *T. hornemannianum* Hayne; *T. mossambicense* Klotzsch]
S.A. no: —
Rhod. no: —   Gum copal

A medium sized to large tree, 6 to 25 m in height; occurring in coastal evergreen bush, woodland or forest; rare towards the southern limit of its range but becoming increasingly frequent further north. **Bark:** pale grey, smooth to roughish. **Leaves:** alternate, compound, with 1 pair of leaflets; leaflets ovate-elliptic, 3 to 12 × 2 to 6 cm, copiously gland-dotted; apex tapering; base markedly asymmetric, rounded on one side, tapering on the other; margin entire; petiolules very short, petiole about 1 cm long. Stipules very small and falling early. **Flowers:** in large, loose sprays, or panicles, up to 30 × 20 cm. Bracteoles well developed; sepals 4, curving back; petals 5, the upper 3 large, white and quite showy, the lower 2 very small and inconspicuous; stamens 10, conspicuous (February to March). **Fruit:** an unusual and distinctive pod, thickly woody, stout, oblong-cylindric, up to 5 × 3 cm, indehiscent and knobby with coarse gummy warts (found on the tree at most times of the year). This valuable timber tree is exploited in East Africa. The gum which exudes from the trunk and branches, known as gum copal, is exported from East Africa for incorporation into superior quality varnishes. The gum drops to the ground and, in time, becomes semi-fossilised; long after the parent trees are dead, this fossilised gum may be dug up, at which stage it is said to be of even better quality than when it is fresh.

6. BRACHYSTEGIA Benth.

Trees. **Leaves:** paripinnate, stipulate; leaflets few to many, sessile, very variable in size and shape, normally opposite. **Flowers:** small, inconspicuous, in short racemes or spikes or branched to form panicles; but completely enclosed by 2 large bracteoles which persist; calyx with 1 to 10 lobes, or absent; petals absent; stamens usually 10, free or shortly joined at the base; ovary oblong, asymmetric, flattened. **Pod:** flat, woody, splitting explosively, the 2 valves springing into spirals and throwing the seeds considerable distances. **Seeds:** flattened, hard and shiny.
This large and taxonomically difficult genus is confined to tropical Africa. Eight species are known to occur south of the Zambezi River and one of these, *B. spiciformis*, reaches its southernmost limit at about 25°S in Moçambique. The genus as a whole is noted for the striking colours of the young foliage produced during the spring flush – from salmon-pink to crimson and dark wine-red; these often brilliant colours rapidly fade through shades of yellow to pale, fresh green and soon darken to the shade of the mature leaves.
Some of the species hybridise freely with one another, and their existence adds to the problem of classification. Such hybrids are mentioned in the text.

269

CAESALPINIOIDEAE

The various species of *Brachystegia*, especially *B. spiciformis*, *B. boehmii* and *B. glaucescens* together with the related *Julbernardia globiflora*, dominate the Rhodesian highveld vegetation. They yield a timber of poor quality, but the wood is widely used as a fuel and the trees are of great ecological importance. Although they come to within 90 km of the South African border, and in Moçambique they reach well south of this, they have never been recorded from the Republic of South Africa itself.

Key to the species of *Brachystegia*:

1 Leaflets numerous, usually in 25 to 55 pairs, conspicuously narrow, usually about 3 mm wide and 0,5 to 1,5 cm long, set closely together (Hybrids with *B. spiciformis* occur in which leaflets are broader, but still many and set closely together) .... **B. microphylla**
   Leaflets larger and usually fewer, than in the above species 2
2 Leaves usually with not more than 4 pairs of leaflets 3
   Leaves usually with 5 or more pairs of leaflets .... '4
3 Leaves usually with only 3 pairs of leaflets, broadly elliptic, apex rounded and notched; inflorescence short, lax and branched. Not extending further south than the extreme north of Rhodesia .... **B. manga**
   Leaves with usually 4 pairs of leaflets, elliptic to oblong, tapering to the apex; inflorescence a dense, compact, unbranched spike. Widespread in Rhodesia and parts of Moçambique .... **B. spiciformis**
4 Leaves usually with 5 to 7 pairs of leaflets 5
   Leaves usually with more than 7 pairs of leaflets 6
5 Leaflets broadly elliptic, 1,5 to 2,5 cm broad, twisted to right angles with the main axis. Occurring in the north-east of Rhodesia and adjacent areas of Moçambique and northwards .... **B. allenii**
   Leaflets narrowly oblong or triangular, seldom more than 9 mm broad, occurring in extreme north-east and south-east of Rhodesia and adjacent areas in Moçambique ..... **B. sp. No. 1**
6 Leaflets rather small, slender, 1,3 to 3 × 0,4 to 1 cm, always associated with rocky koppies.. .... **B. glaucescens**
   Leaflets larger than above, in open woodland 7
7 Leaves with 5 to 12 pairs of leaflets, oblong to elliptic, 2 to 4 × 0,5 to 1,5 cm ..... **B. utilis**
   Leaves with 13 to 28 pairs of leaflets, narrowly oblong to narrowly triangular, 3 to 6 × 1 to 1,5 cm .... **B. boehmii**

Brachystegia allenii Burtt Davy & Hutch.
S.A. no: —
Rhod. no: 247   Escarpment brachystegia

A small to medium sized tree, usually 5 to 6 m in height and rarely above 10 m; confined to the dry, rocky escarpment country verging the Zambezi valley. **Bark:** pale grey, rough, deeply fissured vertically and cracked transversely. **Leaves:** compound, usually with 5 pairs of opposite leaflets; leaflets ovate-elliptic to almost spherical, 2 to 4 × 1,5 to 2,5 cm, without hairs; apex rounded, notched; base asymmetric, lobed, clasping the rachis and each pair of leaflets twisted into a plane at right angles to the main axis; this is a distinguishing feature. The flush of young leaves is bright maroon-red, the mature leaves bluish or greyish-green. **Flowers:** in short, terminal branched heads, or panicles, up to 7 × 7 cm; sepals small and white, (September to October). **Fruit:** a pinkish-brown

270

pod, 10 to 15 cm long, at right angles to the stalk and all produced on the crown of the tree above the foliage (April to August).

Pure *B. allenii* is rare in Rhodesia, most of the material consisting of hybrids with *B. boehmii,* the main feature of this cross being a fine hairiness on the leaves. The distribution map includes these hybrids.

Brachystegia boehmii Taub.   Illust. 73
[*B. woodiana* Harms]
S.A. no: —
Rhod. no: 248   Mufuti, Prince-of-Wales' feathers

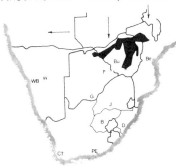

A sturdy, spreading tree 5 to 16 m in height; common in open deciduous woodland, and frequently locally dominant, particularly on poorly-drained soils. **Bark:** grey or brownish, rough and coarsely flaking in squarish woody scales. **Leaves:** with 13 to 28 pairs of closely ranked, overlapping leaflets; leaflets narrowly oblong to narrowly triangular, 3 to 6 × 1 to 1,5 cm, the sides almost parallel, the upper surface of mature leaves without hairs, but all other parts finely hairy; apex rounded and finely notched; base asymmetric and slightly lobed; margin entire. **Flowers:** sweetly scented, in short, compact, branched heads, or panicles, up to 10 × 8 cm, terminal or axillary; bracteoles green; sepals small, white (September to December). **Fruit:** a large brown pod, up to 15 cm long (May to July).

The bark contains 3% tannin; an extract which imparts a red-brown colour to the finished hide has been used for tanning as the final dressing. It also provides the most durable bark rope which Africans use extensively: the inner bark is stripped off in long, narrow lengths which are then chewed and rolled alternately until they are soft and pliable, thus forming an excellent cord. The leaf buds are conspicuously large and the newly opened young leaves often bright red.

Brachystegia glaucescens Burtt Davy & Hutch.   Illust. 74
[*B. tamarindoides* auct.]
S.A. no: —
Rhod. no: 249   Mountain-acacia

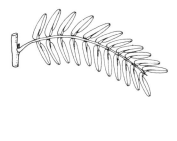

A spreading, beautiful tree up to 15 m in height, inclined to develop a flat top; confined to the summits and slopes of rocky hills and koppies. **Bark:** smooth, grey, sparsely flaking in round discs. **Leaves:** with 10 to 16 pairs of leaflets, or even more; leaflets rather small, oblong, 1,3 to 3 × 0,4 to 1 cm, bluish-green to dark green above, paler below; apex broadly tapering to rounded; base asymmetric, the inner side tapering, the outer side lobed; margin entire; petiolules almost absent, petiole up to

271

1,5 cm. **Flowers:** small, creamy-white, in a short, terminal, branched head, or panicle up to 4 × 4 cm (September to October). **Fruit:** a dark brown, to purplish, woody pod, 8 to 13 cm long, splitting explosively and immediately spiralling, throwing the seeds considerable distances (April to July). This species produces some of the most vivid flush colours. Hybrids between this and *B. spiciformis* are relatively frequent. The wood, very liable to borer attack, is durable if treated and is a useful general purpose timber.

Brachystegia manga De Wild.

S.A. no: —
Rhod. no: 250   Blue-leaved brachystegia

A small to medium sized tree, 4 to 15 m in height; reaching its southern limit in deciduous woodland on the hot, dry Zambezi valley escarpment. **Bark:** smooth, silvery-grey in young trees, later becoming rather rough, brownish-grey and cracked into square scales, but not flaking. **Leaves:** usually with only 3 pairs of leaflets, sometimes with 4 pairs, widely spaced, rather stiff, broad, oval to almost circular, 2 to 8 × 1,5 to 5 cm, without hairs or occasionally very finely hairy, bluish-green, becoming pale yellowish grey-green in autumn; apex rounded, notched; base asymmetric, broadly tapering and lobed; margin entire. **Flowers:** very small, yellowish-green, in terminal branched heads or panicles, up to 9 × 5 cm (October to November). **Fruit:** a rather small pod, up to 10 × 3 cm, usually less, pinkish-brown to purplish and conspicuously pendulous (April to October).
The bunched young leaves in dark, vivid flush colours are very characteristic of this species.

Brachystegia microphylla Harms

S.A. no: —
Rhod. no: 251   Small-leaved brachystegia

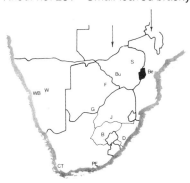 

A small to medium sized tree, 6 to 15 m in height and inclined to be flat-topped; occurring in deciduous woodland usually associated with hills or mountains. **Bark:** pale grey, smoothish, inclined to flake, exposing orange or yellow patches of underbark. **Leaves:** short, with 25 to 55 pairs of very fine, slender leaflets, 0,5 to 1,5 × 0,1 to 0,3 cm, narrowly triangular and often curved; apex tapering; base obliquely and shallowly lobed; margin entire. Stipules fall very early. **Flowers:** small, in small, rather loose, terminal panicles or branched heads, 2 to 4 × 2 to 4 cm (September to October). **Fruit:** a small, flat pod, thinly woody, usually less than 9 cm long, brownish-purple (June to September).
272 This species commonly hybridises with *B. spiciformis* and hybrids are also recorded with *B. utilis*.

Brachystegia spiciformis Benth. Illust. 75

[*B. randii* E. G. Baker]
S.A. no: —
Rhod. no: 252 Msasa

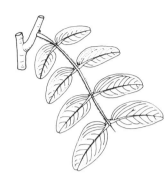

A medium to large tree, 8 to 15 m in height; the branches are heavy, thrusting upwards and outwards, often twisting and curving, giving the tree a beautiful shape and balance; this is the most widespread species of *Brachystegia* in Rhodesia and Moçambique and it is dominant and ecologically important over large areas of its range; occurring in open, deciduous woodland, tolerating a wide range of soil types. **Bark:** pale grey and smooth when young, later becoming rough, dark grey, deeply fissured vertically and coarsely, horizontally cracked, slowly flaking in thick, irregular scales. **Leaves:** pendulous, dark green, shiny; leaflets usually in 4 pairs, the terminal pair being the largest, oblong-elliptic, 2,5 to 8 × 1 to 4,5 cm with or without very fine hairs; apex tapering, finally rounded, notched, and tipped with a fine hair-like bristle; base markedly asymmetric; margin entire; petiolules very short, petiole up to 2,5 cm long, very finely hairy. Stipules threadlike, falling very early. **Flowers:** small, greenish; produced in short, dense, thickset, terminal spikes, 3 to 6 cm long; sweetly scented (August to November). **Fruit:** a large, woody pod, flattened, up to 14 cm in length, dark brown and smooth when mature, splitting exposively (May to August).

The bark is astringent, containing 13% tannin, and an extract of this is used by Africans as a final dressing in tanning hides; it imparts a reddish colour to the finished product. An infusion of the roots provides a treatment for dysentery and diarrhoea and a decoction is applied as an eyewash in cases of conjunctivitis. The flush colours of the young leaves vary from pale fawn to deep claret-red and these trees are important among the contributors to the splendid colour displays in spring; at all times of the year they must be among the most beautiful trees in the world. They provide fine shade and are being increasingly cultivated; the seed germinates readily, but the seedlings are difficult to transplant and the trees are rather slow-growing. The wood is brown in colour, coarse and not durable; even when treated it is a rather inferior general purpose timber, but it is widely used as fuel.

This species hybridises readily with *B. glaucescens* and with *B. microphylla*. It is also easily confused in the field with *Julbernardia globiflora* and the differences between these two are given under the latter species.

Brachystegia utilis Burtt Davy & Hutch.
S.A. no: —
Rhod. no: 253 False mufuti

273

CAESALPINIOIDEAE

Often a slender tree, reaching 10 m in height, at first sight somewhat resembling *B. boehmii;* occurring in mixed woodland, often on ridges or hill slopes in stony or gravelly soil. **Bark:** pale grey and smooth at first, later becoming rough, grey or brownish. **Leaves:** with 5 to 12 pairs of leaflets (usually more than 7); leaflets oblong to elliptic, 2 to 4 × 0,5 to 1,5 cm; almost without hairs to densely velvety; apex and base rounded, base asymmetric; margin entire; petiole short, 4 to 8 mm long. Stipules rather leaf-like, up to 1,5 cm long, falling early. The leaflets are more rounded and more widely spaced than those of *B. boehmii.* **Flowers:** small, greenish, in terminal or axillary rather lax branched heads or panicles, about 5 × 5 cm (October to November). **Fruit:** a thinly woody pod, pinkish-brown to plum-coloured, quite large, up to 12 cm in length (April to August).

Brachystegia sp. no. 1
S.A. no: —
Rhod. no: 254   Torre's brachystegia

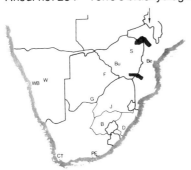

A large tree up to 15 m in height with a spreading crown; often forming almost pure stands on rocky outcrops and hills. **Bark:** grey, smooth, or slightly flaking or scaling. **Leaves:** with 6 to 7 pairs of leaflets; leaflets narrowly oblong or slightly triangular, usually about 2,8 × 0,9 cm; apex tapering, finally rounded; base asymmetric, slightly lobed; margins entire. **Flowers:** small, in short, few-flowered heads about 2 × 2 cm (December). **Fruit:** a flattened pod, about 9 × 3 cm (September). There is some doubt as to the correct status of this species; it seems that it may be advisable to regard it as part of the very variable *Brachystegia spiciformis/glaucescens/microphylla* complex.

7. SCHOTIA Jacq.

Shrubs or trees, unarmed. **Leaves:** alternate, compound, paripinnate; with 3 to 18 pairs of leaflets. **Flowers:** in short, terminal or lateral, many-flowered panicles, often produced on the old wood. Bracts small, falling early; flower stalks (pedicels) short, producing compact heads; calyx 4, joined at the base to form a tube, persistent, red or reddish-brown; petals 5, sometimes long and narrow, red or pink, arising from the mouth of the calyx tube, falling early; stamens 10, arising with the petals, free or joined at the base; ovary oblong with a short stalk. **Pods:** woody, flattened, often curved, beaked, with a hard, persistent rim which often remains on the tree after the tardily dehiscent valves have eventually split away. The brown smooth seeds, 1 to 2 cm in diameter, with or without a yellow aril, may remain attached to this hard rim.

Key to the species of *Schotia:*
1 Usually with more than 6 pairs of leaflets, and the leaflets less than 1 cm in width, flowers with the stamens free from the base. Occurring in the eastern, southern, northern, north-western Cape and South West Africa .... **S. afra**
   Usually with less than 6 pairs of leaflets, and the leaflets more than 1 cm in width 2
2 Occurring in the eastern and southern Cape, reaching its eastern limit at about the Kei River. Leaflets comparatively large, 2,5 to 6 × 1,4 to 3 cm; flower heads comparatively lax; stamens joined at the base; petals well formed .... **S. latifolia**
   From Umtata in Transkei eastwards and northwards 3

3 A shrub or slender tree, up to 7 m in height, sometimes semi-climbing; leaflets rarely more than 2,5 cm long; flowers forming a congested head, 3 to 8 cm in diameter, terminally or on short lateral branches; stamens joined at the base forming a distinct sheath; petals well developed .... **S. capitata**

A medium to large tree, 10 to 16 m in height; leaflets usually larger than 2,5 cm long, up to 8,5 cm long; flowers forming congested heads, 6 to 13 cm in diameter, usually on the old wood; stamens joined at the base; some petals reduced in size and narrow, or may be absent .... **S. brachypetala**

In addition to these four species, there appear to be 2 hybrids: one is a cross between *S. latifolia* and *S. afra*, which retains the free stamens of *S. afra* but has only 4 to 5 pairs of leaflets, and is confined to a small area near Port Elizabeth in the eastern Cape; the other, near East London, also seems to be a cross between *S. latifolia* and *S. afra*, and its small leaves more closely resemble those of *S. afra* (4 to 10 pairs), but the stamens are joined at the base.

Schotia afra (L.) Bodin   Illust. 76

[*S. speciosa* Jacq.; *S. tamarindifolia* Afzel. ex Sims; *S. parvifolia* Jacq.; *S. angustifolia* E. Meyer; *S. venusta* Mason]
S.A. no: 201 and 201,1   Karoo boer-bean. Karooboerboon
Rhod. no: —

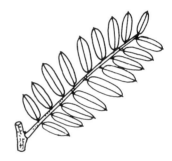

A small, many-branched tree, 3 to 5 m in height, often shrubby, with a twisted, gnarled trunk and stiff, pale branches; common in karroid bush and scrub and in rocky semi-desert regions often along dry watercourses. **Bark:** charcoal-grey, rather smooth, the larger stems tending to be longitudinally cracked and fissured. **Leaves:** fine and feathery, tending to be crowded on short lateral shoots; leaflets in 6 to 18 pairs, small, linear to oblong, 0,5 to 2,5 × 0,15 to 1 cm, dark green; apex very broadly tapering to rounded; base rounded, asymmetric; margin entire. **Flowers:** very showy, producing red splashes of colour in the dry countryside. Sepals red; petals sometimes pink but usually red, up to 2,5 cm long; stamens free. Flowers produced in dense, branched heads, or panicles about 7 to 8 cm long, on short lateral branches or, very occasionally, terminally (August to October). **Pods:** woody, shortly oblong, 5,5 to 12 × 3 to 3,5 cm, the hard rim persisting; seeds roundish, slightly flattened, pale brown, without the yellow aril (October to March, or later).
Africans either eat the seeds while they are still partly green, or roast the mature seeds in the fire and grind them into a meal, as did the early settlers. The wood is hard, tough and reddish-brown, but has little value because of the small size of the trees.

There are two varieties of this species:
In the coastal districts of the eastern and southern Cape; leaflets fewer and larger, 6 to 12 pairs, leaflets 3 to 10 mm wide ....var. *afra*
Inland and in Namaqualand and South West Africa; leaflets very small, fine, and feathery, 11 to 18 pairs, leaflets 1,5 to 3 mm wide .... var. *angustifolia* (E. Meyer) Harvey

Schotia brachypetala Sonder   Illust. 77
[*S. rogersii* Burtt Davy; *S. semireducta* Merxm.]
S.A. no: 202   Weeping boer-bean. Huilboerboon
Rhod. no: 255   Weeping schotia

A large tree, up to 16 m in height, with a rounded crown. Occurs in open, deciduous woodland and in drier types of woodland and scrub forest; frequently associated with termite mounds and also found along river banks. **Bark:** brown or brownish-grey and rough. **Leaves:** with 4 to 6 (occasionally 7) pairs of opposite or sub-opposite leaflets; leaflets oblong to ovate-oblong, 2 - 4,5 × 1,2 - 2,5 cm, with or without sparse hairs; apex rounded or abruptly finely pointed; base rounded, asymmetric; margin entire, wavy. **Flowers:** deep red with slender, pink petals up to 1,5 cm long, which are sometimes reduced or absent; stamens joined at the base. The flowers are produced in dense branched heads, or panicles, 6 to 13 cm long, borne on the old wood; copious nectar is produced (September to October). **Fruit:** a flattened, woody pod, usually 6 to 10 cm long with the characteristic persistent rim; seeds ovoid, flattened, pale brown, about 2 cm in diameter, with a large, conspicuous yellow aril (February to May).

The copious nectar which attracts insects and birds drips from the flowers and thus gives the tree its common name. The seeds are roasted and then eaten and the wood, which is hard, heavy and very dark in colour, produces handsome furniture. The bark has been used in tanning, and also to make a decoction which is taken for heartburn and also to alleviate a hangover.

Schotia capitata Bolle
[*S. tamarindifolia* Afzel. ex Sims var. *forbesiana* Baillon; *S. transvaalensis* Rolfe]
S.A. no: 203   Dwarf boer-bean. Kleinboerboon
Rhod. no: 256   Dwarf schotia

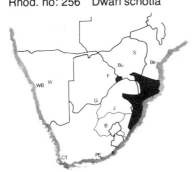 

A shrub or small, slender tree up to 7 m, sometimes semi-climbing, otten forming tangled thickets; occurring in hot dry localities, frequently associated with thornscrub. **Bark:** grey and smoothish. **Leaves:** with 3 to 5 pairs of opposite leaflets; leaflets elliptic to almost round, 1,5 to 2,5 × 1 to 1,8 cm; apex broadly tapering and abruptly narrowly pointed to rounded and notched; base tapering to rounded, often asymmetric; margin entire. **Flowers:** a dense, congested, almost spherical, branched head, or panicle, 3 to 8 cm in diameter; produced on short lateral branches, or, occasionally, terminally; the conspicuous stamens, joined at the base to form a distinct sheath, give the flowers a 'bottle-brush' appearance; the petals are well developed and, with the sepals, are blood red (October to November). **Fruit:** a flattened pod, up to 12 × 4 cm, with the characteristic persistent rim; the seeds are oval, 1,5 to 2 cm in diameter, pale brown, with a large yellow aril (February to May).

Schotia latifolia Jacq.
[*S. cuneifolia* Gaudich.; *S. diversifolia* Walp.]
S.A. no: 204   Bush boer-bean. Bosboerboon
Rhod. no: —

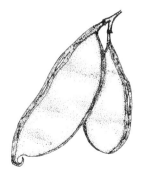

A small to medium sized, slender tree 3 to 10 m in height; occurring in dry bushveld often on stony slopes (Transvaal), and in scrub, scrub forest and fringing evergreen forest (eastern Cape). **Bark:** grey to reddish-brown, smooth. **Leaves:** with 3 to 5 pairs of opposite leaflets; leaflets elliptic-oblong, 2,5 to 6 × 1,4 to 3 cm; apex tapering to rounded; base tapering to rounded, asymmetric; margin entire. **Flowers:** much paler than those of the other species, pink to whitish rather than crimson-red, in rather loose, open, terminal heads, or panicles, about 8 × 8 cm; petals well developed, up to 2 to 2,5 cm long (November to January). **Fruit:** a flattened pod, broadly oval to oblong, about 10 × 4 cm, pale cinnamon-brown with the characteristic persistent rim which sometimes almost forms a narrow wing; the seeds are oval, flattened, up to 2 cm in diameter, with a large yellow aril (April to August). The geographical isolation of these two populations is interesting: those on the dry stony hillsides of the Transvaal are small, slender trees with a rather rounded crown, up to about 3 m in height; while those in the eastern Cape are short, stout trees of about 5 m in height when growing in the arid Fish River scrub, or slender, graceful trees when growing on forest margins.

8. UMTIZA T. R. Sim

Umtiza listerana T. R. Sim
S.A. no: 205   Umtiza. Omtisa
Rhod. no: —

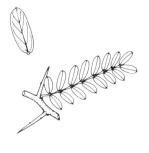

A small, erect, many-branched, strongly armed, evergreen tree up to 8 m in height; growing in or close to deep, wooded ravines. **Bark:** rough, dark brown to grey-black, sometimes rather rust-coloured; the stem may be deeply fluted; many of the axillary shoots are modified to form thickset spines. **Leaves:** alternate, compound, with 7 to 12 pairs of sub-opposite leaflets, without hairs, shining dark green, small, about 1 × 0,5 cm; apex square; base sharply tapering; margin entire. Stipules absent. **Flowers:** small, white, star-shaped; all floral parts in fives; calyx joined, bell-shaped; petals free, sometimes reduced; stamens 10; ovary shortly stalked. The flowers are produced in short, loose heads, or panicles, up to 8 × 5 cm, terminal on short lateral branches, borne on the top of the tree above the leaves; the strong spines make them difficult to reach so they are seldom collected; the flowers fall soon after opening (March to July). **Fruit:** an oblong, flat, woody pod, brown, about 5 cm long, splitting when ripe (the following May to June).

277

CAESALPINIOIDEAE

Although locally common in the forests and kloofs along the Buffalo River, this is almost the limit of its distribution; it sets seed in quantity but does not extend its range. The heartwood is small, but heavy, very hard and oily. Eve Palmer says that it was once used as bearings for propeller shafts in small boats, and that this natural oiliness provided constant lubrication. These trees feature in African myth and legend: pieces of bark are hung in huts as a protection against lightning and also to ward off evil spirits. Witchdoctors use sticks from these trees as healing wands, and in times of trouble the Xhosas make pilgrimages to a tree near East London which is reputed to possess particular powers. This is a rare tree in southern Africa and in South Africa it has been declared a protected species.

9. BAIKIAEA Benth.

Baikiaea plurijuga Harms   Illust. 78
S.A. no: 206   Rhodesian teak. Rhodesiese kiaat
Rhod. no: 257   Rhodesian teak

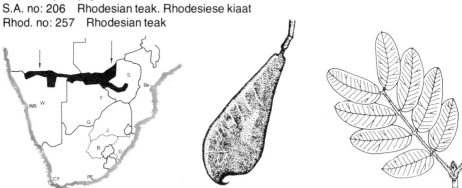

A medium to large tree, 8 to 16 m in height, with a large, dense, spreading crown; characteristic of areas of deep Kalahari sand, usually in open, deciduous woodland. **Bark:** smoothish and pale in young specimens, later becoming vertically fissured and cracked, and brown to grey in colour. **Leaves:** alternate, compound, with 4 to 5 pairs of opposite leaflets; leaflets oblong to elliptic, 3,5 to 7 × 2 to 2,5 cm; apex broadly tapering to rounded, often notched, bristle-tipped; base square to lobed; margin entire, inclined to be wavy, finely rolled under; petiole short. The swelling on the margin near the base of each leaflet appears to be very obscure in this species, although considered important in the other tropical species of *Baikiaea*. **Flowers:** very attractive, large, in strong, axillary racemes up to 30 cm long; buds dark brown or golden-brown and densely velvety. Sepals 4, sepals and stalks with dark brown velvety hairs; petals 5, pinkish mauve, crinkly, 2 to 3 × 1 to 1,5 cm; stamens 10; ovary stalked (December to March). **Fruit:** a flattened, woody, pod up to 13 × 5 cm broadest near the apex and tapering to the base, with dark brown velvety hairs which are frequently rubbed off to reveal golden-yellow patches; dehiscent, splitting explosively and immediately spiralling and throwing the seeds some distance (June to September).

The wood is even textured, hard, strong, durable and a beautiful dark red-brown; it has been used for furniture, flooring and railway sleepers and is exported in considerable quantities. When the London Corn Exchange was rebuilt in 1952 a special grooved floor was designed to take the grain thrown down by the merchants, and *B. plurijuga* was selected for the parquet blocks because of its ability to withstand abrasion without splintering.

10. TAMARINDUS L.

Tamarindus indica L.   Illust. 79
S.A. no: Tamarind. Tamarinde
Rhod. no: 258   Tamarind

A medium to large evergreen tree reaching 20 to 24 m in height, with a dense rounded crown and drooping branches; occurring in low altitude woodland, wooded grassland and bush, often associated with termite mounds and most frequently found along rivers in deep alluvial soil. **Bark:** pale grey, tending to be scaly and rough. **Leaves:** alternate, compound, with 10 to 18 pairs of opposite leaflets; leaflets narrowly oblong 1,2 to 3,2 × 0,3 to 1,1 cm, the petiole and rachis finely hairy, the midrib and net-veining more or less conspicuous on both surfaces; apex rounded to almost square, slightly

278

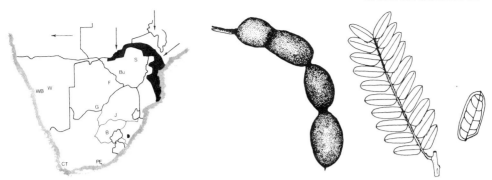

notched; base rounded, asymmetric, with a tuft of yellow hairs; margin entire, finely hair-fringed Stipules present, falling very early. **Flowers:** attractive pale yellow or pinkish, in small, lax spikes about 2,5 cm in width. The flower buds are completely enclosed by 2 bracteoles which fall very early; sepals 4; petals 5, the upper 3 well developed, the lower 2 minute; stamens 8, joined for half their length to form a band which separates near the top into 3 fertile stamens and 5 sterile teeth (November to March). **Fruit:** a pod, indehiscent, sausage-shaped, usually up to 10 to 18 cm long, slightly curved, velvety, rusty-brown; the shell of the pod is brittle and the seeds are embedded in a sticky, edible pulp (June to July).

These valuable trees probably had their origin in Africa and the Far East and from there they were carried to other countries, eventually spreading throughout the tropics in both the Old World and the New. They were known in Egypt four centuries before the birth of Christ and early Arab and Persian merchants came across the tree while trading with India. As the dark brown pulp made from the fruit resembled their own dried dates they called it *Tamare-hindi,* or Indian date, and this inspired Linnaeus, in the 18th century, to name the tree *Tamarindus indica.* It now reaches the southern limit of its range in Moçambique, and has also become naturalised round Durban.

The fruit pulp, mixed with a little salt, is a favourite ingredient of the curries and chutneys popular throughout India, though most of the tamarind imported into Europe today comes from the West Indies where sugar is added as a preservative. When freshly prepared, the pulp is a light brown colour but it darkens with time; it consists of 8% to 14% tartaric acid and acid potassium bitartrate, and 30% to 40% sugar. Its medicinal value has been recognised for centuries: it is still used as a laxative and a drink is prepared from it for treating fevers and inflammatory conditions. Dr W. J. Eggeling, in *Indigenous Trees of the Uganda Protectorate,* gives the following recipe for a refreshing drink: 'To 60 grams of pulp add about 1 litre of cold water and a little sugar; stir and leave in a cool place to mature for several days.' The flowers, leaves and seeds can also be eaten and are prepared in a variety of dishes, while the fruits can be made into jam, preserves and sweets. Even over-ripe fruits have their uses: they clean and brighten silver, copper and brass and Indian silversmiths polish their wares with a strong infusion of roots mixed with sea salt. Considering the ancient tradition of these trees and their variety of uses, it is not surprising that they are worshipped in certain areas of the Far East. The dark brown heartwood is hard, tough and difficult to work, but it takes a good polish. In the Sudan it has been found suitable for general carpentry and boat-building.

11. AFZELIA Smith

Afzelia quanzensis Welw.   Illust. 80
S.A. no: 207   Pod mahogany. Peulmahonie
Rhod. no: 259   Pod mahogany. Chamfuti

A medium to large spreading deciduous tree, usually 12 to 15 m in height, but reaching 35 m under ideal conditions; occurring in low altitude woodland and dry forest. **Bark:** greyish-brown and characteristically flaking in roundish woody scales, leaving pale patches. **Leaves:** alternate, compound, with 4 to 6 pairs of opposite to sub-opposite leaflets; leaflets oblong-elliptic, 2,3 to 9 × 1,5 to 6 cm, without hairs, shiny dark green above, much paler green below, leathery; apex broadly tapering to rounded, sometimes slightly notched; base broadly tapering; margin entire, wavy; petiolules of the leaflets twisted, petioles present. Stipules with a basal section joined which persists as a small scale when the upper section falls away. **Flowers:** in simple sprays, or once-branched racemes; stalks jointed. The bud is covered by 2 large bracteoles but these fall before the bud opens; sepals 4, unequal;

279

a single petal, large, clawed, expanded, red with yellow veining; stamens 7 plus 2 staminodes (July to November). **Fruit:** a large, flat, thickly woody pod, 10 to 17 cm long, dark brown; inside the pod there is a white pith, embedded in which are 6 to 10 distinctive dark blackish-brown seeds, oblong, up to 3 × 1,2 cm, each with a scarlet to orange aril enveloping the lower third to half of the seed (June to November).

The seeds are much in demand for ornaments and charms and are often strung into necklaces or made into trinkets which are sold as curios. The Zulu name for the tree, *mkehli,* means 'betrothed girl' for the black seed with its red aril suggests the head of a maiden with the red-ochred head-dress which she wears in the period prior to her marriage. The light red-brown timber has a good figure, is hard, works well and takes a fine polish. It has been used for building, plywood, furniture, panelling and in flooring blocks. The Africans make their dugout canoes from the trunks, while an infusion of the roots provides a remedy for bilharzia, a cupful of the liquid being blown into the bladder through a very thin reed and, in addition, being taken by the patient orally. It is also used for certain eye complaints. Washing in an infusion of the bark and roots which has steeped overnight is believed to bring a huntsman good luck while powdered bark mixed with one's own body oil is said to ward off attack or even provocation by others.

12. JULBERNARDIA Pellegr.

Trees. **Leaves:** alternate, compound, paripinnate; leaflets opposite, rather markedly asymmetric; petiolules often twisted. Stipulate. **Flowers:** in much-branched terminal panicles. All floral parts in fives; the bud is enclosed by bracteoles which fall early; sepals fringed with hairs; 1 petal larger than the other 4; stamens 10, 1 of which is free, the other 9 being joined shortly at the base. **Fruit:** a flat pod.

Key to the species of *Julbernardia:*
Leaflets large, usually 9 × 5 cm, in 3 to 4 pairs; sepals broadly spatula-shaped, 3 to 5 mm wide; the largest petal rotund or triangular, about 6 mm long .... **J. paniculata**
Leaflets considerably smaller, usually 6 × 2 cm, in 4 to 6 pairs; sepals oblong, 1,5 mm wide; the largest petal ovate and 6 to 9 mm long .... **J. globiflora**

Julbernardia globiflora (Benth.) Troupin   Illust. 81
[*Isoberlinia globiflora* (Benth.) Hutch. ex Greenway]
S.A. no: —
Rhod. no: 260   Munondo

A well branched, deciduous, rounded tree up to 15 m in height; occurring in mixed deciduous woodland; this is an ecologically important species, which is co-dominant with *Brachystegia spiciformis* over large areas in Rhodesia, Moçambique and countries to the north; it does not extend into South Africa. **Bark:** grey, smooth when young, rough later. **Leaves:** with 4 to 6 pairs of opposite leaflets; leaflets oblong to oblong-lanceolate, 2,5 to 8 × 1 to 3 cm, dark green, both surfaces finely hairy; apex rounded, often slightly notched; base broadly tapering, asymmetric; margin entire, finely hair-fringed; petiolules short, petioles hairy. **Flowers:** inconspicuous, white, with the calyx and stalks covered with dense, dark brown velvety hairs. The flowers are tightly clustered in large branched heads, or panicles, 6 to 30 cm long (January to May). **Fruit:** a dark brown, velvety pod, 4 to 9 × 2 to

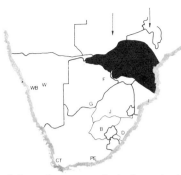
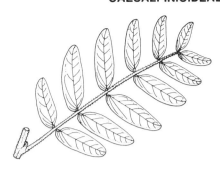

3,5 cm, borne as a cloak above the leaves, splitting explosively when mature (May to July or on to November).

With *Brachystegia spiciformis*, *B. glaucescens* and *B. boehmii*, this tree helps to provide a fine display of leaf colour in the spring. It is often confused with *B. spiciformis*, but there are very clear differences between the two. With *Julbernardia* the leaves usually have about 6 pairs of leaflets, the longest being the third or fourth pair; there are no stipels at the base of the leaflets and the flush colours are usually soft pinks and fawns; it flowers from January to May; the pods are velvety and borne on the top of the tree, well above the foliage. With *Brachystegia spiciformis* the leaves have only 4 pairs of leaflets, the largest being the terminal pair; there is a minute triangular structure, or stipel, at the base of each leaflet and the flush colours are pinks to intense reds; it flowers from August to November; the pods are without hairs and are borne among the leaves. The wood is hard, coarse and uneven but very durable. It is difficult to work, tending to tear when sawn and split badly when nailed, but it has been used quite widely as a general purpose timber and also for mortars and canoes. The bark rope from this tree is inferior to that obtained from the species of *Brachystegia*, but it is nevertheless useful for ropes, beehives, stitched canoes, cornbins and sacks.

Julbernardia paniculata (Benth.) Troupin
[*Berlinia paniculata* Benth.; *Isoberlinia paniculata* (Benth.) Greenway]
S.A. no: —
Rhod. no: —   Large-leaved munondo

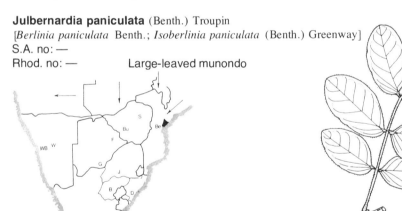

A semi-evergreen, flat-topped tree up to 15 m in height; occurring in deciduous *Brachystegia* woodland. **Bark:** pale grey, becoming dark grey and rough with age. **Leaves:** with 3 to 4 pairs of leaflets; leaflets large, oblong-elliptic, usually about 9 × 5 cm, both surfaces glossy green; apex rounded; base asymmetric; margin entire. Stipules fall early. **Flowers:** inconspicuous, creamy-white, with the calyx and stalks covered with brown velvety hairs. Flowers in a branched head, or panicle, up to 25 × 30 cm long, but usually smaller (April). **Fruit:** a dark brown, velvety pod, 5 to 11 × 2 to 4 cm (June to August).

13. ADENOLOBUS (Harvey) Torre & Hillcoat

Adenolobus garipensis (E. Meyer) Torre & Hillcoat   Illust. 82
[*Bauhinia garipensis* E. Meyer]
S.A. no: 208   Butterfly leaf. Bloubeesklou
Rhod. no: —

A bushy shrub or small tree up to 4 m in height; occurring on rocky hills, usually growing in coarse sand; it is common round the Augrabies Falls where it grows in pockets of sand among the impressive rocks. **Bark:** pale, with a meal-like bloom; the branches are long, slender and rod-like. **Leaves:** alternate, or clustered on dwarf lateral shoots, simple, small, rather wider than they are long, 0,7 to 2,5 cm long, dark green with a bluish tinge, thick and rather fleshy, deeply apically notched giving twin lobes very similar to a *Bauhinia* leaf, usually folded along the central midrib. **Flowers:** the sepals and petals are tightly furled, producing a tubular structure up to 2,5 cm in length; the general effect is dark claret-maroon, the petals being greyish, streaked and net-veined with maroon and protruding from the calyx; the stamens protrude from the tightly furled petals (September to January). **Fruit:** a small, flat, kidney-shaped pod, about 2,5 cm in length and up to 2 cm wide, straw-coloured (October to March).

14. BAUHINIA L.

Shrubs, trees or sometimes climbers. **Leaves:** alternate, simple, deeply 2-lobed. Stipules fall early. **Flowers:** in simple sprays or racemes, or branched heads, forming panicles or corymbs. Bisexual or unisexual; all floral parts in fives; calyx tube shortly bell-shaped; petals large or short, may be widely spreading, somewhat unequal in size and shape; stamens 10 in 2 whorls, free or shortly joined; ovary stalked. **Fruit:** a pod.

The name *Bauhinia* is associated with the characteristic butterfly leaves; the genus was named after the brothers, John and Caspar Bauhin, famous botanists of the 16th century, who are represented by the twin lobes of the leaves. The suggestion that *Bauhinia bowkeri* and *B. tomentosa* be placed in the genus *Pauletia* Cav., and all the other species dealt with here be placed in *Perlebia* Mart., is not followed in the present work.

Key to the tree species of *Bauhinia:*
1 Flowers bright red, brick-red or pink 2
  Flowers white or yellow, not red or pink 3
2 Flowers brick-red, or bright salmon-red; petals paddle-shaped; not occurring in South West Africa
  .... **B. galpinii**
  Flowers pale pink, or white flushed with pink; petals long and narrow, strap-shaped; not extending
  further south than the extreme north-east of South West Africa .... **B. urbaniana**
3 Petals large, deep yellow, broad and overlapping .... **B. tomentosa**
  Flowers white 4
4 In the eastern Cape, Transkei and extreme south of Natal only .... **B. bowkeri**
  In Rhodesia, Moçambique, northern areas of South Africa and South West Africa; not occurring in
  the eastern Cape or Natal .... **B. petersiana**
  Flowers unisexual; fruits indehiscent .... **B. thonningii**

Bauhinia bowkeri Harvey
S.A. no: 208,4   Kei white bauhinia. Keibeesklou
Rhod. no: —

A shrub with a tendency to scramble, or a small straggly tree up to 6 m in height; occurring on mountain slopes and in scrub, along the coastal belt. **Bark:** grey-brown; the young branches are pale brown and more or less heavily lenticellate. **Leaves:** rather small, 1 to 4 × 2 to 5 cm, but usually about 2 × 2,5 to 3 cm, divided for almost half their length; petioles up to 1,5 cm long, slender. **Flowers:**

white, the petals up to 2,5 × 2,5 cm, very similar to *B. petersiana* (October to December). **Fruit:** a long, slender, flat pod up to 16 × 3 cm, dehiscent (December to April).

Bauhinia galpinii N. E. Brown   Illust. 83
[*B. punctata* Bolle, non Jacq.]
S.A. no: 208,2   Pride-of-De Kaap. Vlam-van-die-vlakte
Rhod. no: 261   Red bauhinia

A shrub, frequently a vigorous climber, occasionally a low, spreading tree up to 3 to 5 m in height; occurring usually in hot areas, in various types of woodland and thicket. **Bark:** light brown and powdery. **Leaves:** characteristically twin-lobed up to 7 × 7 cm, deeply notched rather than divided, conspicuously veined on the under surface; apex deeply notched; base lobed; margin entire; petiolate. **Flowers:** bright salmon-red to brick-red, about 6 to 8 cm in diameter, the petals paddle-shaped and not long and slender. The flowers are in large, branched sprays up to 20 cm in diameter, clustered near the ends of the branchlets (November to March). **Fruit:** a narrow, brown pod up to 10 cm long, dehiscent (June to August).
This species is becoming increasingly popular as a hardy garden plant as the seeds germinate well and the plants resist drought and tolerate poor soil. It is extremely beautiful when in full flower.

Bauhinia petersiana Bolle   Illust. 84
[*B. macrantha* Baker]
S.A. no: 208,3   White bauhinia. Koffiebeesklou
Rhod. no: 263   White bauhinia

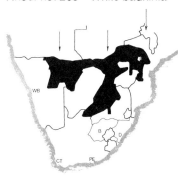

283

Rather inclined to form an untidy, spreading bush, but often a small tree usually 3 to 4 m in height, occasionally reaching 7 m; occurring in woodland and wooded grassland at medium to low altitudes. **Bark:** dark greyish-brown, powdery, flaking in vertical strips in larger specimens. **Leaves:** lobed for almost half their length; lobes ovate, 3,5 to 6 × 3 to 8 cm, with 6 to 9 prominent veins on the under surface; apex of the lobes very broadly tapering to rounded; base of the leaf deeply lobed; margin entire; petiolate. **Flowers:** with long, crinkly, white petals about 8 × 1 to 1,5 cm; stamens pinkish (December to January). **Fruit:** a large, brown, smooth pod, 12 to 18 × 3 to 6 cm, splitting and spiralling explosively when mature (July to September).

The leaves are used in a very widely known African remedy for the common cold: they are boiled in water and the steam inhaled, the liquid is allowed to cool and it is then swallowed. Thomas Baines, in his *Goldfields Diaries*, wrote that on his journey to the Zambezi in 1863, he and his companions collected the seeds of this tree which, after being roasted and ground, were used as a substitute for coffee. Because of this, the tree was known to early hunters and explorers as Zambezi coffee.

The former *B. macrantha* becomes subsp. *serpae* (Ficalho & Hiern) Brummitt & J. H. Ross and occurs in South Africa, South West Africa, Rhodesia and Angola; the typical subsp. *petersiana* tends to have a more easterly distribution, occurring in the north and east of Rhodesia, Moçambique and northwards.

Bauhinia thonningii Schumacher   Illust. 86
[*Piliostigma thonningii* (Schumach.) Milne-Redh.]
S.A. no: 209   Camel's foot. Kameelspoor
Rhod. no: 265   Monkeybread

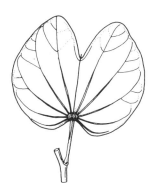

A small to medium sized rounded tree, usually 3 to 5 m in height, but reaching 10 m under ideal conditions; occurring in woodland and wooded grassland at medium to low altitudes. **Bark:** dark brownish-grey, rough, longitudinally furrowed. **Leaves:** alternate, simple, large, leathery, 2-lobed, up to 12 cm long and almost as broad; apex deeply notched, with a small bristle-like structure in the notch; base of the whole leaf square to shallowly lobed; margin entire; petiole thickset. **Flowers:** inconspicuous in axillary, leaf-opposed or terminal sprays which are simple or branched, i.e. racemes or panicles; sexes separate on different trees. Floral parts in fours or fives; calyx forming a short tube, the tube and the calyx lobes covered with dark brown velvety hairs; petals short, white, crinkled, overlapping. Male flower: stamens 10; ovary aborted. Female flower: stamens sterile; ovary without a stalk (December to February). **Fruit:** a large pod, 22 × 7 cm, thick, woody, reddish-brown and tough, not splitting on reaching maturity but falling to the ground where they decay or are broken up (June to September).

The ash from the burnt wood is soapy and the green fruits provide Africans with a soap-substitute. The bark contains a fibre which is used as string and is also made into rope while the pods, which are much sought after by game and stock, can be ground into a meal which is said to equal mealie meal in its nutritional value. However, it is essential to dry the pods first for otherwise they tend to jam the crushing machines. In times of famine Africans eat both the pods and seeds and all parts of the tree are widely used medicinally. The wood makes a good fuel but other than this it has little value.

Bauhinia tomentosa L.   Illust. 85
S.A. no: 208,1   Yellow tree bauhinia. Bosbeesklou
Rhod. no: 264   Yellow tree bauhinia

A shrub or small tree reaching 4 m in height, the branches often drooping; occurring in low altitude woodland, often forming part of riverine thicket, in bushveld and in coastal dune bush. **Bark:** grey or

brown. **Leaves:** deeply divided for almost half their length, with a small apical appendage between the lobes; each lobe is oval to almost elliptic, most often smallish, about 2,5 × 2,5 cm, but may be up to 7,5 cm, pale fresh green; apex of each lobe broadly tapering; base of the whole leaf shallowly lobed; margin entire; petiolate. **Flowers:** bell-shaped, up to 7 cm long, beautiful and distinctive, with large yellow petals, 1 to 3 of which have a dark maroon patch at the base (December to March). **Fruit:** a slender, pale brown velvety pod, 10 to 11 × 1,5 to 2 cm, dehiscent (young fruits in January, mature fruits may be found as late as June or even later).

Bauhinia urbaniana Schinz
S.A. no: Pink bauhinia. Sandbeesklou
Rhod. no: —

Usually a shrub, occasionally a small bushy tree about 3 m in height; occurring in dry, sandy woodland. **Bark:** greyish-brown; the young branchlets are covered with golden-brown, velvety hairs. **Leaves:** deeply divided for almost half their length; each lobe oval to elliptic, 2,5 to 6 × 3 to 7 cm, the under surface conspicuously veined with 3 to 4 veins per lobe and with fine rust-coloured velvety hairs, especially along the veins; apex of each lobe rounded; base of the whole leaf shallowly lobed; margin entire; shortly petiolate. **Flowers:** usually pink, sometimes white flushed with pink or veined with pink; petals about 2,5 × 1 to 1,5 cm (mainly July to February, but may be found at almost any time during the year). **Fruit:** a narrow, dark brown, finely velvety pod, dehiscent (may be found at almost any time of the year).

15. DIALIUM L.

Trees. **Leaves:** alternate or opposite, compound, imparipinnate. Stipules fall early. **Flowers:** in terminal and axillary, many-flowered panicles. Flowers bisexual, asymmetric; sepals 5; petals absent; stamens 2 to 10. **Fruit:** ovoid, with floury pith; indehiscent.

Key to the species of *Dialium:*
Leaflets ovate, an average size being 4,5 × 2,5 cm; leaf base symmetric; extending no further south than the extreme northern areas of South West Africa, Botswana and Rhodesia ....
.... **D. engleranum**
Leaflets oblong, an average size being 2 × 1 cm; leaf base extremely asymmetric; Zululand and Moçambique only .... **D. schlechteri**   **285**

CAESALPINIOIDEAE

Dialium engleranum Henriques
[*D. simii* Phillips]
S.A. no: 210 Kalahari podberry. Kalaharipeulbessie
Rhod. no: 266 Kalahari podberry

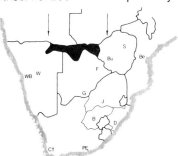

A medium to large tree, 7 to 20 m in height; occurring in mixed forest or woodland, usually growing in deep white sand. **Bark:** dark grey, generally smooth, peeling in small, thin flakes. **Leaves:** alternate, with 4 pairs of leaflets plus a terminal leaflet, ovate to elliptic, 3 to 8 × 1 to 3,5 cm, leathery, glossy, upper surface dark green, the under surface paler green, with yellow, velvety hairs; apex broadly tapering, shortly attenuate; base symmetric; margin entire. **Flowers:** small, the sepals with golden-brown, velvety hairs on the outside, creamy-white within. The flowers are produced in loose, branched, axillary and terminal sprays up to 8 cm long, together forming terminal heads about 20 cm long (July to August). **Fruit:** ovoid, velvety, up to 3 × 1,5 to 2 cm, dark brown, containing 1 to 2 bright vermilion seeds embedded in a floury pith (July to October).

The fruits are an important food of the indigenous peoples in Botswana and South West Africa. The fruit is soaked in water and eaten fresh or with milk, or boiled with meal. The crushed wood is used as a disinfectant, an infusion of the leaves provides a remedy for coughs and a decoction of the roots a treatment for dysentery.

Dialium schlechteri Harms
S.A. no: 211 Zulu podberry. Zoeloepeulbessie
Rhod. no: —

Usually a small tree, 5 to 8 m in height, but reaching 15 m under favourable conditions; occurring in coastal bush and forest, frequently a canopy tree on dry sandy soils. **Bark:** pale grey, smooth and mottled. **Leaves:** opposite, sub-opposite to alternate, with 3 to 6 pairs of leaflets plus a terminal leaflet; leaflets oblong, 0,8 to 3,5 × 0,5 to 1,9 cm, shiny green, without hairs; apex broadly tapering; base markedly asymmetric, one side almost concave while the other is bellied out into a wide lobe; margin entire; petiolules and petiole present. **Flowers:** white, about 10 mm in diameter, sweetly scented; the buds, branchlets, flower stalks and the backs of the calyx lobes are covered with golden-brown, velvety hairs. The flowers are produced in rather compact, branched heads, axillary and terminal, together about 8 × 8 cm (September to November). **Fruit:** almost spherical, about 2,5 cm long, with velvety, red-brown hairs; a bright orange, dry pith surrounds the seeds (December to June).

286

The fruits are often borne in profusion and the powdery pulp mixed with water makes a refreshing drink. The wood is fine, hard and heavy, reddish in colour with a beautiful close grain; it is insect proof. The Zulus use the powdered bark to treat burns.

16. CASSIA L.

Shrubs or trees. **Leaves:** alternate, compound, paripinnate; rachis often with conspicuous glands. Stipulate. **Flowers:** in axillary or terminal racemes, corymbs or fascicles. All floral parts in fives; calyx tube very short; petals large, spreading, showy, somewhat asymmetric, usually yellow, sometimes red, occasionally white; stamens 10; ovary usually stalked. **Fruit:** a pod, cylindric or somewhat flattened, indehiscent.

In addition to the three indigenous and one naturalised tree species dealt with in the following pages, the following exotic species have become naturalised. They are usually shrubs but may possibly be encountered as small trees: *C. bicapsularis* L., in the northern, central and eastern areas of Rhodesia; *C. coluteoides* Collad., in the northern and eastern areas of Rhodesia; *C. floribunda* Cav., in Natal and fairly widespread in Rhodesia; *C. hirsuta* L., in the eastern areas of Rhodesia.

Key to the tree species of *Cassia* (exotic species marked*):
1 Rachis without glands 2
  Rachis with conspicuous glands between each pair of leaflets 3
2 Flowers in lax, branched sprays; flower stalks, both pedicels and peduncles, long and slender; pods
    cylindric, very long, up to 90 cm in length .... **C. abbreviata**
  Flowers in compact, rigid, bold spikes; flower stalks, or pedicels, very short, with the main axis
    thickset; pods flat, 9 to 15 × 2 cm .... ***C. didymobotrya**
3 Leaflets narrowly ovate to lanceolate; apex tapering and pointed; stipules large, conspicuous and
    leaf-like .... **C. petersiana**
  Leaflets more or less oval; apex rather rounded; stipules not large, leaf-like, nor conspicuous..
    .... **C. singueana**

Cassia abbreviata Oliver Illust. 87
[*C. granitica* E. G. Baker; *C. abbreviata* Oliver var. *granitica* (E. G. Baker) E. G. Baker]
S.A. no: 212 Sjambok pod. Sambokpeul
Rhod. no: 267 Long-tail cassia

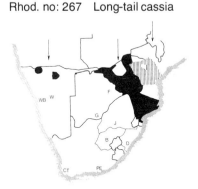

A shrub or small to medium sized tree, 3 to 10 m in height; occurring at medium to low altitudes, in open woodland or wooded grassland, along rivers, on hillsides and frequently associated with termite mounds. **Bark:** brownish-grey and rough. **Leaves:** with 5 to 12 pairs of leaflets; leaflets ovate-elliptic, 3 to 6 × 1,2 to 3 cm, thinly textured, dull green, finely velvety at first, usually losing these hairs later; apex rounded; base broadly tapering; margin entire; petiolules and petiole present, slender. **Flowers:** large, up to 4,5 cm in diameter, pale yellow, with long, slender pedicels and peduncles in beautiful, large, loose sprays up to 15 × 20 cm (mainly September to October, but continuing into November). **Fruit:** a very long, cylindric pod, up to 90 × 2,5 cm, golden-brown to brown, velvety (December to April, the remains often hanging on the tree for months).

This species has been sub-divided into three subspecies, two of which, subsp. *abbreviata* (vertical lines on the map) and subsp. *beareana* (Holmes) Brenan (black areas on the map), extend south of the **287**

Zambezi River. Of these two, subsp. *beareana* is more widespread and more likely to be encountered. The only difference between them lies in the hairiness and the type of hairs on the under surface of the leaflets; subsp. *beareana* has very fine, straight hairs pressed flat against the surface while subsp. *abbreviata* has loose, sometimes curly hairs. Often it is not easy to see these differences with the naked eye. Various parts of the tree feature in African medicine. The seeds are sucked as a tonic, the roots are used to relieve severe cases of abdominal pain and as a remedy for toothache, and the smoke from a burning twig is inhaled to cure headaches. Subspecies *beareana* was named after Dr O'Sullivan Beare who, in 1902, noted that the Africans used a decoction of the roots to cure blackwater fever. He tried this remedy himself and found that it was effective, so he arranged to have a fluid extract from the roots prepared commercially and placed on the market under the name *Cassia beareana*. Since then this has been used from time to time by medical men for the treatment of blackwater fever. The Shangaan believe that the bark has magical properties and they cook their meat with it to ensure success in hunting. The seed germinates well and the tree makes a good garden subject; however, it is tender to frost, particularly when young.

*Cassia didymobotrya Fresen.

This shrub or small tree, the peanut cassia, was introduced from East Africa and has now become naturalised in forest patches in Natal, the Transvaal and Mocambique, and has become widespread in Rhodesia (Rhod. no: 270).

Cassia petersiana Bolle
S.A. no: 213   Monkey pod. Apiespeul
Rhod. no: 275   Eared cassia

A shrub, or small to medium sized tree reaching 12 m in height; occurring most frequently along rivers and streams in riverine fringe thicket. **Bark:** brown, rough and fissured. **Leaves:** with 4 to 10 pairs of leaflets; leaflets narrowly ovate to lanceolate, 2,5 to 6,5 × 1 to 3 cm, dark glossy green above, with fine velvety hairs on the under surface and conspicuous glands between each pair of leaflets; apex conspicuously attenuate; base very broadly tapering to rounded; margin entire, rolled under; petiolules and petiole finely hairy. Stipules large, conspicuous, leaf-like. **Flowers:** very showy, yellow, in large, loose, branched sprays up to 26 × 20 cm (January to June). **Fruit:** a long, slender pod, up to 25 × 1 cm, with a very marked rim, minutely hairy, often slightly constricted between the seeds (May to August).
Various parts of the tree are used in African medicine as a purgative and to treat fevers, gonorrhoea and skin infections. The root bark is given in soup or in milk to a dog injured by the horns of an antelope, or to make a lazy hunting dog lean and hungry and so more eager for the chase.

Cassia singueana Delile   Illust. 88
[*C. singueana* Delile var. *glabra* (E. G. Baker) Brenan]
S.A. no: 213,1   Winter cassia. Kleefpeul
Rhod. no: 276   Winter cassia

A small deciduous tree, usually about 4 to 5 cm in height; occurring in open woodland, frequently associated with termite mounds. **Bark:** brown and rough. **Leaves:** with 4 to 10 pairs of leaflets; leaflets oval, 2,5 to 5 × 1 to 1,5 cm, fresh green with conspicuous glands between each pair of leaflets; apex and base rounded; margin entire. Stipules small and falling early. **Flowers:** very striking, deep

288

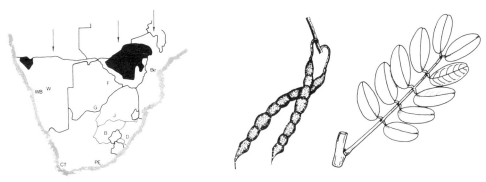

yellow, in large, loose sprays about 15 × 20 cm (April to September). **Fruit:** a narrow, cylindric pod, up to 25 cm long, but usually rather smaller, slightly constricted between the seeds, yellow when ripe, usually without hairs but may be very finely velvety (September onwards, even as late as June). This tree, which is one of the earliest trees to flower in spring, is often damaged by fires, cattle or game and so is frequently distorted. The bark is used by African doctors to 'chase devils out' and the ash from the burnt roots mixed with porridge provides a remedy for stomach pains.

17. PARKINSONIA L.

*Parkinsonia aculeata L.

This attractive small tree, which has minute leaflets similar to those of *P. africana* (see plate on page 290), was introduced from Mexico and is widely cultivated in gardens. It has now become naturalised in Moçambique along the Limpopo River and is common between Nelspruit in the Transvaal and Maputo in Moçambique. It has also escaped near Bulawayo (Rhod. no: 277).

Parkinsonia africana Sonder   Illust. 89
S.A. no: 214   Wild green-hair tree. Wildegroenhaarboom
Rhod. no: —

A tall bush or small tree, thin and sparse, usually 3 to 4 m in height; but reaching 6 m on occasions; occurring in country bordering the desert and in the Namib desert itself. **Bark:** pale brown or grey and rather smooth; the branches are yellowish-green, bent in angular patterns, rigid and spiny. **Leaves:** alternate, or more often clustered in the axils of stipular spines, compound, the leaflets very small to minute, or even absent, leaving only the dark green rachis hanging down like a midrib stripped of its surrounding leaf; if present, the leaflets are opposite, widely spaced along the rachis, scarcely larger than 1 to 2 mm long; the clusters of almost bare to completely bare rachides resemble bunches of green hair. **Flowers:** attractive, yellow, up to 1,3 cm in diameter, in rather compact short heads, clustered along the stem in the axils of the spines (October). **Fruit:** a slender pod, up to 9 × 0,8 cm, reddish-brown when young, pale straw-coloured when mature (December to January).
In desert areas where so little grows that is edible, these trees are browsed on by animals. Coffee is said to be made from the seeds. Illust. 89 shows a small tree growing near an outlier of the Namib desert in South West Africa; the ground is carpeted by the small herb *Tribulus pterophorus* Presl.   **289**

The bare rachides with minute, widely spaced leaflets, about 1 mm long, give Parkinsonia africana *the common name wild green-hair tree*

18. CAESALPINIA L.

Caesalpinia bonduc (L.) Roxb.
S.A. no: Bonduc
Rhod. no: —

A shrub with a tendency to scramble, or a small shrubby tree, up to 3 m in height; confined to the coastal belt, in dune bush and in littoral scrub. **Bark:** smooth, greenish-brown; the stems and branches are beset with dense, straight or recurved prickles. **Leaves:** opposite, compound, large, up to 50 cm long including the petiole, with prickles along the lower side of the petiole and rachis, 2-pinnate, with 3 to 9 pairs of pinnae each bearing 6 to 9 pairs of leaflets; leaflets elliptic-oblong, 1,2 to 4,5 × 0,8 to 2,2 cm; apex broadly tapering to rounded, bristle-tipped; base square to slightly rounded, asymmetric; margin entire; petiole, rachis and the under surface of the leaflets with golden-brown, velvety hairs. Stipules leaf-like and conspicuous. **Flowers:** rather small, in simple or 1- to 2-branched axillary spikes, 11 to 23 cm long or more. All floral parts in fives; sepals green, with golden-brown velvety hairs on the back; petals yellow or greenish-yellow, up to 1,3 × 0,4 cm; stamens 10 (March to May). **Fruit:** a pod, up to 7,6 × 5 cm, very distinctive, broadly oval, densely prickly and hedgehog-like, splitting to release the rather large, spherical, hard, leaden-grey seeds up to 2 cm in diameter (May to August).

Only the colour of the seeds separates this species from *C. major* (Medik.) Dandy & Exell, which has yellowish seeds. The seeds of the Natal plants have not yet been seen, so it is possible that *C. major* may occur as well, although the seed colour of the plants on Inhaca island in southern Moçambique has been verified as grey. The very hard-shelled seeds float well in the sea and have been found to be viable after being in the water as long as two and a half years; in this way they are dispersed far and wide and are therefore characteristic of coastal regions.

290

*Caesalpinia decapetala (Roth) Alston

This, the Mauritius thorn, was originally introduced from tropical Asia as a hedge plant. It has now become a serious weed, in the form of a robust liane, in natural forest and plantations, particularly in high-rainfall areas, in Natal, the eastern Transvaal and Rhodesia (Rhod. no: 279).

19. BUSSEA Harms

Bussea xylocarpa (Sprague) Sprague & Craib
[*Calliandra xylocarpa* Sprague]
S.A. no: —
Rhod. no: —   Bussea

A tree 10 to 15 m tall; occurring in *Brachystegia/Combretum* woodland, favouring stony soils. **Bark:** grey to brown; the young shoots are covered with dark brown velvety hairs. **Leaves:** compound, 2-pinnate, with 3 to 7 pairs of pinnae, each bearing 10 to 15 pairs of leaflets; leaflets oblong, about 2 × 0,7 cm; apex rounded, finely notched; base asymmetric; margin entire. **Flowers:** said to be in terminal panicles, 12 to 15 cm long. **Fruit:** a very distinctive oblanceolate-cylindric pod, 7 to 10 × 2 cm, thickly woody, narrowly tapering to the base, abruptly rounded and shallowly pointed at the apex, deeply channelled above and below with dark chocolate velvety hairs which rub off in places; the pod splits down both sides but remains attached at the base, the 2 valves curving backwards and upwards so releasing the 1 to 2 large smooth glossy seeds which are flattened, pale yellowish-brown and about 2 × 1 cm.

This species is apparently endemic to the particular small area near the Zambezi River, downstream from the Cabora-Bassa dam site.

20. PELTOPHORUM Walp.

Peltophorum africanum Sonder   Illust. 90
S.A. no: 215   Weeping wattle. Huilboom
Rhod. no: 280   African-wattle

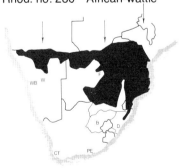

A small to medium sized tree with a spreading crown, 5 to 10 m in height, frequently branched from near the ground or 2- to 3-stemmed from ground level; occurring commonly in medium to low altitudes in wooded grassland and along the margins of vleis. **Bark:** brown, rough and longitudinally fissured. **Leaves:** alternate, compound, 2-pinnate, with 4 to 7 pairs of pinnae, each bearing 10 to 12   **291**

(or up to 23) pairs of feathery leaflets; leaflets oblong, averaging 7 × 2 mm, but variable in size, dull green above, pale green below; apex rounded with a fine hair-like tip; base asymmetric; margin entire; petiole and rachis covered with dense rusty-brown, velvety hairs. Stipules distinctive in appearance, like small compound leaves, but falling early. **Flowers:** very showy, bright yellow, in dense axillary sprays up to 15 cm long. All floral parts in fives; flower stalks and the backs of the sepals covered with brown velvety hairs; petals about 2 cm in diameter, bright yellow and crinkled (September to February). **Fruit:** a flat pod, elliptic, tapering to apex and base, up to 10 × 2 cm with a wing-like margin, very thinly woody, almost leathery, greyish-brown or yellow-tan and ripening to a dark brown, hanging in dense clusters, indehiscent (February to June).

The bark is used medicinally by the African peoples: it is chewed to relieve colic, an infusion is taken orally to relieve a variety of stomach disorders and the steam from a hot decoction is applied to sore eyes. The wood is soft with a black heartwood, and is suitable for carving. Eve Palmer says that this is one of the rain trees of Africa as, in spring, water drips from the branches wetting the ground beneath. Almost certainly this phenomenon is caused by small insects (see under *Lonchocarpus capassa* page 325, where the cause of this 'raining' is described). This is a very good garden shade tree and is beautiful in flower. The seed germinates well, the young plants transplant easily, are fairly fast-growning and will withstand some frost although they need protection for the first few seasons. On a quick field impression it is easy to confuse this species with *Acacia amythethophylla*. However, the latter is sparsely spiny, has no distinctive leaf-like stipules and has flowers which are the typical acacia fluffy balls, while *Peltophorum africanum* has no spines, possesses leaf-like stipules and has flowers with large, beautiful crinkly yellow petals.

21. CORDYLA Lour.

This genus and the following one, *Swartzia*, represent intermediates between the subfamilies Caesalpinioideae and Papilionoideae. For this reason both have been keyed out here, although they have been keyed out also, and fully described, in Papilionoideae. See genus no. 1 *Cordyla*, in that subfamily.

22. SWARTZIA Schreb.

This genus is intermediate between Caesalpinioideae and Papilionoideae. Refer to the note under the preceding genus, *Cordyla*, and see genus no. 2, *Swartzia*, in Papilionoideae.

PAPILIONOIDEAE *(The pea subfamily)*

Key to the genera:

1 Leaves simple 2

Leaves compound, pinnate or digitately foliolate 4

2 Flowers white, often with a yellow patch near the base; produced in simple or branched sprays; pods without hairs .... **9. Baphia**

Flowers pink or purple, solitary, in groups of 2 to 4, or in sprays; pods covered with velvety or woolly hairs 3

3 Flowers solitary or in groups of 1 to 4; pods covered with woolly hairs. Occurring in the south-western and southern Cape only .... **10. Podalyria**

Flowers in sprays or racemes; pods finely velvety. Not extending further south than South West Africa, Botswana and Rhodesia .... **26. Lonchocarpus**

4 Leaves with more than 3 leaflets 5

Leaves pinnately or digitately 3-foliolate.. 35

5 Fruits fleshy, indehiscent 6

Fruits not fleshy 7

PAPILIONOIDEAE

34 Flowers small, standard petal about 6 mm long; pods oblong, 5 to 10 cm long, slightly rimmed (more markedly so in 1 species), usually 1-seeded, seeds brown .... **26. Lonchocarpus**

Flowers larger than those of the preceding species, the standard petal up to 1,3 or 1,6 cm long; pods long and narrow, 10 to 24 × 2 to 4 cm, markedly rimmed, producing more than 1 seed, seeds red .... **4. Pericopsis**

35 Pods cylindric 36

Pods usually flat 37

36 Pods thin-walled, not constricted between the seeds; flowers yellow, the keel petal distinctly beaked, standard petal broad and spreading .... **13. Crotalaria**

Pods woody, markedly constricted between the seeds; flowers scarlet, keel petal not beaked, standard petal hooded and enclosing the other petals .... **28. Erythrina**

37 Leaves digitately 3-foliolate, i.e. the petiolules of the 3 leaflets all join together at one point .... **11. Lebeckia**

Leaves pinnately 3-foliolate, i.e. the terminal leaflet is separated from the 2 lateral leaflets by a short section of rachis with which the petiolule of the terminal leaflet is more or less clearly articulated, or jointed 38

38 Plants occurring only in the Clanwilliam area of the western Cape, in the Cedarberg mountains and nearby ranges to the north; a bush or small tree 2 to 4 m in height; branchlets and leaves covered with dense, silvery, silky hairs .... **12. Wiborgia**

Not occurring in the Clanwilliam area of the western Cape... 39

39 Plants distinctively shaggy with long, golden hairs; flowers yellow streaked with maroon; pods small, up to 2,5 × 0,8 cm, splitting and spiralling when mature; stipules very distinctive, large, sheath-like, reddish-brown, persisting for some time .... **29. Rhynchosia**

Plants without shaggy hairs; if hairs are present then these are fine and velvety and usually confined to the under surface of the leaflets, or even to the midribs; flowers blue, lilac or purple, or whitish, tinged and veined with purple; pods 5 to 12 × 1 to 2,5 cm, indehiscent, with or without velvety hairs; stipules not conspicuous .... **26. Lonchocarpus**

1. CORDYLA Lour.

Cordyla africana Lour.   Illust. 91
S.A. no: 216   Wild mango. Wildemango
Rhod. no: 281   Wild mango

A large, spreading, deciduous tree up to 25 m in height; occurring at low altitudes in hot areas, most often forming part of riverine forest, and also in swamp forest. **Bark:** brown or greyish and rough. **Leaves:** alternate, compound, imparipinnate, with 11 to 28 pairs of leaflets plus a terminal leaflet; leaflets oblong, 2 to 5 × 1,2 to 2,4 cm, with characteristic pellucid dots and streaks; apex rounded, slightly notched; base rounded; margin entire; petiolule and petiole present. **Flowers:** a semi-spherical head of orange-yellow stamens up to 2,5 cm long; the flowers are produced in short dense

295

axillary sprays, or clustered in the leaf axils; petals absent. The flowers somewhat resemble the characteristic 'powder-puff' of the species of *Albizia,* but in *Cordyla* the stamens are stouter and more robust (July to October). **Fruit:** a very unusual pod resembling a semi-fleshy drupe, more or less spherical, 4 to 8 × 3 to 6 cm, thin walled, indehiscent, yellow when ripe with the seeds embedded in an edible, fleshy pulp (November to December).

The fruits have a high vitamin C content and are much sought after, being eaten either fresh or cooked. The heartwood is brown and hard and is used for building and also for making African drums. The tree exudes a gum-resin.

2. SWARTZIA Schreb.

Swartzia madagascariensis Desv.   Illust. 92
S.A. no: 217   Snake bean. Slangboon
Rhod. no: 282   Snake bean

A small tree, usually 3 to 4 m in height, but it may be larger, reaching 15 m under favourable conditions; occurring at medium and low altitudes, in deciduous woodland and wooded grassland. **Bark:** dark grey, rough; the stem often twisted and the branches rather contorted. **Leaves:** alternate, compound, with 7 to 11 alternate leaflets plus a terminal leaflet; leaflets elliptic, 2,5 to 7 × 1,8 to 3,7 cm, leathery, the upper surface dark green and without hairs, the under surface with fine, yellowish, velvety hairs; apex rounded, notched; base tapering; margin entire; petiolules short and thick, petiole up to 2,5 cm. **Flowers:** distinctive, sweetly scented in rather sparse, 2- to 10-flowered sprays. Flowers bisexual; calyx tube with 2 to 5 lobes; a single, large petal, 1,5 to 2 cm long, white with a grey edging, upstanding, crinkled, conspicuous; stamens numerous, orange-yellow; ovary with a long stalk (October to November, but may be as late as January). **Fruit:** a cylindric, indehiscent pod, dark brown, slender and sausage-shaped, up to 30 × 1,3 cm (March to August).

This species is widely distributed in Africa, extending from Gambia and Cameroun to South West Africa, Rhodesia and Moçambique, but it does not occur in Madagascar in spite of its specific name. The pods have a far greater reputation for being poisonous than, apparently, they deserve. They are widely exploited as a fish poison – with some justification, as the powdered pods have killed goldfish in a test trial, though a fairly high concentration was necessary. Bushmen use them in the preparation of their arrow poison; however, injected subcutaneously into a cat, they produced no effect. The powdered pods have also been used with murderous intent, the powder being slipped into the beer of an intended victim. However, it is very doubtful whether this produced any physical effect, for the ripe fruits are an excellent stock food and cattle have been seen butting the stems of the trees to shake down the fruits. Trevor Gordon has observed that it is common to find rapoko grass, *Eleusine indica* (L.) Gaertn., growing round these trees as this is a hardy species and better able to withstand trampling by cattle. It is also an effective insecticide and insect repellant, and grain storage bins are lined with the powder to repel termites and weevils. Africans treat cases of leprosy with a decoction of the pods. The wood is even and close-grained; it is usually red-brown in colour and can develop a purplish-black heartwood which is very decorative. It is durable and termite-resistant, and is used for carving, cabinet work and inlay; it is considered second only to *Dalbergia melanoxylon* for making small ornaments and curios, such as the ashtrays and jars carved by Africans and familiar to visitors to the Victoria Falls. This interesting small tree is difficult to establish in gardens; the seed germinates easily but the plants die when about 30 cm high.

3. XANTHOCERCIS Baillon

Xanthocercis zambesiaca (Baker) Dumaz-le Grand   Illust. 93
S.A. no: 241   Nyala tree. Njalaboom
Rhod. no: 283   Nyala tree

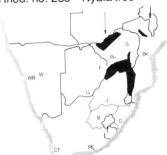

A very large, beautiful, round topped, evergreen tree, the finest specimens reaching 25 to 30 m in height; occurring at low altitudes in hot areas, in the rich alluvial soils of the great river valleys. **Bark:** brown to dark brown, rough; the branchlets are long and slender, hanging down vertically from the main branches. **Leaves:** alternate, compound with up to 7 pairs of sub-opposite to alternate leaflets plus a terminal leaflet; leaflets oval, up to 5,5 × 2 cm, dark green and glossy above, paler green and dull below, sometimes sparsely and finely hairy; apex rounded, notched; base broadly tapering to rounded, asymmetric; margin entire; petiolules and petiole short and velvety. **Flowers:** small, white, somewhat pea-shaped, rose-scented; produced in short sprays, 5 to 10 cm long, axillary or terminal (September to December). **Fruit:** unusual for a legume, being more like a large berry, up to 2,5 × 1,7 cm, yellowish-brown when ripe; containing a floury, fleshy, rather sticky pulp and a single, black, shiny seed (from November onwards almost throughout the year).
The fruits are eaten by Africans when fresh, or are wrapped in a hide and buried for several weeks; when mature the resultant mass is made into a porridge or dried and ground into a meal. The wood is attractive and fine-textured; it works well but causes irritation to the nose and throat while being handled. Termite mounds are frequently found growing up round the bases of these trees. The seed germinates readily and many seedlings may be found round the parent tree. The plants grow slowly and will tolerate only very mild frosts, but they could be cultivated and would provide fine shade trees in large gardens or parks. This is a protected plant in South Africa.

4. PERICOPSIS Thwaites

Pericopsis angolensis (Baker) van Meeuwen   Illust. 94
[*Afrormosia angolensis* (Baker) Harms]
S.A. no: —
Rhod. no: 284   Afrormosia. Muwanga

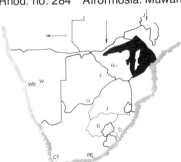

A medium to large tree, usually about 10 m in height, but reaching 20 m under favourable conditions; it is locally common in open or closed woodland and wooded grassland at medium to low altitudes. **Bark:** pale whitish-grey or creamy-brown, fairly smooth, characteristically irregularly fissured and flaking. **Leaves:** alternate, compound, with 8 to 20 sub-opposite to alternate leaflets plus a terminal

297

The crooked symmetry of the muvanga, Pericopsis angolensis.

leaflet; leaflets ovate to elliptic, 3,5 to 6,5 × 2 to 3,5 cm, leathery, without hairs; apex rounded, notched; base tapering; margin entire; petiolules and petiole present. Stipules falling early. **Flowers:** attractive, pale pink to purple, or whitish tinged with violet and veined with purple, the standard petal up to 1,3 cm long; the flower stalks and the backs of the calyx lobes are covered with pale brown, velvety hairs. The flowers are in terminal, branched sprays about 15 cm long (September to November). **Fruit:** a flattened pod, 7 to 24 cm long, usually narrowly winged along both margins, pale dusty straw-coloured, hanging in loose, untidy bunches; seeds red (April to May but the pods may remain on the tree into July).

These trees are strongly fire-resistant, but sensitive to frost. The Africans use a warm infusion of the bark and roots to bathe the eyes, and a decoction of the leaves to relieve headaches: the leaves are pounded and soaked in water and the face and head are then bathed in the liquid. It is said that the smell of the leaves alone is sometimes enough to cure a headache. The wood is a fine, highly esteemed, general purpose timber, being close-grained and virtually indestructable. Commercially it is known as 'afrormosia' (for many years the tree was known by the name *Afrormosia angolensis),* and is used for flooring blocks and panelling. It is only in Moçambique that the trees are large enough and found in sufficient quantities to be exploited commercially.

5. SOPHORA L.

Sophora inhambanensis Klotzsch
S.A. no: 218   Coast bean bush. Kusboontjiebos
Rhod. no: —

A shrub or small tree, 2 to 3 m in height; confined to coastal sand dunes. Young branches, leaves and flowers are densely covered with silver or gold silky hairs. **Leaves:** alternate, compound, with 10 to 14 leaflets, usually alternate; leaflets elliptic, 1,8 to 4 × 0,7 to 1,5 cm, both surfaces densely covered with silvery to golden silky hairs; apex broadly tapering; base tapering, slightly asymmetric; margin entire. **Flowers:** attractive, yellow, pea-like, produced in dense, terminal, axillary sprays up to 25 cm long. Bisexual; calyx shortly toothed; petals 5, characteristically shaped and arranged; stamens 5, free or shortly joined at the base; ovary with many ovules (February to March). **Fruit:** a cylindric, silvery

298

or golden, velvety, small pod, 7 to 11 × 1 cm, narrow, sharply constricted between the 2 to 5 seeds, producing the appearance of a string of beads (July to October).

This remarkably beautiful small tree is often a pioneer on sand dunes and is common from Kenya to the north of Zululand. It would be a very worth-while introduction into gardens, given a sandy soil.

6. CALPURNIA E. Meyer

Shrubs or small trees. Leaves: alternate, compound, imparipinnate. Stipules small, falling early. **Flowers:** in axillary or terminal racemes; typically pea-like, yellow. **Pods:** narrowly oblong, flat, thinly textured, with a narrow wing or rim along the upper edge; usually indehiscent.

This genus looks very much like a yellow flowered form of *Virgilia* and, indeed, was classified as such for some time. However, E. Meyer separated it, naming the new genus after Titus Calpurnius Sicilus who, in the early part of Nero's reign, wrote poetry in direct imitation of Virgil. This generic name is a whimsical reference to Virgil's imitator.

Other species may possibly occur as small trees on occasions and therefore they merit mention: *C. floribunda* Harvey, from the eastern Cape through to the eastern Transvaal; *C. intrusa* E. Meyer, a higher altitude species from Transkei, Pondoland, Lesotho, the eastern Orange Free State, Natal and the Transvaal; and *C. glabrata* Brummitt, from the eastern Transvaal and adjacent areas in Swaziland.

Key to the tree species of *Calpurnia:*

Leaves with 3 to 4 pairs of leaflets plus the terminal leaflet; essentially a high altitude species. Confined to Lesotho and adjacent areas in the Cape, eastern Orange Free State and just into the Transvaal .... **C. robinioides**

Leaves with 5 to 15 pairs of leaflets plus the terminal leaflet; from sea level to about 1 500 m. More widespread than the previous species, extending from the eastern Cape, through Natal and the Transvaal to Rhodesia .... **C. aurea**

Calpurnia aurea (Ait.) Benth.

[*C. subdecandra* (L'Hérit.) Schweickerdt]
S.A. no: 219 and 220   Wild laburnum. Wildegeelkeur
Rhod. no: 286   Wild laburnum

299

Frequently a shrub, but it may be a small, bushy tree up to 4 m in height, even reaching 15 m in the forests in the east of Rhodesia; occurring in evergreen forest and riverine fringe forest, along the margins and in clearings. **Bark:** pale brown on small bushes becoming dark brown as the trees become larger. **Leaves:** with 5 to 15 pairs of leaflets plus a terminal leaflet; leaflets ovate to oblong, 2,5 to 4 × 1,2 to 1,6 cm, fresh light green; apex rounded with a fine hair-like tip; base rounded to shallowly lobed; margin entire. **Flowers:** attractive, yellow, pea-shaped flowers in axillary or terminal sprays 7 to 24 cm long (mainly December to February, but flowers may be found at almost all times of the year). **Fruit:** a light-weight thin pod, up to 10 × 1,5 cm, straw-coloured or light brown, with a narrow wing, or rim, along the upper edge, indehiscent (may be found on the tree at almost any time of the year).

Two subspecies are involved: the typical subsp. *aurea,* with the ovary clothed with silky hairs and subsp. *sylvatica* (Burch.) Brummitt, in which the ovary is without hairs. The subsp. *sylvatica* is confined to the south-eastern Cape, near Somerset East, Port Elizabeth and East London; from there northwards, it is replaced by subsp. *aurea.* This is sometimes grown as an ornamental tree or shrub in gardens and also as a shade tree in coffee plantations.

Calpurnia robinioides (DC.) E. Meyer
S.A. no: 220,1   Free State laburnum. Vrystaatse geelkeur
Rhod. no: —

A bush or small tree up to 3 to 4 m in height; a high altitude species occurring in mountain ravines. **Bark:** grey or brown. **Leaves:** with 3 to 4 pairs of leaflets plus a terminal leaflet; leaflets oval to ovate, 2 to 3,5 × 1 to 2 cm, fresh green in colour; apex rounded to slightly notched with a fine bristle at the tip; base broadly tapering to rounded; margin entire; petiole up to 2,5 cm long. **Flowers:** attractive, bright yellow, pea-shaped, about 10 mm long, in axillary sprays about 5 cm in length (November to December). **Fruit:** a small, flat pod, 3 to 5 × 1 cm, straw-coloured with conspicuous transverse wrinkles and with a narrow wing, or rim, along the upper edge, indehiscent (January).

7. BOLUSANTHUS Harms

Bolusanthus speciosus (Bolus) Harms   Illust. 95
S.A. no: 222   Tree wistaria. Vanwykshout
Rhod. no: 287   Tree wistaria

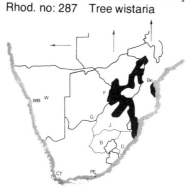
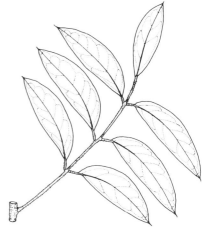

A graceful tree, 4 to 7 m in height; occurring at medium to low altitudes in wooded grassland on a variety of soils. **Bark:** brown to blackish-brown, rough and deeply longitudinally fissured. **Leaves:** alternate, compound, with 3 to 7 pairs of leaflets plus a terminal leaflet; leaflets lanceolate, up to 7 × 1 cm, yellowish-green, with the midrib and lateral veins pale yellowish and conspicuous, bright shining green above, dull green below; apex narrowly tapering; base broadly tapering to rounded, markedly asymmetric; margin slightly and irregularly scalloped. **Flowers:** very beautiful, blue to mauve, pea-shaped, in loose terminal sprays up to 30 cm long (September to October extending sometimes to November and even on to December or January). **Fruit:** a flat, narrow pod, about 7 to 10 × 1 cm, light brown or straw-coloured but may be grey or even blackish with age, tardily dehiscent (February to March or later).

In the Transvaal Africans use the dried inner bark to relieve abdominal disorders. The wood is one of the best and hardest of indigenous timbers and has a wide variety of uses although the pieces are usually small. This is one of the most beautiful of the wild trees and is an excellent garden subject; the seed germinates readily but the seedlings do not transplant easily. However, given a good, well-drained soil and a sunny position free from frost, they can be fast-growing.

8. VIRGILIA Lam.

Virgilia oroboides (Berg.) Salter   Illust. 96
[including **V. divaricata** Adamson; *Virgilia capensis* Lam.]
S.A. no: 221 and 221,1   Keurboom. Keurboom
Rhod. no: —

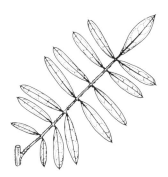

A rather sparse, rounded, medium sized tree, rarely exceeding 10 m in height; occurring on forest edges and in river valleys, confined to the coastal strip from the south-western to southern Cape. **Bark:** pale brownish-grey and smooth. **Leaves:** alternate, compound, with 5 to 20 pairs of leaflets plus a terminal leaflet; leaflets narrowly oblong 1,3 to 2,5 × 0,6 to 0,8 cm, glossy green above with brownish, velvety hairs below; apex broadly tapering with a fine, hair-like tip; base very broadly tapering to rounded; margin entire. Stipules fall early. **Flowers:** very beautiful, pea-shaped, in short, terminal sprays about 10 cm long, often produced in profusion (August to September, or December to January). **Fruit:** a velvety, brown, flat pod, up to 8 × 1 to 1,5 cm, becoming nearly black with age (December to January, or March to April).

This is one of the most beautiful of indigenous trees. The seed germinates readily, although the seed coat is very hard and germination must be assisted in some way, such as by soaking the seeds in hot water or by cracking the seed coat. Once started, these trees grow rapidly and can reach full size in 4 to 5 years; although they are somewhat short-lived their beauty makes them worth-while. They require plenty of water and will not survive much exposure to frost. Their strongly spreading surface roots make them greedy feeders in a small garden. A second species, *V. divaricata* Adamson which occurrs in the Knysna area, may prove to be no more than a darker coloured form of *V. oroboides*. This has been included in the distribution map.

9. BAPHIA DC.

Shrubs with a tendency to scramble, or small to medium sized trees. **Leaves:** alternate, simple; petioles with 1 or 2 characteristic swellings. Stipules fall very early. **Flowers:** in axillary or **301**

6 Leaflets alternate with translucent dots and streaks, fruits up to 8 × 6 cm .... **1. Cordyla**

Leaflets opposite or alternate, without translucent dots and streaks; fruits up to 2,5 × 1,7 cm .... **3. Xanthocercis**

7 Leaflets markedly alternate 8

Leaflets usually opposite or sub-opposite 16

8 Pods long, cylindric, up to 30 cm long, indehiscent .... **2. Swartzia**

Pods flattened or, if cylindric, either dehiscent or small to very small and not longer than 11 cm 9

9 Pods cylindric with bristle-like hairs; or with silver or golden velvety hairs 10

Pods usually flat; if cylindric then without either bristle-like hairs or silver to golden velvety hairs 11

10 Pods either very small, curled and scarcely protruding beyond the remains of the dried petals; or up to 4,5 cm long, more or less straight, covered with long, rather stiff, bristly, gold to yellowish hairs, resembling a caterpillar .... **21. Ormocarpum**

Pods straight, up to 11 cm long, with silver or golden velvety hairs .... **5. Sophora**

11 Leaflets few, 3 to 7 in number only 12

Leaflets usually 8 to 20 in number 13

12 Pods thin, flat, indehiscent .... **23. Dalbergia**

Pods woody, dehiscent, splitting and spiralling .... **19. Craibia**

13 Pod encircled by a wing, broad or narrow, with the seed case raised and with or without spiny hairs; flowers yellow to orange .... **25. Pterocarpus**

Pods flat, narrow, without an encircling wing, but may have a narrow wing along both margins 14

14 Bark with a blood-red exudate from a slash or from wounds; pods very conspicuously veined .... **27. Xeroderris**

Bark without a blood-red exudate from wounds 15

15 Bark pale whitish-grey or creamy-brown, generally smooth, with sparse irregular flakes; flowers pale pink to purple, or whitish-tinged and veined with purple .... **4. Pericopsis**

Bark grey to brown, often dark, rough, sometimes spiny; flowers small, white .... **23. Dalbergia**

16 Branchelets, flower stalks and calyces covered with more or less long, silky, white, silver or golden hairs; the leaves may have similar hairs on one or both surfaces 17

Leaves and all young parts without long, silky, white, silver or golden hairs 19

17 Flowers yellow, in dense terminal sprays; fruit cylindric, tightly constricted between the seeds, resembling a string of beads. Confined to coastal sand dunes and extending no further south than the extreme north of Zululand .... **5. Sophora**

Flowers pink, mauve or purple. Occurring in open woodland, or high altitude forest, not confined to coastal dunes 18

18 A shrub or small tree of open woodland, widely distributed; leaves with 4 to 6 pairs of leaflets; flowers usually 0,8 to 2 cm long .... **17. Mundulea**

A shrub or small tree of high altitude, evergreen forest, known only from a very restricted area in the east of Rhodesia and the adjacent area in Moçambique; flowers usually 2,5 to 3 cm long .... **16. Tephrosia**

293

subterminal, bracteate racemes, sometimes fascicled. Calyx tube splitting to the base on one side, or on both sides; petals pea-shaped; stamens free; ovary almost without a stalk. **Pods:** linear-oblong.

Key to the tree species of *Baphia:*

In the north-eastern Transvaal and northwards; leaves conspicuously obovate, with 6 to 10 pairs of very conspicuous veins on the under surface; apex broadly tapering to rounded .... **B. massaiensis**

In the coastal areas of Natal only; leaves ovate to narrowly so, the under surface not so conspicuously veined, apex narrowly tapering .... **B. racemosa**

Baphia massaiensis Taub.   Illust. 97
[*B. obovata* Schinz]
S.A. no: 223   Sand camwood. Sandkamhout
Rhod. no: 288   Jasmine pea

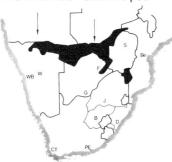 

A shrub to small tree, usually 2 to 4 m in height, but reaching 6 m on occasions; occurring on deep Kalahari sand and, in South West Africa, on sand dunes. **Bark:** dark brown to reddish-black and smooth; branchlets often velvety. **Leaves:** simple, obovate, 4 to 9 × 2 to 5,5 cm, dull green above and pale green below, with 6 to 10 conspicuous lateral veins especially on the under surface, the leaf often being folded inwards along the midrib; apex broadly tapering to rounded and notched; base tapering; margin entire; petiole with 2 distinct swellings. **Flowers:** attractive, white, in short sprays 5 to 8 cm long. Sepals pinkish; petals white and crinkled, the standard petal with a yellow patch near the base; strongly jasmine-scented (October to January). **Fruit:** a long (up to 12 cm), narrow pod; hard, rather woody, reddish-brown to dark shiny brown, splitting when mature (April to May).

The sprecies has been divided into four subspecies, one of which, subsp. *obovata* (Schinz) Brummitt, extends south of the Zambezi River.

Baphia racemosa (Hochst.) Baker
S.A. no: 224   Natal camwood. Natalkamhout
Rhod. no: —

Usually a shrub to small tree, 3 to 5 m tall, but reaching 7 to 10 m under ideal conditions; usually occurring in riverine forest. **Bark:** smooth and grey when young becoming brown and rather rough with age. **Leaves:** simple, ovate, 5 to 9 × 2 to 5 cm; apex and base tapering; margin entire, wavy; petiolate. **Flowers:** attractive, white, in short sprays, or racemes, 5 to 10 cm long, strongly violet scented; the standard petal has the yellow spot at its base (November to December). **Fruit:** a flat brown pod, up to 12 cm long (April to May).

The wood is yellowish and is subject to borer attack; however, if seasoned it makes good hoe handles. It is pliant and easily bent and in the past was made into frames for wagon tents. Eve Palmer states that it is not, as a rule, used in building huts as it is thought to bring bad luck. This is a larger tree than *B. massaiensis* and can become a canopy tree in disturbed forest.

10. PODALYRIA Lam.

Podalyria calyptrata Willd.   Illust. 98
S.A. no: 225   Water blossom pea. Waterkeurtjie
Rhod. no: —

Usually a much-branched shrub about 2 m in height but it may develop into a small tree up to 4 m; occurring in mountainous areas, along streams and fringing forest. Young branches are velvety. **Leaves:** alternate, simple, obovate-elliptic to obovate, 1 to 4,5 × 0,8 to 2,5 cm, greyish-green, only sparsely hairy on the upper surface, though the under surface may have tawny, silky hairs; apex broadly tapering to rounded or notched; base tapering; margin entire, rolled under; petiolate. **Flowers:** showy, mauve to pink, pea-shaped, sweetly scented, up to 2,5 cm in diameter. Solitary, or produced in 1- to 4-flowered axillary clusters which cover the plants in spring (July to September). **Fruit:** a pod, up to 4 × 1,5 cm, hard, inflated, covered with brown, woolly hairs (October to January or later). This species is distinguished from all other species of *Podalyria* by the small, silky, hairy bracts which are joined together to form a hood over the flower bud, but which fall as soon as the flower opens; the specific name refers to these.

11. LEBECKIA Thunb.

Lebeckia sericea Thunb.
S.A. no: Silver pea
Rhod. no: —

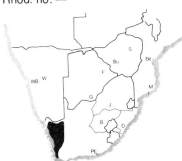

A silvery-grey, rounded shrub or small tree, 2 to 3 m in height; occurring on dry hills and in stony deserts. **Bark:** grey to creamy-brown. **Leaves:** alternate, 3-foliolate, very narrow, 2 to 5 × 0,3 to 0,6 cm, but may be smaller, covered with silky grey hairs; apex and base tapering; petiole slender up to 6 cm long. **Flowers:** pale to deep yellow, occasionally tinged with purple, pea-shaped, up to

303

1,5 cm long, produced in slender, terminal sprays or racemes (June to September). **Fruit:** a small pod, 3 × 0,3 cm, cylindric, straw-coloured, covered with silky hairs (July to October).

A second species, *L. macrantha* Harvey, the *ystervarkbos,* of the dry arid hillsides of the north-western Cape, can exceed 2 m in height and may even attain the stature of a small tree. Its branches are spine-tipped and its leaves are so small that it may seem almost leafless.

12. WIBORGIA Thunb.

Wiborgia sericea Thunb.
S.A. no: 225,1   Silky wing pea. Syvlerkertjie
Rhod. no: —

A robust, dense shrub or small tree 2 to 4 m in height; occurring on dry rocky mountainsides. **Bark:** light brown and deeply ribbed; the whole plant is covered with silky, silvery hairs; the lateral branches sometimes short, leafy and spine-tipped; branchlets covered with silky hairs. **Leaves:** alternate, pinnately 3-foliolate, crowded and tightly clustered along the stems; leaflets small, oblong, up to 8 × 2 to 3 mm, densely covered with silky hairs; apex broadly tapering to rounded and notched; base tapering; margin entire; petiolate. **Flowers:** pale yellow, pea-shaped, up to 10 mm long, in short sprays, 3 to 4 cm long (June to August). **Fruit:** a small, indehiscent pod, about 1,2 × 0,7 cm, reddish-brown, the central section domed and wrinkled, surrounded by a narrow wing, about 2 mm wide (September).

13. CROTALARIA L.

This is a very large genus with about 100 species in southern Africa; some are fodder plants and a few are toxic. One species sometimes becomes a tree.

Crotalaria capensis Jacq.   Illust. 99
[*C. ceciliae* Verdoorn]
S.A. no: 224,1   Cape Rattle-pod. Kaapse klapperpeul
Rhod. no: 290   Rattle-pod

A much-branched shrub or small tree, about 3 m in height, occasionally reaching 6 m; occurring in a wide variety of habitats, but most often associated with evergreen forest. **Bark:** light coloured, greyish to brownish and fissured. **Leaves:** alternate, digitately 3-foliolate; leaflets oval to ovate, up to 6 × 2,5 cm, fresh green, thinly textured, finely hairy; apex generally broadly tapering with a fine bristle-tip; base tapering; margin entire; petiole slender. Stipules very characteristic, like 2 small leaves at the base of the petiole. **Flowers:** bright yellow, pea-shaped, with the keel petal distinctly beaked; produced in showy, pendulous sprays up to 20 cm long (October to February). **Fruit:** a cylindric, almost inflated pod, 6 to 8 × 1,5 cm, light brown in colour (January to May).

These plants are sometimes used as a hedge. They are browsed on by stock, but in certain areas are reported to be poisonous; this may be due to confusion with *C. burkeana* Benth. which causes 'stiff-sickness' in cattle.

14. INDIGOFERA L.

A very large, tropical and subtropical genus with over 200 species in southern Africa: the majority of these are small herbs or shrubs, only 5 of which reach tree size. **Leaves:** alternate, compound, imparipinnate. Stipules present. **Flowers:** in axillary racemes, occasionally branched. Petals usually white, pink or red, smallish, usually about 10 mm long; stamens joined. **Fruit:** a cylindric pod, usually dehiscent.

Key to the tree species of *Indigofera:*

1 Flowers pink or deep wine-red 2
  Flowers white 4
2 Flowers deep wine-red .... **I. lyallii**
  Flowers rose-pink 3
3 Occurring in the eastern Cape and Natal only .... **I. cylindrica**
  Occurring in the Transvaal, Rhodesia and Moçambique .... **I. swaziensis** (var. *perplexa*)
4 Flowers very small, white, occasionally tinged with mauve; pod straight; Natal and the eastern
    Cape only .... **I. natalensis**
  Flowers up to 8 mm long, white or tinged with mauve; pod with a conspicuous, beak-like hook at
    the tip; not extending further south than northern and eastern Rhodesia ... **I. rhynchocarpa**

Indigofera cylindrica DC.
S.A. no: 225,4   River indigo. Rivierverfbos
Rhod. no: —

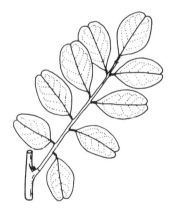

A much-branched, graceful shrub, often with a tendency to scramble, or a small tree sometimes reaching 7 m in height; occurring on dry hillsides, in scrub skirting forest and in riverine bush and fringe forest. **Bark:** greyish or brown. **Leaves:** with 4 to 7 pairs of leaflets plus a terminal leaflet; leaflets obovate, 0,8 to 2,5 × 0,5 to 1,3 cm, well spaced along the rachis, dark green, without hairs; apex rounded, notched; base tapering; margin entire; petiolules and petiole present. **Flowers:** attractive, rose-pink, sweetly scented, pea-shaped; produced in short, almost cylindric, axillary sprays up to 5 cm long, the stalk, or peduncle, almost equalling this in length. The 2 wing petals are a brilliant pink to red, producing a sharply contrasting colour, but these fall early. Paler, sometimes almost white, forms do occur (January to February). **Fruit:** a straight, cylindric pod, 4 × 0,3 cm; the young pods are ensheathed by a white staminal tube for some time; they finally mature to a reddish-brown colour and split and spiral (March to May).

305

PAPILIONOIDEAE

The Africans use the roots as a remedy for intestinal worms. This species makes an attractive and successful garden plant.

Indigofera lyallii Baker
S.A. no: Red indigo
Rhod. no: 306   Red indigo tree

Usually a shrub 2 to 3 m in height, or a small tree up to 7 m under favourable conditions; occurring on open, grassy mountain slopes, fringing forest and in ravine forest. **Leaves:** with 8 to 12 pairs of leaflets plus a terminal leaflet; leaflets squarely oval, up to 2 × 0,5 to 0,8 cm, dark green above, paler green below, finely velvety; apex and base square; margin entire; petiolules and petiole present. **Flowers:** small, dark wine-red, produced in compact, short racemes about 5 cm long. Despite the colour, they are not very conspicuous (March to April, but odd flowers can be found at almost any time of the year). **Fruit:** a distinctive, small, cylindric pod, about 3 × 0,3 mm, reddish-brown, splitting and partly twisting when mature (June to September).

This species has been divided into two subspecies, only the typical subspecies, subsp. *lyallii*, extending south of the Zambezi River.

Indigofera natalensis Bolus
S.A. no: 225,6   Forest indigo, Bosverfbos
Rhod. no: —

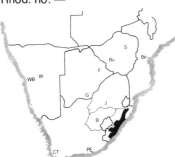 

Very often a shrub, sometimes a small tree up to 3 m in height; confined to the coastal forests where it often grows thickly along the paths. **Bark:** pale grey. **Leaves:** with 1 to 2 pairs of leaflets plus a terminal leaflet; leaflets narrowly ovate, 1,5 to 4 × 0,8 to 1,5 cm, dark green and rather shiny; apex tapering to attenuate; base broadly tapering; margin entire; petiole about 10 mm long. **Flowers:** small, white, occasionally tinged with mauve, about 5 mm long, produced in short axillary sprays, or racemes, up to 5 cm in length (December to March). **Fruit:** a cylindric pod, 4 to 0,4 cm, red-brown, splitting and spiralling when mature (May to June).

Indigofera rhynchocarpa Welw. ex Baker
S.A. no: —
Rhod. no: 308   Beak-fruited indigo tree

Usually a shrub up to 2 m, but frequently smaller, occasionally becoming a small tree up to 3 m in height; occurring in *Brachystegia* woodland. **Leaves:** with 2 to 3 pairs of leaflets plus a terminal

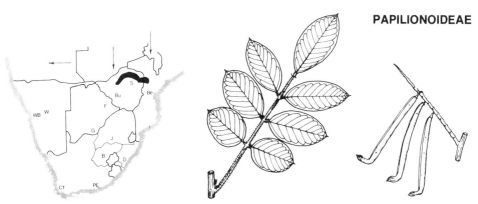

leaflet; leaflets fairly large, ovate, 2 to 7 × 1 to 3 cm, light green, without hairs; apex tapering to rounded, bristle-tipped; base broadly tapering to rounded; margin entire; petiolules and petiole present. **Flowers:** small, inconspicuous, white tinged with mauve, pea-shaped, about 8 mm long, produced in small, compact sprays, or racemes, 3 to 5 cm long among the leaves (October to December). **Fruit:** a strange and distinctive small pod, about 5 cm long, reddish-brown, cylindric, straight, except for the tip which hooks upwards like a small beak; the specific name refers to this (February to July).

This species has been divided into three varieties, only the typical variety, var. *rhynchocarpa*, extending south of the Zambezi River.

Indigofera swaziensis Bolus
S.A. no: Velvet indigo
Rhod. no: 310   Velvet indigo tree

A shrub or a slender tree 3 to 6 m in height; occurring on the margins of evergreen forest or in riverine fringe forest. **Bark:** dark grey, smooth; branchelets and young leaves with fine, brown, velvety hairs. **Leaves:** with 7 to 8 pairs of leaflets plus a terminal leaflet; leaflets elliptic to oblanceolate, 0,6 to 2,5 × 0,4 to 0,7 cm; apex broadly tapering to rounded with a conspicuous hair-like tip; base broadly tapering to square; margin entire; petiolules and petiole short and, with the rachis, covered with dark brown, velvety hairs. **Flowers:** small, pea-shaped, about 5 mm long; the overall impression is pink with the wing petals a deep pink, the standard petal brownish and the keel whitish-pink; produced in many-flowered, axillary or terminal sprays, up to 6 cm long (February). **Fruit:** a small cylindric pod, about 3 × 0,3 cm, covered with brown, velvety hairs, the tip sharply pointed, dehiscent (March to June).

The typical variety, var. *swaziensis*, remains a shrub. Only var. *perplexa* (N. E. Brown) J. B. Gillett reaches tree size.

15. PSORALEA L.

Psoralea pinnata L.
S.A. no: 225,7   Fountain bush. Fonteinbos
Rhod. no: —

An erect shrub or small tree up to 4 m in height; occurring along streams, fringing vleis and forests, and on mountain slopes. **Bark:** pale brown with whitish markings, smooth. **Leaves:** alternate, **307**

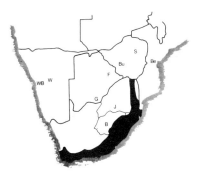 

compound, with 3 to 4 pairs of opposite to sub-opposite leaflets and a terminal leaflet; leaflets very fine and slender, sometimes almost thread-like, 1,5 to 2,5 × 0,1 to 0,4 cm, produced in small clusters towards the tips of the slender branchlets, aromatic when crushed; apex and base tapering; margin entire; petiolules very short to absent, petiole present. **Flowers:** pea-shaped, light to rich blue or mauve (occasionally whitish), clustered, or fascicled, in the axils of the terminal leaves. The calyx lobes are gland-dotted (October to December in the western Cape; February to June in the eastern Cape; August to September in Natal and the Transvaal). **Fruit:** a much reduced, small pod, only about 5 × 3 mm, remaining hidden inside the remains of the persistent calyx (shortly after flowering season).

The common name – 'fountain bush' – arises from the fact that it is frequently found growing around springs and fringing vleis.

16. TEPHROSIA Pers.

Tephrosia praecana Brummitt
S.A. no: —
Rhod. no: 319   Tephrosia

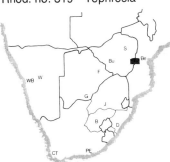  

A shrub or a spreading, well-branched but rather sparse tree up to 7 m in height; occurring on the fringe of high altitude evergreen forest. **Bark:** brownish to grey; branchlets with dense, grey, velvety to silky hairs. **Leaves:** alternate, compound, with 6 to 11 pairs of opposite leaflets plus a terminal leaflet, the very young leaves being covered with dense, silky hairs; leaflets elliptic to oblong, up to 3,8 × 1 cm, the upper surface without hairs, the lower surface with very fine appressed hairs, lateral veins many, ascending, giving a series of fine, parallel streak-lines on both surfaces; apex and base broadly tapering to rounded; margin entire, the blade being inclined to fold upward along the midrib; petiolules short, petiole and rachis often with fine, grey or brown hairs. **Flowers:** rather large, mauve, showy, pea-shaped, up to 3 cm long, the stalks, calyces and the backs of the petals covered with dense, white, silky hairs; produced in leaf opposed, branched sprays (December to March). **Fruit:** a slender, flattened pod, up to 10 × 1 cm, very thinly woody, densely covered with rich brown velvety hairs, with a thickened margin, splitting and spiralling when mature (March to July; the old pods may remain on the tree almost into the following flowering season).

17. MUNDULEA Benth.

Mundulea sericea (Willd.) Chev.   Illust. 100
[*M. suberosa* Benth.]
S.A. no: 226   Cork bush. Kurkbos
Rhod. no: 321   Cork bush

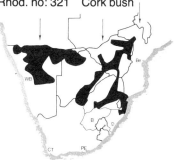

A very attractive shrub or small tree usually 2 to 3 m in height, but occasionally reaching 4 to 5 m; occurring in open woodland, wooded grassland, on wooded hillsides, rocky koppies and dry, sandy flats. **Bark:** light grey, deeply furrowed and corky; branchlets, flower stalks and calyces covered with silky hairs. **Leaves:** alternate, compound, with 4 to 6 (occasionally 11) pairs of opposite to sub-opposite leaflets plus a terminal leaflet; leaflets lanceolate, 2 to 6,5 × 0,5 to 2,5 cm, pale green, covered with silvery, silky hairs; apex somewhat attenuate, finally narrowly rounded; base broadly tapering to rounded; margin entire; petiolules and petiole short. **Flowers:** beautiful, mauve to purple, or lilac, pea-shaped, 0,8 to 2 cm long, in sprays, or pseudo-racemes, 8 to 14 cm long (October to January). **Fruit:** an attractive, small pod, 7,5 to 9 × 1 cm, flat, with a marked rim and covered with golden-brown velvety hairs which become grey with age, tardily dehiscent (February to April, but they stay on the tree even into the next summer).

The bark contains rotenone, the insecticide obtained from some species of *Derris*. Both the bark and seeds of the tree are widely used as fish poisons – they actually kill the fish rather than merely stupify them; nevertheless, the leaves are browsed on by game animals and stock. Zulus use the bark as an emetic to treat cases of poisoning. Venda doctors treat married couples with the powdered root when the wife has had a series of miscarriages, the man and wife being tied together with their backs to one of these trees during the ritual. This is a most attractive plant and well worth introducing into a garden; the seed germinates well if soaked in hot water, but the plants are slow-growing and need a well-drained soil.

18. MILLETTIA Wight & Arn.

Shrubs, lianes or trees. **Leaves:** alternate, compound, imparipinnate, with a characteristic swelling at the base of the rachis. **Inflorescence:** a panicle, or a pseudo-raceme by contraction of the floral branches into lateral knobs each bearing 2 flowers. Flowers pea-shaped. **Fruit:** a flat pod, dehiscent.

Key to the tree species of *Millettia:*
1 In the eastern Cape to Natal and Zululand only 2
  Extending no further south than the east of Rhodesia and Moçambique 3
2 A medium sized tree up to 13 m; leaflets in 6 to 7 pairs plus the terminal leaflet, up to 6,5 cm long; wood of superior quality .... **M. grandis**
  A large forest tree up to 30 m; leaflets in 3 to 4 pairs plus the terminal leaflet, smaller than those of the preceding species, about 4 cm long; wood of poor quality .... **M. sutherlandii**
3 Leaflets large, usually 9 to 10 × 4 to 6 cm; elliptic-obovate, comparatively broad ....
  .... **M. stuhlmannii**
  Leaflets much smaller, usually 2 to 5,5 × 1,5 to 2,5 cm, oblanceolate, narrower than those of the preceding species .... **M. usaramensis**   **309**

PAPILIONOIDEAE

Millettia grandis (E. Meyer) Skeels   Illust. 101
[*M. caffra* Meissner]
S.A. no: 227   Umzimbeet. Omsambeet
Rhod. no: —

A medium sized tree reaching 13 m in height under favourable conditions, but remaining a stunted, gnarled small tree when growing on shale soils; occurring in coastal forests and at low altitudes, seldom found more than 20 km from the coast or at altitudes higher than 600 m. **Bark:** grey to dark grey or light brown, smooth to rather flaky. **Leaves:** with 6 to 7 pairs of opposite leaflets plus a terminal leaflet; leaflets oblong, 4 to 6,5 × 0,8 to 2,2 cm, the under surface covered with silky hairs, the young leaves and petiolules dark reddish-brown, the colour running into the veins; apex and base tapering; margin entire; petiolules and petiole short. **Flowers:** beautiful, purple to mauve, pea-shaped, in upright spikes, up to 25 cm long; the calyces and stems are covered with dark brown, velvety hairs (January). **Fruit:** a large, woody, flat pod, up to 15 cm long, covered with brown, velvety hairs, splitting and spiralling when mature (June to September).

The wood is heavy, hard and strong and makes very beautiful and durable furniture and domestic implements. The heartwood is dark brown and the sapwood yellow. The seeds are poisonous if eaten in quantity, but when ground and soaked in milk provide a remedy for roundworm. The ground roots, prepared in various ways, are used to induce sleep and as a tranquilliser. These plants are easily raised from seed and make well-shaped, shady, decorative, garden trees; they are fairly fast-growning and able to withstand several degrees of frost.

Millettia stuhlmannii Taub.
S.A. no: —
Rhod. no: 322   Panga Panga

A large, fine, spreading tree up to 20 m in height; occurring in low altitude, high-rainfall forest and riverine fringe forest where it reaches its greatest size; away from these areas, on rocky hillsides, it is often only 7 to 10 m in height. **Bark:** yellow or greenish-grey and smooth; the young twigs, leaf rachis and the under surface of the leaflets are covered with very fine, white hairs. **Leaves:** large, compound, with 7 to 9 pairs of opposite leaflets plus a terminal leaflet; leaflets variable in size and shape but generally oval to elliptic-obovate, usually about 9 to 10 × 6 cm, pale green above, slightly bluish-green below; apex rounded, often widely notched but also frequently abruptly attenuate producing a short, narrow tip; base rounded to lobed; margin entire. **Flowers:** very beautiful, large,

310

lilac, pea-shaped, in long, rather lax sprays up to 35 cm long (November to January). **Fruit:** a woody, flat pod, about 25 cm long, with golden-brown, velvety hairs, dehiscent (April to May)
The timber, dark brown to almost black and finely grained, is of an excellent quality and is used particularly for flooring blocks. It is sold commercially under the name 'panga panga'.

Millettia sutherlandii Harvey
S.A. no: 228   Bastard umzimbeet. Basteromsambeet
Rhod. no: —

A very large, forest tree reaching 30 m in height; apparently confined to the 3 small areas shown on the map, where it is locally abundant. **Bark:** pale grey, smooth, finely flaking; the stems of the large specimens are buttressed. **Leaves:** compound, with 3 to 4 pairs of opposite leaflets plus a terminal leaflet, 2 to 5 × 0,6 to 1,8 cm; the leaflets, fewer and rather smaller than those of *M. grandis,* are dark green and form a dense crown. **Flowers:** deep pink to purple, pea-shaped, in conspicuous sprays up to 15 cm long. The buds and stalks are covered with golden-brown, velvety hairs (December to January). **Fruit:** a large, flat, woody, light brown, velvety pod, up to 12 cm long, dehiscent (April to September, but the old pods may remain on the tree longer).
The wood is of little value for a tree of this size as it tends to flake away in rings and T. R. Sim, writing in 1906, described this unfortunate species as 'one of the largest, most abundant and most useless trees in the Egossa forest'. This is a protected plant in South Africa.

Millettia usaramensis Taub.
S.A. no: —
Rhod. no: 323   Lesser millettia

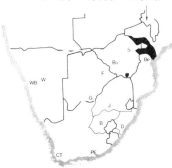

A shrub or small tree about 7 m in height, occasionally reaching 10 m; occurring in hot, low altitude areas. **Bark:** grey and flaking. **Leaves:** compound, with 4 pairs of opposite leaflets plus a terminal leaflet; leaflets oval to oblanceolate, 2 to 5,5 × 1 to 2,5 cm, light fresh green; apex tapering, often attenuate, bristle-tipped; base broadly tapering to rounded; margin entire; petiole and rachis slender, with the leaflets widely spaced. **Flowers:** mauve to purple, pea-shaped, in loose open sprays up to 14 cm long (November to December). **Fruit:** a small, flat pod, 5 to 6 × 1 cm, thinly woody, reddish-brown and velvety, splitting and partly spiralling when mature (April to June).
All the material south of the Zambezi River is placed in subsp. *australis* Gillett. The typical subspecies, subsp. *usaramensis,* extends southwards to northern Moçambique and it is possible that it crosses the Zambezi River near Chemba.

311

PAPILIONOIDEAE

19. CRAIBIA Harms & Dunn

Shrubs or trees, frequently with golden-brown or black hairs. **Leaves:** alternate, compound, usually imparipinnate; leaflets alternate; petiole with a characteristic swelling. **Inflorescence:** a raceme, with dense brown to blackish velvety hairs. Flowers white, pea-shaped. **Fruit:** a flat, woody pod; dehiscent.

Key to the tree species of *Craibia:*
Calyx and flower stalk almost without hairs or completely so; leaflets 3 to 6 in number. In Natal, Zululand, Moçambique .... **C. zimmermannii**
Calyx and flower stalks covered with dense, velvety hairs; leaflets 5 to 7 in number; not extending further south than the Limpopo River .... **C. brevicaudata**

Craibia brevicaudata (Vatke) Dunn   Illust. 102
[*Schefflerodendron gazense* E. G. Baker]
S.A. no: —
Rhod. no: 234   Craibia

A medium to large, rounded, evergreen tree up to 18 m in height; occurring on forested mountain-sides, often dominant in relic evergreen forest. **Bark:** pale grey and flaking. **Leaves:** with 5 to 7 alternate leaflets and a terminal leaflet; leaflets elliptic to oblong- oblanceolate, 6 to 11 × 2 to 3,5 cm, deep green, leathery, almost without hairs; apex tapering to attenuate; base broadly tapering to rounded; margin entire; petiolules wrinkled, petiole with a characteristic swelling. **Flowers:** pink to white, resembling small sweet peas; produced in short compact sprays, or racemes, about 15 cm long, near the ends of the branches. The branches, flower stalks and calyces are covered with dense, golden-brown, velvety hairs. When in full flower the trees are very showy (October to January). **Fruit:** a distinctive, flat, creamy-grey pod, about 8 to 10 × 3,5 to 5 cm, dehiscent. The seeds are a rich red-brown (May to June).
This species has been divided into 4 subspecies, only 2 of which extend south of the Zambezi River. The one treated above is subsp. *baptistarum* (Büttn.) Gillett. The other, subsp. *schliebenii* (Harms) Gillett, has an attenuate leaf apex forming a narrow drip-tip, and floral parts which are covered with black velvety hairs; the only known locality south of the Zambezi River is Mount Gorongoza in Mocambique.

Craibia zimmermannii (Harms) Harms ex Dunn
S.A. no: 229   Small craibia. Ertjiehout
Rhod. no: —

Usually rather a small evergreen tree, 4 to 5 m in height, but reaching 15 m under favourable conditions, as near Lake Sibayi in Zululand; it is a common middle-storey tree in sand forest and on forest margins. **Bark:** pale grey and slightly flaking; the young twigs, leaf petioles and rachides have reddish-brown, velvety hairs. **Leaves:** with 3 to 5 alternate leaflets plus a terminal leaflet; leaflets ovate to lanceolate, 5 to 9 × 2 to 4 cm, shiny green, leathery; apex attenuate; base very broadly tapering to square; margin entire; petiole with reddish-brown, velvety hairs and a characteristic swelling. **Flowers:** white, sweetly scented, quite large, pea-shaped, up to 2 cm in diameter, produced in 5- to 10-flowered sprays, or racemes, about 15 to 20 cm long (September to November). **Fruit:** a flat, woody pod, up to 6 to 11 cm long, pale cream almost with a greyish bloom, dehiscent (March to September, but the old pods may remain on the tree longer). This is a protected plant in South Africa.

312

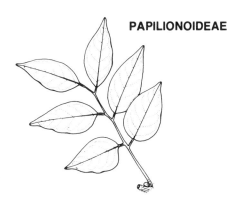

20. SESBANIA Scop.

Frequently annual or briefly perennial shrubs, or woody shrubs, occasionally small trees, with white or golden hairs. Stipules present. **Leaves:** alternate, compound, pinnate, 10 to 46 pairs of opposite leaflets. **Flowers:** in axillary racemes; bracts and bracteoles present, but fall early; calyx bell-shaped; petals characteristically pea-shaped, usually yellow often streaked or spotted with purple; stamens mainly joined with the uppermost stamen free; ovary with or without fine velvety hairs. **Fruit:** a long, slender, semi-cylindric, beaked pod; indehiscent.

Key to the tree species of *Sesbania:*
1 Flowers blue; sometimes a large, almost tree-like annual plant, very occasionally semi-woody and
   perennial .... **S. coerulescens**
   Flowers yellow; plants more or less woody perennials 2
2 All parts densely covered with grey hairs; not extending further south than the north-eastern areas of
   South West Africa and the north-western areas of Botswana .... **S. cinerascens**
   All parts without hairs, or very finely hairy, not with conspicuous, dense, grey hairs; much more
   widespread, extending as far south as Pondoland .... **S. sesban**

Sesbania cinerascens Welw. ex Baker
S.A. no: 229,2   Grey river bean. Vaalrivierboontjie
Rhod. no: —

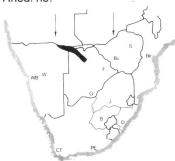

A shrub or small tree, 3 to 4 m in height, with slender branches; occurring along river banks and in damp places. **Bark:** reddish-brown, branches covered with grey hairs. **Leaves:** with 12 to 34 pairs of opposite leaflets; leaflets small, oblong, 10 × 2 mm, blue-grey and densely covered with grey hairs. **Flowers:** very showy, deep yellow, large, pea-shaped, up to 3,5 cm in diameter, produced in long, axillary sprays, or racemes, up to 30 cm long; the stems and flower stalks are densely covered with grey, woolly hairs (February to March). **Fruit:** a very long, slender pod, 25 to 35 × 0,4 cm, red-brown, slightly constricted between the seeds (April to July).

Sesbania coerulescens Harms
S.A. no: Blue river bean
Rhod. no: —   Blue river bean

Usually an annual, very occasionally a shrub, included here because of its size and sometimes tree-like habit, 3 to 5 m in height; occurring in wet vleis or pans on sandy soil. **Bark:** green or

313

 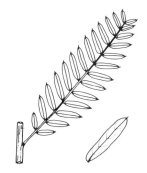

brownish-green and smooth. **Leaves:** with 12 to 46 pairs of opposite leaflets; leaflets oblong, up to 20 × 4 mm; apex rounded with a fine hair-like tip; base rounded; margin entire; petiole running into the stem forming a clearly marked ridge. **Flowers:** very showy, pale blue to lavender, large, pea-shaped; produced in lax, axillary sprays up to 20 cm long (February to April). **Fruit:** a long slender pod, up to 30 × 1 cm, reddish-brown, slightly constricted between the many seeds (April to July).

Sesbania sesban (L.) Merr.
S.A. no: 229,1   River bean. Rivierboontjie
Rhod. no: 326   River bean

 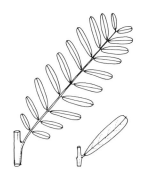

A shrub, or a small, softly woody, short-lived tree, 1 to 7 m in height; occurring in low lying areas usually near water, often on river or stream banks. **Bark:** reddish-brown. **Leaves:** with 10 to 25 pairs of opposite leaflets; leaflets oblong, up to 15 × 3 mm; apex and base tapering to narrowly rounded; margin entire. **Flowers:** attractive, yellow, pea-shaped, with the standard petal often speckled and finely veined with dark maroon; produced in many-flowered sprays up to 15 cm long (March to September). **Fruit:** a distinctive, very long, slender, cylindric pod, up to 30 × 0,3 cm, often slightly curved with a distinct beak (June to December). The fruits develop rapidly and both flowers and fruits may be found together on the plant at almost any time of the year.
This species has been divided into two subspecies, only the typical subspecies, subsp. *sesban*, occurring south of the Sudan; the further subdivision at varietal level is not maintained in the present work.

21. ORMOCARPUM Beauv.

Shrubs or small trees with 2 types of hairs: weak, whitish hairs which soon fall, and stiff, dark, swollen-based hairs which persist. **Leaves:** compound, imparipinnate, often fascicled on dwarfed side shoots; leaflets alternate, almost without hairs. **Flowers:** solitary or in axillary racemes. Bracts and bracteoles persistent at the base of the primary flower stalks, or pedicels; flowers pea-shaped, 0,9 to 2,6 cm long, the petals often conspicuously veined. **Fruit:** a small pod, not splitting but breaking up into a number of 1-seeded segments.

Key to the tree species of *Ormocarpum:*
Pod small, 1 to 1,5 cm long, coiled, remaining almost hidden in the dry remains of the petals ...

.... **O. kirkii**

Pod up to 4,5 cm long, more or less straight, covered with stiff, bristle-like hairs, so that they resemble hairy caterpillars .... **O. trichocarpum**

Ormocarpum kirkii S. Moore   Illust. 103
[*O. mimosoides* S. Moore]
S.A. no: 230,1   Small caterpillar pod. Basterrusperboontjie
Rhod. no: 327   Small caterpillar pod

A shrub or small, rather long-branched tree up to 7 m in height; occurring in dry types of woodland or grassland, along rivers and streams, sometimes associated with termite mounds. **Bark:** dark brown, rough and scaly. **Leaves:** usually clustered, or fascicled, on dwarf side branchlets, with 7 to 13 pairs of leaflets plus a terminal leaflet; leaflets elliptic to oblong, 7 to 11 × 3 to 6 mm, well spaced along the rachis, darker green above, paler green below; apex sharp tipped; base rounded; margin entire, tightly rolled under. **Flowers:** large, pink, flushed with deep mauve in the centre, pea-shaped; closely clustered towards the ends of the branches (September to January). **Fruit:** a very small pod, barely 2 cm long, hairy, curled, often almost into a ring and remaining almost entirely hidden within the dry remains of the petals (Illust. 103) (October to March).

Ormocarpum trichocarpum (Taub.) Engl.   Illust. 104
[*O. setosum* Burtt Davy]
S.A. no: 230   Caterpillar pod. Rusperboontjie
Rhod. no: 328   Large caterpillar pod

Shrubs or small trees rarely exceeding 3 m in height; occurring in hot areas in stony valleys and on rocky hillsides. **Bark:** blackish-brown and rough. **Leaves:** clustered, or fascicled, on dwarfed lateral side shoots, with 7 to 13 pairs of leaflets plus a terminal leaflet; leaflets elliptic to oblong, up to 11 × 5 mm, darker green above than below; apex sharp tipped; base rounded; margin entire, but not rolled under as in the previous species. **Flowers:** violet to mauve-pink, pea-shaped, in 1- to 4-flowered clusters along the stems (September to January). **Fruit:** an unmistakable small pod, up to 4,5 cm long, covered with long, but rather stiff, gold to yellowish hairs, so that it resembles a small, fat, hairy caterpillar (October to March).

22. AESCHYNOMENE L.

Annual or perennial herbs and sub-shrubs, occasionally shrubs or small trees, usually covered with tubercle-based hairs. **Leaves:** compound, alternate, or fascicled on dwarfed lateral branchlets. **315**

PAPILIONOIDEAE

Flowers: pea-shaped, solitary, in clusters, in false racemes or in panicles, axillary, terminal or leaf opposed. **Pods:** flat, narrow or elliptic.

Key to the more tree-like species of *Aeschynomene:*
Leaflets generally small and narrow, up to 1,8 × 0,6 cm; in eastern and southern mountainous areas of Rhodesia, adjacent areas in Moçambique and in the northern Transvaal .... **A. nodulosa**
Leaflets considerably larger than those of the preceding species, 1 to 3,5 × 0,7 to 2,2 cm; in the mountainous areas in the east of Rhodesia and adjacent areas in Moçambique only ....
.... **A. megalophylla**

Aeschynomene megalophylla Harms
S.A. no: —
Rhod. no: 332   Large-leaved false-teeth tree

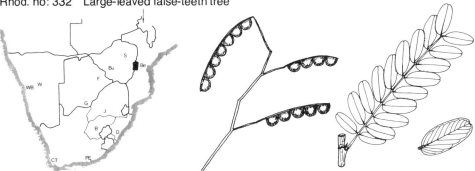

A shrub to small tree, 1 to 6 m in height; this is a mountain species, occurring in mountain grassland or fringing forest. **Bark:** grey to brown, smooth, with conspicuous lenticels; branchlets with conspicuous glandular hairs. **Leaves:** once-pinnate, with 12 to 18 pairs of opposite leaflets; leaflets oblong-elliptic, 1 to 3,5 × 0,7 to 2,2 cm, clear bright green; apex rounded, often notched; base asymmetric; margin entire, reddish; petiolules and petiole present. **Flowers:** pea-shaped; sepals red; petals orange flushed with crimson, 1,7 to 2,2 cm long, produced in axillary sprays near the ends of the branches, together forming large terminal heads (May to October). **Fruit:** an unusual pod made up of almost separate sections, each almost circular and joined together by a narrow band along one edge only, resembling water droplets hanging from a thread, or a row of false teeth (July onwards).

Aeschynomene nodulosa (Baker) E. G. Baker
S.A. no: 230,2   Small-leaved false-teeth tree. Kneukelboontjie
Rhod. no: 334   Small-leaved false-teeth tree

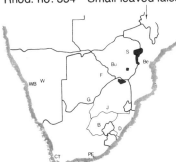

An aromatic shrub or small, rather sparse tree up to 5 m in height; found in open grassland and bracken scrub, in open woodland, along stream banks and on exposed rocky ridges. **Bark:** brown, rather smooth, lenticellate, splitting longitudinally in the larger specimens; the branches are covered with short, glandular hairs. **Leaves:** compound, once-pinnate, with 8 to 32 pairs of opposite to sub-opposite leaflets; leaflets narrowly oblong, 0,3 to 1,8 × 0,2 to 0,6 cm, with or without very sparse hairs; apex rounded with a fine hair-like tip; base rounded or square; margin entire; petiolules and

316

petiole present. **Flowers:** attractive, yellow to orange with red veining, pea-shaped; calyx reddish; the standard petal up to 1,6 cm long; produced in axillary, branched sprays near the ends of the branches so forming large terminal heads (April to November). **Fruit:** very distinctive, made up of 3 to 6 almost separate, circular sections, 5 to 6 mm in diameter, joined together along one side only, resembling beads of water hanging from a thread, or a row of false teeth (May).

There are two varieties of this species:
var. *nodulosa:* with the stem, petiole, rachis and flower stalks densely hairy.
var. *glabrescens* Gillett: with the stem, petioles, and flower stalks without hairs or very nearly so.

23. DALBERGIA L.f.

Trees or vigorous climbers. **Leaves:** alternate, compound, imparipinnate; leaflets opposite or alternate. **Flowers:** in axillary or terminal, dichotomous cymes, or subcorymbose panicles. Flowers pea-shaped, small, often many; bracts small, broad, persistent. Calyx tube bell-shaped; standard petal ovate and clawed, wing petals oblong, keel petals oblong to rounded; stamens in 1 to 2 bundles; ovary stalked. **Fruit:** a pod, oblong or strap-shaped, flat, thin, indehiscent.

Key to the tree species of *Dalbergia:*
1 Plants without spines 2
  Plants spiny 6
2 Branchlets conspicuously rough with tubercular-based glands .... **D. martinii**
  Branchlets without tubercular-based glands 3
3 Leaflets small, up to 1,5 cm .... **D. multijuga**
  Leaflets large, more than 1,5 cm long 4
4 Leaflets in 4 to 7 pairs, opposite to sub-opposite .... **D. nitidula**
  Leaflets 4 to 9, usually alternate, occasionally sub-opposite 5
5 Extending no further north than the extreme south of Moçambique .... **D. obovata**
  Extending no further south than the south-eastern area of Rhodesia and adjacent areas in Moçambique .... **D. boehmii**
6 Reaching the southern limit of its range in the eastern Transvaal; with 8 to 13 leaflets, sub-opposite to alternate, heart-shaped to oval; occurring in low altitude mixed woodland and thicket, on rocky outcrops and on termite mounds, avoiding moist situations .... **D. melanoxylon**
  Reaching the northern limit of its range in the eastern Transvaal; with 10 to 16 leaflets, alternate, oblong to oblong-elliptic; a forest species, occurring in evergreen forest, riverine forest and in densely wooded ravines .... **D. armata**

Dalbergia armata E. Meyer
S.A. no: 231   Thorny rope. Doringtou
Rhod. no: —

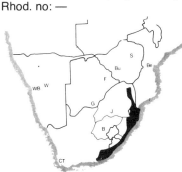

Usually a woody climber, but it can also develop into a shrub and occasionally into a small tree up to 5 m in height; common in wooded ravines, in evergreen forest and in riverine fringe forest. **Bark:** brown, with strong spines from the main stem and branches. **Leaves:** somewhat acacia-like, with 10 to 16 leaflets, alternate; leaflets oblong or elliptic-oblong, 0,6 to 1,1 × 0,3 to 0,8 cm, dark green above, paler green below, with fine velvety hairs when young which are lost later; apex and base **317**

broadly tapering to rounded; margin entire. **Flowers:** small, white to cream, pea-shaped, sweetly scented; produced in many-flowered, axillary or terminal heads up to 10 cm long (October to November). **Fruit:** a rather thin, papery pod, about 5 × 2 cm, often produced in profusion, indehiscent (January to May).

The Zulu name for the tree – *umhluhluwe* – gives the name to the whole area. These people use the slender, monkey-rope-like branches to make muzzles for their calves to prevent them from taking milk from the cows and in Transkei the plant is used as a love charm.

Dalbergia boehmii Taub.
S.A. no: —
Rhod. no: 344   Large-leaved dalbergia

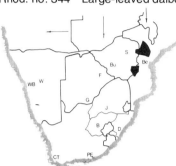

A large, unarmed shrub to medium sized tree up to 10 m in height; occurring in various types of woodland and forest, covering a considerable range of altitudes. **Bark:** dark grey to brown, rough and flaking in old trees. **Leaves:** with 4 to 8 alternate or sub-opposite leaflets; leaflets ovate to lanceolate, up to 7,5 × 3,5 cm, rather pendulous; apex tapering to rounded; base broadly tapering to rounded; margin entire. Stipules present, usually falling early. **Flowers:** small, creamy-white, pea-shaped, sweetly scented, produced in masses either just before the new leaves, or with them (October to December). **Fruit:** a flat, thin pod, 6 to 11 × 1 to 2 cm, reddish-brown, indehiscent (December to May).

Dalbergia martinii F. White
[*D. glandulosa* Dunkley]
S.A. no: Zambezi flat-bean
Rhod. no: 347   Zambezi dalbergia

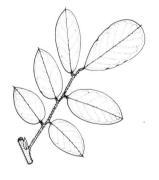

Most often a shrub, or a climber using well-developed coiled stem tendrils, but occasionally becoming a small tree, 3 to 4 m in height, often branching low down or several-stemmed from ground level; occurring in low altitude woodland and riverine fringe thicket. **Bark:** dark chocolate-brown; main trunk and branches unarmed; branchlets conspicuously rough with tubercular-based glands. **Leaves:** with 5 to 8 alternate leaflets; leaflets elliptic to obovate, 2 to 7 × 1 to 3,8 cm. **Flowers:** smallish, white, pea-shaped, 6 mm long, sweetly scented, produced in sprays up to 8 cm long (December). **Fruit:** a very characteristic pod, up to 9 × 2 cm, flattened, almost winged round the raised seed section which is covered by sticky, glandular hairs which harden when they dry, indehiscent (January to April).

318

Dalbergia melanoxylon Guillemin & Perrottet   Illust. 105
S.A. no: 232   Zebrawood. Sebrahout
Rhod. no: 348   Blackwood dalbergia

A shrub or straggling tree, 5 to 7 m in height, occasionally taller; fairly common, although scattered, at medium to low altitudes in mixed woodland, thicket, on rocky outcrops and on termite mounds. **Bark:** pale grey and smooth, darkening and roughening with age when it sometimes peels in strips; it is characteristically several-stemmed and much-branched, with stem and branches armed with spines. **Leaves:** clustered, or fascicled, on dwarfed, hard branchlets, along the smaller spinescent branches; with 8 to 13 opposite to alternate leaflets plus a terminal leaflet; leaflets variable in shape and size, heart-shaped to oval, usually about 1,5 × 1 cm, but may be up to 3 × 1,8 to 2 cm, dark green; apex rounded; base broadly tapering; margin entire. Stipules leaf-like, about 5 mm long, falling very early. **Flowers:** small, white, pea-shaped, sweetly scented, produced in short branched sprays up to 10 cm long, which burst into a profusion of blooms with the first rains, either just before, or with the new leaves (October to December). **Fruit:** a small, oblong pod, up to 7 × 1,5 cm, flattened, thin, almost papery, with a slight swelling over the 1 to 2 seeds, indehiscent (January to March).
The sapwood is yellow to white surrounding a very hard, beautiful, purplish heartwood which becomes black on exposure; it is close-grained and very heavy, pleasantly scented and, if the pieces are of a reasonable size, of considerable commercial value. However, the trees are usually small, the stems twisted and contorted and very often the wood is defective; it is suitable only therefore for trinket boxes, chessmen and small ornaments and particularly for woodwind musical instruments. Africans use the wood to make arrow tips and wooden hammers for beating bark cloth. A preparation to relieve toothache is made from the roots.

Dalbergia multijuga E. Meyer
S.A. no: 233   Hairy flat-bean. Harige platboontjie
Rhod. no: —

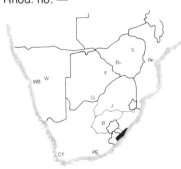
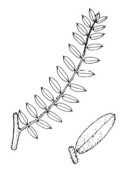

A climber or a small tree up to 5 m in height; occurring in forest and dune bush. **Bark:** brown; the young branches with dense, rusty, woolly hairs; the stem and branches are unarmed. **Leaves:** with 10 to 16 pairs of sub-opposite leaflets plus a terminal leaflet; leaflets rather small, oblong, up to 1,5 × 0,7 cm, finely velvety; apex broadly tapering to rounded, often with a hair-like tip; base shallowly lobed; margin entire; petiolules very short to almost absent, petiole present. **Flowers:** small, creamy-white, pea-shaped, produced in short branched sprays up to 8 cm long, crowded towards the ends of the branches (August to October). **Fruit:** a small pod, 5 to 7,5 × 1,5 to 2 cm, yellowish-

319

brown, finely hairy, swollen and wrinkled over the seeds (November to March, but they remain on the tree longer).

Dalbergia nitidula Welw. ex Baker   Illust 106
S.A. no: 234   Glossy flat-bean. Blinkplatboontjie
Rhod. no: 349   Purplewood dalbergia

 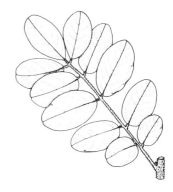

A slender shrub, or a small straggling tree, usually only 5 to 7 m in height, but it may be rather taller; found in various types of woodland over a wide range of altitudes. **Bark:** grey-brown, or reddish, very rough and fissured; the stem and branches are unarmed. **Leaves:** with 4 to 7 pairs of opposite to sub-opposite leaflets plus a terminal leaflet; leaflets oval, usually 2 to 3,5 × 1,3 to 2 cm, but may be as large as 5 × 2 cm; apex rounded and notched; base rounded; margin entire; petiolules and petiole present. Stipules oblong, about 6 mm long, falling early. **Flowers:** small, white, pea-shaped, sweetly scented, produced in dense, branched heads up to 10 cm long, before or with the new leaves (August to September). **Fruit:** a flat, thin, brown pod, up to 7 × 1,5 cm, scarcely swollen over the seeds, usually without hairs but sometimes finely velvety, indehiscent. When the tree is covered with a profusion of pods it is conspicuous (October to December).

The heartwood remains purple when dry and is used for making walking sticks. The roots are toxic.

Dalbergia obovata E. Meyer
S.A. no: 235   Climbing flat-bean. Rankplatboontjie
Rhod. no: —

Often an unarmed woody climber, but can become a small tree up to 6 m in height; occurring on hill slopes, fringing evergreen forest and in dune bush. **Bark:** grey and rough when old. **Leaves:** with 5 to 9 sub-opposite to alternate leaflets; leaflets oval to obovate, up to 6 × 3 cm, but usually smaller, dark green above, paler green below, without hairs, the midrib and veins prominent below; apex and base tapering or rounded; margin entire; stipules about 6 mm long, falling early. **Flowers:** small, creamy-white, sweetly scented, in dense branched heads up to 10 cm long (October to November). **Fruit:** a narrow, flat, oblong pod, up to 9 × 1,8 cm, with the seed case thickened and heavily and conspicuously veined; indehiscent (February to April).

The wood is heavy, red and handsome. Africans use the branches to make fishing baskets. The bark is burnt and the ash mixed with snuff; it is also used to treat sore mouths in babies while the roots provide love charms popular with Zulu youths.

24. DALBERGIELLA E. G. Baker

Dalbergiella nyasae E. G. Baker
S.A. no: —
Rhod. no: 351   Mane-pod

A medium sized deciduous tree, 7 to 9 m in height; occurring in medium to low altitude deciduous woodland and thicket. **Bark:** grey-brown, rather thick and vertically fissured; the young branches and leaves are covered with short, brown hairs. **Leaves:** tend to be crowded near the ends of the branches; alternate, compound, imparipinnate, with 6 to 9 pairs of opposite to sub-opposite leaflets; leaflets oval to oblong, 3 to 6 × 1 to 3 cm, greyish-green; apex and base rounded, base asymmetric; margin entire, slightly rolled under. **Flowers:** small, pea-shaped, whitish-cream to pink, with a large mauve spot at the base of the standard petal; produced in long sprays, up to 25 cm long, the stems and flower stalks covered with dense, brown, velvety hairs. The flowers, when produced in profusion, are very striking (August to October). **Fruit:** a very distinctive, oblong, flat, velvety pod, 6 to 8 × 2 to 3 cm, thin, yellowish, leathery, with a remarkable fringe of dense, long, brown, plumose hairs completely edging the whole pod (October to April).

This is an interesting small tree and well worth cultivation.

25. PTEROCARPUS L.

Trees, with a red, resinous exudate from injuries. **Leaves:** alternate, compound, imparipinnate; leaflets opposite to sub-opposite, occasionally alternate, often with minute glands on the lower surface. Stipules falling early. **Flowers:** in axillary or terminal racemes or panicles. All floral parts in fives. Calyx cup-shaped; petals pea-shaped; stamens joined; ovary stalked. **Fruits:** flattened, indehiscent, with a markedly thickened seed case and surrounded by a narrow or broad, membraneous wing.

Key to the species of *Pterocarpus:*
1 Central 'seed case' covered with long, rigid bristles; wing broad and wavy ..... **P. angolensis**
  Central 'seed case' without long rigid bristles 2
2 Leaflets very large, commonly 12 × 8 to 12 cm, the smallest being 5,5 × 4 cm **P. brenanii**
  Leaflets seldom more than 6,5 cm long 3
3 Leaflets conspicuously small, only 2 to 3 cm long, oval to oblanceolate .... **P. lucens**
  Leaflets not as small as preceding species, usually 4 to 6 cm long, broadly oval to almost circular
  .... **P. rotundifolius**

Pterocarpus angolensis DC.   Illust. 107
S.A. no: 236   Kiaat. Kiaat
Rhod. no: 352   Mukwa. Bloodwood

A medium sized to large tree up to 16 m in height, but reaching 20 m under ideal conditions; occurring in woodland and wooded grassland. **Bark:** dark grey to brown, rough and longitudinally fissured. **Leaves:** with 5 to 9 pairs of sub-opposite to alternate leaflets; leaflets elliptic-lanceolate to obovate, 2,5 to 7 × 2 to 4,5 cm, the upper surface without hairs, the lower surface hairy when young but losing these by maturity; apex tapering to a narrow point, bristle-tipped; base rounded; margin entire, wavy, tightly rolled under; petiolules and petiole velvety. Stipules narrow, up to 8 mm long, velvety, falling early. **Flowers:** orange-yellow, pea-shaped, produced in large, branched sprays, 10 to 20 cm long

321

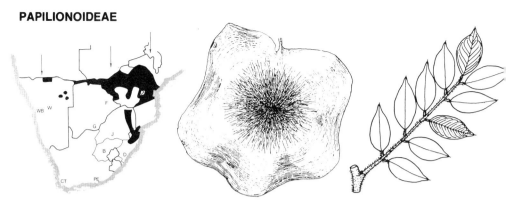

(August to December). **Fruit:** a very distinctive, indehiscent, circular pod. The seed case, which is densely covered with harsh bristles up to 1,3 cm in length, is surrounded by a broad, membraneous, wavy wing, up to 3 cm in width (January to April).

This tree serves a number of purposes, both utilitarian and in African folk-medicine. When cut, it exudes a red, sticky and blood-like sap; this leaves a permanent stain on cloth and therefore makes an effective dye though in some areas, curiously enough, it is used as a cure for nose-bleeding. In Ovambo the inner bark of the roots is sold in small bundles: powdered and mixed with fat, this provides an ointment for anointing the body. The bark has several uses: heated in water and mixed with figs it is massaged on to the breasts to stimulate lactation while a cold infusion from the bark alone provides a remedy for nettle rash or may be taken to relieve stomach disorders, headaches and mouth ulcers. Either the bark or the root, boiled with fresh meat, is used as a preliminary accelerator in the treatment of gonorrhoea and a decoction of the root is believed to be a cure for malaria and blackwater fever. Corneal ulcers are bathed with an eyewash obtained when roots of this tree are first cleaned and then left to soak in water for six hours. In the follow-up treatment of this complaint, the flowers are placed in boiling water over which the patient holds his face allowing the steam to fill his eyes. A remedy for ringworm consists of an ointment containing more or less equal parts of crushed flowers, fowl manure and the fruits of a shrubby species of *Solanum,* which are burned and combined with fat to form a paste. Very often the patch of ringworm is scrubbed vigorously with a dried maize cob before the ointment is rubbed on to it. These trees are very resistant to fire, but repeated heavy burning produces a 'stag-headed' appearance, which also occurs if the tree is suffering as a result of unfavourable conditions such as shallow, stony soil, or too much water. Truncheons, if planted in October when the sap is rising, grow easily and make good garden subjects; they are often seen around a chief's enclosure where they form a live fence. This is one of the best-known, most generally used and most valuable of all woods in south tropical Africa. The golden, or reddish-brown heartwood makes high quality furniture as it is easily worked, glues and screws well and takes a fine polish. It shrinks very little when drying from the green condition, and this quality, together with its high durability, makes it particularly suitable for boat-building; indeed, Africans consider it to be one of the best woods for canoe construction. They also use it to make dishes, mortars and drums, and it is one of the few woods favoured for canoe paddles and game and fish spears. Although the white sapwood is susceptible to borer attack, the heartwood is very durable and resistant to both borers and termites.

Pterocarpus brenanii Barbosa & Torre
S.A. no: —
Rhod. no: 354   Large-leaved bloodwood

A shrub 2 to 3 m in height, or a small tree reaching 6 m; occurring in hot, dry areas at low altitudes in mixed deciduous woodland. **Bark:** pale brown to dark grey, slightly scaling to rough, peeling in narrow, vertical strips in larger specimens. **Leaves:** with 5 to 7 leaflets, large to very large, ovate, oblong or almost circular, occasionally as small as 5,5 × 4 cm, but frequently 12 × 12 cm and even up to 17 cm, shiny green; apex round to square; base markedly square, may be slightly lobed; margin entire. Stipules conspicuous and definitive, large, leafy, almost shield-like, up to 2,5 × 1,8 cm, clasping the stem and persisting for some time. **Flowers:** yellow, pea-shaped, in large, beautiful, branched sprays up to 25 to 30 cm long (October to November). **Fruit:** a flattened, oval pod, usually about 10 × 7,5 to 10 cm, with a markedly swollen seed case which is surrounded by a large, hard,

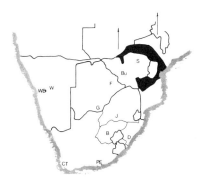 

membraneous wing, becoming brown to reddish-brown when mature (February to May, but they may be found on the tree at most times of the year).

Pterocarpus lucens Guillemin & Perrottet
[*P. antunesii* (Taub.) Harms; *P. stevensonii* Burtt Davy]
S.A. no: 236,1   Small-leaved kiaat. Doringkiaat
Rhod. no: 353   Small-leaved bloodwood

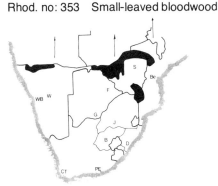 

A medium sized tree with a strong tendency to become shrubby; south of the Zambezi, at its vest, it reaches 7 to 10 m in height; occurring in low altitude woodland, often on deep, sandy soils; it can form thickets. **Bark:** smooth, pale grey, thin, tending to flake like the bark of the guava, *Psidium guajava* L. **Leaves:** with 2 to 4 pairs of opposite to sub-opposite leaflets plus a terminal leaflet; leaflets rather small, ovate to oval, sometimes oblanceolate, usually only 2 to 3 × 1 to 2 cm, but occasionally up to 8 × 5 cm, light green, drooping; apex broadly tapering, rounded or notched, asymmetric; base tapering, asymmetric; margin entire; petiolules and petiole present. **Flowers:** pale yellow, pea-shaped, sweetly scented, in long, slender, lax, delicate sprays, 7 to 22 cm long; the flowering period is short, often only a few days (November to December). **Fruit:** a small, oval, flattened pod, up to 5 × 3 cm, with a conspicuous swelling over the seed case and surrounded by a hard membraneous wing, apex rounded, asymmetric, tapering to the base, pale creamy-brown, occasionally with a reddish tinge, indehiscent (January to May).

This species is confined to southern Africa where it is fairly widespread at low altitudes, especially in Rhodesia and the Transvaal, but it is nowhere common. The wood is light yellow, hard and does not split. It has been used to make axe handles and felloes.

All the material occurring south of the Zambezi is placed in subsp. *antunesii* (Taub.) Rojo. It is a protected plant in South Africa.

Pterocarpus rotundifolius (Sonder) Druce   Illust. 108
[*P. martinii* Dunkley]
S.A. no: 237   Round-leaved kiaat. Dopperkiaat
Rhod. no: 355   Round-leaved bloodwood

A medium to large tree, frequently 10 m in height, but reaching 20 m under favourable conditions; occurring in woodland and wooded grassland over a wide range of altitudes. **Bark:** grey to brown and   **323**

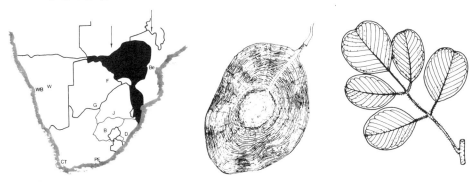

rough to deeply longitudinally fissured. **Leaves:** with 2 to 5 (or more in subsp. *polyanthus*) pairs of opposite to sub-opposite leaflets plus a terminal leaflet; leaflets ovoid to elliptic, 3,5 to 7,5 cm and almost as broad, dark green above, much paler green below, finely velvety (or with tawny hairs in subsp. *polyanthus);* apex rounded, notched; base broadly tapering to rounded; margin entire; petiolules short and thickset, petiole up to 5 cm long. **Flowers:** deep yellow, pea-shaped, with the petals crisped, produced in axillary and terminal sprays up to 15 cm long, together forming large heads up to 30 cm long (September to December). **Fruit:** a flattened pod, 2,5 to 3,5 cm long and nearly as wide, usually 1-seeded, thickened over the seed coat which is heavily veined and surrounded by a membraneous wing (November to April).

This species has been divided into two subspecies and two varieties:

(a) subsp. *rotundifolius:* with 1 to 3 pairs of leaflets, paler green with an ashen bloom, the lateral veining conspicuous on the upper surface and with fine velvety hairs. This is the subspecies which is widespread south of the Zambezi River.

(b) subsp. *polyanthus* Mendonça & E. P. Sousa: with 4 to 8 pairs of leaflets, dark green, with a yellowish bloom, the lateral veins not distinct on the upper surface and with tawny hairs. This subspecies has, in turn, been divided into 2 varieties:

var. *polyanthus:* the ovary and fruit without hairs. This occurs only to the north of the Zambezi valley.

var. *martinii* (Dunkley) Mendonca & E. P. Sousa: the ovary and fruit hairy. This does not occur far south of the Zambezi escarpment.

These trees are a splendid sight when in flower. During hot, dry weather the flower buds remain closed, but with the first shower of rain they seem to burst into bloom. The wood is light-coloured with an attractive grain. It is difficult to saw but works quite well and has been used as a general purpose timber, but is not very durable. However, some reports from South Africa describe it as being of poor quality since the pieces are too small to be of any value. The cut wood has an unpleasant scent.

26. LONCHOCARPUS Kunth

Shrubs, rarely woody climbers, or trees. **Leaves:** alternate, compound, imparipinnate, 1-foliolate (when apparently simple), 3-foliolate or with more than 3 leaflets. Stipules fall early. **Flowers:** in terminal and also axillary panicles. Flowers characteristically pea-shaped. All floral parts in fives; calyx cup-shaped, shortly 5-toothed; petals much longer than the calyx, white, pink or purple; stamens united to form a tube, split to the base on either side; ovary shortly stalked. **Fruit:** a flattened pod, broadly ovate to linear, indehiscent, slightly rimmed, usually 1-seeded; seeds brown.

Key to the species of *Lonchocarpus:*
1 Leaflets large, usually 8 cm or more in length 2
  Leaflets smaller, usually up to 7 cm in length 3
2 Leaves always 3- to 5-foliolate; leaflets more or less narrowly elliptic, densely velvety at first, but
  losing almost all the hairs later; pods large, 7 to 15 × 2 to 3,5 cm; flowers appear with the leaves
  .... **L. capassa**

324

Leaves usually 1-foliolate, but may be 3- to 5-foliolate, leaflets oval to ovate, the young leaflets densely velvety and even the mature leaves velvety to the touch; pods small, usually 4 to 6 cm long, not more than 9 cm long and not more than 1 cm wide; flowers appear before the new leaves .... **L. nelsii**

3 Calyx without hairs; flowers appear before the new leaves; pods thin and narrow, 1,5 cm wide at the most and without hairs .... **L. bussei**

Calyx very hairy; flowers appear with the leaves; pods thick, broad, often 2,5 to 4 cm wide, not less than 2 cm wide and densely velvety .... **L. eriocalyx**

Lonchocarpus bussei Harms

[*L. menyharthii* Schinz]
S.A. no: —
Rhod. no: 356   Narrow lance-pod

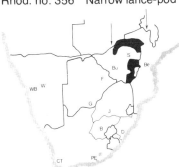

A rather slender tree, usually about 10 m in height, but reaching 15 m under favourable conditions; occurring at low altitudes, on rocky outcrops and in a variety of types of woodland and thicket. **Bark:** grey, smooth, powdery, later becoming darker, roughish, flaking and cracking into square sections **Leaves:** with 2 to 6 pairs of leaflets plus a terminal leaflet; leaflets oblong to oblanceolate, 4 to 9 × 2 to 4,5 cm, dark green above, paler green below, the young leaflets softly velvety, especially below, these hairs being lost by maturity; apex and base tapering; margin entire; petiolules and petiole present. **Flowers:** pea-shaped, smallish, the standard petal magenta-purple to pale mauve, the stamens joined to form a yellow tube round the style; produced in attractive lax, pendant sprays 10 to 20 cm long, before the new leaves (August to October). **Fruit:** a small pod, 4 to 10 × 1 to 1,5 cm, pale straw-coloured to light brown, hanging down in loose clusters, indehiscent (September to January).

Generally very similar to *L. capassa* but smaller in stature; the leaves are smaller and the fruits much smaller. It tolerates a wide range of habitats and is widespread in countries to the north of the Zambezi River, but in Rhodesia it is confined to low altitudes.

Lonchocarpus capassa Rolfe   Illust. 109

[*Capassa violacea* Klotzsch]
S.A. no: 238   Apple-leaf. Appelblaar
Rhod. no: 357   Rain tree

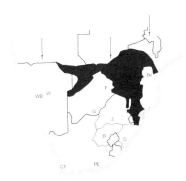

PAPILIONOIDEAE

A small to medium sized tree with a rounded crown, reaching 10 m in height; scattered in various types of woodland at medium to low altitudes, frequently along rivers. **Bark:** creamy-brown and smooth to cracked and rather flaking; a red, sticky sap exudes from wounds. **Leaves:** with 1 to 2 pairs of opposite leaflets plus a large terminal leaflet; leaflets oblong to ovate, 4 to 15 × 2,5 to 7,5 cm, grey-green, densely velvety when young, losing most of these hairs at maturity; apex broadly tapering to rounded with a fine hair-like tip; base tapering to rounded; margin entire; petiolules and petiole short, thickset and velvety. Stipules small, falling early. **Flowers:** small, blue to violet, pea-shaped, sweetly fragrant, the calyx covered with grey, velvety hairs. The flowers are produced in terminal sprays up to 30 cm long, before the leaves (September to November). **Fruit:** a flat, indehiscent pod, 7 to 15 × 2 to 3,5 cm, creamy-grey, with a narrow rim which may be wing-like (January to August). Many Africans are very superstitious about *L. capassa* for it is one of the so-called rain trees, and some specimens do 'rain' for a week or more during the hot dry months just prior to the actual breaking of the rains. This phenomenon is found in other unrelated genera and in this case is caused by the nymph of a small insect, a species of frog-hopper, *Ptyelus grossus,* belonging to the order Hemiptera. As a protection against the sun, the nymph covers itself with a frothy substance similar to patches of foam, popularly called 'cuckoo-spit', caused by common, closely related species. The insects obtain their nourishment by piercing the bark of the tree with their stylets (sucking mouthparts) and sucking up the sap at a great speed. They eject almost pure water equally fast, and this drips from the tree in sufficient quantity to form pools on the ground below. This rain-tree was certainly known to the early hunters and explorers, and Thomas Baines refers to it in his *Goldfields Diaries.* The trees are very sensitive to fire. The leaves are heavily browsed on by game and stock although the roots and bark are said to be poisonous. According to African folk-medicine, colds may be relieved by inhaling smoke from the burning roots which are also used occasionally for treating snakebite and for poisoning fish. The wood is yellow to brown in colour and fairly hard and heavy. Apart from its use in making tool-handles, grain mortars and dugout canoes, it is of little commercial value. This is a protected plant in South Africa.

Lonchocarpus eriocalyx Harms
S.A. no: —
Rhod. no: 358   Broad lance-pod

A slender tree up to 10 m in height; occurring in hot dry areas at low altitudes, on rocky outcrops, in woodland, wooded grassland and bush. **Bark:** dark grey, flaking; the branchlets and all young parts are covered with grey, woolly hairs. **Leaves:** with 3 to 5 pairs of opposite to sub-opposite leaflets plus a terminal leaflet; leaflets ovate to elliptic, 3 to 6 × 1,6 to 4 cm, hairy above, with woolly hairs below which sometimes persist along the midrib and veins only; the under surface has prominent veining; apex very broadly tapering to rounded; base asymmetric, generally tapering, finally narrowly rounded and even slightly lobed; margin entire; petiolules and petiole present. Stipules fall early. **Flowers:** attractive, small, pale violet to lilac or pale blue, pea-shaped; produced in terminal and axillary sprays up to 30 cm long, clustered near the tips of the branches among the leaves (December to January). **Fruit:** a flattened, creamy-brown pod up to 8 × 3 cm with a conspicuously thickened rim and thick, velvety hairs, otherwise very similar to those of *L. capassa,* but much shorter and more oval (May). All the material south of the Zambezi River is assigned to subsp. *wankieënsis* Mendonça & E. P. Sousa; the typical subspecies extends no further south than the extreme north of Zambia.

Lonchocarpus nelsii (Schinz) Schinz ex Heering & Grimme
S.A. no: 239   Kalahari apple-leaf. Kalahari-appelblaar
Rhod. no: 359   Apple-leaf lance-pod

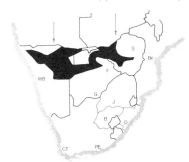

A small, bushy tree often about 4 m in height, but reaching 7 to 10 m under favourable conditions; occurring in various types of hot, dry woodland. **Bark:** pale yellow-grey, rather smooth. **Leaves:** compound, often reduced to a single leaflet, but in higher rainfall areas the number of leaflets tends to increase to 1 to 2 pairs of opposite to sub-opposite leaflets plus a terminal leaflet and leaves with 1, 3 or 5 leaflets can all occur on the same tree; leaflets oval to ovate, up to 12 × 5 to 6 cm, when young often densely velvety and resembling the leaves of *Combretum molle,* most of these hairs being lost by maturity when the leaves are dark green and rather glossy; the mature leaves resemble those of *C. zeyheri,* and this is especially the case when both trees are in their autumn colours; leathery in texture, with conspicuous net-veining on the under surface, the upper surface being puckered; apex and base rounded; margin entire; petiolules and petiole present. **Flowers:** attractive, mauve to lilac or purplish, pea-shaped; produced in branched sprays up to 30 cm long. The stems, buds and calyces are covered with dense, greyish-white, woolly hairs. The flowers usually appear in profusion before the new leaves (September to October). **Fruit:** a small, flat pod, 5 to 9 × 1 cm, straw-coloured, very finely velvety to the touch, indehiscent (October to December).
In the Wankie National Park these trees grow in association with *Acacia erioloba;* their flowering times coincide and the deep yellow of the *Acacia* and the lilac of the *Lonchocarpus* make a beautiful contrast. The leaves are an excellent fodder.

27. XERODERRIS Roberty

Xeroderris stuhlmannii (Taub.) Mendonça & E. P. Sousa   Illust. 110
[*Ostryoderris stuhlmannii* (Taub.) Dunn ex Harms]
S.A. no: 240   Wing pod. Vlerkboon
Rhod. no: 360   Wing pod

A medium to large, spreading tree, usually about 10 m in height, but may be larger; a common and widespread constituent of deciduous woodland and bush in hot, dry areas. **Bark:** grey-brown, fairly smooth to rough, flaking, with a blood-red exudate from wounds. **Leaves:** compound, with 15 alternate to sub-opposite leaflets; leaflets oblong to ovate, 5 to 13 × 3,5 to 6 cm, fresh green, crowded near the tips of the branchlets, and initially covered with fine, golden or silvery, silky hairs which are lost later; apex rather rounded to abruptly attenuate; base rounded to shallowly lobed, asymmetric;

327

margin entire, rather wavy, slightly rolled under; petiolules and petiole present. Stipules fall early.
Flowers: rather small, pea-shaped, white to greenish-white, in branched, terminal and axillary sprays of panicles, each 10 to 20 cm long, crowded at the ends of the branchlets and together forming heads up to 20 × 20 cm, frequently smaller; the calyces and the stalks are densely covered with creamy to rusty velvety hairs; all floral parts in fives; calyx widely bell-shaped; the standard petal with a short claw and widely spreading; stamens joined but the uppermost stamen free; ovary without a stalk (September to October). **Fruit:** a large, flattened pod, usually 10 to 18 × 3 to 4,5 cm, conspicuously swollen over the seed cases, with very distinctive ridged veining over the swellings; running round the edge of the pod is a prominent rim and *outside this* is a hard, membraneous wing up to 10 mm wide in the larger pods (January to August, but they may stay on the tree longer and even persist into the next fruiting season).

The fruits are often parasitized and malformed so that they look like small berries (See Illust. 110). The wood is hard and dark yellow; it has been used for planks and canoe-building. The blood-red sap makes a good dye and is suitable for tanning leather. Africans make an infusion of the roots with which they treat stomach disorders. The fruits and leaves are heavily browsed on by stock and game, and the seeds are ground to produce a meal. The tree has been reported as being poisonous, which may be the case at certain times of the year.

28. ERYTHRINA L.

Trees, sometimes shrubs, often armed with prickles. **Leaves:** pinnately 3-foliolate. Stipules fall early. **Flowers:** in many-flowered, axillary or terminal, false racemes, usually appearing before the new leaves, the flowers being produced in 2- to several-flowered groups along the main axis. All floral parts in fives; calyx tubular; the standard petal large and conspicuous, folded downwards along the centre line, the wing and keel petals usually much smaller and enveloped by the standard; stamens joined to form a tube, the uppermost stamen free; ovary stalked. **Fruit:** a cylindric pod, constricted between the seeds, dehiscent. Seeds red to orange with a black patch (or white, in 1 species) round the point of attachment.

Key to the tree species of *Erythrina:*
1 In South West Africa only; a shrubby tree 3 to 4 m in height .... **E. decora**
  Not in South West Africa 2
2 Leaflets large, usually more than 9,5 cm long, up to 21 cm and even 30 cm 3
  Leaflets usually less than 9,5 cm long 6
3 Leaflets deeply divided into 3 lobes, the apical lobe triangular and tapering to the apex, the lateral lobes sharply squared-off, or truncate; flowers in long sturdy racemes, with flowers extending along the main axis for a distance of 20 cm; rare, in isolated areas in Rhodesia and Moçambique .... **E. livingstoniana**
  Leaflets 3-lobed, but may be obscurely so, and the lateral lobes not truncate; flowers in compact racemes, the flowers themselves seldom extending for more than 10 cm along the main axis 4
4 Bark rather smooth, grey, not thickly corky; young leaves, and petiole, rachis and the under surface of leaflets without dense hairs; calyx not divided into fine, slender, distinctive lobes.......... .... **E. lysistemon**
  Bark thickly corky and prickly; young leaves, petiole, rachis and under surface of leaflets covered with woolly hairs; calyx divided into very distinctive, fine lobes 5
5 Leaflets may be up to 30 × 32 cm; the standard petal 4 to 5,5 cm long; calyx bright red or crimson to brownish-red .... **E. latissima**
  Leaflets generally smaller than those of the above species, up to 17 × 18 cm; the standard petal usually 3 to 3,5 cm long; calyx scarlet to brick-red .... **E. abyssinica**
6 Leaflets sharply triangularly 3-lobed, arrowhead-like, the apical lobe drawn out into a conspicuous long, slender point .... **E. humeana**
  Leaflets may be 3-lobed, but not arrowhead-like as above 7

7 Standard petal relatively short and broad, opening slightly to expose the stamens; length of the wings and keel petals 2 to 2,5 cm; colour of the standard petal orange-scarlet, occasionally cream. Southern and eastern Cape and Natal .... **E. caffra**

 Standard petal relatively long, narrow and enclosing the stamens; length of the wing and keel petals 0,9 to 1,8; colour of the standard petal scarlet, never cream. Northern areas of Transkei, through Natal, Swaziland, Transvaal to Rhodesia and Moçambique .... **E. lysistemon**

Erythrina abyssinica Lam. ex DC.   Illust. 111

[*E. tomentosa* R. Br. ex A. Rich.]

S.A. no: —

Rhod. no: 363   Red-hot-poker tree

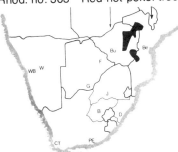

A medium sized, thickset tree with a well-branched, rounded, spreading crown, usually 5 to 10 m in height; occurring in woodland and open wooded grassland. **Bark:** light brown, thickly corky and often spiny. **Leaves:** 3-foliolate; leaflets almost as broad as long, 5,5 to 14 × 6 to 14 cm, the lateral leaflets rather smaller than this, if 3-lobed then obscurely so, densely woolly when young, losing most of these hairs by maturity, the midrib and main veins on the under surface often bear scattered prickles; apex rounded; base broadly tapering; margin entire; petiolules and petiole often with scattered prickles. **Flowers:** spectacular, in strong, sturdy racemes. Calyx joined to form a tube, split along the under surface almost to the base and separating away into long, slender, distinctive lobes at the apex; calyx and standard petal striking scarlet to brick-red (July to November). **Fruit:** a cylindric pod about 10 cm in length, deeply constricted between the seeds, densely furry, light brown in colour (November to March).

The tree grows easily from a trucheon planted in spring, and in 3 to 4 years will have reached a fair size though it should be protected from heavy frosts until it is well-established. The wood is soft and greyish white in colour, with a shot-silk effect and although it is somewhat woolly to work, stools, toys, drums and pestles have been made from it. The seeds are used to decorate trinkets, bracelets and necklaces and are sold as curios. Seeds of *E. abyssinica* and *E. caffra* Thunb., and possibly certain other species of *Erythrina,* contain a curare-like poison which, if injected into the blood-stream, produces anaesthesia, paralysis and even death by respiratory failure. There is no danger involved in buying or selling these seeds, however, and it is unlikely that, if swallowed, they would produce any effect at all. This species closely resembles *E. latissima* E. Meyer (see paragraph 5 of the key).

Erythrina caffra Thunb.

S.A. no: 242   Coast erythrina. Kuskoraalboom

Rhod. no: —

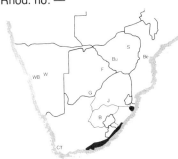

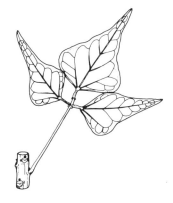

329

PAPILIONOIDEAE

A medium to large tree, usually 9 to 12 m in height, but reaching 20 m under favourable conditions; occurring in coastal forest and riverine fringe forest. **Bark:** grey, often with short, sharp prickles. **Leaves:** 3-foliolate, the terminal leaflet being the largest; leaflets broadly ovate to elliptic, 8 to 16 × 8 to 18 cm, the lateral leaflets slightly smaller, without hairs or spines; apex tapering; base tapering, the base of the lateral leaflets asymmetric; margin entire. **Flowers:** orange-scarlet, produced before the leaves, in large, spectacular, thickset racemes up to 10 cm long, the flowers themselves crowded near the end; standard petal relatively short and broad, opening slightly to expose the stamens; cream-coloured flowers do occur (August to September). **Fruit:** a dark-coloured, cylindric pod, up to 6,5 cm long, deeply constricted between the seeds, without hairs (October to December).

The wood is greyish in colour, light, soft and spongy. These trees are shrouded in superstition and many Africans will not burn the wood for fear of attracting lightning. They are easy to propagate from seed or from truncheons and make splendid garden subjects; in fact, they are doubly desirable for, apart from their beauty, the nectar in the flowers attracts sunbirds. This species closely resembles *E. lysistemon* Hutch. (see paragraph 7 of the key).

Erythrina decora Harms
S.A. no: 243   Namib erythrina. Namibkoraalboom
Rhod. no: —

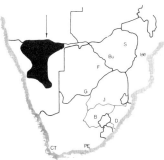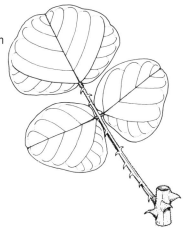

A shrubby tree, usually 3 to 4 m in height, sometimes reaching 8 m or even slightly more; however, it may become dwarfed, barely attaining 50 cm in height when growing under very harsh conditions; occurring in dry, arid country, often among rocks. **Bark:** grey, thickly corky and deeply fissured. **Leaves:** 3-foliolate, the leaflets varying in size and shape, the terminal leaflet frequently broader than long and larger than the 2 lateral leaflets; leaflets ovate to very broadly ovate, 3 to 18 cm long and broad, with odd scattered prickles along the petiole, rachis and midribs; apex broadly tapering to rounded; base square to slightly lobed; margin entire. **Flowers:** bright red, the standard petal is large, 3 to 4 cm long; the branchlets and buds are covered with greyish-white, woolly hairs. The flowers are produced in sturdy racemes about 15 cm long, with the flowers crowded over the terminal 7 cm (November to April). **Fruit:** a short, cylindric pod, about 12 × 1,5 cm, deeply constricted and narrowly waisted between the seeds, grey-brown (April to August).

Erythrina humeana Sprengel   Illust. 112
[*E. princeps* A. Dietrich]
S.A. no: 243,1   Dwarf erythrina. Kleinkoraalboom
Rhod. no: —

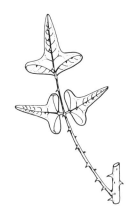

Usually a shrub, occasionally a small tree reaching 4 m in height; occurring in dry scrub, in open wooded grassland, on rocky outcrops, on mountain slopes and on coastal dunes. **Bark:** grey, rather smooth, beset with prickles. **Leaves:** 3-foliolate, the leaflets markedly triangularly 3-lobed, usually about 9 × 8 cm, but up to 13 × 12 cm, dark shiny green, the midrib and main veins beset with strong prickles; apex of the leaflets drawn out into a long, slender tip, arrowhead-like; bases rounded; margins entire, wavy; petiolules and petiole with prickles. **Flowers:** brilliant scarlet, including the calyx, in long-stalked racemes, about 10 cm long on bare stalks as long as the flowering section (September to February). **Fruit:** a deeply constricted, purplish-black pod, up to 15 cm long (December to May).

Africans burn and powder the bark and this is applied to the umbilical cord of newborn babies. An extract of the root is used externally as a hot fomentation applied to sprains and is also taken internally in the treatment of tuberculosis, bronchitis and other chest complaints.

Erythrina latissima E. Meyer

[*E. gibbsae* E. G. Baker]
S.A. no: 244   Broad-leaved erythrina. Breëblaarkoraalboom
Rhod. no: 364   Broad-leaved erythrina

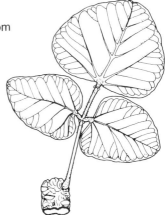

A rather thickset tree, usually 5 to 8 m in height; occurring in a variety of habitats including various types of woodland. **Bark:** grey, thickly corky. **Leaves:** 3-foliolate; leaflets large, ovate, 5,5 to 30 × 7,5 to 32 cm, the lateral leaflets being rather smaller, grey-green, unarmed or very occasionally with a few scattered prickles, the upper and under surfaces covered with dense, woolly hairs which are lost almost entirely by maturity; apex rounded; base broadly tapering; margin entire. **Flowers:** striking, large, crimson to brownish-red, produced in sturdy, cylindric heads about 11 cm long on long, bare stalks, almost equalling the flowering section. Calyx red, separating into slender lobes, as in *E. abyssinica;* the petals are also red and the calyx and petals are covered with velvety hairs (July to October, when the trees are almost leafless). **Fruit:** a large, cylindric pod, up to 30 × 2,5 cm, brownish-black, constricted between the seeds (November to April).

This species can be propagated easily from truncheons and also from seeds, but the growth is slower than in other *Erythrina* species; it is able to withstand a fair amount of frost, but is sensitive to fire damage. In African medicine the bark is burnt, powdered and used as a dressing for open sores. This species closely resembles *E. abyssinica* (see paragraph 5 of the key).

Erythrina livingstoniana Baker

S.A. no: —
Rhod. no: 365   Aloe erythrina

A medium to large spreading tree, up to 15 m in height; this rare and beautiful *Erythrina* is confined to low altitude, hot, dry areas and even where it does occur, it is seldom encountered; when growing among rocks it can become stunted and thickset. **Bark:** a conspicuous colour, thick, furrowed, with distinctive, large, hard, thorny bosses; the branches and branchlets are covered with thorns. **Leaves:** 3-foliolate; leaflets large, almost as broad as long, usually about 13 × 12 cm, but 17 × 17 cm are not uncommon, more or less deeply divided into 3 lobes, the terminal lobe triangular with the apex broadly tapering to rounded, and the lateral lobes very characteristically squared-off, or truncate, sometimes almost 2-lobed; base of the leaflet square; margin entire; petiolules very short and thickset, petiole long up to 20 cm. **Flowers:** most striking, large, brilliant scarlet, in racemes resembling an

331

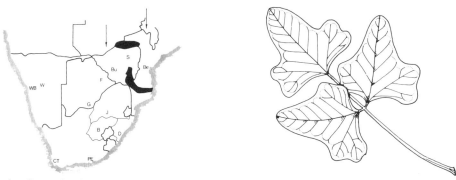

aloe flower head, up to 20 cm long; these flowers are larger and more beautiful than any other southern African species of *Erythrina* (January to February). **Fruit:** a large, cylindric pod, up to 35 × 4 cm, very deeply constricted, yellowish (May to June onwards). The seeds are bright red or vermilion, with a white spot, instead of a black spot, at the point of attachment.

Erythrina lysistemon Hutch.   Illust. 113
S.A. no: 245   Common coral tree. Gewone koraalboom
Rhod. no: 366   Lucky-bean tree.

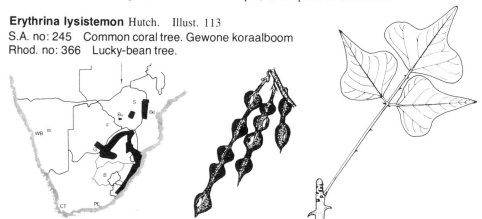

A small to medium sized, rather thickset tree, often about 6 m in height, but it can reach 10 m; with its extensive distribution it covers a wide range of altitudes and habitats; in South Africa it grows in scrub forest, in dry woodland and coastal dune bush, and also in high-rainfall areas; in Rhodesia it is a tree of high altitude woodland, on mountain sides and grassland. **Bark:** dark grey to grey-brown, rather smooth, not corky. **Leaves:** 3-foliolate; leaflets large, ovate, usually up to 17 × 18 cm; apex tapering, sometimes slightly attenuate; base very broadly tapering to square; margin entire; petiolules and petiole present; the petiole, rachis and the midrib of the leaflets may carry scattered, hooked prickles. **Flowers:** beautiful, clear scarlet, in short dense heads about 9 cm long, on long naked stalks almost as long as the flowering section; the standard petal long, narrow and enclosing the other petals and the stamens (July to October, usually before or with the new leaves). **Fruit:** a rather slender, black, cylindric pod up to 15 cm long, sharply constricted and waisted between the seeds (December onwards).

E. lysistemon is used fairly widely in African folk-lore and medicine. There is a custom, in the eastern Transvaal, that when a man dies a truncheon is taken from a tree growing near his hut and planted on his grave. Strips of bark are cut from all four sides of the trunk and used to bind together a bundle of herbs from which an infusion is made to ease labour in childbirth. Crushed leaves are applied to suppurating sores, while open wounds are treated with the powdered burnt bark. Leaf infusions are used as drops to relieve earache, decoctions of the roots are applied to sprains as fomentations, and a chief believes that he will ensure the respect of his people by washing in water in which the bark has been soaked. The trees are easily propagated from truncheons and from seed; they make excellent garden subjects and have been planted with effect along streets in a number of South African towns. This species is very similar to *E. caffra* (see paragraph 7 of the key).

29. RHYNCHOSIA Lour.

Rhynchosia clivorum S. Moore
S.A. no: Shaggybush
Rhod. no: 371   Shaggybush

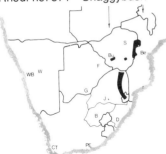

An erect, branched shrub or small tree, usually about 3 to 4 m in height, but reaching 6 m under favourable conditions; occurring at high altitudes in forested gullies, at forest margins and in open grassland and bracken scrub. **Bark:** dark greyish or reddish-brown, smooth; all the younger parts are densely covered with long, tawny hairs. **Leaves:** alternate, compound, 3-foliolate; leaflets oblong-elliptic to narrowly ovate, 2,5 to 11 × 1 to 5 cm, both surfaces covered with fine, velvety hairs, densely so on the younger leaflets, upper surface puckered, lower surface with conspicuous net veining and dotted with resin glands; apex narrowly tapering; base rounded, asymmetric on the lateral leaflets; margin entire; petiolules and petiole densely velvety. Stipules very conspicuous, large, reddish, sheath-like, persisting for some time but falling eventually. **Flowers:** characteristically pea-shaped; sepals with long, silvery, silky hairs; the standard petal up to 1,5 cm long, yellow or greenish-yellow, often streaked with maroon outside and bright clear yellow inside. The flowers are produced in very compact, dense, terminal sprays, or racemes, about 4 to 6 cm long (July to September). **Fruit:** a small, flat pod, 1,7 to 2,5 × 0,8 cm, densely covered with yellowish, silky hairs, splitting and tightly spiralling at maturity (September to November).
The plants are densely shaggy with long, yellow or golden hairs and this is a distinctive character together with the conspicuous, reddish, sheath-like stipules which persist for some time.

LINACEAE *(The flax family)*

HUGONIA L.

Hugonia orientalis Engl.
[*H. busseana* Engl.]
S.A. no: Hugonia
Rhod. no: 377   Hugonia

A shrub with a strong tendency to scramble, or rarely a small tree up to 4 m in height; occurring in low altitude woodland and thicket in dry, sandy soils, very often along rivers and at forest margins. **Bark:** yellowish-white to brown, thick and corky; the climbing branches have conspicuous thick, woody

333

tendrils, curving like a ram's horn and sometimes forming a complete circle, but on shrubs or trees these seem to be absent. **Leaves:** alternate, simple, usually in crowded, terminal clusters on short lateral shoots, oblong to elliptic, usually 5 to 7 × 1,5 to 2 cm, but they can reach 11 × 2,5 cm, midrib and lateral veins very prominent below; apex tapering to rounded; base rounded to tapering; margin entire to serrate and conspicuously wavy. **Flowers:** solitary, axillary, showy, yellow, sweetly scented. All floral parts in fives; sepals free; petals unequal, spreading, the flower being about 2 cm in diameter; stamens in 2 whorls of 5, joined at the base to form a shallow cup (October to December). **Fruit:** oval, perfectly symmetric, fleshy, about 1,5 cm long, pendulous, bright, shiny green when young, becoming yellow when mature (February to June).

This is a very attractive shrub or small tree; no information is available concerning the ease of its propagation, or of its response to cultivation, but it would make a good garden subject.

ERYTHROXYLACEAE *(The coca family)*

Key to the genera:

Leaf apex attenuate; styles 2, joined; nectaries at the base of the petals small and hidden by the sepals, or absent .... **1. Nectaropetalum**

Leaf apex usually rounded; styles usually 3, occasionally 2, free or only partly joined; nectaries large, convolute, longer than the sepals .... **2. Erythroxylum**

1. NECTAROPETALUM Engl.

Shrubs or small trees. **Leaves:** alternate, simple, leathery. Stipules intrapetiolar. **Flowers:** axillary, solitary, or in few-flowered clusters, or fascicles. Bisexual; all floral parts in fives; sepals joined at the base; petals white, free, clawed, with or without a small nectariferous appendage at the base, on the lower surface; stamens in 2 whorls of 5, joined at the base to form a shallow cup; ovary with styles joined, stigmas 2, free. **Fruit:** spherical or ovoid, fleshy.

Key to the tree species of *Nectaropetalum:*

Mainly in Transkei, just entering the south of Natal; leaf veining clearly defined on the upper surface; nectary appendage at the base of the petal absent; flower stalks short, about 1,5 mm long .... **N. capense**
Natal and Zululand only, the range barely overlapping that of the previous species; leaf veining on the upper surface not clearly defined; a small, bi-lobed, pocket-like nectary present at the base of the petals; flower stalks up to 10 mm, longer than those of the previous species ...... **N. zuluense**

Nectaropetalum capense (H. Bolus) Stapf & Boodle
[*Erythroxylum capense* (H. Bolus) Stapf]
S.A. no: 246   Cape nectar petal. Keibasterkokaboom
Rhod. no: —

Frequently a small tree about 4 m in height, but reaching 15 m under favourable conditions; occurring in forest or at forest margins, often tolerating poor soils, common in the coastal forests of Transkei. **Bark:** grey to brownish, smooth; the branches are smooth and without hairs. **Leaves:** elliptic, up to 10 × 5,5 cm, but usually much smaller, fresh bright green, the veining clearly defined on the upper surface; apex tapering to slightly attenuate; base rounded to square; margin entire, wavy; petiole about 6 mm long. Stipules spike-like, at the base of new leaves, falling early. **Flowers:** generally greenish, solitary, or in pairs, on very short stalks, about 1,5 mm long, in the axils of the leaves, but the nodes are close together and this often gives the appearance of tight clusters of flowers; each flower is about 10 mm in diameter with narrow white petals, the pocket-like nectary at the base absent; the stamens form a central mass (January to March). **Fruit:** said to be small, fleshy, oval and 5 to 10 mm long.

Nectaropetalum zuluense (Schönl.) Corbishley
[*Erythroxylon zuluense* Schönl.]
S.A. no: 247   Natal nectar petal. Natalbasterkokaboom
Rhod. no: —

A small tree rarely reaching 10 m in height; occurring at altitudes up to 500 m, in rocky places, where it often becomes dominant, and also in evergreen forest. **Bark:** grey to brownish, smooth. **Leaves:** oblong, 4 to 8 × 2,5 to 4 cm; apex attenuate; base broadly tapering; margin entire, wavy; petiole about 3,5 mm long. Stipules falling early. **Flowers:** green, about 10 mm in diameter, on stalks up to 10 mm in length, solitary or in clusters of 2 to 4, in the axils of the leaves; a small, bi-lobed, pocket-like nectary is present at the base of the petals (June to July, occasionally on to December). **Fruit:** oval, small and fleshy, probably 5 to 10 mm long (October to January).
The wood is tough, red and somewhat elastic and has been used to make small articles and implements.

2. ERYTHROXYLUM   P. Browne

Shrublets, shrubs or small trees. **Leaves:** alternate, simple. Stipules intrapetiolar. **Flowers:** solitary or in fascicles, axillary. Bisexual; all floral parts in fives; sepals triangular, joined; petals white to creamy-yellow, free, clawed; stamens in 2 whorls of 5, joined at the base forming a deep cup with a toothed rim; nectaries large, convoluted, longer than the sepals. **Fruit:** fleshy.

Key to the tree species of *Erythroxylum:*
1 Leaves consistently small, usually less than 3 cm long .... **E. delagoense**
  Leaves usually 3 to 9 cm long 2
2 Extending no further south than the extreme north and west of Rhodesia and the extreme north of
      Botswana; almost confined to the Zambezi valley area .... **E. zambesiacum**
  Not confined to the Zambezi valley area 3
3 Leaf veining usually obscure; eastern Cape to Zululand only .... **E. pictum**
  Leaf veining usually prominent; widespread from Transkei to Rhodesia...... **E. emarginatum**

Erythroxylum delagoense Schinz
[*E. brownianum* Burtt Davy]
S.A. no: 248   Small-leaved coca tree. Fynblaarkokaboom
Rhod. no: —

A shrub or small tree up to 6 m in height; occurring in dry woodland or scrub, sometimes on forest margins, usually on dry sandy soils and often among rocks. **Bark:** grey, rough and rather warty; branches many, erect and slender. **Leaves:** small, oblanceolate to obovate, often rather rounded, 1 to

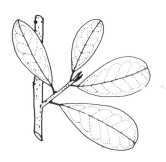

3 × 0,7 to 1,5 cm, pale green above, paler green below, thinly textured; apex rounded; base narrowly tapering; margin entire; petiole short, 1,5 to 3 mm long, slender. **Flowers:** small, inconspicuous, white, yellowish or greenish, shortly stalked, solitary or paired (rarely in groups of 3 to 4), in the axils of the leaves (October to November). **Fruit:** ellipsoidal, 8 to 10 mm long, fleshy, bright red when mature, edible (March to April).

Erythroxylum emarginatum Thonn.   Illust. 114
S.A. no: 249   Common coca tree. Gewone kokaboom
Rhod. no: 378   Common coca tree

Very often a straggling shrub about 1 m in height, but it may become a tree up to 9 m; occurring in forested ravines, fringing forest and forming part of the under-storey in evergreen forest, also on rocky outcrops and in coastal bush. **Bark:** dark grey to grey-brown, smooth to vertically fissured and rough. **Leaves:** oblanceolate to elliptic, rather small, 2 to 12,5 × 1 to 4,5 cm, but usually about 3 to 5 cm long, dark green above, paler green below, rather stiffly textured and hard, leaf veining prominent; apex rounded, abruptly pointed and slightly notched; base tapering; margin entire; petiole 1,5 to 6 mm long, slender. Stipules are small, stiff and triangular, and persist on the branchlets for some time. **Flowers:** white, small, about 10 mm in diameter, sweetly scented, inconspicuous, on short stalks 5 to 14 mm long, solitary or in small clusters, or fascicles, in the leaf axils (September to December). **Fruit:** small, barely more than 10 mm long, ellipsoidal, fleshy, red when mature (January to May).

Erythroxylum pictum E. Meyer ex Sonder
S.A. no: 250   Forest coca tree. Boskokaboom
Rhod. no: —

A shrub to medium sized, well-branched, spreading tree, usually up to 13 m in height, but occasionally taller; occurring from sea level to about 1 800 m, in forest and at forest margins, along river and stream banks and on hillsides among rocks. **Bark:** grey, longitudinally fissured and cracked. **Leaves:** rather small, oval to ovate, 3 to 6 × 1,5 to 3,5 cm, fresh mid-green above, slightly paler green below, veining not prominent; apex rounded, notched; base tapering; margin entire, often yellow edged. **Flowers:** small, greenish-white or white to yellowish, inconspicuous, shortly stalked, solitary or in small groups of 2 to 3 in leaf axils (November to February). **Fruit:** small, ellipsoidal, up to 10 mm long, bright, shiny, cherry-red when mature; falling early while still quite fresh (January to April). The small fruits are edible and the wood has been used for carving.

Erythroxylum zambesiacum N. K. B. Robson
S.A. no: —
Rhod. no: 379   Zambezi coca tree

A shrub or small tree usually 3 to 7 m in height; it is more or less confined to the Zambezi valley, encroaching up some of the valleys of the larger tributaries, in dry woodland and on rocky hillsides. **Bark:** grey, smooth. **Leaves:** rather small, obovate to oblong, 1,8 to 6,7 × 1,3 to 4 cm, thinly textured, pale green above, paler green below, veining rather prominent on the upper surface, with net-veining more or less conspicuous below; apex rounded or square and notched; base narrowly tapering and running into the petiole; margin entire; petiole up to 10 mm long. Stipules triangular, joined, persistent. **Flowers:** small, white or yellowish, inconspicuous, shortly stalked, solitary or in groups of 3 to 5 in the leaf axils (November to December). **Fruit:** ellipsoidal, bright shining green when young becoming red when mature, up to 8 mm long (January to March).

BALANITACEAE

BALANITES Delile

Shrubs or trees, strongly spinescent, the spines either simple or forked. **Leaves:** spirally arranged, compound, 2-foliolate, petiolule and petiole short to almost absent; leaflets leathery to subsucculent. **Flowers:** fascicled or in umbel-like cymes, axillary. Bisexual; all floral parts in fives; sepals free, usually deciduous; petals overlapping, with or without hairs; stamens 10, free; receptacle disc fleshy, cup-shaped, partly surrounding the semi-spherical ovary. **Fruit:** fleshy.

Key to the tree spcies of *Balanites:*
1 Spines most often forked; petals densely hairy on the outer surface; fruits large up to 6 × 3 cm
   .... **B. maughamii**
   Spines always straight and simple; petals without hairs on either surface 2
2 Petiole 1,5 to 6 mm long; leaflets 1 to 3 × 0,5 to 2,3 cm, without stalks; petals narrowly elliptic,
   2,8 to 3,4 mm broad; fruit broadly oval to almost spherical, up to 2,5 × 2 cm ....
   .... **B. pedicellaris**
   Petiole longer than the preceding species, 8 to 20 mm long; leaflets always shortly but distinctly
   stalked; leaflets 2,5 to 6 × 1,5 to 4 cm; the petals 2 to 2,8 mm broad, elliptic oblong; fruits
   longer, more cylindric, up to 5 × 2,5 cm .... **B. aegyptiaca**   **337**

BALANITACEAE

Balanites aegyptiaca (L.) Delile
S.A. no: —
Rhod. no: 380   Simple-thorned torchwood

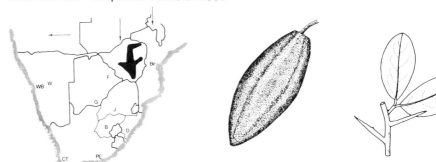

A small evergreen tree, usually 3 to 5 m in height, but it may be taller; occurring in dry, wooded grassland and also near rivers on alluvial flats, not common in Rhodesia. **Bark:** dark brown to grey, cracked into small, square flakes; the branches are greyish-green, stiff and brittle, armed with stout, green or yellow spines. **Leaves:** with 2 separate leaflets; leaflets elliptic obovate, asymmetric, 2,5 to 6 × 1,5 to 4 cm, bright green, leathery, finely hairy when young, the hairs sometimes persisting on the lower surface but usually lost on the upper surface when mature; apex broadly tapering to rounded, occasionally slightly notched; base tapering to rounded; margin entire; petiolules short, petiole 8 to 20 mm long. **Flowers:** greenish-white, 1,5 to 2 cm in diameter, inconspicuous, without hairs, in groups, or fascicled, in the axils of the leaves (November). **Fruit:** rather long and narrow, up to 5 × 2,5 cm, becoming yellowish-red when mature (April).

This species could be confused with *Ximenia caffra,* but the paired leaves of *Balanites* are distinctive. The fruits are edible, very bitter when green, but bitter-sweet when ripe and, in African medicine, provide a treatment for liver and spleen complaints. The bark is used quite extensively as a fish poison and, with the fruit and roots, has been proved lethal to snails, some fish, tadpoles and also to the miracidia and cercariae of the bilharzia fluke. The toxicity takes effect as soon as the fruits are placed in the water, and increases as they soak. One fruit will kill all the snails in 30 litres of water, a dilution of 1 part to 30 000 of fruit pulp being sufficient. *B. maughamii* is even more potent, requiring only concentrations as low as 1:100 000 to 1:250 000. The solution is not harmful to man, and 'air-breathers' such as mosquito larvae and pupae are not affected.

Balanites maughamii Sprague
S.A. no: 251   Torchwood. Fakkelhout
Rhod. no: 381   Y-thorned torchwood

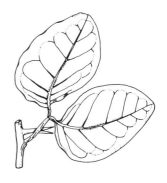

A medium to tall deciduous tree 10 to 20 m in height; occurring in dry, open bush country, in woodland, in sand forest and also along river banks, near springs and round pans. **Bark:** grey and smooth; the trunk conspicuously fluted in large specimens; young branches are distinctly zigzag in appearance and bear conspicuous, forked spines, one arm usually being longer than the other. **Leaves:** with 2 leaflets; leaflets oval to almost round, 2,5 to 6 × 2,2 to 5,7 cm, dark grey-green, with velvety hairs when young which persist on the under surface to maturity, leathery; apex rounded; base broadly tapering; margin entire; petiole and petiolules short and densely velvety. **Flowers:** small, up to 2 cm

338

in diameter, yellowish-green, petals with dense hairs on the outer surface, inconspicuous, produced in small, dense, 3- to 7-flowered umbel-like cymes. The flower-bearing branches are almost unarmed (September to October). **Fruit:** somewhat resembling large dates, 4 to 6 × 2 to 3 cm, yellowish when mature, 5-grooved from the base to the tip, a thin fleshy layer surrounding the hard kernel (November to January).

The fruits are edible but not sought after. The seeds of this species together with those of *B. aegyptiaca* yield a good quality, tasteless and colourless oil, said to equal the best olive oil. This burns with a bright flame and for this reason the dry kernels are sometimes used as torches. These fruits, in common with those of *B. aegyptiaca*, are lethal to snails and some other forms of aquatic life; details of this are given under *B. aegyptiaca*. The tree has certain magico-medicinal uses: an emetic is prepared from a decoction of the bark and witchdoctors ward off evil spirits with a froth made by beating together the roots and bark soaked in water with certain other ingredients. The ritual is to lick the froth three times a day and then to throw the remainder over the roof of the hut so that it spills on to the entrance. A bath taken in water in which the bark has been infused is both stimulating and exhilarating. The wood is hard and of good quality and has been used to make handles for implements and the stocks for guns. The forked thorns of this species could be confused with those of *Carissa bispinosa* (L.) Desf. ex Brenan, but the paired leaflets of *Balanites* are distinctive.

Balanites pedicellaris Mildbr. & Schlechter
[*B. australis* Bremek.]
S.A. no: 252   Small torchwood. Kleinfakkelhout
Rhod. no: 382   Lesser torchwood

A much-branched shrub or small tree up to 6 m in height; occurring in low altitude, dry woodland or scrub, also on alluvial flood-plains among scattered trees. **Bark:** dark grey, cracking into small flakes; the stem is fluted in larger specimens; the branches yellowish or greyish-green, rather stiff and bearing hard, long spines, green, velvety and spirally arranged. **Leaves:** with 2 leaflets; leaflets broadly obovate, 1 to 3 × 0,5 to 2,3 cm, rather fleshy, pale green to pale brownish-green, velvety; apex rounded or square, occasionally slightly notched; base narrowly tapering; margin entire; petiolules absent, petiole short, 1,5 to 6 mm, stout, velvety. **Flowers:** greenish-white, about 1,4 cm in diameter, not conspicuous, produced in small, axillary clusters, sometimes with 2 to 3 flowers on the one stalk (September to October). **Fruit:** rather small, up to 2,5 × 2 cm, usually about the size and shape of a grape, orange when mature, edible but not greatly sought after (May to June).

B. welwitschii (Van Tieghem) Exell & Mendonça, a species which just reaches the Kaokoveld of South West Africa, resembles *B. pedicellaris* but it has characteristically grey-green leaves and has been recorded only as a shrub.

RUTACEAE *(The citrus family)*

Key to the genera (exotic genera marked*):
1 Leaves simple or compound but with a single leaflet 2

  Leaves compound with 3 or more leaflets 3   **339**

RUTACEAE

2 Flowers large, showy, pink to mauve; fruit a rough, warty capsule up to 3,5 cm in diameter .... **3. Calodendrum**

Flowers small, white; fruit a fleshy berry, oval to spherical, about 8 cm long (the lemon or orange) .... **10. *Citrus**

3 Leaves pinnate, with 2 or more pairs of leaflets (or alternate) 4

Leaves 3-foliolate 7

4 Leaf rachis winged .... **9. Citropsis**

Leaf rachis without a wing 5

5 Stem, leaf stalks and sometimes the flower stalks with large or small prickles **1. Zanthoxylum**

Stem and all parts without prickles 6

6 Deciduous trees; flowers with sexes separate, produced in terminal panicles (or branched sprays) .... **2. Fagaropsis**

Evergreen shrubs or small trees; flowers bisexual in axillary, branched sprays .... **8. Clausena**

7 Stamens 4 (or 5), as many as the petals 8

Stamens 8, twice as many as the petals 9

8 Ovary made up of 2 to 4 carpels which are entirely free except for the joined stigmas .... **4. Oricia**

Ovary with carpels joined and single-chambered; fruit single, globose or ovoid, fleshy .... **7. Teclea**

9 Fruit smooth .... **5. Vepris**

Fruit very warty .... **6. Toddaliopsis**

1. ZANTHOXYLUM L.

Deciduous or evergreen spiny shrubs or trees, the stems usually with conspicuous woody or corky bosses, often spine-tipped. **Leaves:** alternate, compound, imparipinnate, with scattered, aromatic, translucent glands (in some species only between the marginal teeth). **Flowers:** usually in terminal or axillary panicles. Sexes separate on the same tree. All floral parts in fives; sepals very small; petals much longer than the sepals, overlapping; stamens opposite the petals in the male flowers, reduced to staminodes in female flowers; ovary raised on a short gynophore, vestigial in the male flowers. **Fruit:** an almost spherical, dehiscent follicle.

Key to the tree species of *Zanthoxylum* (N.B. the pellucid, or translucent, glands can be seen by holding the leaves up to a bright light):
1 Leaflets on the flowering shoots with pellucid glands along the margins only 2
  Leaflets on the flowering shoots with pellucid glands dotted over the surface generally 3
2 Leaflets ovate, elliptic or obovate; apex more or less rounded; 4 to 8 pairs of main lateral veins .... **Z. capense**
  Leaflets lanceolate, oblong or narrowly elliptic; apex tapering; 16 to 20 pairs of lateral veins (or more) .... **Z. davyi**
3 Leaves and leaflets very large and robust; leaves up to 60 cm long, leaflets up to 17 × 5,5 cm, thick and leathery; very large trees up to 30 m in height .... **Z. gilletii**
  Leaves and leaflets not very large, leaflets up to 8 cm long; usually small to medium sized trees, 3 to 10 m, seldom up to 20 m 4

4 Leaves with 5 to 8 pairs of opposite to sub-opposite leaflets plus a terminal leaflet; leaflets usually about 5 cm long, with apex attenuate forming a slender tip .... **Z. leprieurii**
   Leaves with up to 5 pairs of leaflets plus the terminal leaflet; apex may or may not be attenuate and is not very slender 5
5 Leaflets large, usually 8 to 11 × 3,5 to 5,5 cm .... **Z. trijugum**
   Leaflets usually smaller than those of the above species, usually about 5 cm long and seldom more than 7 cm 6
6 Leaves with 3 to 5 pairs of leaflets (very occasionally 2 pairs) plus the terminal leaflet; flowers and fruits produced at the base of new branches, below the leaves .... **Z. chalybeum**
   Leaves usually with 2 pairs of leaflets (very occasionally 3 or 4 pairs) plus the terminal leaflet; flowers and fruits produced in terminal or axillary heads. Known only from the coastal dunes of southern Moçambique .... **Z. delagoense**

Zanthoxylum capense (Thunb.) Harv.

[*Fagara magalismontana* Engl.; *F. thorncroftii* Verdoorn; *F. capensis* Thunb.]
S.A. no: 253   Small knobwood. Kleinperdepram
Rhod. no: 383   Small knobwood

Usually a small, much-branched tree about 4 to 7 m in height, occasionally reaching 10 m; occurring in a variety of habitats, dry woodland or bush, often in rocky places and also at higher altitudes among rocks and even into the mist-belt. **Bark:** grey, characteristically armed with thorny bosses; the stems are sometimes armed with prickles. **Leaves:** with 4 to 8 pairs of leaflets plus a terminal leaflet, the smallest leaflets being near the base (the terminal leaflet tends to abort and is often absent); leaflets ovate to elliptic or obovate, 1 to 4 × 1 to 2 cm, smelling strongly of citrus oil when crushed; the margin only is dotted with pellucid glands; 4 to 8 pairs of main lateral veins; apex more or less rounded; base tapering, with 2 minute, hard lobes against the petiole; margin scalloped to shallowly toothed; petiole short about 10 mm long. **Flowers:** small, greenish-white, inconspicuous, in short, terminal, branched sprays 2 to 6 cm long (January). **Fruit:** small, brownish-red, about 5 mm in diameter, produced in clusters, each fruit splitting open to reveal a shiny black seed which half emerges (February to May).

The thorny stem of the small knobwood,
Zanthoxylum capense

RUTACEAE

The fruit is acrid and tastes strongly of lemon, leaving a persistent burning sensation in the mouth. It has been used to ease colic, especially flatulence, and to treat palsy. Gastric and intestinal disorders, as well as intestinal parasites, are treated with an infusion of the leaves. The bark, which may be taken as a tonic or chewed to relieve toothache, is also widely used as a remedy for snakebite, either as an oral medicine or as a local application to the wound. A decoction and infusion of the leaves is said to be effective against colds and was a popular treatment during the influenza epidemic of 1918. The wood is of little value.

Zanthoxylum chalybeum Engl.
[*Fagara chalybea* (Engl.) Engl.]
S.A. no: —
Rhod. no: 384   Kundanyoka knobwood

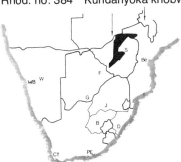

A deciduous shrub or small tree up to 6 m in height; occurring in dry woodland, often on termite mounds. **Bark:** pale grey and smooth except for the knobby thorns; the branches also bear scattered thorns and there are conspicuous dark scales protecting the terminal buds. **Leaves:** much larger than those of *F. capensis,* with usually 3 to 5 pairs (very occasionally 2 pairs) of leaflets plus a terminal leaflet; leaflets oblong to elliptic or lanceolate, 2,5 to 7 × 1 to 2,5 cm, with a strong citrus smell when crushed, sparsely dotted with pellucid glands; apex broadly tapering to rounded; base rounded to tapering; margin almost entire to slightly scalloped; petiole 1 to 5 cm long, the petiole and rachis with small, hooked prickles scattered along their length. **Flowers:** inconspicuous, greenish-white, in short sprays (racemes or panicles) 5 to 10 cm long, produced immediately below the leaves, which is unusual (November to March). **Fruit:** spherical, about 5 mm in diameter, reddish-brown, splitting to allow the shiny, black seed to partly protrude (February to May).

Zanthoxylum davyi (Verdoorn) Waterman
[*Fagara davyi* Verdoorn]
S.A. no: 254   Knobwood. Perdepram
Rhod. no: 385   Knobwood

A small to large tree 8 to 30 m in height; occurring in forest – it is a fairly common species in montane forest. **Bark:** light grey on young trees, dark brown on older trees, both with conspicuous knobby thorns. **Leaves:** with 3 to 6 pairs of leaflets and a terminal leaflet; leaflet size and shape is variable and depends on the locality, but is usually lanceolate, oblong to narrowly elliptic, 2 to 7 × 0,8 to 2,5 cm, with pellucid glands confined to the margin; 16 to 20 pairs of main lateral veins or more; apex tapering, slightly notched; base tapering with slight hardened knobs against the petiole; margin finely

342

The thorny knobs on the stem of the knobwood, Zanthoxylum davyi.

toothed. **Flowers:** greenish-yellow, inconspicuous, in small, terminal sprays, or panicles, 4 to 6 cm long (October to January). **Fruit:** spherical, about 5 mm in diameter, reddish-brown, splitting to allow the single, shiny, black seed to partly protrude (January to May).

The timber appears to be potentially good; it is light in colour with a pronounced grain, finely textured, hard, strong, elastic and polishes well. It has been used for handles of all kinds, for walking sticks, and is said to make good fishing rods.

Zanthoxylum delagoense Waterman
[*Fagara schlechteri* Engl.]
S.A. no: —
Rhod. no: —   Dune knobwood

A shrub or small tree up to 4 m in height; so far known only from the coastal dunes of southern Moçambique. **Bark:** with spiny bosses; young branches reddish-brown and sparsely spiny. **Leaves:** with 2 pairs (very occasionally 3 or 4 pairs) of leaflets plus the terminal leaflet; leaflets elliptic, 3 to 7 × 2 to 3,5 cm, thinly leathery, with very conspicuous pellucid glands dotted over the surface; apex rounded; base abruptly and sharply narrowed; margin scalloped; petiolules almost absent on the lateral leaflets, but up to 0,5 to 2,5 cm on the terminal leaflet. **Flowers:** white, 7 to 9 mm in diameter, produced in branched heads, about 5 cm long, either axillary or terminal (November). **Fruit:** spherical, about 8 mm in diameter, orange-red when mature, splitting to allow the single, black, shiny seed to partly protrude (February).

Zanthoxylum gilletii (De Wild.) Waterman
[*Fagara macrophylla* (Oliver) Engl.]
S.A. no: —
Rhod. no: 388   Large-leaved knobwood

A medium to large tree 10 to 30 m in height; occurring in moist evergreen forest. **Bark:** grey to brown with conspicuous spiny bosses on the trunk. **Leaves:** large, with 11 to 15 sub-opposite to alternate leaflets; leaflets large, broadly elliptic, 8 to 17 × 3,5 to 5,5 cm, thick and leathery; the gland dots are inconspicuous; apex broadly tapering, abruptly attenuate into a short drip-tip; base very asymmetric, the midrib conspicuously off-centre; margin entire or slightly scalloped and markedly rolled under. **343**

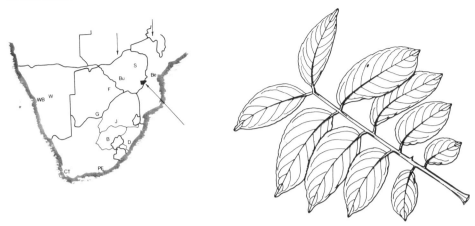

Flowers: greenish-white, not very conspicuous, in dense, compact, axillary, branched sprays, about 5 cm long, near the tips of the branchlets (March). **Fruit:** small, 3,5 mm in diameter, splitting to allow the single, black, shiny seed to partly protrude (July).

Zanthoxylum leprieurii Guillemin & Perrottet
[**Fagara leprieurii** (Guillemin & Perrottet) Engl.]

S.A. no: 255,1   Sand knobwood. Sandperdepram
Rhod. no: 387   Sand knobwood

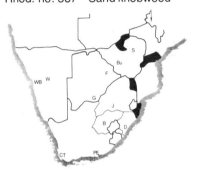

A small to large tree depending upon its habitat, 5 to 10 m in height, or, in forest, reaching 15 to 20 m; occurring in isolated populations, as part of the under-storey in evergreen forest, at forest margins, or at low altitudes, in hot, dry, alluvial soils, in river valleys and near pans, often on termite mounds, or in sand forest near the coast. **Bark:** pale grey, with spiny bosses. **Leaves:** with 5 to 8 pairs of opposite or subopposite leaflets plus a terminal leaflet, the smallest leaflets being near the base; leaflets ovate to elliptic, 1,7 to 7,5 × 1,2 to 3,5 cm, dark green and glossy to yellowish-green above, paler green below, dotted with pellucid glands; apex attenuate forming a slender tip; base tapering to square and asymmetric; margin finely and rather obscurely toothed to finely scalloped; petiole slender, with prickles running onto the rachis. **Flowers:** small, creamy-white, in rather large, lax, terminal, branched panicles about 6 cm long (October). **Fruit:** small, 5 mm in diameter, orange to red, splitting to allow the single, shiny, black seed to partly protrude (March). The fruits are produced in pendulous, branched heads. This is a protected plant in South Africa.

Zanthoxylum trijugum (Dunkley) Waterman
[*Fagara trijuga* Dunkley]
S.A. no: . .—
Rhod. no: 389   Rusty knobwood

A shrub or small tree 3 to 7 m in height; occurring in dry types of woodland and thicket. **Bark:** with sparse prickles; branches, leaves and the stalks in the flower sprays are densely covered with rusty hairs. **Leaves:** with 3 to 4 pairs of leaflets plus a terminal leaflet; leaflets ovate to elliptic, 8 to 11 × 3,5 to 5,5 cm, densely dotted with pellucid glands; apex tapering, may be attenuate; base rounded; margin scalloped or minutely toothed; petiolules and petiole present, the stem, petiole and rachis bearing

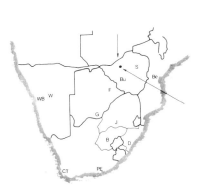

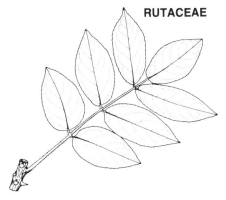

scattered, small, hooked prickles. **Flowers:** small, greenish-white, inconspicuous, in short, branched, terminal sprays about 4 cm long (December). **Fruit:** small, spherical, about 4 to 7 mm in diameter, rusty-brown, splitting to partly release the single, black, shiny seed (January to March).

2. FAGAROPSIS Mildbr. ex Siebenlist

Fagaropsis angolensis (Engl.) Dale
[*Clausenopsis angolensis* (Engl.) var. *mollis* Suesseng.]
S.A. no: —
Rhod. no: 390   Fagaropsis

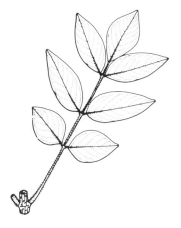

A small to medium sized, deciduous tree, 7 to 15 m in height, well foliaged, with a good shape; occurring in woodland, often on termite mounds, on mountain slopes and in rocky places. **Bark:** grey or brown, rough and slightly corky; the bole may be buttressed; young branches, leaves and flower sprays are covered with ashen hairs, these being lost on the older branches; unarmed. **Leaves:** opposite, compound, large, with 2 to 4 pairs of leaflets plus a terminal leaflet; leaflets lanceolate, ovate to oblong, 4 to 9 × 2 to 4 cm, softly velvety on both surfaces, aromatic, the leaf buds covered with long, silvery-grey hairs; apex tapering; base asymmetric; margin entire with a row of closely spaced glandular dots; petiole up to 7 cm long. **Flowers:** small, inconspicuous, greenish-yellow but sometimes appearing yellow in the sunlight, produced in heads, or panicles, up to 5 cm long, on the previous year's wood. Sexes separate on the same tree. All floral parts in fours; stamens 8 in 2 whorls in male flowers, absent in the female; ovary globose in female flowers, absent in the male (October to November). **Fruit:** almost spherical, 6 to 7 mm in diameter, pale green becoming black, pitted with glands, produced in dense, branched heads (December to May).
All the material south of the Zambezi River is assigned to var. *mollis* (Suesseng.) Mendonça; the typical variety occurs in countries to the north.

3. CALODENDRUM Thunb.

Calodendrum capense (L.f.) Thunb.   Illust. 115
S.A. no: 256   Cape chestnut. Wildekastaiing
Rhod. no: 391   Cape chestnut

A small to tall tree varying form 7 to 20 m in height, depending upon the habitat; occurring in forest, in wooded ravines, in evergreen fringe forest, sometimes in scrub and at altitudes varying from sea level

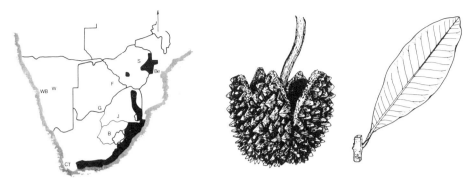

to 2 000 m. **Bark:** grey and smooth; the bole is buttressed in large specimens. **Leaves:** opposite, simple, large, elliptic, 6 to 13 × 3,5 to 7,5 cm, but may reach 22 cm in length, dark green, with scattered pellucid gland-dots; aromatic; apex tapering to rounded; base tapering to slightly lobed; margin entire, rather wavy; the midrib and lateral veins are prominent on the under surface. **Flowers:** large, striking, the petals varying in colour from almost white to pale pink, long and narrow, up to 4 × 0,5 cm, alternating with 5 petal-like staminodes, or sterile stamens, also pale pink but conspicuously dotted with purplish to maroon glands; in terminal, branched heads, or panicles. Bisexual; all floral parts in fives; sepals small; fertile stamens 5; ovary on a long gynophore (October to December). **Fruit:** a brown capsule, 3,5 cm in diameter, 5-lobed, woody, with a knobby surface (January to May).

The wood is hard and generally useful. Although surprisingly little known, these trees grow well in cultivation and are slowly gaining in popularity as beautiful garden subjects.

4. ORICIA Pierre

Oricia bachmannii (Engl.) Verdoorn
[*O. swynnertonii* (E. G. Baker) Verdoorn; *O. transvaalensis* Verdoorn]
S.A. no: 257   Twin-berry tree. Tweelingbessieboom
Rhod. no: 392   Twin-berry tree

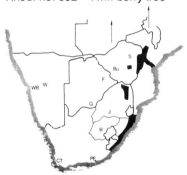

A small to medium sized tree, 5 to 15 m in height, slender and much-branched; occurring in high altitude, evergreen forest. **Bark:** pale grey, smoothish, becoming rather rough with corky flakes. **Leaves:** alternate or opposite, compound, 3-foliolate; the leaflets oblong, 7 to 15 × 3 to 7 cm, leathery, shiny dark green, with or without hairs, conspicuously gland-dotted all over and aromatic when crushed; apex rather rounded to attenuate; base tapering; margin entire; petiolules short, petiole up to 5 cm long. **Flowers:** small, creamy-white, inconspicuous, but they can be attractive when produced in profusion in lax, terminal or axillary heads, or panicles, among the leaves. Sexes separate on the same tree; all floral parts in fours; ovary formed from 2 to 4 separate carpels, joined only by the stigmas (July to October). **Fruit:** fleshy, oblong about 2 cm long, dotted with glands, yellowish-green to brown or orange when mature (April).

5. VEPRIS Commerson ex Adr. Juss.

Shrubs with a tendency to scramble, or trees. **Leaves:** alternate or rarely opposite, 3-foliolate, dotted **346** with pellucid glands. **Flowers:** in axillary or terminal racemes or panicles, or in clustered cymes, sometimes on the old wood. Sexes separate on the same tree. All floral parts in fours (occasionally twos or threes); stamens 8 in 2 whorls in the male flowers, absent in female flowers; ovary with 4 compartments in the female flowers, absent in male flowers. **Fruit:** smooth, fleshy.

Key to the tree species of *Vepris:*
1 Petioles markedly winged 2
  Petioles not winged 3
2 Young branches and leaves with dense, grey hairs .... **V. zambesiaca**
  Young branches and leaves without hairs .... **V. carringtoniana**
3 Flowers and fruits in terminal heads .... **V. undulata**
  Flowers and fruits in axillary heads .... **V. reflexa**

Vepris carringtoniana Mendonça
S.A. no: Coastal white ironwood
Rhod. no: —

A shrub or small tree up to 3 to 4 m in height; occurring on dry, alluvial or sandy soils in thickets, usually near the coast. **Bark:** pale, smooth. **Leaves:** 3-foliolate; leaflets narrowly elliptic to obovate, 1,5 to 4 × 0,6 to 1,5 cm, thinly textured, densely gland-dotted, pungently scented when crushed, the veining conspicuous on both surfaces; apex rounded; base tapering; margin scalloped; petiolules absent, petiole up to 2,3 cm and conspicuously winged, the wings up to 4 mm broad. **Flowers:** small, yellowish, in short, terminal sprays up to 2 cm long, branched or unbranched (November). **Fruit:** fleshy, smooth, ellipsoidal, about 12 × 8 mm, orange when mature (January).

Vepris reflexa Verdoorn
S.A. no: 260   Bastard white ironwood. Basterwitysterhout
Rhod. no: 394   Woodland vepris

A shrub or small, dense tree up to 6 m in height; occurring in dry, deciduous woodland and wooded grassland. **Bark:** grey to dark grey, smoothish. **Leaves:** 3-foliolate; leaflets narrowly elliptic, 3 to 8 × 1 to 4 cm, shiny green, leathery, conspicuously gland-dotted, aromatic when crushed, veining conspicuous; apex tapering to more or less rounded; base tapering; margin entire; petiole not winged. **Flowers:** small, greenish-yellow, not conspicuous, in short, axillary heads up to 3,5 cm long (September to December). **Fruit:** smooth, fleshy, ellipsoidal, 1,2 cm long, orange-red when mature (January to May).

347

RUTACEAE

This species is difficult to separate from the shrub, *Teclea rogersii* Mendonça; *Vepris reflexa* has 8 stamens and can become a small tree, while *Teclea rogersii* has 4 to 5 stamens and has been recorded only as a shrub; however, in the Matopos where they both occur, it is extremely difficult to separate them when flowers are not available.

Vepris undulata (Thunb.) Verdoorn & C. A. Smith
[*V. lanceolata* (Lam.) G. Don]
S.A. no: 261   White ironwood. Witysterhout
Rhod. no: —

Often an evergreen shrub or small tree about 5 m in height but, when growing in tall evergreen forest, it can reach 20 m; occurring in dry types of forest and, at the coast, in littoral evergreen thicket on sandy soils and on dunes. **Bark:** grey to dark grey and smoothish. **Leaves:** 3-foliolate; leaflets narrowly elliptic, 5 to 12 × 1,5 to 3,2 cm, without hairs, strongly lemon-scented when crushed, densely gland-dotted; apex tapering to more or less rounded; base tapering; margin entire, markedly wavy or undulate; petiole not winged. **Flowers:** small, yellowish, inconspicuous in dense, terminal heads, or panicles, 2,5 to 12 cm long (December to March). **Fruit:** smooth, fleshy, 5 mm in diameter, black when mature (May to July).

The wood is white, even-grained, hard, strong and elastic and has been used to make implement handles and beams. The powdered root provides a remedy for influenza. Eve Palmer records that porcupines eat the bark from these trees, a practice which eventually kills them and local farmers believe that, as a result, the species is endangered in the valleys near the Kei Road.

Vepris zambesiaca S. Moore
S.A. no: —
Rhod. no: 395   Rare woodland vepris

Most often a deciduous shrub about 1,5 m in height, but occasionally a small tree up to 3,5 m; occurring in low altitude, dry woodland or scrub, nowhere common. **Bark:** light grey, smooth. **Leaves:** 3-foliolate; leaflets narrowly elliptic, 1,8 to 4,5 × 0,8 to 1,5 cm, softly velvety, especially when young, generally dotted with pellucid glands; apex rounded, notched; base tapering; margin entire, slightly wavy; petiole winged, but narrowly so. **Flowers:** very small, greenish-white to yellow, in very dense, short, terminal heads, 2 to 4 cm long, but produced in profusion (November to December, and occasionally in July). **Fruit:** small, smooth, fleshy, ellipsoidal, 1,3 × 0,8 cm, blackish when mature (January to March).

6. TODDALIOPSIS Engl.

Toddaliopsis bremekampii Verdoorn
S.A. no: 262   Wild mandarin. Wildenartjie
Rhod. no: 397   Wart-berry

Often an evergreen, rather xerophytic shrub, or a small tree up to 6 m in height; occurring in dry woodland or scrub on sandy soils. **Bark:** grey, rather smooth; branches reddish or grey and smooth. **Leaves:** alternate, compound, 3-foliolate; leaflets elliptic, 3,5 to 8 × 1,2 to 3,5 cm, densely gland-dotted, shiny bright green above, yellowish below; apex tapering to rounded; base tapering; margin entire, slightly rolled under; petiolules absent, petiole up to 4 cm long. **Flowers:** small, creamy-white, in small clusters, or short panicles, either axillary or terminal, up to 4 cm long. Sexes separate on the same tree; all floral parts in fours; stamens 8 in 2 whorls, reduced to staminodes in female flowers; ovary slightly 4-lobed, absent in male flowers (November). **Fruit:** characteristic, about 1,4 cm in diameter, the skin wrinkled, warty and loose, somewhat resembling a small litchi, orange-green to reddish-brown when mature (February to March).

7. TECLEA Delile

Shrubs or trees, unarmed. **Leaves:** alternate, compound, 3-foliolate, densely gland-dotted. **Flowers:** in axillary or terminal, simple or branched racemes. Sexes separate on different trees; floral parts in fours to fives; calyx cup-shaped; petals longer than the sepals; stamens reduced to staminodes in female flowers; ovary spherical, carpels joined, vestigial in male flowers. **Fruit:** globose, rather fleshy.

Key to the tree species of *Teclea:*
1 Flowers and fruits in branched sprays, or panicles, axillary or terminal 2
  Flowers and fruits in short unbranched sprays, clustered in the leaf axils 3
2 In the eastern Cape, Natal, Swaziland and the Transvaal only .... **T. natalensis**
  In Moçambique, Rhodesia and northwards; not extending further south than Chirinda forest in Rhodesia .... **T. nobilis**
3 Fruits densely velvety to furry when mature .... **T. trichocarpa**
  Fruits almost without hairs when mature 4
4 Fruits almost spherical, about 10 mm in diameter; apices of leaflets rounded .... **T. gerrardii**
  Fruits ovoid, about 10 × 6 mm; apices of leaflets attenuate .... **T. myrei**

Teclea gerrardii Verdoorn
S.A. no: 263   Zulu teclea. Zoeloekersielemoen
Rhod. no: —

A shrub or small evergreen tree reaching 6 m in height; occurring in evergreen thicket, on forest margins, on littoral dunes and in dune scrub. **Bark:** grey, smooth, rather mottled, yellowish-grey, finely longitudinally cracked and sometimes flaking in circular segments. **Leaves:** 3-foliolate; leaflets elliptic to obovate, 3,5 to 10 × 1 to 4 cm, light dull green, aromatic when crushed; apex rounded; base tapering; margin entire; petiole sometimes narrowly winged. **Flowers:** small, greenish-white, inconspicuous in unbranched axillary clusters about 5 cm long (August to October). **Fruit:** small, **349**

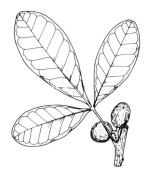

spherical, about 10 mm in diameter, velvety when young, losing most of the hairs and becoming orange when mature; almost without stalks, produced in small groups of 1 to 3 in the leaf axils, closely clustered along the stem (December to January).

Teclea myrei Exell & Mendonça
S.A. no: —
Rhod. no: 398,1   Oval-fruited teclea

A small tree 2 to 5 m in height; occurring in thicket. **Bark:** mottled grey to grey-brown. **Leaves:** 3-foliolate; leaflets elliptic, 4 to 11 × 1,3 to 3,5 cm, shiny green; apex rather abruptly attenuate; base tapering; margin entire, often wavy; petiole up to 4 cm long. **Flowers:** very small, greenish, in tight axillary clusters (January to April). **Fruit:** small, ovoid, about 10 × 6 mm, orange-red when mature; almost without stalks, produced in tight clusters of 1 to 4 in the leaf axils (January to April).

Teclea natalensis (Sonder) Engl.
S.A. no: 264   Natal teclea. Natalkersielemoen
Rhod. no: —

An evergreen shrub or slender heavily foliaged tree up to 8 m in height; occurring in coastal and inland forests, at forest margins and in dune bush; it can be locally common. **Bark:** yellowish-brown, flaking off in small patches. **Leaves:** 3-foliolate; leaflets oblanceolate to elliptic, 5 to 15 × 2 to 4 cm, without hairs, drooping, gland-dotted; apex tapering to notched, often rather broadly and somewhat obscurely attenuate, ultimately very narrowly rounded; base tapering and running into the petiole; margin entire, tending to roll under; petiole up to 10 mm long. **Flowers:** greenish-cream, small, inconspicuous, the male flowers falling early; produced in small, axillary or terminal, branched heads, or panicles, 2 to 3 cm long (August to September, or later). **Fruit:** small, fleshy, spherical, about 10 × 7 mm, orange-red when mature, on distinct stalks, produced along the stem among the leaves (November to January).

Teclea nobilis Delile
S.A. no: —
Rhod. no: 399   Small-fruited teclea

One of the largest of this genus, being an evergreen shrub or a tree up to 13 m in height; occurring in riverine forest and fringing evergreen forest. **Bark:** grey, smoothish. **Leaves:** 3-foliolate; leaflets narrowly elliptic, 5 to 15 × 1,5 to 4 cm, dark glossy green, aromatic when crushed; apex tapering, attenuate, sometimes bluntly so; base tapering; margin entire, wavy. **Flowers:** very small, creamy-yellow, sweetly scented; produced in quite large, branched, terminal or axillary loose sprays, 3 to 12 cm long (August to December). **Fruit:** small, fleshy, 5 to 6 mm in diameter, orange-red when ripe, produced in quite large heads, 10 to 20 cm in diameter, attractive and conspicuous when heavily in fruit (August to December).

This species resembles *Oricia bachmannii,* but can be distinguished by the differences in their respective flowers.

Teclea trichocarpa (Engl.) Engl.
S.A. no: —
Rhod. no: 401   Furry-fruited teclea

A shrub or small tree up to 6 m in height. This species closely resembles *T. gerrardii* but the latter has almost no hairs on the mature fruits, while the mature fruits in *T. trichocarpa* are densely velvety or furry; also the two species are clearly geographically distinct.

8. CLAUSENA N. L. Burm.

Clausena anisata (Willd.) J. D. Hook. ex Benth.   Illust. 116
S.A. no: 265   Horsewood. Perdepis
Rhod. no: 402   Clausena

A shrub or small, unarmed tree, usually 3 to 5 m in height, but occasionally reaching 10 m under ideal conditions; occurring in evergreen forest and fringing forest or in low altitude woodland and palm

351

veld, along stream and river banks, from sea level to about 2 200 m. **Bark:** greyish-brown, rather mottled and smoothish. **Leaves:** alternate, compound, with 10 to 17 alternate to sub-opposite leaflets including a terminal leaflet; leaflets ovate to narrowly elliptic, 1 to 6 × 0,6 to 2,5 cm, dark green, densely gland-dotted, purplish-brown when young, with a strong scent, pleasant or unpleasant, often resembling aniseed; apex tapering and notched; base tapering to rounded; margin toothed to scalloped; petiolules short, petiole present. **Flowers:** small but rather attractive, yellow or white, about 10 mm in diameter, produced in rather sparse, axillary, branched sprays, or cymose panicles, up to 16 cm long. Bisexual; floral parts in fours to fives; stamens 8 to 10 in 2 whorls, yellow (August to November). **Fruit:** spherical, fleshy, 7 mm in diameter, becoming red to black when mature (October to February).

The wood is hard, heavy, strong and elastic, but the small size of the tree limits its use. Zulus hold newly-born babies in the wood-smoke to fumigate them, and in the steam rising from boiling leaves to cleanse the body internally, strengthen the heart and cure rheumatism and fevers. Adults also steam their bodies in this leaf infusion as a deodorant.

9. CITROPSIS Swingle & Kellerman

Citropsis daweana Swingle & Kellerman
S.A. no: 266   Wild citrus. Wildesitroen
Rhod. no: 403   Wild citrus

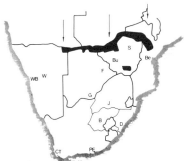 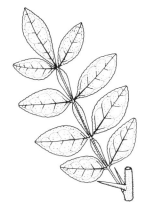

A shrub or small tree up to 6 m in height, with arching branches; occurring in low altitude, hot, dry woodland. **Bark:** grey; the younger branches armed with more or less straight spines, about 2 cm long; the older branches are unarmed. **Leaves:** alternate, compound, with 2 to 4 pairs of leaflets plus a terminal leaflet; leaflets elliptic to obovate, 2 to 4,5 × 0,7 to 2,5 cm, with fine, greyish hairs, aromatic; apex rounded; base tapering; margins scalloped; petiole and rachis winged, petiole up to 2,5 cm long. **Flowers:** small, lemon-yellow to white, about 10 mm in diameter, produced in clusters, or small branched racemes, 2 to 3 cm long, along the stems in the leaf axils, or on short lateral branches; bisexual, all floral parts in fours; petals narrow; stamens 8 in 2 whorls (September to October). **Fruit:** spherical, 1 to 1,4 cm in diameter, reddish-brown (April to June).

1. Cones of Wood's cycad.
   Encephalartos woodii, p54
2. Real yellowwood.
   Podocarpus latifolius, p57
3. Receptacles of the real yellowwood.
   Podocarpus latifolius, p57

4

5

6

8

4. Mountain cedar. *Widdringtonia nodiflora.*
The drawing is of a rare giant specimen.
A spray of juvenile leaves is shown on the right, p60
5. *Welwitschia mirabilis,* p61
6. Inflorescence of the kosi palm. *Raphia australis,* p70
7. The krantz aloe. *Aloe arborescens,* p76
8. A kokerboom. *Aloe dichotoma,* p78
9. A bitter aloe. *Aloe ferox,* p80

9

10

11

12

13

14

15

16

17

18

19

20

21

22

23

21. Wild almond.
    Brabejum stellatifolium, p123
22. The Transvaal beechwood.
    Faurea saligna, p127
23. Broad-leaved beechwood.
    Faurea speciosa, p127
24. The waboom.
    Protea nitida, p138
25. The African protea.
    Protea gaguedi, p133
26. Long-bud protea.
    Protea aurea, p130

24

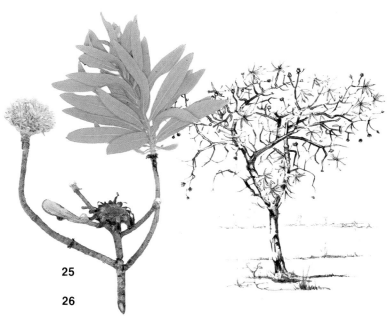

25

26

27 28

29

30

31

32

33

34

35

36

37

38

35. Large sourplum. *Ximenia caffra*, p159
36. The spekboom. *Portulacaria afra*, p162
37. Namaqualand ceraria. *Ceraria namaquensis*, p163
38. One of the dwaba-berries. *Friesodielsia obovata*, p167
39. Flowers of the green-apple. *Monodora junodii*, p174
40. The red-haired laurel. *Cryptocarya wyliei*, p180

39   40

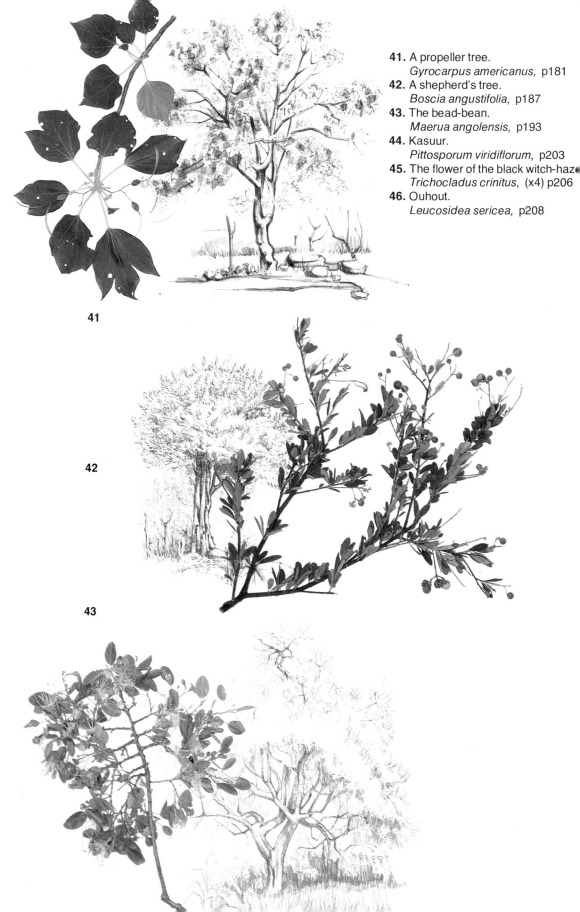

41. A propeller tree.
Gyrocarpus americanus, p181
42. A shepherd's tree.
Boscia angustifolia, p187
43. The bead-bean.
Maerua angolensis, p193
44. Kasuur.
Pittosporum viridiflorum, p203
45. The flower of the black witch-hazel.
Trichocladus crinitus, (x4) p206
46. Ouhout.
Leucosidea sericea, p208

41

42

43

44

45

46

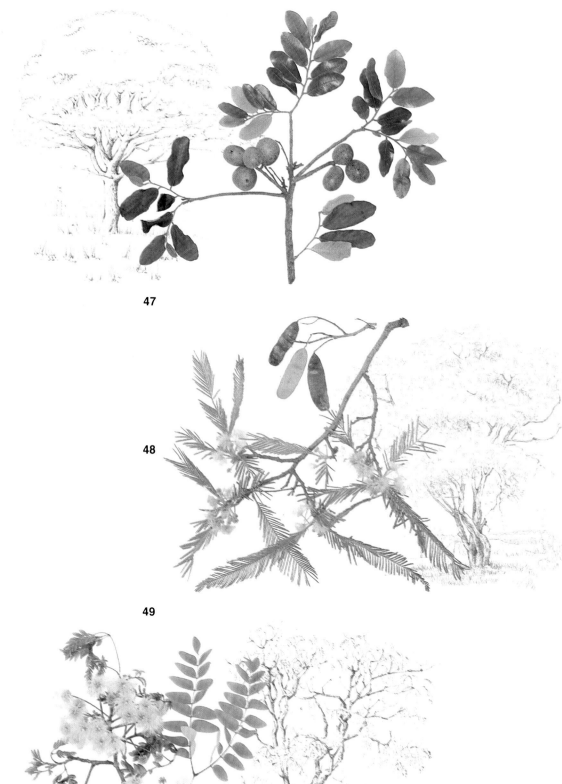

47

48

49

50

51

52

53

54

55

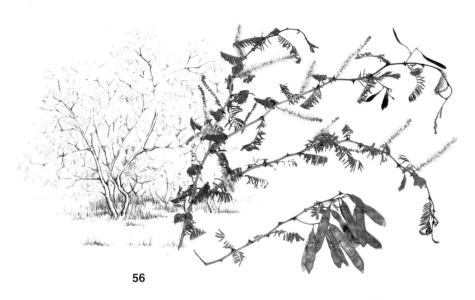

56

57

58

59

58. The red thorn.
    Acacia gerrardii, p238
59. The grey camel thorn.
    Acacia haematoxylon, p239
60. The sweet thorn.
    Acacia karroo, p241
61. The knob thorn.
    Acacia nigrescens, p245
62. The white thorn.
    Acacia polyacantha, p247
63. The paperbark acacia.
    Acacia sieberana, p251

60

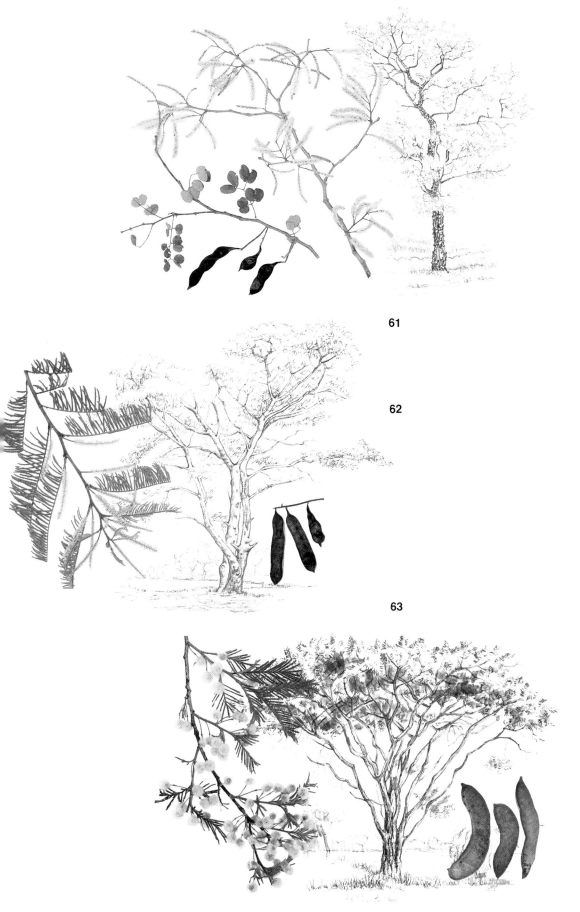

61

62

63

64

65

64. The umbrella thorn.
   Acacia tortilis, p252
65. Fever tree.
   Acacia xanthophloea, p253
66. A sickle bush.
   Dichrostachys cinerea, p254
67. The Scotsman's rattle.
   Amblygonocarpus andongensis, p2
68. One of the sumach beans.
   Elephantorrhiza goetzei, p259
69. The ordeal tree.
   Erythrophleum africanum, p264

66

67

68

69

70

71

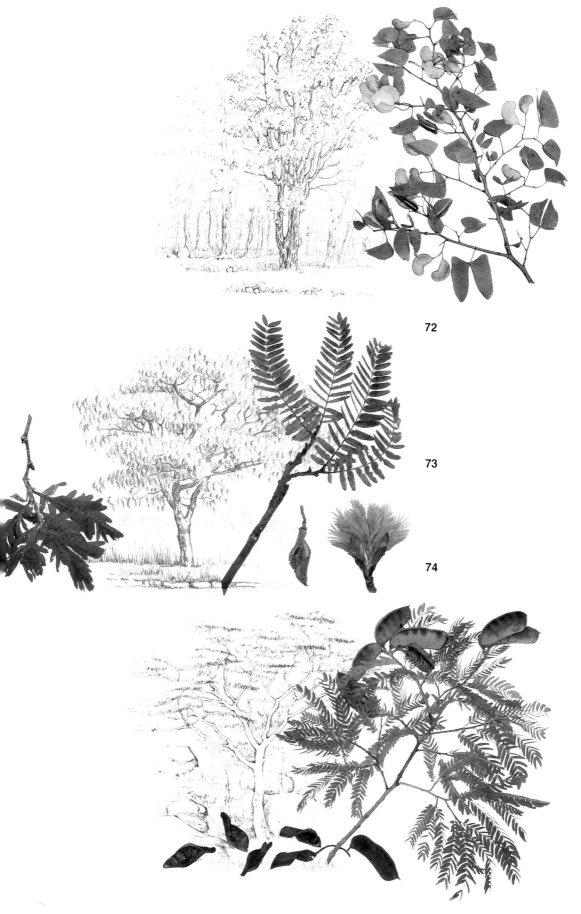

72

73

74

75. The msasa. *Brachystegia spiciformis*, p273
76. The Karoo boer-bean. *Schotia afra*, p275
77. The weeping boer-bean. *Schotia brachypetala*, p275
78. The Rhodesian teak. *Baikiaea plurijuga*, p278
79. The tamarind. *Tamarindus indica*, p278

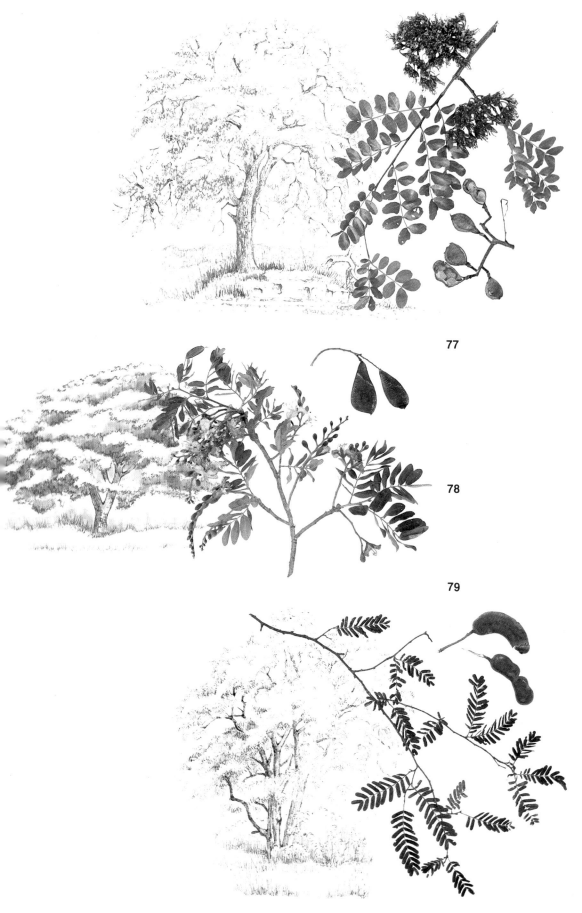

77

78

79

80

81

82

80. Pod mahogany.
    Afzelia quanzensis, p279
81. The munondo.
    Julbernardia globiflora, p280
82. Butterfly leaf.
    Adenolobus garipensis, p281
83. Pride-of-De Kaap.
    Bauhinia galpinii, p283
84. White bauhinia
    Bauhinia petersiana, p283
85. Yellow tree bauhinia.
    Bauhinia tomentosa, p284

83

84

85

86

87

88

89

90

91

92

93

94

95

96

97

100

101

102

103

104

105

106

107

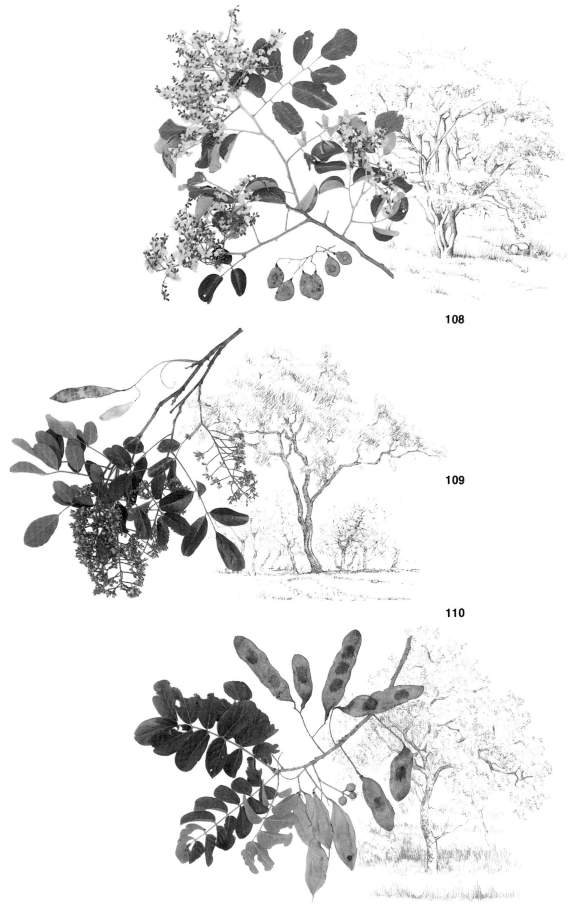

108

109

110

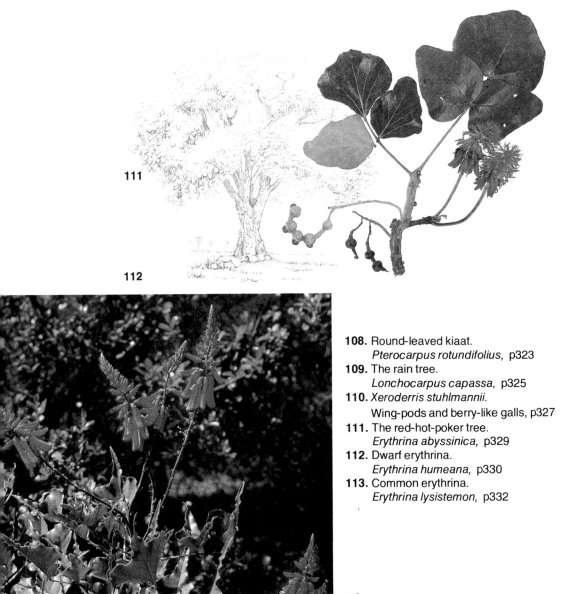

111

112

108. Round-leaved kiaat.
   Pterocarpus rotundifolius, p323
109. The rain tree.
   Lonchocarpus capassa, p325
110. *Xeroderris stuhlmannii.*
   Wing-pods and berry-like galls, p327
111. The red-hot-poker tree.
   Erythrina abyssinica, p329
112. Dwarf erythrina.
   Erythrina humeana, p330
113. Common erythrina.
   Erythrina lysistemon, p332

113

114

114. The common coca tree. *Erythroxylum emarginatum,* p336
115. Cape chestnut. *Calodendrum capense,* p345
116. Horsewood. *Clausena anisata,* p351
117. The white syringa. *Kirkia acuminata,* p354
118. Poison-grub Commiphora. *Commiphora africana,* p357

115

116

117

118

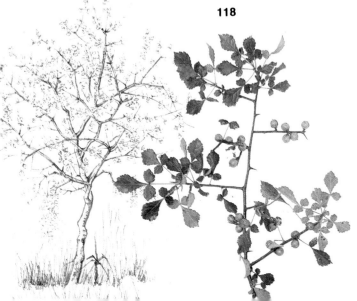

119

120

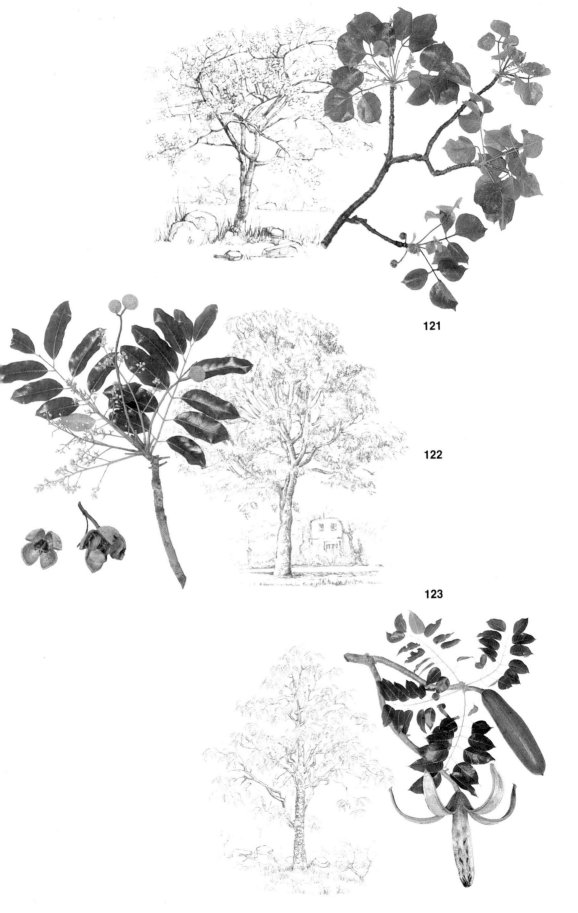

121

122

123

124

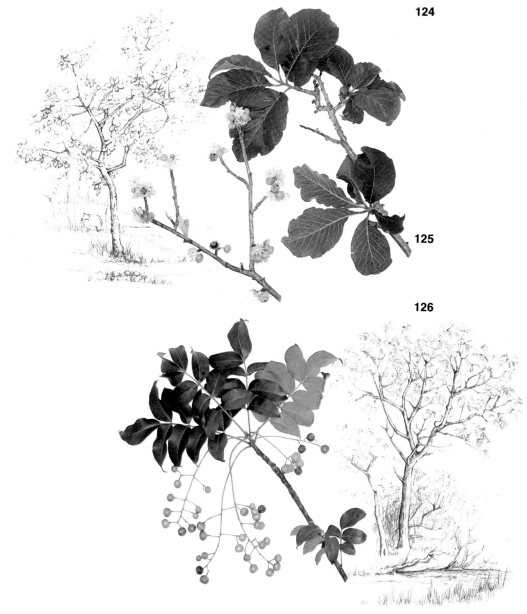

125

126

127

128

129

130

131

132

133

134

135

136

137

138

139

140

141

142

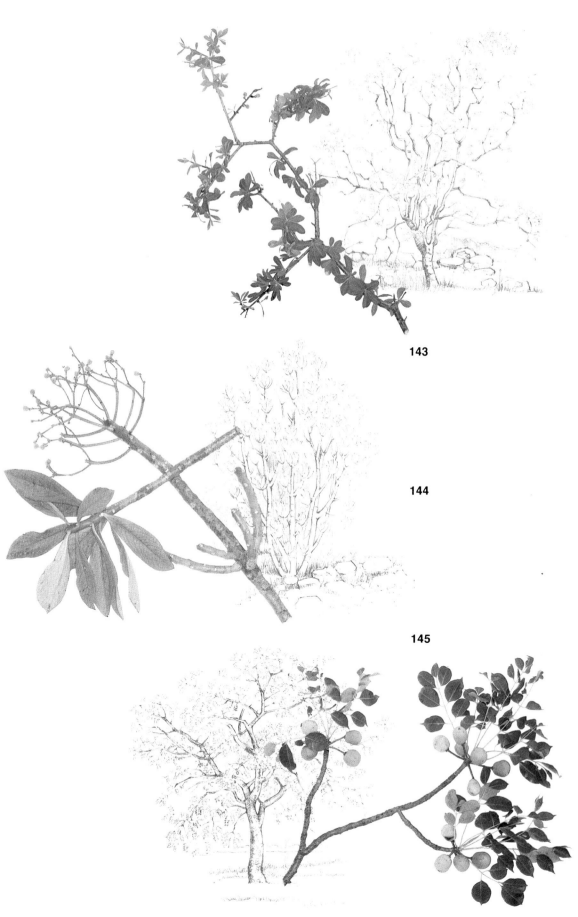

143

144

145

146

148

149

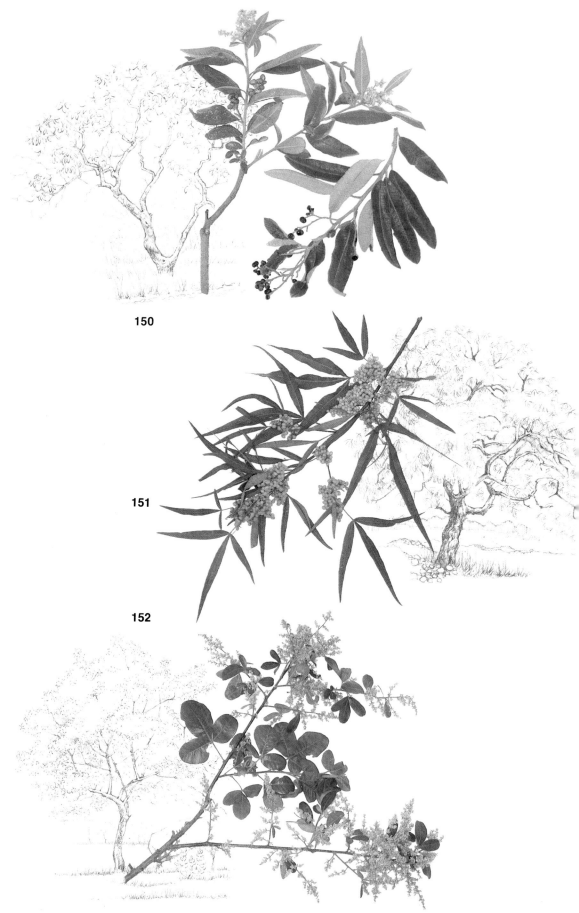

150

151

152

153

154

150. Currant resin tree. *Ozoroa reticulata,* p471
151. The karee. *Rhus lancea,* p481
152. The large-leaved rhus. *Rhus longipes,* p482
153. The common taaibos. *Rhus pyroides,* p487
154. The Cape holly. *Ilex mitis,* p492
155. The confetti tree.
    Maytenus senegalensis, p501

155

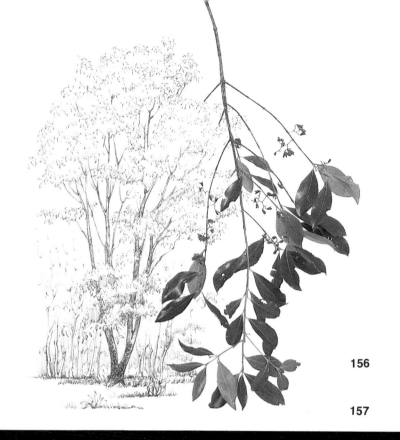

156

157

158

159

160

161

162

163

164

165

166

167

168

169

170

171

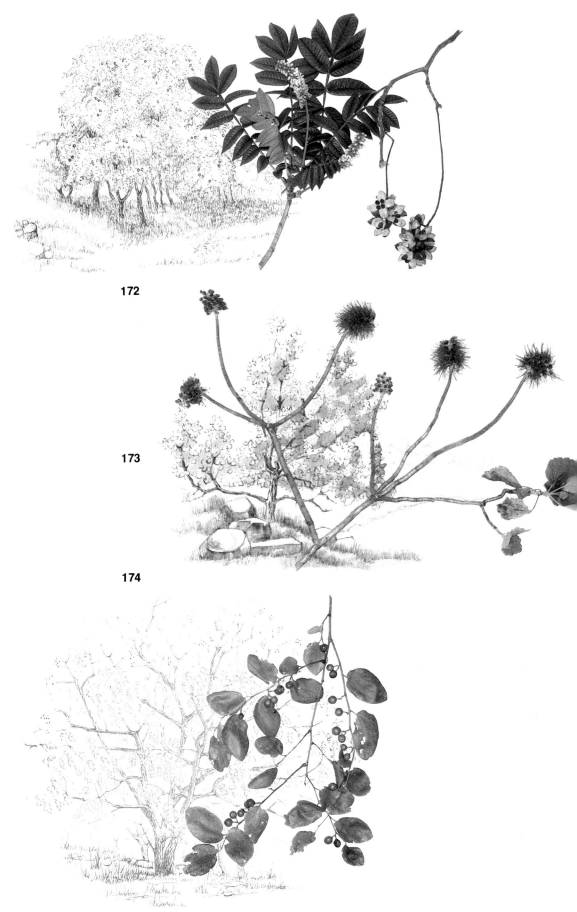

172

173

174

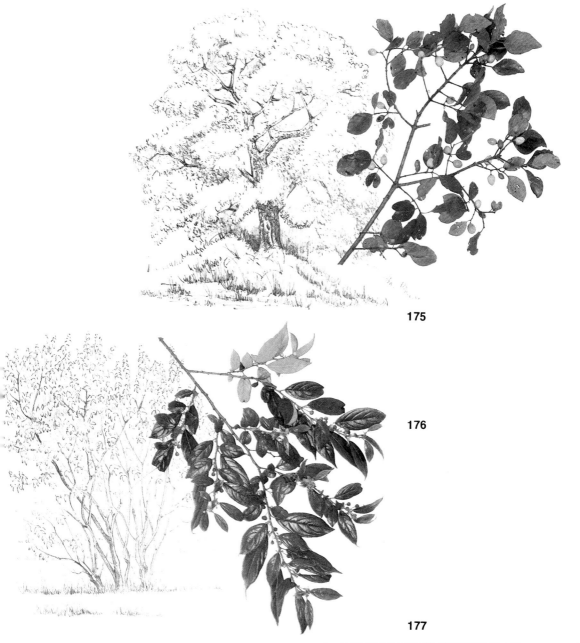

175

176

177

172. Winged bersama.
     Bersama abyssinica, p543
173 The Natal bottlebrush.
     Greyia sutherlandii, p548
174. The buffalo-thorn.
     Ziziphus mucronata, p550
175. The bird plum.
     Berchemia discolor, p552
176. Blinkblaar. *Rhamnus prinoides,* p555
177. The bastard cobas.
     Cyphostemma juttae, p565, growing
     in the Botanic Gardens, Pretoria.

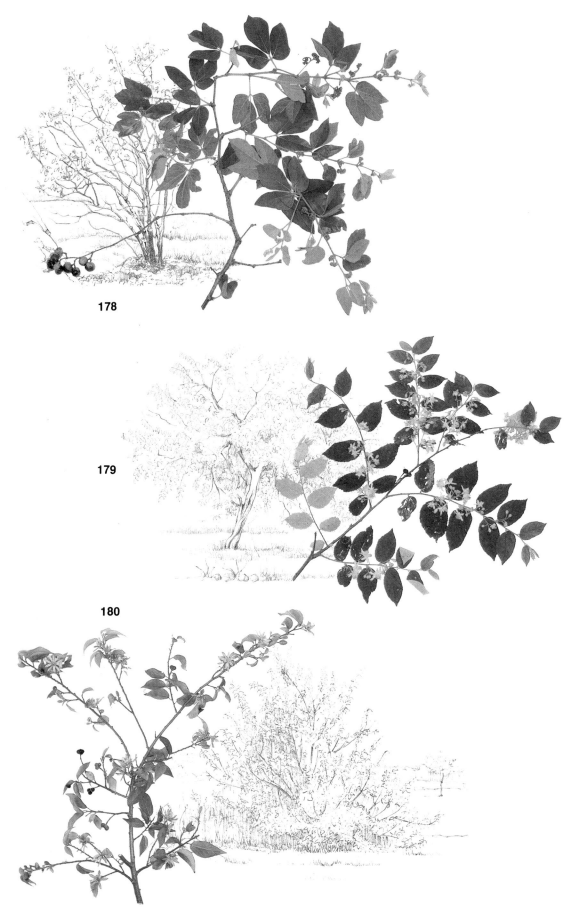

178

179

180

178. The bushveld grape. *Rhoicissus revoilii,* p561, showing characteristic berry-like galls.
179. Silver raisin. *Grewia monticola,* p576
180. The cross-berry. *Grewia occidentalis,* p576
181. Forest raisin. *Grewia lasiocarpa,* p573
182. Coast hibiscus. *Hibiscus tiliaceus,* p584
183. The large-flowered white cross-berry. *Grewia pachycalyx,* p577

181

182

183

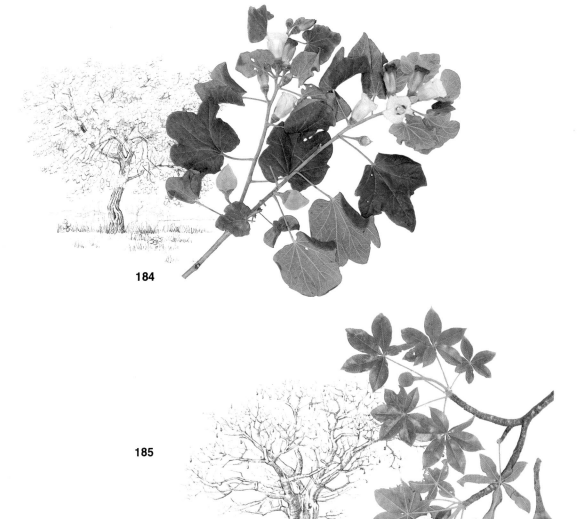

184. The snot apple.
Azanza garckeana, p586
185. A baobab.
Adansonia digitata, p587
186. The pink dombeya.
Dombeya burgessiae, p590
187. Wild pear.
Dombeya rotundifolia, p592
188. African star-chestnut or tick tree.
Sterculia africana, p595
189. The large-leaved star-chestnut.
Sterculia quinqueloba, p597

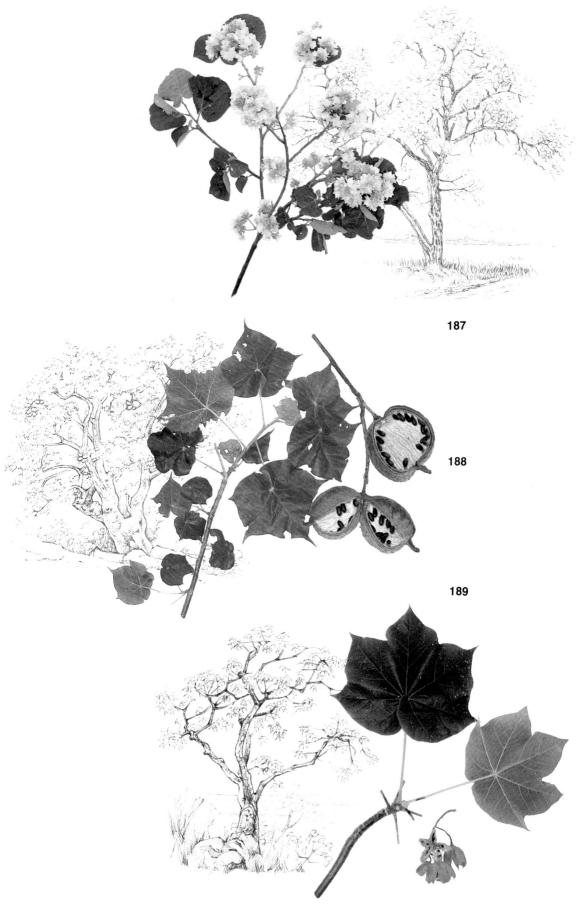

187

188

189

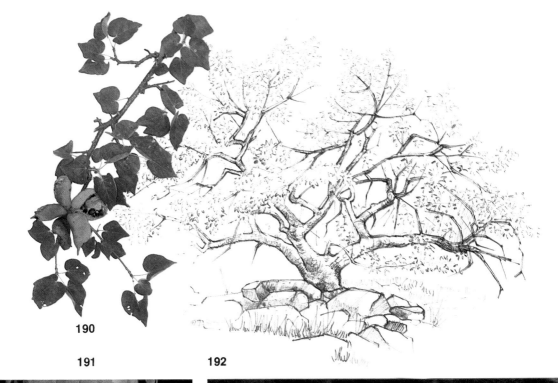

190

191

192

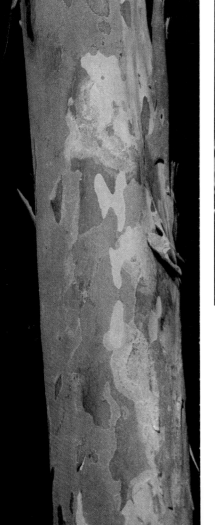

190. Common star-chestnut. *Sterculia rogersii*, p597
191. The Cape plane. *Ochna arborea* var *arborea*, p602
192. The Transvaal plane. *Ochna arborea* var *oconnorii*, p602
193. The lekkerbreek or peeling-bark ochna. *Ochna pulchra*, p607
194. A curry bush. *Hypericum revolutum*, p 610

193

194

195

196

197

198

199

200. The snuff-box tree or fried-egg flower. *Oncoba spinosa,* p624
201. African dog-rose. *Xylotheca kraussiana,* p625
202. Wild peach. *Kiggelaria africana,* p626
203. The thorn pear. *Scolopia zeyheri,* p629

201

202

203

204

205

206

207

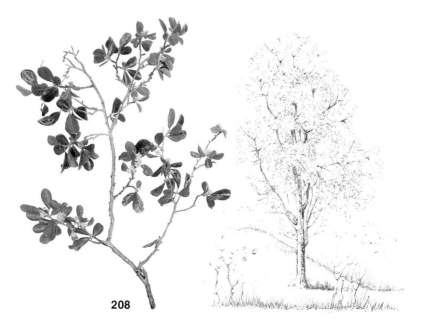

208

209   **210**

211. The silky fibre-bush. *Englerodaphne pilosa,* p647

212. Pompon tree. *Dais cotinifolia,* p649

213. The powder-puff tree. *Barringtonia racemosa,* p652

214. Black mangrove. *Bruguiera gymnorrhiza,* p655

215. Onionwood. *Cassipourea gummiflua,* p658

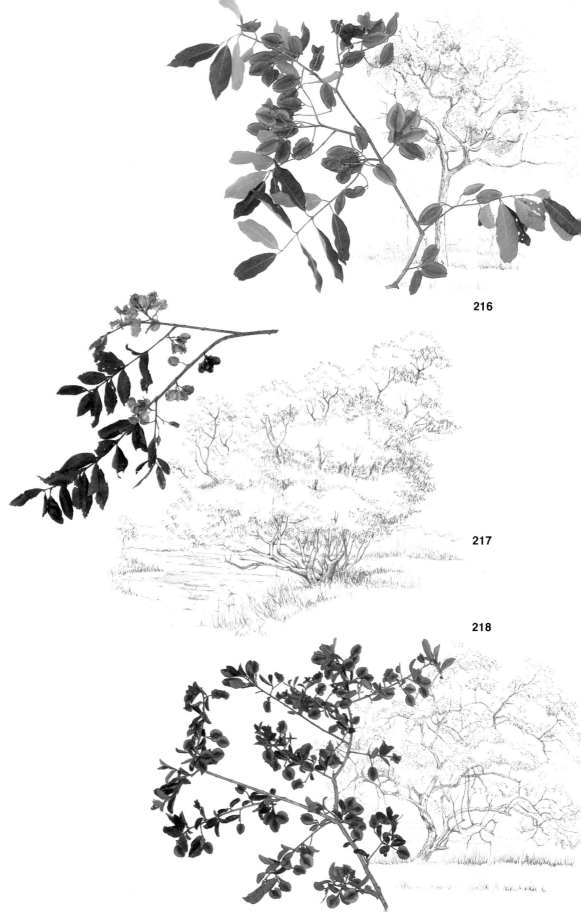

216

217

218

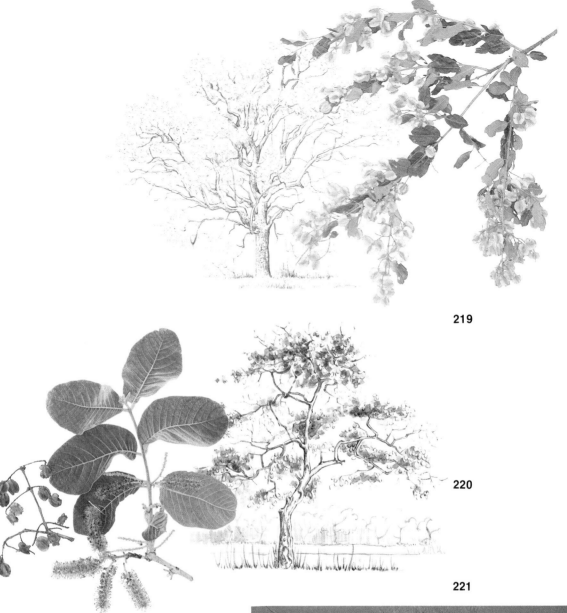

219

220

221

216. The bushwillow.
     Combretum collinum, p665
217. The river bushwillow.
     Combretum erythrophyllum, p667
218. The russet bushwillow.
     Combretum hereroense, p668
219. Leadwood.
     Combretum imberbe, p669
220. The velvet bushwillow.
     Combretum molle, p671
221. Flame combretum or burning-bush.
     Combretum paniculatum, p673,
     with *Euphorbia ingens,* the naboom,
     in the background.

222

223

224

225

226

227

222. The large-fruited bushwillow.
 Combretum zeyheri, p676
223. The large-leaved terminalia.
 Terminalia mollis, p681
224. The purple-pod terminalia.
 Terminalia prunioides, p682
225. Silver terminalia.
 Terminalia sericea, p684
226. The rosette-leaved terminalia.
 Terminalia stenostachya, p685
227. Northern wild myrtle.
 Eugenia nyassensis, p689

228

229

230

228. The water berry or umdoni. *Syzygium cordatum,* p690
229. The forest waterberry. *Syzygium gerrardii,* p692
230. Woodland waterberry.
     Syzygium guineense subsp. *guineense,* p691
231. Lance-leaf myrtle. *Metrosideros angustifolia,* p693

231

232

233

234

235

236

237. The Cape beech.
   Rapanea melanophloeos, p721
238/239. The stamvrug or the stem-fruit.
   Bequaertiodendron magalismontanum, p727
240. The coast red milkwood. *Mimusops caffra,* p7
241. The common red milkwood.
   Mimusops zeyheri, p730

237

238

239

240

241

242

243

244

245

246

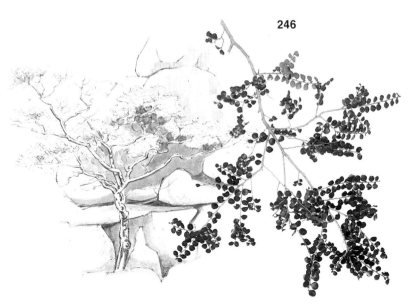

247. Forest monkey plum or bladder-nut. *Diospyros whyteana,* p753   **247**
248. Wing-leaved wooden-pear. *Schrebera alata,* p755
249. The wooden-pear. *Schrebera trichoclada,* p756
250. The Karoo grey form of the wild olive. *Olea europaea* subsp. *africana,* p759
251. Ironwood. *Olea capensis,* p758

248

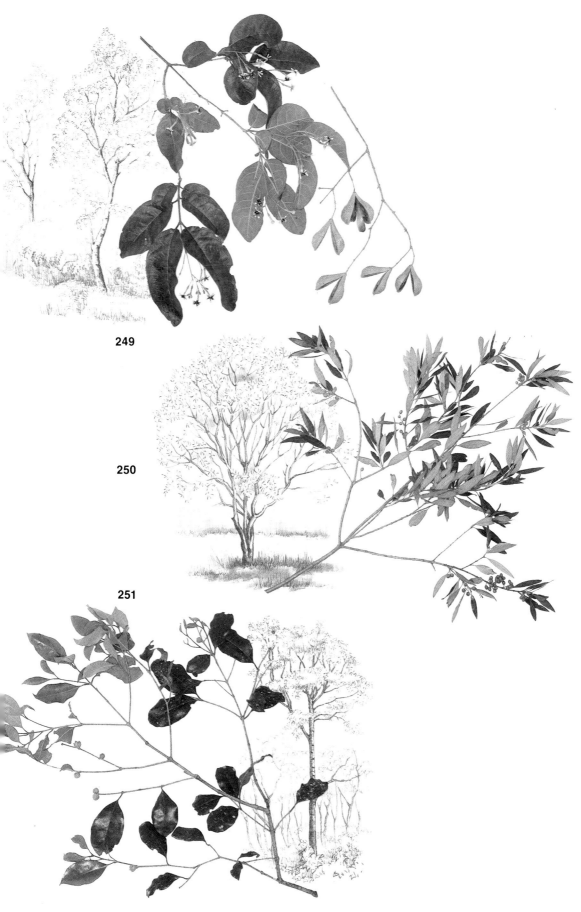

249

250

251

252

253

254

255

256

257

258 **259**

260

258/259. Common poison-bush.
 Acokanthera oppositifolia, p781
260. The num-num. *Carissa bispinosa,* p782
261. The kamassi. *Gonioma kamassi,* p786
262. The jasmine tree.
 Holarrhena pubescens, p786
263. Horn-pod tree or wild rubber.
 Diplorhynchus condylocarpon, p787
264. Toad tree.
 Tabernaemontana elegans, p788

261

262

263

264

265

266

267

268

269

270

271

272

273

274

275

271. Large-leaved cordia. *Cordia abyssinica,* p799
272. The snot-berry or sandpaper cordia. *Cordia ovalis,* p801
273. The puzzle bush. *Ehretia rigida,* p803
274. The chocolate berry. *Vitex payos,* p811
275. The white cat's whiskers. *Clerodendrum glabrum,* p814

276

277

278

279

280

281

282

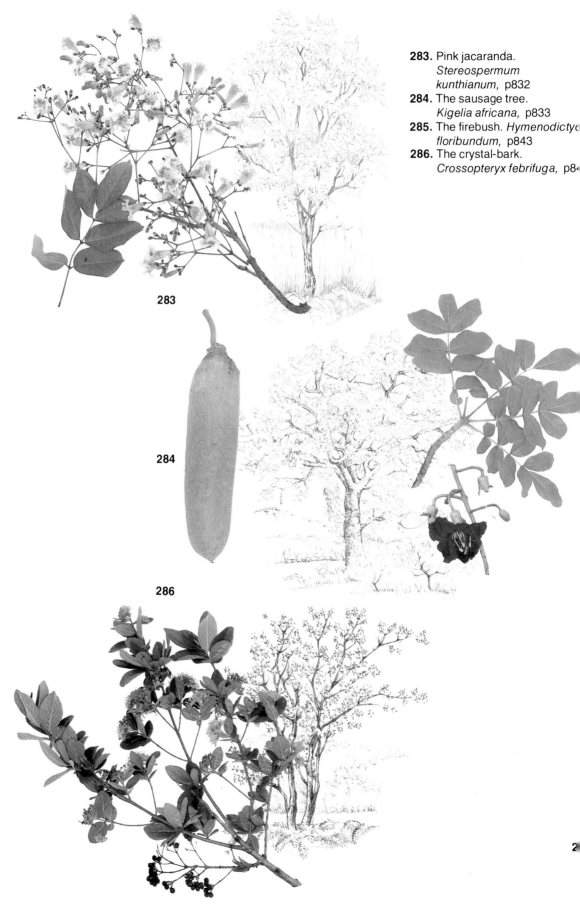

283. Pink jacaranda. *Stereospermum kunthianum*, p832
284. The sausage tree. *Kigelia africana*, p833
285. The firebush. *Hymenodictyc floribundum*, p843
286. The crystal-bark. *Crossopteryx febrifuga*, p8⁴

283

284

286

2

274

275

276

277

278

279   **280**

276. Wild Chinese hats.
   Homskioldia tettensis, p816
277. The tree fuchsia. *Halleria lucida*, p822
278. The yellow shell-flower bush.
   Bowkeria citrina, p825
279. The Cape honeysuckle.
   Tecomaria capensis, p827
280. *Rhigozum zambesiacum*, p829
281. The trumpet thorn.
   Catophractes alexandri, p830
282. The bean tree.
   Markhamia acuminata, p831

281

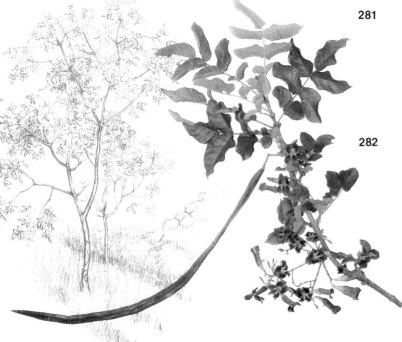

282

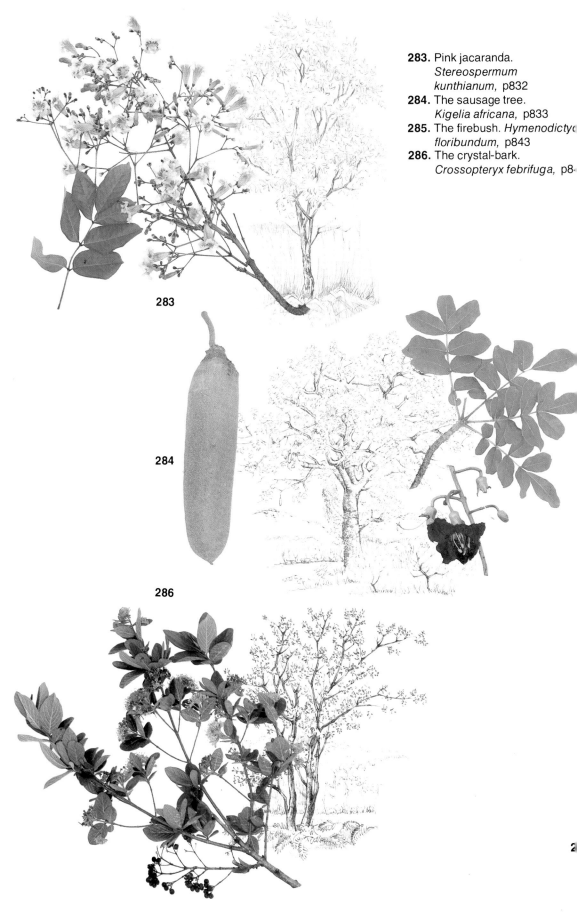

283. Pink jacaranda.
*Stereospermum
kunthianum*, p832
284. The sausage tree.
Kigelia africana, p833
285. The firebush. *Hymenodictyo
floribundum*, p843
286. The crystal-bark.
Crossopteryx febrifuga, p8

283

284

286

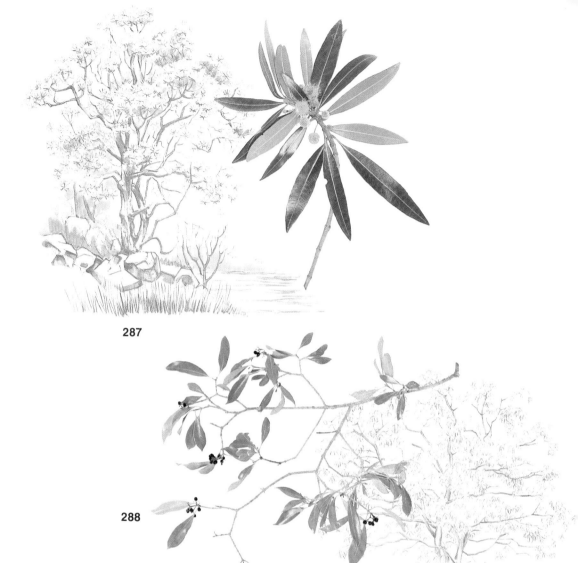

287. The matumi.
Breonadia microcephala, p844
288. *Tarenna neurophylla,* p849
289. Wild pomegranate.
Burchellia bubalina, p850
290. Thorny bone-apple.
Xeromphis obovata, p851
291. Spiny gardenia.
Gardenia amoena, p854
292. Transvaal gardenia.
Gardenia volkensii subsp.
spatulifolia, p857

290

291

292

293   294

295

296

297 298

299

300

301

302

303

304

305

306

307

308

305. The common bride's bush.
   Pavetta gardeniifolia, p894
306. The tree vernonia.
   Vernonia amygdalina, p902
307. *Psychotria capensis,* p899
308. The long-flowering tree vernonia.
   Vernonia hymenolepis
   subsp. *meridionalis,* p904
309. The kloof brachylaena.
   Brachylaena neriifolia, p908
310. The poison tree vernonia.
   Vernonia subuligera, p905
311. The mountain silver oak.
   Brachylaena rotundata, p909

310

311

312

313

314

312. Camphor bush.
Tarchonanthus camphoratus, p910
313. Camphor tree.
Tarchonanthus trilobus, p911
314. Bush-tick berry.
Chrysanthemoides monilifera, p913

10. *CITRUS L.

*Citrus aurantium L.

*Citrus limon (L.) N. L. Burm.

The orange (*C. aurantium*, Rhod. no: 404) and the lemon (*C. limon*, Rhod. no: 405) are widely cultivated in southern Africa. The former has become naturalised to a limited extent in some forests in the east of Rhodesia, while the latter has become naturalised on a wider scale in areas in the north, east and south of Rhodesia and in Moçambique, especially in riverine fringe forest.

SIMAROUBACEAE

Key to the genera:
Petiole and rachis conspicuously winged; leaves with less than 6 pairs of leaflets; flowers with 8 to 10 stamens (or more); fruit fleshy .... **1. Harrisonia**

Petiole and rachis not winged; leaves with 6 or more pairs of leaflets; flowers with 4 stamens (occasionally 3 to 5); fruit a small, thinly woody capsule .... **2. Kirkia**

1. HARRISONIA R. Br. ex Adr. Juss.

Harrisonia abyssinica Oliver
S.A. no: —
Rhod. no: — Harrisonia

A shrub with a tendency to scramble, or a small to medium sized tree up to 10 m in height; occurring in evergreen forest and in the transitional zone between deciduous woodland and evergreen forest. **Bark:** pale brown, corky, often with conical, corky, spine-tipped bosses, 2 cm long, on the trunk; branchlets often prickly and all parts of the plant often softly velvety. **Leaves:** alternate, compound, with 3 to 6 pairs of sub-opposite leaflets plus a terminal leaflet; leaflets elliptic to broadly ovate, 0,7 to 7 × 0,5 to 3 cm, with or without hairs; apex broadly tapering to rounded; base very broadly tapering to almost rounded, asymmetric, one side deeply bellied; margin markedly scalloped to toothed, occasionally almost entire especially near the base; petiolules absent, petiole up to 2,5 cm long, petiole and rachis often conspicuously winged. **Flowers:** small, white to yellow, about 10 mm in diameter, produced in loosely branched, terminal heads or panicles, up to 15 cm long, but usually less. Bisexual; all floral parts in fours to fives; stamens 8 to 10 in 2 whorls, about 3 mm long, forming a central mass (August to October). **Fruit:** almost spherical, about 10 mm in diameter, markedly 5-to 6-lobed with vertical grooves, bright red and fleshy when mature (February to May).
This is the southern limit of the range of this species.

2. KIRKIA Oliver

Shrubs or trees, bark sometimes bitter. **Leaves:** alternate, crowded near the ends of the branchlets, compound, imparipinnate. **Flowers:** sexes separate in the same panicle; all floral parts in fours; calyx lobes free almost to the base; petals narrow, free; stamens opposite the petals, somewhat reduced in

353

size and sterile in female flowers; ovary of 4 united carpels, vestigial in male flowers. **Fruit:** a small capsule.

Key to the tree species of *Kirkia:*
1 Leaflets in 6 to 10 pairs, rather large, 2 to 8 × 1 to 2,5 cm .... **K. acuminata**
   Leaflets in 10 to 20 pairs, or up to 40, alternately arranged, rather small, up to 1,5 × 0,3 cm
   2
2 Leaflets opposite; in the Transvaal only, not in South West Africa .... **K. wilmsii**
   Leaflets alternate; in the north-west of South West Africa only .... **K. dewinteri**

Kirkia acuminata Oliver   Illust. 117
[*K. pubescens* Burtt Davy]
S.A. no: 267 White syringa. Witsering
Rhod. no: 406 White syringa

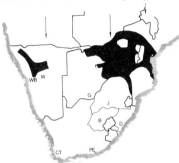

A medium sized deciduous tree 6 to 15 m in height; occurring in various types of woodland at medium to low altitudes, often on rocky ridges and outcrops. **Bark:** grey and smooth when young, inclined to become flaky with age; branchlets are conspicuously marked with leaf scars. **Leaves:** sticky when young, with 6 to 10 pairs of leaflets plus a terminal leaflet; leaflets narrowly ovate, 2 to 8 × 1 to 2,5 cm, with or without hairs; apex narrowly tapering; base asymmetric; margin scalloped to finely toothed; petiolules more or less absent, petiole 3 to 10 cm long. The leaves become splendidly coloured gold and red in autumn. **Flowers:** small, greenish-cream, produced in many-branched but rather lax heads up to 7 cm long, in the axils of the leaves (October to November). **Fruit:** a thinly woody capsule, about 1,5 × 0,5 cm, splitting into 4 valves (January onwards, the old fruits sometimes overlapping the following flowering season).

The wood is a yellowish-brown colour, light and soft; it is difficult to work because of the presence of silica crystals which rapidly blunt saw blades; it is not durable, although it polishes well and has been used for laminated wood and veneers, for furniture and for household utensils such as bowls and spoons. Eve Palmer says that the roots are swollen and act as water-storage organs to which Africans have recourse in times of drought; also game animals are known to dig for them. These trees are sacred to some African tribes in Rhodesia and are protected in all the Black Homelands in South Africa. The trees can be propagated easily either from seed or from truncheons, are fast growing and drought resistant, but are susceptible to frost. With their striking autumn colours they would make fine subjects for warmer gardens.

Kirkia dewinteri Merxm. & Heine
S.A. no: 268 Kaoko syringa. Kaokosering
Rhod. no: —

A small to medium sized tree 3 to 9 m in height, with slender, upright, rigid branches; occurring in desert areas on rocky outcrops; this is a rare species. **Bark:** yellow with blackish spots 'like a leopard' (De Winter's description). **Leaves:** crowded near the ends of the branches with 20 to 40 alternate leaflets; leaflets small, lanceolate, about 15 × 3 mm, without hairs; apex narrowly tapering with a hair-like tip; base asymmetric; margin toothed. **Flowers:** small, white, in sparse 9- to 12-flowered, branched sprays, or panicles. **Fruit:** a small capsule, splitting by 8 valves. The flowering and fruiting times are not known to the author.

Kirkia wilmsii Engl.
S.A. no: 269   Mountain syringa. Bergsering
Rhod. no: —

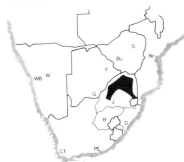

A small tree reaching 8 m in height; occurring on mountain slopes and rocky hills. **Bark:** grey and smooth; branchlets marked with conspicuous leaf scars. **Leaves:** crowded at the ends of the branchlets, with 10 to 15 pairs of opposite leaflets plus a terminal leaflet; leaflet small, slender, up 1,5 × 0,3 cm; apex tapering; base rounded; margin coarsely toothed; petiolules very short to absent, petiole up to 4 cm long. The leaves produce brilliant autumn colours. **Flowers:** small, greenish-white, in much-branched, rather compact heads, or panicles, 4 to 7 cm long, on conspicuous, long, slender stalks, in the axils of the leaves (October to December). **Fruit:** a small capsule, narrowly oval, up to 12 × 5 mm, 4-angled, brown when mature, splitting into 4 valves which remain joined at the apex (January to April).

The wood is light, coarse-grained, greyish, but is little used. The bark provides a good strong fibre. Plants are grown easily from seed and from cuttings and, if given a well-drained soil in a warm, sheltered position, respond well in cultivation.

BURSERACEAE *(The myrrh family)*

COMMIPHORA Jacq.

Shrubs or trees, often spinescent; bark smooth, or papery. **Leaves:** simple or compound, 1- to 3-foliolate or pinnate. **Flowers:** small, produced in axillary panicles, or dichasial cymes, on dwarf lateral shoots, sexes separate, usually on different plants; all floral parts in fours; calyx persistent; petals straight, spreading; stamens 8 in 2 whorls, reduced to vestiges in female flowers; ovary usually 2-chambered (rarely 3), vestigial in male flowers. **Fruit:** ovoid or spherical, thinly fleshy, splitting when ripe into two sections which fall away from the single stone. The stone is only slightly smaller than the fruit and most frequently has a pseudaril, often brightly coloured, at the base, which clasps the stone and which may or may not be lobed.

Most of the species of *Commiphora* produce aromatic resins, *C. myrrha* (Nees) Engl. of Arabia and *C. molimol* Engl. producing the fragrant resinous substance, myrrh, used in medicine and as incense, and *C. gileadensis* (L.) Christensen from Arabia and north-east Africa providing the medicinal resin, 'Balm of Gilead'.

355

BURSERACEAE

Key to the tree species of *Commiphora*:

1 Branchlets spine-tipped 2
  Branchlets not spine-tipped 11
2 Leaves apparently simple (with 1 leaflet only) or 3-foliolate, but with the lower 2 leaflets less than
    half the size of the terminal leaflet 3
  Leaves 3-foliolate, with the lower 2 leaflets at least half the size of the terminal leaflet, or leaves
    with 2 or more pairs of leaflets 4
3 Bark grey or greenish-yellow, zebra-striped, having very characteristic horizontal, dark blackish
    lenticellate rings or bands .... **C. merkeri**
  Bark without the black bands or rings; grey-green, yellowish or reddish, smooth, flaking in small
    strips .... **C. pyracanthoides**
4 Leaves 3-foliolate 5
  Leaves with 2 or more pairs of leaflets 10
5 Leaflets very small, the terminal leaflet no more than 2 cm long .... **C. dinteri**
  Terminal leaflet usually more than 2 cm long 6
6 Leaves covered with velvety hairs 7
  Leaves without hairs, or with only a few scattered hairs 8
7 Leaves 3-foliolate; leaflets obovate or elliptic .... **C. africana**
  Leaves with 2 to 6 pairs of leaflets plus a terminal leaflet; leaflets elliptic .... **C. mollis**
8 Occurring in the extreme north-west of South West Africa and northwards only ....
    .... **C. discolor**
  Not occurring in South West Africa 9
9 Branchlets and leaves completely without hairs; leaflet margins coarsely toothed ....
    .... **C. schimperi**
  Branchlets and leaves with a few scattered hairs; leaflet margins entire or very finely toothed along
    the upper half .... **C. neglecta**
10 Leaflets in 4 to 8 pairs plus the terminal leaflet; apex narrowly tapering. A coastal species
    .... **C. serrata**
  Leaflets in 6 to 10 pairs plus the terminal leaflet; apex broadly tapering to rounded. Occurring in
    the north-east and north-west of Rhodesia and north of the Zambezi River only ....
    .... **C. ugogensis**
11 Bark very conspicuously milky blue in colour .... **C. caerulea**
  Bark green, grey or brownish, but not blue 12
12 Leaves small, only 1 to 4 cm long. Occurring in South West Africa only 13
  Leaves more than 4 cm long, either with a single leaflet, 3-foliolate or with 2 or more pairs of
    leaflets 14
13 Petiole and rachis with a conspicuous wing which merges with the blades of the 5 to 7 leaflets,
    producing the appearance of a deeply lobed simple leaf .... **C. wildii**
  Petiole not winged; leaves 3-foliolate, the leaflets seldom exceeding 1,5 × 0,5 cm...............
    .... **C. oblanceolata**
14 Leaves with a single leaflet or simple 15
  Leaves with 3 or more leaflets 17
15 Leaves large, up to 12 cm long, thickly leathery .... **C. anacardiifolia**
  Leaves not conspicuously large, seldom more than 5 × 2 cm, not thickly leathery........ 16
16 Branchlets and leaves with velvety hairs; leaves up to 5 × 2 cm; margin entire ....
    .... **C. glaucescens**
  Branchlets and leaves without hairs; leaves up to 1,5 × 1,3 cm; margin very finely toothed ....
    .... **C. namaensis**
17 Leaves 3-foliolate 18
  Leaves with 2 or more pairs of leaflets plus the terminal leaflet 25
18 Branchlets and leaves with fine velvety hairs 19
  Branchlets and leaves without hairs 20
19 Leaflet margins entire .... **C. mossambicensis**
  Leaflet margins scalloped to finely toothed .... **C. angolensis**
20 Leaflets small, terminal leaflet 1 to 2 cm long only 21
  Leaflets larger, terminal leaflet usually more than 2 cm long 22

356

21 Lateral leaflets heart-shaped, with the apex deeply notched or obtuse .... **C. capensis**
   Lateral leaflets with the apex rounded, not notched .... **C. virgata**
22 Bark smooth, not peeling, dark grey, reddish-brown to yellowish-brown ....
   .... **C. gracilifrondosa**
   Bark peeling in flakes 23
23 Bark peeling in large, bronze, papery flakes .... **C. harveyi**
   Bark peeling in greyish to silver-white papery flakes 24
24 A coastal species. Found in Moçambique and Swaziland; not yet recorded from South Africa....
   .... **C. schlechteri**
   An inland species. From Rhodesia, northern Transvaal and South West Africa ....
   .... **C. tenuipetiolata**
25 Leaves without hairs 26
   Leaves finely velvety to hairy 34
26 Leaflets very slender and narrow – hair-like .... **C. kraeuseliana**
   Leaflets may be narrow, but not hair-like 27
27 Bark with a papery peel 28
   Bark not peeling 31
28 Leaflet margins entire, or with very few blunt teeth 29
   Leaflet margins with many small, blunt teeth 30
29 Leaflets large, oblong-lanceolate, up to 9,5 to 3 cm .... **C. zanzibarica**
   Leaflets small, elliptic, up to 4 × 2,5 cm long .... **C. tenuipetiolata**
30 Leaflets rather small, up to 7 × 3,2 cm .... **C. schlechteri**
   Leaflets large, 7 to 12 × 2,5 cm .... **C. woodii**
31 Leaflets small, ovate to obovate, to broadly so, up to 3 × 2,2 cm 32
   Leaflets large, oblong-lanceolate, up to 12 × 3 cm 33
32 Leaflet margins entire; petiolules long and conspicuously slender .... **C. multijuga**
   Leaflet margins finely scalloped; petiolules not conspicuously long and slender.................
   .... **C. saxicola**
33 Leaflets in 3 to 4 pairs plus the terminal leaflet .... **C. zanzibarica**
   Leaflets in 7 to 9 pairs plus the terminal leaflet .... **C. woodii**
34 Stem characteristically fluted or longitudinally ridged .... **C. karibensis**
   Stem not fluted or longitudinally ridged, or occasionally irregularly and obscurely so...... 35
35 Leaf margins entire 36
   Leaf margins with many blunt teeth 38
36 Leaflets large, ovate to almost circular .... **C. mossambicensis**
   Leaflets elliptic to oblong 37
37 Leaflets with soft, velvety hairs; conspicuously paler below .... **C. mollis**
   Leaflets harshly hairy; not conspicuously paler below .... **C. edulis**
38 Leaflets usually in 6 pairs plus the terminal leaflet .... **C. crenato-serrata**
   Leaflets usually in less than 6 pairs 39
39 Leaflets very sparsely and shortly hairy .... **C. harveyi**
   Leaflets velvety 40
40 Usually a well-formed tree, 6 to 13 m tall, with a thickset bole and heavy branches. Almost always
    among rocks .... **C. marlothii**
   Usually a shrub or a small tree up to 6 m in height; often on deep Kalahari sand ....
   .... **C. angolensis**

Commiphora africana (A. Rich.) Engl.   Illust. 118
[*C. pilosa* (Engl.) Engl.]
S.A. no: 270   Poison-grub commiphora. Harige kanniedood
Rhod. no: 407   Poison-grub commiphora

A shrub to small tree 2 to 5 m in height; occurring at medium to low altitudes in dry types of woodland
and bush, often among rocks. **Bark:** grey to green, smooth and rather succulent, exuding a pale gum if
damaged; branchlets spine-tipped. **Leaves:** 3-foliolate; leaflets usually obovate, the terminal leaflet
up to 8 × 5 cm, the lateral leaflets about half to three-quarters that size, upper and lower surfaces
finely velvety; apex broadly tapering to rounded; base tapering; margin scalloped; petiole up to

357

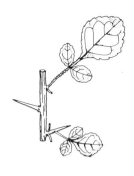

4,5 cm long. **Flowers:** small, green, pink to red, petals up to 5 mm long, inconspicuous; produced in tight, axillary clusters (October). **Fruit:** almost spherical, about 1,2 cm in diameter, pinkish-red; the stone may have a 4-lobed, red, fleshy pseudaril (November to March).

This species has been divided into two varieties. The typical variety, var. *africana*, has the calyx and the flower stalks completely without hairs, while var. *rubriflora* (Engl.) Wild has the calyx and the flower stalks covered with velvety hairs, and its leaves and stems are more densely hairy. The typical variety is the one most often encountered in South Africa, although one record of var. *rubriflora* is known from the Soutpansberg. The gum and resin which exude from the tree are made into a plaster which is applied in cases of abdominal spasms and to the head in cases of fever; it is sometimes mixed with fat and used as a perfumed body lotion and is also considered to be a good insecticide, especially against termites. The washed bark mixed with salt is applied to snakebites, and the fruit provides a remedy for stomach ailments. The soft, sappy wood and clean stems are employed by Africans in the construction of drop-traps for leopards and lions, while the trees are widely used as live fences. The larva of the beetle *Diamphidia*, from which bushmen make their arrow poison, feeds exclusively on these trees.

Commiphora anacardiifolia Dinter & Engl.

S.A. no: 271   Large-leaved commiphora. Grootblaarkanniedood
Rhod. no: —

A deciduous, medium sized but thickset tree, reaching 10 m in height; occurring on the fringes of the Namib desert. **Bark:** yellowish-brown with papery flakes and corky patches; the branchlets are not spine-tipped. **Leaves:** simple, clustered near the ends of the branches; obovate to almost circular, up to 12 cm or more in length and nearly as wide, with or without hairs which may make them harsh to the touch, thickly leathery, blue-green to dark green, paler below, with the veining conspicuous; apex rounded; base tapering; margin entire; petiolule and petiole short. **Flowers:** small, yellow, on long slender stalks; produced in sparse, lax heads (November). **Fruit:** almost spherical, about 10 mm in diameter, apex pointed; the stone has an orange, cup-shaped pseudaril (May).

Commiphora angolensis Engl.

S.A. no: 272   Sand commiphora. Sandkanniedood
Rhod. no: 408   Sand commiphora

A bush or small tree up to 6 m in height; often thicket-forming, occurring at low altitudes in hot, dry woodland, on deep Kalahari sand. **Bark:** chestnut-brown and flaking in polygonal pieces, or peeling

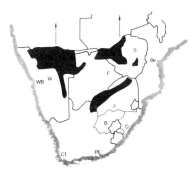

in silvery-white to yellowish papery strips revealing the green underbark; the branchlets are not spine-tipped. **Leaves:** 3-foliolate, or more often with 2 to 4 pairs of leaflets plus the terminal leaflet; leaflets oblong, up to 6 × 2,3 cm, leaves and branchlets covered with velvety hairs; apex broadly tapering; base often tapering, but may be very broadly tapering to rounded; margin scalloped to finely toothed; petiolules very short and thick, petiole up to 5 cm long. **Flowers:** small, yellow, produced in sparse heads up to 8 cm long, on conspicuous long thin stalks, appearing with the young leaves (October to November). **Fruit:** ovoid to spherical, about 10 mm in diameter, becoming pink when ripe (February to March).

Commiphora caerulea B. D. Burtt   Illust. 119
S.A. no: —
Rhod. no: 409   Blue-bark commiphora

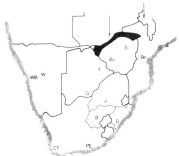

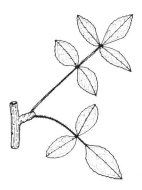

A deciduous, clean-stemmed, medium sized to large tree up to 13 m in height; occurring in thicketed ravines and on rocky hill slopes. **Bark:** smooth, succulent looking, conspicuously milky blue with a translucent, yellowish, papery peel; the branchlets are not spine-tipped. **Leaves:** 3-foliolate, or with 2 pairs of leaflets plus the terminal leaflet, both types of leaves occurring on the same tree; leaflets elliptic, up to 8 × 4,7 cm, thinly textured, with grey, short, soft hairs on the under surface and a few sparse hairs on the upper surface; apex tapering; base rounded, asymmetric; margin scalloped to toothed. **Flowers:** small, greenish-yellow, produced with the very young leaves, singly or in small clusters on the ends of dwarfed lateral twigs; the calyces and flower stalks are covered with dense, grey hairs (November to December). **Fruit:** almost spherical, about 1,5 cm in diameter, with a thin layer of aromatic pulp; a pseudaril covers about three-quarters of the stone (February onwards).

Commiphora capensis (Sonder) Engl.
S.A. no: 273   Namaqua commiphora. Namakwakanniedood
Rhod. no: —

A short, squat, thick-stemmed shrub or small tree up to 4 m in height; occurring in semi-desert areas, on rocky koppies and stony hills. **Bark:** brown to green, occasionally peeling in small, papery flakes; there may be scattered, dark patches; the branchlets are not spinescent, but the very short, rigid, dwarf lateral shoots give the impression of spines. **Leaves:** 3-foliolate; leaflets broadly obovate to almost circular, the terminal leaflet up to 1,8 × 1,4 cm, the lateral leaflets about 0,6 × 0,4 cm, without hairs; apex rounded and sometimes conspicuously notched; base tapering to rounded, even slightly lobed; margin finely scalloped; petiolules absent, petiole short, about 5 mm long. **Flowers:** small, incon-

359

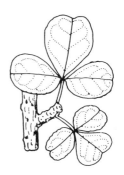

spicuous, greenish to yellow, solitary or in small, axillary clusters, appearing with the leaves (December to March). **Fruit:** oval, about 13 × 10 mm, somewhat flattened, with a pointed apex, greenish tinged with dull reddish-brown (May to October). The stone has no pseudaril.

Commiphora crenato-serrata Engl.
S.A. no: 274   Damara commiphora. Damarakanniedood
Rhod. no: —

A tree 3 to 10 m in height; occurring in dry, stony situations, often rooted in crevices in rocks. **Bark:** greyish to brownish and smooth; the branches are thickset, and the branchlets are not spine-tipped. **Leaves:** with 3 to 7 pairs of opposite leaflets plus a terminal leaflet, clustered at the ends of the branches; leaflets broadly lanceolate, 5 to 9 × 2,5 to 4 cm, velvety when young but losing most of these hairs by maturity except along the midrib and lateral veins which tend to remain hairy; thinly textured; the under surface much paler green than the upper surface; apex narrowly tapering to finely attenuate; base square to shallowly lobed; margin finely to irregularly toothed; petiolules slender, up to 1,5 cm long, petiole slender, up to 7 cm long. **Flowers:** small, yellowish, produced in short sprays about 3 cm long, in the axils of the leaves (November to December). **Fruit:** brownish-green to dark, golden-brown, about 1,5 × 0,7 cm, velvety, the apex drawn out into a long point; the stone is black with a scarlet pseudaril covering the lower one-third (December to January).

Commiphora dinteri Engl.
S.A. no: 274,2   Small-leaved commiphora, Namibkanniedood
Rhod. no. —

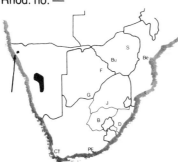

A thick-stemmed tree up to 3 m in height, although sometimes almost prostrate; occurring on stony mountainsides fringing the desert. **Bark:** grey, smooth, mottled and pitted; branchlets very slender and spine-tipped. **Leaves:** clustered on dwarf, knobby side shoots; 3-foliolate, leaflets very small, oval to broadly ovate, up to 7 × 5 mm; apex rounded; base tapering; margin almost entire to toothed; petiolules almost absent, petiole slender. **Flowers:** small, reddish, in short, axillary clusters (November). **Fruit:** oval, green to reddish-brown, about 10 mm long, apex pointed (January to March). The stone is partly enveloped by a red, 4-lobed pseudaril, 2 of the lobes being long and 2 short.

Commiphora discolor Mendes
S.A. no: 274,1   Kaoko commiphora. Kaokokanniedood
Rhod. no: —

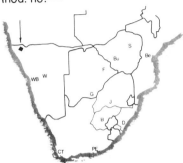

A climbing shrub or small tree up to 9 m in height; occurring in arid, rocky, desert areas. **Bark:** smooth, with a papery peel; branchlets either straight up to 40 cm long, or dwarfed lateral branchlets only 2,5 cm long and spine-tipped. **Leaves:** alternate, or crowded on the dwarfed branchlets; 3-foliolate or 1-foliate, leaflets elliptic to lanceolate, the terminal leaflet about 6 × 2,5 cm, the lateral leaflets more than half this size, without hairs, conspicuously paler green below than above; apex tapering; base tapering; margin toothed; petiolules absent, petiole up to 1,3 cm long. **Flowers:** dark purple, without hairs, produced in small lax heads at the ends of the dwarf, lateral branchlets (September to October). **Fruit:** almost spherical, about 10 mm in diameter, fleshy, purplish when mature (December).

Commiphora edulis (Klotzsch) Engl.
S.A. no: 275   Rough-leaved commiphora. Skurweblaarkanniedood
Rhod. no: 410   Rough-leaved commiphora

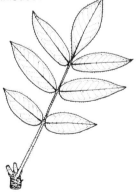

A many-stemmed shrub or small tree, 3 to 8 m in height, occasionally reaching 10 m; occurring in hot, dry types of thicket, woodland or bush, often on rocky hillsides. **Bark:** very pale grey to whitish, smooth, with small, papery flakes; the branchlets are not spine-tipped. **Leaves:** with 2 to 4 pairs of leaflets plus a larger terminal leaflet; leaflets elliptic to oblong, up to 9,5 × 4 cm, light green with long, rather stiff hairs, rough to the touch; apex tapering; base rounded, or tapering on the terminal leaflet; margin entire; petiolules very short, petiole up to 8 cm long. **Flowers:** small, yellow, inconspicuous, produced in long, slender, branched heads up to 15 cm long (October to December).

361

Fruit: almost spherical, quite large, 2 to 2,5 cm in diameter, becoming apricot-coloured when mature (December to February).

The wood has great vitality and truncheons strike even under most unfavourable conditions. Despite its name, which means 'edible', the fruits are apparently not eaten.

Commiphora glaucescens Engl.
S.A. no: 276   Blue-leaved commiphora. Bloublaarkanniedood
Rhod. no: —

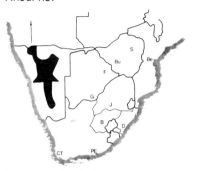

A tree up to 8 m in height, thickset and rather spreading; occurring on rocky hillsides and mountain slopes. **Bark:** smooth, with golden to reddish, peeling, papery flakes; branchlets hard and rigid but not spine-tipped. **Leaves:** crowded on dwarf lateral shoots, with a single leaflet, oval to obovate, 2,5 to 5 × 1,3 to 3 cm, bluish-green above, paler green below, without hairs or with very fine hairs; apex broadly tapering to rounded and notched; base tapering; margin entire. **Flowers:** small, creamy-white to rose pink, inconspicuous, produced in small, sparse, axillary clusters (November to February). **Fruit:** almost spherical, about 10 mm in diameter and velvety; the stone has a cup-like fleshy pseudaril (February to March or even later).

Commiphora gracilifrondosa Dinter ex J. J. A. van der Walt
S.A. no: 284   Karee-leaved commiphora, Kareekanniedood
Rhod. no: —

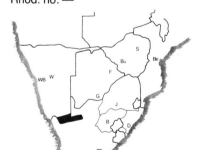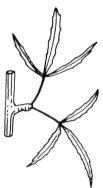

A shrub or thickly stemmed small tree up to 3 m in height; occurring in arid mountains and on rocky hills. **Bark:** reddish-brown to yellowish-brown and smooth, with no papery peel; the branchlets are not spine-tipped. **Leaves:** 3-foliolate; the leaflets very narrow, up to 6 × 0,5 cm, the terminal leaflet frequently 3-lobed; apex narrowly rounded; base tapering; margin irregularly toothed; petiole slender. **Flowers:** small, yellow to green, produced in short, axillary clusters 1 to 5 cm long (probably October). **Fruit:** somewhat flattened, almost circular, about 10 mm in diameter, ultimately and abruptly sharply tipped, green tinged with red (January to February).

It seems likely that the plants growing along the Orange River, approximately from the Augrabies Falls to Springbok and previously regarded as *C. oblanceolata*, are now correctly placed in this newly revived species. Both species have only 4 stamens per flower, while the other species of *Commiphora* have 8; true *C. oblanceolata* apparently occurs only near Swakopmund, in South West Africa, and has leaves that are comparatively broader and shorter (seldom exceeding 1,5 cm in length) than those of *C. gracilifrondosa*.

Commiphora harveyi (Engl.) Engl.
S.A. no: 277   Bronze paper commiphora. Rooistamkanniedood
Rhod. no: —

A small, squat, deciduous tree about 5 m in height in the Cape, but reaching 18 m in the north; occurring on stony hill slopes, in hot, rocky river valleys in the bushveld and also fringing forests in Swaziland. **Bark:** greenish, smooth, peeling off in large, bronze, papery flakes; branchlets without spines. **Leaves:** with sometimes 1 pair, but usually 2 to 3 pairs of opposite leaflets plus a terminal leaflet; leaflets broadly lanceolate, 5 to 7 × 1,5 to 2,5 cm, without hairs; apex and base tapering; margin scalloped to coarsely toothed. **Flowers:** small, whitish, produced in short, axillary heads on slender stalks up to 10 cm long, which have a few short hairs especially when young (October to December). **Fruit:** oval to almost spherical, about 10 mm in diameter, becoming red when mature; the stone is partially enveloped by a 4-lobed, orange or red pseudaril (January to March).
The soft, white wood is used by Africans to make spoons and small stools which are sold to tourists in Pondoland. This species has been confused with *Commiphora woodii*, but the latter is a larger tree with more (7 to 9 pairs) leaflets and larger fruits; the bark does not have a papery peel and the stone is partially enveloped by a pseudaril which has no lobes.

Commiphora karibensis Wild
S.A. no: Angular-stemmed commiphora
Rhod. no: 411   Angular-stemmed commiphora

A small to medium sized tree, usually up to 7 m in height, but it may reach 13 m in some localities; occurring in riverine thicket and on clay soils in mopane woodland; it is quite often associated with *C. mollis*, which it resembles, but it is much more restricted in its distribution than *C. mollis* and its leaves are darker green. **Bark:** silvery-grey to dark grey and smooth; the bole is characteristically fluted, or longitudinally ridged and is often twisted. Younger trees are often almost square-stemmed; the branchelets are not spinescent. **Leaves:** with 3 to 6 pairs of leaflets plus a terminal leaflet; leaflets narrowly ovate, up to 7 × 3,3 cm, dark green, with velvety, soft hairs; apex tapering; base broadly tapering to rounded; margin entire; petiolules almost absent, petiole up to 4,5 cm. **Flowers:** small, yellowish, in small heads on long, slender stalks up to 8 cm long (November to January). **Fruit:** almost spherical, about 12 × 10 mm with scented flesh, remaining on the tree for some time, becoming tinged with red when mature, finally splitting to reveal a single black seed with a bright scarlet, 4-lobed pseudaril (March to April).

363

BURSERACEAE

Commiphora kraeuseliana Heine
S.A. no: Thread-leaved commiphora
Rhod. no: —

A many-stemmed, very short but sturdy tree, seldom more than 2 m in height; occurring on rocky hillsides and stony slopes in areas fringing the desert. **Bark:** reddish to yellowish-brown, sometimes with an orange to yellowish, papery peel; the side branches are short and rigid, but not spinescent. **Leaves:** clustered on dwarf lateral shoots, with about 6 to 8 pairs of leaflets plus a terminal leaflet; leaflets exceedingly narrow and threadlike, about 1,9 cm long, resembling bunches of hair caught in the branchlets. **Flowers:** small, yellowish, in few-flowered clusters, crowded at the ends of long, slender stalks. **Fruit:** almost spherical, up to 2 cm in diameter; the stone has no pseudaril.

Commiphora marlothii Engl.   Illust. 120
S.A. no: 278   Paperbark commiphora. Papierbaskanniedood
Rhod. no: 412   Paperbark commiphora

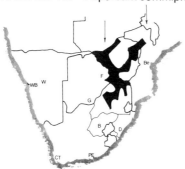 

A small to medium sized tree, often thickset with a heavy bole and branches, reaching 13 m under favourable conditions; sometimes occurring in woodland, but almost always associated with rocky koppies or stony hill slopes. **Bark:** green, peeling into large, yellow, papery sheets, which flap audibly in the wind. **Leaves:** with 3 to 4 pairs of opposite leaflets plus a terminal leaflet; leaflets oblong to obovate, 3 to 7,5 × 2 to 4 cm, fresh, pale green or yellowish green, rather soft and finely velvety especially below; apex tapering to rounded; base of the terminal leaflet tapering, those of the lateral leaflets rounded and asymmetric; margins scalloped to toothed; petiolules short and thick, petiole up to 10 cm long. **Flowers:** small, yellow, axillary, produced in dense compact heads, or paniculate cymes, about 1,8 cm broad, on long stalks up to 4 cm long, appearing with the first new leaves (October but may be as late as November). **Fruit:** ellipsoidal, green or brownish-red with a minute, sharp tip; the stone has a 4-lobed, yellow or red pseudaril (November to March).
This tree is remarkable for the paper which peels abundantly from the thick, rather succulent trunk. The paper itself is rather brittle and tears easily, but it can be written on with a soft lead-pencil.

Commiphora merkeri Engl.
S.A. no: 279   Zebra-bark commiphora. Sebrabaskanniedood
Rhod. no: 413   Zebra-bark commiphora

The striped zebra-bark commiphora, Commiphora merkeri.

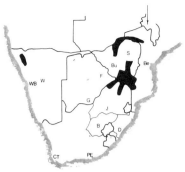 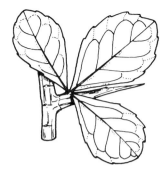

A small tree up to 6 m in height; occurring in low altitude, hot, dry areas, often associated with mopane woodland. **Bark:** grey or greenish-yellow, zebra-striped with very characteristic, horizontal, dark blackish, lenticellate bands; branchlets dark brown with a purplish sheen and spine-tipped. **Leaves:** tightly clustered in rosettes on dwarf, spine-tipped side shoots, with 1 leaflet (very occasionally 3-foliolate) obovate to narrowly obovate, up to 4,5 × 2,5 cm; when 3 leaflets are present the lateral leaflets are considerably less than half the size of the terminal leaflet; without hairs, bluish-green with a distinct, greyish bloom, fresh and attractive in appearance; apex rounded; base tapering; margin scalloped; petiolules almost absent, petiole short and slender. **Flowers:** very small, yellowish, in small, inconspicuous clusters, produced with, or just before, the new leaves (November to December). **Fruit:** ellipsoidal, about 1,3 to 0,7 cm, without hairs, becoming reddish-brown; stones with a 3- to 4-lobed yellow to red pseudaril (January to March).

The tree contains a resin which, in Kenya, is used by Africans to rub on to their skin to treat skin diseases.

Commiphora mollis (Oliver) Engl.
S.A. no: 280   Velvet commiphora. Fluweelkanniedood
Rhod. no: 414   Soft-leaved commiphora

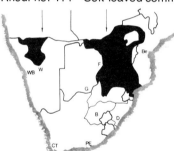 

A small to medium sized tree up to 8 m in height; occurring at medium to low altitudes in hot, dry types of woodland; it can be thicket forming. **Bark:** dark greenish to grey, becoming silvery where exposed to the sun, smooth, tending to peel in yellowish, papery strips; the trunk is often fluted. **Leaves:** with 2 to 6 pairs of leaflets plus a terminal leaflet; the lower pair or 2 pairs are often markedly smaller; leaflets elliptic, 6 × 3 cm, grey-green to pale green tending to be paler below and becoming yellow in autumn, with dense, short, soft hairs; apex tapering to rounded; base broadly tapering; margin entire. **Flowers:** small, yellowish to pinkish, in axillary clusters, appearing before, or with, the new leaves (September to January, but mainly October to November). **Fruit:** almost spherical, about 10 mm in diameter, densely furry, green to brownish becoming dull red; the base of the black stone is completely surrounded by a flat, scarlet pseudaril with 4 winged arms (February to April).

This is a widespread and variable species. It strikes easily from truncheons, but is frost-tender. It is browsed on by game and stock and elephants are said to dig up the succulent roots.

Commiphora mossambicensis (Oliver) Engl.   Illust. 121
[*C. fischeri* Engl.]
S.A. no: 281   Pepper-leaved commiphora. Peperblaarkanniedood
366   Rhod. no: 415   Pepper-leaved commiphora

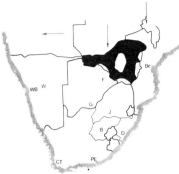 

A small, deciduous tree, 3 to 10 m in height; occurring at low altitudes in hot, dry types of woodland, often on rocky hills. **Bark:** brown, or pinkish-grey, smooth, occasionally showing a tendency to peel; the branchlets are not spinescent, and young branches and leaves are more or less velvety. **Leaves:** 3-foliolate, or occasionally with 2 pairs of leaflets plus a terminal leaflet; leaflets large, ovate or almost circular, up to 8,5 × 7 cm, a most distinctive, light, fresh green and, from a distance, shiny in appearance; apex almost rounded and abruptly attenuate into a short, narrow point; base broadly tapering to rounded; margin entire, finely hair-fringed especially when young; minute, golden glands are present. **Flowers:** small, creamy-yellow to pinkish-red, in small, axillary, branched heads, or paniculate cymes, up to 7 cm long; there are conspicuous leafy bracts among the flowers (October to December). **Fruit:** almost spherical, about 10 mm in diameter, slightly furry, becoming reddish to blackish when mature (April to May, and even as late as August).

The tree readily exudes a resin, and the wood is used by Africans to make household utensils. The leaves are aromatic with a peppery smell.

Commiphora multijuga (Hiern) K. Schum.
S.A. no: 282   Purple-stem commiphora. Persstamkanniedood
Rhod. no: —

A shrub or small tree, often about 3 to 4 m in height, but reaching 8 m on occasions; occurring in hot, dry, arid areas. **Bark:** dark brown-grey to purplish-grey, very smooth, but not peeling; the branchlets are not spinescent. **Leaves:** with 3 to 7, occasionally 10 pairs of leaflets plus a terminal leaflet; leaflets ovate to very broadly ovate, 1,3 to 2,5 × 0,9 to 1,5 cm, without hairs, thinly textured, fresh green, aromatic; apex broadly tapering and finally abruptly pointed, sometimes attenuate, forming a slender tip; base broadly tapering, rounded or square; margin entire; petiolules long and conspicuously slender, petiole slender. **Flowers:** small, creamy-yellow, in few-flowered, loose, axillary clusters (October). **Fruit:** small, oval, about 12 mm long (January to March).

Commiphora namaensis Schinz
S.A. no: 282, 1   Nama commiphora, Namakanniedood
Rhod. no: —

A low spreading shrub or small tree about 3 m in height; occurring in dry, desert regions. **Bark:** light grey to dark grey, not peeling; branchlets grey and not spinescent. **Leaves:** simple, occasionally 3-foliolate, fascicled in clusters of 2 to 4 on dwarf lateral branches which are hardly more than slight

367

swellings; small, broadly oval to almost circular, up to 1,5 × 1 to 1,3 cm, but usually smaller, blue-green, without hairs; apex rounded; base broadly tapering; margin very finely toothed; petiole slender, up to 7 mm. **Flowers:** very small, yellowish, on short lateral shoots (October). **Fruit:** attractive, ovate, up to 10 mm long and possibly more, greenish, but the outer covering dries to a thin layer which splits down both sides, opening outwards to reveal the black stone still firmly attached to the lateral branch and embedded in a bright orange pseudaril which has two arms reaching upwards for half the length of the stone (April).

Commiphora neglecta Verdoorn
S.A. no: 283   Sweet-root commiphora. Soetwortelkanniedood
Rhod. no: 415/1

A small tree, usually about 3 to 5 m in height, very occasionally reaching 8 m under ideal conditions; found in wooded grassland, sand forest and on hot, rocky hillsides, often in small groves. **Bark:** green, smooth, peeling away in straw-coloured, papery strips; the thickset trunk often branches from just above ground level; the tree is given a twiggy appearance by the spine-tipped, dwarf, lateral branches. **Leaves:** 3-foliolate; leaflets obovate, up to 6 × 3,5 cm, clear bright green or grey-green with the yellow midrib prominent, usually without hairs or with very sparse hairs, aromatic when crushed; apex rounded and shortly pointed; base tapering; margin entire near the base, finely scalloped or toothed over the upper half to two-thirds; petioles long and slender. **Flowers:** very small, yellowish, in clusters produced on short side shoots, before the leaves (September to October). **Fruit:** almost spherical, bright red when ripe, about 10 mm in diameter; the stone is black with a 4-lobed, red, claw-like pseudaril at the base (November but remains on the tree until May).
Eve Palmer records that Zulus peel the roots and eat them like sugar-cane. Material recently collected in the extreme south-east of Rhodesia shows considerable similarity to *C. neglecta,* but this has the leaflet apices conspicuously attenuate. Both this specimen and *C. neglecta* appear to closely resemble *C. pteleifolia* Engl. from areas north of the Zambezi River.

Commiphora oblanceolata Schinz
S.A. no: 284, 1   Swakopmund commiphora, Basterkareekanniedood
Rhod. no: —

This species closely resembles *C. gracilifrondosa* and the description of the latter species, with its accompanying note, should be referred to.

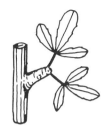

Commiphora pyracanthoides Engl.
[*C. glandulosa* Schinz]
S.A. no: 285   Common commiphora. Gewone kanniedood
Rhod. no: 416   Common commiphora

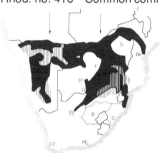

A sprawling, spiny shrub or small tree up to 8 m in height; occurring at low altitudes in dry woodland, occasionally on termite mounds. **Bark:** grey, green, yellowish or reddish, flaking in small, papery strips; the short, lateral branches are spinescent. **Leaves:** clustered on the short, spiny branchlets; compound, but with a single leaflet, narrowly obovate, up to 7,5 × 3,2 cm but usually·smaller, fresh bright green above, paler green below, without hairs; the midrib and lateral veins are yellow and conspicuous on the upper surface; apex narrowly to broadly tapering; base tapering; margin toothed; petiolule and petiole almost absent. **Flowers:** small, pink or reddish, in clusters on the dwarf branchlets, appearing before the leaves (September to October). **Fruit:** oval, about 10 mm long, without hairs; the stone has a 3- to 4-armed pseudaril (November, often remaining on the tree until February).

There are two subspecies involved in southern Africa. The typical subspecies, subsp. *pyracanthoides* (refer to the black area on the map), is usually a low, spreading, thicket-forming bush, about 1 to 3 m tall; the stone has an irregularly formed pseudaril, and the calyx is completely lacking hairs. The subsp. *glandulosa* (Schinz) Wild (refer to the lined area on the map), is more often a small tree up to 8 m in height; the pseudaril is regularly formed and the calyx is densely covered on the outside with glandular hairs. Van der Walt *(Bothalia* Vol. 11, Part 1, pp 57-60) considers these differences to be sufficient for regarding *C. glandulosa* as a separate species. However, these two entities are difficult to separate, especially without reference to flowers or fruits, and for practical purposes it is considered preferable to differentiate them at subspecific level as proposed by Wild *Flora Zambesiaca* Vol. 2, Part 1, pp 268-269).

The wood is sometimes made into household utensils and the trees are planted as live fences. The bark exudes a gum which is said to be edible, although bitter.

Commiphora saxicola Engl.
S.A. no: 286   Rock commiphora. Rotskanniedood
Rhod. no: —

A bush or small tree, barely reaching 4 m in height; occurring on stony hills and rocky mountain slopes fringing the desert. **Bark:** yellowish-green, very smooth, but not peeling; the stem is thick and swollen, and the branches have no spines. **Leaves:** with 3 to 6 pairs of leaflets plus a terminal leaflet; leaflets obovate to almost round, 0,6 to 3 × 0,4 to 2,2 cm, shiny delicate green, without hairs; apex

abruptly tapering; base rounded to square; margin finely scalloped; petioles slender. **Flowers:** very small, yellowish, in short sprays up to 2 cm long (January). **Fruit:** oblong, about 10 × 5 mm, apex pointed (May).

Commiphora schimperi (O. Berg) Engl.

[*C. betschuanica* Engl.]
S.A. no: 287 Glossy-leaved commiphora. Blinkblaarkanniedood
Rhod. no: 417 Glossy-leaved commiphora

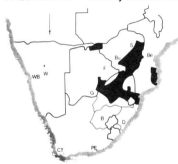

A shrub or small tree up to 8 m in height; occurring at medium to low altitudes in hot, dry bush, woodland or thicket. **Bark:** greenish, smooth, peeling in golden-brown to yellowish, papery flakes; the branchlets are spine-tipped. **Leaves:** in dense clusters, 3-foliolate; leaflets narrowly obovate, the terminal leaflet up to 2,6 × 1,4 cm, the lateral leaflets about half this size, rather shiny green, without hairs; apex and base tapering; margin coarsely scalloped or toothed; petiole up to 2,5 cm long. **Flowers:** small, yellowish, inconspicuous, in small clusters almost without stalks, appearing before the leaves (August to October). **Fruit:** oval, about 1,3 cm long, apex pointed, very pale pink when ripe; the black stone is completely enveloped by a scarlet pseudaril (December to January).

Although widely distributed, this species is nowhere common. Twigs from this tree are used by Africans to produce fire by friction.

Commiphora schlechteri Engl.

S.A. no: —
Rhod. no: — Dune commiphora

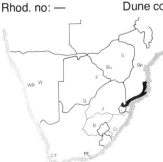

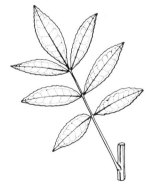

A low-growing tree up to 6 m in heigh; characteristically growing on coastal sand dunes, but occurring also in mixed woodland at higher altitudes. **Bark:** grey-green, smooth and peeling in papery flakes; the branchlets are not spine-tipped and all parts are without hairs. **Leaves:** 3-foliolate, or with 2 to 3 pairs of leaflets plus a terminal leaflet; leaflets oblong to lanceolate, the terminal leaflet about 7 × 3,2 cm, the other leaflets smaller than this; apex and base tapering; margin scalloped to toothed. **Flowers:** small, whitish, in loose heads or sprays up to 11 cm long, with the leaves (October to December). **Fruit:** narrowly oval, up to 2,3 × 1,2 cm, tapering to a conspicuous narrow point, red when mature (February to April). The stone has a 4-armed pseudaril.

Apparently this species has not yet been collected in South Africa.

Commiphora serrata Engl.

S.A. no: —
Rhod. no: —   Coastal commiphora

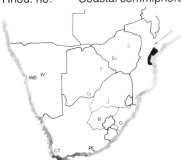

A shrub or small tree up to 8 m in height; occurring in coastal woodland and thicket. **Bark:** green and smooth; branchlets spiny. **Leaves:** with 4 to 8 pairs of leaflets plus a terminal leaflet; leaflets oblong-elliptic, up to 5,5 × 1,5 cm; both surfaces may or may not have hairs, but the midrib and lateral veins always have short hairs; apex narrowly tapering; base broadly tapering to rounded; margin scalloped to finely toothed; petiolules very short, petiole up to 5,5 cm. **Flowers:** small, greenish-yellow, about 8 mm in diameter, in branched, hairy, axillary heads, or dichasial cymes, up to 8 cm long, produced before or with the young leaves (October to November). **Fruit:** quite large, about 2 cm in diameter, almost spherical; the lower third of the stone is covered with a fleshy, cup-shaped pseudaril (November to January).

Commiphora tenuipetiolata Engl.

S.A. no: 289   Satin-bark commiphora. Witstamkanniedood
Rhod. no: 418   Satin-bark commiphora

A bush or small tree up to 5 m in height, but sometimes reaching 12 m or more; occurring in low altitude, dry types of woodland. **Bark:** pale grey or yellowish-green, smooth, peeling into silver-white, papery flakes; branchlets not spinescent; all parts mostly without hairs. **Leaves:** 3-foliolate, or with 2 to 4 pairs of leaflets plus a terminal leaflet; leaflets elliptic, the terminal leaflet up to 4 × 2,5 cm, the lateral leaflets smaller; apex tapering; base rounded; margin entire or with very few scallops; petiole long and slender, up to 4,5 cm. **Flowers:** small, greenish, in few-flowered, loose clusters appearing with the young leaves (December to January). **Fruit:** spherical, about 1,2 cm in diameter (February to April). A thin pseudaril covers about two-thirds of the stone.

371

BURSERACEAE

Commiphora ugogensis Engl.
S.A. no: —
Rhod. no: 419   River commiphora

A small, spiny, deciduous tree usually up to 8 m in height, very occasionally reaching 15 m, much-branched, the branches spreading, angular and inclined to zigzag; occurring on alluvial flats along rivers, inclined to be thicket-forming. **Bark:** green to rusty-brown and peeling in small flakes; the young branches are spine-like and are covered with fine, short hairs. **Leaves:** with 6 to 10 pairs of leaflets plus a terminal leaflet; leaflets ovate to narrowly oblong, up to 7,5 × 2,3 cm; the lateral leaflets are smaller; apex broadly tapering to rounded; base rounded, often asymmetric; margin finely toothed; petiole short. **Flowers:** small, yellowish, in dense clusters on dwarf side shoots (October to December). **Fruit:** almost spherical, 1,8 to 2 cm in diameter (January to April). The stone is partly enveloped by a 4-lobed pseudaril, the arms of which have wavy margins.

Commiphora virgata Engl.
S.A. no: 290   Twiggy commiphora. Slapkanniedood
Rhod. no: —

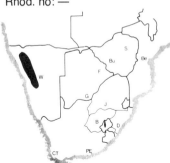
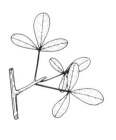

A small, many-branched tree, 2 to 3 m in height; occurring in desert regions. **Bark:** grey to reddish-brown and peeling in horizontal strips; the branchlets are not spinescent. **Leaves:** closely clustered along the slender branchlets; 3-foliolate; leaflets obovate to almost circular, small, the terminal leaflet usually 1 × 0,6 cm, but occasionally up to 2 cm long, the lateral leaflets being slightly smaller, without hairs; apex rounded; base tapering; margin entire or obscurely scalloped; petioles very short. **Flowers:** small, greenish or yellowish, inconspicuous, closely clustered along the branches, appearing before the leaves (October to November). **Fruit:** more or less ovoid, about 10 mm in diameter, red when ripe (February to April).

Commiphora wildii Merxm.
S.A. no: 290,1   Oak-leaved commiphora. Eikblaarkanniedood
Rhod. no: —

A shrub or small spreading tree, barely more than 2 m in height; occurring in stony places fringing desert. **Bark:** grey-green to brownish, which may or may not peel in small, papery flakes; the lateral branches are short and stubby but not spinescent. **Leaves:** very distinctive; with 2 to 4 pairs of leaflets plus a terminal leaflet; the blades of the leaflets run into a winged petiole and rachis, producing the appearance of a deeply divided single leaf; the whole structure is 2 to 4 cm long, covered with short,

fine, grey hairs; apices of the leaflets broadly tapering to rounded; margin entire; terminal leaflet is fairly distinct. **Flowers:** small, about 3 mm in diameter, yellowish, solitary or in pairs, on long, slender stalks up to 2 cm long, in the axils of the leaves (December to January). **Fruit:** ovoid, orange to pale red, about 10 mm long, on long slender stalks up to 4 cm long; stone with a 4-lobed pseudaril (February to May).

Commiphora woodii Engl.

[*C. caryaefolia* Oliver]
S.A. no: 291   Forest commiphora. Boskanniedood
Rhod. no: —

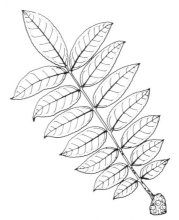

A medium to large tree up to 15 m in height; occurring in forest, bush and thornveld. **Bark:** greenish to grey, rather mottled with white, sometimes peeling in papery flakes; the branchlets are not spinescent. **Leaves:** with 7 to 9 pairs of leaflets plus a terminal leaflet; leaflets conspicuously large, oblong-lanceolate, 7 to 12 × 2,5 cm, without hairs, leathery; apex narrowly tapering; base rounded, asymmetric; margin scalloped to finely toothed. **Flowers:** small, creamy-green, in short, dense sprays, about 2 cm long, produced before the leaves or with the first flush of new, reddish leaves (October to December). **Fruit:** large, oval to almost spherical, up to 2,5 cm long, becoming red when mature; the stone has a red, cup-shaped pseudaril (February to April).
The wood is very light and has been used for fishing floats. In warm areas these trees produce leaves and flowers twice during the year and therefore are hardly ever bare. When damaged, the bark yields a gum.

Commiphora zanzibarica (Baillon) Engl.

S.A. no: 291,1   Zanzibar commiphora. Zanzibarkanniedood
Rhod. no: 420   Pendulous-fruited commiphora

A shrub or tree up to 12 m in height; occurring in low altitude river valleys and in coastal thickets. **Bark:** pale grey, smooth; may or may not peel in straw-coloured strips; the branchlets are not spinescent. **Leaves:** with 3 to 4 pairs of leaflets plus a terminal leaflet; leaflets large, oblong-lanceolate, up to 9,5 × 3 cm, without hairs, slightly aromatic when crushed; apex tapering; base tapering; margin entire. **Flowers:** small, creamy-green to yellow-green, in large, loose heads up to 25 cm long, appearing with the leaves (November to January). **Fruit:** large, up to 1,6 × 0,9 cm, pendulous, brownish-red when mature; the stone has a very fleshy, cup-shaped pseudaril (March to June).

373

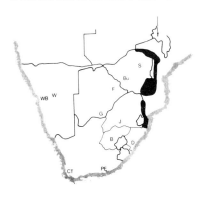

MELIACEAE (*The mahogany family*)

Key to the genera (naturalised exotic species marked*):
1 Leaves always simple 2
  Leaves compound, with 3 or more leaflets 3
2 Leaves always small, narrow, 0,8 to 4 × 0,2 to 0,6 cm, tightly fascicled on dwarf lateral shoots;
    flowers solitary, petals bell-shaped or cylindric; petals oblong-elliptic, pink, scarlet or claret
    red; stamens joined at the base only; fruit a greatly inflated, papery thin capsule, balloon-like,
    rose-red when mature .... **6. Nymania**
  Leaves vary from small and narrow to large and almost circular, up to 16 × 10 cm; flowers
    fascicled in axillary clusters of 2 or more; petals spreading, usually strap-shaped, white or
    greenish to cream, aging to yellow; stamens joined to form a distinctive tube; fruit a woody
    capsule splitting into 5 valves .... **7. Turraea**
3 Leaves always ending in an even pair of leaflets 4
  Leaves always ending in an odd terminal leaflet 8
4 Fruit an elongate, cylindric capsule 5
  Fruit an ovoid to spherical capsule 7
5 Capsule more than 12 cm long .... **3. Entandrophragma**
  Capsule less than 6 cm long 6
6 Capsule about 5 × 2 cm; south of the Zambezi River, it occurs in the Chirinda forest in Rhodesia
    and near Garuso in Moçambique .... **4. Lovoa**
  Capsule small, about 2 × 0,8 cm; a naturalised exotic in a variety of habitats, usually open
    woodland .... **1. *Toona**
7 Capsule woody, about 3 to 5 cm in diameter, splitting neatly into 4 to 5 valves; seeds winged.
    Occurring in evergreen forest often near water .... **2. Khaya**
  Capsule leathery, or with a thinly woody shell, very large, up to 20 cm in diameter, irregularly
    circular, not dehiscing evenly into valves but breaking up to release the seeds; seeds not winged
    but with a thick corky outer layer. Occurring in mangrove swamps .... **5. Xylocarpus**
8 Fruit a dry, thinly woody capsule, splitting into 2 to 5 valves 9
  Fruit fleshy, indehiscent, berry-like 10
9 Capsule splitting into 2 to 4 valves, with the surfaces rather smooth or only slightly wrinkled,
    creamy-brown .... **10. Trichilia**
  Capsule splitting into 4 to 5 valves, the surface covered with remarkable, woody, antler-like
    appendages .... **11. Pseudobersama**
10 Leaves 2- to 3-pinnate; leaflet margins toothed or scalloped .... **8. *Melia**
   Leaves 1-pinnate; leaflet margins entire .... **9. Ekebergia**

1. *TOONA M. Roemer

*Toona ciliata M. Roemer

The toon tree, or, less correctly, cedrela, is a native of tropical Asia and has been extensively planted
as a shade tree. It has now become naturalised to a limited extent in some areas in central Rhodesia
(Rhod. no: 421), in Moçambique and in some areas in the Transvaal.

2. KHAYA Adr. Juss.

Khaya nyasica Stapf ex E. G. Baker   Illust. 122
S.A. no: —
Rhod. no: 422   Red mahogany

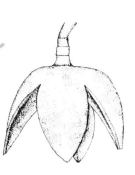

A large to very large tree, sometimes exceeding 60 m in height; occurring at medium to low altitudes, in evergreen forest and riverine fringe forest. **Bark:** grey to brown, mainly smooth but flaking in characteristic scales; the trunks of large specimens are markedly buttressed, very straight, and reaching considerable heights before branching. **Leaves:** compound, paripinnate, large, with 2 to 7 pairs of leaflets; leaflets oblong-elliptic, up to 17 × 7 cm, the upper surface dark glossy green, paler green below; apex abruptly and shortly attenuate; base broadly tapering to rounded; margin entire; petiolules and petioles slender. **Flowers:** white, up to 10 mm in diameter, sweetly scented, inconspicuous, produced in large, many-flowered, axillary, branched sprays, or panicles. Floral parts in fours to fives; sexes separate but on the same tree, the male and female flowers closely resembling each other as each has well developed, but sterile, organs of the opposite sex; sepals joined at the base; petals free; stamens joined to form a tube up to 6 mm long (September to December). **Fruit:** an ovoid, woody capsule, 3 to 5 cm in diameter, creamy-brown, splitting into 4 to 5 valves; seeds winged (March to July and even later).

The bark is bitter, resembling quinine, and Africans drink an infusion of this to relieve colds. In parts of Moçambique the stems are used to make dugout canoes. Over large areas of Moçambique, Malawi and Zambia, this is one of the most important timber woods. It is reddish in colour with a handsome grain, hard, but works easily and takes a fine polish; it is very suitable for furniture; it weathers well and resists borers and termites. This is the 'big tree' in the Chirinda forest in the east of Rhodesia. It seems that this famous tree is dying of old age for large parts of it are now dead.

3. ENTANDROPHRAGMA C. DC.

Usually large trees. **Leaves:** alternate, compound, paripinnate. **Flowers:** sexes usually separate but on the same tree. All floral parts in fives; sepals joined for half their length; petals free; stamens joined to form a cup with 10 anthers round the rim, sterile in female flowers; ovary enveloped by the disc, sterile in male flowers. **Fruit:** a large, elongate, cylindric capsule.

Key to the species of *Entandrophragma:*
Occurring only in the extreme north and north-west of South West Africa and northwards; leaflets
    ovoid to almost circular .... **E. spicatum**
Not occurring in South West Africa outside the Caprivi Strip; leaflets oblong-elliptic ....
.... **E. caudatum**

Entandrophragma caudatum (Sprague) Sprague   Illust. 123
S.A. no: 293   Wooden-banana. Bergmahonie
Rhod. no: 423   Wooden-babana

A large deciduous tree up to 30 m in height; occurring at low altitudes in river valleys and also in open woodland on rocky hill slopes. **Bark:** grey to grey-brown, flaking in large scales; the stem does not form buttresses. **Leaves:** with 6 to 7 pairs of leaflets; leaflets ovate to lanceolate, up to 11 × 3,5 cm, dark green above, much paler green below, both surfaces without hairs; apex narrowly attenuate; base

375

rounded, asymmetric; margin entire, translucent; petiolules slender, up to 2 cm long, allowing the leaflets to droop, petiole up to 4 cm long. **Flowers:** pale green, inconspicuous, produced in rather sparse, branched sprays, or panicles, up to 20 cm long in the axils of leaves (October). **Fruit:** a woody capsule, up to 15 cm long, splitting into 5 valves which curve back, giving the appearance of a stiff, peeled banana, releasing large winged seeds from the central column which remains intact (December to March and even later).

This was the royal tree of Barotseland in Zambia and from it barges were made for the Paramount Chief. The wood is dark brown or reddish-brown and attractively figured; it is esteemed as a furniture wood but supplies are limited. The bark is used for dyeing and tanning.

The seed germinates well when fresh, and the plants are fairly fast-growing although they are probably tender to frost. The tree is seldom without leaves, the new flush appearing almost as soon as the old leaves have fallen.

Entandrophragma spicatum (C. DC.) Sprague
S.A. no: 294   Ovambo wooden banana. Ovambomahonie
Rhod. no: —

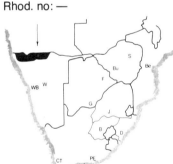

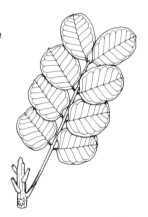

A large tree up to 16 m in height; occurring in mixed woodland, usually on deep sand. **Bark:** grey, smooth, flaking in large round sections. **Leaves:** crowded at the ends of the branches, with 3 to 7 pairs of leaflets (usually 4 to 5); leaflets ovoid to almost circular, 2,5 to 9 × 2 to 6,5 cm, closely ranked, with short, soft hairs on both surfaces, but losing most of these by maturity; paler green below than above; apex rounded, often notched; base rounded to shallowly lobed; margin entire; petiolules short and thickset; petiole slender, up to 8 cm long. **Flowers:** small, greenish, in slender, sparse spikes, up to 20 cm long, clustered round the tips of the branches, appearing before the leaves (October). **Fruit:** a cylindric woody capsule, up to 15 cm long, very similar in shape and appearance to the fruit of *E. caudatum,* but tending to be smoother and pinkish-brown (February to September).

4. LOVOA Harms

Lovoa swynnertonii E. G. Baker
S.A. no: —
Rhod. no: 424   Miniature wooden banana

A large, evergreen tree occasionally reaching heights of 50 m; occurring in evergreen forest, reaching the southern limit of its range in the Chirinda forest in Rhodesia and at Garuso in Moçambique. **Bark:** grey to brown and tending to flake in circular segments; the stem is seldom buttressed. **Leaves:** large,

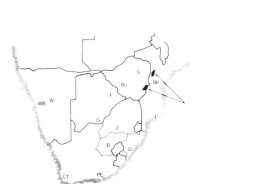
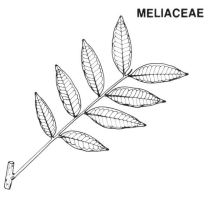

compound, paripinnate with 3 to 8 pairs of opposite to sub-opposite leaflets; leaflets oblong-elliptic to lanceolate, up to 10 × 4 cm, but usually smaller, the upper surface glossy green; apex somewhat abruptly and shortly attenuate; base conspicuously asymmetric; margin entire, wavy. **Flowers:** white, inconspicuous, but produced in profusion in rather dense, terminal heads up to 15 cm long, and visited by many species of butterflies. Sexes separate but on the same tree. All floral parts in fours; sepals joined at the base only; petals free; staminal tube cup-shaped, anthers 8 in male flowers, absent in female flowers; ovary enveloped by the receptacle disc, sterile in male flowers (January to March). **Fruit:** a cylindric, woody capsule, resembling a miniature fruit of *Entandrophragma caudatum*, 5 × 2 cm, dark brown, splitting into the 5 characteristic valves to release winged seeds (September to October but could be several months later).

The wood has been called 'brown mahogany'; the heartwood is handsome but often difficult to work. It is very durable and is resistant to attack by borers.

5. XYLOCARPUS Koenig

Xylocarpus granatum Koenig
S.A. no: —
Rhod. no: —   Mangrove mahogany

A much-branched, evergreen tree, 4 to 7 m in height; one of the constituents of mangrove swamps occurring in tidal mud, especially near the upper limits of the swamp. **Bark:** yellowish, brownish or greenish and smooth, breaking into flakes with age; the surface roots send out almost horizontal, ribbon-like pneumatophores, with the upper edges protruding above the mud and suggesting a mass of snakes. **Leaves:** compound (which is unusual for a mangrove), paripinnate, with 1 to 2 pairs of leaflets (occasionally 3); leaflets elliptic to obovate, up to 12 × 5 cm, but usually 5 to 8 cm long, thick, leathery, the veins conspicuous on both surfaces; apex rounded or square, quite frequently notched and sometimes deeply so; base narrowly tapering; margin entire, finely rolled under and often wavy; petiolules up to 5 mm long, petiole about 3 cm long. **Flowers:** cream or pale pink, about 12 mm in diameter, sweetly scented, in loose, axillary, branched sprays up to 7 cm long. Sexes separate but probably on the same tree, even in the same sprays, or the flowers may be bisexual; all floral parts in fours; calyx lobes small; petals up to 7 × 3 mm; stamens 8, joined to form a tube up to 5 mm long, present also in the female flower where they lack the anthers and so are sterile; ovary very small, the lower half embedded in the red receptacle disc, vestigial in the male flower (November to January). **Fruit:** large, irregularly spherical, about 20 cm in diameter, leathery, or with a thin, woody   **377**

shell which breaks open unevenly to release a number of tightly packed, large, angular, chocolate-brown seeds with a thick, corky, outer layer, 4 to 8 cm long (June to September).

6. NYMANIA Lindb.

Nymania capensis (Thunb.) Lindb.
S.A. no: 295   Chinese lanterns. Klapperbos
Rhod. no: —

Usually a shrub, occasionally a small tree reaching 4 m in height; occurring in hot, dry, arid areas. **Bark:** dark grey; the young branchlets brown. **Leaves:** alternate, simple, fascicled on dwarf lateral shoots, closely clustered along the slender branchlets, small, linear to linear-lanceolate, 0,8 to 4 × 0,2 to 0,6 cm, bright green, leathery; apex narrowly rounded; base tapering; margin entire; petiole very short. **Flowers:** attractive, pink to scarlet or dark claret-red, up to 3 cm long, solitary in the axils of the leaves. Bisexual; all floral parts in fours; petals overlapping, so forming a cylindric tube, or slightly bell-shaped; stamens joined at the base only (July onwards). **Fruit:** greatly inflated, papery thin capsules, like small, rose-red balloons when mature, 3 to 4 × 3 to 4 cm (October to December).
Although the flowers are attractive, they are eclipsed by the beautiful fruits which make fine splashes of colour in the dry, stony countryside. This species is very drought-resistant and, while grown easily from seed, it does not survive for long in high-rainfall areas.

7. TURRAEA L.

Shrubs, occasionally scrambling, or small trees. **Leaves:** alternate, simple. **Flowers:** bisexual, solitary, fascicled, or in axillary or terminal cymes. Floral parts in fours to fives; calyx cup-shaped, persistent; petals long and narrow; stamens joined to form a cylindric tube; ovary small. **Fruit:** a small, leathery or woody dehiscent capsule.

Key to the tree species of *Turraea:*
1 Mature leaves large, usually more than 10 cm in length 2
  Mature leaves usually less than 10 cm in length 3
2 Leaf apices rounded or very broadly tapering; flowers in dense, tight clusters along the stems; staminal tube 1 to 1,5 cm long; valves of the mature fruits 5 to 10 mm long .... **T. nilotica**
  Leaf apices more narrowly tapering than in the above species and frequently abruptly attenuate into a marked narrowed tip; flowers in large, lax clusters along the stems; staminal tube up to 4,5 cm in length; valves of mature fruits up to 2,4 cm long .... **T. floribunda**
3 Petiole very short, or absent; apex broadly tapering to rounded; blade oblanceolate, widest just below the apex, often with 2 blunt lobes at the widest point; leaves usually small and narrow, about 3 × 0,8 cm but can be larger .... **T. obtusifolia**
  Petiole always distinct, at least 5 mm long; apex tapering to attenuate; leaves not conspicuously small or slender, and widest about the middle or below the middle 4
4 Leaves usually shorter than 5,5 cm. Confined to the Matopos hills in Rhodesia.... **T. fischeri**
  Leaves usually 5,5 cm long or more. Does not occur in the Matopos 5
5 Petals very long and narrow, up to 6 × 0,15 cm; staminal tube up to 5 cm long. In the coastal belt in Moçambique only .... **T. wakefieldii**
  Petals shorter and broader, up to 2,2 × 0,3 cm; staminal tube up to 1,5 cm. Along the Zambezi River and extending up the lower reaches of its tributaries .... **T. zambesica**

Turraea fischeri Gurke
S.A. no: —
Rhod. no: 425   Matopos honeysuckle tree

A deciduous shrub or small tree up to 8 m in height; confined to the Matopos granite hills in Rhodesia.
Bark: grey to brown and rather scaly; the young branchlets are reddish-brown or grey and smooth.
Leaves: ovate to elliptic, usually less than 5,5 × 3 cm, but may reach 10 × 6 cm; lower surface without hairs; apex abruptly attenuate; base broadly tapering; margin entire, rather wavy; petiole slender. **Flowers:** greenish, petals up to 3 × 0,4 cm; staminal tube conspicuous, white, up to 2,5 cm long; solitary or in pairs on the dwarfed lateral branchlets (December to January). **Fruit:** a reddish-brown capsule up to 1,3 cm long (February to May).
The Matopos population is separated as subsp. *eylesii* (E. G. Baker) Styles & F. White, and occurs only in this area. The species as a whole has a remarkably discontinuous distribution, the typical subsp. *fischeri* being known only from rocky hills in the northern and central areas of Tanzania, with an outlying population in Uganda.

Turraea floribunda Hochst.   Illust. 124
S.A. no: 296   Wild honeysuckle tree. Wildekamperfoelieboom
Rhod. no: 426   Wild honeysuckle tree

A deciduous shrub, with a tendency to scramble, or a small tree 3 to 5 m in height, occasionally reaching 10 m or even 13 m under ideal conditions; occurring in open woodland or among rocks and also as a constituent of forest, particularly in ravines, where it reaches its greatest size. **Bark:** light brown to dark brown and roughish; young branchlets finely velvety and reddish to purplish-brown, the hairs being lost on the older branches. **Leaves:** ovate to lanceolate, up to 14 × 7 cm, densely bristly but losing these hairs by maturity; apex broadly tapering, frequently attenuate into a markedly narrowed tip; base tapering; margin entire; petiole short. **Flowers:** cream to greenish-white, sweetly scented; petals long and narrow, up to 5,5 × 0,3 cm; staminal tube conspicuous, up to 4,5 cm, pure white; in showy, large, lax, axillary clusters appearing with the leaves (October to January, but mainly November to December). **Fruit:** a thick, woody, pendulous capsule, almost spherical, up to 2,4 cm in diameter but usually about 1,5 cm, turning black when mature (February to July).
In African medicine rheumatism, dropsy and heart disease are treated with a preparation from the root and bark while the bark alone is used by witchdoctors to induce a trance prior to their divining dances. An overdose is said to be poisonous.

379

MELIACEAE

Turraea nilotica Kotschy & Peyr.   Illust. 125
[*T. randii* E. G. Baker]
S.A. no: 297   Bushveld honeysuckle tree. Bosveldkamperfoelieboom
Rhod. no: 427   Small mahogany

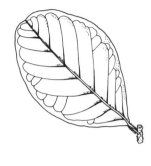

A deciduous shrub or small tree usually 2 to 4 m in height, very occasionally reaching 10 m; occurring in open wooded grassland, on rocky ridges and often on termite mounds. **Bark:** greyish, smooth to rather rough. **Leaves:** large, elliptic, up to 16 × 10 cm, the lower surface usually densely covered with short, soft hairs, the upper surface more sparsely so; apex very broadly tapering to rounded; base tapering and running into the petiole; margin entire; petiole short and obscure. **Flowers:** greenish-white turning yellow with age; petals short, up to 2,2 × 0,3 cm; staminal tube 1 to 1,5 cm long; in compact, dense clusters along the younger branches, appearing before the leaves (June to October). **Fruit:** an almost spherical, thinly woody capsule, usually 5 to 10 mm in diameter, splitting to release blackish seeds (September to February).
The roots are used in African medicine to treat headaches.

Turraea obtusifolia Hochst.
[*T. obtusifolia* var. *matopensis* E. G. Baker]
S.A. no: 297,2   Small honeysuckle tree. Kleinkamperfoelieboom
Rhod. no: 428   Lesser honeysuckle tree

Most often a deciduous shrub or a small bushy tree up to 3 m in height; occurring from low to medium altitudes, from coastal dunes to rocky koppies. **Bark:** grey-brown, smooth, lenticellate; young shoots with extremely fine hairs. **Leaves:** clustered, or fascicled, on very dwarf lateral shoots, oblanceolate to obovate, small, usually about 3 × 0,8 cm but possibly reaching 5 × 2,5 cm, glossy green; apex very broadly tapering to rounded; base narrowly tapering; margin entire, frequently with 2 lobes just below the apex giving a rather triangular shape to the end of the leaf; petiole very short or absent. **Flowers:** large, showy, pure white, almost gardenia-like; petals up to 3,5 × 0,5 cm; staminal tube conspicuous, up to 3,2 cm long; in lax, 1 to 3-flowered axillary clusters (January to February). **Fruit:** a distinctive, 5-lobed, thinly woody capsule about 2,5 cm in diameter, splitting and opening back, star-like, into its 5 valves, crimson when mature, becoming reddish-brown on the outside and straw-coloured within. The fruits develop very rapidly and mature fruits and flowers are often found on the tree together (February to June).

Turraea wakefieldii Oliver
S.A. no: —
Rhod. no: —   Moçambique honeysuckle tree

A deciduous shrub with a tendency to scramble, or a small tree up to 7 m in height; occurring in coastal secondary forest. **Bark:** grey to brown; young branches purplish-brown. **Leaves:** broadly ovate, up to 8 × 4 cm, leathery, dark shiny green above, dull green below, without hairs except for tufts of small hairs in the axils of the veins; apex shortly and abruptly tapering; base tapering; margin entire; petiole up to 1,5 cm long. **Flowers:** large, white; petals narrow and strap-like, up to 6 × 0,15 cm; staminal tube up to 5 cm long; produced singly or in small groups of up to 4 in the axils of the leaves (January to June). **Fruit:** a small, woody capsule, deeply ribbed, about 7 × 12 mm (February to July).
This species reaches the southern limit of its range along the coast of Moçambique.

Turraea zambesica Styles & F. White
S.A. no: 297,1   Zambezi honeysuckle tree. Zambezikamperfoelieboom
Rhod. no: 429   Zambezi honeysuckle tree

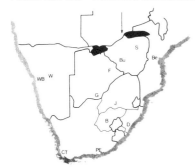 

A shrub to small, slender tree, sometimes erect and much-branched, reaching 5 m in height; occurring in riverine woodland and thicket, apparently confined to the Zambezi valley and its tributaries. **Bark:** grey-brown, smooth. **Leaves:** elliptic, up to 10 × 5 cm, but usually rather smaller, the lower surface almost without hairs, the upper surface completely so; apex and base tapering; margin entire; petiole thickset. **Flowers:** creamy-white, turning yellow with age; petals up to 2,2 × 0,3 cm; staminal tube up to 1,5 cm long; in small, axillary clusters along the stem (July to September). **Fruit:** a thinly woody capsule, up to 7 × 12 mm (August to October).
This species resembles *T. nilotica,* but the leaves are rather smaller (usually less than 10 cm long), the under surface almost completely lacking hairs, and it is confined mainly to the Zambezi valley; while *T. nilotica* has larger leaves, (usually more than 10 cm long) and the under surface is covered with dense velvety hairs.

8. *MELIA L.

*Melia azedarach L.

The Persian lilac was introduced from India as an ornamental tree. It has now become naturalised in many areas in Rhodesia (Rhod. no: 430), Moçambique and South Africa and Van Wyk states that an   **381** incessant and costly war is being waged in an attempt to keep it under control in the Kruger National Park. So far, in Rhodesia, it has not proved such a vigorous colonist. The fruits are very poisonous.

9. EKEBERGIA Sparrm.

Small to medium sized trees. **Leaves:** alternate, compound, imparipinnate. **Flowers:** in axillary, cymose panicles, or may be produced below the leaves towards the base of the current year's wood. Sexes separate on different trees. Floral parts in fours to fives; calyx lobes divided to half the length of the tube; petals free; stamens joined to form a tube with 8 to 10 teeth each bearing an anther; the anthers are sterile in female flowers; receptacle disc free from the ovary but joined to the staminal tube; ovary with 2 to 5 compartments, vestigial in male flowers. **Fruit:** fleshy, more or less spherical.

Key to the species of *Ekebergia:*
1 Petiole and rachis slightly or, more often, markedly winged; leaflets small .... **E. pterophylla**
  Petiole and rachis not winged 2
2 Second year branchlets slender, usually less than 6 mm in diameter, smooth, with scattered leaf scars and conspicuous white lenticels; apex of leaflets tapering to narrowly so, attenuate .... **E. capensis**
  Second year branchlets stout, usually more than 7 mm in diameter, rough and corky, with many crowded leaf scars, but without conspicuous lenticels; apex of leaflets rounded to square .... **E. benguelensis**

Ekebergia benguelensis Welw. ex C. DC.
[*E. arborea* E. G. Baker; *E. velutina* Dunkley]
S.A. no: —
Rhod. no: 431   Woodland dogplum

A small to medium sized, semi-evergreen tree up to 13 m in height; occurring in open woodland. **Bark:** grey to dark grey, rough, with irregular, thick flakes; the second year branchlets are stout, usually more than 7 mm in diameter, rough, with thick, corky bark and many crowded leaf scars; lenticels scattered along the branches but not conspicuous. **Leaves:** with 3 to 4 pairs of opposite to sub-opposite leaflets plus a terminal leaflet; leaflets ovate, oblong to elliptic, up to 9 × 5 cm, with or without hairs, but often densely velvety; apex rounded to almost square; base broadly tapering, asymmetric; margin entire, often rolled under; petiolules short and sometimes obscure, petiole up to 7 cm long, often reddish. **Flowers:** white or pinkish-white, about 10 mm in diameter, sweetly scented, in many-flowered heads, or cymose panicles, about 7 cm long (September to October). **Fruit:** fleshy, more or less spherical, about 1,5 cm in diameter, pink to bright red when mature (November to February).

Ekebergia capensis Sparrm.   Illust. 126
[*E. meyeri* Presl ex C. DC.]
S.A. no: 298   Cape ash. Essenhout
Rhod. no: 432   Dogplum

A medium sized to large evergreen, or semi-evergreen tree, spreading if given the opportunity, 7 to 10 m or up to 20 m in height, even reaching 30 m on occasions; occurring in a variety of habitats,

from scrub to high altitude evergreen forest and riverine forest, and from sea level to about 1 500 m. **Bark:** light grey to almost black, smooth; the trunk may be slightly buttressed or fluted at the base; second year branchlets slender, usually less than 6 mm in diameter, conspicuously dotted with white lenticels. **Leaves:** with 3 to 5 pairs of leaflets plus a terminal leaflet, lanceolate to oblong-lanceolate, up to 14 × 6 cm, but usually much smaller, glossy green, frequently without hairs; apex tapering, attenuate; base tapering, asymmetric; margin entire. **Flowers:** small, white, occasionally touched with pink, sweetly scented, not very conspicuous, produced in loose sprays about 8 cm long (September to November). **Fruit:** fleshy, berry-like, almost spherical, about 1,5 cm in diameter, turning pink to bright red when mature (December to April, or even as late as June).

The wood is light, soft and straw-coloured with an even grain; it works easily and makes attractive furniture. The bark is used as an emetic and in the treatment of dysentery, and also for tanning. A decoction of the root is said to relieve headaches and chronic coughs, while the leaves provide a remedy for intestinal worms. The fresh seed germinates readily and the tree is reasonably fast-growing, but is sensitive to severe frost. It makes a good shade tree and has been planted, for instance, along the streets of Port Elizabeth.

Ekebergia pterophylla (C. DC.) Hofmeyr
S.A. no: 299   Rock ash. Rotsessenhout
Rhod. no: —

Usually a small, stout, evergreen tree, 3 to 4 m in height, but reaching 10 m on occasions; occurring among rocks, in ravines or on krantzes, often in rocky crevices. **Bark:** light to dark grey, smooth, sometimes mottled, or rough. **Leaves:** 3-foliolate, or with 2 pairs of leaflets plus a terminal leaflet; leaflets small, oval, up to 5 × 2,5 cm, but usually smaller, the terminal leaflet being the largest, bluish-green with conspicuous, pale veining; apex broadly tapering; base narrowly tapering; margin entire; petiolules absent, petiole and rachis, especially the rachis, usually conspicuously winged (the specific name refers to this). The leaflets are jointed to the rachis where they break away on falling. **Flowers:** small, white, sweetly scented, produced in compact short heads, 1,5 to 5 cm long (August to November). **Fruit:** small, fleshy, berry-like, about 7 to 9 mm in diameter, maturing to pale yellow or red (January to February onwards).

10. TRICHILIA P. Browne

Sometimes shrubs but usually large trees. **Leaves:** alternate, compound, imparipinnate. **Flowers:** in cymes or cymose panicles. Sexes separate, but the male and female flowers are similar in appearance.   **383**

MELIACEAE

All floral parts in fives; calyx cup-shaped; petals free; stamens joined to form a staminal tube with 10 anthers round its rim, sterile in female flowers; ovary small, sterile in male flowers. **Fruit:** a leathery capsule.

Key to the tree species of *Trichilia:*.
1 Leaves usually 15 to 21 cm long; leaflets usually about 7 × 3 cm, rather thinly textured with fine, soft hairs on both surfaces; leaf apex shortly attenuate; fruits small, about 1,5 cm in diameter. Only in the extreme north-east of Rhodesia and Moçambique (and Malawi)..... **T. capitata**
  Leaves usually up to 28 cm long; leaflets usually about 12,5 × 5,5 cm; upper surface dark glossy green, under surface with or without hairs, apex tapering to rounded, rarely attenuate; fruits about 3 cm in diameter. Widespread 2
2 A medium to large tree of low altitude woodland and coastal and riverine forest; leaflets not markedly broadest near the apex; apex rounded, notched; lateral veins generally in 13 to 16 pairs, closely spaced; under surface with dense curly hairs; the fruit has a distinct cylindric neck which connects the base of the fruit to the stalk .... **T. emetica**
  A large tree of evergreen forest; leaflets markedly broadest near the apex; apex tapering; lateral veins generally in 8 to 9 pairs, widely spaced; under surface without hairs, or a few hairs only along the midrib and lateral veins; the fruit without the neck, or stipe, the stalk joining directly on to the base of the fruit .... **T. dregeana**

Trichilia capitata Klotzsch
S.A. no: —
Rhod. no: 433   Small trichilia

A shrub with a tendency to scramble or a small to medium sized tree; in Rhodesia seldom more than 3 m in height, but in Moçambique and Malawi reaching 15 m; occurring at low altitudes in deciduous thicket or woodland along stream banks. **Bark:** grey, smooth, becoming finely cracked in small squares. **Leaves:** with 4 to 6 pairs of opposite to alternate leaflets plus a terminal leaflet; leaflets ovate to elliptic, usually about 7 × 3 cm, but up to 11,5 × 5 cm, rather thinly textured, dull green, the upper surface finely velvety, the lower surface usually densely so; apex tapering and usually shortly attenuate; base broadly tapering to rounded, asymmetric; margin entire; petiolule very short, petiole up to 6 cm long and densely hairy. **Flowers:** very small, white to yellow, the petals only 3 to 4 mm long; crowded together in short heads about 4 cm in diameter, on long stalks up to 6 cm long, in the axils of the leaves (January to April). **Fruit:** a small, creamy-brown, woody capsule, about 1,5 cm in diameter, splitting into 3 valves. The seeds are very similar to those of the other 2 species of *Trichilia*, but are smaller and not as conspicuous; the dull, dark red aril covers less than one third of the black seed (April to September).

Trichilia dregeana Sonder   Illust. 127
[*T. chirindensis* Swynnerton & E. G. Baker]
S.A. no: 300   Forest Natal mahogany. Bosrooiessenhout
Rhod. no: 434   Forest Natal mahogany

A very large tree reaching heights of 30 m or more; occurring in evergreen forest. **Bark:** grey, smooth; the trunk may be slightly buttressed. **Leaves:** with 3 to 4 pairs of opposite to alternate leaflets plus a terminal leaflet; leaflets obovate to oblanceolate, up to 21 × 8,5 cm, but usually about 12,5 ×

384

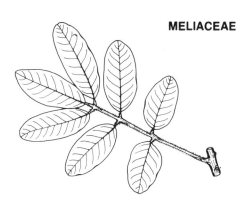

5,5 cm, almost always distinctly wider near the apex, dark glossy green above, the lower surface usually without hairs or with a few hairs along the veins, only very occasionally hairy; apex tapering; base tapering to rounded; margin entire, may be broadly rolled under; petiolules thickset up to 10 mm long, petiole up to 8 to 10 cm long, with or without hairs. **Flowers:** large, creamy-white, petals up to 2,4 cm long; produced in short, branched, axillary sprays up to 5 cm long, not conspicuous (October to November). **Fruit:** an almost spherical, creamy-brown capsule, up to 3 cm in diameter, splitting into 3 to 4 valves, with no neck, or stipe, connecting the capsule to the stalk. The black seeds are almost completely enveloped by the scarlet aril (January to May). The timber is pink, easily worked and polishes well, but should be treated to prevent borer attack. Africans carve dishes and headrests from it. Various parts of the tree are probably used in a similar way to those of *T. emetica*.

Trichilia emetica Vahl
[*T. roka* Chiov.]
S.A. no: 301   Natal mahogany. Rooiessenhout
Rhod. no: 435   Natal mahogany

A medium sized to large, handsome, evergreen tree, 8 to 20 m in height; occurring at medium to low altitudes, in woodland, in riverine fringe forest and in coastal forest. **Bark:** dark grey to brown, smoothish to rather rough. **Leaves:** with 4 to 5 pairs of opposite to sub-opposite leaflets plus a terminal leaflet; leaflets elliptic to oblong-elliptic, frequently 12 × 5,5 cm, but up to 15 × 6 cm, dark green and glossy above, the lower surface covered with dense, short, curly hairs; apex rounded, notched; base broadly tapering to rounded; margin entire, often widely rolled under; petiolules short and thickset, petiole 7 to 12 cm long, velvety. **Flowers:** creamy-green, fragrant; petals about 1,6 cm long; produced in short, compact, branched, axillary heads, about 5 cm long, not conspicuous (August to October). **Fruit:** an almost spherical creamy-brown capsule, 2,5 to 3 cm in diameter, splitting into 2 to 3 valves; with a distinct neck, or stipe, connecting the base of the capsule to the stalk. The black seeds, almost completely enveloped by the scarlet aril, are fascinating, as they have the vacant expression of a doll's eyes (December to March).

The wood is pinkish-brown to brownish-grey, but it darkens with age. It works well and takes a good polish but should be treated against borer attack. It has been found suitable for furniture, household utensils, shelving and dugout canoes. In African medicine, the bark is soaked in warm water and the liquid used as an emetic (the specific name refers to this) or, preferably, as an enema. The seeds provide a superior quality oil which is obtained by skimming the surface of water in which they have been boiled after being ground and pounded. This oil is rubbed into cuts made on a fractured limb in order to hasten healing and is also used to anoint the body generally. It may be taken internally for the

385

relief of rheumatism and can be made into good quality soap. The leaves are said to induce sleep when placed in one's bed at night, and a hot infusion may be prepared from them and applied to bruises as a soothing lotion.

All the material south of the Zambezi River is placed in the typical subspecies, subsp. *emetica;* subsp. *suberosa* De Wilde, a shrub or small tree with a corky bark, reaches no further south than Lake Victoria.

11. PSEUDOBERSAMA Verdc.

Pseudobersama mossambicensis (T. R. Sim) Verdc.
S.A. no: 302 False white ash. Valswitessenhout
Rhod. no: —

A small to medium sized tree 7 to 15 m in height; occurring in coastal forest and woodland. **Bark:** grey; young branches red-brown. **Leaves:** compound, with 4 to 7 pairs of sub-opposite to alternate leaflets plus a terminal leaflet; leaflets elliptic to oblong-elliptic, 3,5 to 8,5 × 1,1 to 3,7 cm, dark green; apex tapering to attenuate; base tapering, markedly asymmetric; margin entire, tightly rolled under; petiolules very short, petiole about 5 cm long. **Flowers:** whitish, inconspicuous, produced in 3- to 12-flowered heads, or cymes, in the axils of the leaves near the ends of the branches; functionally male or female, apparently separate on different trees, but differing only very slightly in appearance since the organs of the opposite sex are well-formed, though sterile, in each flower; all floral parts in fives; stamens joined for about half their length (December). **Fruit:** a very distinctive, thickly woody capsule up to 4 cm in diameter, scarlet when mature and covered with remarkable antler-like appendages resembling a coating of shaggy, hard, woody wool; the capsule splits into 4 to 5 valves which open out wide. The seeds are shiny brown with a red aril (April to September).

These trees are characteristic of coastal forest from Kenya southwards to Zululand. The wood is durable and light. This is a protected plant in South Africa.

MALPIGHIACEAE

ACRIDOCARPUS Guillemin & Perrottet

Acridocarpus natalitius Adr. Juss.
S.A. no: Moth-fruit
Rhod. no: —

A shrub with a marked tendency to scramble, usually becoming a strong climber reaching the forest canopy, but sometimes developing into a small tree up to 5 m in height; occurring in riverine fringe forest, along forest margins and clearings, or on rocky outcrops and wooded hillsides. **Bark:** grey; the tips of the branchlets often twining. **Leaves:** alternate, simple, oblong to linear-lanceolate, 7 to 12 × 0,5 to 4,5 cm, leathery, both surfaces usually without hairs; midrib and veining prominent below, net-veining fairly clearly defined; 2 glands occur near the base of the leaf; apex tapering to rounded, notched; base tapering to broadly so; margin entire; petiole stout, 2 to 10 mm long. **Flowers:** deep yellow and very striking, about 3 cm in diameter, produced in sturdy, pyramidal spikes, sometimes borne clear above the forest canopy, very distinctive but difficult to reach. Bisexual; all floral parts in

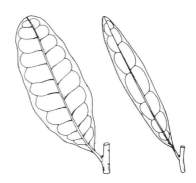

fives; petals bold and spreading, almost circular; stamens 10 in 2 whorls; flower stalks red-brown with velvety hairs (November to February). **Fruit:** twin nutlets, each with a broad membraneous wing up to 3 × 2,2 cm, the 2 wings together resembling a dark reddish-brown moth (December to March). This species has been divided into two varieties: var. *natalitius* – with leaves oblong to oblong-oblanceolate, and always more than 10 mm broad; var. *linearifolius* Launert – with leaves narrow, linear to linear-oblanceolate, up to 10 mm broad but seldom more. It appears that the distribution of these two varieties overlaps.

Eve Palmer records that the wood has a faint peppery smell when cut.

This tree or climber would make a striking garden subject and it is easily propagated from both seed and cuttings. The roots are reputed to be a love charm; they are also used by African doctors in the preparation of an ointment which is believed to safe-guard warriors in battle. Sticks placed in a roof are said to ward off lightning and, when planted round a house, will protect the occupants from witches. Both Pondos and Zulus believe that the leaves have the power to prevent a person from performing some undesirable deed, from uttering undesirable words or passing on secret information.

POLYGALACEAE *(The milkwort family)*

Key to the tree genera:

1 Petals 5, almost equal in size and shape; fruit fleshy .... **3. Carpolobia**

  Petals 3 (or 5, but with 2 very reduced); fruit a capsule or a winged nut, or samara 2

2 Usually a shrub, seldom more than 2 to 3 m in height; fruit a small dehiscent capsule, may be shortly winged but not conspicuously so. Occurring in the Cape and Natal only .... **1. Polygala**

  Usually a small tree, sometimes a shrub; fruit an indehiscent nut with a large conspicuous wing. Reaching the southern limit of its range in the central Transvaal .... **2. Securidaca**

1. POLYGALA L.

Polygala myrtifolia L.   Illust. 128
S.A. no: September bush. Septemberbossie
Rhod. no: —

POLYGALACEAE

Usually a shrub 1 to 2 m in height, but occasionally a small tree reaching 4 m; occurring in a variety of habitats, from moist evergreen forest to open grassy hillsides, in dune bush and even on sand dunes. **Bark:** grey to brown. **Leaves:** closely crowded along the branchlets, alternate, simple, usually narrowly oblong, 2 to 5 × 0,8 to 1,3 cm, fresh green; apex rounded, tipped with a short bristle; base tapering; margin entire; petiole almost absent. Plants fringing the Karoo develop very small, narrow, almost needle-like leaves, with the margins rolled under. **Flowers:** showy, pale mauve, pinkish to purple, often conspicuously veined. Bisexual; floral parts in threes to fives; the 2 lateral sepals resemble petals, being wing-like; petals united at the base, the lower petal keel-shaped, often with a distinctive crest, lateral petals lobed, the uppermost petals absent; stamens 8, joined to form a split tube (May to September, but intermittently at most times of the year). **Fruit:** a small, oval, brown, dehiscent capsule, slightly winged, ensheathed by the persistent sepals (at most times of the year). Pappe wrote that, in the past, the Cape Malays mixed the bark with water, beating it to a froth, and then bathed their dead before burial in this infusion. Seed germinates readily and this is a most attractive plant for the garden.

2. SECURIDACA L.

Securidaca longipedunculata Fresen.   Illust. 129
S.A. no: 303   Violet tree. Krinkhout
Rhod. no: 442   Violet tree

A small tree up to about 6 m in height; occurring in various types of woodland and bush from sea level to about 1 600 m. **Bark:** light grey and smooth. **Leaves:** alternate, or clustered on dwarf lateral branchlets, simple, variable in size and shape, broadly oblong to narrowly elliptic, 1 to 5 × 0,5 to 2 cm, with very fine hairs when young but losing these by maturity; apex rounded; base narrowly tapering; margin entire; petiole slender, up to 5 mm long. **Flowers:** rather small, about 10 mm long, pink to lilac or purple, sweetly scented, on long slender stalks (the specific name refers to this), produced in beautiful profusion in terminal and axillary sprays 3 to 5 cm long, appearing with the very young leaves. Bisexual; sepals 5, unequal, the lateral 2 being petalloid, large and wing-like; petals 3, free, the median petal hooked; stamens 8, joined to form a split tube (August to September, and sometimes on to November). **Fruit:** a more or less round nut, somewhat heavily veined, occasionally smooth, bearing a single, oblong, rather curved, membraneous wing up to 4 cm long (the hatchet-like appearance of this is referred to in the generic name); purplish-green when young becoming pale, straw-coloured when mature (April to August).

The roots of this tree, when crushed and powdered, are used as an intra-vaginal or intra-rectal poison; this is the accepted means of suicide for the women of the Lovale tribes in Zambia and there have been many authenticated cases recorded. Dr W. Gilges, in his occasional paper *Some African Poison Plants and Medicines of Northern Rhodesia,* found the same pattern of symptoms in all the cases he examined: rapid pulse rate, repeated vomiting and extreme weakness with death following sometimes within 30 to 36 hours. Post-mortem examinations showed multiple submucus haemorrhages in the respiratory system, the stomach, intestines, bladder and uterus, with a complete breakdown of the vaginal mucosa. In spite of the well-known dangers involved, the roots are widely used in Rhodesia and elsewhere as an abortifacient and sometimes as a contraceptive, often with very harmful effects. An infusion of the roots is used as a mouthwash in cases of toothache and is applied to cuts on the legs to treat inflammatory conditions. Powder from the burned roots is rubbed into small incisions made on the temple and forehead to relieve headaches. Root scrapings contain methyl salicylate and so have the characteristic smell of oil of wintergreen; this is regarded as a remedy for fibrositis and is supposed to drive away snakes. The leaves are used to treat snakebite and, when pounded with water and salt, are taken to relieve coughs. Soap is made from the bark which also provides a good fibre for fishing nets and for thread to sew bark cloth. This beautiful tree is not easy to cultivate. The seeds germinate with difficulty and young plants do not transplant well, but Eve Palmer reports that fairly good results have been obtained by soaking the seeds thoroughly and then sowing them in sandy soil where the plants are to remain.

3. CARPOLOBIA G. Don

Carpolobia conradsiana Engl.
S.A. no. —
Rhod. no: 442/1   Carpolobia

A shrub or small tree up to 5 m in height; occurring in dry types of open woodland, in riverine fringe thicket and on coastal dunes. **Bark:** grey, smooth; branchlets pale, whitish-grey, finely scaly, frequently abbreviated and spine-tipped. **Leaves:** alternate, simple, narrowly obovate to elliptic, 3 to 11 × 1 to 4 cm, thinly leathery, net-veining prominent on both surfaces; apex broadly tapering to rounded; base tapering; margin entire, finely rolled under; petiole short and slender, up to 3 mm long. **Flowers:** white to cream, sometimes fragrant, in very short, axillary sprays, or racemes. Bisexual, all floral parts in fives; sepals up to 7 mm long with brownish hairs; petals almost equal in size and shape (unusual in this family, where flowers are usually markedly and characteristically asymmetric), up to 1,5 cm long, the lower 3 slightly longer than the upper 2, somewhat bell-shaped (October to November). **Fruit:** fleshy (also unusual in this family), spherical, about 1,3 cm in diameter, becoming orange and finally black when mature (December to February).

DICHAPETALACEAE *(The gifblaar family)*

TAPURA Aubl.

Tapura fischeri Engl.
S.A. no: 304   Leaf-berry tree. Blaarbessieboom
Rhod. no: 443/1   Leaf-berry tree

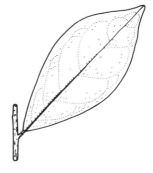

389

A small tree 4 to 6 m in height, but reaching 12 m, even occasionally 20 m; occurring in evergreen forest, on forest margins and in riverine forest. **Bark:** grey or mottled, greenish-brown and thinly scaly. **Leaves:** alternate, simple, elliptic to broadly lanceolate, 2,5 to 6,5 × 1,2 to 3 cm, light green, thinly textured, sparsely hairy to densely so; apex bluntly attenuate; base broadly tapering to almost rounded; margin entire, wavy; petiole up to 5 mm long. **Flowers:** very small, white, 2 to 3 mm in diameter, produced singly or in small clusters of up to 12, each cluster up to 10 mm in diameter, on a slender common stalk, or peduncle, up to 5 mm long. A very unusual feature is that the flower stalk, arising in the axil of a leaf, combines with the leaf petiole so that the flowers appear to rise at the top of the petiole where it joins the base of the leaf. Bisexual, asymmetric; all floral parts in fives; sepals joined; petals joined to the base of the stamens to form an unequal lobed tube; stamens 2 to 3 fertile, 2 sterile; ovary 3-chambered (November to December). **Fruit:** fleshy, ovoid, about 4 mm long, without hairs, also apparently rising at the top of the petiole (February).

All the material occurring south of the Zambezi River is assigned to var. *pubescens* Verdc. & Torre as it has only 2 fertile stamens in the flower and, in comparison with the typical variety, is more hairy. The typical variety does not extend south of the Zambezi River, almost completely lacks hairs and has 3 fertile stamens in the flower.

EUPHORBIACEAE *(The euphorbia family)*

A large and somewhat loose family, held together by the following characters: Milky latex often present. **Leaves:** usually alternate, usually simple but may be variously compound, rudimentary or absent. Stipules usually present. **Flowers:** sexes always in separate flowers; perianth occasionally absent from one or both sexes, or sepals present; petals rarely present. Male flower: stamens 1 to many, filaments free. Female flower: ovary frequently comparatively large, resembling a miniature fruit, usually clearly 2- to 4-chambered, or even lobed. **Fruit:** most often a dehiscent capsule, but may be indehiscent and fleshy although the 2 to 4 lobes are usually still clearly visible.

Key to the tree genera (Exotic species are marked*):

1 Plants succulent. Leaves present or much reduced to almost absent and falling very early, in which case the branches are thick, round, square or winged, green, frequently spiny, fleshy, with copious milky latex; or leaves may be well-developed, but falling easily, the stems usually soft and semi-succulent although sometimes woody. Apparent flowers are, in fact, heads, or cyathia, made up of male flowers, each with 1 stamen only – there may or may not be a single female flower present, consisting of a naked ovary with styles and stigmas only; this whole head of minute flowers is encircled by an involucre with a ring of glands at its rim 2

Leaves usually present. Male and female flowers not produced in the specialised heads described above; male flowers usually with more than 1 stamen 3

2 Involucre with 2 to 8 distinct glands, often 5, fleshy, frequently brightly coloured and resembling thick lip-like petals .... **36. Euphorbia**

Leaves usually present. Involucre not divided, forming one continuous saucer-shaped or cup-shaped structure .... **37. Synadenium**

3 Leaves in whorls of 4 at the nodes; confined to the arid mountains in the Clanwilliam district .... **11. Hyaenanche**

Leaves alternate or opposite 4

4 Leaves digitately compound, with 5 to 7 leaflets .... **30. Ricinodendron**

Leaves simple, although they sometimes give the illusion of being pinnately compound ... 5

5 Leaves opposite 6

Leaves usually alternate.. 8

6 Leaves elliptic .... **32. Excoecaria**

Leaves broadly ovate or heart-shaped 7

7 Both leaves in each pair approximately equal in size; leaves thickly leathery with the under surface densely matted with whitish-grey hairs; stipules large and very conspicuous, silvery outside, reddish-brown inside, up to 2,5 cm long; occurring on rocky hillsides and stony outcrops .... **15. Androstachys**

One leaf of each pair usually markedly smaller than the other; leaves thinly but firmly textured with the under surface lacking dense whitish hairs; stipules small, inconspicuous; occurring in evergreen forest .... **21. Mallotus**

8 Fruit a flattened capsule with two broad wings .... **9. Hymenocardia**

Fruit not flattened, without wings 9

9 Flowers in long sprays or heads, more than 4 cm long 10

Flowers in small, usually dense, axillary clusters, or small sprays up to 4 cm long, or solitary 26

10 Fruits fleshy, hanging in pendulant bunches .... **10. Antidesma**

Fruit a dehiscent, often woody capsule 11

11 Leaves large, ovate to almost circular, usually more than 10 cm long 12

Leaves small, (or large) but elliptic and not broadly ovate to almost circular 15

12 Leaves without conspicuous greenish, whitish or silvery hairs 13

Leaves with conspicuous whitish to silver, silky or stellate hairs 14

13 Mature leaves usually more than 4 cm broad; base usually narrowly to distinctly peltate, but may be lobed .... **26. Macaranga**

Mature leaves usually less than 4 cm broad; base tapering to rounded, not lobed .... **34. Sapium**

14 Leaves – at least when young – with long, silky, silvery or whitish, appressed hairs on the under surface .... **16. Croton**

Both surfaces of the leaves (but particularly the under surface) with very conspicuous white, stellate hairs, especially along the net-veining, giving a white, lace-like appearance .... **25. Neoboutonia**

15 Petiole shortly curved and thickened into the leaf; young leaves strikingly red; female flowers set sparsely along a large spike up to 19 cm long, the styles and stigmas large and conspicuous, branched and antler-like .... **24. Neopalissya**

Petiole not thickened into the leaf base; in female flowers, styles and stigmas not antler-like 16

16 Leaves small, usually less than 7 cm long 17

Leaves usually more than 7 cm long 20

17 Leaf margins entire, or with very fine, sparse teeth, may or may not have satiny silvery scales below .... **16. Croton**

Leaf margins markedly toothed to scalloped, or somewhat shallowly so 18

18 Upper surface of the leaves harshly hairy and rough to the touch .... **19. Micrococca**

Upper surface of the leaves may be hairy but not harsh to the touch 19

19 Leaves broadly ovate; apex narrowly attenuate; margins jaggedly and conspicuously toothed or bluntly scalloped .... **27. Acalypha**

Leaves somewhat narrowly ovate, narrowly elliptic to lanceolate; apex tapering, may be attenuate; margin rather finely or obscurely toothed .... **20. Erythrococca**

391

20 Leaves with hairs 21

    Leaves without hairs 23

21 Leaves with petioles almost absent due to the narrow, decurrent leaf bases; leaves large and velvety, up to 31 × 8,5 .... **22. Argomuellera**

    Leaves with distinct petioles 22

22 Hairs mainly confined to the very young leaves and to the midrib and petiole, mature leaves may be without hairs .... **23. Alchornea**

    Hairs always conspicuous; in some species the under surface of the leaves is satiny silver with glistening scales, frequently with conspicuous coloured scales dotting the surface .... **16. Croton**

23 Fruit a distinctive inflated capsule, large, 5 × 4,5 cm, thin-walled and light .... **32. Excoecaria**

    Fruit not thin-walled and inflated and up to 1 to 2 cm in diameter 24

24 Leaf margins conspicuously toothed .... **19. Micrococca**

    Leaf margins entire 25

25 Leaves 3-veined from the base, the lateral veins terminating in the margin ... **18. Tannodia**

    Leaves not 3-veined from the base, the lateral veins not reaching the margin, but looping to form a sub-marginal vein .... **17. Cavacoa**

26 Base of the young leaves peltate; disc and female parts absent in male flowers; sepals 3 .... **3. Heywoodia**

    Base of leaves not peltate; disc always present in male flowers and vestiges of the ovary may or may not be present 27

27 Fruits fleshy 28

    Fruit not fleshy, dehiscent or indehiscent 33

28 Fruits small, 10 mm or less in diameter 29

    Fruits larger, about 10 mm or more in diameter 30

29 Fruits black or blackish-brown when mature .... **14. Bridelia**

    Fruits white when mature .... **5. Securinega**

30 Leaf margins toothed; leaves markedly asymmetric .... **8. Drypetes**

    Leaf margins entire; leaves symmetric or nearly so 31

31 Leaves oval to obovate, large, thickly leathery, usually 10 cm long, but may reach up to 22 cm .... **12. Uapaca**

    Leaves ovate to elliptic, usually 10 cm long or less 32

32 Petioles conspicuously long and slender, up to 5 cm in length ..... **12. Uapaca**

    Petioles not longer than 10 mm .... **8. Drypetes**

33 Leaves large, 12 cm or more in length 34

    Leaves less than 12 cm in length 36

34 Leaves very broadly heart-shaped to almost circular, usually about 18 × 15 cm .... **28. *Jatropha**

392   Leaves usually elliptic to ovate or obovate, only occasionally more than 12 cm long 35

35 In the flowers the sexes are separate on different trees; under surface of leaves not covered with silvery hairs .... **6. Margaritaria**

In the flowers the sexes are separate but on the same tree, and in the same flower spike; the under surface of the leaves covered with silver, stellate hairs .... **16. Croton**

36 Leaves simple, but on the flowering branches they are produced on very slender branchlets and are so placed as to strongly resemble leaflets in a compound leaf .... **7. Phyllanthus**

Leaves simple, not so placed as to resemble compound leaves 37

37 Fruits 2 cm or more in diameter; leaves fresh green, developing magnificent autumn colours .... **4. Pseudolachnostylis**

Fruits less than 2 cm in diameter 38

38 Leaf margins toothed to obscurely toothed 39

Leaf margins entire 43

39 Male flowers in distinctive catkins, up to 3 cm long, the reddish-brown scale-like bracts overlapping and giving the appearance of a rat's tail; large trees characteristic of low altitude riverine fringes, woodland and thicket; leaves ovate to elliptic, 2,5 to 7 × 1,8 to 3,5 cm, light green ....**33. Spirostachys**

Male flowers lacking the overlapping reddish-brown bracts 40

40 Flowers in compact axillary or leaf-opposed clusters without stalks .... **31. Suregada**

Flowers either catkins or solitary but always stalked 41

41 Flowers with sexes separate on different trees; flowers individually on hair-like stalks making up cobwebby branched heads, or rather compact heads on long slender peduncles; female flowers fewer, but also stalked on long slender peduncles .... **20. Erythrococca**

Flowers with sexes separate but on the same tree; may be in the same spike 42

42 Leaves thinly textured; flowers in small, narrow, rather sparse, wispy spikes, frequently all male, or with a solitary female flower near the base or apex of the spike; fruit usually a 3-lobed capsule .... **27. Acalypha**

Leaves firm and leathery; flowers in well-formed spikes up to 3 cm long, frequently with sexes in different spikes, or with 1 or 2 female flowers at the base of the male spike; fruit a spherical or 2-lobed capsule, thickly woody to thinly fleshy, 10 to 15 mm in diameter ...... **34. Sapium**

43 Flowers in compact, almost spherical clusters, about 5 mm in diameter, the whole cluster on a stalk 2 to 5 mm long; capsules about 10 mm long reddening from the base upwards as they mature ....**35. Maprounea**

Flowers axillary, solitary, in leaf-opposed fascicles or in short, branched sprays 44

44 Leaves with lateral veins immersed and very obscure on both surfaces; capsule 3-lobed, about 10 mm in diameter, the lobes slightly keeled .... **1. Andrachne**

Leaves with lateral veining clearly visible, even conspicuous 45

45 Capsules very small, about 5 to 7 mm in diameter 46

Capsules about 10 mm in diameter or slightly more 48

46 In Natal, Lesotho, the Orange Free State, Swaziland, the Transvaal, Rhodesia and adjacent areas in Moçambique .... **29. Clutia**

In southern and eastern Cape only 47

47 Capsules warty .... **29. Clutia**

Capsules without warts .... **2. Lachnostylis**   **393**

48 Flowers axillary, solitary, in clusters, or in pairs; male flowers very small, without petals, about 2 mm in diameter; leaves with primary lateral veins in 8 to 12 pairs .... **7. Phyllanthus**

Flowers in clusters or in short sprays; male flowers about 10 mm in diameter; leaves with primary lateral veins in 4 to 7 pairs .... **13. Cleistanthus**

1. ANDRACHNE L.

Andrachne ovalis Muell. Arg.

S.A. no: 305   Bastard lightning bush. Basterbliksembos
Rhod. no: 444   Insecticide-root

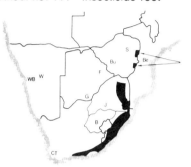

Usually a small bushy shrub about 2 m in height occasionally reaching 6 m; occurring as an undershrub in evergreen forest and at forest margins. **Bark:** light grey, smooth. **Leaves:** closely arranged along the slender branchlets, alternate, simple, ovate to ovate-elliptic, 2 to 5 × 1,2 to 3 cm, deep bright green; veining obscure; apex tapering to rounded; base tapering; margin entire; petioles short. Stipules small, triangular. **Flowers:** very small, greenish-yellow. Sexes separate. Floral parts in fives or sixes; petals membraneous. Male flowers: in small axillary clusters; disc present; stamens free, absent in the female flowers. Female flowers: solitary, axillary; ovary 3-chambered, vestigial in the male flowers (November to January). **Fruit:** a capsule up to 10 mm in diameter, 3-lobed, slightly keeled, dehiscent (January to March).

Snakes are said to be driven away by the pungent smell of the roots which also have a number of uses in African folk-medicine. Powdered, they are considered an effective insecticide, a cure for chest complaints, a snuff to treat headaches and a snakebite remedy. Mixed with milk this powder poisons flies and, infused with water to make a wash, it destroys scalp parasites.

2. LACHNOSTYLIS Turcz.

Shrubs or small trees. **Leaves:** alternate, simple, petiolate. Stipules present, falling early. **Flowers:** clustered, or fascicled, in the leaf axils. Sexes separate on different trees, male flowers more numerous than female flowers. All floral parts in fives; disc present in both sexes; stamens free or joined for half their length, absent in the female flowers; ovary spherical, 2- to 3-chambered, absent in the male flowers. **Fruit:** a capsule with 2 to 3 chambers.

Key to the tree species of *Lachnostylis:*
The fruit and the ovary in the female flowers 2-chambered; female flowers on long, slender stalks; male flowers with the stamens free to the base. Confined to inland rocky slopes and cliffs on the Swartberg and nearby hills .... **L. bilocularis**
The fruit and the ovary in the female flowers 3-chambered; female flowers on short stalks; male flower with the stamens joined for half their length. Confined to coastal bush and forest..... **L. hirta**

Lachnostylis bilocularis R. A. Dyer

S.A. no: 307,1   Rock coalwood. Klipkoolhout
Rhod. no: —

A shrub or small, much-branched tree up to 3 m, rarely larger; occurring on dry rocky mountainsides, among rocks, in crevices and on ledges. **Bark:** light brown and corky, splitting into rectangular

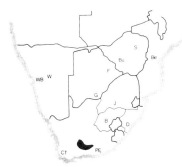

flakes; the branchlets are covered with thick hairs when young but these are lost by maturity. **Leaves:** clustered on short lateral branchlets, small, elliptic-oblong, up to 3,5 × 1,8 cm, bright green, lateral veining clearly visible; apex broadly tapering to rounded, often sharp-tipped; base tapering; margin entire; petiole up to 5 mm long. **Flowers:** greenish-yellow, on slender stalks up to 10 mm long (male flowers more numerous than the female flowers and with shorter stalks), produced in pendulous, axillary clusters near the ends of the branches; petals ovate, up to 10 mm in diameter; ovary 2-chambered (November to January). **Fruit:** a small, 2-chambered capsule, 5 to 7 mm in diameter, dehiscent (February to May).

Lachnostylis hirta (L.f.) Muell. Arg.   Illust. 130
S.A. no: 307   Coalwood. Koolhout
Rhod. no: —

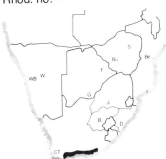

A shrub or small tree confined to coastal bush and forest. This species closely resembles *Lachnostylis bilocularis*. The wood makes a good charcoal.

3. HEYWOODIA T. R. Sim

Heywoodia lucens T. R. Sim
S.A. no: 306   Stink ebony. Stinkebbehout
Rhod. no: —

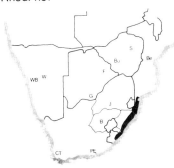
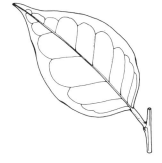

395

EUPHORBIACEAE

A large tree up to 25 m in height, often growing gregariously; occurring in evergreen forest. **Bark:** grey-brown, slightly rough in older trees, flaking away in thin, large, patchy pieces. **Leaves:** alternate, simple, ovate to lanceolate, 5 to 10 × 2,5 to 7,5 cm, leathery, glossy green, veining clearly visible; apex broadly tapering, often attenuate; base very broadly tapering to rounded, narrowly peltate when young; margin entire; petiole 1 to 2 cm long. **Flowers:** small, greenish to cream, inconspicuous, dropping very easily; produced in small dense axillary heads. Sexes separate on different trees; sepals 3; petals 5; stamens 8 to 12 in 2 whorls, absent in the female flower; ovary 4-chambered, absent in the male flower (October). **Fruit:** a capsule, about 1 cm long × 2 cm wide, splitting into 5 valves each of which splits again forming 10 segments (November onwards).

The timber is coarse-grained, heavy, hard and strong, the heartwood being dark to nearly black and foetid smelling. Juvenile specimens of both this species and *Macaranga capensis* are the only trees in the forests of south Natal which produce peltate leaves.

4. PSEUDOLACHNOSTYLIS Pax

Pseudolachnostylis maprouneifolia Pax   Illust. 131
[*P. dekindtii* Pax]
S.A. no: 308   Kudu-berry. Koedoebessie
Rhod. no: 445   Kudu-berry

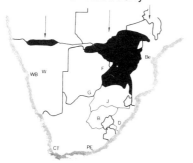

An attractive rounded tree, often 4 to 6 m in height, but reaching 12 m under favourable conditions; occurring in deciduous woodland, wooded grassland and on rocky outcrops over a wide range of altitudes, its habit varying very much according to the habitat. **Bark:** light greyish-brown, fissured and cracked. **Leaves:** alternate, simple, ovate, ovate-elliptic to almost circular, 2,5 to 8 × 2 to 6 cm, without hairs, clear fresh green to blue-green, paler green below, thinly textured; apex very broadly tapering to rounded; base tapering to rounded; margin entire; petiole up to 1,5 cm, yellowish. **Flowers:** small, greenish-white, in few-flowered axillary clusters, or cymes, 2 to 3 cm long. Sexes separate on different trees; all floral parts in fives; stamens joined for half their length, absent in female flowers; female flowers solitary, styles 3, ovary 3-chambered, vestigial in male flowers (July to November). **Fruit:** spherical, 2 cm or more in diameter, pale yellow when mature, tipped by the remains of the persistent styles, indehiscent (May onwards, the old fruits and the very young fruits often on the tree together).

This is an attractive tree at all times, but it is at its best in autumn and winter when its leaves take on spectacular, fiery colours. Antelope eat the fruits and Africans inhale smoke from burning roots to treat pneumonia; they use a bark extract to remedy diarrhoea. The trees are fire-resistant but they respond well if protected and become shapely with good crowns and straight boles. The wood is smooth, even-grained, moderately heavy and has been used in toy making, turnery and handicrafts. There is a belief among some tribes in Malawi that the tree harbours a spirit, and women going into the field to harvest crops must placate this 'msolo' by laying a small offering of a few bunches of grain at the foot of the tree.

5. SECURINEGA Commerson ex Juss.

Securinega virosa (Roxb. ex Willd.) Baillon   Illust. 132
[*Flueggea virosa* (Roxb. ex Willd.) Pax & K. Hoffm.]
S. A. no: 309   White-berry bush. Witbessiesbos
Rhod. no: 446   Snowberry tree

Usually a many-stemmed, bushy shrub 2 to 3 m in height, but it can become a small spreading tree up to 4 m; occurring in deciduous woodland, at forest margins, on rocky outcrops and frequently on termite mounds. **Bark:** reddish-brown to brown; the branches are angular and somewhat rigid. **Leaves:** alternate, simple, crowded along the branchlets, elliptic to obovate, usually 2,5 × 1,5 cm but may be as large as 6 × 3 cm, fresh green, thinly textured; apex tapering to rounded; base tapering; margin entire; petiole slender, up to 3 mm long. **Flowers:** very small, creamy-green, inconspicuous. Sexes separate on different trees, male flowers being produced in few-flowered axillary heads, or cymes, about 5 to 10 mm long, whereas female flowers are solitary in the leaf axils. All floral parts in fives; petals absent; stamens free, absent in the female flowers; ovary 3-chambered, vestigial in the male flowers (October to January). **Fruit:** small, white when mature, fleshy, spherical, about 4 mm in diameter, edible (December to January and often on to March).

The slender branchlets are used to make fish-traps and an infusion of the root is taken with a meat broth to relieve malaria. In Tanzania the roots and fruits are believed to be an effective snakebite remedy. The bark contains tannin and provides a treatment for diarrhoea and pneumonia. *S. virosa* resembles some species of *Phyllanthus* but the two genera are easily recognisable when in flower and fruit. *S. virosa* differs further in having obviously simple leaves, whereas a number of the *Phyllanthus* species dealt with here have apparently compound leaves and possess stipels.

6. MARGARITARIA L.f.

Margaritaria discoidea (Baillon) Webster

[*Phyllanthus flacourtioides* Hutch; *P. discoideus* (Baillon) Muell. Arg.]

S.A. no: 310   Common pheasant-berry. Gewone fisantebessie

Rhod. no: 447   Margaritaria

The appearance of this tree varies according to its habitat; at medium to low altitudes in wooded grassland it is a shrub or small tree reaching 8 m in height which can be thicket forming; in evergreen forest it reaches 20 m in height, and in the forests of Moçambique heights of 35 and even 50 m have been recorded. **Bark:** pale grey, smooth, becoming brown and roughish in large specimens with the stem well buttressed. **Leaves:** ovate or obovate to elliptic, 2 to 8 × 1,3 to 4 cm, but may be as large as 10 to 13 cm in length in the forest specimens, bright green, thinly textured, the veining prominent below, apex broadly tapering to rounded; base broadly tapering; margin entire, rolled under; petiole usually short. **Flowers:** inconspicuous greenish-yellow, sexes separate on different trees. Male flowers: numerous, fascicled in the leaf axils. Female flowers: in pairs in the leaf axils; the swollen

397

ovary can easily be mistaken for a small fruit but the styles and stigmas are clearly visible on the top (September to November). **Fruit:** a 3-lobed capsule, yellowish, about 10 mm in diameter, dehiscent (December to February).

The bark contains tannin, and a decoction of this is taken to relieve pains after childbirth. Ashes from the burnt bark, mixed with salt and palm oil, apparently produce a burning sensation and are applied locally to relieve lumbar pains. A similar preparation, but using ashes from the burnt stem, is rubbed over the body as a stimulant and tonic. The timber is very dense and red in colour.

7. PHYLLANTHUS L.

A large genus of plants, the members of which are usually bushes with many thin stems, forming somewhat tangled masses of growth. They may occasionally develop into small trees and some members are large. **Leaves:** alternate, simple, the flowering branchlets may simulate compound, pinnate leaves. Stipules small, but often conspicuous along the branchlets. **Flowers:** very small, in axillary clusters, or fascicles. Sexes separate, usually on the same tree; sepals 4 to 6, free; petals always absent; stamens 2 to 6, free or joined, or some free and some joined, absent in female flowers; ovary 3-chambered with 3 styles and stigmas, absent in male flowers; receptacle disc glandular, saucer-shaped. **Fruit:** a capsule.

Key to the tree species of *Phyllanthus:*

1 Branches with remarkable spur-shoots, squat, thickset and heavily spinose, having the appearance of galls or growths, up to 2 × 2 cm .... **P. engleri**
  Branches without thickset, spinose spur-shoots 2
2 Leaves small, usually 2 cm long or less 3
  Leaves usually larger than 2 cm long 5
3 Male flowers in very dense, compact clusters on woody cushions representing lateral branches; female flowers and fruits solitary on very long thread-like stalks up to 3 cm long; capsules up to 9 mm in diameter .... **P. kirkianus**
  Male and female flowers produced along very slender branchlets giving the appearance of spikes 4
4 Widespread at low altitudes, always in riverine fringe forest or thicket; in the evenings especially, the flowers produce a very characteristic smell of potatoes .... **P. reticulatus**
  Restricted distribution; usually in or fringing evergreen forest at medium to high altitudes; the flowers do not produce the 'potato smell' but nevertheless have a strong and unpleasant, somewhat foetid odour .... **P. guineensis**
5 Confined to the forests of Transkei and in the Ngoye forest in Zululand; fruit a spherical, rather flattened capsule about 2 cm in diameter .... **P. cedrelifolius**
  Reaching no further south than a small area in the east of Rhodesia and adjacent areas in Moçambique; fruits inflated, thin-walled, bladder-like capsules, up to 1,4 cm in diameter .... **P. inflatus**

Phyllanthus cedrelifolius Verdoorn
S.A. no: 312   Feather-leaved pheasant-berry. Veerblaarfisantebessie
Rhod. no: —

A small deciduous tree, 3 to 5 m in height, but occasionally reaching 9 m; occurring in evergreen forest. **Bark:** rough and warty. **Leaves:** arranged along the slender branchlets to appear as leaflets of large compound leaves (resembling those of cedrela, *Toona ciliata;* the specific name refers to this); elliptic, 1,5 to 5 × 0,7 to 2,5 cm, without hairs, thinly textured, fresh green; apex and base broadly tapering to rounded; margin entire, wavy; petiole short. **Flowers:** very small, yellowish-green, produced in clusters, or fascicles, made up of one female flower and several male flowers; arising from dwarfed lateral shoots along short, very slender leaf branchlets and appearing before the leaves, they give the appearance of spike-like racemes about 5 cm long. The female flowers have slightly longer stalks than do the male flowers (August to September). **Fruit:** an almost spherical, sometimes rather flattened, capsule, about 2 cm in diameter, dehiscent (shortly after the flowering).

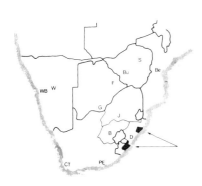

Phyllanthus engleri Pax

S.A. no: —
Rhod. no: 448   Spurred phyllanthus

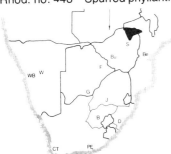

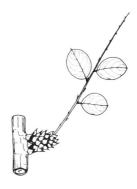

A small tree up to 6 m in height, often branching almost from ground level; occurring at low altitudes in hot, dry woodland. **Bark:** dark grey, rough and deeply fissured. The branchlets are long, stout and unbranched except for remarkable spur-shoots which grow up to 2 × 2 cm and are squat, thickset and heavily spinose – at first sight resembling galls or growths; these spur-shoots are very slow-growing and annually bear leaves and flowers. **Leaves:** closely arranged along the very slender branchlets giving the impression of compound leaves; small, almost circular, occasionally semi-elliptic, up to 2 cm in diameter; apex and base broadly tapering to rounded; margin entire; petiole short. **Flowers:** very small, greenish, bedded in reddish-brown bracts which have split into tufts of hair-like segments giving a reddish appearance, a feature which has led several collectors to describe the flowers as red. Sexes separate on different trees; produced in small groups of 4 to 6 along a very slender short leaf shoot, axillary but appearing before the leaves, giving the impression of a spray or a rather loose catkin, 4 to 7 cm long (October to November). **Fruit:** large, yellow, smooth, spherical, 3 to 4 cm in diameter, roughly 3-lobed and clustered along the stems, dehiscent (June to July, but may be as early as March or as late as September).

Tests have shown that the root bark is highly toxic, but some Africans, who chew the leaf to relieve indigestion and constipation, maintain that all parts of the tree above ground are non-poisonous. No toxicity has been found in the smoke of the burnt bark, although in Zambia it is said that people deliberately inhale it in order to commit suicide.

Phyllanthus guineensis Pax

S.A. no: —
Rhod. no: 449   Small-fruited phyllanthus

Usually a many-branched shrub, 3 to 4 m in height, with a tendency to scramble, but it can become a small tree reaching 6 m; occurring in high altitude, evergreen forest and on forest margins. **Bark:** grey to brown; branches angular with spinescent stipules which are very short, hooked down and scattered along the larger branchlets. **Leaves:** arranged so that the branchlets strongly resemble compound leaves; oblong, up to 1,8 × 0,8 cm, light green; apex rounded; base very broadly tapering to rounded, often asymmetric; margin entire; petiole slender and short. **Flowers:** very small, yellowish-green,

399

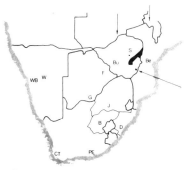

axillary, produced before the leaves along hair-like branchlets up to 6 cm long, thus strongly resembling racemes of small flowers; the under surface of the sepals is reddish, the upper surface creamy-green (August to January, but mainly October to November). **Fruit:** small, ellipsoidal, 3 to 4 mm long, becoming red to purplish-black with a grey bloom when mature (from October onwards).

Phyllanthus inflatus Hutch.
S.A. no: —
Rhod. no: 451 Balloon-fruited phyllanthus

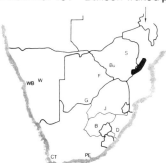

A slender, rather spindly tree 6 to 10 m in height; scattered through evergreen forest, but not common. **Bark:** grey, smooth; the thin, leafy stems are crowded into rosettes at the ends of the branches. **Leaves:** so arranged that the branchlets strongly resemble compound leaves; lanceolate to narrowly ovate, up to 7 × 2 cm; apex broadly tapering to rounded; base rounded; margin entire; petiolate. **Flowers:** very small, yellowish-green in very small axillary clusters; produced on the leaf branchlets before the leaves and strongly resembling spike-like racemes (August). **Fruit:** a yellowish, thin walled, rather inflated, somewhat bladder-like capsule, almost spherical, 1,7 × 1,4 cm, 3-lobed, dehiscent (October to December).

Phyllanthus kirkianus Muell. Arg.
S.A. no: Woody-cushion pheasant-berry
Rhod. no: 452 Woody-cushion phyllanthus

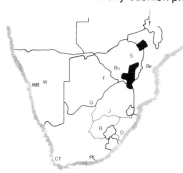

A shrub or small spindly tree 2 to 5 m in height; occurring at low altitudes in hot, dry woodland, sometimes among rocks and along stream and river banks. **Bark:** mottled grey, flaking. **Leaves:** small, oval to almost circular, 1 to 4 × 0,7 to 3 cm, but usually 1 to 2 cm long, thinly textured, delicate green, veining clearly visible; base and apex rounded, occasionally very broadly tapering; margin entire; petiole short and very slender. **Flowers:** sexes separate on different trees. Male flowers: very small, greenish-yellow to yellow, densely clustered, or fascicled, in the leaf axils or on very dwarfed lateral branchlets, no more than woody cushions on the stem. Female flowers: greenish, solitary, on extremely slender, thread-like stalks up to 3 cm long (September to November). **Fruit:** a yellowish capsule about 10 mm in diameter, on a slender stalk, apparently developing rapidly (September to April).

Phyllanthus reticulatus Poiret
S.A. no: 311   Potato bush. Aartappelbos
Rhod. no: 455   Potato-smell

A many-branched shrub, sometimes partially scrambling, or a small, twiggy tree up to 8 m in height; occurring in low altitude riverine vegetation and thicket. **Bark:** grey-brown; the branches arch almost to the ground if they have no support. **Leaves:** oval to elliptic, up to 2,5 × 1,5 cm, so arranged as to give the impression of compound leaves, thinly textured, with rather conspicuous reddish net-veining on the under surface (the specific name refers to this); apex and base broadly tapering to rounded; margin entire; petiole short. **Flowers:** very small, yellow, axillary, clustered on short, very slender branchlets, about 3 cm long appearing before or with the leaves (September to October, but the flowering season can extend from July onwards). **Fruit:** berry-like, black when mature, 4 to 6 mm in diameter, dehiscent (from September onwards).

Flowers and leaves of the potato bush, Phyllanthus reticulatus.

EUPHORBIACEAE

The flowers of this plant are responsible for the strange odour of potatoes which is so often encountered along river banks in the lowveld, particularly on spring and summer evenings. This is one of the fascinating characteristic smells of Africa. The leaves and fruits provide a local treatment for sores and burns; the fruit produces a black dye which has been used for dyeing fishing nets. Although the fruits and roots are said to be toxic, the bushes are browsed on by game and stock.

8. DRYPETES Vahl

Shrubs or trees. **Leaves:** alternate, simple, often large, markedly asymmetric; petiolate. Stipules fall early. **Flowers:** fascicled in the axils of the leaves, sometimes on the old wood. Sexes separate on different trees. Sepals 4 to 5, somewhat leathery, deeply concave; petals absent; stamens 3 to many, free, absent in female flowers; ovary 1- to 4-chambered, absent in male flowers. **Fruit:** fleshy, spherical to ellipsoidal, indehiscent.

Key to the tree species of *Drypetes:*

1 Leaf margins entire, or shallowly and obscurely toothed 2
  Leaf margins markedly toothed 3
2 Leaf apex always narrowed, very frequently attenuate, often forming a long slender tip; fruit almost spherical .... **D. gerrardii**
  Leaf apex usually rounded to broadly tapering, very seldom attenuate and then shortly and rather obscurely so; fruits narrowly ovoid .... **D. mossambicensis**
3 Leaves large, usually longer than 12 cm; margin jaggedly toothed, the teeth almost spine-tipped; the flowers and fruits are produced on the old branches and main stem .... **D. natalensis**
  Leaves usually less than 12 cm long; margin conspicuously and more or less regularly toothed, but not jaggedly so, the teeth not spine-tipped; flowers and fruits axillary .... **D. arguta**

Drypetes arguta (Muell. Arg.) Hutch.
S.A. no: 313   Water drypetes. Waterysterpruim
Rhod. no: 458   Water drypetes

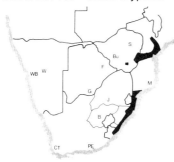 

A straggling shrub or small tree up to 6 m in height; occurring in evergreen forest, often along streams. **Bark:** grey, smoothish. **Leaves:** lanceolate, broadly lanceolate to elliptic, up to 11 × 4 cm, bright green above, dull green below; apex tapering to attenuate; base rounded to shallowly lobed; margin markedly toothed; petiole short. **Flowers:** inconspicuous, greenish to cream, with a strong smell of honey; produced in small, axillary clusters (November to December). **Fruit:** fleshy, almost spherical, about 1,5 × 2 cm, bright orange-red when mature (March to May).
An intoxicating drink is made from the fruits.

Drypetes gerrardii Hutch.
S.A. no: 314   Hairy drypetes. Bosysterpruim
Rhod. no: 459   Hairy drypetes

A shrub or small evergreen tree up to 6 m in height but, when growing in forest, it can reach 15 and even 35 m; occurring in more open woodland at low altitudes, as a shrub or small tree, also as an under-storey tree in evergreen forest or in riverine fringe forest. **Bark:** grey or brownish, rather smooth; stem may be fluted or buttressed in larger specimens; the branchlets are finely hairy. **Leaves:** always arranged in a horizontal plane so giving the tree a feathery appearance; ovate to elliptic, 4 to 9

402

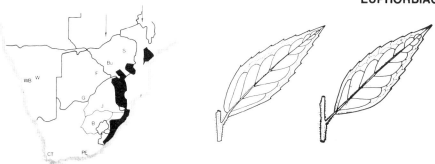

× 2 to 5 cm, dark shiny green above, paler green below, with sparse, brown, woolly hairs near the base of the midrib and nóticeable net-veining on the under surface; apex tapering to attenuate often forming a long slender tip; base tapering; margin broadly and shallowly toothed, or entire; petiole short. **Flowers:** small, yellow; the male flowers in inconspicuous axillary clusters, or fascicles; the female flowers have conspicuous styles and are solitary in the leaf axils (September to November). **Fruit:** almost spherical, about 10 mm in diameter, with short, soft hairs, yellow to orange-red when mature (September to October, and even on to April). The timber is white and heavy.

Drypetes mossambicensis Hutch.

S.A. no: 315   Sand drypetes. Sandysterpruim
Rhod. no: 460   Lowveld drypetes

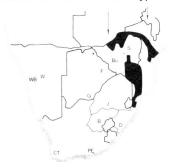

A medium to large, densely foliaged tree varying in height from 3 to 20 m, depending upon the habitat; occurring in low altitude woodland, on rocky outcrops and on termite mounds. **Bark:** pale grey to brownish and smooth when young but, in large specimens, becoming rough and flaking in small squares, sometimes corky and pallid grey, giving the appearance of great age. **Leaves:** ovate, elliptic or oblanceolate, up to 9 × 4,5 cm, but usually much smaller, bright green and shiny, the net-veining clear on both surfaces; apex broadly tapering to rounded and notched; base very asymmetric; margin entire, wavy; petiole short. **Flowers:** very small, yellow, in axillary clusters along the branchlets (September to December but flowering can take place at almost any time of the year). **Fruit:** fleshy, narrowly oval, up to 2 × 1,3 cm, becoming yellow when mature, tipped with the remains of the old styles and bedded into a small, basal cup (May to June, but variable).
The fruits are relished by Africans who begrudge every one taken by birds, fruit-bats and monkeys. Elephants browse heavily on the leaves but seldom break down the trees.

Drypetes natalensis (Harvey) Hutch.

S.A. no: 316   Natal drypetes. Natalysterpruim
Rhod. no: 461   Stem-fruit drypetes

A small to medium sized evergreen tree usually up to 9 m in height, but reaching 15 m under favourable conditions; occurring in evergreen and dune forests. **Bark:** dull grey-green; the branches are angular. **Leaves:** very conspicuous, large, oblong or narrowly elliptic, up to 17 × 6 cm, but usually smaller, rigidly leathery, dark shiny green above, less shiny and paler green below; apex tapering to almost rounded; base tapering to rounded, asymmetric; margin deeply toothed, the teeth   **403**

being almost spine-tipped, resembling the margin of holly leaves; petiole short. **Flowers:** yellow, produced on the main trunk and older branches from just above ground level up to 7 m. The male flowers with their unpleasant smell have been described by a collector as 'stinking of rancid butter or stale ale' (September to October). **Fruit:** fleshy, spherical, about 2,3 × 2 cm, velvety, yellow-orange when mature (December to March).

9. HYMENOCARDIA Wall.

Shrubs or trees. **Leaves:** alternate, simple. **Flowers:** sexes separate on different trees, the male flowers in axillary, catkin-like spikes, the female flowers solitary, or in axillary clusters, or fascicles. Sepals 4 to 5; petals absent; stamens 3 to many, free or joined at the base, the anthers with a conspicuous golden gland on the back, absent in the female flowers; ovary 2-chambered, vestigial in the male flowers. **Fruit:** a winged capsule.

Key to the tree species of *Hymenocardia:*
Leaves usually about 4,5 cm long; the male flowers in spikes up to 6 cm long; fruits with 2 large wings
    on either side of the apex with a deep apical notch, forming the shape of a heart ... **H. acida**
Leaves usually less than 4,5 cm long, usually 2,5 to 3 cm in length; male flowers in spikes barely
    1 cm long; fruit with a papery wing all round except for a narrow apical notch .... **H. ulmoides**

Hymenocardia acida Tul.
S.A. no: —
Rhod. no: 462   Heart-fruit

A shrub or small tree up to 6 m in height; occurring in *Brachystegia* woodland and scrub. **Bark:** light grey, smooth or flaking to reveal patches of bright brown under-bark, or it may be corky; young branches orange to rust-coloured. **Leaves:** elliptic-oblong, 2,5 to 9 × 2 to 4 cm, with brownish velvety hairs when young which are mostly lost by maturity, densely golden gland-dotted on the under surface; apex broadly tapering to rounded and notched; base tapering; margin entire, rolled under; petiolate. **Flowers:** male flowers reddish with cream stamens and anthers, forming catkin-like spikes up to 6 cm long. Female flowers green, each one resembling a miniature fruit but with 2 long, red, velvety styles forked like a snake's tongue; axillary, solitary or in clusters (October to December). **Fruit:** a flattened capsule with 2 wings widely expanded at each side of the apex giving the shape of a deeply indented heart, becoming red and conspicuous when mature (April to July).

404

In African medicine the root ashes are applied to mouth infections and the inner bark is used to treat ulcers. Headaches are relieved by inhaling vapour from boiling leaves which, when they are fresh, have an entirely different use for they are placed in the roof of a house to protect it from lightning.

Hymenocardia ulmoides Oliver
[*H. capensis* Hutch.]
S.A. no: 317   Red heart-fruit. Rooihart
Rhod. no: 463   Lesser heart-fruit

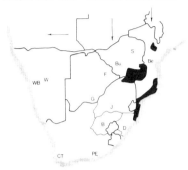 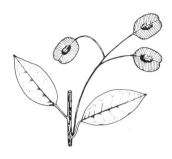

A shrub or small tree up to 5 m in height; occurring at low altitudes in mixed woodland, in riverine forest or thicket, often among rocks. **Bark:** grey and striated. **Leaves:** ovate, elliptic to lanceolate, 2,5 to 3 × 1,8 cm, only sparingly gland-dotted on the under surface; young leaves red, mature leaves dark shiny green; midrib reddish and hairy; apex tapering, often attenuate; base tapering; margin entire, rolled under; petiolate. **Flowers:** male flowers very small, pinkish with cream stamens, produced in catkin-like spikes barely more than 10 mm in length; female flowers green, solitary, resembling a miniature fruit, 6 to 7 mm long, with a pair of long, red, thread-like styles (November to December). **Fruit:** with a rose-coloured wing extending all round the fruit except for a narrow apical notch; frequently the long hair-like styles persist from the base of the notch (from January onwards, especially March to April).

The fruits somewhat resemble those of some species of *Terminalia,* but the latter lack the apical notch, the wing surrounding the seed completely. The wood is strong, straight and elastic and has been used as fencing posts, roofing poles and for fish traps.

10. ANTIDESMA L.

Shrubs or trees. **Leaves:** alternate, simple, large. **Flowers:** sexes separate on different trees. Calyx 3- to 5-lobed; petals absent; stamens 2 to 5, absent in female flowers; ovary 1-chambered (occasionally 2-chambered) vestigial in male flowers. **Fruit:** fleshy.

Key to the tree species of *Antidesma:*
1 Under surface of the leaves without hairs, except for a few which may occur sparsely along the
    midrib; leaves rather thinly textured. Reaching its southern limit in a small area of high altitude
    forest in the east of Rhodesia and adjacent areas in Moçambique .... **A. vogelianum**
    Under surface of the leaves with more or less dense velvety hairs 2
2 Leaves bright, glossy green above, paler green below; fruits about 8 × 4 mm, white when young,
    becoming bright red and finally black in catkins about 8 to 12 m long. Widespread...........
    .... **A. venosum**
    Leaves dark green above, yellowish below; fruits small, about 3 mm in diameter, pink, in
    pendulous catkins up to 10 cm long. Recorded only from extreme east of Rhodesia and
    northwards .... **A. membranaceum**

Antidesma membranaceum Muell. Arg.
S.A. no: —
Rhod. no: 464   Pink tassel berry

A shrub or small tree about 5 m in height, occasionally larger, sometimes reaching 13 m; occurring at low altitudes in riverine fringe forest and thicket. **Bark:** brown and rough; young branchlets are

405

covered with brown, velvety hairs. **Leaves:** oval to elliptic, up to 13 × 5,5 cm, but usually about half this size, dark green and velvety above, yellowish below; apex tapering and attenuate to more or less rounded; base tapering to rounded; margin entire; petiole short. **Flowers:** yellowish-green, in slender catkins up to 10 cm long; the female flowers, lacking stamens, are not so fluffy. The flower catkins are often parasitized and deformed, thus forming dense tangled sterile heads (October to January, usually November to December). **Fruit:** berry-like, about 3 mm in diameter, pinkish in colour, clustered in long pendulous catkins about 10 cm long (February to March).

Antidesma venosum E. Meyer ex Tul.   Illust. 133
S.A. no: 318   Tassel berry. Tosselbessie
Rhod. no: 465   Tassel berry

A shrub or small tree 4 to 5 m in height, occasionally reaching 7 m; occurring at medium to low altitudes, in woodland and wooded grassland, at forest margins and in coastal bush. **Bark:** grey or grey-brown, smooth to rough and flaky. **Leaves:** oval to elliptic, 2,5 to 15 × 2 to 10 cm, leathery, bright glossy green above, paler green and hairy below; apex tapering to rounded; base rounded; margin entire; very shortly petiolate. **Flowers:** the male flowers dull yellowish, the female flowers reddish and not so fluffy, in catkin-like spikes up to 8 cm in length, unpleasantly scented; the young flowering spikes are often parasitized by insects and therefore form distorted, tangled, sterile growths (October to January, but may be found earlier or later). **Fruit:** small, fleshy, about 8 × 4 mm, white when young, becoming bright red and finally purplish-black when mature, in long, pendulous spikes 8 to 12 cm long (March to May, but may be found several months earlier or later).
The flowers are said to have an offensive smell which has been likened to that of rotting water-melons. In African medicine an infusion of the roots is used to bathe the body to ease pains, and is also a constituent of a mixture believed to ensure fertility. This would make a very good tree in the garden as it is attractive at all times of the year and beautiful when in fruit; it should be borne in mind that both a male and a female tree would be necessary to continue propagation.

Antidesma vogelianum Muell. Arg.
S.A. no: —
Rhod. no: 466   Forest tassel berry

A small tree usually 3 to 5 m in height, but very occasionally reaching 7 m, often with long, slender, arching branches, almost liane-like; a constituent of high altitude, evergreen forest. **Bark:** pale grey and smooth in younger specimens becoming brown, vertically fissured and flaking. **Leaves:** oblong-

406

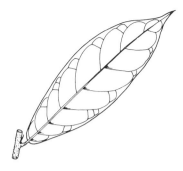

elliptic, usually about 7 × 3 cm, but reaching 10 × 4,5 cm at times, shiny green on both surfaces, thinly textured; apex attenuate; base tapering; margin entire; petiole up to 10 mm long. **Flowers:** small, creamy-green, in pendulous spikes 2,5 to 10 cm long, the stamens being tipped with brown anthers; the female flowers, lacking the stamens, are not so fluffy (October to November, but August and December have also been recorded). **Fruit:** berry-like, broadly conical, about 5 to 6 mm long, very shiny red becoming blackish when mature, produced in pendulous spikes, 3 to 10 cm long (December to January or later).

11. HYAENANCHE Lambert

Hyaenanche globosa (Gaertn.) Lambert
S.A. no: 319   Hyaena poison. Wolwegifboom
Rhod. no: —

The hyaena poison, Hyaenanche globosa, *growing near Vanrhynsdorp on the Gifberg, or 'poison mountain', named after these trees.*

A dense, dark green shrub or small tree 3 to 5 m in height; occurring on arid mountains. **Bark:** pale grey to brown. **Leaves:** simple, in whorls of 4, lanceolate, 6,5 to 10,5 × 1,5 to 3,5 cm, dark green, slightly hairy when young but losing these hairs by maturity, stiffly leathery, midrib conspicuous and yellowish; apex tapering to rounded and notched; base tapering; margin entire; petiole reddish, short and thickset. **Flowers:** small, deep red, in axillary clusters. Sexes separate on different trees, the male flowers in dense clusters, the female flowers solitary or in groups of 2 to 3. Sepals 5 to 6 in 2 whorls; petals absent; stamens many, absent in the female flowers; ovary ovoid, vestigial in the male flowers (July to September). **Fruit:** a 3- to 4-lobed capsule, about 2,5 cm in diameter, brownish-yellow when mature, containing 6 black, shiny seeds (October to December).

The seeds, and possibly the leaves, contain a toxic principal which acts on the heart like strychnine, and it is from the fruits that Bushmen are said to make their deadly arrow poison. In 1886 a collector referred to *H. globosa* as 'this fatal bush . . . ' and, indeed, it was the custom of poisoning hyaenas and other predators with the pounded seeds that gave rise to the plant's generic name. The flat-topped *Gifberg*, or 'poison mountain', near Vanrhynsdorp was so-called because of the trees of this species growing in the area.

12. UAPACA Baillon

Trees. **Leaves:** alternate, simple, usually crowded near the ends of the branchlets, leathery. **Flowers:** axillary on the current year's branchlets, or in the axils of fallen leaves on older wood. Sexes separate on different trees; petals absent in the flowers of both sexes. The apparent 'male flower' is a dense head, up to about 10 mm in diameter, of tightly clustered individual flowers, each with 4 to 6 stamens and a small 5- to 6-lobed calyx; the whole structure forms a central mass of stamens with 5 to 8 large, green, ovate to almost circular, spoon-shaped, calyx-like, involucral bracts. The female flower is a single, large ovary, up to 10 mm in diameter, with thick, branched styles lying flat on the surface, and the calyx-like involucral bracts round the base; it has very small calyx lobes. **Fruit:** fleshy, spherical to ovoid, indehiscent.

Key to the species of *Uapaca:*

1 Leaves with hairs, more or less dense, long or woolly, on the under surface or on the midrib and
    lateral veins 2
  Leaves without hairs on the under surface, which may be scaly 3
2 Leaves large, averaging 17 × 11 cm; base symmetric; petiole short and thickset, seldom more than
    2 cm long; fruits 2,5 to 3 cm in diameter .... **U. kirkiana**
  Leaves usually smaller averaging 11 × 6 cm, although large leaves can occur; base may be rather
    asymmetric; petiole 2 to 3 cm long, rather slender; fruits 1,5 to 2 cm in diameter............
    .... **U. sansibarica**
3 Occurring in low altitude, high-rainfall forest; possessing marked stilt-roots ...... **U. sp. no. 1**
  Not possessing stilt-roots 4
4 Leaves elliptic to oblong-elliptic; petioles conspicuously long and slender, up to 5 cm in length
    .... **U. nitida**
  Leaves obovate; petioles 2 to 3 cm in length, not conspicuously long and slender ....
    .... **U. sansibarica**

Uapaca kirkiana Muell. Arg.   Illust. 134
S.A. no: —
Rhod. no: 467   Mahobohobo

A small tree, 5 to 6 m in height, with a characteristically rounded crown; occurring at medium altitudes in open woodland, sometimes locally dominant on gravelly soils. **Bark:** dark grey and rough. **Leaves:** scattered, clustered at the tips of the branches, ovate to obovate, large, usually about 17 × 11 cm, thickly leathery, the upper surface dark shiny green, the lower surface covered with grey to rust-coloured woolly hairs, midrib prominent above, very prominent below, covered with short grey hairs; apex rounded, notched; base tapering; margin entire and broadly rolled under; petiole thick, up to 2 cm long, velvety. **Flowers:** male and female flowers greenish-yellow, inconspicuous (January to April). **Fruit:** spherical, rusty-yellow, 2,5 to 3 cm in diameter, fleshy, with a rather hard skin surrounding the sweet edible flesh (October to December).

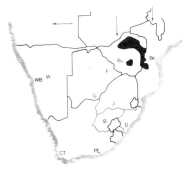

The fruits are delicious and, if allowed to ferment, can be made into a pleasant wine while an infusion of the roots is used to treat indigestion. Hunters declare that *Uapaca* woodland is the very worst in which to hunt, as the large leaves, when dry and brittle, form a crackling carpet which betrays their every move. Thomas Baines, in his *Goldfields Diaries*, often mentioned these trees and once referred to them as a means of telling the age of elephant tracks, because the plucked leaf ' . . . of the makobakoba (a name expressive of the noise it makes) affords the best time-test, for in two to three hours it loses its cool, glossy green and begins to look dry and pale.' The wood is red-brown, reasonably durable and termite and borer proof. It works fairly easily and polishes well; it is useful as a general purpose wood and provides a good charcoal. This tree is frost-tender and cannot survive in chilly hollows but the young shoots are protected to some extent by the large, curved, coarse leaves which, being crowded at the ends of the branches, tend to curl over the growing point.

Uapaca nitida Muell. Arg.
S.A. no: —
Rhod. no: 468   Narrow-leaved mahobohobo

A small to medium sized tree reaching 10 m in height; occurring at low altitudes in *Brachystegia* woodland. **Bark:** dark grey, rough and deeply fissured. **Leaves:** elliptic, oblong-elliptic, 5 to 16 × 1,5 to 4,5 cm, shiny green above, without hairs on either surface, veining conspicuous; apex broadly tapering to rounded; base tapering or narrowly tapering; margin entire, occasionally wavy; petiole slender, up to 5 cm long, yellowish-green, finely velvety. **Flowers:** creamy-green, inconspicuous (March to June, but mainly in April). **Fruit:** ellipsoidal, up to 2 cm long (June to September, but may be found during several months earlier or later than this).
The fruits are edible, but are not nearly as highly esteemed as are those of *U. kirkiana*. The wood makes a good quality charcoal and may also be used for building purposes. *U. nitida* is very fire-sensitive. The leaves and stems often carry black galls, which resemble young fruits in shape.

Uapaca sansibarica Pax
S.A. no: —
Rhod. no: 469   Lesser mahobohobo

A small to medium sized tree 6 to 10 m in height; occurring in low altitude deciduous woodland and bamboo thicket. **Bark:** dark grey, rough. **Leaves:** scattered, clustered near the ends of the branchlets, markedly obovate, 5 to 14,5 × 2,3 to 7 cm, stiffly leathery, dark green above, paler green below, the   **409**

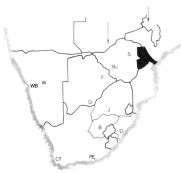

veining very conspicuous on the under surface, either with or without sparse hairs; apex rounded, sometimes notched; base tapering and sometimes asymmetric; margin entire, widely rolled under; petiole up to 3 cm long. **Flowers:** greenish-yellow, inconspicuous (March to April). **Fruit:** yellow, spherical, up to 1,5 to 2 cm in diameter, on stalks 1,4 to 2 cm long (June to July).

This species closely resembles *U. kirkiana*, but its leaves and fruits are conspicuously smaller than those of the latter species; it also tends to occur at low altitudes.

Uapaca sp. no. 1
S.A. no: —
Rhod. no: 470   Stilt-rooted mahobohobo

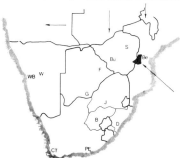

A medium to large tree reaching 18 m in height; occurring in low altitude, high-rainfall, evergreen forest. **Bark:** grey, smooth; the tree develops most conspicuous prop-roots, or stilt-roots. **Leaves:** obovate or frequently oval, 7 to 22 × 4,5 to 13,5 cm, without hairs, veining conspicuous; apex broadly tapering to rounded; base tapering to rounded; margin entire, inclined to roll under; petiole slender, up to 3 cm long (occasionally up to 7 cm). The flowers and fruits and the times of flowering and fruiting closely resemble those of *U. sansibarica*.

This species may well be undescribed. It is possible that it also occurs in north-western Zambia and elsewhere.

13. CLEISTANTHUS J. D. Hook. ex Planchon

Shrubs or trees. **Leaves:** alternate, simple. **Flowers:** small, in axillary clusters, or fascicles, or in very short racemes. Sexes separate, either on different trees or on the same tree. All floral parts in fives; petals usually small or absent; stamens 5, absent in female flowers; ovary 3-chambered, vestigial in male flowers. **Fruit:** a capsule.

Key to the tree species of *Cleistanthus:*
Leaf apex attenuate, forming a long, slender tip; base broadly tapering to rounded ....
.... **C. apetalus**
Leaf apex broadly tapering to rounded, occasionally abruptly and shortly attenuate, but not forming a long, slender tip; base rounded to shallowly lobed .... **C. schlechteri**

410

Cleistanthus apetalus S. Moore

S.A. no: —
Rhod. no: 471   Forest umzithi

A medium to large tree frequently 10 to 12 m in height, but quite often able to reach 20 m; occurring at medium to low altitudes in evergreen and riverine fringe forests. **Bark:** grey-brown; sometimes smooth, but usually lightly longitudinally fissured and slightly scaly to rather rough; the terminal branches are long, slender and drooping. **Leaves:** oval to elliptic, up to 9 × 3 cm but frequently less, without hairs, leathery, shiny, dark green above, paler yellowish-green below, with net-veining on both surfaces; apex attenuate, forming a slender drip-tip; base broadly tapering to rounded; margin entire, wavy; petiolate. **Flowers:** creamy-white, about 10 mm in diameter, with the slender sepals opening out wide; petals absent; sweetly scented; produced in compact sprays, 2 to 3,5 cm long; the stalks and buds are finely covered with very short, soft, golden-brown hairs (September to December). **Fruit:** a small, thinly woody capsule, about 10 mm in diameter, pale creamy-brown, splitting when mature to release small smooth pale brown seeds (December to January).

Cleistanthus schlechteri (Pax) Hutch.

S.A. no: 320   Bastard tamboti. Bastertambotie
Rhod. no: 472   Umzithi

 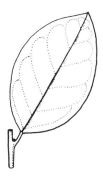

A small to large tree, 4 to 20 m in height, depending upon the locality; occurring in open woodland when it is low-growing, or in riverine vegetation when it reaches its greatest size. **Bark:** dark grey to blackish-brown, roughly striated; the tree is well branched, the branches ending in long, slender, grey, drooping branchlets. **Leaves:** elliptic, usually 3 to 7 × 1 to 2,7 cm, deep glossy green, paler on the under surface, with net-veining visible on both surfaces; apex broadly tapering to rounded, sometimes shortly and abruptly attenuate; base rounded to lobed; margin entire; petiolate. **Flowers:** golden-green, sweetly scented, about 10 mm in diameter, on slender stalks 1,5 to 2 cm long, produced in profusion in axillary clusters or in short sprays; petals absent, the slender calyx lobes opening wide giving the flower a thin, rather spidery look; anthers very pale, creamy-yellow; disc pinkish (September to November). **Fruit:** a thinly woody capsule about 10 mm in diameter, very clearly 3-lobed, with golden-green, soft hairs when young but losing these by maturity. The split capsule breaks apart very easily (October to November).

The wood is dark brown, and considered to be one of the hardest of those which grow in Zululand where the name for the tree is *umZithi*.

411

14. BRIDELIA Willd.

Shrubs or trees. **Leaves:** alternate, simple, characteristically lying in a horizontal plane. **Flowers:** in small heads, or tight clusters, in the leaf axils. Sexes separate on the same tree, the male flowers numerous, the female flowers less so, even solitary. All floral parts in fives; petals small, scale-like, clawed and spathulate. Male flowers: receptacle disc entire or lobed; stamens joined near the base to form a central column, separating away in the upper half; ovary vestigial. Female flowers: sepals narrower than in the male flower; receptacle disc double; stamens absent; ovary 2-chambered. **Fruit:** small and fleshy, spherical.

Bridelia angolensis Welw. ex Muell. Arg. (S.A. no: 321) was thought to occur in South West Africa, but it now appears that this was a case of mistaken identification and that *B. angolensis* does not occur further south than Angola.

Key to the tree species of *Bridelia:*

1 Leaves with velvety hairs, which may be sparse, or with hairs confined to the midrib and lateral veins 2
Leaves without hairs 5
2 Occurring only in the north and east of South West Africa (and northwards from there) .... **B. tenuifolia**
Not confined to South West Africa 3
3 Lateral veins break up, anastomosing, and not reaching the margin .... **B. atroviridis**
Lateral veins terminate in the margin 4
4 Upper surface of the leaves shiny green, without hairs; the lower surface may have sparse hairs, but is usually without hairs .... **B. micrantha**
Both leaf surfaces with dense velvety hairs .... **B. mollis**
5 Lateral veins break up, anastomosing, before reaching the margin .... **B. cathartica** subsp. *melanthesoides*
Lateral veins tend to terminate in the margin 6
6 Leaf apex broadly tapering to rounded, not attenuate.......... **B. cathartica** subsp. *cathartica*
Leaf apex shortly attenuate .... **B. micrantha**

Bridelia atroviridis Muell. Arg.
S.A. no: —
Rhod. no: 473   Rare forest bridelia

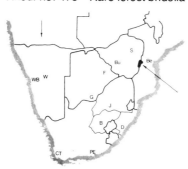

A shrub or small to medium sized tree up to 10 m in height, occasionally reaching 22 m; occurring in medium to low altitude, wet evergreen forest. **Bark:** brown, rough. **Leaves:** elliptic to oblanceolate, up to 12,5 × 5 cm, the veining conspicuous on both surfaces and the midrib very prominent below, the lateral veins arching and anastomosing, not reaching the margin, finely but densely hairy along the veins (the latter feature may be apparent only if the leaf is observed under a 10x lens); apex attenuate, forming a narrow drip-tip; base tapering; margin entire; petiole up to 10 mm long. **Flowers:** very small, greenish-yellow, inconspicuous, in clusters in the axils of the leaves (December to January). **Fruit:** small, berry-like blackish brown (April to May).

Bridelia cathartica Bertol. f.   Illust. 135
S.A. no: 322   Knobby bridelia.   Bloublaarsoetbessie
412   Rhod. no: 474   Knobby bridelia

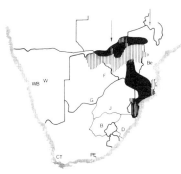 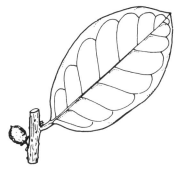

A many-stemmed shrub with a marked tendency to scramble, or a small tree 4 to 6 m in height; occurring along stream banks, in riverine fringe thicket and in littoral scrub, sometimes thicket forming. **Bark:** brown or grey, smooth. **Leaves:** oblong, elliptic to broadly oblanceolate, 3 to 9 × 1,5 to 4,5 cm, but usually about 3,5 × 1,6 cm, dark green and shiny above, pale green and sometimes rust-coloured below, without hairs; apex and base broadly tapering; margin entire, rolled under; petiole short. **Flowers:** male and female flowers very small, greenish to yellowish, in small, tight, axillary clusters along slender branchlets, the bracts and the remains of the sepals which persist after the fruits have fallen give a knobby effect (December to April). **Fruit:** up to 9 × 7 mm, resinous, blackish when mature, edible (April to September).
The species has been divided into 2 subspecies:

subsp. *cathartica* – the leaves have veins which do not branch and tend to end in the margin; the stalks of the male flowers have short soft hairs; the petals of the female flowers have a rounded base; the branchlets do not tend to zigzag. This is a plant of low altitude, riverine fringe thicket and littoral scrub (see black area on distribution map).

subsp. *melanthesoides* (Klotzsch) J. Léonard – the leaves have veins which arch and anastomose near the margin, and do not reach the margin; the male flower stalks lack short soft hairs; the petals of the female flower are narrowed to the base; the branchlets zigzag. This is a plant of mixed open woodland at medium rather than low altitudes; the plants in Zululand, the south-eastern Transvaal and the extreme south of Moçambique are outlying populations (see lined area on distribution map).

Bridelia micrantha (Hochst.) Baillon
S.A. no: 324   Mitzeerie. Mitserie
Rhod. no: 475   Mitzeerie

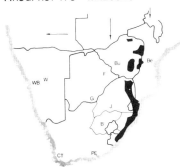 

A small to medium sized tree, 7 to 15 m in height; occurring in riverine forest, patches of relic forest, or in open woodland. **Bark:** brown to grey, rather flaky, becoming rough in older specimens. **Leaves:** rather large, elliptic to obovate, 4 to 18 × 2,5 to 10 cm, usually 7 to 8 × 3,5 to 4 cm, dark glossy green above, paler green below; the lower surface may have sparse hairs but usually lacks them altogether; the veins run right to the margin; apex shortly attenuate; base broadly tapering to rounded; margin entire, slightly wavy or scalloped; petiole short, thickset. The leaves frequently develop bright colours in autumn. **Flowers:** very small, yellowish, in tight clusters in the axils of the leaves (October to December). **Fruit:** ellipsoidal, about 8 × 4 mm, blackish when mature, edible and sweet tasting (January to March).

413

EUPHORBIACEAE

The leaf sap is used in African medicine to soothe sore eyes and the root, which is said to have purgative properties, is taken to relieve stomach pains and possibly to treat gastric ulcers. It is also powdered and, mixed with oil or fat, rubbed into the head to cure headaches. The wood is dark brown, naturally lustrous, fine-grained, very durable and termite-resistant, and it could be used to make fine furniture. This is a fast growing tree, beautiful, shady, and able to stand some degree of frost. It is easily raised from seed which must, however, be fresh when planted.

Bridelia mollis Hutch.   Illust. 136
S.A. no: 325   Velvet bridelia. Fluweelsoetbessie
Rhod. no: 476   Velvet bridelia

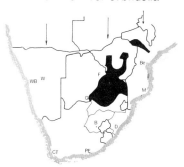 

A shrub or small tree up to 7 m in height, often well-branched and rather spreading; occurring at low altitudes, often among rocks or on granite koppies. **Bark:** dark brown to grey, often with vertical striations, rough. **Leaves:** ovate to obovate, 2,5 to 13 × 1,3 to 9 cm, young leaves golden and furry, older leaves covered with soft, short hairs on both surfaces; the lateral veins are conspicuous and run right to the margin; apex broadly tapering and often notched; base lobed; margin scalloped, though sometimes shallowly and not obviously so; petiole short, thickset, densely velvety. **Flowers:** small, greenish-yellow, in tight clusters in the axils of the leaves (November to February). **Fruit:** almost spherical, about 10 mm in diameter, clustered along the branches, finely velvety when young, becoming black when mature (January to June).
The fruits are edible and are said to make a pleasant jam. Africans fear that if they use the wood as fuel, their cows will never bear heifer calves.

Bridelia tenuifolia Muell. Arg.
S.A. no: 325,1   Tender-leaved bridelia. Sagteblaarsoetbessie
Rhod. no: —

A low shrub or small tree reaching a maximum height of 10 m; occurring on sandy mountain slopes, stony outcrops and in rocky valleys. **Bark:** dark grey, flaking; the branches velvety when young, losing these hairs later. **Leaves:** broadly lanceolate to oval, sometimes almost circular, 4 to 11 × 2 to 6 cm, paler green below than above with both surfaces finely velvety, the lateral veins looping to form a sub-marginal vein and not reaching the margin; apex rounded, or broadly tapering and abruptly pointed; base tapering to rounded; margin entire, wavy; petiole up to 3 to 5 mm long. **Flowers:** small, greenish-yellow, in tight axillary clusters (probably December to January). **Fruit:** fleshy, about 7 mm in diameter, black when mature (July).

414

15. ANDROSTACHYS Prain

Androstachys johnsonii Prain   Illust. 137
S.A. no: 327   Lebombo ironwood. Lebombo-ysterhout
Rhod. no: 477   Simbi tree

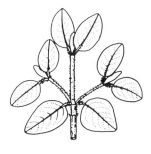

A medium sized erect tree up to 15 m in height, although it may be taller; occurring at low altitudes, on rocky hillsides and stony outcrops, in deciduous woodland, frequently in more or less pure stands forming *Androstachys* thickets. **Bark:** dark, distinctive and rough; the smaller branchlets are angular and articulated, densely covered with soft white to silvery almost woolly hairs. **Leaves:** simple, opposite, 1 pair set at right angles to the next, conspicuously heart-shaped, 2,5 to 6 × 2 to 4 cm, shiny dark green above, the under surface covered with a matt of short, white, felt-like hairs, thickly leathery; apex very broadly tapering; base lobed, often narrowly peltate; margin entire, rolled under; petiole up to 2 cm long, thickset, densely covered with whitish, woolly hairs. The very distinctive stipules, up to 2,5 × 0,6 to 1 cm, ensheathe the leaf bud but, as the shoot thrusts upwards, they open out and stand side by side like a pair of wings, silvery on the outside, reddish-brown within (see Illust. 137); they fall quite early. **Flowers:** sexes separate on different trees, the flowers of both sexes being distinctive and unusual. Male flowers: yellow, with a remarkable, very slender staminal column rising from the centre, upon which many stamens are produced, giving the appearance of a catkin 1,5 to 2,5 cm long (the generic name refers to this), and at the base of which are 5 small, yellow, bract-like sepals; the flowers are produced in groups of 3, shortly joined at the base, in the leaf axils, each one borne on a slender, thread-like stalk, or pedicel. Female flowers: small, yellowish, 5 to 7 mm in diameter, with 5 sepal lobes; borne on the end of an unusual stalk up to 1,7 cm long, resembling a calyx tube, fairly thick, ribbed, slightly curved, creamy-white, with silvery silky hairs; ovary large, conspicuously 3-lobed, velvety, with 3 stigmas (October to November). **Fruit:** a pale yellowish-brown capsule, about 1,2 cm in diameter, conspicuously 3-lobed (occasionally 4- to 5-lobed), dehiscent (November to March).

The wood is valuable, extremely hard, fine-grained, durable and almost completely termite proof. Poles used for building rest huts in the Shingwidzi and Punda Milia camps in the Kruger National Park have stood for 40 years and still show no sign of deterioration. All African names for the tree, variations of *msimbiti,* mean 'iron wood'. The timber has a characteristic smell of honey while it is being cut and when it is burning but the honey produced from the flowers is said to be poisonous and to have a purgative effect. The leaves turn yellow-brown in winter and are shed irregularly; the seeds germinate very readily and the young plants are hardy, though they are very slow-growing and will not withstand cold.

16. CROTON L.

Evergreen shrubs or trees, usually with stellate hairs and rounded scales. **Leaves:** alternate, sometimes opposite, rarely whorled, simple, usually with 2 glands at the top of the petiole. **Flowers:** in spikes, or racemes. Sexes separate on the same tree, rarely on different trees, and usually in the same flower spike; a few female fowers occur at the base with many male flowers above them; floral parts in fours to fives. Male flowers: calyx lobes usually deeply divided, to free; petals usually present, small; stamens 5 to many; ovary absent. Female flowers: sepals and petals smaller than in the male; stamens absent; ovary 3-chambered. **Fruit:** a 3-lobed capsule.

415

EUPHORBIACEAE

Key to the tree species of *Croton:*

1 Under surface of the leaves with a distinctive and beautiful silver or golden satiny sheen produced by dense scales, which may also be present on the branchlets 2
  Under surface of the leaves without the silver or golden satiny sheen, though sparse whitish or even silvery stellate hairs may be present, especially when the leaf is young 5
2 The silver under surface not, or very rarely, dotted with yellow to red scales .... **C. steenkampianus**
  The under surface dotted with more or less numerous yellow to red scales 3
3 Upper surface roughish to the touch, especially when dry .... **C. menyhartii**
  Upper surface with or without hairs, but not rough to the touch 4
4 Under surface of the leaves dotted with cinnamon-brown scales; petioles and young branchlets may be pale yellowish to brownish; flowers in racemes up to 10 cm long......... **C. gratissimus**
  Under surface of the leaves with conspicuous dark reddish-brown to red scale-dots; flowers in small compact racemes only about 10 mm long .... **C. pseudopulchellus**
5 Flower sprays usually more than 9 cm in length; conspicuous lateral veins usually in more than 6 pairs 6
  Flower sprays usually less than 9 cm long; conspicuous lateral veins in 4 to 5 pairs 7
6 Occurring only in areas adjacent to the Victoria Falls .... **C. leuconeurus**
  Not occurring near the Victoria Falls .... **C. sylvaticus**
7 Leaf margins irregularly and roughly toothed; fruits 3 to 4 cm in diameter .... **C. megalobotrys**
  Leaf margins finely, and sparsely toothed; fruits about 10 mm in diameter .... **C. scheffleri**

Croton gratissimus Burch.   Illust. 138 and photograph on page 186
[*C. zambesicus* Muell. Arg.]
S.A. no: 328 and 328,1   Lavender croton. Laventelkoorsbessie
Rhod. no: 478   Lavender croton

A shrub or small tree reaching 10 m in height; occurring over a wide range of altitudes, in a variety of woodland types, often associated with rocky outcrops. **Bark:** grey, rough, petioles and young branchlets may be yellowish to brownish. **Leaves:** alternate, with a beautiful and striking silvery under surface, lanceolate to elliptic, the size somewhat variable, but usually about 7 to 8 × 2 to 4 cm, the upper surface without hairs, rather dark shiny green, the lower surface covered with dense, silvery scales, and dotted with small cinnamon-coloured glandular scales; apex tapering to broadly so; base rounded to shallowly lobed; margin entire, sometimes wavy; petiole slender, pale yellowish to brownish-green, up to 3 cm long. **Flowers:** small, cream to golden-yellow, about 6 mm in diameter, in spikes up to 10 cm long; the buds are conspicuous and are on the tree for months before the flowers open. The sexes are separate but both present in the same spike, with only 1 or 2 female flowers at the base and many male flowers above, therefore little seed is set (September to November). **Fruit:** a 3-lobed capsule, yellow when mature, about 10 mm in diameter, dehiscent (March).

This species has been divided into two varieties – var. *gratissimus,* which has no hairs on the upper surface and var. *subgratissimus* (Prain) Burtt Davy, which has stellate hairs on the upper surface and occurs in the south of Rhodesia, the central areas of the Transvaal and in Botswana.

The branches of this tree are brittle; the leaves, when crushed, are pleasantly aromatic and are dried and powdered by Bushman girls to make a perfume. In the Transvaal the charred and powdered bark is used to treat bleeding gums and although the plant in general is believed to be toxic it is valued as an important stock-feed in South West Africa. This is an ornamental tree (the specific name means 'most pleasant') and it would be well worth introducing into gardens.

Croton leuconeurus Pax
[*C. barotsensis* Gibbs]
S.A. no: Barotse croton
Rhod. no: 479   Barotse croton

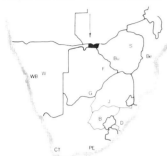

This species is very similar to *Croton megalobotrys;* however, it differs in that the leaf apex is broadly tapering, the flower spike is up to 22 cm long, there are 8 or more pairs of major lateral veins in the leaf and it is recorded only from the immediate vicinity of the Victoria Falls; whereas in *C. megalobotrys* the leaf apex is attenuate, the flower spikes reach only 9 cm long, there are 4 pairs of major lateral veins in the leaf, and it is widespread.

Croton megalobotrys Muell. Arg.   Illust. 139
[*C. gubouga* S. Moore]
S.A. no: 329   Fever-berry. Grootkoorsbessie
Rhod. no: 480   Fever-berry croton

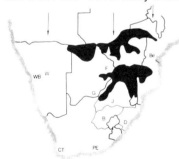
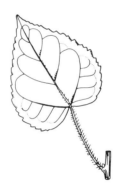

A shrubby to medium sized, densely leafy tree reaching 15 m in height; occurring on alluvial flats and almost always a constituent of riverine fringe forest or thicket. **Bark:** pale grey, smooth; branches lenticellate. **Leaves:** alternate, roughly triangular, 2,5 to 18 × 1,3 to 13 cm, but usually about 8 × 5 cm, with pale, whitish silvery-green stellate hairs, especially on the under surface when young, tending to lose these by maturity, but never with the dense, silvery scales found in *C. gratissimus* and some other species; with 4 to 5 pairs of conspicuous lateral veins; apex attenuate, forming a slender tip; base square to shallowly lobed; margin irregularly and roughly toothed; petiole long and slender. **Flowers:** yellowish-green, in sturdy spikes up to 8 to 9 cm long; male and female flowers generally on the same spike (September to November). **Fruit:** a woody capsule, 3-lobed, 3 to 4 cm in diameter, fig-shaped, covered with greyish-white, woolly hairs when young, losing most of these by maturity, yellowish-brown when mature (December to January).

The wood, which is light-coloured, is said to be a useful timber and a clear golden-yellow oil can be obtained from the seeds. In 1899 the medical journal, *The Lancet,* published an account by a Dr Maberley of an old prospector who claimed his life had been saved when, stricken with malaria, he had taken 'some beans' and bark given to him by an African doctor. Later the old man had given the 'beans' to Dr Maberley who used them to make a preparation with which he successfully treated his   **417** own bouts of fever as well as those of his patients. It was some 20 years before he was able to identify the tree as *Croton megalobotrys,* the bark and seeds of which were used as a purgative and were well-known among Africans and early pioneers in malarial areas not only as a cure for the fever but also as a prophylactic. It appears, however, that no further research into the medicinal properties of this species has been carried out. It closely resembles *C. leuconeurus* and the differences are discussed under the latter species.

Croton menyhartii Pax

S.A. no: Rough-leaved croton
Rhod. no: 481   Rough-leaved croton

This species closely resembles *C. gratissimus;* however, it differs in that the upper surface of the leaves is covered with stellate hairs which make them rough to the touch, the flowers are in short, dense heads, scarcely more than 4 cm long, the leaves are smaller, reaching a maximum size of 7 × 3 cm, and the scale-dots on the silver under surface are yellow; whereas in *C. gratissimus* the upper surface of the leaves is not harsh to the touch in either of the varieties, the flowers are in longer spikes up to 9 cm long, the leaves are usually about 7 to 8 cm long and the silver under surface is covered with cinnamon-brown scale-dots.

Croton pseudopulchellus Pax

S.A. no: Small lavender croton. Kleinlaventelkoorsbessie
Rhod. no: 482   Lesser lavender croton

Usually a small, often spindly, shrub 1 to 2 m in height, but it can become a small tree up to 4 m; occurring at low altitudes, becoming very common in some areas, even forming the dominant under-shrub in certain types of woodland. **Bark:** grey, smooth to roughish; the ultimate branchlets are often a true red with a satiny sheen caused by the presence of glandular scales. **Leaves:** alternate, small, lanceolate to elliptic, up to 6 × 2 cm, but frequently smaller, the upper surface dark green without hairs, the under surface densely covered with scales producing a beautiful, silvery or golden sheen which is copiously scale-dotted with red-brown to red scales, the latter frequently covering the young leaves and flower buds as well; apex tapering; base broadly tapering to rounded; margin entire, rolled under; petiole short, red. **Flowers:** small, yellow, in very short, compact heads only about 10 mm long, in the axils of the leaves, male and female flowers in the same head; the buds can be produced as early as February, the flowers opening only some 10 months later (November to

December). **Fruit:** a 3-lobed capsule, about 10 mm in diameter, yellowish with rusty-red scales dotting the surface, dehiscent (November to January).
In African medicine a decoction of the root is used to treat asthma.

Croton scheffleri Pax
[*C. madandensis* S. Moore]
S.A. no: Thicket croton
Rhod. no: 483   Thicket croton

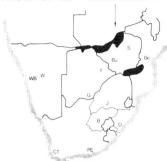 

Usually a shrub, often with a tendency to scramble, or a small tree 3 to 4 m in height; occurring at low altitudes in woodland or thicket, frequently itself thicket forming. **Bark:** light brown. **Leaves:** alternate, without a silvery sheen on the under surface, lanceolate to ovate-lanceolate, 4 to 7 × 1,5 to 3,5 cm, finely hairy on both surfaces; apex attenuate forming a long slender tip; base broadly tapering to rounded; margin very finely and sparsely toothed; petioles long and very slender. **Flowers:** male flowers yellow, in sparsely flowered spikes up to 6 cm long. Female flowers: greenish-yellow, sepals leaf-like up to 8 mm long; produced on slender stalks 10 to 18 mm long, solitary or in groups of 2 to 3, arising in the leaf axils, often produced at the base of the male spike (November to January). **Fruit:** a 3-lobed capsule, greenish-yellow, up to 10 mm in diameter, seated in the remains of the persistent calyx (January to March).

Croton steenkampianus Gerstner
S.A. no: 329,1   Marsh croton. Vleikoorsbessie
Rhod. no: —

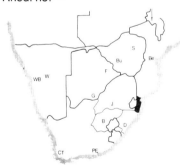 

Usually a shrub 2 to 3 m in height, but it can become a small tree reaching 7 m; occurring in open woodland, at forest edges, frequently along river banks and fringing swamps. The young branches, the under surface of the leaves and the ovary are covered with silvery, stellate hairs and scales, but the dark orange to red-brown scale-dots so characteristic of *C. gratissimus* and *C. pseudopulchellus* are absent or rarely seen. **Leaves:** alternate, heart-shaped to almost circular, 5 to 15 × 3 to 8 cm, usually about 13 × 7 cm, much larger and broader than those of *C. gratissimus;* apex narrowly tapering; base lobed; margin entire; petiolate. **Flowers:** creamy-green, in spikes up to 4 cm long, with a few female flowers near the base of the spike (November). **Fruit:** a 3-lobed capsule, about 6 mm in diameter, yellow and velvety when mature (November to January).

419

EUPHORBIACEAE

Croton sylvaticus Hochst.   Illust. 140
S.A. no: 330   Forest croton. Boskoorsbessie
Rhod. no: 484   Forest croton

Varying in size from a small to a large tree usually 7 to 13 m in height, but when growing under favourable conditions, can reach 30 m or more; always associated with forest or dense woodland. **Bark:** pale to dark grey, smooth in young specimens, becoming rough with age. **Leaves:** alternate, broadly lanceolate to ovate, 4 to 13,5 × 2,5 to 10 cm, uniform green on both surfaces, sometimes with short soft hairs on the under surface when young, although mature leaves are usually without hairs on either surface; with 6 or more pairs of main lateral veins; apex narrowly to abruptly attenuate; base rounded to lobed; margin toothed; petiole long and slender up to 10 cm in length. **Flowers:** cream or pale yellow, male and female flowers produced together in spikes up to 15 cm long, consisting of many male flowers with only a few female flowers among them, the latter occurring mainly towards the base of the spike (October to December). **Fruit:** a 3-lobed capsule, 8 to 10 mm in diameter, bright orange when ripe, forming conspicuous clusters among the leaves (March to April).

In certain areas, such as the southern parts of the Kruger National Park, this species occurs only as a small shrub. The wood is light in colour, sometimes with dark streaks, soft and easily worked. It burns even when green. Parts of the tree are said to be toxic, and the bark has been used as a fish poison. In African medicine the leaves are made into a poultice to treat pleurisy and the bark provides a remedy for rheumatism. This is a decorative, shady tree and well worth growing in any garden.

17. CAVACOA J. Léonard

Cavacoa aurea (Cavaco) J. Léonard
S.A. no: 332   Natal hickory. Natalokkerneut
Rhod. no: —

A canopy tree up to 15 m in height, occurring in evergreen forest. **Bark:** brown, thinly scaly; the stem is conspicuously folded and fluted. **Leaves:** alternate, simple, broadly elliptic to oblanceolate, 4 to 13 × 1,7 to 5,5 cm, usually 8 to 10 cm long, the lateral veins looping to form a sub-marginal vein, deep dull green, leathery, without hairs, minutely pellucid gland-dotted, conspicuously net-veined; apex broadly tapering and abruptly attenuate; base tapering; margin entire; petiole rather long and slender. **Flowers:** small, conspicuous yellow, sweetly scented, in loose racemes up to 7 cm long, clustered, or fascicled, in leaf axils. Sexes separate on different trees. All floral parts in fives. Male flowers: calyx membraneous; petals free, small; disc glandular; stamens 15 to 30; ovary absent. Female

420

flowers: solitary, on long stalks, or pedicels, up to 2 cm long, or in axillary sprays up to 7 cm long; stamens absent; ovary 3- to 5-chambered (October to December). **Fruit:** a smooth, woody capsule, up to 1,5 to 2 cm in diameter, dark brown to black by maturity, dehiscent (December to February). The fruits drop to the ground while still closed and split open on contact with the damp soil. Fresh seed germinates well and plants thrive in either sun or shade. An infusion of the roots is taken to ease pain and to treat fevers, and the steam rising from it is used to clear sinuses. This is a protected plant in South Africa.

18. TANNODIA Baillon

Tannodia swynnertonii (S. Moore) Prain
S.A. no: —
Rhod. no: 486   Tannodia

A small to medium sized tree up to 13 m in height, but occasionally reaching 20 m in some areas in Moçambique; occurring in evergreen forest. **Bark:** grey to dark brown and smooth; the trunk is fluted and buttressed in larger specimens; branchlets lenticellate. **Leaves:** alternate, simple, oblong to oblong-elliptic, sometimes ovate, 6 to 12 × 3,5 to 7 cm, light green, without hairs on either surface, 3-veined from the base, the lateral veins terminating in the margin; apex attenuate; base broadly tapering to rounded; margin entire, wavy; petiole up to 2,5 cm, channelled above. **Flowers:** sexes separate on different trees. Male flowers: creamy-white, sepals and petals very small; stamens 7 to 8; ovary absent; produced in spikes up to 12 cm long. Female flowers: creamy-green, in sparsely flowered spikes up to 20 cm long; petals up to 4 mm long; stamens absent; ovary ovoid. Many more male than female flowers are produced and the trees do not set much fruit (October to December). **Fruit:** a greenish, woody capsule, 3- to 5-lobed, dehiscent (February to March).

19. MICROCOCCA Benth.

Micrococca capensis (Baillon) Prain
S.A. no: 332,2   Common bead-string. Gewone kralesnoer
Rhod. no: —

A tall shrub or small tree up to 5 m in height; occurring in evergreen forest. **Bark:** grey, smooth. **Leaves:** alternate, simple, broadly elliptic to narrowly elliptic, 4 to 14 × 2 to 5,5 cm but usually about 5 × 2,5 cm, very dark green, upper surface harshly hairy and rough to the touch; apex narrowly

421

attenuate; base tapering; margin sharply toothed; petiolate. **Flowers:** minute, greenish. Sexes separate on different trees. Floral parts in twos to fours; petals absent. Male flowers: in small clusters of 6 to 20 flowers, each cluster in the axil of a bract and sparsely spaced along slender, thread-like spikes up to 15 cm long; calyx splitting into lobes; stamens about 15; ovary absent. Female flowers: solitary in the axils of each bract, spaced along shorter spikes, up to 10 cm long; calyx lobes small; stamens absent; ovary 3-chambered (August to January). **Fruit:** a 3-lobed capsule, about 10 mm in diameter yellow when mature, dehiscent (October to May).

20. ERYTHROCOCCA Benth.

Shrubs with slender branches, or small trees. **Leaves:** alternate, simple, petiolate, with scalloped or toothed margins, the teeth being glandular. Stipules may be modified to form weakened thorns or, occasionally, pungent spines. **Flowers:** small, in axillary fascicles, or in racemes, or in very tight, compact heads. Floral parts in twos to fours; petals absent; arising in the axils of bracts, and all produced in leaf axils. Sexes separate on different trees. Male flowers: calyx lobes 3 to 4; stamens 2 to 60, free, often mixed with glandular hairs; disc present; ovary vestigial. Female flowers: usually solitary in the axil of each bract; calyx 2-lobed (rarely 3 to 4); stamens absent; ovary with 2 to 3 compartments. **Fruit:** a capsule.

Key to the tree species of *Erythrococca:*
1 Occurring only in Natal and possibly in the extreme south of Moçambique ..... **E. berberidea**
  Occurring more to the north, not in Natal or in the extreme south of Moçambique 2
2 Confined to areas of high altitude, evergreen forest; leaves dark green with a purplish tinge,
    especially when young .... **E. polyandra**
  Not a high altitude species; occurring at medium to low altitudes in various types of woodland
    3
3 Occurring in north and central Rhodesia, adjacent areas in Moçambique, and in Botswana
    .... **E. menyharthii**
  Occurring in the east and west of Rhodesia and adjacent areas in Moçambique, not in Botswana
    .... **E. trichogyne**

Erythrococca berberidea Prain
S.A. no: 332,1   Prickly red-berry. Dorinkiebessie
Rhod. no: —

A small tree up to 5 m in height, frequently spinescent; occurring in evergreen forest. **Bark:** grey, smooth, often dotted with lenticels, especially on the branches. **Leaves:** elliptic to ovate-elliptic, 2,5 to 8 × 1,3 to 5 cm, bright green, with or without fine hairs which are often confined to the veins of the under surface; apex attenuate; base tapering; margin rather coarsely toothed; petiolate. Stipules form short, yellowish spines 1 to 3 mm long. **Flowers:** minute, yellowish or green, on the thread-like stalks, forming misty or cobweb-like heads up to 2,5 cm in diameter (November to December). **Fruit:** a 3-lobed capsule, about 6 mm in diameter, reddish-brown to bright orange and conspicuous when mature, dehiscent (December to February).

422

Erythrococca menyharthii (Pax) Prain
S.A. no: Northern red-berry
Rhod. no: 488   Northern red-berry

Usually a small slender shrub 1 to 2 m in height, but it can become a small tree reaching 6 m; occurring at medium to low altitudes in mixed woodland, often associated with rocky outcrops or termite mounds. **Bark:** pale grey, smooth to slightly corky. **Leaves:** arising in clusters, or fascicles, on short, lateral branches, lanceolate, elliptic or ovate-elliptic, 3 to 8 × 1,5 to 4,8 cm, pale green, thinly textured, finely velvety on both surfaces; apex markedly attenuate; base tapering; margin almost entire, or with large, blunt teeth; petiole slender. Stipules rather horny, but falling early. **Flowers:** male flowers: minute, yellowish-green, in small, compact heads 1 to 4 cm long (the head being rather longer than in the other species), the whole head borne on a very slender stalk 8 to 15 mm long. Female flowers: greenish-yellow, about 5 mm in diameter, on slender stalks 1,5 to 3 cm long; axillary, in 2- to 4-flowered fascicles (October to December). **Fruit:** a 3-lobed capsule, up to 10 mm in diameter, becoming red when mature, dehiscent (December to January).
The fruits are edible, and Africans use the leaves as a vegetable.

Erythrococca polyandra (Pax & K. Hoffm.) Prain
S.A. no: —
Rhod. no: 489   Forest red-berry

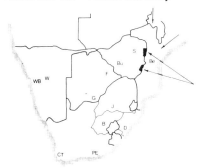 

A shrub to small tree up to 4 m in height; occurring as a constituent of the under-storey in closed canopy forest. **Bark:** greyish-brown, rough; the branches are often long and arching. **Leaves:** lanceolate to broadly lanceolate, 5 to 12 × 2 to 5,5 cm, dark green, sometimes tinged with purple especially when young, without hairs on either surface; apex narrowly attenuate; base tapering; margin irregularly but more or less deeply toothed; petiole slender, up to 10 mm long. **Flowers:** small, greenish, inconspicuous. Male flowers: in very thin, sparse, branched axillary sprays. Female flowers: on slender stalks or peduncles up to 3 cm long, in 2- to 3-flowered clusters (October to November). **Fruit:** a 3-lobed capsule, 5 to 7 mm in diameter, becoming red when mature, dehiscent (October to January).

Erythrococca trichogyne (Muell. Arg.) Prain
S.A. no: —
Rhod. no: 490   Twin red-berry

423

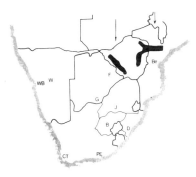 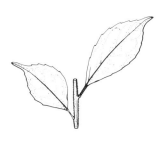

A shrub or small tree up to 4,5 m in height; occurring at medium to low altitudes, in open woodland or in riverine fringe forest or thicket. **Bark:** grey or yellowish-grey to pale brown, smooth in young specimens becoming roughish with age. **Leaves:** broadly lanceolate to ovate, 2 to 7 × 1 to 3,5 cm, but usually about 3 × 1,5 cm, pale green to yellowish-green, thinly textured, with sparse hairs on both surfaces, on the petioles and on the young stems; apex and base tapering; margin irregularly toothed, sometimes bluntly so; petiolate. **Flowers:** minute, pale yellow, in small branched heads, on slender stalks in the axils of the very young leaves (October to December). **Fruit:** a 1- to 2-lobed capsule, about 5 mm long × 10 mm wide, yellowish, splitting and falling away leaving 1 to 2 seeds remaining attached to the branch; each seed is completely covered with a bright orange-red to scarlet, fleshy aril so that the seeds strongly resemble two red berries (January to February).

21. MALLOTUS Lour.

Mallotus oppositifolius (Geiseler) Muell. Arg.
S.A. no: —
Rhod. no: 490/1   Mallotus

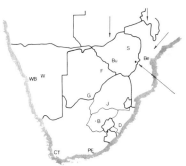 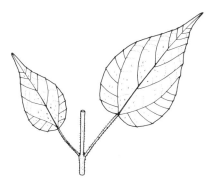

A shrub or small tree up to 6 m in height; occurring in riverine fringes and evergreen forest. **Bark:** brown and scaly. **Leaves:** simple, opposite with one leaf of the pair markedly smaller and shorter-stalked than the other; heart-shaped or broadly ovate, 3 to 14 × 2 to 10 cm, thinly but firmly textured, deep green above, paler green below, gland-dotted on the under surface; 3-veined from the base with rusty-coloured stellate hairs; apex attenuate; base sometimes very broadly tapering but usually square to lobed; margin entire, inclined to be wavy; petiole up to 9 cm long on the larger leaves, stipules small. **Flowers:** small, greenish-yellow, the male flowers having purple anthers to the stamens, produced in spike-like racemes up to 8 cm long in the axils of the leaves. Sexes separate, usually on different trees; calyx 3- to 5-lobed; petals absent; stamens usually many in the male flowers, absent in the female flowers; ovary usually 3-chambered, absent in the male flowers (November to December). **Fruit:** a deeply 3-lobed capsule about 10 mm in diameter, the lobes separate for almost one-third of their length; greenish-yellow when mature (December to January).

22. ARGOMUELLERA Pax

Argomuellera macrophylla Pax
S.A. no: —
424   Rhod. no: 491   Undershrub big-leaf

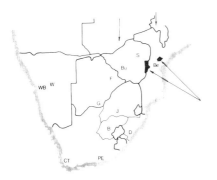

A shrub or small, evergreen tree up to 4,5 m in height; occurring as part of the low, shrubby undergrowth in evergreen forest. **Bark:** green to grey, rather smooth. **Leaves:** alternate, simple, large, oblanceolate, up to 31 × 8,5 cm, the upper surface without hairs, the lower surface with spreading hairs; the young leaves are red; apex tapering; base tapering almost to the stem; margin sharply toothed; petiole almost absent due to the decurrent leaf base. **Flowers:** clustered near the ends of the branchlets, in showy, white or pinkish, spike-like racemes, up to 13 cm long, fluffy with the conspicuous stamens. Sexes separate but usually in the same spike, frequently 1 female flower among many male flowers. Male flowers: calyx 3- to 4-lobed; petals absent; stamens many, free; ovary vestigial. Female flowers: small; calyx 5-lobed; stamens absent; ovary about 2 mm in diameter with velvety golden hairs (October). **Fruit:** a 3-lobed capsule with velvety golden hairs, especially when young (October to November).

23. ALCHORNEA Swartz

Shrubs or trees. **Leaves:** alternate, simple, may be 3-veined from the base, with glands between the veins. **Flowers:** in simple or branched, axillary spikes. Sexes separate on different trees. Floral parts usually in fours; petals absent. Male flowers: usually several flowers clustered in the axil of a bract, these groups making up the spike; stamens up to 8; ovary absent. Female flowers: usually solitary in the axil of a bract; stamens absent; ovary 3-chambered. **Fruit:** a capsule.

Key to the tree species of *Alchornea:*
Leaf base tapering, blade usually elliptic to narrowly ovate; in evergreen forest. Occurring in the extreme east of Rhodesia, in adjacent areas in Moçambique and in Zululand ...... **A. hirtella**
Leaf base rounded to narrowly lobed, blade usually broadly obovate to broadly oblong; in low altitude woodland, or in riverine fringe forest or thicket. Occurring in the southern (and central) areas of Rhodesia and adjacent areas in Moçambique .... **A. laxiflora**

Alchornea hirtella Benth.
[*A. glabrata* Prain]
S.A. no: 333   Zulu bead-string. Zoeloekralesnoer
Rhod. no: 492   Forest bead-string

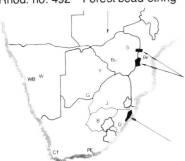

A slender, spindly shrub or tree occasionally reaching 12 m in height; occurring as a constituent of the under-storey in evergreen forest. **Bark:** pale; often with lax branches and sometimes bearing aerial

425

roots. **Leaves:** elliptic, up to 15 × 5,5 cm, light green, the young leaves reddish with short soft hairs; apex and base tapering; margin irregularly and shallowly toothed; petiolate. **Flowers:** male flowers: minute, yellowish, in very slender, delicate sprays about 20 × 15 cm. Female flowers: greenish in few-flowered spikes, 2 to 5 cm long, the velvety ovaries each with 3 long, rather fleshy, conspicuous stigmas (October to December). **Fruit:** a 3-lobed capsule, about 10 mm in diameter (December to February).

Alchornea laxiflora (Benth.) Pax & K. Hoffm.
[*A. schlechteri* Pax]
S.A. no: 334   Venda bead-string. Vendakralesnoer
Rhod. no: 493   Lowveld bead-string

A shrub or small tree up to 6 m in height; occurring at low altitudes, in well wooded places or in riverine fringe forest or thicket. **Bark:** light grey; the ultimate branchlets covered with velvety hairs. **Leaves:** large, ovate to elliptic, up to 20 × 9 cm, light green developing attractive colours in autumn, varying from plum to golden-yellow, leaves velvety when young, the hairs sometimes persisting to maturity along the midrib on the under surface; apex attenuate; base tapering to rounded; margin irregularly toothed to scalloped; petiole slender, 2 to 7 cm long, frequently with 2 hair-like stipellae where the base joins the petiole. **Flowers:** in quite conspicuous, reddish spikes. Male flowers: minute, grouped in clusters of 2 to 4, each cluster with very conspicuous, reddish bracts and hairs which give the spike its colour; the spikes are up to 4 cm long in small groups in the axils of the leaves. Female flowers: small, velvety ovaries 1 to 1,5 mm in diameter, with thread-like styles 10 to 15 mm long, produced among the leaves (September to December). **Fruit:** a 2- to 4-lobed, thinly woody capsule, about 5 to 7 mm in diameter, dark brown (January to February).

24. NEOPALISSYA Pax

Neopalissya castaneifolia (Baillon) Pax
S.A. no: —
Rhod. no: 494   Mock lemon tree

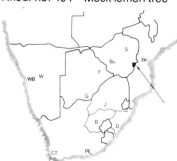
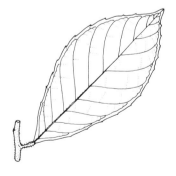

A small tree up to 4 m in height; occurring as part of the under-storey in evergreen forest, often growing gregariously, although never common. **Bark:** dark, smooth. **Leaves:** alternate, simple, oval to elliptic, 7 to 18 × 3 to 6,5 cm, although usually 12 × 3,5 cm, dull green with the midrib prominent on both surfaces; the young leaves are strikingly red; apex attenuate; base tapering; margin coarsely, sometimes rather obscurely, toothed and wavy, occasionally almost entire; petiole shortly curved and thickened into the base of the leaf which is a conspicuous feature. **Flowers:** sexes separate on the same tree. Male flowers: very small, whitish to yellow, in short racemes about 10 mm long, forming tight, dense, axillary clusters; calyx 4- to 5-lobed; petals absent; stamens many; each flower in the axil of a bract. Female flowers: greenish-yellow, sparsely set along slender spikes up to 19 cm long; calyx 4- to 6-lobed, persistent; disc saucer-shaped; petals absent; stamens absent; ovary velvety, with very conspicuous, large, branched, antler-like stigmas (October). **Fruit:** a capsule, conspicuously 3-lobed, each lobe about 8 mm in diameter, finely velvety with a pinkish bloom, dehiscent (January to March).

An immediate field impression is that of a thornless lemon tree. Outside Rhodesia this species is known only from the Malagasy Republic.

25. NEOBOUTONIA Muell. Arg.

Neoboutonia melleri (Muell. Arg.) Prain
S.A. no: —
Rhod. no: 495   Lace-leaf

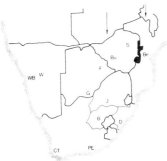
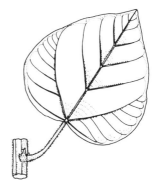

A medium to large tree up to 13 m tall, but heights of 20 m have been recorded in countries to the north; occurring in evergreen forest. **Bark:** grey to brown and smooth; young branchlets velvety. **Leaves:** alternate, simple, large, ovate to almost circular, about 15 × 15 cm, but shade and sapling leaves may be much larger, up to 30 × 30 cm; the net-veining is conspicuous, being picked out with dense, white, stellate hairs, giving a characteristic resemblance to fine delicate lace, which is especially noticeable on the under surface but often apparent, to a lesser extent, on the upper surface also; young leaves are densely covered with furry hairs; apex shortly attenuate; base usually deeply lobed; margin finely toothed, the small teeth projecting from the margin and not being indented; petiole sturdy. **Flowers:** sexes separate on different trees; all floral parts in fives; petals absent. Male flowers: very small, yellowish, in fine, loose heads, 27 × 17 cm; stamens 15 to 30; ovary vestigial; much more numerous than the female flowers. Female flowers: greenish, also produced in branched heads, but more thickset, compact and densely velvety than are the male flowers; stamens absent (September onwards but mainly in December). **Fruit:** a markedly 2-lobed, thinly woody, dehiscent capsule, each lobe being about 10 mm in diameter, densely velvety when young (December onwards).

26. MACARANGA Thouars

Shrubs or trees. **Leaves:** alternate, simple, the base more or less peltate. **Flowers:** in axillary spikes, racemes or panicles. Sexes separate on different trees. Floral parts in threes to fours; petals absent. Male flowers: stamens usually 3 to 30; ovary vestigial. Female flowers: stamens absent; ovary 2- to 3-celled; stigma stout and short. **Fruit:** a capsule.

Key to the species of *Macaranga:*
Stipules small and narrow, about 5 × 1 mm, dark-coloured, falling early; base of the leaves very narrowly peltate, frequently only lobed and not joined across the petiole; leaves ovate to oblong; petiole and midrib green; stem and branches without thorns. A tree of medium to high altitude evergreen forest .... **M. mellifera**   **427**

EUPHORBIACEAE

Stipules large, lanceolate, up to 2 × 0,5 cm, leaf-like, green, persisting for some time; base of the leaves more markedly peltate, especially on younger plants; leaves broadly ovate; petiole and midrib often rose-pink; stem and branches may be spiny. A tree of low altitude evergreen forest .... **M. capensis**

Macaranga capensis (Baillon) Benth. ex T. R. Sim
S.A. no: 335   Wild poplar. Wildepopulier
Rhod. no: 496   Spiny macaranga

A medium to large tree usually 7 to 13 m in height, but reaching 25 m under favourable conditions; occurring at low altitudes in evergreen forest, often fringing the forest or along stream banks. **Bark:** pale grey to light brown and smooth; frequently with a wide branching, rounded crown; the trunk and branches are sometimes armed with spines. **Leaves:** large, ovate to almost triangular-ovate, occasionally tending towards elliptic, usually 10 to 15 × 8 to 12 cm, but can be considerably larger, up to 30 × 30 cm on juvenile trees, dark dull green above, pale fresh green below, the young leaves conspicuously pale-coloured, even whitish; 3 to 4 main veins which are prominent and densely hairy on the under surface; apex narrowly but shortly attenuate; base may be lobed but usually the petiole joins the leaf well inside the blade so that a 'frill', as broad as 1,5 cm, runs round the bottom, that is, the base of the leaf is peltate, but it tends to become narrower in leaves on mature trees; margin entire; petiole long, slender, up to 16 cm in length, often rose-pink, the colour extending along the midrib and main veins. Stipules large, lanceolate, up to 2 × 0,5 cm, leaf-like, green, persisting for some time. **Flowers:** male flowers: small, yellowish-green, in short, branched, axillary sprays up to 6 cm long. Female flowers: greenish, in simple, few-flowered, axillary spikes up to 5 cm long (October to January). **Fruit:** a small, single-lobed, yellowish-green capsule, 4 to 5 × 3 to 4 mm, splitting quite explosively to reveal a single seed covered with a fleshy, red to purplish aril (March to April). This tree, and *Heywoodia lucens,* are the only two tree species with peltate leaves in the forests of southern Natal. The wood is dense, strong and greyish with dark brown lining; it has been used to make handsome furniture and is suitable for boxes and planking. It is fire-resistant and fast-growing; the flowers are honey-scented and attract bees.

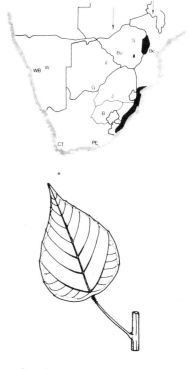

The peltate leaves of Macaranga capensis.

428

Macaranga mellifera Prain
S.A. no: —
Rhod. no: 497   Mountain macaranga

A medium to large tree 7 to 20 m in height; occurring in medium to high altitude, evergreen forest and on forest margins. **Bark:** grey, smooth. **Leaves:** ovate to oblong, 6 to 17 × 3 to 11 cm, dark green, the young leaves conspicuously pale, not inclined to be 3- to 4-veined from the base; apex generally narrowly attenuate forming a long, slender tip; base, in general outline, usually broadly tapering but occasionally square, often shallowly lobed but sometimes narrowly peltate, although this is frequently scarcely noticeable; margin entire, occasionally with a few, scattered, obscure teeth; petiole up to 10 cm long, green, not tinged with pink. Stipules small and narrow, about 5 × 1 mm, dark-coloured, falling early. **Flowers:** greenish-yellow, in short spikes, 4 to 6 cm long (September to October). **Fruit:** a spherical capsule, about 5 mm in diameter, brown, with short, soft, golden hairs, crowned with the remains of the 3 persistent styles, and clustered into catkin-like spikes, about 6 cm long; the capsule splits into 2 valves to reveal a single seed almost as large as the capsule (March to June).

27. ACALYPHA L.

Herbs, shrubs or trees. **Leaves:** alternate, simple, 3- to 7-veined from the base. **Flowers:** axillary or terminal, unisexual or bisexual. If unisexual, then the female flowers are usually at the base of the spike with the male flowers above them. Floral parts in threes to fours; petals absent; disc absent. Male flowers: very small, in clusters above small inconspicuous bracts, forming slender, catkin-like spikes or racemes; stamens usually 8; ovary absent. Female flowers: solitary, or in groups of rarely more than 2 within a toothed or lobed bract, usually becoming leaf-like as the fruit develops; stamens absent; ovary 3-chambered, hairy. **Fruit:** a capsule.

Key to the tree species of *Acalypha*:

Leaf apex rounded; branches spinescent; flower spikes with a terminal female flower and male flowers
    below it .... **A. sonderana**
Leaf apex attenuate; branches without spines; flower spikes with one or more female flowers at the
    base of the spike and male flowers above .... **A. glabrata**

Acalypha glabrata Thunb.
S.A. no: 335,1   Forest false-nettle. Bosvalsnetel
Rhod. no: 500   Silky-berry

A scrambling shrub or a small, heavily foliaged tree up to 5 m in height; abundant in coastal forest, but also found inland, in evergreen forest, in bush and woodland, often along stream banks. **Bark:** smooth, grey; branchlets long and slender, velvety, unarmed. **Leaves:** ovate, 2 to 8 × 1,2 to 4,5 cm; the young leaves are reddish and covered with fine hairs, but the mature leaves lose most of these, except on the under surface which may remain sparsely hairy, chiefly along the veins; mature leaves light green, thinly textured, becoming vivid red in autumn; apex narrowly attenuate; base very broadly tapering to square; margin roughly toothed to scalloped; petiolate. **Flowers:** in sparse, axillary spikes, 3 to 4 cm long. Male flowers: very small, whitish to yellowish. Female flowers: greenish-yellow, with a small ovary, densely covered with silky hairs and crowned with much-branched styles; occurring on the same flower spike as the male flowers, but usually near the base (October onwards).

429

Fruit: a slightly 3-lobed capsule about 5 to 7 mm in diameter, yellowish, covered with silky hairs, splitting to release the seeds (December to January).
The wood has been used for fencing posts and for stakes in the ground. Fish traps are made from the long, tough, elastic branchlets.

Acalypha sonderana Muell. Arg.
S.A. no: 335,2   Thorny false-nettle. Doringvalsnetel
Rhod. no: —

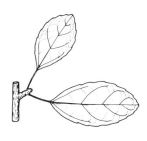

A shrub or small tree up to 4 m in height, occasionally reaching 10 m; occurring in evergreen forest and coastal bush. **Bark:** grey, smooth; the short, lateral branchlets are occasionally spinescent. **Leaves:** clustered on the branchlets, ovate to elliptic, 2,5 to 5,8 × 1,5 to 2,5 cm, thinly textured; apex rounded; base rounded; margin bluntly scalloped to almost entire; petiolate. **Flowers:** greenish-yellow in slender but quite well-flowered spikes up to 4 cm long, the male flowers near the base, the single female flower with its red styles at the apex (August to October). **Fruit:** a 3-lobed capsule, about 4 mm in diameter, reddish-brown, with short, brown bristles, dehiscent (November to December).

28. *JATROPHA L.

*Jatropha curcas L.

The physic nut, or *purgeerboontjie,* was introduced from tropical America probably centuries ago and, it is thought, gradually spread from Moçambique through Rhodesia to the Transvaal and Natal. In all these areas it is frequently planted as living fences round African and Indian villages, and has become naturalised. It is a sturdy shrub or small tree, its bark yellowish with a papery peel. The leaves are large and lobed, the flowers small, greenish and produced among the leaves, and the fruit is a large capsule about 4 cm in diameter. The seeds provide an oil favoured by Africans for cosmetic purposes and to make candles and soap. The seeds, taken in small quantities, have a purgative action (hence the common names); overdoses can produce a violent reaction, but recovery is rapid. However, some confusing information is that this plant is very poisonous with several deaths in S.W.A. 1979-1980. It has been used as a fish and arrow poison.

29. CLUTIA L.

Undershrubs, shrubs, or occasionally small trees. **Leaves:** alternate, simple, often without a petiole. **Flowers:** sexes separate on different trees, or occasionally on the same tree. Floral parts in fours to

430

fives; petals almost as long as the sepals; disc often with one or more glands at the base. Male flowers: on short stalks in axillary clusters; stamens joined at the base to surround the vestigial ovary. Female flowers: on longer stalks, usually solitary, occasionally in fascicles, in the axils of the leaves; stamens absent; ovary with or without hairs or warty; styles 2- to 3-branched. **Fruit:** a woody, almost spherical capsule.

Key to the tree species of *Clutia:*
Capsules smooth .... **C. abyssinica**
Capsules warty .... **C. pulchella**

Clutia abyssinica Jaub. & Spach
[*C. glabrescens* Knauf]
S.A. no: 336 Smooth-fruited clutia. Grootbliksembos
Rhod. no: 506 Smooth-fruited clutia

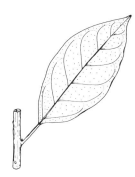

Usually a shrub 1 to 2 m in height, but it can become a small tree reaching 6 m; occurring in evergreen forest, riverine forest and often in forested ravines. **Bark:** greenish to pale brown; branches brittle. **Leaves:** elliptic, 3 to 11 × 1,3 to 3,5 cm, thinly textured, pellucid gland-dotted, light green becoming red to gold in autumn; apex and base tapering; margin entire; petiole slender up to 2,5 cm long. **Flowers:** very small, greenish to white. Male flowers: in tight, axillary clusters along the young branches. Female flowers: solitary, occasionally among the male flowers; the ovary is comparatively large and soon starts swelling into the fruit (March to June, or even later). **Fruit:** a capsule, about 4 to 5 mm in diameter, dehiscent (April to September).
The roots are used in African medicine as a laxative.

Clutia pulchella L.
S.A. no: Warty-fruited clutia. Gewone bliksembos
Rhod. no. 509 Warty-fruited clutia

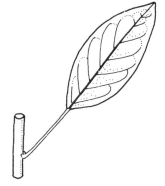

A shrub or small tree up to 6 m in height; occurring over a wide range of altitudes and in a variety of habitats, from karroid scrub to evergreen forest. **Bark:** brown; branchlets with or without warts. **Leaves:** ovate to elliptic, occasionally even circular, 1 to 7,5 × 0,5 to 7,5 cm, thinly textured, pellucid gland-dotted, light green above, bluish-green below, becoming orange and red in autumn; the veining on the leaves is translucent; apex broadly tapering; base tapering; margin entire, finely rolled under; petiole slender, up to 2,5 cm long. **Flowers:** very small, white, inconspicuous (November to

431

January). **Fruit:** a spherical, warty capsule about 5 mm in diameter, dehiscent (January to May). This species has been divided into 3 varieties:

var. *pulchella* – branchlets warty; leaves ovate to ovate-oblong with long appressed hairs when young. Widespread from the south-western Cape to Rhodesia.

var. *franksiae* Prain – branchlets not warty; leaves ovate, small up to 2,5 cm long only, with soft spreading persistent hairs. Apparently occurring only from Transkei through to Zululand.

var. *obtusata* Sonder – branchlets not warty; leaves almost circular, up to 7,5 cm in diameter, with hairs only when young. Occurring from the eastern Cape to the Transvaal.

30. RICINODENDRON Muell. Arg.

Ricinodendron rautanenii Schinz
S.A. no: 337   Manketti tree. Mankettiboom
Rhod. no: 511   Manketti tree

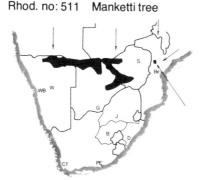

A large spreading tree, 15 to 20 m in height; occurring on wooded hills and among sand dunes, always on Kalahari sand and sometimes forming pure stands. **Bark:** grey to light golden-brown, smooth, with a tendency to peel; the stem is thickset and stout, and the thick young branchlets are densely covered with soft rust-coloured furry hairs which later fall; the branches and stems exude a white gum. **Leaves:** alternate, digitately compound, with 5 to 7 leaflets; leaflets oval, 6 to 11 × 3,5 to 5,5 cm, dark green above, pale grey below with stellate hairs on both surfaces; the leaf buds are covered with dense rusty furry hairs; apex broadly tapering; base tapering; margin entire; petiolules and petiole covered with rusty hairs, petiole up to 15 cm long. Stipules small. **Flowers:** yellow, about 10 mm in diameter, produced in slender loose sprays, or panicled cymes, up to 12 cm long. Sexes separate on different trees. Floral parts in fours to fives; sepals densely covered with golden to rusty, furry, stellate hairs; petals joined to form a wide tube. Male flowers: stamens 10 to 18, free, forming a central head; disc 4- to 5-lobed, each lobe attached to the base of the stamens; ovary absent. Female flowers: stamens absent; disc saucer-shaped; ovary densely covered with stellate hairs; produced in few-flowered sprays, shorter than those of the male flowers (October to November). **Fruit:** egg-shaped, up to 3,5 × 2,5 cm, light grey-green and covered with velvety hairs; inside the fruit there is a single, very hard seed which, when cracked open, reveals an edible kernel which provides a bright yellow edible oil (February onwards).
In South West Africa a porridge is made from the dried fruit which has been scraped away from the kernel. The fresh pulp has a fruity smell and an astringent but not unpleasant taste. The wood is pale yellowish-white, the grain is wavy and the texture coarse, but it is comparatively strong for its very light weight and therefore makes a reasonable substitute for South American balsa wood. It has also been used for light packing cases, insulating material, floats, toys, drawing boards and dart boards. It should be sawn immediately after cutting and dried as rapidly as possible to prevent discolouration. This is a protected plant in South Africa.

31. SUREGADA Roxb. ex Rottler

Shrubs or trees. **Leaves:** alternate, simple, almost without a petiole, pellucid gland-dotted. Stipules joined, falling early. **Flowers:** in leaf-opposed, dense heads, without stalks. Sexes separate on different trees. All floral parts in fives; calyx lobes unequal, the 3 outer lobes concave; petals absent. Male flowers: disc saucer-shaped; stamens 6 to 60; ovary absent. Female flowers: disc shallowly saucer-shaped, sometimes with vestiges of staminodes on the rim; ovary without hairs. **Fruit:** a somewhat woody, or fleshy, capsule.

Key to the tree species of *Suregada:*
1 Leaves usually less than 5 cm long .... **S. africana**
  Leaves usually more than 5 cm long 2
2 Leaf margin entire, or sinuate, or obscurely and broadly toothed; apex tapering, very rarely abruptly and very shortly attenuate; sepals without glands; flowers with sexes separate on different trees .... **S. procera**
  Leaf margins entire to sharply and jaggedly toothed; apex narrowly attenuate; sepals with glands on the back; flowers with sexes separate but on the same tree .... **S. zanzibariensis**

Suregada africana (Sonder) Kuntze
S.A. no: 338   Common suregada. Gewone kanariebessie
Rhod. no: —

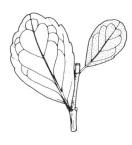

A slender, lax-stemmed tree up to 6 m in height; occurring in evergreen forest. **Bark:** pale grey to brown. **Leaves:** oblanceolate to obovate, up to 5 × 3 cm, pellucid gland-dotted; apex rounded; base tapering; margin scalloped, or obscurely toothed; petiole short, about 1 to 2 mm long. **Flowers:** small, yellow to greenish-white, in tight clusters produced on very short, dwarf, lateral branchlets, opposite or just below the leaves (September to October). **Fruit:** a 3-lobed capsule, about 10 mm in diameter, becoming yellowish when mature, dehiscent (November).

Suregada procera (Prain) Croizat
[*Gelonium procerum* Prain]
S.A. no: 339   Forest suregada. Boskanariebessie
Rhod. no: 512   Forest suregada

A small to medium sized tree up to 9 m in height, with a superficial resemblance to a lemon tree; occurring in evergreen forest. **Bark:** grey, smooth, or minutely vertically fissured; the branches are usually long and slender. **Leaves:** elliptic to oblanceolate, 2,5 to 11 × 1,3 to 5,5 cm, leathery, dark green above, paler green below, with conspicuous pellucid dots over the whole surface; apex broadly tapering to rounded; base tapering and running into the petiole; margin entire or obscurely serrate;

433

petiole almost absent, or very short, due to the decurrent leaf base. Stipules fall early, leaving scars. **Flowers:** small, whitish to greenish, solitary or in axillary clusters; the male flowers have conspicuous yellow stamens; the sepals lack glands (September to November, but buds may be on the tree again by February to March). **Fruit:** a 3-lobed, golden-brown capsule, broader than it is long, up to 8 × 10 mm, dehiscent (December to February).

Suregada zanzibariensis Baillon
S.A. no: 340   Woodland suregada. Sandkanariebessie
Rhcd. no: 513   Woodland suregada

 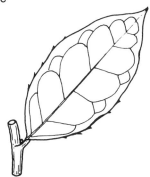

A shrub or small tree reaching up to 5 m in height, somewhat resembling a citrus tree; occurring in woodland at low altitudes. **Bark:** grey, smooth, scaling towards the base. **Leaves:** obovate, 4 to 9 × 2,5 to 5 cm, pellucid-dotted; apex rounded and abruptly attenuate; base tapering; margin usually very finely but irregularly toothed, although it may be conspicuously toothed so that it almost resembles a holly leaf. **Flowers:** very small, creamy-green, solitary or in clusters in the axils of the leaves; the sepals have glands on the back (March). **Fruit:** a 3-lobed capsule, about 7 mm in diameter, pale brown, thinly woody (June).

32. EXCOECARIA L.

Shrubs or trees; all parts without hairs. **Leaves:** alternate or opposite, simple. Stipules minute, falling early. **Flowers:** in axillary spikes, the male spike usually dense, the female spike lax; produced with the leaves. Sexes separate on the same tree or on different trees. Floral parts usually in threes (occasionally in twos or fours); petals absent; disc absent; stamens 2 to 3, free, absent in female flowers; ovary 3-celled, with 3 stigmas joined at the base, vestigial in male flowers. **Fruit:** a dehiscent capsule.

Key to the tree species of *Excoecaria:*
Leaves opposite, narrowly elliptic to lanceolate, not broader than 5 cm; flowers in short spikes, barely more than 2 cm long. Occurring in medium altitude evergreen forest. ....
.... **E. madagascariensis**
Leaves alternate, broadly ovate, up to 8 cm broad; flowers in long spikes up to 12 cm long. Occurring in low altitude riverine fringe forest and thicket .... **E. bussei**

Excoecaria bussei (Pax) Pax
[*Sapium bussei* Pax]
S.A. no: —
Rhod. no: 514   Pawn-broker tree

A small to medium sized tree up to 10 m in height; occurring at low altitudes, in hot dry areas, frequently in thicket or riverine fringe thicket. **Bark:** pale grey to brown, varying from rather smooth to rough; the tree exudes a milky latex when damaged. **Leaves:** alternate, elliptic, 4,5 to 15 × 3 to 8 cm, thinly textured; apex shortly attenuate; base tapering; margin scalloped; petiole slender, up to 10 mm long. **Flowers:** small, greenish-yellow, in slender, axillary spikes up to 12 cm long. Sexes separate on the same tree; the flower spikes are almost always made up entirely of male flowers, but occasionally 1 to 2 female flowers are produced near the base (November). **Fruit:** a distinctive, bladder-like, 3-lobed capsule, 5 × 4,5 cm, dark brown when mature, very thin walled and light; each

434

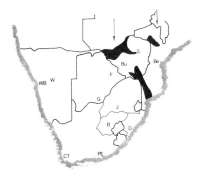

lobe contains a single, spherical, light brown seed, about 10 mm in diameter, and the three seeds are joined together to form a neat arrangement that somewhat resembles the sign above a pawn-broker's shop (February to March, and later).

If these seeds are chewed, they are tasteless at first but later produce a peppery, burning sensation which lasts for a considerable time. Africans maintain that the latex is harmful to the eyes and that all game avoid this tree.

Excoecaria madagascariensis (Baillon) Muell. Arg.

[*E. sylvestris* S. Moore]
S.A. no: —
Rhod. no: 515   Red-ears

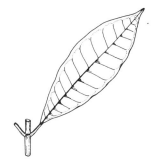

A shrub or small tree up to 4 m in height; occurring as an under-storey tree in evergreen forest. **Bark:** dark blackish-brown and smooth; a milky latex exudes if the stem or branches are damaged. **Leaves:** opposite, ovate-lanceolate, 3,5 to 15 × 1,7 to 5 cm; apex and base narrowly tapering; margin entire; petiole rather thick, about 10 mm long, channelled above; the tree is made conspicuous by the young leaves, about 2 at the end of each branch, which are erect and a deep coppery-red in colour. **Flowers:** greenish-white or yellowish, in short spikes, about 2 cm long, almost concealed behind the bright red young leaves; the spikes are often made up entirely of male flowers, but occasionally a few female flowers occur at the base (October to November). **Fruit:** a thinly woody capsule, about 6 mm in diameter, bright red, becoming yellowish-brown when mature and dry; splitting to release the seeds (February to March).

33. SPIROSTACHYS Sonder

Spirostachys africana Sonder   Illust. 141
S.A. no: 341   Tamboti. Tambotie
Rhod. no: 516   Tamboti

A medium sized tree with a rounded crown, usually about 10 m in height, but occasionally reaching 15 m; occurring in low altitude bush, often along rivers and streams. **Bark:** dark grey to blackish and rough, forming rectangular, chunky flakes. **Leaves:** alternate, simple, small, ovate to elliptic, 2,5 to 7 × 1,8 to 3,5 cm, usually about 5 × 2,5 cm, with 2 glands at the junction with the petiole, light green, hairy, becoming brilliant yellow to red in autumn; apex and base tapering to rounded; margin finely toothed or scalloped; petiole slender, about 6 mm long. Stipules small, falling early. **Flowers:** very

435

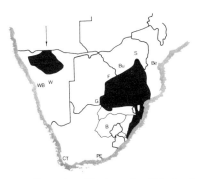

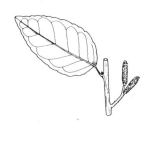

small, produced in the axils of distinctive reddish bracts in slender catkin-like spikes up to 3 cm long, the overlapping bracts somewhat resembling a rat's tail; each spike is usually made up of many male flowers, but there may be a few female flowers at the base. All floral parts in fives; petals absent; disc absent; stamens 3, joined to form a slender tube, absent in female flowers; ovary 3-celled, with 3 styles joined to form a thick cylindric column, vestigial in male flowers (September onwards, but the first flowers appear very early and last well into the new year). **Fruit:** a 3-lobed capsule (occasionally 2-lobed), about 10 mm in diameter, yellowish-brown, splitting when mature (about October to December, but also at most times of the year).

The copious milky latex is very poisonous and causes extreme irritation to sensitive skin and severe pain and even damage to the eyes. Africans use it as a fish poison and to tip arrow heads. P. van Wyk quotes the case of a ranger in the Kruger National Park who, while on a foot patrol, suddenly developed severe toothache. The African ranger with him put a drop of *Spirostachys* latex into the cavity in the tooth and, after a moment of intense pain, the nerve quickly became deadened. The wood is hard, heavy, durable, close-grained and not touched by termites or borers; the sapwood is creamy-white and the heartwood rich brown with a satin-like lustre. It is inclined to be oily and, when freshly worked, has a distinctive, sweetish smell; care should be taken to keep sawdust out of the eyes. This wood is not suitable for fuel: it burns with a strange, sweetish odour, initially pleasant and aromatic, but later becoming sickening and causing headache and nausea, while the smoke itself is said to taint food. It does not make satisfactory ox-yokes either as it causes burn-like sores on the animals' necks and its effects on insects are so unpleasant to them that pieces of wood are placed among clothing as a repellent. Africans are warned against this tree from early childhood, their fear sometimes amounting almost to a taboo which prevents them from damaging any living specimens. Nevertheless, splendid furniture has been made from the timber though large pieces are difficult to come by as the trunks of the trees are often hollow. The wood itself is almost indestructible and samples in a very good state of preservation were taken from the Zimbabwe Ruins for carbon-dating: they were reported as being between 1 240 and 1 530 years old so the trees must have been of considerable age when the timber was collected. This is one of the 'jumping bean' trees, the seeds often becoming infested with the larvae of a small grey moth, which, by spasmodic straightening of the body, cause the seed to spring several centimetres into the air.

34. SAPIUM P. Browne

Shrubs or trees; milky latex present. **Leaves:** alternate, simple. **Flowers:** in an axillary or terminal spike, bearing both male and female flowers, usually with many male flowers in the upper section of the spike and a few female flowers near the base. Those along the spike solitary, or in few-flowered clusters in the axils of bracts. Floral parts in twos or threes; petals absent; disc absent; stamens 2 to 3, free, absent in female flowers; ovary 3-celled, with 3 styles, free, sometimes lying back flat over the surface of the ovary reaching almost to its base, absent in male flowers. **Fruit:** a woody capsule.

Key to the tree species of *Sapium*:
Leaves 5 to 9 × 2 to 3 cm; fruits 3-lobed, splitting into 6 valves, each valve with a distinct horn near
    the apex .... **S. integerrimum**
Leaves tending to be larger than those of the preceding species, 6 to 14 × 2,5 to 4 cm; fruits 2-lobed,
    reluctantly dehiscent, without the horns, but usually crowned with the remains of the persistent
    styles .... **S. ellipticum**

Sapium ellipticum (Hochst.) Pax
S.A. no: 342   Jumping seed tree. Springsaadboom
Rhod. no: 517   Jumping seed tree

A small to medium sized tree up to 12 m in height, occasionally reaching 20 m; common on the outskirts of evergreen forest and in wooded ravines; in Zululand it occurs as a canopy tree in swamp forest. **Bark:** light brown to very dark and almost black, rough; the branches tend to droop. **Leaves:** elliptic, oblong to lanceolate, 6 to 14 × 2,5 to 4 cm, dark green; apex tapering, often attenuate; base tapering to almost rounded; margin irregularly toothed to scalloped; petiole up to 10 mm long.
Flowers: yellow, in axillary or terminal catkin-like spikes about 5 cm long (November to April).
Fruit: a 1- to 2-lobed capsule about 10 × 7 mm, reddish, usually crowned with the remains of the persistent styles, but without horns, reluctantly dehiscent (March to August).
Insect larvae frequently infest the seeds which they cause to jump several centimetres into the air by straightening their bodies convulsively.

Sapium integerrimum (Hochst.) J. Léonard   Illust. 142
S.A. no: 343   Duiker-berry. Duikerbessie
Rhod. no: 518   Duiker-berry

Usually a small deciduous tree up to 7 m in height, but it may be taller; occurring in open woodland or fringing forest. **Bark:** pale grey, smoothish; young branches lax. **Leaves:** oblong-ovate to elliptic, 5 to 9 × 2 to 3 cm, without hairs, dull dark green above, paler dull green below; apex tapering, sometimes narrowly so; base tapering to rounded; margin widely scalloped; petiole short. **Flowers:** greenish-yellow, in catkin-like spikes up to 7 cm long (October to January). **Fruit:** a very hard 3-lobed capsule, up to 1,7 cm in diameter, greenish-yellow when mature; splitting into 6 valves, each lobe containing a single, smooth, satiny, coppery-brown seed, about 6 × 5 mm, slightly streaked and mottled, resembling a castor oil (*Ricinus*) seed (November to March and later, the fruits often remaining on the tree for a considerable time).
In years past ink was made from the fruits and they have also been used in tanning. An infusion is prepared from the roots as a mouthwash to ease toothache. The wood is heavy, hard and durable; it is a useful general purpose timber and can make attractive furniture.

EUPHORBIACEAE

35. MAPROUNEA Aubl.

Maprounea africana Muell. Arg.
S.A. no: 343,1   Redskin. Rooitakkie
Rhod. no: 519   Redskin

 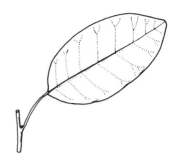

A small deciduous tree with spreading branches, reaching 7 m in height, but usually about 4 to 5 m; occurring in open woodland, sometimes in riverine fringe forest, often on sandy soils and occasionally on dunes. **Bark:** thick, grey or blackish, very rough, deeply and irregularly fissured. **Leaves:** alternate, simple, ovate to shortly lanceolate or elliptic, 3 to 5 × 2,2 to 3 cm; the young leaves are bright red, becoming light green when mature and then again red with age; apex broadly tapering, finally narrowly rounded and notched; base rounded to shallowly lobed; margin entire; petiole very slender, up to 15 cm long; stipules small. **Flowers:** yellowish, in characteristic, contracted spikes, almost forming round balls about 5 mm in diameter, but they may become more elongate, up to 8 × 4 mm, as they mature. Sexes separate but in the same spike, the male flowers very small and densely packed into the congested heads, the female flowers solitary on longer stalks, just below the male flowers. Floral parts in twos to threes; petals and disc absent; stamens 1 to 3, joined at the base to form a slender column, absent in female flowers; ovary 3-celled, the styles joined at the base to form a short column, vestigal in male flowers (August to October). **Fruit:** a 3-lobed capsule about 10 mm in diameter, red when mature, drying to brown (November to January).

36. EUPHORBIA L.

Herbs, shrubs or trees, very variable in habit, all producing a milky and often copious latex. Most of the trees are succulent, spiny and somewhat cactus-like, but a few unarmed and woody species occur. **Leaves:** alternate, opposite or whorled; in the succulent species they are usually inconspicuous and often fleeting. Branches mostly angular, usually constricted into segments, the shape of which is often characteristic of the species; the angles are often compressed, becoming wing-like, with the margins frequently slightly toothed or shallowly indented and armed with paired spines (a much smaller pair, often reduced to a mere asperity, usually occurs above) arising from horny bases known as spine shields. These are sometimes wholly or partly united to form a continuous or subcontinuous horny margin. **Inflorescence:** bisexual or unisexual; reduced to a fleshy flower-like structure, called a *cyathium* which consists of a fleshy involucre with a ring of glands (nectaries) at its rim, and usually contains a single female flower reduced to an ovary with a rudimentary perianth/calyx which may be carried on a distinct sometimes curved pedicel, or may be almost without a stalk; this female flower is surrounded by groups (usually 5) of male flowers alternating with the glands, each male flower being reduced to a pedicel and a single stamen with a pair of anther cells, and usually being subtended by a pair of membraneous bracteoles. The cyathia are usually arranged vertically or horizontally in groups of 3 (occasionally 5) to form a cyme, with the initial or central cyathium usually being male and subsequent cyathia being bisexual; wholly female cyathia are rare. **Fruit:** a capsule, dehiscent.

All species of *Euphorbia* should be treated with caution. The milky latex is poisonous and causes damage to the eyes and intense irritation and inflamation to the skin. In fact, in some species it is so toxic that it can prove fatal if taken internally.

Key to the woody species of *Euphorbia:*
1 Tips of the branchlets spinescent .... **E. matabelensis**
  Tips of the branchlets not distinctly hardened into spines 2

2 Bark olive-green with a yellow-brown papery peel; cyathia solitary, produced on lateral branches so reduced as to be slight cushions only .... **E. espinosa**
Bark dark brown; cyathia solitary but produced on distinct dwarf lateral branchlets..............
.... **E. guerichiana**

Key to the succulent species of *Euphorbia* (because of the complexities and the close relationships of these species it has been found necessary to key out on a geographical basis):

A. On Goa island only, off the coast of northern Moçambique .... **E. angularis**

B. Extreme north-west of SOUTH WEST AFRICA and northwards only

A tall, candelabriform *Euphorbia* on stony, rocky hills .... **E. eduardoi**

C. EASTERN CAPE

1 Without spines, many-branched; branchlets narrowly cylindric up to 7 mm in diameter
.... **E. tirucalli**
With spines; branches square or winged, more than 7 mm in diameter 2
2 Branches not markedly winged, being somewhat square in cross section 3
Branches distinctly winged 4
3 Branchlets markedly slender, 1 to 2 cm in diameter, 2- to 3-angled, forming conspicuously small crowns usually only 0,5 to 1 m in diameter .... **E. grandidens**
Branchlets slender, but up to 2,5 to 5 cm in diameter, 4- to 5-angled, forming small crowns, but larger than those of the preceding species, being 1,5 to 2 m in diameter ...... **E. tetragona**
4 Fruits very shortly stalked, almost sessile; branches curve upwards, but tend to be horizontal where they join the main stem; dark green; crown 2 to 3 m in diameter.............. **E. curvirama**
Fruits with a distinct stalk; branches tend to be ascending from the base; yellowish-green; crown somewhat smaller than that of the preceding species, about 1,5 to 2,5 m in diameter
.... **E. triangularis**

D. NATAL, SWAZILAND and extreme southern MOÇAMBIQUE

1 Without spines; many-branched; branchlets narrowly cylindric, up to 7 mm in diameter
.... **E. tirucalli**
With spines; branches square or winged 2
2 Branches not, or only slightly, constricted to form segments; not conspicuously winged 3
Branches deeply constricted to form conspicuous segments; winged 4
3 Branches usually 2- to 3-angled (only occasionally 4-angled), the crests of the undulate margins with wart-like cushions; spines often accompanied by 2 prickles; trees reaching 16 m in height
.... **E. grandidens**
Branches 3- to 4-angled, the margins without warty cushions; spines never accompanied by prickles; reaching a maximum height of 10 m .... **E. evansii**
4 A massively branched tree, the heavy branches arising from fairly low down, neither the candelabriform shape nor the individual crowns of branchlets being evident .... **E. ingens**
Distinctly candelabriform; may be branched, in which case each branch has its own conspicuous crown of branchlets 5
5 Segments of the branchlets comparatively short and broad, conspicuously triangular in outline, up to 15 cm long × 12 cm broad, broad at the top of each segment, tapering sharply to the base
.... **E. cooperi**
Segments of the branchlets with parallel sides, not triangular in outline, each segment up to 30 cm long and not more than 9 cm broad 6
6 Spine shields forming a continuous horny margin to the wings; spines 5 to 8 mm long, fairly stout; branchlets usually 5-winged, only 3 to 4 cm in diameter. Occurring near Stegi in Swaziland only
.... **E. keithii**
Spine shields usually separate, occasionally continuous; spines 3 to 8 mm long, widely diverging, slender; branchlets usually 3-winged, 4 to 9 cm in diameter. Widespread along the coast from the eastern Cape to Zululand and Swaziland and into Moçambique .... **E. triangularis**　　**439**

EUPHORBIACEAE

Spine shields subcontinuous or separate, spines generally less than 5 mm long, slender; branchlets usually 4-winged (or 6-winged in subsp. *rhodesiaca),* about 6 to 7 cm in diameter. Extending south to Swaziland and southern Moçambique .... **E. confinalis**

E. TRANSVAAL

1 Without spines, many-branched; branchlets narrowly cylindric up to 7 mm in diameter .... **E. tirucalli**
  With spines, branchlets either 2- to 5-angled, or -winged 2
2 Branchlets not deeply constricted to form segments 3
  Branchlets deeply and conspicuously constricted to form segments 6
3 In the south-eastern Transvaal 4
  In central-eastern Transvaal, Sekukuniland only 5
4 Branchlets usually 2- to 3-angled (only rarely 4-angled), the crests of the undulate wing margins with wart-like cushions; spines often accompanied by 2 prickles; reaching 16 m in height. Possibly only just occurring in the Transvaal .... **E. grandidens**
  Branchlets 3- to 4-angled, without warty cushions; spines never accompanied by prickles; reaching a maximum height of 10 m .... **E. evansii**
5 Stem with 8 to 10 dark, horny, slight vertical ridges, being obsolete wings which have filled out; spine shields on the branchlet wings united to form a continuous horny margin to the wings, this horny margin widening at each pair of spines and tapering towards the next pair above it; branchlets 4- to 5-angled, not deeply winged; slightly constricted at intervals of about 20 cm and frequently rebranching immediately above these points .... **E. sekukuniensis**
  Stem without the dark vertical ridges; spine shields united to form a continuous margin of almost uniform width; branchlets usually 4-angled, nearly square in cross-section, slightly constricted at intervals of 8 to 15 cm, but not markedly inclined to rebranch above these points .... **E. excelsa**
6 A massively branched tree, the heavy branches arising from fairly low down, not candelabriform in shape and without individual crowns of branchlets .... **E. ingens**
  Distinctly candelabriform with or without trunk-like branches, each with its own crown of branchlets 7
7 Segments conspicuously triangular in outline, up to 15 × 12 cm .... **E. cooperi**
  Segments not triangular in outline, sides parallel 8
8 Branches conspicuously slender and graceful, 2 to 3,5 cm in diameter. Endemic to the area round Wyllie's Poort in the Soutpansberg .... **E. zoutpansbergensis**
  Branchlets more thickset than those of the preceding species, 6 to 7 cm in diameter. More widespread .... **E. confinalis**

F. RHODESIA, BOTSWANA and MOÇAMBIQUE

1 Without spines; many-branched; branchlets narrowly cylindric, up to 7 mm in diameter .... **E. tirucalli**
  With spines; branches 4- to 6-angled or winged 2
2 A massively branched tree, the heavy branches arising from fairly low down, not candelabriform in shape and without individual crowns of branchlets being evident .... **E. ingens**
  Distinctly candelabriform, with or without trunk-like branches each with its distinctive crown of branchlets 3
3 Spines large, 10 to 15 mm long. In Moçambique and only just into the south-east of Rhodesia .... **E. halipedicola**
  Spines up to 7 mm long (very occasionally longer, up to 15 mm in *E. cooperi)* 4
4 Spine shields merge to form a continuous horny margin to the wings on the branches 5
  Spine shields not continuous 6
5 Trees rarely more than 5 m in height; trunk conspicuously short and branching low down, the branches being sub-persistent; branch segments broadly elliptic to almost spherical in outline. Confined to the Zambezi valley .... **E. fortissima**
  Trees reaching 7 m with a long naked trunk 3 m or more in length. Branch segments triangular in outline. Not confined to the Zambezi valley .... **E. cooperi**

440

6 Branchlets usually 5 to 7 cm in diameter; spines and shields relatively strong; involucral glands in the flower heads greenish-yellow .... **E. confinalis**

Branchlets slender, usually about 2 to 2,5 cm in diameter; spines and shields small and weak; flowers distinctive and conspicuous, involucral glands reddish-purple with 5 bright red overlapping lobes .... **E. lividiflora**

Euphorbia angularis Klotzsch, with short, thickset segments, previously thought to occur in the Transvaal, is now known to occur only on Goa island, just off the northern coast of Moçambique.

Euphorbia confinalis R. A. Dyer
S.A. no: 345   Confinalis. Lebombo-naboom
Rhod. no: 520   Confinalis

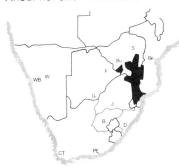

A spiny, succulent candelabriform tree up to 10 m in height with a sturdy main stem which may develop trunk-like branches, each with the characteristic crown of branchlets; occurring on rocky hill slopes and, in Moçambique, on deep alluvial soils. The branchlets are 4-winged (occasionally 3- or 5-winged), and not much more than 6 to 7 cm in diameter. The spines are slender, up to 5 mm long, but frequently shorter; spine-shields conspicuous, but usually separate, only occasionally continuous. The branchlets are constricted at intervals, forming segments with parallel sides. **Inflorescence:** greenish-yellow, with the cyathia of the usual pattern in groups of 3 cymes (June to August). **Fruit:** a 3-lobed capsule, 6 to 7 mm in diameter, ruby-red when mature, on a slender stalk (July to September). A second subspecies, subsp. *rhodesiaca* Leach occurs in the Matopos, Chibi and Bikita areas in the west and south of Rhodesia. It differs from the single stemmed subsp. *confinalis* in being generally more robust and stout, having a trunk which is 5- to 6-angled (instead of being 3- to 4-angled) and usually branched, and being generally more strongly armed, with hornier, wider and more distinct spine shields. Its latex has no scent and is somewhat thin and watery.

Euphorbia cooperi N. E. Brown ex A. Berger
S.A. no: 346   Lesser candelabra tree. Transvaalse kandelaarnaboom
Rhod. no: 521   Lesser candelabra tree

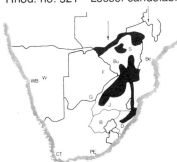

A spiny, succulent, candelabriform tree up to 7 m in height, with a naked trunk up to 3 m in length; occurring on rocky outcrops, in wooded grassland and in scrub. The branchlets are deeply divided, producing triangular or heart-shaped segments resembling chunky strings of beads; the segments are 5

441

The lesser candelabra tree, Euphorbia cooperi.

to 15 cm long and up to 12 cm broad, very conspicuously 4- to 6-winged. Spines usually 5 to 7 mm long, occasionally up to 15 mm; the spine shields run into each other forming a continuous, horny margin to the wings on the branchlets. **Inflorescence:** yellowish-green; cyathia of the usual pattern in groups of 3 cymes towards the tips of the branches; bisexual (September to October). **Fruit:** a markedly 3-lobed capsule, 15 × 8 mm, green with reddish markings, becoming dull red when mature (September to October onwards). The flowering and fruiting times often overlap.

The species comprises 3 varieties: the typical variety, var. *cooperi,* (refer to the dotted area on the map) has segments 5 to 15 cm long, branchlets 4- to 6-winged and wings 5 to 6 mm thick, and is widely distributed; var. *calidicola* Leach (refer to the vertical lines on the map) has rather larger segments, 10 to 15 cm long, its branches are 3- to 4-winged, the wings are thin, being about 3 mm at the margin and it is confined to the Zambezi valley; the third variety, *ussanquensis* (N. E. Brown) Leach, occurs only in countries to the north.

The latex has a pungent, acrid smell and is said to be one of the most poisonous of the *Euphorbia* species, causing intense skin irritation and even producing a burning sensation in the throat if one stands too close to a bleeding plant. If material is being collected, care should be taken to wrap the branches in some protective covering. The latex is used as fish poison by the method described under *E. ingens.*

Euphorbia curvirama R. A. Dyer
S.A. no: 347   Cape candelabra tree. Kaapse kandelaarnaboom
Rhod. no: —

A spiny, succulent, candelabriform tree seldom exceeding 5 m in height; occurring in dry, thorny scrub, on rocky hillsides and in river valleys. The stem is usually single, but it may produce 1 to 3 trunk-like branches, each with a round crown, 2 to 3 m in diameter, of dark green branchlets, which leave the stem almost at right angles and then curve sharply before growing upright. The branchlets

are usually 4-winged (occasionally 3- or 5-winged) constricted into segments. Spines stout, up to 1,5 cm long, grey, widely diverging; spine shields united to form a broad, conspicuous, horny margin. **Inflorescence:** greenish-yellow; cyathia of the usual pattern in 1 to 3 cymes produced above the spines (June). **Fruit:** a 3-lobed capsule, about 7 mm in diameter, very shortly stalked (July onwards).

This species closely resembles *E. triangularis*.

Euphorbia eduardoi Leach
S.A. no: 347,1   Kaoko euphorbia. Kaokonaboom
Rhod. no: —

A spiny, succulent candelabriform tree reaching 10 m in height; occurring on stony and rocky hills, sometimes forming well-populated colonies. Stem unbranched, stout, 5- to 6-angled, with a relatively small rather sparse crown. Branches ascending round the crown, almost horizontal lower down, slender, about 7,5 cm in diameter, only slightly constricted, not markedly winged (except on very young sections), 4- to 5-angled. Spines stout, up to 15 mm long, the spine shields reddish-brown, soon becoming cracked, grey and corky. **Inflorescence:** greenish-yellow; cyathia of the usual pattern (January to May). **Fruit:** ovoid, about 1,8 cm in diameter (May).

Euphorbia curvirama *on the left with* Euphorbia triangularis *(page 452) in the Great Fish River Valley.*

Euphorbia espinosa Pax
S.A. no: Woody euphorbia
Rhod. no: 522   Woody euphorbia

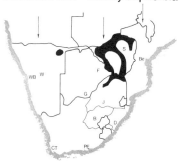

A woody shrub or small tree up to 3,5 m in height, often many-branched and twiggy; occurring on rocky outcrops or hillsides, but nowhere common. **Bark:** olive-green with a yellowish-brown papery peel; the stem is succulent; the branchlets are not spinescent. **Leaves:** oval to elliptic, 3,5 to 4 × 2 to 2,5 cm; apex rounded, finally very shortly but finely pointed; base broadly tapering; margin entire. The new leaves appear in December. **Inflorescence:** green or greenish-yellow, without stalks, produced on lateral branches which are so reduced as to be slight cushions only, clustered along the main branches; the cyathia are of the usual pattern (July to November). **Fruit:** a blue-green, 3-lobed capsule, about 8 mm in diameter (October to December).
This species resembles *E. matabelensis,* but the latter has spine-tipped branches.

Euphorbia evansii Pax
S.A. no: 348   Small-toothed euphorbia. Kleintandnaboom
Rhod. no: —

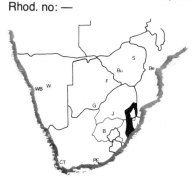

A spiny, succulent, candelabriform tree, reaching a maximum height of 10 m; occurring at medium to low altitudes, in hot dry woodland and bush, often among rocks. The main trunk is cylindric or angled with one to several trunk-like branches, each ending in a small thin head of characteristically slender ascending branches which often divide into secondary branchlets, the whole crown being conspicu-
444 ously sparse and thin. The branches and branchlets are only about 1,5 cm in diameter, 3- to 4-angled

rather than winged, and not constricted into segments although the margins are frequently sinuate. Spines paired, up to 6 mm long, the spine shields horny but separate. **Inflorescence:** greenish-yellow; cyathia of the usual pattern shortly stalked, along the upper part of the flowering branches (September). **Fruit:** a 3-lobed capsule, 6 mm in diameter (October onwards).

This species resembles *E. grandidens*, but both are geographically distinct; the differences are discussed under the latter species.

Euphorbia excelsa White, Dyer & Sloane

S.A. no: 349   Olifants River euphorbia. Olifantsriviernaboom

Rhod. no: —

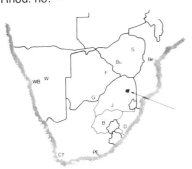

A spiny succulent candelabriform tree, up to 10 m in height, occasionally reaching 15 m; occurring on dry rocky hillsides. The main stem is sub-cylindric, and rarely produces stem-like branches; it has a small somewhat compact crown, the general impression being of a long stem with a small head; young trees are bluish-green; the branches are only slightly constricted at intervals of 8 to 15 cm, usually 4-angled (rarely 2- to 5-angled), square in cross-section, 2,5 to 3 cm in diameter. Spines obsolete on the older branches but on the younger branches are paired and up to 8 mm long. The spine shields form a continous horny margin. The rudimentary leaves fall very early. **Inflorescence:** greenish-yellow; cyathia of the usual pattern (January to March). **Fruit:** a 3-lobed capsule, about 5 × 8 mm, on a short stalk about 5 mm long (February onwards).

In all other tree species of *Euphorbia* the stalk of the cyme has only 2 bracts while in *E. excelsa* there are 4. This species resembles *E. tetragona* which occurs only in the eastern Cape.

Euphorbia fortissima Leach

S.A. no: —

Rhod. no: 523   Zambezi candelabra tree

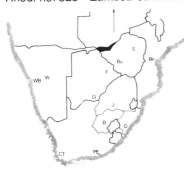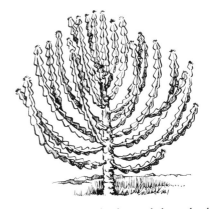

A spiny candelabriform succulent tree rarely exceeding 5 m in height, occurring in wooded grassland, on rocky hillsides and stony slopes. The main stem is conspicuously short and stout, branching low down, the branches being sub-persistent and forming a large, round, ball-like head. The branches are 3- to 4-winged (usually 3-winged), deeply divided, forming almost spherical to ellipsoidal segments up to 10 × 9 cm near the apex, lengthening near the base; secondary branchlets and terminal branchlets which are usually very short, are frequently produced from the margins of the stout wings. Paired, diverging spines, 2 to 7 mm long, are produced along the margins of the wings, the spine shields uniting to form a continuous pale brown horny margin (becoming grey with age). Minute

445

rudimentary leaves fall very early. **Inflorescence:** yellow; cyathia of the usual pattern arranged vertically (January to April). **Fruit:** a 3-lobed capsule up to 1 × 2,4 cm, becoming reddish-brown when mature (March to June).

Candelabra Pool at the Victoria Falls probably derived its name from the large and almost certainly very old specimen of *E. fortissima* which grows there. This tree is unusual in having a long naked trunk, 3 m or more in length.

Euphorbia grandidens Haw.
S.A. no: 350   Large-toothed euphorbia. Groottandnaboom
Rhod. no: —

A spiny candelabriform succulent tree up to 16 m in height; occurring in karroid scrub and scrub forest. This is one of the largest of the tree euphorbias, often with one to several stem-like branches, each bearing numerous secondary branchlets with slender, clustered, terminal branchlets, only 1 to 2 cm in diameter, giving the appearance of small, tufty heads 0,5 to 1 m in diameter on the ends of the thickset branches; the branches are 2- to 3-angled, (usually 3-angled), the faces being concave rather than winged, with wavy margins crested with wart-like encrustations. Spines rather small, paired, up to 6 mm long or very short to almost absent, divergent, grey, frequently with a pair of minute prickles immediately above them. Small, rudimentary leaves are produced but fall very early. **Inflorescence:** greenish-yellow; cyathia of the usual pattern, almost without stalks (October). **Fruit:** a 3-lobed capsule, about 8 mm in diameter (October onwards).

In general habit this species is easily confused with *E. evansii*. However, it can be considerably taller, reaching heights of 16 m, the branches are usually 3-angled, the margins are toothed with warty cushions, and the spines are frequently accompanied by 2 small prickles; whereas *E. evansii* reaches a maximum height of 10 m, its branches are usually 3- to 4-angled with the margins gently sinuate, and the spines are never accompanied by prickles.

The latex is cohesive and has been used in Moçambique for caulking boats and for other adhesive purposes. African superstition regarding this tree is described under *E. triangularis*.

Euphorbia guerichiana Pax
S.A. no: 344   Western woody euphorbia, Papiermelkbos
Rhod. no: 525   Western woody euphorbia

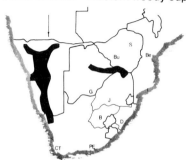

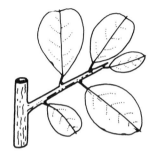

A spineless, woody shrub or small tree up to 6 m in height; occurring at low altitudes in hot dry areas, often on sand and among rocks. **Bark:** dark brown, characteristically peeling in light yellow, papery sheets; the young branches are long and whip-like. **Leaves:** alternate, small, obovate to oblanceolate, 3 to 15 × 1,3 to 5 mm, rather fleshy in texture; apex rounded; base tapering; margin entire; petiole short. The leaves fall early and the plant stands as a twiggy, bare clump for many months during the year. **Inflorescence:** yellow; cyathia of the usual pattern arising at the ends of short, lateral branchlets, appearing when the tree is bare (October to January). **Fruit:** a 3-lobed capsule, about 6 mm in diameter, smooth (January to March).

Euphorbia halipedicola Leach
S.A. no: —
Rhod. no: 526   Zig-zag candelabra tree

A spiny, candelabriform succulent shrub or small tree up to 5 m in height, usually single-stemmed with its distinctive crown of branches; occurring at low altitudes in mixed woodland, on deep alluvial soils. The branches are 3- to 4-winged, the wings being very thin, only 2 mm thick at the margin which is conspicuously zigzag and wavy, with paired spines, up to 1,5 cm long on the crests; the spine shields form a horny margin, not always completely continuous. **Inflorescence:** deep yellow to orange, in clusters of up to 6 cymes, produced on short stalks up to 10 mm long, above the spines (May to August). **Fruit:** a 3-lobed capsule, up to 2 × 0,8 cm (July to August).
This species is somewhat similar in general appearance to *E. cooperi,* but the segments are much larger, being up to 32 cm long, and the zigzag margins to the wings are conspicuous.

Euphorbia ingens E. Meyer ex Boiss.
S.A. no: 351   Candelabra tree. Gewone naboom
Rhod. no: 527   Candelabra tree

A massively branched tree up to 10 m in height; occurring at medium to low altitudes in various types of decidous woodland, most frequently on rocky koppies and often associated with termite mounds. The heavy branches arise fairly low down, neither the candelabriform shape nor the individual crown of branchlets being evident. In the other tree species of *Euphorbia* the lower branches are shed each year as new ones are added at the top, thus producing an increasingly long, naked stem with the characteristic crown of branchlets; this does not take place in *E. ingens,* which therefore has a massive, many-branched, rounded crown (the specific name, meaning 'huge', refers to this). The branches are usually 4- to 5-winged and irregularly constricted. Spines paired, often reduced, up to 2 mm long, or absent; spine shields are usually obsolescent, becoming corky and senescent. **Inflorescence:** yellowish-green; cyathia of the usual pattern (April). **Fruit:** a 3-lobed capsule up to 10 mm in diameter (August).

447

The candelabra tree, Euphorbia ingens.

This tree is common in parts of the central Transvaal and has given its name to the town Naboomspruit. The latex is toxic, causing intense irritation and blistering to the skin and, if coming into contact with the eyes, leading to temporary or even permanent blindness. Cattle driven through groves of these trees have been burned on the lips, face and eyes, sometimes so severely that they have had to be destroyed. Africans in the Limpopo valley prepare a fish poison from this tree: they soak a bundle of grass in the latex, tie it to a stone and throw it into a pool. The fish are said to rise to the surface within 15 minutes, paralysed but still breathing. It is also used, in very small doses, as a drastic purgative, a remedy for dipsomania and to treat cancer. However, in these cases the patients run a grave risk for there have been several recorded deaths from an over-dose, the symptoms being vomiting, violent abdominal pain and excessive, intractable purging. The flowers of this and several other species of *Euphorbia* produce quantities of nectar, but honey from this – known as 'noors honey' – causes a burning in the mouth which is only aggravated by drinking water. It is said that the Zulu king, Dingaan, built his throne under a large *E. ingens* near which the Boer leader, Piet Retief, and 100 of his men were murdered in 1838.

Euphorbia keithii R. A. Dyer
S.A. no: 352   Swazi euphorbia. Swazinaboom
Rhod. no: —

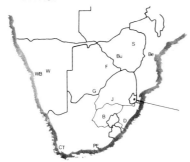

448

A spiny succulent candelabriform shrub or small tree, 2 to 7 m in height; occurring on rocky mountainsides and cliff faces. The branches are dark green, spreading and finally ascending, 1 to 2 m long, 5-winged (occasionally 3- to 6-winged); they are constricted into segments of varying length, up to 25 cm long and only 3 to 4 cm broad, the sides being almost parallel. Spines paired, up to 8 mm long, rather stout; the spine shields form a continuous, horny margin. Rudimentary leaves are produced but fall very early. **Inflorescence:** greenish-yellow; cyathia of the usual pattern, in clusters of 2 to 3 cymes arranged vertically (October to January). **Fruit:** a 3-lobed capsule, 6 to 7 mm in diameter, greenish-red, on a conspicuous, curved stalk up to 6 mm long (December onwards).

Euphorbia lividiflora Leach
S.A. no: —
Rhod. no: 528   Red-flowered euphorbia

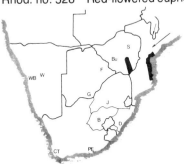

A rare species. A much-branched spiny succulent candelabriform tree up to 10 m in height, but usually about 4 m; occurring in small colonies, in dense thicket and patches of woodland. The branches spreading, the secondary branchlets somewhat lax, slender, about 2 to 2,5 cm in diameter, 3- to 4-angled; branches constricted but not conspicuously so, the segments up to 30 cm long, with a sinuate margin with paired spines on the crests; the spines up to 5 mm long, the spine shields very small and not conspicuous. It produces well-formed fleshy leaves, almost circular in shape, about 13 mm in diameter, but falling very early. **Inflorescence:** distinctive, the involucre being red to reddish-purple with 5 bright red overlapping lobes and 5 bluish-purple glands; cyathia of the usual pattern, horizontally arranged (December to January). **Fruit:** a deeply 3-lobed capsule up to 2,5 × 1 cm, on a conspicuous stalk (March to June).

Euphorbia matabelensis Pax   Illust. 143
S.A. no: Three-forked euphorbia
Rhod. no: 529   Three-forked euphorbia

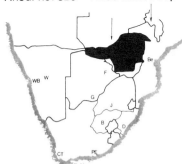

A woody and leafy shrub or small tree, 2 to 4 m in height; occurring on granite koppies, domes and whale-backs, growing round the base, in soil pockets on the rock itself and in crevices and cracks in the rock; in some areas it is fairly common along streams, and in poorly drained areas it is found near hills and also in woodland. **Bark:** light grey, smooth; branchlets spine-tipped; the secondary branches and branchlets usually develop in whorls of 3 from the apex of the previous year's growth. **Leaves:** produced in small clusters, or fascicles, at the apex of lateral, spur-like branchlets; narrowly lanceolate, usually about 3 × 1,2 cm, but may be larger; delicate and graceful, developing attractive **449**

flush colours in November and December and falling from May to July. **Inflorescence:** greenish-yellow, in dense heads, about 1,5 cm in diameter, on very short, lateral, spur-like shoots; the heads consist of up to 5 cyathia, usually produced when the tree is leafless but they may occur at almost any time of the year (May to June and later). **Fruit:** a 3-lobed capsule, up to 8 mm in diameter (June onwards).

Euphorbia sekukuniensis R. A. Dyer
S.A. no: 353   Sekukuni euphorbia. Sekukuninaboom
Rhod. no: —

A small succulent candelabriform spiny tree up to 7 m in height, with a comparatively thickset main trunk and a small head of slender branches; occurring on rocky hillsides. The trunk carries 8 to 10 vertical stripes made up of old spine shields, the latter representing obsolete angles which have filled out; the branches are about 1 m long, very slender, only 1,5 to 2 cm in diameter, 4- to 5-angled, not deeply winged (the sides tending to be flat), only slightly constricted. Spines in pairs, up to 8 mm long, stout, rigid; spine shields united to form a horny margin which widens at each pair of spines and tapers towards the next pair above it. **Inflorescence:** yellowish-green; cyathia of the usual pattern horizontally arranged, on very short stalks (August). **Fruit:** a deeply 3-lobed capsule, about 8 to 9 mm in diameter, on a short stalk (September onwards).

Euphorbia tetragona Haw.
S.A. no: 354   Honey euphorbia. Heuningnaboom
Rhod. no: —

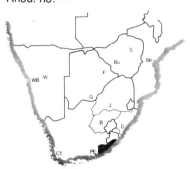

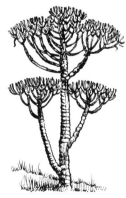

A robust spiny succulent candelabriform tree reaching 13 m in height; occurring on hillsides and valley slopes, in dry thorn scrub and scrub forest. The main stem may be single, but frequently divides from near ground level into 2 to 5 stout, stem-like branches; young trees are deep green. The branchlets form small crowns 1,5 to 2 m in diameter; they are slender, 2,5 to 5 cm in diameter and are 4- to 5-angled but flat-sided, the edges being slightly tubercled. Spines in pairs up to 1,2 cm long, widely diverging, on the apex of the tubercles; spine shields separate. Old branches may be spineless. **Inflorescence:** greenish-yellow; cyathia of the usual pattern, horizontally arranged. **Fruit:** somewhat rounded, 3-lobed capsule, about 9 mm in diameter.

This species closely resembles *E. excelsa;* the differences are discussed under that species. *E. tetragona* is easily recognised by the square appearance of the branches, to which the specific name refers. The flowers produce copious nectar, but the honey is of no value as it is unpleasantly flavoured

450

causing a hot, burning sensation in the mouth and throat (see 'noors honey' under *E. ingens*). The Xhosa burn dry stems on their maize fields to ensure a good crop and use the latex as a remedy for toothache. African superstition regarding this tree is described under *E. triangularis*.

Euphorbia tirucalli L.
S.A. no: 355   Rubber hedge euphorbia. Kraalnaboom
Rhod. no: 352   Rubber hedge euphorbia

A small succulent many-branched and variably shaped tree, without spines, usually 3 to 5 m in height, but reaching 10 m on occasions; occurring in a wide variety of habitats. The leaves, small and slender, up to 1,2 × 0,15 cm, are rarely seen as they fall very early. The cylindric, smooth, green branches, 5 to 7 mm in diameter, form brush-like masses, and are the best known feature of this species. **Inflorescence:** yellow, inconspicuous; the cyathia in clusters at the apex of the branches or in the angles of the branches (October to December). **Fruit:** a somewhat rounded, 3-lobed capsule, about 8 mm in diameter (November to January).
This is the ubiquitous rubber-hedge. It has been widely cultivated and used as a hedge plant, to the

Large specimens of the rubber hedge euphorbia, Euphorbia tirucalli.

extent that it is now difficult to say where it is growing naturally and where it has been introduced. Early traders and sailors carried plants from South Africa to India and the Far East and the fact that these have all flourished gives some indication of its resilience. The plant was named *tirucalli* by Linnaeus in 1753 as this was the name used by the natives of Malabar. It was once thought to be a species of *Euphorbia* yielding true rubber, but numerous tests on a commercial scale have shown that the latex contains too high a percentage of resin. The toxic latex of this species possibly accounts for its very widespread use by Africans as a hedge round smallholdings or habitations, as its presence would probably deter marauders. In African medicine it is regarded as a remedy for sexual impotence, although there is at least one recorded case of its causing death from gastro-intestinal haemorrhage. It is also considered to be an effective insect repellant, an insecticide and a fish poison; the roots have been used as a treatment for snakebite.

Euphorbia triangularis Desf.   Photograph on page 443
S.A. no: 356   River euphorbia. Riviernaboom
Rhod. no: —

A spiny succulent candelabriform tree up to 18 m in height; occurring in dry arid country, on rocky hillsides and river valleys, and along tidal rivers almost reaching the water's edge. The cylindric trunk, which has traces of 4 angles, may develop 2 or more stem-like branches, each bearing a rounded crown of upward-curving branchlets, 1,5 to 2,5 m in length. Branchlets usually 3-winged (occasionally 4- or 5-winged), constricted, forming segments with parallel sides 7,5 to 30 cm long, 4 to 9 cm in diameter, yellowish-green. The margins of the wings are sinuate, with or without tubercles. Spines slender, inconspicuous, up to 8 mm long, brown to grey, diverging. The spine shields may be separate, or merge to form a continuous horny margin. **Inflorescence:** greenish-yellow; cyathia of the usual pattern in 2 to 3 cymes vertically arranged (June). **Fruit:** a somewhat rounded 3-lobed capsule, 6 to 8 mm in diameter, with a distinct curved stalk (July).

Superstition surrounds many species of *Euphorbia,* including this species. The Xhosa in Transkei believe that if twins are born, the father must go into the veld and bring back two of these trees and plant them, side by side, in front of the hut. This custom has been observed for hundreds of years and carries great significance: it is believed that the tree will protect the two children from witchcraft, and that the trees and the twins will influence each other throughout their lives, so that if one dies so will the other. The same belief is held regarding *E. tetragona* and *E. grandidens.*

Euphorbia zoutpansbergensis R. A. Dyer
S.A. no: 357   Soutpansberg euphorbia. Soutpansbergnaboom
Rhod. no: —

A spiny succulent candelabriform shrub or small tree up to 5 m in height; occurring on cliffs and rocky mountainsides, endemic to the area round Wyllie's Poort in the Soutpansberg. The trunk supports a crown of slender branches, the lower ones hanging down. Branches 6-winged (occasionally 5- or 7-winged), constricted into segments 5 to 10 cm long and 2 to 3,5 cm in diameter, the sides parallel. Spines in pairs, up to 10 mm long, stout, very sharp; the spine shields unite to form a continuous, horny margin. **Inflorescence:** yellow; cyathia of the usual type, usually 1 cyme, but may be 2 or 3. **Fruit:** pale green, a 3-lobed capsule, up to 10 mm in diameter, with a conspicuous stalk up to 6 cm long.

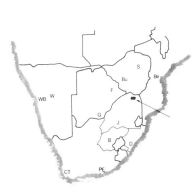

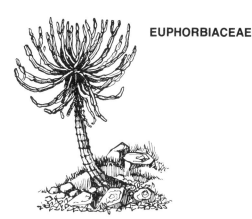

This is an attractive species with its graceful, slender branches and the delicate yellow and pale green colouring of the cyathia and the capsules.

37. SYNADENIUM Boiss.

Shrubs or small trees with cylindric fleshy branches containing milky latex. **Leaves:** alternate, often crowded, relatively large, rather fleshy, deciduous. Stipules absent. **Inflorescence:** axillary; the apparent flowers, or cyathia, in umbellate compound cymes. Each cyathium bisexual or unisexual, comprising a fleshy cup-shaped or plate-like disc with a ring of glands (nectaries) at its rim; usually containing a single female flower reduced to an ovary with a rudimentary perianth/calyx and surrounded by groups of male flowers alternating with the glands, each male flower being reduced to a single stamen with a pair of anther cells and usually subtended by a pair of membraneous bracteoles. The cyathia are usually arranged in groups of 3 (occasionally 5), with the central or initial cyathium often male and the subsequent cyathia bisexual. **Fruit:** a capsule, dehiscent.

Key to the species of *Synadenium:*
Occurring in Natal, Swaziland and the Transvaal; the involucre cup-shaped .... **S. cupulare**
Occurring in Rhodesia and adjacent areas of Moçambique; the involucre with a flat disc-like gland
.... **S. sp.** aff. **S. grantii**

Synadenium cupulare (Boiss.) L. C. Wheeler   Illust. 144
S.A. no: 357,1   Dead-man's tree. Dooiemansboom
Rhod. no: —

A spreading, sparsely branched shrub 1 to 2 m in height, or a small tree reaching 5 m; occurring in woodland and thicket, often on rocky outcrops. **Bark:** green to greyish and smooth. **Leaves:** obovate 1,5 to 10 × 2 to 6 cm, rich green and fleshy, the midrib prominent and tinged with purple or red, deciduous, leaving conspicuous leaf scars; apex rounded, finally sharp-tipped; base narrowly tapering; margin entire; petiole very short due to the narrowly tapering leaf base. **Flowers:** yellowish-green, in terminal or axillary spreading heads (April to May). **Fruit:** a small capsule, about 5 mm in diameter, pale brown, dehiscent (June to August).

The latex is poisonous and tests have shown that it is equally as irritant as that of *Euphorbia ingens;* it is said that the skin, eyes and mouth can be affected simply by the handling of specimens. Whether it is as poisonous as this is open to question, but the author once had the misfortune to get a drop of latex   **453** into his eye and, while no permanent damage was done, for some three hours the pain was so intense that it seemed that only blindness could follow; vision was partially impaired for several days as the cornea had been blistered. Africans are sure that this is one of the most evil of trees; they firmly believe that it cries like a plumed snake (which is said to bleat like a goat!) and that it lures people and animals towards it in order to kill them. They are convinced that the ground round the trees is white with the bones of slain animals and that birds flying above will fall dead from the sky.

Synadenium sp. aff. **S. grantii** N. E. Brown   cf. Illust. 144

S.A. no: —

Rhod. no: 535   Northern dead man's tree

This species is very similar in general habit and appearance to *S. cupulare*, but it differs in that it has a flat disc-like gland, whereas *S. cupulare* has a cup-shaped involucre. The collection made near the coast and shown on the distribution map as just south of Beira certainly represents a third species and it is possible that yet more are involved as the genus is in need of revision.

BUXACEAE *(The box family)*

BUXUS L.

Shrubs or trees, usually many-branched. **Leaves:** opposite, simple, evergreen. **Flowers:** in axillary racemes or cymes, with or without stalks; bracts resemble the perianth segments. Sexes separate on the same tree. Male flowers: perianth segments 4 in 2 whorls; stamens 4, opposite the perianth segments, filaments either free and fleshy or absent; ovary vestigial. Female flowers: perianth segments 4 to 6; stamens absent; ovary 3-celled; styles persistent. **Fruit:** a woody capsule, crowned with the persistent styles.

Key to the species of *Buxus:*

Leaves small, 1,5 to 3 × 0,7 to 1,8 cm, stiffly leathery .... **B. macowanii**
Leaves large, 6 to 11 × 2 to 5 cm, thinly leathery .... **B. natalensis**

Buxus macowanii Oliver

[*Notobuxus macowanii* (Oliver) Phillips]

S.A. no: 358   Cape box. Kaapse buksboom

Rhod. no: —

A small, slow-growing tree up to 7 m in height; occurring sporadically and erratically, but frequently locally common in warm valleys near the sea and on coastal dunes; often gregarious and forming pure stands; the Transvaal population is an unexpected outlier. **Bark:** greyish or brownish, rather smooth. **Leaves:** ovate to ovate-oblong, 1,5 to 3 × 0,7 to 1,8 cm, deep green, without hairs, stiffly leathery; apex and base tapering; margin entire; petiole very short. **Flowers:** very small, greenish, the male flowers in axillary clusters or contracted cymes, the female flowers solitary or 1 between 2 male clusters (July to October). **Fruit:** a brown dehiscent capsule, about 7 mm in diameter, crowned with three conspicuous horns which are the hardened remains of the persistent styles (February to June).

The wood is yellow, heavy, hard and close-grained with an exceptionally even and smooth texture. At

one time it was in great demand for engraving, especially for printing, and is still used for carving and in the manufacture of clay modelling tools, musical and mathematical instruments, and various parts of machinery connected with the cotton-spinning industry. It closely resembles the European box, *B. sempervirens* L.

Buxus natalensis (Oliver) Hutch.

[*Notobuxus natalensis* Oliver]
S.A. no: 359   Natal box. Natalse buksboom
Rhod. no: —

A shrub or small tree seldom reaching 10 m in height; occurring as an undershrub or an under-storey tree in coastal evergreen forest and bush. **Bark:** grey to brown. **Leaves:** ovate-lanceolate to elliptic, 6 to 11 × 2 to 5 cm, thinly leathery, dark shiny green, without hairs; apex broadly tapering; base

The horned fruit and leathery leaves of the natal box, Buxus natalensis.

tapering; margin entire; petiole short and thickest. **Flowers:** small, green, in axillary clusters on short, branches stalks, the male and female flowers together in the same cluster (August to September). **Fruit:** a brown, dehiscent capsule, about 2 cm long, crowned with three conspicuous horns which are the hard remains of the persistent styles (from September onwards).
The wood is very similar to that of *B. macowanii*.

ANACARDIACEAE *(The mango family)*

Mostly trees or shrubs, a few species producing useful, edible fruits; the mango, the cashew nut and the pistachio nut all belong to this family.

Key to the genera (Exotic species marked*):
1 Leaves simple 2

  Leaves compound 7

2 Female flower conspicuous with large, thick woody, persistent antler-like bracts .... **11. Laurophyllus**

  Female flowers without antler-like bracts 3

3 Trees with characteristically brightly coloured red, orange or yellow leaves scattered throughout the crown .... **8. Protorhus**

  Trees without conspicuous scattered brightly coloured leaves 4

4 Fruit kidney-shaped, up to 3 cm long (the cashew nut), on a very conspicuous stalk, so thickened that it resembles a second section of the true fruit .... **2. *Anacardium**

  Fruit without a very conspicuously thickened stalk 5

5 Fruit large and fleshy (the mango), 8 cm long or more .... **1. *Mangifera**

  Fruits not much more than 2,5 cm long 6

6 Fruits leathery, about 1,5 × 2,5 cm; ovary asymmetric; stamens 5 to 10 .... **14. Heeria**

  Fruits thinly fleshy, about 0,8 × 1,3 cm; ovary symmetric; stamens 5 .... **13. Ozoroa**

7 Leaves 3-foliolate 8

  Leaves imparipinnately compound 9

8 Fruits compressed, with a conspicuous circular wing .... **12. Smodingium**

  Fruits may be somewhat compressed but are usually spherical to ovoid, not winged .... **15. Rhus**

9 Petiole ridged or winged and rachis winged 10

  Petiole and rachis not ridged or winged 11

10 Flowers and fruits with large, showy, red petal-like sepals, the small creamy-white petals falling early; fruits dry, somewhat flattened, inconspicuous among the persistent sepals .... **10. Loxostylis**

  Flowers and fruits without large brightly coloured persistent sepals; fruits small, round, fleshy, shiny red, in conspicuous bunches .... **9. *Schinus**

11 Fruits usually up to 10 mm in diameter, occasionally up to 15 mm 12

  Fruits larger than 15 mm in diameter 15

12 Leaflets numerous, well-spaced, very slender, about 4 × 0,5 cm .... **9. *Schinus**

  Leaflets not conspicuously slender, more than 8 mm broad 13

13 Male flowers with 4 to 5 stamens only; leaf margin may be conspicuously wavy. Occurring only in the extreme east of Rhodesia and adjacent areas in Moçambique and northwards .... **7. Trichoscypha**

Male flowers with more than 5 stamens; leaf margin usually not conspicuously wavy 14

14 Young parts covered with dense woolly hairs; male flowers with 8 stamens; flower heads usually small, up to 15 cm long, rarely reaching 23 cm .... **5. Lannea**

Young parts without conspicuous woolly hairs; male flowers with 10 to 20 stamens; flowers in large, loose, branched heads, 30 to 70 cm long .... **6. Sorindeia**

15 Leaflets ovate to elliptic; flowers in unbranched spikes; fruits very fleshy .... **3. Sclerocarya**

Leaflets lanceolate, occasionally ovate, sickle-shaped; flowers in branched heads or panicles; fruits thinly fleshy .... **4. Harpephyllum**

1. *MANGIFERA L.

*Mangifera indica L.

The mango, originally introduced from east tropical Asia, has become naturalised and, in places, well-established in Moçambique, in the east of Rhodesia (Rhod. no: 536) and along the Natal coast in Zululand.

2. *ANACARDIUM L.

*Anacardium occidentale L.

The cashew nut, introduced from tropical America, is occasionally planted in Natal and, after the coconut, is perhaps the most commonly cultivated tree in Moçambique; it is occasionally planted in suitable areas in the east of Rhodesia. It would seem probable that this tree sometimes becomes naturalised in Moçambique.

3. SCLEROCARYA Hochst.

Sclerocarya birrea (A. Rich.) Hochst.   Illust. 145
[*S. caffra* Sonder]
S.A. no: 360   Marula. Maroela
Rhod. no: 537   Marula

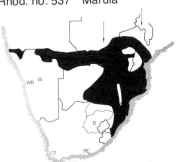

A medium sized tree up to 10 m in height, but it may reach 15 m under favourable conditions; occurring in medium to low altitude, open woodland and bush. **Bark:** grey, rough, flaking in patchy sections giving a mottled appearance. **Leaves:** alternate, compound, crowded near the ends of the branches, with 7 to 13 (occasionally up to 17) pairs of opposite to sub-opposite leaflets plus a terminal leaflet; leaflets ovate to elliptic; 3 to 10 × 1,5 to 4 cm, dark green above, much paler and bluish-green below, early deciduous, the trees standing bare for several months in the year; apex broadly tapering, finally abruptly and narrowly attenuate; base broadly tapering to rounded, asymmetric; margin entire, the young leaves, or coppice leaves toothed; petiolules and petioles long and slender and, like the rachis, often tinged with pink. **Flowers:** in unbranched sprays, 5 to 8 cm long. Sexes separate, on the

457

same tree or on different trees. Floral parts in fours to fives; sepals red; petals yellow, small. Male flowers: stamens 15 to 25; ovary vestigial. Female flowers: staminodes 15 to 25; ovary almost spherical (September to November). **Fruit:** fleshy, almost spherical, up to 3,5 cm in diameter, with three rather obscure points just below the apex, yellow when mature, indehiscent (February to June).

These trees are among the most highly valued of the indigenous species; indeed, the Tonga people celebrate the Feast of the First Fruits by pouring a libation of the fresh juice over the tombs of their dead chiefs and the branches feature in their funeral rites. The fruits have a rich scent; they can be made into an alcoholic drink of some potency, an excellent conserve and a delicious amber-coloured jelly, all of which must have considerable nutritious value as the pulp contains four times as much vitamin C as orange juice. Game, which feed eagerly on them, may possibly become intoxicated after eating the over-ripe, fermenting fruits lying on the ground. Each has a single stone, inside which there are two or three seeds containing an oil rich in protein. These 'nuts' may be eaten either raw or cooked with porridge; the Zulus crush and boil them with water, skimming off the oil which they massage into the skin as a cosmetic, while Shangaan witchdoctors regard the stones as 'medicine' in their divining dice. The bark, which has an astringent taste, is widely used in the treatment of dysentery and diarrhoea. It is believed to prevent malaria, particularly if gathered before the first flush of leaves and, when taken as a tincture in brandy or powdered and swallowed in teaspoonsful, is thought to provide an effective cure for the fever. It is doubtful, however, whether there is any scientific basis to these theories. The Venda give the powdered bark to a pregnant woman to make certain that the child will be of the desired sex: for a girl she must take the bark from a female tree while that from a male tree will plants are susceptible to frost. They have been declared protected trees in South Africa.

Only subsp. *caffra* (Sonder) Kokwaro occurs south of the Zambezi river.

4. HARPEPHYLLUM Bernh.

Harpephyllum caffrum Bernh.
S.A. no: 361   Wild plum. Wildepruim
Rhod. no: —

A small to medium sized evergreen tree 6 to 10 m in height, sometimes reaching 15 m; occurring in riverine forest. **Bark:** dark brown, rough. **Leaves:** alternate, crowded at the ends of the branchlets, compound, with 4 to 8 pairs of opposite leaflets plus a terminal leaflet; leaflets lanceolate, occasionally ovate, sickle-shaped, 5 to 10 × 1,3 to 2,5 cm, without hairs, dark shiny green, the midrib lying well to one side; apex narrowly tapering; base tapering, markedly asymmetric; margin entire, tightly rolled under; petiolules very short. The leaves remain on the tree for approximately two years, finally turning red before they fall and consequently the trees are never bare. **Flowers:** small, whitish to yellowish-green, in small branched sprays near the ends of the branches. Sexes separate on different trees. Floral parts in fours to fives; petals longer than the calyx lobes; stamens 7 to 10, represented by conspicuous staminodes in female flowers; ovary 1-chambered with 4 to 5 sessile stigmas, vestigial in male flowers (February). **Fruit:** oblong, thinly fleshy, up to 2,5 cm long, red when mature, indehiscent (August).

The rather sour fruits, which are relished by children, make a good rosé wine and also a jelly. The wood is pale reddish, fairly heavy, takes polish well but is not very durable. It has been used for furniture, beams and as a general purpose timber. This decorative tree has been planted along streets in a number of South African towns and cities; it is cultivated in Rhodesia and is fairly frequently planted as a garden ornamental.

5. LANNEA A. Rich.

Shrubs, trees, or shrublets growing from a rootstock; all young parts densely covered with woolly stellate hairs. **Leaves:** alternate, compound, imparipinnate or 3-foliolate, clustered at the tips of the branches. **Flowers:** in terminal or axillary panicles. Sexes often separate on the same tree or on different trees, but the flowers may be bisexual. All floral parts in fours; stamens 8 (as short staminodes in female flowers); ovary ovoid or sub-spherical (vestigial in male flowers). **Fruit:** ovoid, fleshy, indehiscent.

Key to the tree species of *Lannea:*

1 Leaves with 9 to 21 leaflets; leaflets small, up to 3 cm long; fruits hairy .... **L. humilis**
  Leaves with 3 to 11 leaflets; leaflets larger than those of the above species, usually more than 3 cm long; fruits without hairs 2
2 Leaflets with dense woolly hairs on the under surface 3
  Leaflets without dense woolly hairs on the under surface, although some hairs may be present 4
3 Mature leaflets with a dense felt of whitish hairs on the under surface, but with net-veining still conspicuous, the veins being darker than the matted hairs .... **L. discolor**
  Mature leaflets with the under surface densely covered with pale, rusty, woolly hairs, somewhat obscuring the veining .... **L. schimperi**
4 Flowers produced with the leaves: young leaflets without pink or white glandular hairs; widespread .... **L. stuhlmannii**
  Flowers produced before the new leaves; young leaflets with dense, pink to white glandular hairs which are lost by maturity, except for pockets in the axils of the veins on the under surface; south of the Zambezi River known only from southern Moçambique .... **L. antiscorbutica**

Lannea antiscorbutica (Hiern) Engl.
S.A. no: —
Rhod. no: —   Pink-haired lannea

A shrub or medium sized tree up to 15 m in height; occurring in woodland, on alluvial soils and often on termite mounds. **Bark:** greyish. **Leaves:** usually with 2 to 4 pairs of leaflets plus a terminal leaflet; leaflets lanceolate to elliptic or oblong, variable in size, 4 to 14 × 1,8 to 7 cm, thinly textured, almost the same colour green above and below; the young leaves resinous and densely covered with pink or white glandular hairs among which there may be some stellate hairs; all these hairs are lost by maturity except for pockets persisting in the axils of the veins on the under surface; net-veining is just visible on the under surface of old leaves; apex attenuate, sometimes abruptly so; base broadly tapering to rounded, asymmetric on the lateral leaflets, symmetric on the terminal leaflet; margin entire; petiolules short, 1 to 6 mm on the lateral leaflets, 2 to 4 cm on the terminal leaflet; petiole present. **Flowers:** creamy-yellow, in spikes up to 10 cm long, clustered at the tips of the branchlets, appearing before the leaves and densely covered with pinkish woolly stellate hairs (October). **Fruit:** almost spherical to ovoid, up to 9 × 7 mm, fleshy (October to November).

Lannea discolor (Sonder) Engl.   Illust. 146
S.A. no: 362   Live-long. Dikbas
Rhod. no: 538   Live-long   **459**

A medium sized tree up to 15 m in height; occurring in open woodland, on rocky outcrops or stony slopes, often on termite mounds. **Bark:** grey with a coppery tinge, smooth to slightly rough. **Leaves:** appear after the flowers; with 5 to 11 opposite to sub-opposite leaflets, including a terminal leaflet; leaflets elliptic to oblong, 3 to 10,5 × 1,5 to 5,5 cm, the upper surface dark green, the under surface covered with a dense felt of whitish hairs, the dark net-veining remaining conspicuous through the pale hairs; apex tapering to almost rounded; base tapering, asymmetric on the lateral leaflets, symmetric on the terminal leaflet; margin entire; petiolules of the lateral leaflets about 3 mm long, that of the terminal leaflet up to 20 mm long; petiole hairy. **Flowers:** small, cream to yellow, sweetly scented, produced in long spikes up to 23 cm in length, crowded near the ends of short branchlets (September to October). **Fruit:** fleshy, ovoid, about 10 mm long, rather resembling a miniature marula, but produced in short sprays, and reddish to grape-purple when mature (September to November).

Poles used as fencing standards strike and grow easily, while the wood which is soft and light is suitable for fishing net floats and also for dishes and stamping blocks. If the bark on the young branchlet is carefully tapped it can be slipped off the wood and children use it to make effective pop-guns. The bark and roots are taken medicinally by Africans for a variety of ailments, particularly children's complaints ranging from fever to constipation. Twine may be made from the stripped bark.

Lannea humilis (Oliver) Engl.
S.A. no: —
Rhod. no: 539   Small-leaved lannea

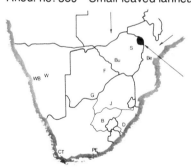

A shrub or small tree about 3 m in height but reaching 6 m on occasions; south of the Zambezi River this is a rare tree, occurring in low altitude mixed woodland. **Bark:** brownish-grey; the branches are cylindric, striated, smooth, with conspicuous lenticels; the branchlets are densely covered with whitish hairs. **Leaves:** with 4 to 10 pairs of leaflets plus a terminal leaflet; leaflets small, oblong or elliptic, 1 to 3 × 0,8 to 1,3 cm, the terminal leaflet tending to be larger; upper surface dark green, under surface prominently veined and densely covered with white woolly hairs, most of which are lost by maturity; apex very broadly tapering to rounded; base asymmetrically rounded to lobed; margin entire. **Flowers:** small, creamy-yellow, produced in spikes up to 5 cm long, clustered on short lateral branchlets, the axes of the spikes densely covered with white furry hairs (September to October). **Fruit:** fleshy, oblong, about 10 mm long, covered with dense, greyish, furry hairs (September to October).

460

Lannea schimperi (Hochst. ex A. Rich.) Engl.
S.A. no: —
Rhod. no: —   Rusty-leaved lannea

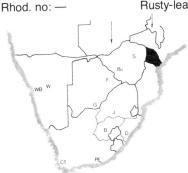

A small to medium sized tree 5 to 10 m in height; occurring in open woodland. **Bark:** grey to nearly black, roughish. **Leaves:** with 2 to 5 pairs of leaflets plus a terminal leaflet; leaflets elliptic to oblong-elliptic, 6 to 15 × 4 to 7,5 cm, the lower leaflets being comparatively shorter and broader; young leaves covered with dense, pinkish to rusty woolly hairs, but by maturity the upper surface is dark green and more or less without hairs and the lower surface is covered with pale rusty woolly hairs which somewhat obscure the veining; apex tapering to rounded; base rounded, square or lobed, asymmetric in the lateral leaflets, symmetric in the terminal leaflet; margin entire; petiolules very short on the lateral leaflets, 1 to 3 mm long, but up to 3,5 cm on the terminal leaflet, petiole present. **Flowers:** small, greenish to yellow, produced in dense clusters in branched spikes, or panicles, crowded at the ends of short branchlets. The male spikes up to 22 cm long, the female spikes up to 8 cm long (August to November). **Fruit:** obliquely ovoid, up to 10 × 6 mm, fleshy, red when ripe (September to December). The flowers and fruits appear before the leaves.
This species is divided into 2 varieties, var. *stolzii* (Engl. & V. Brehm.) R. & A. Fernandes with persistent stellate and simple hairs, and the typical variety with only stellate hairs.

Lannea stuhlmannii (Engl.) Engl.
[*L. stuhlmannii* (Engl.) Engl. var. *tomentosa* Dunkley]
S.A. no: 363   False marula. Bastermaroela
Rhod. no: 540   False marula

A small to medium sized tree, usually 7 to 9 m in height but occasionally reaching 20 m, with spreading drooping branches; occurring over a wide range of altitudes from riverine forest to open woodland and rocky outcrops, often associated with termite mounds; it is sometimes locally common. **Bark:** grey to light brown, flaking in rectangular pieces to reveal the cream-orange underbark, producing a mottled effect; the branchlets and leaves are slightly aromatic. **Leaves:** with 1 to 2 (occasionally 4) pairs of leaflets plus a terminal leaflet; leaflets ovate or elliptic to almost circular, 2 to 9 × 1,7 to 6 cm, fresh pale green, shiny, turning yellow before they fall, the lateral leaflets smaller than the terminal leaflet, the young leaflets densely hairy, the mature leaflets with or without hairs; apex abruptly, but broadly attenuate; base asymmetric on the lateral leaflets, symmetric on the terminal leaflet; margin entire; petiolules absent, petiole long and slender. **Flowers:** small, creamy-white to yellow, in rather loose, catkin-like spikes, branched or simple, up to 12 cm long, in the axils

461

of the leaves near the tips of the branches (November to January). **Fruit:** oblong, about 1,2 cm long, fleshy, reddish to dark brown-black when mature, produced along a common slender axis, 5 to 6 cm long (November to March).

The Swazi name for this tree – 'the tree of forgetfulness' – is probably derived from the fact that it features in certain ceremonies which take place when two former enemies meet and agree to forget their past quarrels. It is believed to harbour a benevolent spirit which is often invoked to protect and heal by ritual. In more orthodox African medicine, a paste made from the leaves is applied as a dressing on sores and abscesses. The fruits have a pleasant flavour; the wood has been used as a general purpose timber and the bark for tanning and as a purple dye.

6. SORINDEIA Thouars

Sorindeia juglandifolia (A. Rich.) Planchon ex Oliver
S.A. no: —
Rhod. no: —   Sorindeia

A climbing shrub or a small tree up to 9 m in height; occurring in dense coastal dune bush. Young branches often densely lenticellate. **Leaves:** alternate, compound, with 2 to 4 pairs of sub-opposite to alternate leaflets plus a terminal leaflet; leaflets obovate to elliptic, up to 22 × 11 cm, the terminal leaflet being the largest; leathery, both surfaces a uniform green, the midrib very prominent below, without hairs, apex almost rounded, finally abruptly attenuate into a short narrow tip; base tapering to rounded; margin entire; petiolules purplish, thick, wrinkled, 3 to 10 mm long, petiole present. **Flowers:** small, creamy-white tinged with pink, or dusky pink, in large, loose, branched heads, or panicles, up to 70 cm long, in the axils of the leaves or terminal. Sexes separate on different trees. All floral parts in fives; calyx cup-shaped, with 5 lobes or teeth; petals longer than the calyx; stamens 10 to 20, reduced to 5 staminodes in female flowers; ovary ovoid with a persistent style, absent in male flowers (September to October). **Fruit:** broadly elliptic, fleshy, about 10 mm long, yellow when mature, indehiscent (October to November).

7. TRICHOSCYPHA J. D. Hook.

Trichoscypha ulugurensis Mildbr.
S.A. no: —
Rhod. no: 541   Agony tree

A medium sized evergreen tree up to 10 m in height; occurring in evergreen forest. **Bark:** brown. **Leaves:** alternate, compound, with 3 to 5 pairs of opposite to sub-opposite (rarely alternate) leaflets plus a terminal leaflet; leaflets elliptic to oblong, 5 to 13 × 3 to 5,5 cm, usually about 11 × 4 cm, thinly leathery, veining anastomosing towards the margin and forming a more or less conspicuous sub-marginal vein; midrib and veins may be hairy on both surfaces, whitish above, brownish below; apex shortly and bluntly attenuate; base tapering to rounded, asymmetric; margin entire, sometimes wavy; petiolules short, thick; petiole up to 3,5 cm long. **Flowers:** small, whitish-green, in narrow branched heads, or many-flowered panicles, up to 28 cm long. The floral branches are covered with fine reddish hairs. Sexes separate on different trees. Floral parts in fours to fives; calyx shortly cup-shaped with 4 to 5 lobes; petals reflexed; stamens 4 to 5, sterile in female flowers; ovary ovoid, absent in male flowers (March to August). **Fruit:** ovoid, fleshy, about 1,4 cm in diameter, indehiscent, becoming wine-red when mature, often with black, tar-like patches, produced in heavy terminal heads (January to February).

The plants should be approached with caution as contact is liable to cause an allergic rash, similar to that caused by *Smodingium argutum* and the American poison ivy, *Toxicodendron radicans* (L.) Kuntze.

8. PROTORHUS Engl.

Protorhus longifolia (Bernh.) Engl.   Illust. 147

[*Rhus longifolia* Bernh.]

S.A. no: 364   Red beech. Rooiboekenhout

Rhod. no: —

A medium sized evergreen tree up to 15 m in height; occurring in forest, on forest margins, in open woodland and on river banks. **Bark:** dark brown, rough. **Leaves:** opposite to sub-opposite, simple, linear-oblong or narrowly elliptic, 8 to 15 × 2,4 to 4 cm, upper surface dark green and glossy, undersurface paler green, with conspicuous parallel secondary veins; odd, striking, bright red to yellow leaves dotted about the tree are a conspicuous feature; apex and base tapering; margin entire, markedly frilled and tightly rolled under; petiolate. **Flowers:** greenish-white to yellow, up to 4 mm in diameter, in dense, many-flowered, short, axillary heads, or panicles. Sexes separate on different trees, with some bisexual flowers. All floral parts in fives; calyx saucer-shaped, 5-lobed; petals erect, oblong, longer than the calyx; stamens 5; ovary ovoid (August to October). **Fruit:** asymmetrically oblong, fleshy, up to 1,2 cm long, becoming purple when mature, indehiscent (October to December).

The wood is not very durable but provides a general purpose timber from which quite attractive furniture can be made. The bark exudes a sticky gum which Africans use to fix the blades of assegais into their handles, and also as a depilatory.

9. *SCHINUS L.

*Schinus molle L.

The pepper tree, with its light, rather sparse compound leaves and pink to reddish fruits, was introduced from South America and is now extensively planted in South Africa. It is favoured for its shade, especially in the Karoo, where few other species will survive both the drought conditions and the winter cold. There is evidence that it may have escaped in some areas.

ANACARDIACEAE

*Schinus terebinthifolius Raddi

The Brazilian pepper tree has broader leaflets than those of the preceding species. It was originally introduced from Brazil and is also widely planted in South Africa, often as a hedge plant, and Rhodesia, being found in areas where conditions are not quite as harsh as those tolerated by *S. molle*. There is some evidence that *S. terebinthifolius* may have escaped locally in some areas in Natal.

10. LOXOSTYLIS A. Sprengel ex Reichenb.

Loxostylis alata A. Sprengel ex Reichenb.   Illust. 148
S.A. no: 365   Loxostylis. Tierhout
Rhod. no: —

A small evergreen tree up to 5 m in height; often occurring in areas adjoining the Karoo, growing on rocky outcrops and cliffs, but also fringing forest and along river banks in Transkei and Natal. **Bark:** pale grey, with shallow vertical fissures, flaking. **Leaves:** alternate, compound, with 2 to 5 pairs of leaflets plus a terminal leaflet, and a conspicuous, winged rachis; leaflets slender, narrowly elliptic, usually 6 × 1 cm, yellowish-green, the young leaves often conspicuously yellow tinged with red, tough and without hairs; apex narrowly rounded with a hair-like tip; base narrowly tapering; margin entire, rolled under; petiolules absent, petiole not winged but ridged. **Flowers:** in dense terminal branched heads, or panicles, about 20 to 30 cm long. Sexes separate on different trees. Floral parts in fours to fives; calyx divided almost to the base, soon becoming large, elliptic, petal-like, brightly coloured pink to brick red; petals themselves small, narrow, star-like, creamy-white, falling very early; stamens 4 to 5; ovary obliquely ovoid. The brightly coloured sepals are the most conspicuous part of the flower (September to January, occasionally as late as April). **Fruit:** small, fleshy, about 4 mm in diameter, embedded in the persistent brightly coloured sepals which enlarge slightly and deepen in colour (January to April).

This tree resembles fairly closely the introduced Brazilian pepper tree, *Schinus terebinthifolius*, but the latter does not have the large, brightly coloured, showy sepals, nor are the margins of its leaves entire.

11. LAUROPHYLLUS Thunb.

Laurophyllus capensis Thunb.   Illust. 149
S.A. no: 366   Iron martin. Ystermartiens
Rhod. no: —

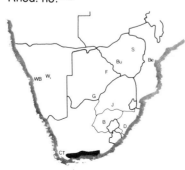

A large shrub or small tree up to 6 m in height, resinous, densely leafy and evergreen; occurring on wooded hill slopes and along stream banks. **Bark:** charcoal-grey to brown, smooth. **Leaves:** alternate, simple, elliptic-oblong, 3 to 12 × 2,5 to 4 cm, leathery, glossy green with conspicuous veining above, light green below; apex broadly tapering; base tapering; margin roughly and bluntly toothed; petiole up to 2 cm long. **Flowers:** small, white, in terminal heads or panicles, 15 × 8 cm. Sexes separate on different trees. The female flowers are produced in very dense, branched, woody, persistent antler-like structures formed from bracts, resembling a parasitized deformity, and described as such by many collectors. Floral parts in fours to fives; calyx and corolla both 5-cleft almost to the base; stamens 4 to 5, absent in female flowers; ovary almost spherical, absent in male flowers (November to January). **Fruit:** oval, compressed, hard, slightly winged, about 4 to 5 mm in diameter, in tight bracteate panicles of congested fruits (May to July, possibly remaining on the tree longer).

12. SMODINGIUM E. Meyer ex Sonder

Smodingium argutum E. Meyer ex Sonder
S.A. no: 367   African poison oak. Pynbos
Rhod. no: —

A shrub to small tree up to 6 m in height; occurring in shaded valleys, often in *Acacia* dominated thorn bush in low rainfall areas. **Bark:** grey to brown. **Leaves:** alternate, compound, digitately 3-foliolate, the terminal leaflet rather larger than the two lateral leaflets; leaflets narrowly ovate, up to 9 × 4 cm, dark green, leathery, without hairs; apex very narrowly tapering and finely pointed; base tapering; margin coarsely toothed; petiolules more or less absent on all three leaflets, petiole slender. **Flowers:** small, creamy-green, in large, loose, axillary and terminal, branched sprays, or panicles, together up to 30 cm or more in length. Sexes separate on different trees. All floral parts in fives; calyx 5-lobed; petals reflexed; stamens 5, reduced to staminodes in female flowers; ovary almost spherical with 3 persistent styles, absent in male flowers (November to March). **Fruit:** a small flattened nut, completely encircled by a red papery wing, 10 × 7 mm in diameter, produced in dense, attractive heads (May).

This species closely resembles the genus *Rhus*, but is distinguished by its winged fruits which contain an aromatic oil. This is a poisonous plant and gardeners should be warned that it may be dangerous to cultivate. The sap causes a livid rash which swells and blisters, accompanied by great discomfort, itching and intense burning pain which persists for a long time, even weeks, and is difficult to bring under control. Simply handling the branches or leaves is enough to bring on the allergy in susceptible people. Soon after its discovery early in the 19th century it became known as 'the terrible tovana plant of Pondoland' – a name of Xhosa and Zulu derivation. Many African people fear and revere it, believing that all the allergic symptoms will develop if the tree is not greeted with deference whenever it is seen.

13. OZOROA Delile

Shrubs, suffrutices or trees with milky, resinous latex. **Leaves:** alternate, opposite, or fascicled, simple, hairy; lateral veins many, parallel, usually unbranched almost to the thickened margin. **Flowers:** in axillary and terminal panicles, with the stalks jointed near the base. Sexes separate on different trees. All floral parts in fives; calyx lobes ovate to lanceolate; petals flat or with the apex curved back; stamens 5, reduced to staminodes in female flowers; ovary spherical, vestigial in male flowers. **Fruit:** usually kidney-shaped, thinly fleshy, small, indehiscent.

465

ANACARDIACEAE

Key to the tree species of *Ozoroa*:
1 Net-veining clearly visible, even conspicuous, on the under surface 2
 Net-veining not clearly visible on the under surface 6
2 In South West Africa and north-western Cape 3
 Not in South West Africa or north-western Cape 5
3 Under surface not thickly matted with pale hairs .... **O. concolor**
 Under surface matted with pale hairs 4
4 Leaves large, up to 11 × 7,8 cm, obovate; under surface has thick heavy veining, and grey felted
 hairs not tinged with yellow. Widespread in South West Africa and also in Namaqualand
 .... **O. crassinervia**
 Leaves smaller, usually about 5 × 2 cm; net-veining on the under surface somewhat obscure, but
 clearly distinct on the upper surface; the matted hairs yellow-grey. In the south of South West
 Africa and in Namaqualand only .... **O. dispar**
5 Margin much thickened and rolled under; petiole usually less than 10 mm, usually about 3 to
 6 mm; fruits almost spherical, not flattened .... **O. sphaerocarpa**
 Margin not as thickened as in the preceding species; petiole usually more than 10 mm long; fruits
 flattened .... **O. reticulata**
6 Leaves almost circular with an abruptly and very shortly attenuate apex; petiole slender, up to half
 the length of the leaf .... **O. longipes**
 Leaves elliptic, oblong to lanceolate; petiole less than half as long as the leaf 7
7 Petiole conspicuously long, up to 6,5 cm; leaves up to 15 cm long. Occurring only on the chrome
 hills of the Great Dyke in the north of Rhodesia .... **O. longepetiolata**
 Petioles usually less than 3 cm long 8
8 In the south of South West Africa only .... **O. namaensis**
 Not in the south of South West Africa 9
9 Occurring in an area round East London in the eastern Cape only .... **O. mucronata**
 Not occurring in the eastern Cape 10
10 Under surface of the leaves velvety with short, fine, creamy-grey to whitish hairs; occurring in
 north-central South West Africa only (and in countries to the north) .... **O. insignis**
 Under surface of the leaves with a silvery or silky sheen 11
11 Leaf apex narrowly tapering .... **O. engleri**
 Leaf apex broadly tapering, rounded to square, often notched 12
12 Midrib and lateral veins raised and conspicuous on the under surface; leaf blade comparatively
 narrow, narrowly elliptic, 4 to 12 × 1 to 4 cm .... **O. paniculosa**
 Midrib and lateral veins not clearly raised on the under surface; leaf blade comparatively broader,
 elliptic, obovate to oblong, 2,5 to 12 × 1,5 to 4 cm .... **O. obovata**

Ozoroa concolor (Presl ex Sonder) De Winter
S.A. no: 369,1   Green resin tree. Groenharpuisboom
Rhod. no: —

A small tree up to 4 m in height; occurring in dry, arid, windswept areas, along dry watercourses.
Bark: grey. **Leaves:** alternate, or fascicled; obovate to elliptic, up to 5 × 2,5 cm, leathery, dark vivid
green on both surfaces, without hairs, the midrib and net-veining yellow and conspicuous on both
surfaces; apex rounded, slightly notched; base tapering; margin entire, conspicuously wavy; petiole

466

short. **Flowers:** small, creamy-yellow, in branched heads 4 to 8 cm long, sweetly scented (September to October). **Fruit:** thinly fleshy, rather broader than it is long, up to 10 mm wide, reddish when mature (September to November).

Ozoroa crassinervia (Engl.) R. & A. Fernandes
S.A. no: 369   Namibian resin tree. Namibiese harpuisboom
Rhod. no: —

A small tree up to 9 m in height; occurring in various types of woodland, on rocky hills and in stony arid areas. **Bark:** dark grey. **Leaves:** clustered at the ends of the branchlets, broadly obovate, 2,5 to 11 × 1,9 to 7,8 cm; the midrib and lateral veins are conspicuous on both surfaces, the net-veining thick and heavy on the under surface (the specific name refers to this) which is densely covered with grey-felted hairs; apex rounded, notched; base tapering; margin entire; petiole short. **Flowers:** small whitish, in terminal sprays. **Fruit:** 5 to 7 × 6 to 9 mm, on rather long stalks, becoming blackish and wrinkled when mature.

Ozoroa dispar (Presl) R. & A. Fernandes
S.A. no: 370   Namaqua resin tree. Namakwaharpuisboom
Rhod. no: —

A small, compact, leafy tree up to 5 m in height; occurring among rocks and on stony hillsides, rocky hills and karroid flats, the roots often splitting the rocks among which they grow. **Bark:** grey, longitudinally fissured. **Leaves:** crowded at the ends of the branchlets, elliptic, 2 to 7 × 2 to 3 cm, usually about 5 × 2 cm, thick, leathery, strongly and conspicuously veined, particularly on the upper surface which is bright green; the under surface is densely covered with fine, grey to yellow, velvety hairs; apex rounded, slightly notched; base tapering, margin entire, rather wavy; petiole short, 2 to 4 mm long. **Flowers:** creamy-white, about 3 to 4 mm in diameter, in compact, terminal, branched heads usually about 3 cm long, but up to 7 cm (May). **Fruit:** rather large, kidney-shaped, 10 to 13 mm wide, bright green and shiny becoming black when mature (September to November).

Ozoroa engleri R. & A. Fernandes
[*O. insignis* sensu Codd *Trees and Shrubs of the Kruger National Park*]
S.A. no: 371   White resin tree. Witharpuisboom
Rhod. no: —

A robust shrub or a small tree up to 8 m in height, but usually about 4 to 5 m; occurring in open woodland and bush, characteristic of low altitude, dry sandy flats and rocky hill slopes. **Bark:** dark   **467**

 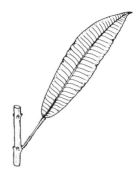

brown to grey and rough, flaking in small square segments; latex thin and watery. **Leaves:** alternate, but inclined to occur in whorls of 3; oblong to narrowly elliptic, 4 to 14 × 1 to 3,3 cm, thinly textured, upper surface dark green without hairs, the under surface densely covered with fine appressed hairs giving a silver sheen; midrib somewhat depressed above but very prominent below, lateral veins obscure; apex narrowly tapering with a hair-like tip; base tapering; margin entire, thickened; petioles hairy, pinkish-brown to yellowish or grey, 1 to 3 cm long. **Flowers:** small, creamy-white, sweetly scented, in axillary and terminal sprays (October to February). **Fruit:** kidney-shaped to rounded, up to 5 × 10 mm, becoming reddish and finally black when mature (February to June).

This is an attractive small tree and would make a good garden subject.

Ozoroa insignis Delile

S.A. no: Tropical resin tree. Tropiese harpuisboom

Rhod. no: —

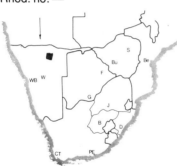 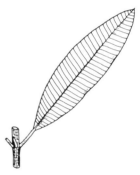

A shrub or small tree 2 to 4 m in height; occurring in dry open woodland. Branchlets hairy. **Leaves:** usually in whorls of 3; elliptic to lanceolate, 5 to 13 × 2 to 4 cm, densely covered with very fine, creamy-grey to whitish, velvety hairs on the under surface, the upper surface without hairs, lateral veining somewhat obscure; apex tapering to rounded, with a conspicuous bristle-like tip; base broadly tapering; margin entire; petiole long and slender, up to 3 cm long. **Flowers:** small, white, in short branched sprays (October). **Fruit:** kidney-shaped, 4,5 × 7,5 mm, becoming black when mature (February).

The material collected in South West Africa is placed in subsp. *latifolius* (Engl.) R. Fernandes; the typical subspecies does not extend as far south as this.

Ozoroa longepetiolata R. & A. Fernandes

S.A. no: —

Rhod. no: 542   Great Dyke raisin-berry

A small, round-topped tree up to 7 m in height; occurring only on serpentine-derived soils on the chrome hills of the northern part of the Great Dyke in Rhodesia. **Bark:** dark grey, smooth, although it may break into rectangular flakes near the base; branches round and cinnamon-coloured. **Leaves:** opposite or alternate, narrowly lanceolate, 10 to 15 × 2 to 4 cm, although occasionally larger, often slightly sickle-shaped, glossy green above, with conspicuously silvery silky hairs below; midrib and lateral veins more or less conspicuous; apex tapering; base broadly tapering; margin entire, thickened; petiole long and slender, up to 6,5 cm long. **Flowers:** small, white, inconspicuous, in loose axillary

468

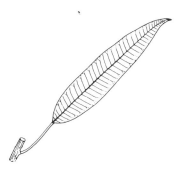

and terminal heads, altogether up to 24 cm long (December to March). **Fruit:** kidney-shaped, 7 × 8 mm, becoming black and shiny when mature (May).

Ozoroa longipes (Engl. & Gilg) R. & A. Fernandes
S.A. no: 372   Round-leaved resin tree. Rondeblaarharpuisboom
Rhod. no: —

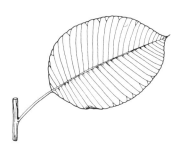

A shrub or rarely a small tree up to 3 to 4 m in height; occurring in deciduous woodland, frequently on Kalahari sand. **Bark:** dark brown. **Leaves:** alternate, often in 2 vertical ranks, probably the most distinctive leaves of all the species of *Ozoroa,* very broadly ovate to almost circular, usually about 6,5 × 4,5 cm, but may be larger; the upper surface shiny green, the lower surface covered with silvery silky hairs; midrib very prominent below, lateral veins slender; apex rounded, finally abruptly and very shortly attenuate with a conspicuous bristle-like tip; base very broadly tapering to rounded; margin entire; petiole slender, up to 4 cm long, making the leaves pendulous. **Flowers:** small, creamy-white, in rather loose terminal heads (December). **Fruit:** kidney-shaped, about 7 × 10 mm, becoming black and shiny when mature (March).

Ozoroa mucronata (Bernh.) R. & A. Fernandes
S.A. no: 373   Eastern Cape resin tree. Oos-Kaapse harpuisboom
Rhod. no: —

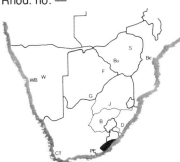

A small tree 3 to 4 m in height; occurring in evergreen forest and in riverine fringe forest. **Bark:** grey.
Leaves: alternate, oblong to lanceolate, up to 7,5 × 2,5 cm, but usually smaller, the upper surface

469

dark green without hairs, the under surface with silvery silky hairs, veining somewhat obscure; apex broadly tapering to rounded with a fine hair-like tip; base very broadly tapering; margin entire, broadly rolled under; petiole short. **Flowers:** small, greenish-white, in compact, branched, terminal and axillary heads, up to 4 cm long (November to December). **Fruit:** kidney-shaped, about 8 × 10 mm, becoming black and shiny when mature (June).

Ozoroa namaensis (Schinz & Dinter) R. Fernandes
S.A. no: 373,1   Nama resin tree. Namaharpuisboom
Rhod. no: —

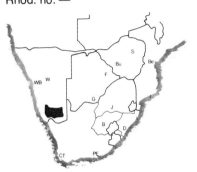

A small tree up to 4 m in height; occurring among rocks and on gravel flats. **Bark:** brown, very rough. **Leaves:** small, oval, 1,3 to 4 × 1 to 1,3 cm, blue-green and finely velvety above; the under surface has a thick prominent midrib, obscure lateral veins, and is covered with fine, dense, velvety hairs; apex rounded, often notched; base tapering; margin entire, rolled under; petiole very short, 1 to 3 mm long. **Flowers:** small, creamy-white, in short, dense, axillary and terminal, branched heads (April to September, and sometimes as late as November). **Fruit:** kidney-shaped, 5 × 10 mm, black when mature (August to December).

Ozoroa obovata (Oliver) R. & A. Fernandes
S.A. no: 374   Broad-leaved resin tree. Breëblaarharpuisboom
Rhod. no: 543   Eastern raisin-berry

A much-branched shrub or small tree up to 8 m in height; occurring in coastal dune bush, in several types of forest, and on the islands off the Moçambique coast. **Bark:** grey and rough in larger specimens. **Leaves:** alternate or whorled in threes, elliptic, obovate to oblong, 2,5 to 12 × 1,5 to 4 cm, yellowish-green, the under surface much paler green with a conspicuous silky sheen and short appressed hairs; midrib and lateral veins not clearly raised on the under surface; apex broadly tapering to square, notched, with a hair-like tip; base tapering to rounded; margin entire; petiole 1 to 2 cm long. **Flowers:** small, white, inconspicuous, in dense terminal and axillary heads, together forming pyramids about 10 cm long (January to May). **Fruit:** kidney-shaped, about 7 × 10 mm, becoming black when mature (April to August).

The typical variety, var. *obovata,* hugs the coastline, seldom being found far from the sea and is replaced further inland by var. *elliptica* R. & A. Fernandes; the latter has elliptic to oblong-elliptic leaves which have tapering apices, occasionally with a marked hair-like tip up to 8 mm in length and rounded bases, and slender floral branches, about 3 mm in diameter at their base; var. *obovata* has obovate to obovate-oblong leaves which have square and notched apices, tapering bases, and floral branches about 7 mm in diameter at their base. However, the situation is somewhat confused by intermediates, and their geographical distribution is not very clear.

Ozoroa paniculosa (Sonder) R. & A. Fernandes

[*O. paniculosa* var. *paniculosa; O. paniculosa* var. *salicina* (Sonder) R. &. A. Fernandes]
S.A. no: 375   Common resin tree. Gewone harpuisboom
Rhod. no: 544   Resin tree

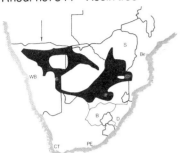 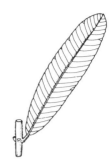

A compact shrub or small tree up to 6 m in height, but occasionally larger; occurring at low altitudes in hot deciduous woodland, often on hillsides. **Bark:** grey, rough in larger specimens; branches brownish-red. **Leaves:** alternate, or in whorls of 3, narrowly elliptic, 4 to 12 × 1 to 4 cm, conspicuously long and slender, the upper surface with or without fine velvety hairs, the under surface silvery to silky green with appressed hairs; midrib and lateral veins clearly raised below; apex broadly tapering to rounded with a hair-like tip; base tapering; margin entire, undulate; petiole 2,5 to 12 mm long. **Flowers:** small, whitish, in rather loose, short, terminal heads about 4 cm long (November to February). **Fruit:** kidney-shaped, 7 × 10 mm, becoming black when mature (March).
The division of this species at varietal level is not followed in the present work as many intermediates are found between the two varieties.

Ozoroa reticulata (E. G. Baker) R. & A. Fernandes   Illust. 150

S.A. no: 376   Currant resin tree. Korenteharpuisboom
Rhod. no: 545   Tarberry

 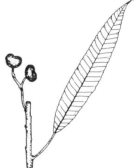

A much-branched tree up to 15 m in height; occurring in open deciduous woodland, often among rocks. **Bark:** dark grey to brown, rough and flaking in small squares; branchlets densely hairy, yellowish to reddish. **Leaves:** alternate or in whorls of 3, very variable in size and shape, frequently elliptic, about 4 times as long as broad, up to 17 × 4 cm, varying from more or less uniform green above and below to conspicuously pale yellowish or rusty below, with dense, coarse, woolly hairs and very conspicuous net-veining (the specific name refers to this); the hairs on the under surface are distinctive, there being 2 layers, a lower, finely appressed layer which is obscured by an upper, woolly layer of green, yellow or rusty hairs, but these 2 layers are very difficult to distinguish even under a microscope; apex tapering to rounded, often with a bristle-like tip, base tapering to rounded; margin entire, thickened; petiole short and thickset, 0,5 to 3 cm long. **Flowers:** small, creamy-green, in branched terminal heads up to 17 cm long (November to February). **Fruit:** kidney-shaped, 8 × 11 mm, flattened, black when mature (February to May).

471

ANACARDIACEAE

This species has been divided into 3 subspecies and varieties according to the degree of net-veining and hairiness of the leaves. Two of the subspecies are found south of the Zambezi River:

subsp. *reticulata:* occurring in South Africa and Rhodesia.
subsp. *grandifolia* R. & A. Fernandes: occurring in the Chimoio area of the Manica e Sofala province of Moçambique.

The divisions at varietal level seem of doubtful value and have been ignored. There is also considerable overlap between the subspecies. The situation is further complicated by the fact that *O. reticulata* is very close to *O. paniculosa,* but differs in that the latter usually has a fine silky silvery sheen on the under surface of the leaves, with inconspicuous net-veining, while *O. reticulata* has woolly hairs standing away from the leaf and very conspicuous net-veining. It is possible that *O. reticulata* is not genuinely distinguishable from *O. paniculosa* at species level, or at least that some of the infra-specific taxa presently included under *O. reticulata* would belong better with *O. paniculosa.* The present classification is not the complete answer and some sections of *Ozoroa* need to be examined afresh.

Ozoroa sphaerocarpa R. & A. Fernandes
S.A. no: 377   Bastard currant resin tree. Basterkorenteharpuisboom
Rhod. no: —

A small tree up to 7 m in height; occurring in deciduous woodland and on rocky hillsides. This species closely resembles *O. reticulata* and *O. paniculosa,* but differs in the structure of its leaf margin which is much more thickened, slightly curled under, and wavy, and also in its fruits which are spherical and not flattened and kidney-shaped as are those of the other two species.

14. HEERIA Meissner

Heeria argentea (Thunb.) Meissner
S.A. no: 368   Rockwood. Kliphout
Rhod. no: —

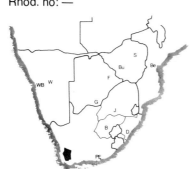 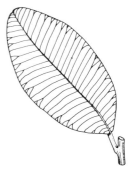

A small, sturdy shrub or bushy tree up to 5 m in height; occurring among rocks and boulders on dry arid mountain slopes. **Bark:** grey to brown, mottled and rough. **Leaves:** alternate, simple, oblong to ovate, 2,5 to 5,5 × 1,5 to 4 cm, dark green above, with fine silvery-white hairs below, the veining characteristically and conspicuously parallel, resembling that in the genus *Ozoroa;* apex rounded, notched; base broadly tapering to rounded; margin entire, inclined to be wavy; petiole about 5 mm long. **Flowers:** cream to white with orange stamens; produced in terminal and axillary sprays or panicles, 3 to 5 cm long. Sexes usually separate on different trees; all floral parts in fives; stamens 5 to 10; ovary asymmetric (January to July). **Fruit:** oblong, about 1,5 × 2,5 cm, leathery, yellow-green and rough (September to January).

15. RHUS L.

Shrublets, shrubs or trees. **Leaves:** alternate, 3-foliolate, or up to 5- to 7-foliolate (other species not dealt with here have simple or imparipinnate leaves). **Flowers:** very small, in branched heads, or panicles, axillary and/or terminal, collectively forming large heads. Sexes usually separate on different trees. All floral parts in fives; calyx segments overlapping; petals longer than the calyx lobes; stamens reduced to staminodes in the female flower; ovary ovoid, usually absent in the male flower. **Fruit:** small, fleshy, often flattened, indehiscent, in many-fruited, branched heads.

This is a taxonomically difficult genus, the flowers and fruits being remarkably constant through all the species while the leaves may be variable within a species. The leaf size and shape are the most useful characters in separating the species and in view of this, and because of the difficulties of compiling a key to the species of *Rhus*, drawings of the leaves have been substituted for the usual key. In all cases a leaf has been chosen which is considered to be generally characteristic.

The 3-foliolate leaves of the *Rhus* species are easily, and frequently, confused with those of species of *Allophylus* (Sapindaceae); differences between the two genera are discussed under the latter.

Rhus angustifolia L.
S.A. no: 377,1   Lance-leaf taaibos. Smalblad
Rhod. no: —

Usually a shrub up to 2,5 m, but it may become a small tree reaching 4 m in height; occurring along streams and river banks. **Bark:** brown. **Leaves:** 3-foliolate; leaflets narrowly elliptic to lanceolate, the terminal leaflet up to 5 × 0,7 cm, the lateral leaflets slightly shorter, leathery, the under surface with short grey hairs, the upper surface shiny, without hairs, the veining not distinct; apex and base tapering; margin entire, may be slightly rolled under; petiolules very short, usually no more than 5 mm, rarely up to 10 or 15 mm long, petiole up to 4 cm long. **Flowers:** small, yellowish, in terminal and axillary heads up to 9 cm long; the stalks and calyces are covered with greyish hairs (October to November). **Fruit:** thinly fleshy, flattened, up to 5 mm in diameter, covered with dense, velvety, greyish hairs (November to April).

This species resembles *R. tomentosa*, but the latter species has longer petioles, the leaflets are more oval and, although their distribution overlaps, *R. angustifolia* is confined to the south-western Cape.

Rhus carnosula Schönl.
S.A. no: 379   Bastard nana-berry. Basternanabessie
Rhod. no: —

A shrub to small tree up to 5 m in height; occurring in, and at the margins of, coastal bush and forest, and on grassy hill slopes. **Bark:** brown. **Leaves:** 3-foliolate; leaflets oblong to ovate, 3 to 7 × 1 to 3 cm, thick, almost fleshy (the specific name refers to this), under surface finely net-veined; apex tapering with a wispy hair-like tip; base narrowly tapering; margin with 1 or 2 large teeth on each side

473

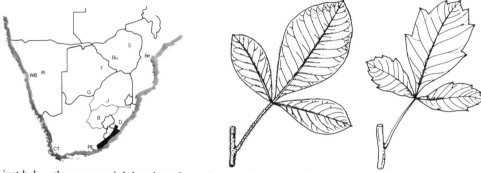

just below the apex; petiolules about 2 mm long on the apical leaflet, absent on the lateral leaflets, petiole up to 6 cm long. **Flowers:** very small, yellowish-green to yellow, in delicate branched sprays up to 5 cm long, axillary, near the tips of the branchlets (October to February). **Fruit:** about 5 mm in diameter, reddish-brown, in heavy clusters (December to April).

Rhus chirindensis E. G. Baker
[*R. legatii* Schönl.]
S.A. no: 380   Bostaaibos. Bostaaibos
Rhod. no: 546   Red currant rhus

Sometimes a shrub, but usually a small tree, often straggling, 3 to 4 m in height, occasionally reaching 6 m or even 10 m; occurring in a wide variety of habitats, from stony hillsides and open woodland to mountain scrub and forest, frequently along streams. **Bark:** brown, smooth; branches spreading. **Leaves:** 3-foliolate; leaflets large, ovate to ovate-lanceolate, 6 to 13 × 2,5 to 4 cm, dark green, young leaves tinged with red, with or without fine hairs, veining more or less conspicuous on both surfaces, but net-veining somewhat obscure; apex tapering to a sharp tip, often curved, ending in a hair-like point; base broadly tapering; margin entire; petiolules very short to absent, petiole long and slender, up to 7 cm long. **Flowers:** minute, yellowish-green, in axillary and terminal misty heads, up to 20 cm long, near the ends of the branchlets (November to December). **Fruit:** up to 5 mm in diameter, thinly fleshy, yellowish-pink becoming shiny red when mature (November to February). The tree is attractive when fruiting heavily. The wood is red, heavy and strong with an attractive sheen; it has considerable potential but is not widely used.

A small tree, reaching 5 m in height, occurs as an under-storey tree in closed woodland and on the margins of forests in Natal and the Transvaal. The leaves are 3-foliolate, and the leaflets large, elliptic, up to 11 × 5 cm, thinly textured and bright green. This has been described as *R. intermedia* Schönl., but it seems quite likely that it may be a hybrid between *R. chirindensis* and *R. macowanii*.

Rhus crenata Thunb.
S.A. no: 380,1   Dune crow-berry. Duinekraaibessie
Rhod. no: —

A shrub or many branched small tree 3 to 5 m in height; occurring on coastal dunes. **Bark:** brownish. **Leaves:** 3-foliolate; leaflets narrowly obovate to oblanceolate, 1 to 2 × 0,3 to 0,8 cm, thinly leathery, dark or greyish-green above, paler yellow-green below; apex tapering; base narrowly tapering; margin scalloped over the upper third, tightly rolled under; midrib prominent below and reddish-

brown; petiolules absent, petiole very short. **Flowers:** very small, white to cream, in small terminal heads. **Fruit:** thinly fleshy round berries, red-brown to blackish when mature.

Rhus culminum R. & A. Fernandes

S.A. no: —
Rhod. no: 547   Mountain scrambling rhus

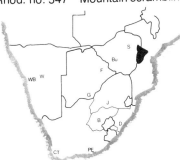
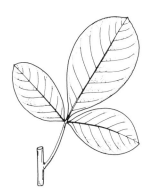

Usually a shrub inclined to scramble, but it can become a small slender-stemmed tree up to 4 m in height; occurring in, or fringing, high altitude evergreen forest, occasionally on rocky mountainsides. **Bark:** brown, smooth; branchlets red. **Leaves:** 3-foliolate; leaflets obovate to elliptic, 5 to 10 × 2,8 to 5,5 cm, the lateral leaflets slightly smaller than the terminal leaflet, glossy green, leathery, usually without hairs but may be slightly furry; the close net-veining is distinctive; apex rounded and finally shortly pointed; base broadly tapering; margin entire; petiolules more or less absent, petiole up to 4 cm long. **Flowers:** very small, yellow, in fine heads up to 24 cm long (September to October). **Fruit:** 4 to 5 mm in diameter, thinly fleshy, red when mature, in large masses (October to December).

Rhus dentata Thunb.

S.A. no: 381,1   Nana-berry. Nanabessie
Rhod. no: 548   Nana-berry

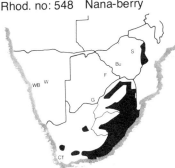

A shrub to small tree up to 6 m in height; occurring from medium to high altitudes, in a variety of habitats, from rocky hillsides to thorn veld, open woodland, at the margins of evergreen forest and in riverine forest. **Bark:** greyish-brown, smooth or striated. **Leaves:** 3-foliolate; leaflets lanceolate to

475

elliptic, the terminal leaflet 2 to 8 × 1 to 5 cm, the lateral leaflets about half this size, upper surface dark green, under surface paler green, occasionally without hairs, but usually with rather long hairs mainly on the prominent midrib and veins; apex rather broadly tapering; base narrowly tapering; margin roughly and deeply toothed, occasionally almost entire, but always toothed to some extent; petiolule short on the terminal leaflet, absent on the lateral leaflets; petiole slender, up to 4 cm long. **Flowers:** small, yellow, in narrow, terminal and axillary heads up to 14 cm long; when borne in profusion they are quite attractive (September to November). **Fruit:** about 4 mm in diameter, bright shiny red when mature, in fairly heavy clusters (November to January).

The fruits are edible, but are probably eaten in quantity only in times of famine. This species grows easily from seed or cuttings and would make an attractive garden subject.

Rhus dura Schönl.
S.A. no: 381,2   Hard-leaved taaibos. Hardetaaibos
Rhod. no: —

A shrub to small tree up to 4 m in height; occurring on mountain slopes and in evergreen forest. **Bark:** brown; the trunk is often twisted and gnarled. **Leaves:** 3-foliolate; leaflets ovate to obovate or oblong, the terminal leaflet up to 6 × 3 cm, the lateral leaflets about half this size, leathery, upper surface bright green, under surface paler green and with fine but marked net-veining, which may be finely hairy; apex very broadly tapering to rounded with a final, abrupt, short sharp tip; base broadly tapering; margin often entire, sometimes irregularly and shallowly toothed; petiolules absent, petiole stout, up to 3 cm long, finely hairy. **Flowers:** very small, greenish, in loose axillary heads about 8 cm long, more or less hidden by the leaves (September to November). **Fruit:** about 3 mm in diameter, shiny reddish when mature (October to January.)

Rhus engleri Britten
S.A. no: 382   Velvet karee. Fluweelkaree
Rhod. no: —

A bushy shrub or small tree up to 4 m in height; occurring in low altitude, deciduous woodland and thorn veld, where it may be locally common. **Bark:** brown; the branches are sometimes spinescent and the branchlets densely covered with long grey hairs. **Leaves:** 3-foliolate; leaflets oblanceolate, the terminal leaflet up to 3,5 cm long, the lateral leaflets about two-thirds of this size, upper surface dark green, under surface covered with grey furry hairs; apex and base tapering; margin frequently entire but may be roughly and irregularly toothed; petiolules absent, petiole up to 1,5 cm long. **Flowers:** very small, yellowish, in terminal and axillary, loose, misty heads about 5 cm long (October to March). **Fruit:** about 4 mm in diameter, flattened, often asymmetric, with a swelling on one side, shiny brown (April to August).

The wood is reddish-brown and tough. It has been used to make implement handles although it is said to be inferior to the wood of *R. pyroides*.

Rhus erosa Thunb.
S.A. no: 383   Broom karee. Besemkaree
Rhod. no: —

A much-branched sprawling shrub or small tree 3 to 4 m in height; occurring on stony koppies. **Bark:** brown; the young branchlets are cinnamon-brown. **Leaves:** 3-foliolate, very conspicuous, long, very narrow and strikingly toothed; leaflets linear, the terminal leaflet up to 12 × 0,5 cm, the lateral leaflets only slightly shorter, yellowish-green, shiny above, leathery, without hairs; apex and base tapering; margin jaggedly toothed (the specific name, meaning 'gnawed', refers to this); petiolules absent, petiole up to 3 cm long. **Flowers:** small, in loose slender-stemmed heads about 9 cm long (October to December). **Fruit:** yellowish, about 5 mm in diameter (January to March).

This species closely resembles *R. tenuipes*, but the two are widely separated geographically. It is a valuable tree in consolidating the soil, its removal often being followed by serious erosion. The branches and leaves are suitable for thatching outbuildings, and also for making rough brooms; it features in 'rain-making' ceremonies in Lesotho, and parts are used to treat diarrhoea in both man and cattle. This attractive species has been grown in gardens, sometimes as a hedge.

Rhus fastigiata Ecklon & Zeyher
S.A. no: 383,1   Broom crow-berry. Besemkraaibessie
Rhod. no: —

A much-branched shrub or small tree up to 3 m in height, with slender, erect branchlets; occurring in wooded ravines, in woodland and forest. **Bark:** brown; branchlets and leaves covered with close, flat hairs. **Leaves:** 3- foliolate; leaflets oblong or elliptic to lanceolate, the terminal leaflet 2 to 3 × 0,4 to 0,8 cm, the lateral leaflets about two thirds of this size, dark green above, paler green below, net-veining absent; apex broadly tapering; base narrowly tapering; margin entire, narrowly rolled under; petiolules minute or absent, petiole up to 10 mm long. **Flowers:** small, cream to yellowish, in sparse heads about 3 to 4 cm long (December to April). **Fruit:** thinly fleshy, about 3 to 4 mm in diameter, shiny brown (January to August).

477

ANACARDIACEAE

This species resembles the hairy forms of *R. pyroides*, but in the latter the net-veining is always more or less conspicuous on the leaves, while in *R. fastigiata* the leaves are without net-veining.

Rhus fraseri Schönl.
S.A. no: Rusty currant
Rhod. no: —

A shrub or small tree up to 3 m in height; occurring in grassland, along forest margins and in scrub forest. **Bark:** brown. **Leaves:** 3-foliolate; leaflets lanceolate to elliptic, the terminal leaflet up to 7,5 × 2,5 cm, the lateral leaflets only slightly smaller, finely velvety above, with dense, grey to rusty, velvety hairs below; apex broadly tapering, ultimately sharp-tipped; base narrowly tapering; margin sometimes almost entire, usually with large jagged teeth especially in the upper third; petiolule on the terminal leaflet about 6 mm long, absent on the lateral leaflets, petiole up to 3 cm long. **Flowers:** very small, yellow, in many-flowered misty heads up to 15 cm long, axillary and terminal (October to March). **Fruit:** almost spherical, about 4 mm in diameter, only slightly asymmetric, greenish-yellow (March to May).

Rhus glauca Thunb.
Rhod. no: 383,2   Blue kuni-bush. Bloukoenibos
Rhod. no: —

 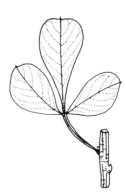

Usually a shrub, rarely a small tree up to 8 m in height; occurring on hill slopes and sometimes along watercourses. **Bark:** grey; the branches are conspicuously angular. **Leaves:** 3-foliolate, scattered closely along the reddish branchlets, often in clusters (or 'tufts'); leaflets obovate, small, the terminal leaflet usually about 2 × 1 cm, the lateral leaflets about two-thirds of this size, firmly textured, highly glossy green, caused by a resinous coating which dries to a greyish powdery layer; veining not clearly visible; apex characteristically square to slightly concave with a short hair-like tip; base narrowly tapering; margin entire, rather wavy; petiolules absent, petiole 5 to 10 mm long, narrowly winged. **Flowers:** very small, whitish or greenish-white to yellowish, in many-flowered, axillary and terminal, branched heads up to 4 cm long (June to July). **Fruit:** spherical, about 5 to 6 mm in diameter, shiny reddish-brown when mature (August to September).

478

Rhus gueinzii Sonder
[*R. simii* Sonder; *R. spinescens* Diels; *R. gueinzii* Sonder var. *spinescens* (Diels) R. & A.
Fernandes; *R. crispa* (Engl.) Harvey ex Sonder]
S.A. no: 384   Thorny karee. Doringkaree
Rhod. no: 549   Spiny rhus

A shrub or small tree up to 3 m in height, with rather spreading, flexuous branches; occurring at low altitudes in a variety of habitats, in open woodland, in thicket or at the margins of riverine forest, often on termite mounds. **Bark:** grey or brown; the branches greyish pubescent and most often bearing spines; these may be confined to near the base of the stems, or may be conspicuous on all parts of the tree. **Leaves:** 3-foliolate, occasionally 4-foliolate; leaflets lanceolate to oblong, the terminal leaflet 3,5 to 7 × 0,6 to 1,3 cm, the lateral leaflets about two thirds of this size, pale blue- to grey-green above, paler green below, thinly textured, without hairs, midrib slender, prominent on both surfaces; apex tapering, finely rounded, often notched; base narrowly tapering; margin entire or shallowly and irregularly toothed or scalloped; petiolules absent, petiole slender, up to 4 cm long. **Flowers:** very small, greenish-yellow, produced in fine delicate heads 4 to 6 cm long, rather obscured by the leaves; flower stalks with dense, whitish, velvety hairs (November to March). **Fruit:** thinly fleshy, about 4 mm in diameter, flattened, shiny brown when mature (February to May).
Preparations from this tree are used in treating eye-complaints: a lotion may be made from an infusion of the branches, while smoke drifting into the eyes from a burning stick is regarded as another remedy. The wood is hard, red and very tough but is little used.

Rhus incisa L.f.
[*R. incisa* var. *typica* Schönl.; *R. incisa* var. *obovata* (Sonder) Schönl.]
S.A. no: 385   Rub-rub berry. Baardbessie
Rhod. no: —

A shrub or small tree 3 to 4 m in height; scattered through open scrub and frequently occurring along the banks of rivers. Branches rigid and spreading. **Leaves:** very distinctive, 3-foliolate; leaflets ovate to obovate in general outline, the terminal leaflet up to 2 × 1,2 cm, the lateral leaflets about half this size, dark green and minutely hairy above, the under surface covered with whitish, woolly hairs; apex broadly tapering or deeply incised; base narrowly tapering; margin deeply toothed to very deeply incised forming almost separate lobes, often resembling an oak leaf; petiolules absent, petiole up to 10 mm long. **Flowers:** small, although slightly larger than in many other species of *Rhus*, greenish-yellow, distinctive; the calyces and stalks covered with grey woolly hairs, in terminal and axillary

479

heads up to 6 cm long, produced among the leaves (June to November). **Fruit:** thinly fleshy but shaggy with long soft hairs, cream to pinkish-brown, 5 to 7 mm in diameter, occasionally splitting to release the seeds (August to January).

The degree of dissection of the leaflet varies a great deal even on the same tree, but the typical variety, var. *incisa*, with very deeply dissected leaflets, does not appear to occur further east than Riversdale, while the eastern variety, var. *effusa* (Presl) R. Fernandes, tends to have less deeply dissected leaflets.

Rhus krebsiana Presl ex Engl.
S.A. no: 385,1   Bastard sour taaibos. Bastersuurtaaibos
Rhod. no: —

A shrub or small bushy tree up to 4 m in height; occurring at medium to high altitudes in bush and fringing forest. **Bark:** brown; young branches are somewhat corrugated and angular and may be tinged with red. **Leaves:** 3-foliolate; leaflets oblong to oblong-obovate, the terminal leaflet up to 6 × 2,5 cm, the lateral leaflets about two-thirds of this size, with net-veining distinct on both surfaces; apex rounded, abruptly attenuate; base narrowly tapering; margin entire, slightly rolled under; petiolules absent, petiole up to 2,5 cm, slightly winged. **Flowers:** small, yellowish, in axillary, loose heads, about 4 to 5 cm long (March to August). **Fruit:** thinly fleshy, about 7 mm in diameter (September to November).

Rhus laevigata L.
[*R. mucronata* Thunb.]
S.A. no: 385,2   Dune taaibos. Duinetaaibos
Rhod. no: —

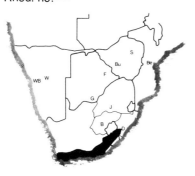 

A dense shrub or small, bushy, spreading tree up to 4 m in height; occurring in the *fynbos* on stony hills, and on coastal dunes. Branches with or without spines. **Leaves:** 3-foliolate; leaflets lanceolate to obovate, the terminal leaflet up to 4 × 2,5 cm, the lateral leaflets somewhat smaller, glossy green above, paler green below with the midrib and veins conspicuous on both surfaces, with or without fine velvety hairs; apex more or less rounded, finally sharp-tipped; base narrowly tapering; margin entire, finely rolled under; petiolules absent, petiole up to 2 cm long. **Flowers:** small, greenish-yellow, in axillary and terminal branched heads up to 7 cm long (November to April). **Fruit:** almost spherical, about 4 mm in diameter, russet-red when ripe (January to June).

480

Rhus lancea L.f.   Illust. 151
S.A. no: 386   Karee. Karee
Rhod. no: 550   Willow rhus

A small to medium sized evergreen tree, usually about 8 m in height, but sometimes taller; occurring over a variety of altitudes and habitats, in open woodland, along river and stream banks and often on termite mounds. **Bark:** dark grey or brown, rough; the branches are reddish-brown. **Leaves:** 3-foliolate; leaflets narrowly lanceolate, the terminal leaflet 9 to 12 × 0,6 to 1,5 cm, the lateral leaflets only slightly less than this, dark green above, paler green below, without hairs, leathery, frequently slightly sickle-shaped, with fine net-veining clearly visible on the upper surface; apex narrowly tapering; base tapering; margin entire; petiolules absent, petiole 3 to 4 cm long, slender. **Flowers:** very small, pale greenish-yellow, in dense clusters, about 6 × 6 cm, at the ends of the branchlets; sweetly scented, attracting bees and other insects (June to September). **Fruit:** almost spherical, often slightly asymmetric, about 4 to 5 mm in diameter, greyish-yellow to shiny brown when mature, sometimes sticky (September to January).

This species resembles *R. viminalis,* a characteristic tree of riverine fringe thicket which is confined to the central and northern Cape and has more thinly textured leaves; *R. lancea* almost takes over in distribution in South West Africa, the Orange Free State, the Transvaal and further north. The fruits of *R. lancea,* pounded with water and allowed to ferment, make a good beer. The wood, which is said to have a sweet spicy scent, is reddish brown, hard, tough and durable but the trunks are frequently so twisted and crooked that they cannot be made into satisfactory planks. However, they are valuable as fencing posts and are used to make implement handles. The trees grow easily from seed, cuttings or truncheons and are reasonably fast-growning. They make attractive garden subjects.

Rhus leptodictya Diels
[*R. gueinzii* auct. non Sonder; *R. amerina* Meikle]
S.A. no: 387   Mountain karee. Bergkaree
Rhod. no: 551   Rock rhus

A shrub or small tree usually 3 to 4 m in height but sometimes reaching 8 m; occurring in a variety of habitats, in open woodland, at the margins of forest, often on hillsides and in rocky places. **Bark:** dark brown to blackish, rough. **Leaves:** 3-foliolate; leaflets lanceolate to oblong-lanceolate, the terminal leaflet 4 to 14 × 1 to 3,5 cm, the lateral leaflets about two-thirds of this size, fresh green, or greyish-green, only slightly paler below than above, without hairs, or with very short hairs sometimes present on the midrib which is slender and raised on both surfaces, the lateral veins not conspicuous; apex narrowly tapering; base tapering; margin usually shallowly toothed or scalloped, occasionally almost entire; petiolules absent, petiole slender up to 4 cm long. **Flowers:** very small, pale yellow, in

481

fine heads up to 15 cm long, axillary and terminal, collectively forming large clusters (January to April). **Fruit:** flattened, slightly asymmetric, about 5 mm in diameter, yellowish-brown to orange when mature (March to June).

The plants are easily raised from seed and grow well in cultivation. They are hardy to all but the most severe frosts, and are fairly drought-resistant. An intoxicating liquor can be made from the fruit.

Rhus longipes Engl.   Illust. 152
S.A. no: —
Rhod. no: 552   Large-leaved rhus

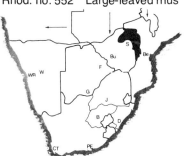
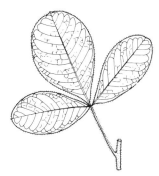

Usually a small straggling shrub or small tree with long weak stems, growing to 5 m in height, but it can reach 9 m; occurring in open woodland and thicket, often along river banks. **Bark:** grey-brown, becoming rough. **Leaves:** 3-foliolate; leaflets elliptic or obovate-elliptic, the terminal leaflet 4 to 13 × 1,5 to 8 cm, the lateral leaflets about three-quarters of this size; net-veining conspicuous; with or without slender hairs; young leaves conspicuously fresh apple-green, mature leaves firmly leathery, clear yellowish-green; apex rounded, hair-tipped; base asymmetric, tapering; margin entire; petiolule on the terminal leaflet short, absent on the lateral leaflets, petiole up to 6 cm long, hairy. **Flowers:** small, yellow to yellowish-green, in loose heads up to 8 cm long, axillary and terminal, collectively forming large clusters up to 24 cm long (June to September). **Fruit:** 6 to 7 mm in diameter, reddish-brown when mature (September to December).

All the material south of the Zambezi River is placed in the typical variety, var. *longipes;* var. *schinoides* R. Fernandes, is known only from Zambia.

Rhus longispina Ecklon & Zeyher
S.A. no: 388   Thorny taaibos. Doringtaaibos
Rhod. no: —

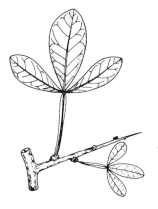

A spiny scaly-rough shrub or small tree 3 to 5 m in height; occurring in dry, rather arid areas. **Bark:** grey; the young branchlets, leaflets and flower heads are covered with red glands which disappear with maturity; the branchlets are spine-tipped and short side branches, up to 10 cm long, develop which also become spiny, the spines projecting some 4 cm beyond the leaves. **Leaves:** 3-foliolate; leaflets obovate to oblong, 1 to 5 × 0,5 to 2,2 cm, usually greyish-green but variable in colour; coarse net-veining is conspicuous on both surfaces; apex bluntly tapering to square, sometimes notched; base tapering; petiolules absent, petiole up to 4 cm long, winged. **Flowers:** small, pale yellowish, in compact heads, 4 to 6 cm long, among the leaves and densely covered with red glandular hairs (March to May). **Fruit:** thinly fleshy, flattened, up to 5 to 6 mm in diameter, asymmetric, turning brown when mature (April to August).

482

Rhus lucens Hutch.
S.A. no: —
Rhod. no: 553   Shiny-fruited rhus

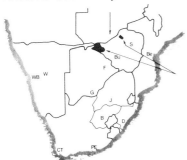 

A shrub or small tree 4 to 5 m in height; occurring at low altitudes in mixed woodland, on stony hills, in escarpment woodland and open areas in dry forest. **Bark:** grey. **Leaves:** 3-foliolate; leaflets obovate to almost circular, the terminal leaflet 3,5 to 8 × 1,5 to 6 cm, the lateral leaflets half this size, leathery, upper surface greyish-green, lower surface somewhat paler green, net-veining visible above and below, with or without hairs; apex rounded, notched; base tapering; margin shallowly scalloped, often wavy; petiolules absent, petiole up to 2,5 cm long, slender. **Flowers:** small, creamy-white to yellowish, in fine heads about 6 cm long, almost lost among the leaves (April to May). **Fruit:** thinly fleshy, up to 6 mm in diameter, somewhat asymmetric and flattened, becoming very glossy, yellowish-brown when mature, with a polished look to which the specific name refers (July).
This species is nowhere common.

Rhus lucida L.
S.A. no: 381,1   Glossy taaibos. Blinktaaibos
Rhod. no: 554   Shiny-leaved rhus

A shrub or small tree usually 3 to 4 m in height but it can reach 7 m; occurring in scrub and forest, from sea level to 2 000 m. **Bark:** grey to brown; branchlets reddish-brown or greyish, with short, white hairs, the young parts often covered with shiny resin. **Leaves:** 3-foliolate; leaflets obovate to oblong, the terminal leaflet 1,5 to 7 × 0,5 to 2,5 cm, the lateral leaflets about two-thirds of this size, dark green on both surfaces, often very glossy (the specific name refers to this); net-veining is not conspicuous, without hairs; apex broadly tapering, most often rounded, notched; base tapering; margin entire; petiolules absent; petiole short, about 2,5 cm long, slightly winged. **Flowers:** often bisexual, small, creamy-white, in rather sparse terminal and axillary heads about 7 cm long (August to October). **Fruit:** thinly fleshy, 3 to 5 mm in diameter, becoming shiny brown when mature (October to November).
The wood is hard, tough and durable, and makes good fence posts. The bark from the roots and branches was once used for tanning.

Rhus macowanii Schönl.
S.A. no: 389   Sour taaibos. Suurtaaibos
Rhod. no: —

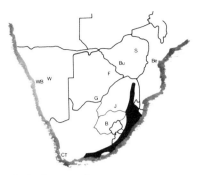

A shrub or small tree occasionally reaching 10 m in height; occurring in scrub, bush and at forest margins. **Bark:** grey to brown. **Leaves:** usually 3-foliolate, although specimens with 4 or 5 leaflets may be found; leaflets ovate to obovate, the terminal leaflet up to 3,5 × 2 cm, the lateral leaflets about two-thirds of this size, fine net-veining is visible on both surfaces especially on older leaves, younger leaflets finely velvety; apex broadly tapering; base narrowly tapering; margin entire, or occasionally slightly scalloped or toothed; petiolules absent, petiole short, up to 1,5 cm long. **Flowers:** small, greenish-yellow, in compact heads about 4 cm long, axillary, among the leaves (December to April). **Fruit:** thinly fleshy, only about 3 mm in diameter, cream, becoming tinged with red, slightly juicy at first (January to June).

Although this species resembles *R. pyroides,* it differs in that it lacks spines, the branches do not spread at such a wide angle, the petioles are shorter and thicker, the flower heads are larger and more dense although the individual flowers are smaller, the leaves are furry rather than silky and the hairs tend to drop as the leaves mature. The possibility that *R. intermedia* is a hybrid between *R. macowanii* and *R. chirindensis* is mentioned under the latter species.

Rhus marlothii Engl.
S.A. no: 389,2   Bitter karee. Bitterkaree
Rhod. no: —

A woody dense shrub or small evergreen tree up to 3 m in height; occurring along stony watercourses, in rocky crevices, on grassy hillsides and in mountainous areas. **Bark:** grey to brown. **Leaves:** 3-foliolate; leaflets ovate to oblong, the terminal leaflet 2 to 4,5 × 1 to 1,8 cm, the lateral leaflets about two-thirds of this size, thinly textured, blue-green and sparsely hairy on both surfaces, midrib raised on both surfaces, lateral veins somewhat obscure; apex rounded; base tapering; margin slightly scalloped in the upper part; petiolules absent, petiole up to 1,2 cm long. **Flowers:** small, yellowish, in axillary, branched heads, or panicles, about 3 cm long (January to March). **Fruit:** flattened, about 6 mm in diameter, cream to yellowish-brown (March to May).

It is said that stock will not browse on this tree as its leaves are bitter.

Rhus microcarpa Schönl.
S.A. no: 389,1   Natal mountain karee. Natalse bergkaree
Rhod. no: —

A shrub or small tree 2 to 5 m in height; occurring in coastal bush and woodland, and in riverine fringe forest. **Leaves:** 3-foliolate; leaflets narrowly oblong to obovate, the terminal leaflet 4 to 6 × 1,4 to 2 cm, the lateral leaflets only slightly smaller than this, thinly textured, blue-green above and below,

484

the under surface slightly paler, with or without sparse flattened hairs, especially along the midrib and veins which are more or less prominent on both surfaces; apex narrowly tapering; base conspicuously narrowed; margin entire; petiolules absent, petiole slender, up to 3 cm long, densely hairy. **Flowers:** small, cream to yellow-green, in loose, axillary heads, about 4 cm long, covered with long thick hairs (October to April). **Fruit:** thinly fleshy, only 2 to 3 mm in diameter, flattened, red when mature (January to July).

Rhus montana Diels

[*R. gerrardii* Harvey & Engl.; *R. gerrardii* Harvey & Diels var. *montana* (Diels) Schönl.; *R. montana* var. *latifolia* (Schönl.) R. Fernandes; *R. montana* var. *basutorum* (Schönl.) R. Fernandes]
S.A. no: 384,1   Drakensberg karee. Drakensbergkaree
Rhod. no: —

A shrub or small tree up to 5 m in height with a graceful drooping habit; occurring in mountain areas, often along river banks. **Bark:** brown to grey. **Leaves:** very variable, from 3- to 5-foliolate, occasionally even 7-foliolate; leaflets oblanceolate to obovate, the terminal leaflet up to 9 × 2 cm, but usually smaller than this, the lateral leaflets becoming progressively smaller towards the base, the leaves turn red in autumn, with or without hairs, midrib prominent especially below, lateral veins somewhat obscure; apex tapering; base narrowly tapering; margin usually deeply toothed, each tooth ending with a sharp hair-like tip, occasionally almost entire; petiolules absent, petiole slender, up to 4 cm long. **Flowers:** small, yellowish, softly hairy or almost without hairs, in many-flowered heads, up to 14 cm long, tightly clustered along the branches (October to February). **Fruit:** thinly fleshy, almost spherical, about 5 mm in diameter, red when mature (November to June).

This species has been divided into 4 varieties, 2 of which, var. *latifolia* (Schönl.) R. Fernandes and var. *basutorum* (Schönl.) R. Fernandes, are not upheld in the present work. The typical variety, var. *montana,* usually has 5 leaflets and occurs from Transkei to the Transvaal; var. *gerrardii* (Harvey ex Engl.) R.Fernandes usually has 3 leaflets and occurs only in the Transvaal. However, there would seem to be almost sufficient grounds for reinstating *R. gerrardii* at specific level.

Rhus natalensis Bernh.

S.A. no: 390   Natal karee. Natalkaree
Rhod. no: 555   Natal rhus

Usually a shrub with a tendency to scramble, but it may become a small tree up to 8 m in height; occurring on coastal dunes, in dune forest, open woodland and at forest margins. **Bark:** grey, rough. **Leaves:** 3- foliolate, leaflets obovate, oblong to elliptic, the terminal leaflet 2,5 to 9 × 1 to 3,5 cm,

485

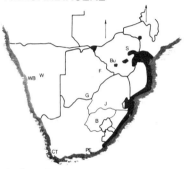

the lateral leaflets about two-thirds this size, both surfaces greyish-green or dark green above with the under surface greyish-green or paler green, rather thinly textured, net-veining not conspicuous, without hairs; apex very broadly tapering to rounded; base tapering; margin almost entire or obscurely and shallowly scalloped and toothed; petiolules absent, petiole up to 4 cm long. **Flowers:** small, greenish-yellow, in fine terminal heads, about 8 cm long, produced among the leaves (March to May). **Fruit:** thinly fleshy, somewhat flattened, about 5 to 6 mm in diameter, yellowish-brown when mature (May to July).

Rhus nebulosa Schönl.
S.A. no: Sand taaibos
Rhod. no: —

A climber, scrambling shrub or small tree up to 3 m in height, sometimes tree-shaped but less than 1 m in height ('like a bonsai tree' wrote one collector); occurring in coastal dune scrub and forest, in evergreen forest and open woodland on sandy soil, often in stream valleys; one of the early colonisers of cleared sands. **Leaves:** 3-foliolate; leaflets obovate to broadly elliptic, the terminal leaflet up to 6 × 3,5 cm, veining very conspicuous on the under surface; apex rounded usually with a small short point and a hair-like tip; base tapering; margin entire; petiolule of the terminal leaflet about 5 mm long, absent on the lateral leaflets, petiole up to 2 cm long. **Flowers:** very small, yellowish, in fine, lax, branched heads, axillary and terminal, up to 17 cm long (February to April). **Fruit:** almost spherical, about 5 mm in diameter, red-brown when mature, often produced in attractive, dense, heavy heads (April to July).

Rhus pentheri Zahlbr.
S.A. no: 391   Common crow-berry. Gewone kraaibessie
Rhod. no: —

A much-branched shrub or small tree up to 6 m in height; occurring in dry types of woodland, thornveld and scrub, often along the stony banks of seasonal streams. **Leaves:** 3-foliolate; leaflets small, obovate, the terminal leaflet up to 3,3 × 1,4 cm, the lateral leaflets about half this size, the upper surface dark green, the under surface conspicuously paler green, thinly textured, at first with fine hairs but losing these by maturity, net-veining not visible; apex very broadly tapering to rounded, notched; base narrowly tapering; margin entire, or occasionally with 3 blunt teeth near the tip; petiolules absent, petiole up to 1,5 cm long. **Flowers:** small, in compact heads, up to 4 cm long, among the leaves (March). **Fruit:** thinly fleshy, 3 to 4 mm in diameter, glossy, orange-brown to dark brown when mature; often produced in profusion (April to May).

Rhus pyroides Burch.   Illust. 153
[*R. pyroides* Burch. var. *gracilis* Burtt Davy; *R. pyroides* Burch. var. *puberula* (Ecklon & Zeyher)
Schönl.; *R. vulgaris* Meikle; *R. baurii* Schönl.]
S.A. no: 392   Common taaibos. Gewone taaibos
Rhod. no: 556   Fire-thorned rhus

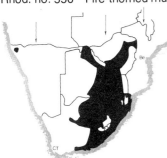

A very variable species in all respects; often a shrub, or a small bushy to spreading tree up to 5 m in
height, occasionally taller and frequently spiny; occurring in open woodland, in dry thornveld
frequently associated with *Acacia karroo*, often on termite mounds, also on rocky hillsides and even
fringing forest and thicket, or along watercourses. **Bark:** dark brown; young stems green, often with
rusty velvety hairs, and often bearing stout thorns. **Leaves:** 3-foliolate; leaflets very variable from
almost lanceolate to obovate, the terminal leaflet 3 to 8 × 1 to 2,3 cm, the lateral leaflets somewhat
shorter, with or without velvety hairs, the lateral veins very conspicuous on the under sufrace, but the
net-veining somewhat obscured in the hairy forms; apex very broadly tapering to rounded, ultimately
sharply pointed; base narrowly tapering; margin entire or irregularly toothed; petiolules absent,
petiole up to 3 cm long. **Flowers:** very small, yellow, in terminal heads up to 20 cm long (October to
February). **Fruit:** 3 to 4 mm in diameter, red when mature (November to May).
A prick or scratch from the thorns stings and burns for some time. The wood is red-brown, cross-
grained, tough and elastic. In the Transvaal this species and *Acacia detinens* are looked upon as
providing the best wood for implement handles, especially for axes; they are considered comparable
to hickory wood. They also make good fencing poles, but the trees are too small to provide timber of
any great size. The specific name means 'like *Pyrus*', or pear-tree.

Rhus quartiniana A. Rich.
S.A. no: 393   River rhus. Savannekorentebos
Rhod. no: 557   River rhus

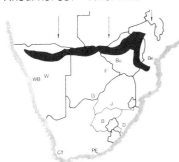

487

ANACARDIACEAE

A willow-like shrub or small tree up to 7 m in height; occurring along river banks, on islands in rivers and in open woodland. **Bark:** brown, rough and striated; the branches tend to droop. **Leaves:** 3-foliolate; leaflets lanceolate to oblong-elliptic, the terminal leaflet 3 to 7 × 1 to 3 cm, the lateral leaflets about half this size, dark green above, pale yellowish-green below, the midrib is prominent on the upper surface, with rather long spreading hairs, but secondary veins and net-veining are not clearly visible; apex tapering to rounded, notched, sometimes forming a sharp, abrupt tip; base tapering; margin entire; petiolules up to 6 mm, or absent, petiole up to 2,5 cm long. **Flowers:** very small, greenish-yellow, in loose heads, up to 10 × 7 cm (November to March). **Fruit:** thinly fleshy, about 3 mm in diameter, reddish to yellowish-brown when mature (March to June).

This species has been divided into 2 varieties, most of the material south of the Zambezi River falling under the typical variety, var. *quartiniana,* which has no spines and entire leaf margins; the other variety, var. *zambesiensis* R. & A. Fernandes, is a spiny tree with toothed leaf margins which occurs round the Victoria Falls and into the Caprivi Strip.

Rhus rehmanniana Engl.
S.A. no: 393,1   Blunt-leaved taaibos. Stompblaartaaibos
Rhod. no:—

A small tree up to 5 m in height; occurring in thicket, in grassland, on forest margins and on mountainsides. **Leaves:** 3-foliolate; leaflets obovate, 2 to 6,5 × 0,5 to 4,5 cm, rather leathery, the under surface paler green than the upper surface, often with fine velvety hairs most of which are lost by maturity; apex flattened, or truncate, with the margin round the apex broken into irregular scallops or teeth, below this the margin is entire; base tapering; petiolules absent, petiole up to 4 cm long. **Flowers:** small, greenish-yellow, axillary heads 5 to 6 cm long, almost lost among the leaves (December to April). **Fruit:** thinly fleshy, up to 3 mm in diameter, reddish-brown when mature (April onwards).

A second variety, var. *longecuneata* R. & A. Fernandes, has been described; it occurs only in the extreme south of Moçambique, near the Maputo River, and is said to differ from the typical var. *rehmanniana* in having rather smaller leaflets which have more narrowly tapering bases.

Rhus tenuinervis Engl.
[*R. commiphoroides* Engl. & Gilg; *R. kwebensis* N. E. Brown]
S.A. no: 393,2   Kalahari taaibos. Kalaharitaaibos
Rhod. no: 558   Commiphora rhus

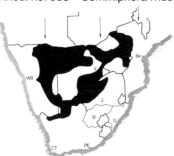
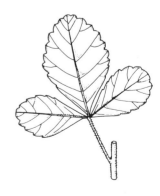

A well-branched shrub or small tree, characteristically rounded and bushy, 5 to 8 m in height; occurring in various types of woodland, on rocky hillsides, on the banks of rivers and on termite mounds. **Bark:** very dark brown to almost black, finely fissured to rough; occasionally with spines on the branches. **Leaves:** 3-foliolate; leaflets comparatively large, obovate; the terminal leaflet 2,5 to 11,5 × 1,5 to 7 cm long, the lateral leaflets half this size, with dense velvety hairs, the upper surface dull green, the under surface conspicuously paler green; the midrib and lateral veins more or less prominent, especially below; apex rounded with a small, sharp tip; base broadly tapering; margin coarsely scalloped and toothed over the upper two-thirds, the lower third entire; petiolules absent, petiole up to 3,5 cm long. **Flowers:** minute, yellowish, in loose heads, terminal and axillary, up to 15 cm long (January to April). **Fruit:** thinly fleshy, flattened, up to 6 mm in diameter, becoming shiny brownish-red when mature, edible (April to June).

A second variety, var. *meikleana* R. & A. Fernandes, just crosses the Zambezi River near Zóbuè in the Tete province of Moçambique; all the other material is placed in the typical variety, var. *tenuinervis*. The wood is medium hard and pinkish-yellow and the bark has been used for tanning. The crushed leaves have a strong and distinctive smell.

Rhus tenuipes R. & A. Fernandes
S.A. no: —
Rhod. no: 559   Serpentine rhus

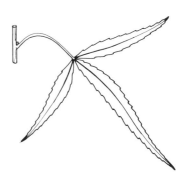

A small graceful tree, 3 to 5 m in height; occurring in woodland and bush, often associated with mineralised soils, such as the serpentine-derived soils of the Great Dyke in Rhodesia where it is locally abundant. **Bark:** dark brownish-grey; the young branchlets are reddish and drooping. **Leaves:** 3-foliolate; leaflets conspicuously long and narrow, the terminal leaflet 4,5 to 12 × 0,4 to 0,8 cm, the lateral leaflets being only slightly shorter than this, veining not conspicuous, without hairs; apex sharply pointed; base narrowly tapering; margin conspicuously toothed; petiolules absent, petiole very slender, up to 5 cm long, so that the leaves hang down. **Flowers:** very small, yellowish, in rather sparse fine heads up to 15 cm long, among the leaves (January to March). **Fruit:** almost square in shape, flattened, 3 to 4,5 mm in diameter, shiny dark brown when mature (March to July).

The leaves of this species closely resemble those of *R. erosa* but there should be no confusion as the two species are widely separated geographically. The leaves are aromatic when crushed and the roots have an unpleasant smell when cut.

Rhus tomentosa L.
S.A. no: 394   Wild currant. Korentebos
Rhod. no: 560   Furry rhus

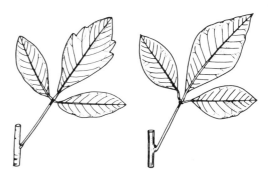

489

ANACARDIACEAE

A shrub or small tree, 3 to 5 m in height; occurring at medium to high altitudes, not below 500 m, on rocky mountainsides and in forest. Branches spreading, red and hairy when young. **Leaves:** 3-foliolate; leaflets lanceolate-elliptic to obovate, the terminal leaflet 3 to 8,5 × 1 to 3,8 cm, the lateral leaflets only slightly less than this, the upper surface dark green, the under surface with short, dense, yellowish to almost white hairs, veining inconspicuous; apex tapering; base broadly tapering, asymmetric on the lateral leaflets, one side being almost rounded; margin entire, sometimes with 1 or 2 teeth in the upper third; petiolules about 6 mm long, petiole slender, often reddish, up to 4 cm long. **Flowers:** very small, in very dense terminal heads, up to 9 × 7 cm, the whole head being densely furry and conspicuous (May to November). **Fruit:** thinly fleshy, asymmetric, up to 6 × 4 mm, covered with dense, greyish, furry hairs (June to February).

The flowers of this tree have an unpleasant scent. The bark, both of the roots and the branches, has been used in tanning, the latter also producing fibre for rough cordage. The wood is hard and tough but because the trees are small the timber is useful only as fuel.

Rhus transvaalensis Engl.
S.A. no: 394,1   Transvaal taaibos. Transvaaltaaibos
Rhod. no: —

A shrub or small well-branched tree, 3 to 5 m in height; occurring at high altitudes, common along streams and in scrub forest. **Bark:** pale grey; branchlets densely hairy. **Leaves:** 3-foliolate; leaflets oblong to elliptic, the terminal leaflet 2,5 to 4 × 0,8 to 1,3 cm, the lateral leaflets about two-thirds this size, rather leathery, young leaves with dense hairs, losing these by maturity, the under surface rather paler green than the upper surface; apex and base tapering; margin entire, thickened, often slightly wavy; petiolules absent, petiole up to 3 cm long, slender, velvety. **Flowers:** very small, greyish yellow-green, in sparse heads, axillary and terminal, up to 4 cm long, rather lost among the leaves (October to November). **Fruit:** about 5 mm in diameter, pale white to yellow becoming deep orange to reddish-brown when mature, in heavy, short clusters (November to December).

Rhus undulata Jacq.
[*R. excisa Thunb.; R. celastroides* Sonder; *R. burchellii* Sonder ex Engl.; *R. rangeana* Engl.]
S.A no: 395   Kuni-bush. Koeniebos
Rhod. no: —

A very variable species. It ranges from a low-growing shrub to a small tree up to 5 m in height, and, having adapted itself to a very wide range of conditions, occurs from dry, arid areas to evergreen forest. **Bark:** grey to brown. **Leaves:** 3-foliolate; leaflets very variable in size, obovate to oblanceolate, the terminal leaflet 1 to 5 × 0,7 to 1,8 cm, lateral leaflets slightly smaller than this, from leathery to thinly textured, the young leaves often shiny and resinous; apex tapering to square, or truncate, even concave in the small-leaved form; base tapering; margin entire to toothed in the upper half, usually markedly wavy (the specific name refers to this); petiolules absent, petiole up to 2,5 cm long, winged, particularly in the upper half. **Flowers:** small, in loose, terminal and axillary heads, 4 to 6 cm long, among the leaves (February to April). **Fruit:** thinly fleshy, up to 3 mm in diameter, reddish, but often green even when mature (March to June).

This species has been divided into 3 varieties:

var. *undulata* – widespread; including the larger-leaved forms.

var. *celastroides* (Sonder) Schönl. – in Namaqualand and South West Africa; usually a low-growing shrub with small leaves.

var. *tricrenata* (Engl.) R. Fernandes – in dry areas of the Cape, Lesotho, Orange Free State, the Transvaal and South West Africa; usually tree-like. The Hottentots, who called this tree '!Kuni', used a decoction of the leaves for postparturient problems; the Namaquas chew them as a treatment for chest colds.

Rhus viminalis Vahl.
S.A. no: 396   White karee. Witkaree
Rhod. no: —

A rather willow-like bush, or a small to medium sized tree up to 10 m in height; occurring along river and stream banks. **Bark:** dark brown, roughish. **Leaves:** 3-foliolate; leaflets lanceolate, the terminal leaflet 4 to 11 × 0,9 to 2,5 cm, the lateral leaflets about three-quarters this size, rather thinly textured, both surfaces a delicate green; fine net-veining is visible above and below; tapering to base and apex; margin entire; petiole slender, up to 6 cm long. **Flowers:** small, greenish-yellow, in delicately branched, many-flowered, axillary and terminal heads, densely furry, up to 8 cm long, among the leaves (September to January). **Fruit:** almost spherical, up to 4 mm in diameter, reddish when mature (December to May).

The leaves, particularly when dry, resemble those of *R. lancea*, but the leaves of the latter species are much more leathery, tend to be larger, and are olive-green rather than the fresh green of *R. viminalis*. In the northern and north-western Cape it often occurs in association with *Salix mucronata*, especially along the banks and on the islands of the Orange River; it often has many slender stems and, at a casual glance, resembles a small-leaved bamboo. Certain African peoples prepare a milk infusion from the leaves and this is given, as an enema, to children suffering from stomach upsets. The wood has a reputation for durability and is suitable for fencing posts and for hut-building. Along the Orange River the slender branchlets are used to make fish traps. This is a protected tree in the northern Cape.

Rhus zeyheri Sonder
S.A. no: 396,1   Blue taaibos. Bloutaaibos
Rhod. no: —

A shrub, occasionally becoming a small tree up to 4 m in height; occurring along stream banks and on rocky koppies. **Leaves:** 3-foliolate; leaflets rather small, obovate to elliptic, the terminal leaflet 2 to 6

491

× 0,8 to 2,2 cm, but usually about 3,5 × 2 cm, the lateral leaflets being only slightly less than this, without hairs, characteristically blue-green with a whitish bloom; apex broadly tapering to almost rounded and sharp tipped, occasionally notched; base tapering; margin entire; petiolules absent, petiole up to 2,5 cm long. **Flowers:** small, greenish-yellow, in axillary and terminal heads up to 4 cm long (October to November). **Fruit:** about 8 mm in diameter, russet-red when mature (November to February).

AQUIFOLIACEAE *(The holly family)*

ILEX L.

Ilex mitis (L.) Radlk.   Illust. 154
S.A. no: 397   African holly. Without
Rhod. no: 561   African holly

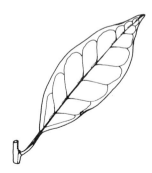

A medium to large tree, 10 to 30 m in height; most frequently occurring along river banks and stream beds, in moist evergreen forest, sometimes straggling and leaning over the water, but often a fine, well-shaped tree. **Bark:** very pale grey to light brown, smooth; young branches tinged with purple. **Leaves:** alternate, simple, narrowly elliptic, 7 to 13 × 1,9 to 4,5 cm, shiny dark green, mid-vein deeply channelled, lateral veins looping, without hairs; the young leaves are characteristically reddish; apex tapering to a sharp point, or square with a very fine hair-like tip; base tapering; margin entire, or with a few shallow, sharp teeth; petiole up to 10 mm long, purplish tinged. **Flowers:** white, about 7 mm in diameter, sweet-scented, in axillary clusters or in few-flowered panicles up to 3 cm long, often produced in profusion. Sexes separate on different trees; floral parts in fours to sixes; calyx small, persistent; petals shortly joined at the base; stamens attached to the mouth of the corolla tube, alternating with the petal lobes, absent in female flowers; ovary 5- to 6-chambered, absent in male flowers (September to December). **Fruit:** berry-like, almost spherical, about 7 mm in diameter, taking a long time to develop, but finally becoming shiny crimson (April to July).
The fruits are conspicuous, edible, and sought after by birds. The wood is white, hard, close-grained, and can be attractively marked; although it would make good furniture, it has been little exploited possibly because the trees grow in areas where other more valuable furniture woods are available. If the fresh leaves are rubbed together in water a lather is produced; the Zulus bathe influenza sufferers in

492

this and it is said that early Knysna woodcutters washed with it in the forest streams. Small pieces of bark are chewed as a purgative and are also used in the preparation of an enema for treating colic in children. Sotho witchdoctors include the plant in their divining dice to protect sick people from being bewitched and it is believed that the presence of this tree is an indication of underground water near the surface.

The most famous member of this genus is *Ilex aquifolium* L., the European holly, which has the spiny-edged leaves and bright red berries traditionally associated with Christmas. Occasionally it is grown in southern Africa, but the trees are either male or female, and therefore berries are seldom produced.

CELASTRACEAE

Key to the genera:

1 Fruit a dehiscent capsule 2

Fruit indehiscent, may be fleshy, or dry and leathery 7

2 Capsules with very distinctive horns or spikes, may be winged, the fruit about 7 to 10 mm in diameter .... **4. Pterocelastrus**

Capsules more or less smooth, lacking distinctive horns or wings 3

3 Capsules flat, long, up to 6 × 2 cm, splitting into 2 distinctive boat-shaped valves .... **10. Hippocratea**

Capsules round or oblong not conspicuously flattened not more than 3 cm long 4

4 Leaves opposite; capsule more or less narrowly oblong, 7 to 10 mm long .... **3. Catha**

Leaves alternate, spirally arranged, or fascicled 5

5 Flowers up to 1,5 cm in diameter, pale greenish-apricot in colour; seeds triangular, smooth, brown .... **12. Pseudosalacia**

Flowers small to minute, in only one species reaching 10 mm in diameter, usually less than 6 mm in diameter; seeds partially or completely enveloped by a thin membraneous aril, the aril may be fleshy, forming a basal cup 6

6 Capsules comparatively large, 1,5 to 2,5 cm in diameter; ovary with 3 to 6 ovules per chamber .... **2. Putterlickia**

Capsules small, not more than 1,3 cm in diameter; ovary with 2 ovules per chamber .... **1. Maytenus**

7 Fruit dry, leathery, internally curved so that the conspicuous remains of the persistent style lie well down towards the base on the one side .... **9. Pleurostylia**

Fruit fleshy or dry, but the remains of the style, or its scar, occur at the apex 8

8 Petals 4 to 5, stamens 3 .... **11. Salacia**

Petals and stamens equal in number, 3, 4 or 5 9

9 Leaves extremely tough and leathery, dark green, broadly ovate to almost circular, 5 to 8 × 3 to 5 cm, petiole very short and stout, only 3 mm or less in length; ultimate branchlets purplish-tinged; confined to the extreme south-western Cape .... **7. Maurocenia**

Leaves variable but petiole longer than 3 mm; the ultimate branches not purple-tinged ... 10

10 Leaves dark glossy blue-green; seeds 2 to 4 per fruit .... **6. Allocassine**

Leaves not dark glossy blue-green, but one species may have a pale bluish bloom; seeds 1 per fruit, rarely 2 11

493

11 Fruits more or less fleshy when young but becoming dry and leathery by maturity. Confined to the extreme south-western and southern Cape .... **8. Hartogia**

Fruits dry to sub-fleshy, sometimes woody; with its various species, very widespread .... **5. Cassine**

1. MAYTENUS Molina

Rhizomatous shrublets, shrubs with a tendency to scramble, or trees. **Leaves:** spirally arranged or fascicled, rarely alternate; simple. Stipules free, small, falling early, or sometimes absent. **Flowers:** in heads, or cymes, with or without stalks, or in clusters, or fascicles. Usually bisexual, occasionally with the sexes separate on different trees or on the same tree; all floral parts in fives (occasionally fours or sixes); sepals small; petals small, white to yellow; stamens free or joined with the base of the receptacle disc, reduced to staminodes in female flowers if unisexual; ovary without a stalk, 2- to 5-chambered, reduced in size and becoming sterile in male flowers if unisexual. **Fruit:** a capsule, leathery or woody, sometimes thinly fleshy, dehiscent; seeds partially to completely surrounded by a thin to fleshy aril.

Key to the tree species of *Maytenus*:
1 When a leaf is snapped across transversely and the two sections pulled apart, very conspicuous latex threads are drawn out like fine, silken strands .... **M. acuminata**
Leaves not as above 2
2 Plants armed with spines; leaves often in clusters, or fascicles, on lateral branchlets 3
Plants unarmed; leaves seldom fascicled 11
3 Leaves with fine velvety hairs 4
Leaves without hairs 5
4 Flowers unusually large, up to 10 mm in diameter, white .... **M. putterlickioides**
Flowers small, up to 4 mm in diameter, pink to red .... **M. mossambicensis** (var. *ruber*)
5 Leaves linear to lanceolate, seldom more than 1,2 cm broad 6
Leaves ovate to obovate, usually more than 2 cm broad 7
6 Leaves long and conspicuously narrow, 2 to 9 × 0,2 to 0,7 cm; capsules 2-lobed **M. linearis**
Leaves small, obovate, about 1,5 × 0,2 to 0,5 cm; capsule 3-lobed .... **M. polyacantha**
7 Leaf margin entire .... **M. heterophylla**
Leaf margin toothed or scalloped 8
8 Flowers unisexual, often on different trees, but with staminodes and sterile ovary fairly well-formed .... **M. senegalensis**
Flowers bisexual 9
9 Leaf apex tapering, often shortly attenuate; seeds enveloped by an orange aril .... **M. mossambicensis**
Leaf apex rounded, often notched; seeds only partially covered by a thin aril, or aril almost absent 10
10 Fruits reddish-brown when mature; seeds dark brownish to blackish, almost without an aril .... **M. nemorosa**
Fruits yellowish-green tinged with red; seeds with a thin yellow aril covering the lower half .... **M. heterophylla**
11 Capsule valves rough, wrinkled, with small projections, green even when mature, about 10 mm in diameter .... **M. chasei**
Capsule valves smooth, yellow, orange, red-brown or red when mature usually less than 10 mm in diameter 12
12 Flowers and fruits on conspicuously long stalks, or peduncles, up to 1,5 to 2,5 cm; petioles and branchlets conspicuously hairy .... **M. peduncularis**
Flower and fruit stalks not conspicuously long; petioles and branchlets may have fine, inconspicuous hairs 13
13 Leaf margins thickened, quite abruptly bent back; tending to be a climber, the branches often drooping or semi-prostrate .... **M. procumbens**
Leaf margins not thickened or bent back; plants upright 14

494

14 Occurring east of Port Elizabeth only 15
    Occurring west of Port Elizabeth only 16
15 Leaves ovate to almost circular, 2 to 13 × 1 to 9 cm, apex very broadly tapering to rounded
    .... **M. undata**
    Leaves narrowly lanceolate, 1,5 to 6 × 0,3 to 1,3 cm, apex narrowly tapering **M. bachmannii**
16 A shrub or small stocky tree, occurring on rocky mountain slopes. Leaves obovate, 2 to 6 × 0,3 to
    3 cm .... **M. oleoides**
    Usually a low-growing shrub, occasionally a small tree, growing in coastal sand and dune bush,
    and on hillsides. Leaves ovate to almost circular, 1,3 to 4 × 0,8 to 4 cm ...... **M. lucida**

Maytenus acuminata (L.f.) Loes.
S.A. no: 398   Silky bark. Sybas
Rhod. no: 562   Silky bark

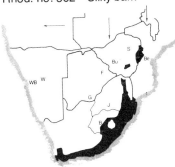
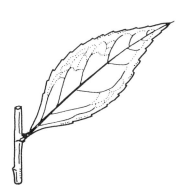

An unarmed shrub or small tree up to 8 m in height, but sometimes reaching 15 m; occurring in evergreen forest and at forest margins, often among rocks near rivers or on mountain slopes. **Bark:** grey to brown, smooth; young branches more or less distinctly 4-lined; young shoots are reddish. **Leaves:** not fascicled, ovate to elliptic, 1,7 to 12 × 0,8 to 5 cm, thick, rather leathery, glossy, dark green above, rather paler green below; the midribs in young leaves are reddish-tinged; net-veining often conspicuous below; apex tapering, rarely rounded, with a fine, hair-like tip; base tapering to rounded or triangularly lobed; margin shallowly scalloped or toothed; petiole up to 7 mm long. **Flowers:** white to creamy-green, about 6 mm in diameter, the petals curving back, stamens with conspicuous orange anthers; in tight, axillary clusters along the stems (January to February, sometimes continuing to June). **Fruit:** an almost spherical red or orange capsule, about 10 mm in diameter, splitting to release seeds completely enveloped by a red or orange aril (May to October).
All the material south of the Zambezi River is placed in the typical variety, var. *acuminata;* a second variety, var. *uva-ursi* Brenan, is confined to Mount Mlanje in Malawi. So-called latex threads are present in the branches, leaves, flowers and fruits; if snapped and gently drawn apart these silky threads become clearly visible. Miss Elsie Esterhuysen of the Bolus Herbarium in Cape Town suggests that these are the elastic thickening of the tracheids, and not viscous latex.

Maytenus bachmannii (Loes.) Marais
S.A. no: Willow maytenus
Rhod. no: —

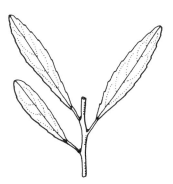

495

A shrub or small straggling tree up to 3 m in height; occurring on rocky banks of rivers and streams in evergreen forest. **Bark:** brownish-grey, generally smooth, vertically striated, revealing orange under-bark; branches without spines. **Leaves:** alternate or spirally arranged, small, narrowly lanceolate, 1,5 to 6 × 0,3 to 1,3 cm, softly textured, clear apple-green above, paler green with rather open net-veining below, without hairs; apex narrowly tapering, finally finely rounded; base tapering; margin finely and irregularly to rather obscurely toothed; petiole up to 5 mm long, tinged with pink which runs on to the stem. **Flowers:** creamy-white, about 4 mm in diameter, star-like, in pairs on the branches forming groups of 2 to 6; pedicels up to 3 mm long on a slender peduncle (common stalk) up to 1,5 cm long (January to March). **Fruit:** a 2- to 3-lobed capsule, 5 to 7 × 4 to 6 mm, becoming pinkish-red when mature (February to March).

When in leaf, these small trees rather resemble a willow.

Maytenus chasei N. K. B. Robson
S.A. no: —
Rhod. no: 563   Rough-fruited maytenus

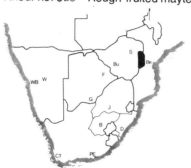 

A shrub or small tree up to 6 m in height; occurring in evergreen forest. **Bark:** dark grey, branchlets without spines, more or less markedly 4-lined when young, later becoming rounded and longitudinally streaked. **Leaves:** alternate, on lateral branchlets, ovate to elliptic, 6,5 to 13 × 2,5 to 7 cm, usually about 9 to 10 cm long, dark green and rather glossy above, paler green below, leathery, without hairs, veins slightly prominent above and below; apex tapering; base narrowly tapering to rounded; margin almost entire or very finely toothed; petiole up to 9 mm long. **Flowers:** creamy-yellow or greenish-white, about 5 mm in diameter, in small axillary clusters (January to April). **Fruit:** a 2- to 3-lobed capsule, about 10 mm in diameter, fleshy at first with a rough, wrinkled coating of small projections, green when mature, splitting to release seeds which are completely enveloped by an orange aril (June to September).

Maytenus heterophylla (Ecklon & Zeyher) N. K. B. Robson
[*Gymnosporia buxifolia* (L.) Szyszyl.]
S.A. no: 399   Common spike-thorn. Gewone pendoring
Rhod. no: 564   Spike-thorn

A shrub or small tree, usually 4 to 5 m in height, but reaching 7 to 9 m at times; occurring over a wide range of altitudes and in a variety of habitats, often on termite mounds. **Bark:** grey, striated; young branches brown, green or reddish-purple, becoming pale to dark grey; with sharp spines, 3 to 4 cm long, very rarely up to 24 cm. **Leaves:** produced in clusters on dwarf lateral branchlets, occasionally on the greenish thorns; ovate to obovate or narrowly lanceolate, 1 to 9 × 0,4 to 5 cm, usually about 4 × 2,5 cm, varying from dark green to pale grey-green or blue-green, frequently paler green below; apex broadly tapering to rounded; base tapering; margin finely and irregularly toothed or entire; petiole up to 10 mm long. **Flowers:** whitish, 2 to 7 mm in diameter, in short heads up to 4 cm long, clustered on short side branches, among the leaves, or occasionally on the spines; the flowers have an unpleasant scent (flowering times differ in various areas, but mainly February to June). **Fruit:** a thinly leathery to semi-fleshy, smooth, more or less spherical capsule, greenish-yellow to yellow tinged with red, about 10 mm in diameter; the seeds have a thin yellow aril covering the lower half (May to January, but at almost all times of the year).

Four subspecies have been recognised. Of these, subsp. *arenaria* N. K. B. Robson is a shrub, or shrublet, occurring in Moçambique and Natal, and subsp. *puberula* N. K. B. Robson is also a shrub, but is confined to the Matopos and areas just south and south-west of Bulawayo. Only subsp. *heterophylla* is widespread. Subsp. *glauca* N. K. B. Robson, a shrub or small tree occurring in Natal, Swaziland, the eastern Transvaal and southern Moçambique, is very similar to *M. senegalensis*. However, it differs in that its flowers are bisexual with a 3- sometimes 2-chambered ovary and its leaves usually have entire margins; while in *M. senegalensis* the flowers are unisexual, usually on different trees, the ovary is usually 2- sometimes 3-chambered and the leaf margins are usually toothed or scalloped.

Maytenus linearis (L.f.) Marais
S.A. no: 399,1   Narrow-leaved spike-thorn. Smalblaarpendoring
Rhod. no: —

A bluish grey-green shrub or small tree up to 5 m in height; occurring in arid places, among rocks and in sand. **Bark:** grey to brown; the branches are long and slender with spines up to 5 cm long, frequently bearing leaves and flowers. **Leaves:** alternate or fascicled, narrow, linear to lanceolate, 2 to 9 × 0,2 to 0,7 cm, leathery, bluish-grey; apex tapering to broadly so; base narrowly tapering; margin irregularly and finely toothed; petiole about 4 mm long with the leaf base running into the petiole. **Flowers:** small, yellow, in small axillary clusters (August to September). **Fruit:** a dry 2-lobed capsule, about 7 mm in diameter, each lobe splitting to release a seed partly covered by a yellowish membraneous aril (November to December).

Maytenus lucida (L.) Loes.
S.A. no: Cape maytenus
Rhod. no: —

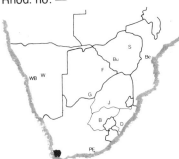

497

CELASTRACEAE

Usually a low-growing shrub, occasionally a small tree, 3 to 4 m in height; occurring in coastal sand and dune bush, and on hillsides. **Bark:** grey to brownish; branches stiff and ascending, without thorns. **Leaves:** alternate, ovate to almost circular, 1,3 to 4 × 0,8 to 4 cm, leathery, without hairs; apex broadly tapering to almost rounded, with a bristle-tip; base rounded; margin entire, rolled under; petiole short. **Flowers:** small, creamy-green, in tight axillary clusters (September). **Fruit:** 3-lobed capsule, about 5 mm in diameter, containing seeds enveloped by a thin aril (October to January).

Maytenus mossambicensis (Klotzsch) Blakelock
S.A. no: 399,2   Red forest spike-thorn. Rooibospendoring
Rhod. no: 565   Long-spined maytenus

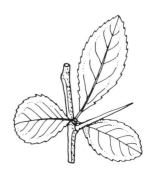

A shrub or small tree up to 8 m in height; occurring in thick woodland, riverine forest and at the margin of evergreen forest. **Bark:** grey-brown, smooth; the stems are usually slender and the young branches bear reddish-brown spines up to 8 cm long. **Leaves:** alternate or fascicled, ovate to elliptic, 1 to 6,5 × 0,6 to 4 cm, shiny bright green above, rather paler green below, without hairs; apex tapering to shortly attenuate; base tapering, rounded, or shallowly lobed; margin irregularly and rather shallowly toothed; petiole up to 6 mm long. Stipules conspicuous, often thread-like. **Flowers:** small, white, usually in axillary clusters along the stems, occasionally forming loose, branched heads, about 4 cm long (October to November, but sporadically on to May). **Fruit:** an attractive 3-lobed capsule, up to 1,3 cm in diameter, pendulous on a long slender stalk; white when young, becoming reddish-brown to carmine red when mature. The seeds are enveloped by an orange aril (March to September).
The plants from the drier areas tend to have ovate leaves with very shallowly toothed margins, and capsules which are rather hard and dry; plants of mountain forests have elliptic to almost circular leaves with more deeply toothed margins, and capsules which are almost fleshy when young. This species has been divided into 3 varieties: the typical variety, var. *mossambicensis,* is the common one south of the Zambezi River; var. *ruber* (Harvey) Blakelock, a low-growing shrub from Kenya and Tanzania and the Soutpansberg in the northern Transvaal, has hairy leaves and stems and velvety pink to red flowers; a third variety, var. *gurueensis* N. K. B. Robson, is a shrublet occurring north of the Zambezi River.

Maytenus nemorosa (Ecklon & Zeyher) Marais
S.A. no: 399,3   White forest spike-thorn. Witbospendoring
Rhod. no: —

A spiny shrub or small tree up to 7 m in height; occurring in evergreen forest, at forest margins and on wooded hill slopes. **Bark:** grey-brown; the branches carry spines 5 cm long on and below the flowering branches. **Leaves:** in clusters, obovate to elliptic, 3 to 6 × 1,5 to 3,5 cm, leathery, glossy dark green above, rather paler green below, sometimes bluish-green; apex rounded, often notched; base tapering; margin finely toothed or scalloped; petiole present. **Flowers:** small, creamy-white, in short slender-stemmed clusters among the leaves (September to March). **Fruit:** a 2- to 3-lobed capsule, reddish when mature, splitting to release dark brownish to blackish seeds with almost no aril (October to June).

Maytenus oleoides (Lam.) Loes.
[*M. angustifolius* Loes.]
S.A. no: 400   Mountain maytenus. Klipkershout
Rhod. no: —

An unarmed shrub or small stocky tree about 4 m in height; occurring on rocky mountain slopes. **Bark:** very pale greyish-brown to ashen grey, corky with tight vertical grooves, becoming smoother about 1 m from the base. **Leaves:** alternate or spiralled, obovate, 2 to 6 × 0,3 to 3 cm, leathery, bright green with a bluish bloom, containing a characteristic pale green sap; apex rounded, often notched; base narrowly tapering; margin entire, tightly rolled under; petiolate. **Flowers:** small, white flecked

The thickset mountain Maytenus, Maytenus oleoides.

with brown, in tight axillary clusters (September to November). **Fruit:** a 2-lobed capsule, about 10 mm in diameter, fleshy at first, becoming orange and dry when mature, splitting to release the seeds which are enveloped by a yellow aril (December).

Maytenus peduncularis (Sonder) Loes.
S.A. no: 401   Blackwood maytenus. Kaapse swarthout
Rhod. no: —

An unarmed, small tree up to 8 m in height; occurring along streams in evergreen forest and scrub, from sea level to 2 000 m. **Bark:** grey-brown, smooth, sometimes becoming dark and rough; branchlets slender and drooping, conspicuously hairy. **Leaves:** alternate, lanceolate to ovate, 1,3 to 9 × 0,8 to 4 cm, glossy dark green above, paler green below, thinly textured, the young leaves more or less densely covered with brownish hairs, most of which are lost by maturity; tapering to base and apex; margin markedly toothed; petiole hairy. **Flowers:** small, greenish-yellow, on slender stalks up to 1,5 to 2,5 cm in length (the specific name refers to this), solitary or in groups of 2 to 3, in the leaf axils (March to August). **Fruit:** a dry, 2-lobed capsule, about 10 mm in diameter, pendulous on long slender stalks; seeds with a yellowish aril (September to November).

Maytenus polyacantha (Sonder) Marais
S.A. no: Kraal spike-thorn. Kraalpendoring
Rhod. no:—

A heavily armed shrub or small tree up to 4 m in height; occurring in dry types of mixed woodland **Bark:** grey; the branches with strong, stout spines up to 6 cm long. **Leaves:** clustered, or fascicled, on dwarf lateral branches in the axils of the spines; small, obovate, about 1,5 × 0,2 to 0,5 cm, grey-green, leathery; apex broadly tapering to rounded, often notched; base tapering; margin entire or obscurely scalloped or toothed; petiole short and thickset; petioles and branchlets may be tinged with pink. **Flowers:** small, white, in sparsely branched heads about 2 cm long, clustered with the leaves on the dwarf lateral branches (February to April). **Fruit:** a 3-lobed capsule, 2 to 4 mm in diameter, reddish-brown when mature, splitting to release small black seeds with yellow arils (May to August). The plants occurring in the Orange Free State and the Transvaal are shorter and less sturdy with very small leaves and slender spines. In the central Transvaal this species can form dense, impenetrable thickets, 1,5 to 2 m high, covering considerable areas; it closely resembles some forms of the very variable *M. heterophylla*.

Maytenus procumbens (L.f.) Loes.
S.A. no: 401,1   Dune kokoboom. Duinekokoboom
Rhod. no: —

A bushy, scrambling or drooping shrub or small tree, about 6 m in height, occasionally reaching 10 m; occurring in coastal dune forest, woodland and scrub, in wooded dune valleys and at the margin of evergreen forest. **Bark:** rather pale, yellowish-brown, smooth, sometimes becoming finely fissured with age; the young branchlets are reddish and without spines. **Leaves:** alternate, oblong, elliptic or obovate, 3 to 7 × 1,3 to 3 cm, pale green above and below, leathery; apex tapering to rounded; base tapering; margin hardened, with 3 to 5 shallow but spine-tipped teeth, conspicuously bent backwards; petiolate. **Flowers:** small, greenish-white, in short, axillary clusters (June to July, but may be on to February). **Fruit:** an almost spherical capsule, about 5 mm in diameter, becoming bright yellow-orange when mature, splitting to release seeds enveloped by orange arils (August to January, but may continue to May).

Maytenus putterlickioides (Loes.) Exell & Mendonça
S.A. no: —
Rhod. no: 568   Large-flowered maytenus

A shrub, rarely a small tree, usually 1 to 3 m in height and many-stemmed from the base, but occasionally reaching 6 m; occurring in dry, deciduous woodland, often on termite mounds; it can form almost impenetrable thickets. **Bark:** pale grey to brown; the branches with pungent spines up to 2 cm long. **Leaves:** in clusters, frequently on the spines; elliptic to obovate, 1,8 to 8 × 1 to 4 cm, distinctively softly textured and finely hairy; apex rounded, sometimes notched; base tapering; margin slightly and shallowly scalloped; petiole up to 5 mm long, velvety. **Flowers:** white or cream, large for the genus being up to 10 mm in diameter, in axillary clusters, often in showy masses, frequently on the spines (September to November). **Fruit:** a 3-lobed capsule, 4 to 6 mm in diameter, orange when mature, splitting to release the seeds which are enveloped by reddish-brown arils (November to January).

Maytenus senegalensis (Lam.) Exell   Illust. 155
S.A. no: 402   Confetti tree. Bloupendoring
Rhod. no: 569   Confetti tree

A shrub or small tree, usually 3 to 5 m in height, but it may reach 9 m; occurring in a wide variety of habitats from sea level to 2 400 m, particularly common in open woodland, often on termite mounds, **501**

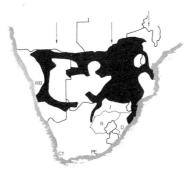

but found also in riverine fringe thicket and at the margins of vleis. **Bark:** light grey, smooth; the young branchlets are markedly reddish and the branches may be armed with straight, rigid spines up to 4 cm long. **Leaves:** alternate or fascicled, oblong to obovate, 2 to 12 × 4 to 6 cm, pale blue-green with a whitish or grey bloom, the petiole and midrib frequently pink-tinged, thick and leathery in texture, veining not conspicuous; apex rounded, often notched; base tapering; margin with shallow, rather rounded teeth, or scalloped; petiole short. **Flowers:** cream, white or greenish-white, 4 to 6 mm in diameter, in dense axillary clusters about 4 cm in diameter, often sweetly scented, produced in profusion. Sexes separate, usually on different trees but occasionally on the same specimen, a feature which is unusual in this genus (May to June, but may be found from March to December). **Fruit:** a 2-lobed capsule, 2 to 6 mm in diameter, greenish with a red flush when mature, occasionally becoming reddish-brown; seeds with yellowish or pinkish arils (October, but may occur from July to January).

This species closely resembles *M. heterophylla* and in particular *M. heterophylla* subsp. *glauca;* this resemblance is discussed under the latter. The beautiful profusion of white flowers is short lived as the blooms fall while still quite fresh and can then be gathered by the handful. The wood is yellowish-white, hard, straight-grained and durable. It could possibly provide suitable box wood but generally the pieces are so small that they cannot be of any practical use. Some African peoples stretch the hides for their drums over the spines and make an aphrodisiac by chipping the roots into fragments which they then drop into beer. These roots have a variety of other uses. In the Transvaal they are boiled and applied as a poultice to relieve chest pains, and at the same time the liquid is added to mealie meal to make an invalid porridge. They also provide a remedy for patients who have been coughing up blood and they are used in the treatment of snakebite. For this they are burnt together with the snake's head; oil is then added to the ashes to form a paste which is applied to the site of the bite and also the victim's tongue. Another reputed snakebite cure is a medicine prepared from an infusion of the leaves, and in India lice are removed from the scalp by the application of an ointment consisting of the powdered bark mixed with mustard oil.

Maytenus undata (Thunb.) Blakelock
S.A. no: 403   Kokoboom. Kokoboom
Rhod. no: 571   Koko tree

Often a shrub 2 to 3 m in height, but frequently becoming a well-branched tree up to 10 m; occurring in forest, at forest margins, in ravine forest among boulders and also in open woodland. **Bark:** grey-brown, smooth, becoming finely fissured in larger specimens; branches without spines. **Leaves:**

502

alternate, ovate, oblong, elliptic to almost circular, 2 to 13 × 1 to 9 cm, pale green (sometimes almost silvery green) through to dark green and frequently glossy, thinly leathery, frequently with a conspicuous white, almost powdery bloom on the under surface or both surfaces; apex very broadly tapering to rounded; base tapering; margin usually conspicuously toothed, each tooth tipped with a small, hard, dark brownish gland; petiole up to 10 mm long. **Flowers:** small, pale yellow to greenish-yellow, inconspicuous, in very shortly stalked axillary clusters, barely 10 × 10 mm (November to January, but may last until June). **Fruit:** a 3-lobed capsule, about 5 to 7 mm in diameter, white to yellow becoming red-brown when mature, splitting to release seeds enveloped by orange-brown arils (March to September).

The wood is red, heavy, close-grained and was once used in wagon construction and for farm tools. It makes a satisfactory fuel. These trees are easily grown from seed or cuttings, and would make good, hardy, evergreen garden subjects.

2. PUTTERLICKIA Endl.

Shrubs or small trees, without hairs, with strong spines which may or may not have small tufts of leaves; branches smooth or wrinkled. **Leaves:** alternate, simple. **Flowers:** in lax, few-flowered cymes. Bisexual; all floral parts in fives; sepals with ciliate margins; petals sometimes unequal, the outer two small, the inner three larger, oblong to ovate; stamens shorter than the petals; ovary 3-chambered. **Fruit:** a 3-lobed capsule, the seeds more or less enveloped by an aril.

Key to the tree species of *Putterlickia:*

1 Leaves large, usually about 10 × 5 cm, elliptic, but may be nearly circular; spines large, about 6 cm long, stout and conspicuously backward curving; capsule greenish-purple   **P. sp. no. 1**

Leaves usually 3 to 5 × 1 to 2 cm, obovate; spines slender, about 2,5 cm long; capsule red to red-brown 2

2 Branches smooth; flower stalks, or pedicels, long and slender up to 10 mm or more, jointed; capsules green tinged with red .... **P. pyracantha**

Branches warty (or covered with large lenticel-like dots); flower stalks 5 to 10 mm long, not jointed; capsules red-brown .... **P. verrucosa**

Putterlickia pyracantha (L.) Szyszyl.
S.A. no: 403,1   Bastard spike-thorn. Basterpendoring
Rhod. no: —

Usually a spiny shrub 2 to 3 m in height, occasionally a small bushy tree 4 to 6 m high; occurring along river banks, in scrub and dune forest. **Bark:** red-brown, with conspicuous lenticels; branches beset with spines; lateral branchlets up to 8 cm long, the final 2 cm of which may form spine-like tips. **Leaves:** singly, in pairs, or clustered on or in the axils of the dwarf branchlets, narrowly obovate, usually 2 to 3 × 1 to 1,5 cm but may reach 8 × 3 cm, glossy dark green; apex usually rounded, frequently shallowly notched; base tapering to rounded; margin entire to finely toothed, or scalloped, wavy; petiolate. **Flowers:** white, 6 to 10 mm in diameter, with 5 oblong spreading petals, produced in loose, branched, spreading heads, about 6 × 6 cm, on very slender stalks, arising from the spiny lateral branchlets with the leaves (November to January). **Fruit:** a 3-lobed woody capsule, about 2 cm long, pendulous on the end of a slender jointed stalk up to 3 cm long, green tinged with red when mature, splitting to release seeds, enveloped by a thin yellowish aril (February to August).

503

CELASTRACEAE

This species is very difficult to separate from *P. verrucosa* but, pending the revision of the genus by Dr. L. E. Codd, the two species are maintained in the present work. According to Ross in his *Flora of Natal*, *P. pyracantha* does not occur in Natal, its place being taken by *P. verrucosa*.

Putterlickia verrucosa (E. Meyer ex Sonder) Szyszyl.
S.A. no: Warted bastard spike-thorn. Vratterige basterpendoring
Rhod. no:—

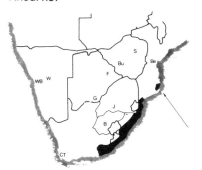

A shrub or small tree 1 to 4 m in height; frequently a scrambler in evergreen forest, dune forest or open deciduous woodland. **Bark:** grey-brown, smooth; the branches reddish to purplish-brown when young, becoming grey-brown and lenticel-dotted; the branches are beset with slender spines up to 4 cm long. **Leaves:** clustered on short lateral shoots; obovate to oblanceolate-spathulate, 1 to 5 × 0,4 to 2,4 cm, leathery, somewhat grey-green; apex rounded, sometimes notched; base tapering; occasionally rounded; margin usually with fine sharp teeth over the upper two-thirds, entire near the base, occasionally quite without teeth; petiolate. **Flowers:** greenish-yellow or creamy-white, in small branched heads, on stalks up to 2 cm long, in the axils of the leaves, clustered on short lateral shoots (July to October). **Fruit:** an ovoid woody capsule, 1,5 to 2,5 cm long, becoming reddish-brown to red when mature, splitting to release the seeds, each of which is enveloped by a thin yellow aril (June).

Putterlickia sp. no. 1
S.A. no: Large-leaved bastard spike-thorn
Rhod. no: —

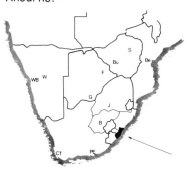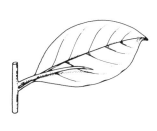

A scrambling shrub or small tree 3 to 4 m in height; occurring in riverine forest, at forest margins and among rocks in wooded valleys. **Bark:** grey and heavily lenticelled when young, becoming black and warty with age; the branches are tinged reddish-brown and densely lenticellate; new shoots pale green with a grey, waxy bloom. The branches bear strong, slightly curved, backward-facing spines, 5 to 7 cm long, arising above the leaves and occasionally bearing leaves on the spines themselves, thus becoming spinescent branchlets. **Leaves:** elliptic to almost circular, about 10 × 5 cm, hard, thick, leathery, glossy dark green above, much paler yellowish-green below, veining conspicuous on both surfaces, yellowish but slightly tinged with pink on the under surface; apex broadly tapering to rounded, often sharply curved down forming a channel-tip; base tapering; margin entire; petiolate. **Flowers:** white, about 7 mm in diameter, in rather loose axillary heads up to 6 cm in diameter, on slender pedicels 1 to 2 cm long; peduncle up to 3,5 cm long (October to December). **Fruit:** a 3- to 4-lobed capsule up to 2,5 × 2 cm, pendulous on pedicels 2 to 3 cm long, peduncles 4 to 5 cm long, produced singly or in clusters of 2 to 4, becoming green tinged with purple at the base by maturity; when the fruit splits the valves curve back and lie horizontally exposing its creamy interior; the seeds each ensheathed in a creamy-white membraneous aril resembling a tight fitting old-fashioned nightdress, hang down from the ribs of the valves (February to March).

It is likely that this plant will be described in the near future.

3. CATHA Forsk. ex Scop.

Shrubs or trees, without hairs or spines. **Leaves:** opposite, simple. **Flowers:** in small axillary cymes, much shorter than the leaves. Bisexual; all floral parts in fives; sepals free, ciliate; petals longer than the sepals, creamy-white; stamens shorter than the petals; ovary 3-chambered. **Fruit:** an oblong, dry, dehiscent capsule.

Key to the species of *Catha:*
Seeds with a small narrow wing .... **C. edulis**
Seeds without a wing .... **C. transvaalensis**

Catha edulis (Vahl) Forsk. ex Endl.   Illust. 156
S.A. no: 404   Bushman's tea. Boesmanstee
Rhod. no: 572   Bushman's tea

A shrub, 1 to 2 m in height, to a medium to large tree, 12 to 25 m in height; occurring in medium to high altitude evergreen forest, in open woodland and on rocky wooded hillsides. **Bark:** grey and smoothish in young specimens, becoming dark brown and rough in large trees. **Leaves:** elliptic to oblong, 5,5 to 11 × 1,5 to 4,5 cm, pendulous (they shake and shimmer in the wind), glossy bright green above, paler green below, thick, rather leathery; close net-veining is visible, especially on the under surface; tapering to apex and base; margin evenly toothed; petiole up to 10 mm long. **Flowers:** pale lemon-yellow or white with a greenish throat, produced in small dense clusters up to 2 cm in diameter (January to October, but mainly April to June). **Fruit:** a 3-lobed capsule, about 10 mm long and comparatively narrow, becoming reddish-brown to brown by maturity, splitting to release narrowly winged seeds which lack arils (March to October, but mainly June to August).

This graceful tree has rather a drooping habit and, from a distance, resembles a *Eucalyptus* or gum. The wood has been used for rafters, building poles, furniture, wood pulp and for carving spoons and combs. The leaves and roots provide a remedy for influenza, and the early pioneers in South Africa knew it as a treatment for coughs, asthma and other chest complaints. This tree is well known as a stimulating, narcotic drug and from early times has been called 'Abyssinian tea'; the name 'Bushman's tea' was recorded in South Africa by Burchell in 1814. The leaves and bark contain three alkaloids, cathine, cathenine and cathidine, all of which have a powerful effect on the nervous system; chewing the leaves produces wakefulness, an artificial feeling of well-being and mental alertness. However, if this drug is taken over a prolonged period it can have dangerous side effects: the character of the addict will deteriorate, the senses become dulled and, in the final stages, insanity may occur, followed by coma and death. There seems to be no evidence that it is taken in countries south of Kenya, and it is not used to any extent in southern Africa, possibly because in this region it is not so potent.

CELASTRACEAE

Catha transvaalensis Codd
S.A. no: 404,1   Transvaal Bushman's tea. Basterboesmanstee
Rhod. no: —

A shrub or small to medium sized tree up to 9 m in height; occurring in ravines and on rocky hill slopes and mountainsides. **Bark:** dark brown; branches at first pale green, later becoming dark reddish-brown. **Leaves:** oblong to elliptic, 2,5 to 8 × 1,3 to 5 cm, grey-green above, paler green below with long brownish hairs and dense prominent net-veining on the under surface; apex shortly tapering to rounded; base tapering; margin toothed; petiole up to 1,2 cm long. **Flowers:** small, in dense axillary clusters, very similar to those of *C. edulis* (April to October). **Fruit:** a slender 3-lobed capsule up to 8 mm long, brownish-green when mature, splitting to release the wingless, 3-angled seeds, each of which has a small white aril at the base (June to January).

In flower this species resembles *Cassine peragua*, but it differs in that it has a 3-lobed, dehiscent capsule, while *Cassine* has a hard or fleshy, indehiscent fruit. It is also very like *Catha edulis*, but may be distinguished by its wingless seed.

4. PTEROCELASTRUS Meissner

Shrubs, sometimes with a tendency to scramble, or trees; unarmed. **Leaves:** alternate, simple. **Flowers:** in cymes. Bisexual; all floral parts in fives; sepals unequal; petals longer than the sepals, often brown-flecked; disc usually saucer-shaped, clasping the base of the 3-chambered ovary; stamens shorter than the petals. **Fruit:** a dry, woody, dehiscent capsule.

Key to the tree species of *Pterocelastrus*:
1 Flowers up to 6 mm in diameter, in rather large, loose heads up to 3,5 cm long; capsules many-horned .... **P. rostratus**
  Flowers smaller, 3 to 4 mm in diameter, in short, compact axillary heads 1 to 2 cm long; capsules have fewer horns, and these may be winged 2
2 Young branchlets, petioles and young leaves pink to red; capsules with winged horns ....
  .... **P. tricuspidatus**
  Young branchlets, petioles and young leaves not pink to red; capsules with 3 to 9 horns, not usually winged .... **P. echinatus**

Pterocelastrus echinatus N. E. Brown
S.A. no: 405   White cherrywood. Witkershout
Rhod. no: 573   Hedgehog tree

A shrub or small tree, usually 2 to 5 m in height, but it may reach 25 m under favourable conditions; occurring in forest, at forest margins, in scrub forest or on rocky hillsides, sometimes along stream banks. **Bark:** pale grey or brown; in average specimens the stems are usually slender and erect with horizontal, rather angular branches; the bark is thin and, in young specimens, distinctive, for if it is very lightly scraped it comes away revealing a bright orange underbark – this is not a slash. **Leaves:** lanceolate to elliptic or ovate, 3 to 9 × 1 to 4 cm, rather thick, leathery, glossy deep green above, paler green below, the veining somewhat submerged; apex bluntly tapering; base tapering; margin entire, often slightly rolled under; petiole up to 8 mm long. **Flowers:** white to cream, about 4 mm in diameter, in compact, axillary clusters, 1 to 2 cm long (February to June, but flowers may be found during every month of the year in the plant's different areas). **Fruit:** a 3-lobed capsule about 10 mm in

diameter, becoming yellow-orange to red when mature, often with a waxy bloom; the fruits are spiky in appearance as each lobe has a very distinctive ridge or point; produced in conspicuous profusion; the specific name means 'armed with prickles or spines' (April to August).

Pterocelastrus rostratus (Thunb.) Walp.
S.A. no: 408   Red cherrywood. Rooikershout
Rhod. no: —

Usually a small tree, but occasionally reaching 20 m in height; occurring on mountainsides and in high altitude evergreen forest. **Bark:** dark grey; young stems red. **Leaves:** oblong-lanceolate, 2 to 9 × 1,3 to 5 cm, leathery, shiny blackish-green above, paler green and dull below, veining prominent on both surfaces, midribs tinged with pink; apex broadly tapering, slightly notched; base tapering; margin entire, wavy; petiole 5 to 7 mm long. **Flowers:** yellowish, up to 6 mm in diameter, in rather lax, branched heads up to 3,5 cm long, in the axils of the leaves near the ends of the branches (October to April). **Fruit:** a 3-lobed capsule, about 10 mm in diameter, becoming dark reddish-brown when mature, covered with coarse triangular spines, 6 to 8 mm long; the capsules split at maturity to release yellow seeds (July to February).
The bark yields 2% tannin; it is used by Zulus, powdered and mixed with the dried carcass of a fruit bat (or 'flying fox') and parts of other plants, to treat spinal diseases.

Pterocelastrus tricuspidatus (Lam.) Sonder   Illust. 157
S.A. no: 409   Cherrywood. Kershout
Rhod. no: —

507

CELASTRACEAE

A shrub or small tree up to 7 m in height, occasionally reaching 25 m; occurring in dry to medium moist forest and often a major constituent of dune scrub. **Bark:** dark brown, smoothish, often fluted or buttressed, with conspicuous lenticels. **Leaves:** broadly oval, 3 to 8 × 1 to 4 cm, but usually about 5 × 3 cm, very thick, leathery, shiny dark green above, paler green below and somewhat wrinkled, the most characteristic feature being that the branchlets, petioles and young leaves are pink to red; apex rounded, slighty notched; base tapering; margin entire, slightly rolled under; petiole stout, about 3 mm long. **Flowers:** yellowish to creamy-white, 3 to 4 mm in diameter, fragrant, in short, compact, axillary heads, 1 to 2 cm long (July to November). **Fruit:** a 3-lobed capsule, each lobe with 1 to 2 wings or teeth (the specific name refers to this), the fruit measuring about 10 mm in diameter including the wings or teeth; becoming orange-yellow when mature (July to March).

5. CASSINE L.

Shrubs, occasionally scrambling, or trees; the ultimate branchlets may be slightly winged. **Leaves:** opposite or alternate, simple. **Flowers:** a cyme. Bisexual; floral parts in fours to fives (occasionally in threes); sepals usually somewhat fleshy, sometimes hairy, usually with short, narrow lobes, as if slashed; petals longer than the sepals; disc fleshy, saucer-shaped or flat; stamens shorter than the petals; ovary 2- to 3-chambered. **Fruit:** dry to thinly fleshy, occasionally woody, indehiscent.

Key to the tree species of *Cassine:*

1 Leaves clustered, or fascicled, on short lateral branchlets .... **C. transvaalensis**
  Leaves opposite or alternate 2
2 Leaves alternate, or sometimes spirally arranged 3
  Leaves opposite, or sub-opposite 6
3 Leaves, when snapped transversely, produce fine latex threads .... **C. eucleiformis**
  Leaves do not produce latex threads 4
4 Leaves apple-green to grey-green, narrowly elliptic to linear; usually fascicled on dwarf side shoots, but may be alternate on young branchlets; fruits yellow when mature (drying to reddish-brown) .... **C. transvaalensis**
  Leaves dark green, oblong-elliptic to ovate or obovate; not fascicled; fruits pink to red when ripe 5
5 A small, dark green, bushy, densely twiggy tree up to 6 m in height; leaves alternate, small, usually 2 cm long (maximum 4 cm); fruits up to 1,3 cm in diameter; flowers sparse, in about 10-flowered axillary clusters .... **C. burkeana**
  Not as distinctively bushy and twiggy as the above species; it may become a medium sized tree up to 12 m in height; leaves spirally arranged, larger than those of the above species being usually 4 to 5 cm long (maximum 12 cm); fruits up to 2 cm long; flowers in slender-stalked terminal heads about 4 cm long .... **C. aethiopica**
6 Leaf margins entire 7
  Leaf margins toothed 8
7 Leaves ovate, margin entire, rolled under; flowers white with a pink calyx, in few-flowered axillary clusters .... **C. parvifolia**
  Leaves almost circular, margin entire, rolled under along the lower half; flowers white, in many-flowered, rather loose, axillary heads .... **C. peragua**
8 Leaves small, usually less than 5 cm long 9
  Leaves usually longer than 5 cm 11
9 Leaves very broadly ovate to almost circular .... **C. peragua**
  Leaves oval to ovate 10
10 Fruits small, about 8 mm in diameter, greenish-blue in colour, almost spherical; bark grey; leaves often with a bluish bloom .... **C. tetragona**
  Fruits about 2 cm long, white to pale yellow, narrowly oval; bark whitish and smooth to yellowish and crusty; leaves very dark green .... **C. crocea**
11 A light scrape (*not* a slash) on the trunk with a stick or even a book reveals a bright yellow or saffron-coloured underbark .... **C. papillosa**
  A scrape on the bark does not expose yellow underbark 12

508

12 Flowers in a simple, branched head, or cyme, in the axils of foliage leaves; margin of juvenile leaves entire or finely toothed; fruits yellow; opposite, but occasionally alternate leaves occur on the same shoot .... **C. matabelica**

Flowers produced on specialised lateral branchlets in the axils of leaves, the branched flower heads produced in the axils of bracts on new shoots; leaf margins always with spreading teeth; fruits white .... **C. schlechterana**

Cassine aethiopica Thunb. Illust. 158

[*Mystroxylon aethiopicum* (Thunb.) Loes.; *Cassine velutinum* (Harvey) Loes. ex Davison]
S.A. no: 410   Kooboo-berry. Koeboebessie
Rhod. no: 574   Kooboo-berry

A shrub or small to medium sized tree up to 12 m in height; occurring in evergreen forest, at forest margins, in riverine fringes and in open woodland, frequently on termite mounds and rocky ridges. **Bark:** grey, smooth in smaller specimens, becoming dark brown and rough in older and larger trees. **Leaves:** spirally arranged, oblong, ovate to obovate, 2 to 12 × 1 to 7 cm, usually about 4 to 5 cm long, handsome, glossy dark green above, paler green and dull below; the veins are yellowish, velvety, and conspicuous on the under surface; apex broadly tapering to rounded, shallowly notched; base broadly tapering; margin finely toothed; petiole up to 8 mm long. **Flowers:** small, yellowish-green, in about 10-flowered heads, with slender stalks about 12 mm long, collectively forming terminal heads about 4 cm long, inconspicuous (December to February, but also occasionally May to June). **Fruit:** berry-like, oval, often pointed at the tip, 1 to 2 cm long, becoming bright red when mature (June to January).

The fruit is edible and sweet. The Zulus prepare a milk infusion from the bark as a drench for worm infestation in calves and the Xhosa use the wood to make handles for their small axes, or knobkerries, and also as fuel.

Cassine burkeana (Sonder) Kuntze

S.A. no: 411   Transvaal kooboo-berry. Transvaalse koeboebessie
Rhod. no: —

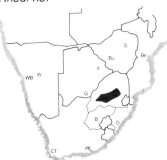

A small, bushy, densely twiggy, dark green tree up to 6 m in height; occurring in dry bush and on rocky outcrops. **Bark:** dark brown, rough. **Leaves:** alternate, elliptic or oblong-elliptic, 1,5 to 4 × 1 to 2 cm, usually about 2 cm long, leathery, dark green and finely hairy above, paler green and more velvety below; apex rounded, notched; base rounded; margin either toothed or entire, and tightly

509

rolled under; petiolate. **Flowers:** small, creamy-green, in few-flowered, short stalked, axillary clusters (January). **Fruit:** berry-like, up to 1,3 cm in diameter, may be oval and slightly pointed to the apex, maturing to a bright orange-red (March to June).

This species closely resembles *C. aethiopica* but it is a recognisable species over most of its range becoming somewhat obscure only round Lydenburg.

Cassine crocea (Thunb.) Kuntze
[*Crocoxylon croceum* (Thunb.) N. K. B. Robson]
S.A. no: 412   Red saffronwood. Rooisaffraan
Rhod. no: —

 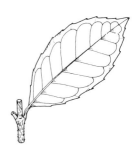

A medium sized spreading tree up to 13 m in height, often gnarled with a stout trunk giving the impression of greater size; occurring in coastal forest. **Bark:** whitish to yellowish, generally smooth but with encrustations. **Leaves:** usually opposite, oval, 2 to 5 × 1 to 3,5 cm, dark green, with conspicuous net-veining; apex rounded, often notched; base broadly tapering; margin with very shallow, widely spaced teeth, or scalloped; petiolate. **Flowers:** small, greenish, in axillary clusters (December to June). **Fruit:** berry-like, narrowly oval, up to 2 cm long, maturing to pale yellow (March to September).

According to Eve Palmer, the fruits are not edible. The wood is brown in colour, tinged with red, fine-grained, hard and tough. It is a useful general purpose timber and beams and furniture have been made from it. The bark can be used for tanning and dyeing and the Xhosa prepare an emetic from the roots. These latter are poisonous and are said to have been employed by witchdoctors in trial by ordeal ceremonies, and to have caused death. In past times a decoction of the outer layer of the bark was thought to be an effective snakebite remedy.

Cassine eucleiformis (Ecklon & Zeyher) Kuntze
S.A. no: 413   White sybas. Witsybas
Rhod. no: —

Usually a small tree, 4 to 5 m in height, but it can reach 10 m; occurring at the margins of forests, on mountainsides and among rocks. **Bark:** grey-brown. **Leaves:** alternate, oval, ovate to elliptic, 2,5 to 4 × 1 to 2,5 cm, glossy dark green above, paler green below and rather wrinkled; apex rounded; base tapering; margin usually entire, wavy, occasionally toothed; petiole about 5 mm long. **Flowers:** small, whitish, inconspicuous, in tight axillary clusters, 6 to 10 mm in diameter (September to

November). **Fruit:** berry-like, thinly fleshy, about 6 mm in diameter, white or pale yellow when mature (November to February).

The leaves, when broken, produce silky latex threads.

Cassine matabelica (Loes.) Steedman Illust. 159
[*Elaeodendron matabelicum* Loes.]
S.A. no: —
Rhod. no: 575 Condiment cassine

Often a shrub, 2 to 3 m, or a small tree, 4 to 7 m in height; very occasionally reaching 20 m under ideal conditions. Occurring at medium to low altitudes, in dry open woodland and wooded grassland, frequently on termite mounds or rocky hillsides. **Bark:** grey, smooth in young trees, later becoming deeply fissured; the young branches are brown and drooping. **Leaves:** some of the leaves may be alternate, but there are always opposite to sub-opposite leaves on the same shoot; oblong to elliptic, 4 to 10 × 1,5 to 4,5 cm, shiny; yellowish, greyish, to dark green above, paler green and dull below; apex tapering to rounded; base tapering; margin finely toothed, occasionally more or less entire; petiole 0,7 to 1,8 cm long. **Flowers:** cream to greenish-yellow, inconspicuous, produced in profusion in dense, axillary heads, visited by many insects (August to December). **Fruit:** berry-like, fleshy, up to 1,8 cm in diameter, becoming yellow when mature (April to July).

The trees are often mutilated by being stripped of their bark as this has a considerable reputation as an aphrodisiac. The Matabele use the wood to carve spoons and the roots provide a yellow dye. Parts of the plant were favoured by hunters away from home to flavour their meats and stews.

Cassine papillosa (Hochst.) Kuntze Illust. 160
[*Elaeodendron capense* Ecklon & Zeyher]
S.A. no: 415 Common saffronwood. Gewone saffraan
Rhod. no: 576 Common saffronwood

A shrub or small tree, 4 to 5 m in height, but not infrequently reaching 10 m; occurring from sea level to about 900 m, at margins of evergreen forest and in wooded ravines and valleys. **Bark:** grey, smooth, very thin with a bright orange underbark which shows through in patches; dotted with prominent black lenticels; very bitter. **Leaves:** opposite to sub-opposite, oblong to elliptic, 5 to 11 × 2 to 4 cm, leathery, thick, dark green above, paler green below, or grey-green on both surfaces in younger leaves, net-veining is clearly defined on both surfaces; apex tapering to broadly so; base tapering; margin hardened and with fine, often widely spaced teeth which are sharp-tipped; petiole up

511

to 10 mm long. **Flowers:** small, whitish or pale green, on the current year's shoots, in the axils or small bracts which soon fall; the flowers are produced in few- to many-flowered, compact heads about 8 mm in diameter (August to March, but mainly October to November). **Fruit:** berry-like, up to 2,5 cm long, ovoid, becoming pale lemon-yellow when mature, often covered with wrinkles and encrustations – the specific name refers to this. The fruits frequently reach full maturity only with the next season's flowers.

Cassine parvifolia Sonder
S.A. no: 415,1   Mountain saffronwood. Bergsaffraan
Rhod. no: —

Usually a shrub, occasionally a small tree, 3 to 5 m in height; occurring in the *fynbos* of the south-western Cape and in dry forest. **Leaves:** opposite, lanceolate to ovate, 1,3 to 6 × 0,3 to 2,5 cm; midrib prominent below; apex tapering to rounded, notched; base tapering; margin entire, rolled under; petiole short. **Flowers:** small, white with a pink calyx, in few-flowered, axillary clusters (August to October). **Fruit:** fleshy, almost spherical, about 7 mm in diameter, becoming dark purplish with a bluish waxy bloom when mature (October to December).

Cassine peragua L.   Illust. 161
[*C. capensis* L.; *C. barbara* L.]
S.A. no: 414   Bastard saffronwood. Bastersaffraan
Rhod. no: —

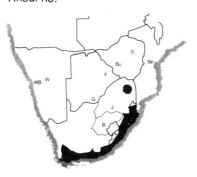

A shrub to small tree, 6 to 10 m in height; occurring on dry rocky ground, on steep mountain slopes, along streams, in dune scrub and occasionally at forest margins. **Bark:** grey-brown to dark grey, finely vertically fissured with horizontal cracks forming square flakes. **Leaves:** opposite, almost circular, 2 to 4,5 × 1,5 to 4 cm, leathery, with prominent net-veining on both surfaces; apex rounded, notched; base tapering to rounded; margin entire, rolled under along the lower half and sometimes toothed along the upper half; petiole short. **Flowers:** small, white, in many-flowered, rather loose, axillary heads (February to May). **Fruit:** berry-like, about 5 mm in diameter, ovoid, dark purple and fleshy when mature (July to August).

The leaves are apparently toxic: when administered to a rabbit, the symtoms were very soon evident, culminating with general paralysis and death as a result of respiratory failure. The wood was used to make large ladles in the time of Simon van der Stel (late 17th century).

Cassine schlechterana Loes.

[*Elaeodendron schlechteranum* (Loes.) Loes.]
S.A. no: —
Rhod. no: 577   Large-leaved cassine

Sometimes a shrub, but usually a small tree up to 7 m in height, occasionally reaching 18 m in low-lying riverine forest. **Bark:** dark grey to almost black, rather smooth; the young branches are reddish-brown to grey with conspicuous lenticels. **Leaves:** opposite to sub-opposite although occasionally the leaves of a branch show a tendency to be alternate; elliptic to oblong, 3,5 to 15 × 2 to 8 cm, but usually about 7 to 10 cm long, grey-green to dark green above, paler green below, sometimes with a greyish bloom, thick, leathery, brittle; apex tapering to rounded, sometimes notched; base broadly tapering; margin hardened with rather widely spaced, stiff, sharp teeth; petiole short and stout. **Flowers:** small, whitish, in short, dense, axillary heads, produced on specialised branches in the axils of bracts on new shoots, or in the axils of leaves (October). **Fruit:** berry-like, olive-shaped, up to 2,5 cm long, white becoming red when mature, smooth (May onwards, even overlapping into the next flowering season).

Cassine tetragona (L.f.) Loes.

[*Allocassine tetragona* (L.f.) N. K. B. Robson]
S.A. no: 411,1   Climbing saffronwood. Ranksaffraan
Rhod. no: —

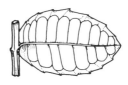

A scrambling shrub or small tree, 3 to 5 m in height; occurring in dune bush and forest and in evergreen forest. **Bark:** grey; branches grey, drooping, with the branchlets conspicuously 4- to 6-angled – the specific name refers to this. **Leaves:** opposite, oblong to ovate, 1,3 to 8 × 0,5 to 5 cm, leathery, often with a bluish bloom, the leaves are larger near the base of the branch and become conspicuously smaller near the tip; apex tapering to rounded with a fine spine-tip; base tapering; margin with sharp hard teeth, somewhat rolled under; petiolate. **Flowers:** small, yellowish to cream, occasionally tinged with pink, in dense, axillary heads, 1 to 2 cm long (September). **Fruit:** fleshy, about 8 mm in diameter, occasionally 2-seeded, red when mature (August to September).

Cassine transvaalensis (Burtt Davy) Codd   Illust. 162

[*Pseudocassine transvaalensis* (Burtt Davy) Bredell; *Crocoxylon transvaalensis* (Burtt Davy) N. K. B. Robson]
S.A. no: 416   Transvaal saffronwood. Transvaalsaffraan
Rhod. no: 578   Three-petalled cassine

513

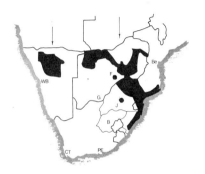

A shrub or more often a small bushy tree, 4 to 5 m in height, occasionally reaching 10 to 15 m; widespread but nowhere common, at medium to low altitudes in open woodland, along streams and on termite mounds. **Bark:** conspicuously pale grey, smooth, sometimes finely fissured. **Leaves:** usually in tight clusters at the end of short, rigid, side shoots, but may be alternate; narrow, linear to narrowly elliptic, 2 to 7 × 1 to 3 cm, apple-green to dull grey-green, with conspicuous net-veining on both surfaces; tapering to apex and base; margin entire or finely to strongly toothed; petiole short and slender. **Flowers:** small, greenish-white, in 20- to 30-flowered heads about 2 cm long, with slender stalks, in the axils of the leaves; petals 3 (December to February). **Fruit:** somewhat elongate, berry-like, broadly tapering to both ends, up to 2,5 × 1,8 cm long, yellow to reddish-brown when mature (June to November).

Two historic trees near Bulawayo, Mzilikazi's tree and Baden-Powell's tree, are both specimens of *C. transvaalensis*. The Zulus drink large quantities of bark infusion as a general stomach conditioner and from it prepare an enema to relieve stomach-ache and fevers. The bark, which has a faint aromatic scent, contains 13,34% tannin which could explain its medicinal use, and the fruit is edible. The wood is pale whitish in colour and brittle, but is used by Africans to make cattle troughs, spoons, ladles, headrests and tobacco pipes. The Zululand district of Ingwavuma is named after this tree.

6. ALLOCASSINE N. K. B. Robson

Allocassine laurifolia (Harvey) N. K. B. Robson
S.A. no: 416,1   Laurel saffronwood. Louriersaffraan
Rhod. no: 579   Allocassine

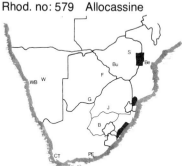

Usually a scrambling shrub, occasionally a small tree, 3 to 5 m in height; occurring at low to medium altitudes, in open woodland and in evergreen forest, especially in forested ravines and gorges. **Bark:** silver-grey to brown; branches drooping. **Leaves:** alternate, simple, becoming opposite on flowering branches; oval to oblong, 6 to 14 × 3 to 7 cm, glossy deep bluish-green on both surfaces, thick, leathery, net-veining visible on both surfaces; apex and base broadly tapering to rounded, the apex often notched; margin entire or with irregular, narrow teeth; petiole stout, less than 10 mm long. Stipules with a fringed margin, falling early. **Flowers:** very small, greenish-yellow, in few-flowered heads, or condensed cymes, produced on specialised, axillary, side shoots towards the ends of the branches, the whole structure giving the appearance of a branched spray, or panicle, about 2 cm long. Bisexual; all floral parts in fives; sepals free; petals often 3; disc deeply concave; stamens joined to the disc at their bases; ovary 2-chambered (September to December). **Fruit:** 2- to 4-seeded, ovoid, up to 2,5 × 1,8 cm, fleshy, tomato-red when mature (October to May).

514

7. MAUROCENIA L.

Maurocenia frangularia (L.) Miller
S.A. no: 417   Hottentot's cherry. Hottentotskersie
Rhod. no: —

A shrub, or small erect rigid tree up to 3 m in height; occurring in coastal bush or along mountain streams. **Bark:** greyish, scaly; branchlets tinged with purple, without spines. **Leaves:** opposite, simple, ovate to almost circular, 5 to 8 × 3 to 5 cm, dark green, tough, leathery, midrib prominent on the lower surface; apex and base tapering, or both rounded; margin hard, ridged, entire, rolled under; petiole very short and stout, not more than 3 mm long. **Flowers:** very small, whitish to dull yellow, solitary or in compact, branched heads, or cymes, barely more than 10 mm long. Bisexual; floral parts in fours to fives; sepals small; petals ovate, longer than the sepals; stamens inserted inside the saucer-shape disc; ovary 2-chambered (May to June). **Fruit:** thinly fleshy, 2-seeded, up to 1,5 cm long, red when mature, indehiscent (July).
The wood is yellow with brownish veins and is fine, hard and tough; it polishes well and has been used to make musical instruments.

8. HARTOGIA L.

Hartogia schinoides C. A. Smith
S.A. no: 418   Spoonwood. Lepelhout
Rhod. no: —

A shrub or small, much-branched tree up to 9 m in height, single- or multi-stemmed from the base; occurring on rocky mountain slopes and in wooded ravines. **Bark:** grey, pale at first becoming dark with age, smooth, often mottled; branches grey and sometimes wrinkled. **Leaves:** opposite, simple, narrowly elliptic to lanceolate, 2,5 to 6 × 0,8 to 2 cm, coppery when young, green when mature, leathery, without hairs; apex broadly tapering, notched; base tapering; margin entire near the base, toothed over the upper half or two-thirds; petiole up to 7 mm long. **Flowers:** small, white, sweetly scented, in slender, axillary, stalked, rather lax heads, or cymes, 1 to 2 cm long. Bisexual; all floral parts in fours; sepals ovate, the margin with small, close-set teeth; petals longer than the sepals; stamens inserted on the outside of the disc; ovary 2-chambered (October to January). **Fruit:** almost spherical, about 9 to 12 mm in diameter, fleshy when young, becoming dry, indehiscent and yellow when mature (January to March).
The wood is light-coloured, fine-grained and hard; it is said to be suitable for turnery and cabinet work, and some fine pieces of furniture have been made from it.

515

9. PLEUROSTYLIA Wight & Arn.

Shrubs or trees, unarmed; the bark contains a red pigment. **Leaves:** opposite, simple. **Flowers:** in small, axillary racemes. Bisexual; floral parts in fours to fives; petals longer than the sepals; stamens longer than the petals; ovary 1-chambered. **Fruit:** dry, more or less club-shaped, curved well over so that the remains of the style are on one side near the base, indehiscent.

Key to the species of *Pleurostylia:*
Occurring in South Africa only, not in Rhodesia .... **P. capensis**
Occurring in Rhodesia and northwards, not in South Africa .... **P. africana**

Pleurostylia africana Loes. Illust. 163
S.A. no: —
Rhod. no: 580   Northern coffee-pear

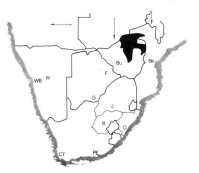

A shrub or small well-branched tree, usually 4 to 5 m in height, but sometimes reaching 10 m; occurring in open woodland and at forest margins, often on termite mounds and on rocky hillsides. **Bark:** grey, becoming dark and rough in large trees; young stems pale grey-green. **Leaves:** elliptic to oblong-elliptic, 4 to 9 × 1 to 4 cm, fresh glossy green to dark green above, slightly paler green and dull below, leathery; apex and base tapering conspicuously; margin entire; petioles up to 8 mm long, slender, so that the leaves are pendulous from the young drooping stems. **Flowers:** very small, greenish-yellow, produced in profusion in compact, rounded, axillary heads, about 8 mm in diameter (October to February). **Fruit:** elongate, berry-like, up to 8 × 3 mm, with the remains of the style well down towards the base on one side; also produced in profusion (February to July).
The flowers have an unpleasant scent – described as 'mousey' – which attracts insects. Parts of the tree have a considerable reputation for having aphrodisiac properties.

Pleurostylia capensis (Turcz.) Oliver
S.A. no: 419   Coffee pear. Koffiepeer
Rhod. no: —

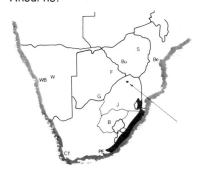

A large tree up to 20 m in height; occurring in scrub, wooded ravines, along rivers and streams, and in coastal and mountain forest where it reaches its greatest size. **Bark:** greyish-brown, fissured and flaking readily to reveal bright orange underbark. **Leaves:** lanceolate to oblong-lanceolate, 2,5 to 6 × 0,8 to 2,3 cm, shiny dark green to fresh green above, somewhat paler green below, apex and base conspicuously tapering; margin entire, somewhat wavy; petiole up to 6 mm long. **Flowers:** small, greenish-yellow, in few-flowered axillary clusters (November). **Fruit:** curved, dry, 1-seeded, about 15 mm long, with the style scar half-way down one side (March to June).

This is a scarce tree. It closely resembles *P. africana,* but differs in having 6 to 8 ovules in each compartment of the ovary, whereas the latter species has only 2 to 3. The wood is white to pale yellow, tinged with pink; it is hard, heavy and compact and has sinuous bands. It was once used in wagon construction.

10. HIPPOCRATEA L.

Shrubs with a tendency to scramble, lianes or trees. **Leaves:** opposite to sub-opposite, simple. Stipules fall early. **Flowers:** small, in axillary and/or terminal cymes or panicles; bisexual; all floral parts in fives; sepals small; petals somewhat leathery, usually larger than the sepals; fertile stamens 3, rarely 5, with 2 remaining sterile, shorter than the petals, free or joined to the ovary; disc saucer-shaped; ovary often 3-lobed. **Fruit:** separating into 3 carpels joined at the base, boat-shaped, either splitting by 2 valves or indehiscent.

Key to the tree species of *Hippocratea:*
1 Leaves densely covered with short soft fawn-coloured hairs .... **H. buchananii**
   Leaves without hairs 2
2 Leaves leathery, margins entire or very obscurely toothed, surface smooth ...... **H. parvifolia**
   Leaves thinly textured; margins with conspicuous rounded or jagged, usually glandular, teeth; surface usually puckered .... **H. volkensii**

Hippocratea buchananii Loes.
S.A. no: —
Rhod. no: 582   Velvet-leaved paddle-pod

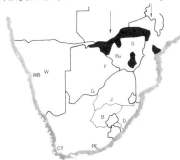
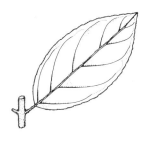

A shrub or small tree up to 8 m in height, often with a tendency to scramble; occurring in dry scrub or mopane woodland. **Bark:** light to dark grey, rough in older specimens; young branches with dense, short, fawn-coloured hairs, becoming reddish to greyish-brown. **Leaves:** oblong-elliptic to obovate, 4,5 to 12 × 2,5 to 6 cm, the upper surface deep green to yellowish-green, the under surface paler green with fairly prominent veining, short soft fawn-coloured hairs on both surfaces; apex tapering to broadly so; base tapering; margin entire, or glandular and shallowly scalloped; petiole up to 10 mm long, with soft hairs. **Flowers:** very small, yellowish, in many-flowered branched heads up to 8 × 4 cm, axillary and terminal, with the stalks covered with short soft hairs (October to January). **Fruit:** distinctive, flat, oblong to elliptic, up to 5 × 2,2 cm, green to yellowish, splitting into 2 boat-shaped valves, releasing 2 winged seeds (December to April).

Hippocratea parvifolia Oliver
S.A. no: Smooth-leaved paddle-pod
Rhod. no: 588   Smooth-leaved paddle-pod

A shrub with a marked tendency to scramble, a liane, or a small tree, about 5 m in height, with spreading whip-like drooping branches; occurring at low altitudes in dry woodland, on rocky outcrops, on the steep sides of gorges and in riverine fringe forest. **Bark:** pale grey to grey-brown, often appearing wrinkled due to many lenticels. **Leaves:** oblong to elliptic, 2,7 to 10 × 1 to 4,5 cm,

517

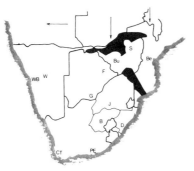

shiny deep green above, paler dull green below, leathery, with distinct veining, without hairs; apex broadly tapering to rounded, notched; base tapering to rounded; margin entire, or with very shallow and inconspicuous teeth; petiole up to 10 mm long, slender. **Flowers:** minute, brownish-green to yellowish, in very open, loose, few-flowered, axillary heads, 2 to 4 cm long (December to March). **Fruit:** distinctive, flat, paddle-shaped, up to 5 × 2 cm, purplish-brown, smooth, splitting longitudinally along the flat faces into 2 boat-shaped valves to release 2 seeds, each with a single, large, paper-thin, red wing (June to July).

Hippocratea volkensii Loes.

S.A. no: —
Rhod. no: 589   Serrate-leaved paddle-pod

A shrub with a tendency to scramble, or a small tree about 5 m in height; occurring at medium to low altitudes, in thicket and dense woodland. **Bark:** grey. **Leaves:** oblong to elliptic, 3,5 to 10 × 2 to 4,5 cm, thinly textured, slightly puckered between the clearly defined net-veining, without hairs, shiny dark green, occasionally yellowish-green on both surfaces with the under surface dull; apex tapering to rounded, slightly notched; base tapering; margin with somewhat rounded or jagged evenly-spaced teeth, which may be glandular; petiole 5 to 10 mm long. **Flowers:** small, yellow to yellowish-green, the sepals and often the petals with conspicuous dark green veins; produced in loose, few-flowered, axillary heads, 2 to 4 cm long (December to January). **Fruit:** flat, paddle-shaped, up to 6 cm long, becoming brown when mature, smooth, splitting down the flat sides to release 6 to 8 seeds, each with a single red papery wing (July to August).

11. SALACIA L.

Salacia leptoclada Tul.

S.A. no: 419,1   Salacia. Lemoentjietou
Rhod. no: 590   Salacia

A shrub with a strong tendency to scramble, or a small tree up to 4 m in height; occurring at low altitudes, fringing forest or in dune forest near the coast. **Bark:** dark grey; young branches dark brown, long and drooping; when given the opportunity the plant climbs by means of twining or hooked side branches. **Leaves:** opposite or alternate, simple, lanceolate, oblong to ovate, 5 to 10 × 2 to 4 cm, dark green above, paler green below, glossy on both surfaces, thinly textured; net-veining

more prominent below than above; apex and base tapering; margin entire or with shallow rounded teeth; petiole up to 10 mm long. **Flowers:** very small, pale lemon to greenish-yellow, on short stalks, axillary, solitary or in groups of 2 to 3, inconspicuous. Bisexual; floral parts in fours to fives; calyx deeply lobed; petals sometimes leathery, spreading, ovate to elliptic; disc thick, conical; stamens 3, rarely 2 to 4, the remaining ones aborted; ovary partially surrounded by the disc, 3-chambered (November to February). **Fruit:** almost spherical, fleshy, up to 2 cm in diameter, bright orange when mature, indehiscent (March).

12. PSEUDOSALACIA Codd

Pseudosalacia streyi Codd
S.A. no: 419,2   False saffronwood. Valssaffraan
Rhod. no:—

A lax shrub or small tree up to 5 m in height; occurring among rocks along river banks in evergreen forest, seldom far from the sea. **Bark:** pale greyish to dark chestnut-brown, smooth. **Leaves:** alternate, simple, oblong-elliptic, 7 to 14 × 4 to 8 cm, greyish-green to dark green, rather glossy above, paler green below, leathery, with the midrib and lateral veins translucent and the lateral veins looping; apex rounded, notched, curved down to form a channel-tip; base rounded; margin entire; petiole up to 1,5 cm long. Stipules absent. **Flowers:** greenish-yellow to dull orange-yellow, waxy, up to 1,5 cm in diameter, produced in axillary clusters. Bisexual; floral parts in fours to fives; stamens inserted outside the disc; ovary partially submerged in the disc (October to November). **Fruit:** a more or less spherical, dark brown capsule, up to 3 cm in diameter; slow to mature and can be found on the tree with the following season's flowers; eventually splitting into 3 valves to release 2 to 5 triangular smooth brown seeds (October to December). This is a protected plant in South Africa.

ICACINACEAE

Key to the tree genera:
Leaves opposite .... **1. Cassinopsis**

Leaves alternate .... **2. Apodytes**   **519**

ICACINACEAE

1. CASSINOPSIS Sonder

Shrubs or small trees, often spiny. **Leaves:** opposite, simple. **Flowers:** small, in dichotymous panicles. Bisexual; all floral parts in fives; calyx bell-shaped; petals longer than the calyx; stamens and petals equal in length; disc absent; ovary 1-chambered, without a stalk. **Fruit:** almost spherical, leathery, almost dry, indehiscent.

Key to the tree species of *Cassinopsis:*

Unarmed; leaves rather thick, apex broadly tapering to rounded; margin entire; fruit elongate, rather narrow, longitudinally ridged .... **C. tinifolia**
Spiny; leaves rather thinly textured, apex narrowly tapering; margin with scattered teeth; fruit ovoid, smooth .... **C. ilicifolia**

Cassinopsis ilicifolia (Hochst.) Kuntze
S.A. no: 420   Spiny cassinopsis. Lemoendoring
Rhod. no: 591   Spiny cassinopsis

A scrambling shrub or small tree up to 5 m in height; occurring at the margins of evergreen forest, in riverine fringe forest, wooded kloofs and along stream banks. **Bark:** pale grey to brown; young branches shiny green, with single, long, slender, straight, very sharp spines up to 5 cm long, rising on one side of the branch only between the petioles of opposite leaves. **Leaves:** narrowly ovate, 4 to 6 × 2 to 2,5 cm, shiny green above, dull green below, thinly textured; apex sharply tapering; base broadly tapering; margin almost entire but with scattered sharply-tipped teeth, rolled under; petiole up to 8 mm long. **Flowers:** small, white, yellowish or creamy-green, in compact heads about 7 mm in diameter, on short stalks about 10 mm long, arising on the side of the branches, opposite the spines between the leaf petioles (September to November). **Fruit:** berry-like, smooth, ovoid, about 10 mm long, tipped by the dry persistent style, becoming bright orange when mature (February).

Cassinopsis tinifolia Harvey
S.A. no: 421   Spineless cassinopsis. Valslemoendoring
Rhod. no: 592   Spineless cassinopsis

A straggling shrub or small tree up to 4 m in height, occasionally reaching 10 m; occurring at the margins of mountain forest, in wooded gullies and riverine fringe forest. **Bark:** grey, smooth; branches long, the young branches bright green, smooth, without spines. **Leaves:** oval, 3 to 9 × 2 to

5 cm, rather thick, glossy dark green above, slightly paler dull green below; apex broadly tapering to rounded; base broadly tapering; margin entire, slightly rolled under; petiolate. **Flowers:** small, white or creamy-green, in axillary, much-branched, dense heads up to 3 cm in diameter, on stalks up to 3 cm long (June to September, but variable). **Fruit:** elongate, rather narrow, up to 8 mm long, longitudinally ridged, berry-like, becoming dark purplish-black when mature (February to March, but variable).

2. APODYTES E. Meyer ex Arn.

Apodytes dimidiata E. Meyer ex Arn.   Illust. 164
S.A. no: 422   White pear. Witpeer
Rhod. no: 593   Bird's-eye

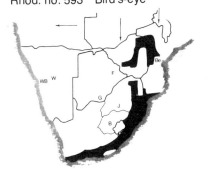

Frequently a small bushy tree 4 to 5 m tall, but reaching heights of 20 m when growing in forest; occurring in coastal evergreen bush, at the margins of medium altitude evergreen forest, in open woodland and on grassy mountain slopes, often among rocks. **Bark:** pale grey, smooth. **Leaves:** alternate, simple ovate-elliptic, 2 to 15 × 1 to 8 cm, usually 5 to 7 cm long, glossy bright green above, paler green and dull below, thinly textured, with or without hairs; the midrib usually conspicuously yellow especially on the under surface and may be flushed with pink, which is carried on to the reddish leafy branchlets; apex narrowly to broadly tapering, may be slightly notched; base broadly tapering; margin entire, very wavy; petioles pink, 0,6 to 2 cm long. **Flowers:** small, white, fragrant, in loose heads, or axillary or terminal cymose panicles, about 11 × 8 cm, frequently produced in striking profusion. Bisexual; all floral parts in fives; calyx saucer-shaped; petals free; stamens shortly joined to the petals at the base; ovary 1-chambered with a conspicuous lateral appendage (October to April). **Fruit:** berry-like, black and flattened, with a scarlet fleshy lateral appendage which gives the fruit a kidney shape, with the persistent, finger-like style in the notch (December to June).

Only the typical subspecies, subsp. *dimidiata,* occurs south of the Zambezi River; the subsp. *acutifolia* (Hochst. ex A. Rich.) Cufod. reaches its southern limit in Malawi. The light pink wood is very hard and is suitable for agricultural implements and furniture; in the past it was valued for wagon construction. The Zulus prepare an infusion from the root bark as an enema for intestinal parasites and the leaf is used in the treatment of ear inflammation. The fruit is not edible and is seldom taken, even by birds. Seedlings are easily raised, though germination is slow, taking from four months to a year; the seed should be sown shallowly in June or July. The young plants should be protected for a further year before being planted out, but once established, they are hardy and will withstand considerable cold.

SAPINDACEAE *(The litchi and soap-berry family)*

Key to the tree genera:
1 Leaves simple 2

  Leaves compound 4

2 Leaves resinous and very glossy; petals absent; fruits 2- to 3-winged .... **16. Dodonaea**

  Leaves not resinous, and not very glossy; petals present; fruits not winged 3   **521**

3 Leaf with base and apex rounded, tough and leathery; fruits about 10 to 15 mm in diameter, splitting to reveal the bright red, semi-fleshy arillode which covers the seed .... **11. Pappea**

Leaf with base and apex tapering, not particularly tough and leathery; fruits themselves thinly fleshy, not splitting; seed with no fleshy arillode .... **1. Allophylus**

4 Leaves trifoliolate .... **1. Allophylus**

Leaves with 1 or more pairs of leaflets, (if 1 pair only, then with no terminal leaflet) 5

5 Leaves, or the pinnae, ending in a terminal leaflet (or, in one species, in a lateral leaflet set to one side) 6

Leaves, or the pinnae ending in a pair of leaflets 8

6 Leaflets alternate, or sub-opposite, but the final leaflet not set terminally, but on one side .... **6. Smelophyllum**

Leaves always with a terminal leaflet 7

7 Leaves 2-pinnate, with 3 to 6 pairs of pinnae each bearing 10 to 30 alternate leaflets plus a terminal leaflet; rachis not winged. Occurring only in central Moçambique and northwards .... **10. Macphersonia**

Leaves 1-pinnate, with 4 to 7 pairs of opposite leaflets plus a terminal leaflet; rachis conspicuously winged. Occurring only in Namaqualand, South West Africa and the Transvaal, not in Moçambique .... **15. Erythrophysa**

8 Fruits 1- to 3-winged .... **2. Atalaya**

Fruits not winged 9

9 Rachis of the leaves conspicuously winged 10

Rachis narrowly winged or without a wing 11

10 Widespread in South Africa from the southern Cape to the Transvaal, not in Rhodesia or central Moçambique; leaves with 3 to 6 pairs of leaflets, obovate, 0,5 to 5 × 0,4 to 2 cm; margins more or less entire but often finely to deeply toothed .... **17. Hippobromus**

Not in South Africa, occurring in the east of Rhodesia and central Moçambique; leaves with up to 11 pairs of leaflets, narrowly oblong to oblong-elliptic, up to 15 × 3 cm; margin entire .... **19. Filicium**

11 Fruit a capsule, splitting when mature 12

Fruit not splitting, either leathery or fleshy when mature 15

12 Fruit a velvety, flattened capsule with a marked rim, greenish-brown, about 1,8 × 2,3 cm, splitting from the apex round the margin so that the two valves curl back like flaps revealing the single dark brown to black seed with a red arillode .... **13. Aporrhiza**

Fruit almost spherical or ovoid, not flattened, and green, orange or pink to red 13

13 A 3-lobed capsule, up to 3 × 3 cm, at no time fleshy, rather pear-shaped, bright pink when mature, splitting from the apex to reveal the dark seed with a yellow arillode, the valves curling back to form contorted and tangled masses .... **14. Blighia**

Fruit 1- to 3-lobed, not more than 1,5 cm in diameter; the seed without a yellow arillode; the old valves of the capsule not forming contorted, tangled masses 14

14 A small tree usually 4 to 7 m in height (occasionally 10 m), on rocky koppies and in gorges; fruit 1- to 3-lobed, about 1,2 cm in diameter, green to red when ripe, splitting from the apex to expose a single seed completely enveloped by an olive-green arillode .... **12. Stadmania**

A densely leafy small tree usually about 7 m in height (occasionally 10 m), frequently a constituent of low altitude riverine fringe, sometimes thicket-forming; fruit ovoid, 1,5 × 1,3 cm, showy orange or pinkish when ripe, reluctantly splitting from the base to expose a single seed enveloped by a bluish-white, fleshy, edible arillode .... **8. Lecaniodiscus**

15 Flowers and fruits produced on the wood and on the main stem; fruits of 2 to 3 carpels joined only at the base, up to 2,5 × 2 cm, orange, hanging in clusters from the stem and main branches .... **5. Pancovia**

Flowers and fruits terminal or in the leaf axils 16

16 Leaves with one pair of leaflets only, arising from a short, spur-like petiole 5 to 12 mm long .... **4. Aphania**

Leaves with 2 or more pairs of leaflets (if only 1 pair then the petiole up to 5,5 cm long) 17

17 Petals present, well developed .... **3. Deinbollia**

Petals absent or much reduced 18

18 The seed without an arillode; stamens 4 to 7 .... **7. Glenniea**

The seed surrounded by an arillode; stamens 5 to 13 19

19 Leaflets large, not less than 4 × 2 cm .... **18. Zanha**

Leaflets small, not more than 2 × 1 cm .... **9. Haplocoelum**

1. ALLOPHYLUS L.

Shrubs or trees. **Leaves:** alternate, simple or 3-foliolate. **Flowers:** very small to minute in simple or branched, axillary racemes. Bisexual; all floral parts in fours; sepals in opposite pairs, the outer two smaller; petals small, sometimes bearded on the inner surface; stamens 8 in 2 whorls of 4, usually hairy; ovary 2-chambered, often hairy. **Fruit:** 1 to 2 fleshy or leathery carpels, indehiscent.

It is difficult to separate vegetative material of this genus from that of *Rhus* (Anacardiaceae), though hairy pockets are present in the axils of the veins on the under surface of the leaves in *Allophylus*. However, the flowers and fruits are very distinctive and remarkably constant. In *Rhus* the flowers are produced in loose, branching, spreading heads and all their parts are in fives; the fruits are usually somewhat flattened and russet or red-brown. In *Allophylus* the minute flowers are produced in spike-like racemes, which may be branched, and all their floral parts are in fours; the fruits are usually round and crimson, sometimes turning purplish-black when mature, and are tightly clustered along the axes.

Allophylus contains at present some 250 species throughout the tropics. Vegetatively there is great variation, the same species having adapted to wide ranges of habitats; there is frequently inter-grading between species and it is extraordinarily difficult to subdivide the genus into meaningful species. Over the past two centuries a taxonomic tangle has developed which will be difficult to unravel.

Key to the tree species of *Allophylus:*
Drawings of the leaves of all the tree species of *Allophylus* which occur south of the Zambezi River are given, and these replace the usual written key. In each case care has been taken to select a leaf which illustrates the shape most usually encountered.

Allophylus abyssinicus (Hochst.) Radlk.
S.A. no: —
Rhod. no: 596   Forest velvet allophylus

A medium to large tree, 10 to 20 m in height; occurring in evergreen forest. **Bark:** grey or greyish-green, smooth; the stem is sometimes fluted; side shoots may arise from the trunk (epicormic shoots), which may be distinctive. **Leaves:** 3-foliolate; leaflets elliptic, 4 to 14 × 2 to 6 cm, thinly textured, more or less equal in size and shape, but frequently with one of the lateral leaflets conspicuously shorter; apex and base broadly tapering; margin irregularly and bluntly toothed;

523

SAPINDACEAE

petiolules short, petiole up to 9 cm long, with very fine soft hairs which can be felt rather than seen. **Flowers:** very small, minutely velvety, in tight clusters, or in catkin-like sprays, up to 8 cm long, on one to two branched stalks (November to March). **Fruit:** almost spherical, about 8 × 6 mm, probably red when mature (February to April).

Allophylus africanus Beauv.   Illust. 165
[*A. transvaalensis* Burtt Davy; *A. rubifolius* (Hochst. ex A. Rich.) Engl.; *A. melanocarpus* (Sonder) Radlk.; *A. rhodesicus* Exell]
S.A. no: 423,1   African allophylus. Afrikaanse bastertaaibos
Rhod. no: 597   African allophylus

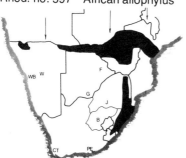

A shrub, 1 to 2 m in height, or a small tree, about 4 to 5 m, occasionally reaching 10 m; occurring over a wide range of altitudes, in riverine thicket, forest or open woodland, frequently on termite mounds. **Bark:** grey to brown. **Leaves:** 3-foliolate; leaflets obovate to elliptic, up to 15 × 8 cm, but usually about 7 to 8 × 4 cm, varying from thinly textured to almost leathery, without hairs or conspicuously velvety, sometimes with one lateral leaflet conspicuously smaller than the other two, usually with fine soft hairs on the under surface except in some forest forms which tend to be without hairs; apex and base tapering to broadly so, the apex sometimes slightly notched; margin entire to broadly toothed or scalloped; petiolules very short or absent, petiole up to 7 cm long. **Flowers:** small, creamy-yellow or greenish, in slender, usually branched, occasionally unbranched, axillary, spike-like racemes up to 26 cm long (December to March). **Fruit:** almost spherical or ovoid, about 6 mm in diameter, rather fleshy, becoming orange, red or sometimes black when mature (February to March).

Allophylus alnifolius (Baker) Radlk.
S.A. no: —
Rhod. no: 598   Lowveld allophylus

A bushy shrub or small tree up to 5 m in height; occurring in low altitude woodland, thicket and riverine fringe forest. **Bark:** grey to greenish, with conspicuous lenticels. **Leaves:** 3-foliolate; leaflets obovate to elliptic, 3 to 8 × 2 to 4 cm, bright glossy green above, paler green below, thinly textured, with or without very fine flattened hairs; apex rounded, notched; base narrowly tapering; margin bluntly toothed to scalloped; petiolules very short or absent, petiole up to 5,5 cm long. **Flowers:** small, cream to yellowish-green, rather thinly distributed along branched or unbranched, axillary, catkin-like racemes, up to 12 cm long (December to March). **Fruit:** ovoid to almost spherical, about 6 mm in diameter, becoming scarlet when mature (March to May).

524

Allophylus chaunostachys Gilg
[*A. gazensis* E. G. Baker]
S.A. no: Forest dotted allophylus
Rhod. no: 599   Forest dotted allophylus

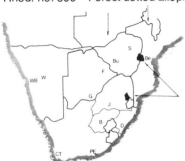

A shrub or small tree, usually 3 to 5 m in height, but occasionally reaching 8 m; occurring in medium altitude evergreen forest, as part of the under-storey. **Bark:** pale grey to brown, with conspicuous lenticels, especially on the branches. **Leaves:** 3-foliolate; leaflets elliptic, up to 15,5 × 6 cm, thinly textured, but the older leaves becoming thinly leathery, shiny dark green above, paler green below, both surfaces without hairs except for fine pockets of hairs in the axils of the veins on the under surface; apex tapering; base tapering to broadly so; margin almost entire to rather shallowly and finely toothed; petiolule of the terminal leaflet up to 1,5 cm long, with or without fine hairs. **Flowers:** small, whitish, in small groups of 2 to 4 along the axis of the slender, unbranched, catkin-like raceme, usually about 10 cm long, but may be up to 24 cm (March to May). **Fruit:** fleshy, almost spherical, about 6 mm in diameter, becoming bright red when mature, drooping in pendulous sprays (August to September).

Allophylus chirindensis E. G. Baker
S.A. no: —
Rhod. no: 600   Large-leaved allophylus

A small to large tree up to 15 m in height; occurring in medium altitude evergreen forest. **Bark:** silver-grey. **Leaves:** large, 3-foliolate; leaflets elliptic, up to 17 × 9 cm, thinly textured, without hairs **525**

or with very fine hairs along the veins only; apex and base tapering; margin toothed or scalloped; petiolules up to 1,2 cm long, petiole up to 11 cm, without hairs. **Flowers:** small, yellowish or greenish-white, in small groups along the main axes of slender, branching, catkin-like racemes up to 27 cm long (November to January). **Fruit:** almost spherical, about 7 mm in diameter, bright red when mature (April to September).

Allophylus decipiens (Sonder) Radlk.
S.A. no: 423   Bastard taaibos. Bastertaaibos
Rhod. no: —

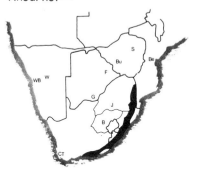

A many-stemmed shrub or small tree, 3 to 4 m in height; occurring at low altitudes, in coastal forest, wooded ravines and in riverine fringe forest and thicket. **Bark:** pale grey. **Leaves:** 3-foliolate; leaflets ovate, 1 to 7 × 0,5 to 2,5 cm, darkish-green above, paler green below, satiny textured, without hairs, except for conspicuous pockets of hairs in the axils of the veins on the under surface; apex broadly tapering; base tapering; margin variable, either deeply toothed or almost entire, slightly rolled under; petiolules very short or absent, petiole up to 3,5 cm long, hairy. **Flowers:** small, whitish, in unbranched, furry, catkin-like racemes, up to 6 cm long (March to May). **Fruit:** almost spherical, about 6 mm in diameter, becoming red when mature (April to June).
The wood is white, hard, dense and, despite its small size, could be suitable for cabinet work. This tree would make an attractive garden subject; the seed germinates easily.

Allophylus dregeanus (Sonder) De Winter
S.A. no: 424   Simple-leaved allophylus. Bosbastertaaibos
Rhod. no: —

A small tree up to 7 m in height; occurring in evergreen forest. **Bark:** grey. **Leaves:** this is the only species of *Allophylus* from southern Africa with 1-foliolate leaves giving the impression of a simple leaf; broadly ovate to elliptic, up to 12,5 × 5 cm, dark green above, paler green below, without hairs or with pockets of hairs in the axils of the veins on the under surface, net-veining fairly conspicuous; apex and base tapering; margin deeply and often sharply toothed; petiole up to 2,5 cm long, finely hairy. **Flowers:** very small, whitish, in small clusters along the main axes of an unbranched, spike-like raceme, up to 9 cm long (March). **Fruit:** ovoid, up to 10 mm long, red when mature (May to August).

Allophylus natalensis (Sonder) De Winter
S.A. no: 426   Dune allophylus. Duinebastertaaibos
Rhod. no: —

A shrub or small tree up to 5 m in height; occurring in coastal forest and on dunes. **Bark:** grey; branchlets greyish-white, minutely hairy. **Leaves:** 3-foliolate; leaflets narrowly elliptic, 3,5 to 8,5 × 1 to 2 cm, thinly leathery, almost without hairs; apex broadly tapering; base narrowly tapering; margin with small shallow teeth; petiolules about 5 mm long or almost absent, petiole up to 3 cm long, almost without hairs. **Flowers:** minute, greenish-yellow, in small clusters along the branched, catkin-like racemes, up to 9 cm long (April). **Fruit:** almost spherical, about 7 mm in diameter, becoming bright red when mature (July).

2. ATALAYA Blume

Shrubs or small trees. **Leaves:** alternate to almost sub-opposite, compound, paripinnate. **Flowers:** in branched terminal sprays, or panicles. Bisexual; all floral parts in fives; the outer sepals smaller than the inner; petals usually shorter than the sepals, with a hairy appendage on the inner face; stamens 8 with 2 aborted, hairy; disc fleshy; ovary 3-chambered. **Fruit:** a 1- to 3-winged nut.

Key to the species of *Atalaya:*
1 Leaflet margins toothed or scalloped along the upper edge .... **A. alata**
  Leaflet margins entire or with 2 teeth only near the apex 2
2 In the Cape only, near Port Elizabeth; leaflets 2,5 to 6,5 × 1 to 2 cm; margin may have 2 large teeth
  only, near the apex .... **A. capensis**
  In Natal only, in forests of Zululand; leaflets 4 to 8 × 1,5 to 2,5 cm; margins entire .. **A. natalensis**

Atalaya alata (T. R. Sim) H. M. L. Forbes   Illust. 166
S.A. no: 427   Lebombo wing-nut. Lebombokransesseboom
Rhod. no: —

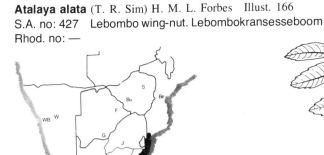 

A small to medium sized tree, 5 to 10 m in height; occurring in coastal scrub forest, *Androstachys* thickets, and at high altitudes along rocky watercourses. **Bark:** pale grey, rather warty. **Leaves:** with 5 to 7 pairs of opposite leaflets; leaflets narrowly elliptic to narrowly ovate, up to 6 × 1,8 cm, rather sickle-shaped, thinly textured, dark green, almost without hairs; apex tapering; base tapering, markedly asymmetric; margin mainly entire along the lower edge, toothed to scalloped along the

527

upper edge; petiole 2 to 3 cm long. **Flowers:** attractive, small, white, in rather loose terminal heads, 3 to 15 cm long (September to December). **Fruit:** a 1- to 3-winged nut (usually 3-winged but 1 or 2 wings may not develop); the wings are stiffly membraneous, elliptic, up to 3,5 × 1,5 cm, pale brown when mature (February to May).

Atalaya capensis R. A. Dyer
S.A. no: 428   Cape wing-nut. Kaapse kransesseboom
Rhod. no: —

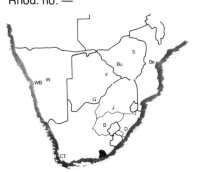

Usually a small tree about 3 m in height, but it may reach 10 m; occurring on steep mountain slopes, in forest and bush. **Bark:** very pale grey to whitish, smooth. **Leaves:** with 3 to 5 pairs of opposite leaflets; leaflets elliptic to oblong, 2,5 to 6,5 × 1 to 2 cm, dark green; net-veining clearly visible on both surfaces; apex tapering; base tapering and running almost parallel to the petiolule, inclined to be asymmetric; margin wavy, entire, or very occasionally (particularly in young plants) with a large tooth on either side near the apex; petiolule very short or absent due to the decurrent leaflet base, petiole up to 3,5 cm long. **Flowers:** cream, about 6 mm in diameter, in many-branched, axillary heads, 4 to 8 cm long, towards the ends of the branches so that the combined effect is a terminal mass of creamy flowers (December to January). **Fruit:** a nut, about 10 × 8 mm, with 1 to 3 brittle yellowish-brown wings, each up to 2,5 × 1,5 cm (April to June). This is a protected plant in South Africa.

Atalaya natalensis R. A. Dyer
S.A. no: 429   Natal wing-nut. Natalse kransesseboom
Rhod. no: —

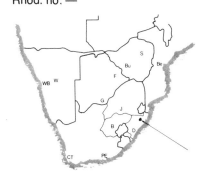

A small to medium sized tree up to 20 m in height; occurring in evergreen forest. **Bark:** pale grey. **Leaves:** with 3 to 5 pairs of opposite to sub-opposite leaflets, the rachis prolonged into a short point between the terminal pair of leaflets, oblong to lanceolate, 4 to 8 × 1,5 to 2,5 cm, dark green; apex tapering; base tapering, asymmetric; margin entire, wavy; petiolules very short, petiole about 6 cm long. **Flowers:** small, greenish-white, in rather dense terminal branched sprays, up to 20 cm long (November to January). **Fruit:** a 1- to 3-winged nutlet, the wings more or less lobed on the under surface, up to 4 × 2 to 2,5 cm, pale brown when mature (February to May).

528

3. DEINBOLLIA Schumacher

Shrubs, rarely shrublets, or trees. **Leaves:** alternate, compound, usually paripinnate, with the rachis slightly prolonged into a short point between the terminal pair of leaflets; leaflets alternate, sub-opposite to opposite. **Flowers:** in a terminal, simple or branched raceme, or paniculate thyrse. Sexes separate on different trees; all floral parts in fives; sepals circular, concave, in 2 whorls; petals about as long as the sepals, broadly obovate to elliptic, often hairy; stamens 10 to 30, in several whorls, reduced to staminodes in female flowers; ovary usually 3-lobed, vestigial in male flowers. **Fruit:** almost spherical, somewhat fleshy, indehiscent.

Key to the tree species of *Deinbollia:*

Occurring in Natal, extreme south-eastern Transvaal and the coastal regions of southern Moçambique; petioles up to 9 cm long .... **D. oblongifolia**

Occurring in Rhodesia, the extreme north-eastern Transvaal and adjacent areas in Moçambique; petiole very short, less than 1 cm long .... **D. xanthocarpa**

Deinbollia oblongifolia (E. Meyer ex Arn.) Radlk.
S.A. no: 430   Dune soap-berry. Duineseepbessie
Rhod. no: —

A shrub with slender woody stems, or a small tree up to 3,5 m in height; occurring in coastal open woodland, dune bush and forest, along riverine fringes and in bush clumps. **Leaves:** with 5 to 7 pairs of opposite to sub-opposite leaflets; leaflets elliptic to oblong-elliptic, 3,5 to 15 × 1,5 to 5 cm, pale green, without hairs; apex and base broadly tapering; margin entire; petiolules about 3 mm long, petiole up to 9 cm long. **Flowers:** white to cream, about 10 mm in diameter, in many-flowered, dense, axillary racemes, making up large, terminal heads up to 35 cm long; the flower stalks and calyces are densely covered with short, soft, greyish-brown to almost silvery hairs (April to May). **Fruit:** berry-like, about 10 mm in diameter, pale yellowish when mature, tightly clustered in terminal heads (July to October).

The Zulus take an infusion of the root for diarrhoea and dysentery, and the Bemba incise the forehead and rub powdered bark into the cuts to relieve headaches. The seed is said to froth and lather when rubbed in water.

Deinbollia xanthocarpa (Klotzsch) Radlk.
S.A. no: 430,1   Transvaal soap-berry. Transvaalse seepbessie
Rhod. no: 601   Soap-berry

A scrambling shrub or small tree up to 7 m in height, occasionally reaching 10 m; occurring at low altitudes in mixed woodland, riverine fringes and on rocky koppies. **Leaves:** 3 to 9 pairs of opposite to sub-opposite leaflets with very short petioles so that the lowest pair of small leaflets is almost on the main stem, thus resembling large stipules; leaflets oblong to oblong-elliptic, up to 8 × 3 cm, much smaller than those of the previous species, light green, without hairs; apex rounded, notched; base tapering to square; margin entire, usually wavy; petiolules 1 to 3 mm long; petiole up to 9 mm long. **Flowers:** white, up to 12 mm in diameter, in dense, branched, catkin-like racemes, forming terminal masses up to 20 cm long (July to September). **Fruit:** berry-like, spherical to ovoid, about 1,4 cm in diameter, becoming yellow when mature (October to November).

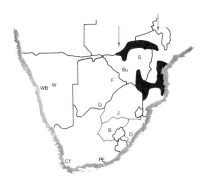

4. APHANIA Blume

Aphania senegalensis (Juss. ex Poiret) Radlk.
S.A. no: —
Rhod. no: —

Aphania

A shrub to medium sized tree, 7 to 15 m in height; occurring in forested ravines and riverine forest. **Bark:** grey, smooth. **Leaves:** alternate to sub-opposite, compound, with 1 pair of leaflets only, arising on a short, spur-like petiole; leaflets elliptic, 8 to 14,5 × 3 to 4,5 cm, leathery; apex tapering, often curved down into a channel-tip; base tapering; margin entire, wavy to almost frilled; petiolules 1 to 3 mm long, thick, wrinkled, petiole 5 to 12 mm long. **Flowers:** greenish-cream, about 6 mm in diameter, in fairly dense, branched, terminal sprays, or panicles, up to 15 × 13 cm. Sexes separate on the same tree, possibly in the same flower head; all floral parts in fives; sepals ovate; petals about 2 to 3 mm long, ovate, with a scale at the base; stamens usually 8, reduced to staminodes in female flowers; ovary usually 2-chambered, vestigial in male flowers (July to September). **Fruit:** fleshy, ovoid, sometimes 2-lobed, about 2 × 1,2 cm, reddish when mature, indehiscent; may be produced in profusion (October onwards).
This is a rare tree south of the Zambezi River and little material has been collected.

5. PANCOVIA Willd.

Pancovia golungensis (Hiern) Exell & Mendonça
S.A. no: 430,2　Bastard soap-berry. Basterseepbessie
Rhod. no: 601/1　Pancovia

A shrub or small slender tree, usually 2 to 4 m in height, but sometimes reaching 12 m; occurring in coastal forest, dune forest and patches of evergreen forest. **Bark:** smooth, pale grey, frequently mottled with green. **Leaves:** alternate, compound, paripinnate, with 3 to 4 pairs of leaflets (sometimes 2 or 5), narrowly oblong to elliptic, up to 14 × 6 cm, but usually about 8 cm long, thinly textured, the young leaflets pink to red; apex narrowly to broadly tapering, often attenuate, forming a drip-tip; base narrowly to broadly tapering; margin entire, often wavy; petiolules up to 6 mm long, petiole up to 17 cm long. **Flowers:** cream, small, in spikes or racemes about 7 cm long, sweetly scented, forming loose heads produced on the old wood and on the main stem. Sexes separate on different trees; sepals 4 to 5, unequally joined for half their length; petals 3 to 4, about 3 mm long, clawed, each with a

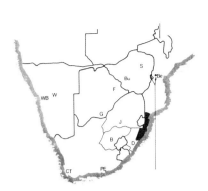

minute, 2-lobed basal scale; stamens 7 to 9, reduced to staminodes in female flowers; ovary with 3 carpels, free for at least half their length, vestigial in male flowers (October to November). **Fruit:** berry-like, the 2 to 3 carpels joined only at the base, each carpel ovoid, up to 2,5 × 2 cm, with or without velvety hairs, becoming orange when mature and hanging in clusters from the stem and main branches (December to February).

6. SMELOPHYLLUM Radlk.

Smelophyllum capense (Sonder) Radlk.
S.A. no: 431   Buig-my-nie. Buig-my-nie
Rhod. no: —

A shrub or small tree, 3 to 4 m in height; occurring in evergreen forest, in kloofs and bush. **Bark:** grey, smooth; the floral branches slender, without hairs. **Leaves:** alternate, compound, with 6 to 8 alternate, occasionally opposite, leaflets (if alternate then the final leaflet is not terminal, but lies to one side); the lowermost leaflets lie close to the stem; leaflets oblong to elliptic, 5 to 6 × 1,2 to 2,5 cm, dark green, leathery; apex and base tapering; margin roughly toothed; petiolules short, petiole up to 2 cm long only. **Flowers:** small, greenish, in branched axillary heads, or panicles, up to 5 cm long. Bisexual; all floral parts in fives; calyx shortly lobed; petals slightly longer than the sepals; stamens 8 to 10 in 2 whorls; ovary 2- to 3-chambered (December). **Fruit:** 2-lobed, almost separating into 2 carpels, joined at the base only; each lobe up to 1,5 cm long, fleshy, containing a single, shiny, purplish-brown seed (December to January).
The branches are brittle. These plants could be cultivated in gardens but they are slow-growing.

7. GLENNIEA J. D. Hook.

Glenniea africana (Radlk.) Leenh.
[*Crossonephelis africanus* (Radlk.) Leenh.; *Melanodiscus oblongus* Radlk. ex Taubert]
S.A. no: —
Rhod. no: 602   Double-litchi

A well-foliaged tree, usually about 7 m in height, but sometimes reaching 12 m; occurring in medium altitude woodland and evergreen forest, in wooded ravines and on rocky mountainsides. **Bark:** grey to brown, smooth becoming rough in large specimens. **Leaves:** alternate, compound, paripinnate, with **531**

SAPINDACEAE

2 to 3 pairs of leaflets; leaflets elliptic, 7 to 19 × 3 to 9 cm, the lowermost leaflets much smaller, the terminal pair being the largest, thinly textured to almost leathery, without hairs or with hairs confined to the midrib on the under surface; young leaves attractive, in delicate shades of yellow, red and green, maturing to dark green; apex rounded, sometimes notched; base tapering; margin entire, often wavy; petiolules pink, petiole up to 7 cm long. **Flowers:** pale pinkish to yellow, about 4 mm in diameter, in short, branched, axillary, spike-like racemes, together making up a spreading terminal head about 20 cm long, the stalks and calyces densely covered with short soft hairs. Sexes separate on different trees; all floral parts in fours; calyx lobed; petals absent; stamens 4 to 7, may be in 2 whorls, bent twice in the bud, reduced to staminodes in female flowers; ovary markedly 3-lobed, with dense woolly hairs, vestigial in male flowers (September to April). **Fruit:** berry-like, spherical, up to 2,5 cm long; or may be 2-lobed, almost completely divided, resembling 2 large berries stuck together; velvety becoming golden-brown when mature; seeds without an arillode (May to June, or even continuing to February).

8. LECANIODISCUS Planchon ex Benth.

Lecaniodiscus fraxinifolius Baker
S.A. no: —
Rhod. no: 603   River litchi

A densely leafy tree, usually about 7 m in height, but able to reach 10 m; occurring at low altitudes, frequently in riverine fringes; it can become thicket forming. **Bark:** brown, grey to dark grey, rough and may be scaly. **Leaves:** alternate, compound, paripinnate, with 3 to 7 pairs of leaflets; leaflets oblong to elliptic, 3 to 11 × 2,2 to 4 cm, usually about 7,5 × 2,5 cm, young leaves red-tinged, becoming light yellowish-green when freshly mature and darkening with age, thinly textured, without hairs on the upper surface, with minute glandular hairs along the veins on the under surface; apex tapering to rounded; base broadly tapering to rounded; margin entire; petiolules almost absent; petiole up to 5,5 cm long. **Flowers:** yellowish or greenish, in rather loose, axillary, spike-like racemes up to 10 cm long. Sexes separate on different trees; the male flowers small, yellow, falling soon after they open; the female flowers resembling miniature urns with black-tipped necks, velvety, clustered along the axes, the racemes shorter than in the male flowers; floral parts in fours to fives; sepals free almost to the base; petals absent; stamens 8 to 13, in 2 or more whorls, reduced to staminodes in female flowers; ovary 3-chambered, much reduced and sterile in male flowers (October to December). **Fruit:** ovoid, up to 1,5 × 1,3 cm, velvety, showy, yellow, orange or pinkish when mature, edible, finally

532

dehiscent, or reluctantly so, splitting irregularly from the base to reveal a single hard seed completely enveloped in a bluish-white, fleshy arillode (December to January).

9. HAPLOCOELUM Radlk.

Shrubs or trees. Leaves: alternate, often almost fascicled on dwarf lateral shoots which frequently become rigid and almost spinescent; compound, paripinnate. **Flowers:** in small dense clusters, or congested axillary polychasia, at the ends of the lateral branchlets. Sexes separate on different trees; floral parts in fives to sixes; calyx very short; petals absent; stamens long and slender, reduced to very short staminodes in female flowers; ovary 3-chambered, vestigial to absent in male flowers. **Fruit:** ovoid, fleshy, indehiscent; the single seed is almost completely enveloped in an arillode.

Key to the species of *Haplocoelum:*
In Zululand only; with 4 pairs of leaflets .... **H. gallense**
In Moçambique and Rhodesia, not in Zululand; leaves with 3 to 14 pairs of leaflets   **H. foliolosum**

Haplocoelum foliolosum (Hiern) Bullock
S.A. no: —
Rhod. no: 604   Northern galla plum

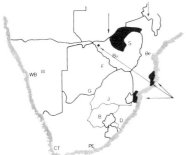

A straggling shrub or small tree, 3 to 4 m in height; occurring at low altitudes in open woodland, on termite mounds and rocky koppies. **Bark:** grey, smooth. **Leaves:** with 3 to 14 pairs of opposite leaflets; leaflets obliquely oblong, up to 1,5 × 0,9 cm, the rachis velvety and often narrowly winged; apex rounded, notched, often with a fine, hair-like tip; base asymmetric, one side tapering, the other more or less rounded; margin entire; petiolules very short to absent, petiole up to 8 cm long, with short soft hairs. **Flowers:** small, cream to yellowish-green, inconspicuous and even difficult to see; the male flowers very small with long slender stamens, produced in small clusters; the female flowers greenish with extremely small staminodes (November). **Fruit:** almost spherical, up to 1,5 cm in diameter, becoming bright orange to red when mature (December to January).

Haplocoelum gallense (Engl.) Radlk.
S.A. no: 432   Galla plum. Gallapruim
Rhod. no: —

533

A small tree 3 to 6 m in height; occurring in dune forest and at low altitudes in dry deciduous woodland. **Bark:** grey, smooth. **Leaves:** with 4 pairs of opposite to sub-opposite leaflets; leaflets oval to obovate, up to 2 × 1 cm, rachis narrowly winged; apex rounded, distinctly notched; base markedly asymmetric, one side tapering, the other almost square; margin entire; petiolules absent, petiole up to 2 cm long. **Flowers:** very small, brownish, the stamens are characteristically long (about 6 mm) in the male flowers, absent in female flowers; female flowers as for *H. foliolosum;* produced in clusters at the ends of the short, rigid, lateral branchlets (June). **Fruit:** more or less spherical, about 1,5 cm in diameter, fleshy, edible, becoming bright pink or deep red when mature (November to February). The wood is hard and strong; the Zulus use it to make huts, and also fashion their sharply pointed fighting sticks from it. This species also occurs north of the Zambezi River.

10. MACPHERSONIA Blume

Macphersonia hildebrandtii O. Hoffm.
S.A. no: —
Rhod. no: —   Macphersonia

A shrub or small tree up to 4 m in height; occurring along stream banks. **Bark:** grey to brownish. **Leaves:** alternate, compound, 2-pinnate; with 3 to 6 pairs of opposite pinnae, each pinna bearing 10 to 30 alternate leaflets plus a terminal leaflet; leaflets obliquely oblong, up to 13 × 6 mm, frequently with one leaflet conspicuously placed right at the junction of the pinna with the rachis; rachis with short soft hairs; apex rounded, notched; base markedly asymmetric, the lower side tapering, the upper side expanded into a wide lobe; margin entire; petiolules almost absent, petiole up to 5 cm long. **Flowers:** small, whitish, the conspicuous stamens up to 4 mm long; produced in a slender, branched, spike-like head, or racemose thyrse, up to 15 cm long, in the axils of the leaves. Sexes separate on different trees; all floral parts in fives; sepals petal-like, free almost to the base; petals small, spurred; stamens 7 to 8 in 2 whorls, with several stamens aborted, reduced to very small staminodes in female flowers; ovary 2- to 3-chambered, vestigial in male flowers (September to October). **Fruit:** spherical to ovoid, berry-like, about 1,3 cm long, often sharp-tipped (September to November).

11. PAPPEA Ecklon & Zeyher

Pappea capensis Ecklon & Zeyher   Illust. 167
[*P. schumanniana* Schinz; *P. capensis* var. *radlkoferi* (Schweinf. ex Radlk.) Schinz]
S.A. no: 433   Doppruim. Doppruim
Rhod. no: 605   Indaba tree

A small to medium sized, usually very spreading, tree, about 7 m in height, but not infrequently reaching 13 m; occurring in open woodland, in riverine fringes, often on termite mounds and among rocks. **Bark:** pale grey to brownish, rather smooth. **Leaves:** alternate, simple, frequently crowded near the ends of the branches; oblong to almost circular, very variable in size, those from arid areas being 2,5 to 4 × 0,8 to 1,2 cm, but those from areas of higher rainfall possibly reaching 10 × 6 cm; leathery, rough, tough, dull green above, paler green below; apex and base rounded; margin often entire or conspicuously and closely spine-toothed; petiole stout, up to 1,5 cm long. **Flowers:** pale yellow or greenish, small, in long, axillary and terminal, catkin-like racemes, up to 16 cm long. Sexes separate on different trees; all floral parts in fives; calyx cup-shaped; petals usually 5 (occasionally 4

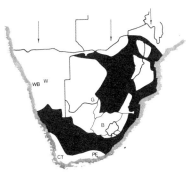

or 6), inconspicuous, each petal with 2 hairy scales at the base; stamens 8 to 10, about 4 mm long, reduced in size and sterile in female flowers; ovary 3-chambered, absent in male flowers (January to May, but over its great range, this can vary considerably). **Fruit:** a furry green capsule about 10 to 15 mm in diameter, almost spherical, splitting to reveal the single shiny black seed which is completely enveloped in a brilliant orange-red, fleshy, jelly-like arillode (February to July).

Lobengula's Indaba tree, now standing in the grounds of Government House in Bulawayo, is an ancient specimen of *P. capensis*. The wood is light to medium brown, hard and tough, with a twisted grain, but the pieces of timber from this species are rarely large enough to be of value. The leaves provide a valuable browse for game and stock. The fruits, which are edible and pleasantly flavoured, can be made into a jelly, an alcoholic beverage and vinegar. The seed yields a golden-yellow, non-drying, fairly heavy oil which is also edible though it has a mildly purgative action. It is claimed to be a remedy for ringworm and also to restore hair; it is suitable for soap-making and lubrication – farmers oil their guns with it. A leaf infusion is used as a cure for sore eyes and a root infusion is given to cattle, either orally or as an enema, as a purge.

Venereal diseases are treated with a preparation from the bark.

12. STADMANIA Lam.

Stadmania oppositifolia Poiret
S.A. no: 435   Silky plum. Sypruim
Rhod. no: 606   Silky plum

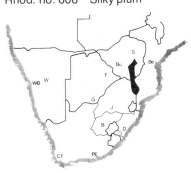

A small to medium sized tree, 4 to 7 m in height, but reaching 10 m on occasions; occurring on rocky koppies and in gorges. **Bark:** grey, scaling, leaving paler patches which give a mottled appearance; sometimes many-stemmed from the base. **Leaves:** alternate, compound, paripinnate, with 2 to 3 pairs of leaflets; leaflets elliptic, up to 8,5 × 3,5 cm, shiny deep green and without hairs on the upper surface, paler dull green and with minute soft hairs on the under surface, leathery; midrib prominent above and below, with fine net-veining; apex rounded, usually notched; base tapering, asymmetric; margin entire, somewhat rolled under; petiolules 2 to 4 mm long, petiole up to 5,5 cm long, with short soft hairs. **Flowers:** small, greenish-yellow, in axillary, catkin-like racemes, up to 10 cm long; sexes separate on the same tree, and even in the same raceme; all floral parts in fives; sepals very small, joined, inconspicuous, about 1 mm long, velvety; petals absent; stamens 6 to 8, reduced in female flowers; ovary markedly 3-lobed, vestigial in male flowers (October to December). **Fruit:** berry-like, **535**

up to 1,2 cm in diameter, 1- to 3-lobed, velvety, green to red when mature, each lobe splitting to reveal a single seed completely enveloped in an olive-green arillode (December to March).

All the material south of the Zambezi River is placed in subsp. *rhodesica* Exell; the typical subspecies, subsp. *oppositifolia,* occurs in the Malagasy Republic and Réunion. The wood is hard.

13. APORRHIZA Radlk.

Aporrhiza nitida Gilg ex Milne-Redh.
S.A. no: —
Rhod. no: 607   Aporrhiza

A medium to large tree, 10 to 16 m in height; occurring at low altitudes, in evergreen forest, riverine fringe forest and swamp forest. **Bark:** grey-brown or grey-green, smooth to fissured. **Leaves:** alternate, compound, paripinnate, with 2 to 4 pairs of opposite or sub-opposite leaflets; leaflets elliptic, 9 to 18 × 4,5 to 7 cm, without hairs; veining prominent below; apex and base broadly tapering; margin entire; petiolules up to 8 mm long, thickset, petiole 4 to 6 cm long. **Flowers:** small, whitish, in a yellow-grey terminal head, or paniculate thyrse, up to 40 × 20 cm. Sexes separate but in the same flower head; all floral parts in fives; sepals 3 to 4 mm long; petals shorter than the sepals; stamens 6 to 8, and 3 to 4 mm long, reduced in female flowers; ovary 2-chambered, vestigial in male flowers (October). **Fruit:** a velvety flattened capsule with a marked rim, up to 1,8 × 2,3 cm, greenish-brown when mature, splitting round the edges so that the 2 valves curl backwards until they lie horizontally; the inner surface is smooth, woody and brown and the single large seed is brown to black, half covered with an oblique red arillode (November to December).

14. BLIGHIA C. Koenig

Blighia unijugata Baker
S.A. no: 436   Triangle tops. Driehoektolletjies
Rhod. no: 608   Triangle tops

A medium to large tree, 7 to 25 m in height; occurring at medium to low altitudes, in evergreen forest, riverine fringe forest and also in open woodland, frequently associated with termite mounds. **Bark:** grey or brownish, smooth, but frequently covered with small, knobby, nipple-like warts; young branchlets covered with orange-brown hairs. **Leaves:** alternate, compound, paripinnate, with up to 3 pairs of opposite to sub-opposite leaflets; leaflets oval to elliptic, up to 15 × 8 cm, the largest at the apex; the leaf buds are covered with soft light brown hairs, and the young leaves are fiery red and very conspicuous, maturing to a glossy deep green above, dull green below, without hairs except for small pockets in the axils of the lateral veins on the under surface; apex broadly tapering, frequently finally attenuate forming a drip-tip; base tapering to rounded; margin entire, often wavy; petiolules 3 to 5 mm long, hairy, petiole 4 to 10 mm long, also hairy. **Flowers:** white, sweetly scented, about 5 mm in diameter, in an axillary, catkin-like raceme, or racemose thyrse, up to 6 cm long. Sexes separate, usually on different trees; all floral parts in fives; each petal with a broad scale covered with long hairs; stamens 8, reduced in female flowers; ovary 3-chambered, vestigial in male flowers (September to October). **Fruit:** a 3-lobed capsule, rather pear-shaped, up to 2,5 to 3 × 2,5 to 3 cm, becoming bright pink when mature, in handsome clusters; each lobe finally splits, the valves curl backwards and form a distinctive, twisted, contorted, wrinkled, woody mass; the shiny dark brown to black seeds have a yellow cup-shaped arillode round the base (September to February).

These trees are dense, round-crowned, and bear a resemblance to mango trees. The heartwood is reddish, durable and suitable for building and for furniture. However, the tree is not common enough to be used to any extent, although it occurs in fair numbers in the dune forests of northern Zululand where the flowers are soaked in water to make a fragrant cosmetic lotion. The brilliant colour of the new leaves and fruits would make this an admirable garden subject; the seed germinates readily and, in Zululand at least, the young trees are fast-growing. The specific name, meaning 'with one pair of leaflets', is somewhat inappropriate as it is more usual for the leaves to have two to three pairs. This is a protected plant in South Africa.

15. ERYTHROPHYSA E. Meyer

Large shrubs or trees. **Leaves:** alternate, compound, imparipinnate, often crowded at the apex of the branches. **Flowers:** small, in branched sprays, or racemose corymbs. Sexes separate on different trees; floral parts in fours to sixes; calyx small, cup-shaped; petals as long as the calyx; stamens 8 to 10, hairy, sterile in female flowers; ovary 2- to 3-lobed, absent in male flowers. **Fruit:** a much-inflated, usually spherical, capsule.

Key to the species of *Erythrophysa:*
Occurring only in Namaqualand and South West Africa; leaflets obovate, small, up to 1,2 to 0,7 cm .... **E. alata**
Occurring only in the western Transvaal; leaflets narrowly lanceolate, 2 to 7 × 0,3 to 0,8 cm .... **E. transvaalensis**

Erythrophysa alata (Ecklon & Zeyher) Hutch.
S.A. no: 436,1   Namaqua red balloon. Namakwarooiklapperbos
Rhod. no: —

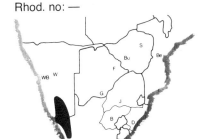

An attractive, rigid, small tree, 3 to 4 m in height; occurring on rocky hillsides. **Bark:** grey, rather rough and flaking in large specimens. **Leaves:** clustered on short lateral side branches; with 4 pairs of opposite leaflets plus a terminal leaflet; leaflets obovate, up to 1,2 × 0,7 cm, dark green, the rachis conspicuously winged; apex and base tapering; margin entire; petiolules very short to absent, petiole 5 to 10 mm long with a wing up to 7 mm wide. **Flowers:** showy, red, about 1,6 cm in diameter, the petals spurred, the stamens long, slender and red (March onwards). **Fruit:** a very attractive, 3-lobed, inflated, red capsule, up to 3,7 × 5 cm, indehiscent (September).

537

SAPINDACEAE

Erythrophysa transvaalensis Verdoorn   Illust. 168
S.A. no: 436,2   Transvaal red balloon. Transvaalse rooiklapperbos
Rhod. no: 608/1   Red balloon

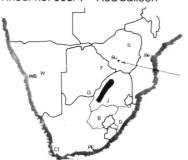

A large shrub or small tree up to 5 m in height; occurring on stony hillsides and rocky koppies. **Bark:** red-brown, smooth and shiny; the stems are slender and brittle. **Leaves:** crowded at the ends of the branchlets, on new growth only; with about 7 pairs of opposite leaflets plus the terminal leaflet set about 1 to 2 cm apart on the winged rachis; leaflets narrowly lanceolate, 2 to 7 × 0,3 to 0,8 cm, dark grey-green, apex narrowly tapering; base broadly tapering, markedly asymmetric; margin entire, although quite frequently broken up into a number of frond-like lobes near the base giving the leaf a delicate appearance; petiolules absent, petiole up to 2,5 cm long, usually without a wing. **Flowers:** attractive, about 15 × 10 mm, green suffused with red, the petals sometimes fully red (September to October). **Fruit:** a beautiful, inflated, bladder-like capsule, strongly 3-angled, green flushed with red or totally red, about 8 × 5 cm, containing 3 seeds in each lobe; the seeds are slightly flattened, smooth, purplish-black, about 2 cm in diameter (October to February).
The seeds, which African women use as beads, germinate readily and the plants respond well in cultivation; this tree would make an excellent garden subject. It is a protected plant in South Africa.

16. DODONAEA Miller

Dodonaea viscosa Jacq.   Illust. 169
S.A. no: 437 and 437,1   Sand olive. Sandolien
Rhod. no: 609   Sand olive

A shrub or small tree, usually 3 to 5 m in height, but occasionally reaching 10 m; occurring in riverine thicket and forest, in open woodland and on rocky koppies; its habitat varies from arid, semi-desert regions to the margins of evergreen forest in high-rainfall areas. **Bark:** dark grey and stringy. **Leaves:** alternate, simple, narrowly elliptic, up to 10 × 3 cm, resinous, shiny light green; apex and base tapering; margin entire; petiole 5 to 10 mm long. **Flowers:** greenish-yellow, in dense axillary or terminal heads, or racemes, corymbs or panicles, about 1,5 cm long. Sexes separate on different trees, or bisexual; floral parts in threes to eights; sepals 3 to 7; petals absent; stamens 4 to 8, sterile or absent in female flowers; ovary 2- to 4-lobed, absent in male flowers (April to August). **Fruit:** a very characteristic capsule with 2 to 3 membraneous, papery wings; greenish-red, about 1,5 cm, in diameter, including the wings which form conspicuous papery masses (May to October).
A decoction of the leaves is used as a mild purgative and also in the treatment of rheumatism, sore

throats and haemorrhoids. From very early times people of all races have regarded an infusion of the roots as a reliable remedy for the common cold. The seed is apparently edible; it germinates readily, plants respond well in cultivation and are used in various parts of the world to consolidate sand and to reclaim marshes.

17. HIPPOBROMUS Ecklon & Zeyher

Hippobromus pauciflorus(L.f.) Radlk.
S.A. no: 438   Basterperdepis. Basterperdepis
Rhod. no: —

A small, densely leafy, resinous tree, usually 3 to 5 m in height; occurring in riverine thicket, in scrub, along stream banks and at margins of evergreen forest. **Bark:** grey-brown, rough, with the yellow underbark showing through the cracks and fissures; branchlets grey or reddish with short, soft hairs. **Leaves:** alternate, compound, paripinnate, with 3 to 6 pairs of leaflets; leaflets narrowly obovate, variable in size, 0,5 to 5 × 0,4 to 2 cm, usually about 3 to 4 cm long, dark green above, paler green below, the rachis winged, apex broadly tapering to rounded; base tapering; margin may be entire, but frequently toothed; petiolules very short to absent, petiole up to 3 cm long, without a wing. **Flowers:** creamy-white, yellowish or reddish, about 4 mm in diameter, in dense, axillary, golden velvety heads, or panicles, about 2 cm long. Bisexual; floral parts in fives; sepals unequal; petals shorter than the sepals; stamens 8; ovary 3-chambered (March to September). **Fruit:** almost spherical, about 10 mm in diameter, fleshy, black when mature, not edible (October to December).

All parts of the tree have a strong, aromatic but not unpleasant scent when bruised or crushed. The generic name means 'a bad smell like a horse' which is not very appropriate. It is thought that Ecklon and Zeyher, in naming the tree, confused it with *Clausena anisata,* the common name of which is *perdepis,* and this they translated directly into Latin. Early this century the tree acquired a reputation for its timber and was declared a protected plant, but it seems that this was scarcely necessary as the wood is not much used. It is hard and strong but owing to the small size of the pieces is not suitable for furniture though it makes sturdy *jukskei* stumps and walking sticks. When the leaves are crushed a vapour is emitted and this may be inhaled to relieve headaches – a simple form of smelling-salts; they also yield a juice which is dropped into inflamed eyes. The root is regarded by the Zulus as a love-charm; it is also believed to cure dysentery and diarrhoea and when rubbed in water it produces a froth which, if swallowed, induces vomiting. An infusion from this root is given to stock suffering from coughs and is inserted into the noses of sheep and goats to stimulate sneezing to clear the nasal passages.

18. ZANHA Hiern

Trees. **Leaves:** alternate to sub-opposite, compound, paripinnate. **Flowers:** small, in short to very short axillary and terminal panicles. Sexes separate on different trees; sepals 4 to 6; petals absent; disc small; stamens 4 to 7, coiled in the bud, reduced to staminodes in female flowers; ovary 2-chambered, vestigial in male flowers. **Fruit:** ovoid, fleshy, indehiscent.

Key to the species of *Zanha:*
Fruits and mature leaves with hairs .... **Z. africana**
Fruits and mature leaves without hairs .... **Z. golungensis**   **539**

SAPINDACEAE

Zanha africana (Radlk.) Exell   Illust. 170

[*Dialiopsis africana* Radlk.]
S.A. no: —
Rhod. no: 610   Velvet-fruited zanha

A medium sized tree up to 10 m in height; occurring at medium to low altitudes, in open woodland, often among rocks and on koppies or ridges and occasionally in riverine forest. **Bark:** dark brown, scaly, flaking away in about 2 cm sections. **Leaves:** with 3 to 5 pairs of opposite to sub-opposite leaflets; leaflets elliptic, 4 to 8 × 2 to 4 cm, leathery, with conspicuous net-veining, especially visible above; the under surface often masked by tawny hairs; the petiole and rachis covered with yellow-tawny hairs; apex broadly tapering to rounded; base rounded to lobed; margin entire, scalloped, or bluntly and shallowly toothed; petiolules very short or absent, petiole up to 6 cm long, hairy. **Flowers:** small, inconspicuous, sweetly scented, with the inner surface of the sepals brown or pale bronze, and the outer surface with tawny hairs; produced in dense heads, about 2 cm in diameter, usually on short branches, either axillary or leaf opposed; the flowers appear before the new leaves (October to December). **Fruit:** ovoid, up to 3 × 2 cm, velvety, fleshy, bright orange when mature, often produced in handsome profusion; the seed is surrounded by an arillode (November to January).

The fruits are generally reported as being inedible, but both Norman Chase and Angus Pardy record that they have a pleasant taste and are eaten at least by birds. Trevor Gordon states that, in one particular year, monkeys ate all the fruit on the trees on his farm. The seed contains 10,5% acid saponin and is reputed to be poisonous; nevertheless it is said to be edible if first boiled in water. An infusion of the roots provides a remedy for dysentery, but is reported to have caused a state of coma and even death in at least one patient; post mortem investigation showed signs of inflammation of the kidneys.

Zanha golungensis Hiern

S.A. no: —
Rhod. no: 611   Smooth-fruited zanha

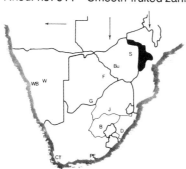

A medium to large spreading tree, 10 to 20 m in height; occurring at medium altitudes, in open woodland, often on termite mounds, in densely wooded ravines and in closed canopy, evergreen forest. **Bark:** grey to brown or reddish, smooth to flaking. **Leaves:** with 3 to 7 pairs of opposite to sub-opposite leaflets; leaflets elliptic, 4 to 10 × 2,5 to 4 cm, glossy light green, without hairs, thinly textured; apex tapering to rounded, often notched; base tapering; margin entire, or often scalloped or bluntly toothed, sometimes markedly so; petiolules up to 2 mm long or absent, petiole up to 7 cm

540

long. **Flowers:** small, inconspicuous, in short, dense, sparsely hairy heads up to 2 cm long, appearing before the first flush of leaves; the male flowers fall very soon (September to October). **Fruit:** ovoid, fleshy, up to 2 × 1,5 cm, without hairs, bright orange when mature, edible, often produced in such profusion that the branches bend under the weight; the seed is surrounded by an arillode (November to January).

The wood is valued by rural Africans for the construction of animal traps and snares, and in some areas most of the large specimens of these trees have been destroyed for this purpose.

19. FILICIUM Thwaites ex J. D. Hook.

Filicium decipiens (Wight & Arn.) Thwaites
S.A. no: —
Rhod. no: 612   Fern-leaf

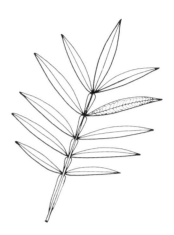

A large tree up to 25 m in height; occurring in evergreen forest, deep ravines, riverine fringe forest and by mountain streams. **Bark:** variable, from greyish-brown, smooth or roughish and peeling easily, to dull chocolate-brown and rough. **Leaves:** alternate, compound, paripinnate, with the rachis conspicuously winged and bearing up to 11 pairs of opposite or sub-opposite leaflets; leaflets narrowly oblong to oblong-elliptic, up to 15 × 3 cm, thinly textured, glossy dark green above, paler green below, resinous, without hairs and rather obscurely gland-dotted; midrib conspicuous on both surfaces; apex tapering, ultimately narrowly rounded and notched; base tapering; margin entire; petiolules absent, petiole up to 10 cm long, conspicuously winged. **Flowers:** very small, inconspicuous, creamy, in axillary branched sprays, or panicles, 8 to 10 cm long, occasionally longer. Sexes separate, but with well-formed sterile organs of the opposite sex present; all floral parts in fives; ovary 2-chambered (November to December). **Fruit:** ovoid to spherical, fleshy, indehiscent, about 6 × 4 mm, without hairs, becoming dark green when mature, inconspicuous (March).

This is a splendid tree with its attractive, glossy, fern-like foliage. The botanical name, freely translated, means 'deceptively fern-like'.

PTAEROXYLACEAE *(The sneezewood family)*

PTAEROXYLON Ecklon & Zeyher

Ptaeroxylon obliquum (Thunb.) Radlk.   Illust. 171
S.A. no: 292   Sneezewood. Nieshout
Rhod. no: 613   Sneezewood

A shrub to large tree up to 20 m in height; occurring in a variety of habitats, from low altitude woodland and scrub forest, where it is small, to evergreen montane forest in the mist-belt, where it reaches its greatest size. **Bark:** pale grey, almost whitish, smooth when young, darkening with age, becoming longitudinally fissured and inclined to flake. **Leaves:** opposite, compound, paripinnate, the rachis slightly winged, with 3 to 7 pairs of opposite leaflets (rarely sub-opposite or alternate); leaflets obliquely rectangular, 1,3 to 5 × 0,6 to 2,4 cm, but usually about 2,5 × 1,3 cm, with fine conspicuous hairs on both surfaces when young, losing these by maturity; apex broadly tapering to rounded, may be notched; base markedly asymmetric, one side narrowly tapering, the other square;

541

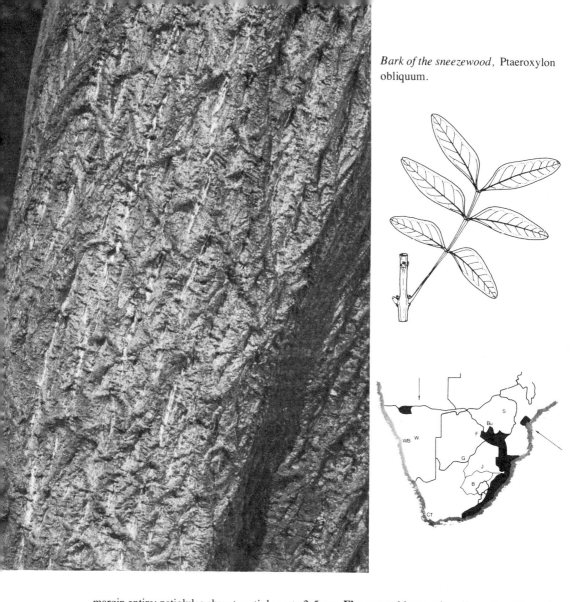

Bark of the sneezewood, Ptaeroxylon obliquum.

margin entire; petiolules absent, petiole up to 2,5 cm. **Flowers:** white to pale yellow, about 7 mm in diameter, sweetly scented, in short branched heads, up to 5 cm long, in the axils of leaves or fallen leaves. Sexes separate on different trees; all floral parts in fours; sepals very small; petals up to 3,5 mm long; stamens about 3,5 mm long, reduced to staminodes in female flowers; ovary 2-chambered, laterally flattened, vestigial in male flowers. A tree in full flower, just before or when the new leaves appear, is very attractive (August to December). **Fruit:** an oblong apically-notched capsule, about 2 × 1,5 cm, becoming reddish-brown and heavily veined when mature, splitting into two valves to release a pair of winged seeds; the old capsules remain on the trees for some time (December to February).

The wood is a very handsome, delicate rose-red colour darkening to golden-brown, and is finely grained with a beautiful satin lustre. The sapwood is liable to decay but well-seasoned heartwood is very durable. It has been widely used as a valuable general purpose timber; it makes handsome furniture and even effective machine bearings, which are said to outlast those made of iron. The wood contains an aromatic resin and also a highly volatile oil which makes it very inflammable; it is therefore not suitable for fencing standards or telegraph poles. Sawdust from the wood is pungent and irritating and causes violent sneezing. The Xhosa make snuff from it to relieve headaches and, with chips of the wood, it has been placed among clothes to repel moths. The resin is applied to warts and is added to a wash to kill ticks on cattle.

542

MELIANTHACEAE

BERSAMA Fresen.

Shrubs or trees, with simple hairs. **Leaves:** alternate, compound, imparipinnate, or occasionally 3-foliolate. Stipules often large and conspicuous. **Flowers:** in conspicuous, dense, terminal or axillary racemes. Bisexual, or with sexes separate on the same tree or on different trees; floral parts in fours to fives; sepals persistent; petals spathulate, densely hairy, much longer than the sepals; stamens 4 to 5 (occasionally up to 8), remaining well formed, but sterile, in female flowers; ovary 4- to 5-chambered, still well formed but sterile in male flowers. Flowers are most often greenish-white to cream, in the axils of conspicuous, usually brown, bracts. **Fruit:** a dehiscent capsule which may be smooth, but is frequently warty or spiny.

All the species of *Bersama,* although varying considerably, have a very characteristic appearance: they are all densely foliaged, the leaves being strong, heavy, tending to curve down, and often slightly flushed with maroon to brown; the flowers and the fruits are usually in firm, upstanding racemes, and the bracts are conspicuous.

Key to the tree species of *Bersama:*

1 Rachis winged; capsule smooth .... **B. abyssinica**
  Rachis without a wing; capsule warty or wrinkled 2
2 Leaves with 1 to 3 pairs of leaflets, plus a terminal leaflet 3
  Leaves with more than 3 pairs of leaflets, plus a terminal leaflet 4
3 Capsule with hairs. Occurring in the eastern Cape, through Natal to the Transvaal and extreme
    southern Moçambique .... **B. lucens**
  Capsule without hairs. Occurring in eastern Rhodesia and adjacent areas in Moçambique
    .... **B. swynnertonii**
4 Flowers in short, sturdy racemes, only about 5 cm long, in the axils of the large, silvery, silky
    bracts, and almost hidden by them. Occurring in Natal and eastern Cape .... **B. swinnyi**
  Flowers in racemes longer than 5 cm; bracts conspicuous but not silvery and silky, and not almost
    concealing the flowers 5
5 Leaflets without hairs on either surface .... **B. tysoniana**
  Leaflets with velvety hairs at least on the under surface 6
6 Flowers in dense racemes up to 8 cm long; leaflets up to 5 × 1,5 cm .... **B. stayneri**
  Flowers in rather lax racemes up to 15 cm long; leaflets 5,5 to 9 × 2 to 3 cm **B. transvaalensis**

Bersama abyssinica Fresen.   Illust. 172
S.A. no: —
Rhod. no: 614   Winged bersama

A handsome, well-foliaged, shapely tree, 7 to 15 m in height; occurring along watercourses, in wooded ravines, at the margins of evergreen forest and also in open woodland, often associated with termite mounds. **Bark:** light brown, rather smooth. **Leaves:** the rachis usually narrowly to broadly winged, with 5 to 10 pairs of opposite leaflets plus a terminal leaflet; leaflets elliptic to lanceolate, up to 14 × 5 cm, but usually about 8 to 10 cm long, with or without hairs, veining conspicuous on both surfaces; apex and base tapering; margin either entire or deeply toothed; petiolules very short to absent, petiole about 8 cm long, with soft golden hairs. **Flowers:** conspicuous, greenish to creamy-yellow tinged with pink, about 2 cm in diameter, velvety; in strong, upstanding, thickset, spike-like racemes up to 35 cm long, resembling candles (November to December). **Fruit:** a spherical capsule, smooth, about 2,5 cm in diameter, golden velvety at first, losing most of these hairs and becoming brown by maturity; splitting into 4 valves to reveal the attractive bright red seeds, about 10 mm long, enveloped for about half their length by a yellow, cup-shaped aril (May to October).

This species has been divided into a number of subspecies:

subsp. *englerana* (Gürke) F. White – the under surface of the leaflets without hairs, or with sparse white hairs along the midrib and lateral veins; occurring in Moçambique, but rare in Rhodesia.

subsp. *nyassae* (E. G. Baker) F. White – the under surface of the leaflets densely covered with long, spreading, golden hairs; this subspecies is the one most likely to be encountered.

The typical subspecies, subsp. *abyssinica,* occurs no further south than Malawi.

A decoction of the bark is used to treat intestinal worms in children and as a mild purgative. The leaves and roots are said to contain an insecticide.

Bersama lucens (Hochst.) Szyszyl.

S.A. no: 439   Glossy bersama. Blinkblaarwitessenhout
Rhod. no: —

A shrub or small to medium sized tree, 3 to 10 m in height; occurring in rocky places, often in crevices. **Bark:** brown, rather rough. **Leaves:** the rachis not winged, with 2 to 3 pairs of opposite leaflets, plus a terminal leaflet, or 3-foliolate; leaflets ovate to oblong, 4 to 7,5 × 2,5 to 4,5 cm, leathery, shiny green, without hairs, veining conspicuous on both surfaces; apex rounded, may be notched; base tapering, often asymmetric; margin entire, thickened, wavy; petiolules short, petiole 2 to 2,5 cm long. **Flowers:** whitish or yellow, petals narrowly oblong, about 6 mm long, in firm, upstanding, quite conspicuous racemes, up to 15 cm long (June to September). **Fruit:** a spherical hairy capsule, up to 2 cm in diameter, wrinkled, dull green when mature; splitting into 4 valves to reveal 4 bright scarlet seeds about half enveloped in a fleshy, yellow-green, cup-shaped aril (August to March).

Parts of this tree have been regarded as poisonous, but the Zulus use the bark to relieve menstrual pains and to treat cases of impotency and barrenness.

Bersama stayneri Phillips

S.A. no: 440   Hairy-leaved bersama. Waterwitessenhout
Rhod. no: —

An under-shrub or small tree, 4 to 5 m in height; occurring at medium to high altitudes in evergreen forest. **Bark:** dark, thick and rough. **Leaves:** rachis not winged, with 4 to 5 pairs of opposite leaflets plus a terminal leaflet; leaflets elliptic to broadly lanceolate, up to 5 × 1,5 cm, dark grey-green; veining conspicuous on both surfaces, with the under surface of the leaflets, the midrib, rachis and petiole covered with dense, long, straight hairs; apex and base tapering to narrowly rounded; margin entire, scalloped or toothed; petiolules short, petiole up to 2 cm long. **Flowers:** rather small, in short, dense, thickset, hairy racemes, 5,5 to 8 cm long (April to May). **Fruit:** an almost spherical, warty capsule, up to 3 cm in diameter, brown when mature; splitting into 4 valves to reveal the reddish seeds which have a cup-shaped yellow aril round the base (July to October).

The hairy leaves, rachis and petiole are said to be distinctive, but there is some doubt about the status of this species; Verdcourt in *Kew Bulletin* 1955: 600 (1956) suggests that *B. stayneri* is possibly only a variety of *B. tysoniana,* and although it is reputed to occur in Natal, Ross in his *Flora of Natal* states 'locality unknown'. The bark is bitter and is used in African medicine; the trees are often deformed or destroyed as a result of being stripped of their bark.

Bersama swinnyi Phillips
S.A. no: 441   Coast bersama. Kuswitessenhout
Rhod. no: —

A small to medium sized tree, 6 to 15 m in height; occurring in evergreen forest and at forest margins. **Bark:** brownish, rough. **Leaves:** crowded at the ends of the branches; rachis not winged, with 5 pairs of opposite leaflets plus a terminal leaflet; leaflets oblong-lanceolate or ovate, 2,5 to 8 × 1 to 3,5 cm, without hairs; lateral veins distinct and midrib prominent on the under surface; margin rounded, notched; base rounded; margin entire; petiolules about 5 mm long, petiole up to 3,5 cm long. **Flowers:** greenish-white, in short, thickset, axillary racemes, up to 5 cm long, with conspicuous bracts almost hiding the flowers and covered with silvery hairs (January). **Fruit:** an almost spherical, very warty capsule produced in dense close clusters; each capsule splits, the valves twisting back and contorting, to reveal the red-brown seeds (May to July).

The bark has a burning taste which is characteristic and very strong. It is used in African medicine to treat a variety of ailments.

Bersama swynnertonii E. G. Baker
S.A. no: —
Rhod. no: 615   Purple bersama

MELIANTHACEAE

A small to medium sized tree, usually up to 10 m in height; occurring in medium altitude evergreen forest, at forest margins and in riverine fringes. **Bark:** mid-grey to brownish-grey often mottled with pale grey. **Leaves:** rachis not winged, with 1 to 3 pairs of opposite leaflets plus a terminal leaflet; leaflets ovate, obovate to lanceolate, up to 8 × 3,5 cm, glossy dark green above, paler green below, leathery; midrib slightly raised above, conspicuously raised below; veining conspicuous on both surfaces; apex tapering, finely notched; base tapering; margin entire; petiolules short, thickset, pinkish-red; petiole pinkish-red. **Flowers:** about 1,8 cm in diameter, opening a greenish-white, rapidly becoming pink and finally a dull purplish-red by the following day; in rather slender upstanding racemes up to 18 cm long, with the flowers clustered over the upper half (November to January). **Fruit:** an almost spherical capsule, about 2 cm in diameter, wrinkled, greenish-brown; splitting into 4 valves to reveal the bright orange-red seeds each with a yellow cup-shaped aril at the base (March to June).

Bersama transvaalensis Turrill
S.A. no: 442   Transvaal bersama. Transvaalse witessenhout
Rhod. no: —

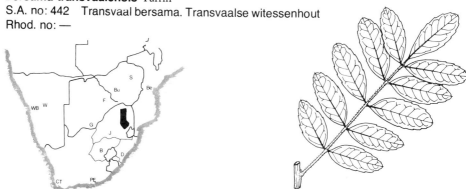

A medium sized tree up to 10 m in height; occurring at high altitudes in evergreen forest. **Bark:** greyish to brownish; the branchlets covered with fine soft hairs and marked by triangular leaf scars. **Leaves:** the rachis not winged, but sparsely hairy and furrowed, with 6 pairs of opposite leaflets plus a terminal leaflet; leaflets ovate to elliptic-lanceolate, 5,5 to 9 × 2 to 3 cm, dark green, veining prominent on both surfaces; apex tapering, notched; base tapering, asymmetric; margin entire or irregularly toothed; petiolules short, petiole 2 to 4 cm long. **Flowers:** creamy-white, in rather slender, terminal, somewhat lax, spike-like racemes up to 15 cm long (November). **Fruit:** a spherical capsule up to 2,5 cm in diameter, densely warty and spiny, brown when mature; splitting into 4 valves to reveal the orange to reddish seeds which have a waxy, yellow, cup-shaped aril round the base (May). There is some doubt regarding the status of this species. Verdcourt, in *Kew Bulletin* 1955 : 600 (1956) suggests that this is no more than a hybrid between *B. tysoniana* and *B. lucens*.

Bersama tysoniana Oliver
S.A. no: 443   Common bersama. Gewone witessenhout
Rhod. no: —

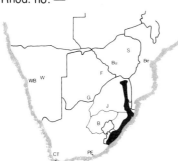

546 A shrub or small to medium sized tree, 3 to 10 m in height; occurring at the margins of evergreen forests and in bush clumps. **Bark:** grey to brownish, thick, rough, corrugated. **Leaves:** rachis not winged, with 4 to 5 pairs of opposite leaflets plus a terminal leaflet; leaflets oblanceolate or oblong to elliptic, up to 6 × 3 cm, without hairs on either surface, midrib prominent below; apex and base rounded; margin entire, or finely toothed over the upper half; petiolate. **Flowers:** greenish-white to cream, with shaggy hairs, in dense, upright, spike-like racemes, up to 17 × 2,5 cm (August to December). **Fruit:** a spherical capsule, about 2,5 cm in diameter, brown when mature, covered with woody protuberances; splitting into 4 valves to reveal the reddish seeds which have a yellow, waxy, cup-shaped aril at the base (February to August).

GREYIACEAE

GREYIA Hook. & Harvey

Shrubs or small trees. **Leaves:** alternate, simple, almost circular. **Flowers:** showy, red, in terminal, shortly branched racemes. Bisexual; all floral parts in fives; calyx persistent; petals longer than the sepals, overlapping, funnel-shaped; stamens 10 in 2 whorls, protruding from the mouth of the petal funnel; ovary deeply 5-furrowed, 1-chambered. **Fruit:** an almost cylindric, 5-grooved schizocarp, dehiscent.

Key to the species of *Greyia:*
1 In the eastern Cape only; flowers point downwards in rather few-flowered heads   **G. flanaganii**
  Not in the eastern Cape; flowers more or less horizontal in dense, many-flowered heads 2
2 Leaves without hairs or minutely hairy but lacking the woolly hairs of the following species, green
    above, paler green below but not white or yellowish .... **G. sutherlandii**
  Leaves sparsely hairy, losing most of these by maturity, green above, but the under surface densely
    covered with white to yellowish woolly hairs .... **G. radlkoferi**

Greyia flanaganii H. Bolus
S.A. no: 444   Kei bottlebrush. Keibaakhout
Rhod. no: —

A shrub or, rarely, a small tree, about 3 m in height; occurring on grassy hillsides and among rocks on the steep sides of river valleys. **Bark:** pale brown, smooth. **Leaves:** crowded at the ends of the branches, ovate or almost circular, 5 to 8 × 5 to 8 cm, grey-green to dark green above, paler green below, heavily veined, sparsely hairy above, densely so below; apex very broadly tapering to rounded; base broadly tapering, rounded to shallowly lobed; margin broadly scalloped, toothed, to slightly lobed; petiolate. **Flowers:** showy, red, bell-shaped, about 2 cm long, the red stamens and style protruding from the mouth of the petal tube; in loose, few-flowered heads pointing downwards, among the leaves (April to November). **Fruit:** 5-partite, cylindric, up to 2,5 × 0,7 cm, brownish when mature, the parts separating away from the tips downwards and splitting along their inner surfaces (October to February).
The Xhosa place roots on either side of their cattle kraals; this is thought to ward off sickness and also to protect the animals from theft.

Greyia radlkoferi Szyszyl.
S.A. no: 445   Transvaal bottlebrush. Transvaalse baakhout
Rhod. no: —

547

GREYIACEAE

A shrub or small tree, often gnarled, up to 5 m in height; occurring in mountain forested gullies, along stream banks, fringing evergreen forest and among rocks. **Bark:** very dark grey, deeply furrowed and rough on old trees, yellowish and smooth on young stems. **Leaves:** ovate, up to 10 × 9 cm, green, sparsely hairy above, losing most of these with age, with dense yellowish-white, woolly hairs below; apex broadly tapering to rounded; base lobed; margin very coarsely toothed to many-lobed; petiolate. **Flowers:** very showy, scarlet, bell-shaped, about 2 cm long, with the scarlet stamens protruding from the mouth of the flowers, densely clustered in spike-like racemes up to 8 cm long, before or with the young leaves (July to October). **Fruit:** cylindric, deeply divided into 4 to 5 long, narrow, cylindric sections, at first tightly pressed together, but later separating away from the tips downwards and splitting along their inner surfaces to release the seeds (September to October).
This is a very attractive species and is becoming increasingly cultivated.

Greyia sutherlandii Hook. & Harvey   Illust. 173
S.A. no: 446   Natal bottlebrush. Natalse baakhout
Rhod. no: —

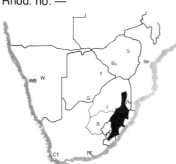

A shrub or small tree, 3 to 7 m in height; occurring in mountainous areas, on mountain slopes and along crests of broken rocky ridges. **Bark:** reddish-grey and smooth when young, becoming dark and rough with age. **Leaves:** ovate-oblong to rounded, up to 10 × 11 cm, green above, pale green below, with or without very fine hairs; apex rounded; base lobed, often almost clasping the stem; margin many-lobed, the lobes themselves scalloped; petiole up to 7 cm long. **Flowers:** showy, red, bell-shaped, about 2 cm long, the red stamens protruding from the mouth of the flower; produced in dense racemes up to about 12 cm long, the flowers crowded in upper half (August to October). **Fruit:** 4- to 5-partite, conical, about 2 cm long, becoming pale grey-brown when mature, the long cylindric sections separating away from the tips downwards and splitting longitudinally along the inner surfaces to release the seeds (September to November).
This small tree is most decorative and is becoming increasingly popular as an ornamental garden subject. It is not difficult to propagate and has proved hardy and fairly fast-growing under suitable conditions. The branches are brittle, and the pale, light, soft wood is used for carvings and to make household utensils.

548

RHAMNACEAE *(The buffalo-thorn family)*

Key to the genera:

1 Leaves opposite or sub-opposite 2

  Leaves alternate 3

2 Fruits ovoid, fleshy, indehiscent .... **2. Berchemia**

  Fruits obscurely 3-lobed capsules, almost spherical, reluctantly dehiscent ..... **8. Lasiodiscus**

3 Armed with stipular or axillary spines 4

  Without spines, or may have spine-tipped branches 5

4 Leaves pinnately veined .... **3. Scutia**

  Leaves 3- to 5-veined from the base .... **1. Ziziphus**

5 Fruit fleshy 6

  Fruit a capsule 8

6 Leaves 3- to 5-veined from the base .... **1. Ziziphus**

  Leaves pinnately veined 7

7 Fruit yellow to orange with 2 seeds .... **2. Berchemia**

  Fruit red to purplish with 3 to 4 seeds .... **4. Rhamnus**

8 Leaves small and often conspicuously narrow, not larger than 2,5 × 1,2 cm ...... **7. Phylica**

  Leaves larger than 4 × 1 cm 9

9 Usually at high altitudes, in open scrub near streams; from south-western Cape to Natal; leaves oblong-lanceolate .... **5. Noltea**

  Always on coastal dunes or in littoral scrub. Along coastal belt in Moçambique and northwards; leaves broadly ovate .... **6. Colubrina**

1. ZIZIPHUS Miller

Shrublets, shrubs or trees. **Leaves:** alternate, simple, 3- to 5-veined from the base. Stipules frequently spinescent. **Flowers:** small, in axillary heads, or cymes. Bisexual; all floral parts in fives; petals may be absent; stamens inserted beneath the cone-shaped disc; ovary enveloped by the disc, 2- to 4-chambered. **Fruit:** fleshy, indehiscent.

Key to the tree species of *Ziziphus* (naturalised exotics marked*):

1 Paired stipular spines present 2
  Stipular spines absent 4
2 Leaf bases frequently symmetric or nearly so, tapering to rounded .... ***Z. mauritiana***
  Leaf bases markedly asymmetric 3
3 Upper surface of the leaf always without hairs and with the veins depressed; under surface always with woolly hairs .... **Z. abyssinica**
  Upper surface of the leaf with or without hairs, the veins not depressed; the under surface almost without hairs or with soft, pale brown, woolly hairs .... **Z. mucronata**
4 Leaf bases markedly asymmetric .... **Z. mucronata**
  Leaf bases not markedly asymmetric, although they may be slightly so 5
5 Flower heads without a common stalk, or peduncle; style 3-branched, ovary 3-chambered; fruit spherical .... **Z. rivularis**
  Flower heads with a common stalk, or peduncle; style 2-branched; ovary 2-chambered; fruit ovoid .... **Z. pubescens**

Ziziphus abyssinica Hochst. ex A. Rich.
S.A. no: —
Rhod. no: 616   Jujube

549

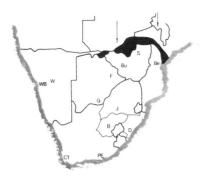

A shrub or small tree reaching 7 m in height; occurring at medium to low altitudes, in open woodland, wooded grassland and along river banks; it reaches its southernmost limit along the southern escarpment of the Zambezi valley. **Bark:** greyish-brown, becoming longitudinally fissured and rough in older specimens. **Leaves:** ovate to broadly ovate, up to 7,7 × 4,7 cm, conspicuously 3-veined from the base, dark green above with the veins depressed, paler green below due to the dense rusty yellow to grey, furry hairs; apex broadly tapering, frequently ending in a hair-like tip; base lobed, markedly asymmetric; margin finely toothed; petiole up to 1,2 cm long, with dense, soft hairs. Stipules spinescent, one sharply hooked downwards, the other slightly curved upwards. **Flowers:** small, yellowish, in dense tight clusters in the axils of the leaves; inconspicuous except when produced in profusion (December to February). **Fruit:** almost spherical, up to 3 cm in diameter, shiny red or reddish-brown when mature, edible (June to September).

The ash from the burnt leaves is mixed with salt and applied as a throat paint to relieve tonsillitis, and hot steaming leaves soaked in boiling water are used as a fomentation on the chest to treat pneumonia.

*Ziziphus mauritiana Lam.

Usually a small tree about 7 m in height; but occasionally reaching 20 m. This was introduced probably from the Middle East or India and is widely cultivated in Moçambique for its edible fruits; it spread up the Zambezi valley and has become naturalised in many areas (Rhod. no: 617). The fruits are used to make 'kachaso', a primitively distilled spirit of considerable potency.

Ziziphus mucronata Willd.   Illust 174
[*Z. abyssinica* sensu Palgrave, *Trees of Central Africa*]
S.A. no: 447   Buffalo-thorn. Blinkblaar-wag-'n-bietjie
Rhod. no: 618   Buffalo-thorn

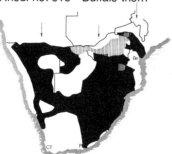

A small to medium sized tree up to 9 m in height, occasionally taller; occurring in a wide variety of habitats, in open woodland, often in alluvial soils along rivers, and frequently on termite mounds; it is said to indicate the presence of underground water. **Bark:** grey to dark grey and fissured; branches often drooping. **Leaves:** ovate to broadly ovate, 3 to 7,7 × 2 to 5 cm, shiny green, only slightly paler green below, either without hairs or with short, soft, pale brown, woolly hairs on the under surface, according to the subspecies; characteristically 3-veined from the base; apex broadly tapering; often

550

with a hair-like tip; base rounded to lobed, markedly asymmetric; margin finely toothed over the upper two-thirds, often wavy; petiole up to 7 mm long, with short soft hairs. Stipular spines, one curved the other straight, may or may not be present. **Flowers:** small, yellowish, inconspicuous, in tight axillary clusters, often producing copious nectar (November to February). **Fruit:** almost spherical, about 1,5 cm in diameter, shiny russet-red when mature, often remaining on the tree over winter until the leaves fall; the pulp is rather dry and meal-like (March to August).

This species has been divided into two subspecies:

subsp. *mucronata* – (refer to the black area on the map) under surface of the leaves with short soft hairs, frequently along the veins only, or without hairs; this subspecies is the most widespread.

subsp. *rhodesica* R. B. Drumm. – (refer to the vertical lines on the map) under surface of the leaves covered with dense, coarse, pale creamy-brown, woolly hairs, which persist to maturity.

In Rhodesia, subsp. *mucronata* tends to occur in dry localities, whereas subsp. *rhodesica* is found in moister areas or those with higher rainfall. In South Africa, subsp. *mucronata* occurs in a wide variety of habitats, but subsp. *rhodesica* is not found at all.

The buffalo thorn has numerous magico-medicinal uses. A widespread remedy for almost any pain is a poultice of the powdered and baked roots which is eaten after removal from the affected area. Boils and other skin infections are treated with a leaf paste, and this, together with a dose of a root decoction, is the accepted treatment among some Africans for tubercular gland-swellings. Sufferers from dysentery and lumbago either chew the root or drink an infusion made from it, while Zulus use the powdered leaf and bark to relieve chest complaints and take an infusion of the bark alone to cure coughs. In Botswana this tree is considered immune to lightning, so any person sheltering under it is thought to be safe. It is also believed that if a tree is felled after the first rains a drought will certainly ensue. The leaves and fallen fruits are browsed on by stock and game and can provide useful fodder in times of drought.

Ziziphus pubescens Oliver

S.A. no: —
Rhod. no: 619   Small jujube

A large shrub or small unarmed tree up to 7 m in height; occurring from coastal forest to low altitude riverine fringe forest and thicket. Young branchlets have soft short hairs which are lost by maturity. **Leaves:** ovate, up to 8 × 4 cm, conspicuously 3-veined from the base, dark green and possibly sparsely hairy above, and with greyish hairs below which may be confined to the main veins; apex broadly tapering, finally narrowly rounded, notched; base tapering, more or less symmetric; margin finely toothed; petiole only 6 mm long. Stipules not spinescent. **Flowers:** small, yellowish, in dense axillary heads; the whole flower head may be shortly stalked (November to December). **Fruit:** ovoid, about 10 × 8 mm, reddish-brown when mature (May to July).

This species has been divided into two subspecies:

subsp. *pubescens* – both surfaces of the leaves with short soft hairs.

subsp. *glabra* R. B. Drumm. – both surfaces of the leaves without hairs, or sometimes with a few hairs on the main veins below; this has been recorded from Moçambique only.

RHAMNACEAE

Ziziphus rivularis Codd
S.A. no: 448   False buffalo-thorn. Valswag-'n-bietjie
Rhod. no: —

A shrub or small unarmed tree up to 7 m in height; occurring among rocks and also along stream banks or in watercourses (the specific name refers to this). **Bark:** grey, smooth. **Leaves:** lanceolate to ovate-lanceolate, up to 6,5 × 3,4 cm, with sparse hairs along the veins only on the under surface, losing the hairs by maturity, conspicuously 3-veined from the base; apex tapering; base rounded, often rather asymmetric; margin finely toothed; petiolate. Stipules minute, not spinescent. **Flowers:** small, yellowish, inconspicuous, in very small, few-flowered, axillary, compact heads, without a common stalk, or peduncle (November). **Fruit:** spherical, about 6 mm in diameter, dark brown when mature, usually solitary per leaf axil (January).
This species resembles *Z. pubescens*.

2. BERCHEMIA Necker ex DC.

Shrubs or trees. **Leaves:** alternate, opposite or sub-opposite, simple. Stipules small, not spinescent. **Flowers:** in axillary or terminal heads, or cymes. Bisexual; all floral parts in fives; petals with a small claw; stamens inserted under the edge of a flattish receptacle disc; ovary may or may not be enveloped in the disc. **Fruit:** ovoid, fleshy, indehiscent.

Key to the species of *Berchemia:*
Leaves small, 1,2 to 4 × 0,6 to 2,5 cm, fruits small, up to 9 × 3 mm; ovary not enveloped in the disc
.... **B. zeyheri**
Leaves larger, 5 to 11 × 3 to 6 cm; fruits larger, up to 2 × 0,8 cm; ovary enveloped in the disc
.... **B. discolor**

Berchemia discolor (Klotzsch) Hemsley   Illust. 175
[*Phyllogeiton discolor* (Klotzsch) Herzog]
S.A. no: 449   Bird plum. Voëlpruim
Rhod. no: 620   Bird plum

Occasionally shrubby, but usually a well-shaped tree, 7 to 20 m in height; occurring at low altitudes, in riverine fringe forest or open dry woodland, often on termite mounds; widespread but seldom common. **Bark:** dark grey, rough, fissured; young branches green, smooth. **Leaves:** alternate, elliptic or oblong-elliptic, 5 to 11 × 3 to 6 cm, usually about 7 cm long, without hairs; shiny dark green above, much paler green below with a single prominent midrib; the lateral veins may be slightly hairy and form a distinct 'herring-bone' pattern on the under surface; apex tapering, often slightly notched; base broadly tapering to rounded; margin entire to finely toothed; petiolate. **Flowers:** small, greenish-yellow, on slender stalks, in rather loose, axillary clusters, often borne in profusion (October to January). **Fruit:** ovoid, up to 2 × 0,8 cm, fleshy, yellow to light orange when mature, edible, with a sweetish flavour (January to May).

The wood is yellow-brown and hard with an attractive short grain; it would make a good furniture wood but its scattered occurrence prevents any large scale use.

Berchemia zeyheri (Sonder) Grubov
[*Rhamnus zeyheri* Sonder]
S.A. no: 450   Red ivory. Rooi-ivoor
Rhod. no: 621   Red ivory

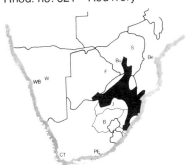

A shrub or well-shaped tree up to 10 m in height; occurring at medium to low altitudes, in open woodland, often on termite mounds, on rocky ridges and along watercourses. **Bark:** grey, smooth, becoming dark grey and rough near the base in larger trees. **Leaves:** usually opposite to sub-opposite, elliptic, 1,2 to 4 × 0,6 to 2,5 cm, greyish-green above, paler green below, without hairs; the veins on the under surface, the petioles and young twigs are often purplish-red; apex broadly tapering; base rounded; margin entire; petiolate. **Flowers:** small, greenish, inconspicuous, in small, tight, axillary clusters (October to December). **Fruit:** ellipsoidal, berry-like, up to 9 × 3 mm, yellow to brownish-red when mature, fleshy with a pleasant taste (November to April).

The Zulus take an infusion of the bark orally, and also use it as an enema to relieve pains in the back and to treat rectal ulceration in children. In the northern Transvaal fruits are stored in grain storage baskets where they eventually form a thick, brown, sugary mass which is highly esteemed as a sweetmeat and condiment. The wood is close-grained, hard and strong. The heartwood is a most striking and unusual bright pink-red shade when freshly cut but this slowly fades to a deep red; it is a startling colour for furniture, but outstanding for ornaments, small boxes and curios. In Natal, only the chiefs were allowed to carry knobkerries made from this wood.

3. SCUTIA Commerson ex Brongn.

Scutia myrtina (N. L. Burm.) Kurz
S.A. no: 451   Cat-thorn. Katdoring
Rhod. no: 622   Cat-thorn

Usually a scrambling shrub or a liane, but it can develop into a small tree up to 8 m in height; occurring at the margins of evergreen forest. **Bark:** light brown; branches bear strongly hooked, single or paired, axillary spines, grey with brown tips, which are aids to climbing. **Leaves:** usually opposite, simple, ovate to elliptic, 3,5 to 6 × 2 to 4 cm, glossy light green above, only slightly paler green below; apex broadly tapering to rounded, often notched and frequently bristle-tipped; base broadly tapering to rounded; margin entire, or occasionally slightly scalloped and wavy; petioles up to 10 mm long. Stipules very small, falling early. **Flowers:** about 4 mm in diameter, yellowish-green, axillary in small, dense clusters, or fascicles, or umbels. Bisexual; all floral parts in fives; petals shorter than the sepals; stamens about as long as the petals; ovary 2- to 4-chambered (September to January).

553

Fruit and leaves of the cat-thorn, Scutia myrtina.

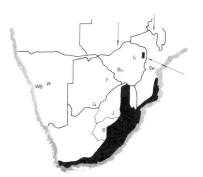

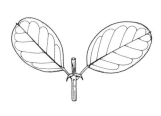

Fruit: almost spherical, berry-like, up to 8 mm in diamater, black when mature, indehiscent (February to April).

The astringent fruit is eaten mainly by children and birds. In India the leaf is used as an ointment applied locally to hasten parturition of both the child and the placenta.

4. RHAMNUS L.

Shrubs or small trees. **Leaves:** alternate opposite or fascicled, simple. Stipules small, falling early. **Flowers:** small, axillary, fascicled. Bisexual; floral parts in fours to fives; petals may be absent; ovary 2- to 4-chambered. Fruit: ovoid, fleshy, indehiscent.

Key to the tree species of *Rhamnus:*
Leaves elliptic to elliptic-oblong, 3 to 10 × 1,5 to 4 cm; petiole 3 to 10 mm long; floral parts in fives .... **R. prinoides**

Leaves narrowly elliptic to obovate, small, 1,2 to 2,5 × 0,7 to 1,5 cm; petiole short, 1 to 3 mm long; floral parts in fours .... **R. staddo**

Rhamnus prinoides L'Hérit.   Illust. 176
S.A. no: 452   Dogwood. Blinkblaar
Rhod. no: 623   Shiny leaf

A shrub, sometimes with a tendency to scramble, or a small tree which may reach 7 m in height; widespread and locally common at medium to high altitudes, along watercourses, in riverine forest and at the margins of evergreen forest. **Bark:** grey to brown, smooth with conspicuous lenticels, becoming dark brown with age. **Leaves:** alternate, elliptic to oblong-elliptic, 3 to 10 × 1,5 to 4 cm, very glossy dark green above, dull green below, without hairs, net-veining very distinct; apex rather narrowly tapering; base tapering to rounded; margin finely toothed or scalloped over the upper two-thirds; petiole 3 to 10 mm long. **Flowers:** greenish, small, inconspicuous, on slender stalks; in sparse, axillary groups or clusters of 2 to 10 (October to December). **Fruit:** berry-like, ovoid to almost circular, about 5 mm in diameter, shiny red becoming dark red when mature, sometimes almost black; edible (January to March).
A decoction of the decorticated root is taken as a blood purifier and to treat pneumonia; the leaves are applied as a liniment to simple sprains. Parts of the plant are widely favoured as a protective charm which is used against lightning, to protect homes and to safeguard the courts of chiefs. Green twigs are burned to smoke away evil spirits from the fields and an infusion of the leaves is sprinkled over members of a hunting party before they set off to bring them luck in the chase. The wood is white, hard and heavy, but usually not large enough to make anything but small articles. The leaves and berries are attractive and make striking floral arrangements. The seed germinates readily and the plants are hardy; they are becoming increasingly popular as garden subjects.

Rhamnus staddo A. Rich.
[*R. rhodesicus* Suesseng.]
S.A. no: —
Rhod. no: 624   Staddo

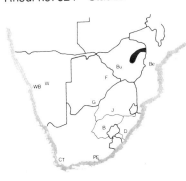

A small, bushy, rigidly branched shrub or small tree, 2 to 4 m in height; occurring on rocky koppies and in open woodland, where it is often associated with termite mounds. **Bark:** grey-brown, smooth. **Leaves:** small, clustered on short, lateral, often spine-tipped branches; narrowly elliptic or narrowly obovate, 1,2 to 2,5 × 0,7 to 1,5 cm, shiny dark green above, dull green below; apex rounded, often notched; base narrowly tapering; margin entire, or obscurely toothed; petioles short, 1 to 3 mm long, slender. **Flowers:** small, greenish-yellow, inconspicuous, in few-flowered, axillary clusters; slightly

555

almond-scented (October to December). **Fruit:** berry-like, about 5 mm in diameter, red to purplish-red when mature (November to April).

This is a rare tree south of the Zambezi River. It also occurs in Tanzania and northwards to Ethiopia where the vernacular name for the plant is 'staddo'.

5. NOLTEA Reichenb.

Noltea africana (L.) Reichenb. f.
S.A. no: 453   Soap dogwood. Seepblinkblaar
Rhod. no: —

A shrub or small bushy unarmed tree up to 4 m in height; occuring at high altitudes, occasionally in open scrub and along stream banks. **Bark:** branchlets reddish. **Leaves:** alternate, simple, oblong-lanceolate, 4 to 7 × 1 to 1,8 cm, leathery, glossy dark green above, paler green below, midrib clearly visible; apex narrowly rounded; base tapering; margin toothed; petiole short. Stipules small, gland-like, green, on the smooth reddish shoots. **Flowers:** very small, white, about 3 mm in diameter, in few-flowered, axillary and/or terminal branched heads up to 3 cm long. Bisexual; all floral parts in fives; calyx tube bell-shaped; petals shorter than the calyx tube and surrounding the stamens; ovary with the lower section joined to the calyx tube (August to September, occasionally on to January). **Fruit:** a dry, shallowly 3-lobed, spherical capsule, up to 10 mm in diameter, ovoid, the persistent calyx cup forming a distinct disc round the base, brownish when mature, splitting, the valves curving back away from a central column; the seeds are blackish (September to November).

The leaves and twigs are soapy when rubbed in water and are used by Africans for their laundry. The Xhosa give their stock a decoction of the leaves both to prevent and to cure 'quarter-evil'.

6. COLUBRINA Rich. ex Brongn.

Colubrina asiatica (L.) Brongn.
S.A. no: —
Rhod. no: —   Colubrina

A shrub with a tendency to scramble, or a small tree up to 5 m in height; occurring on coastal sand dunes and in littoral scrub. **Bark:** brown; branchlets long, thin, reddish-brown with a marked whitish bloom. **Leaves:** alternate, simple, ovate, up to 7,5 × 5 cm, shiny green above, paler green below, conspicuously 3- to 5-veined from the base, with several pairs of lateral veins arising from these,

556

either without or occasionally with a very few sparse hairs along the veins on the under surface; apex tapering; base tapering, rounded, square to lobed; margin shallowly toothed or scalloped; petiole slender, up to 1,5 cm long. Stipules small, falling early. **Flowers:** cream to yellowish, about 4 mm in diameter, on slender stalks up to 7 cm long, in sparse, axillary heads, or cymes. Bisexual; all floral parts in fives (September to May). **Fruit:** a spherical capsule, up to 10 mm in diameter, reddish-brown when mature, dehiscent (February to September).

7. PHYLICA L.

Shrublets, shrubs or small trees. **Leaves:** alternate, simple. Stipules absent. **Flowers:** axillary or terminal, solitary, or in a spike or raceme, a spherical head or capitulum. Bisexual; all floral parts in fives; sepals erect or spreading, often with a prominent median vein on the inner surface; petals may be absent; stamens inserted below the petals; ovary beneath the fleshy disc. **Fruit:** a dehiscent capsule.

Key to the tree species of *Phylica:*
1 Leaves fairly broad and, although the margins are markedly rolled under, the under surface of the leaves is still visible 2
   Leaves very narrow and the margins so rolled under that the leaves are needle-like 4
2 Leaves ovate; net-veining often clearly visible on the under surface; flowers in tight terminal or axillary clusters, on a stalk up to 10 mm long; conspicuous leaf-like bracts below the flower head .... **P. buxifolia**
   Leaves elliptic; net-veining not visible; conspicuous leaf-like bracts below the flower head absent 3
3 In the dry, arid coastal mountains of the south-western Cape only. Leaves usually more than 1,5 cm long; fruits 8 to 10 mm in diameter .... **P. oleifolia**
   Not in the south-western Cape, but widespread elsewhere in high-rainfall areas, from the southern Cape to Rhodesia. Leaves seldom exceeding 1,2 cm in length; fruits about 6 mm in diameter .... **P. paniculata**
4 Leaves with the margins so rolled under that the leaves become cylindric, only 1 mm in diameter and needle-like, up to 2 cm in length. Occurring in the western and south-western Cape only .... **P. villosa**
   Leaves not fully needle-like, but very small, usually less than 10 mm in length. Not in the western and south-western Cape, occurring only in the southern Cape .... **P. purpurea**

Phylica buxifolia L.

S.A. no: 453,1   Box hard-leaf. Bukshardeblaar
Rhod. no: —

A stout, much-branched shrub or small tree, ususally 3 to 4 m in height; occurring only among rocks in mountainous areas. **Bark:** greyish or brownish; young branches are covered with yellowish-brown, short, soft hairs. **Leaves:** small, ovate, up to 2,5 × 1 cm, dark green above, very pale green to almost white below, the upper surface characteristically minutely roughly textured, net-veining clearly visible on the under surface; apex broadly tapering; base more or less rounded; margin entire, markedly and tightly rolled under; petiole short. **Flowers:** small, white, rather unpleasant smelling, in dense axillary or terminal heads up to 10 mm in diameter, on stalks up to 10 mm long, with characteristic, fluffy, leaf-like bracts round the flower heads (March to June). **Fruit:** a capsule up to

557

1,3 cm long, with a square tip and a tuft of small hairs round the rim, densely creamy-green, with short soft hairs (October to November).

Phylica oleifolia Vent.
S.A. no: 453,3   Glossy hard-leaf. Blinkhardeblaar
Rhod. no: —

 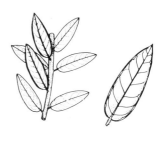

A rounded, dense shrub or small tree about 3 m in height; occurring on rocky mountain slopes. **Bark:** grey, smooth. **Leaves:** closely clustered along the young branches, elliptic, up to 2,5 × 1 cm, dark green above, with white soft hairs below; apex tapering; base rounded; margin entire but tightly and conspicuously rolled under; petiolate. **Flowers:** very small, white, the calyx and stalks covered with dense white hairs, produced in compact, small terminal heads (June). **Fruit:** a clearly 3-lobed, woody capsule, 8 to 10 mm in diameter, shiny reddish-brown when mature, girdled by the vestiges of the old calyx (August to October).

Phylica paniculata Willd.
S.A. no: 453,2   Common hard-leaf. Gewone hardeblaar
Rhod. no: 625   Common hard-leaf

 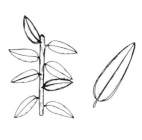

A much-branched shrub or small tree up to 6 m in height; occurring on rocky mountain slopes, along stream banks and in high-rainfall areas. **Bark:** grey; branchlets with grey woolly hairs. **Leaves:** crowded along the branchlets and overlapping, very small, ericoid, elliptic, usually about 10 × 2 mm but can reach 15 × 6 mm, dark green above, with whitish downy hairs below; apex narrowly tapering; base rounded; margin entire, rolled under so that only about half the lower surface is visible. **Flowers:** very small, greyish, greenish or cream, sweetly scented, in short, axillary and terminal, branched heads, or panicles, up to 10 × 4 cm (February to April). **Fruit:** an almost spherical to slightly pear-shaped, thickly woody capsule, about 6 mm in diameter, red-brown, often almost black when mature (August to September).

Phylica purpurea Sonder
S.A. no: Silk-fruited hard-leaf
Rhod. no: —

A dense shrub or small tree, 1 to 3 m in height; occurring in *fynbos,* usually among rocks. **Bark:** grey to brown; young branches covered with grey hairs. **Leaves:** small, narrowly ovate, up to 10 mm long, the margin so conspicuously rolled under that it becomes almost needle-like and the leaf shape is

obscured. **Flowers:** small, white, with dense woolly hairs, in compact heads, crowded near the ends of the brachlets, the flowers collectively giving an almost floss-like appearance to the flower head (April). **Fruit:** an ovoid capsule, about 6 mm long, covered with white silky hairs, with a conspicuous apical ring (May onwards).

Phylica villosa Thunb.
S.A. no: 453,4   Needle hard-leaf. Naaldhardeblaar
Rhod. no: —

Usually a low bushy shrub, occasionally a small tree up to 3 m in height; occurring in coastal and mountain *fynbos*. **Bark:** grey; young branches with dense, creamy, soft hairs. **Leaves:** grey-green, up to 2 cm long and very slender, with the margins so rolled under that the leaves become cylindric and needle-like. **Flowers:** whitish, in short, spreading, axillary and terminal, slender branched heads; the stem, stalks and buds, all covered with creamy, soft woolly hairs (May to October). **Fruit:** a small, obovate capsule, about 7 × 5 mm, reddish-brown when mature, with the remains of the calyx forming a crown-like ring of tiny, white, woolly tufts (October to November).

8. LASIODISCUS J. D. Hook.

Shrubs or small trees. **Leaves:** opposite or sub-opposite, simple. Stipules large, narrow, falling early. **Flowers:** in axillary branched heads, or pedunculate cymes, or in clusters or fascicles. Bisexual; all floral parts in fives; petals slightly spoon-shaped; disc fleshy; stamens inserted below the disc; ovary 3-chambered. **Fruit:** a capsule, reluctantly dehiscent.

Key to the tree species of *Lasiodiscus:*
Leaf base asymmetric, rounded to shallowly lobed; flowers in round branched heads, or corymbose
    pedunculate cymes .... **L. mildbraedii**
Leaf bases symmetric, tapering; flowers in clusters, or fascicles, without stalks   **L. usambarensis**

Lasiodiscus mildbraedii Engl.
S.A. no: 453,5   Lasiodiscus. Rooihaarbos
Rhod. no: —

A shrub or small tree, usually up to 5 m in height, but may reach 9 m; occurring in and at the margins of medium altitude evergreen forest and coastal forest. **Bark:** pale grey to whitish-grey, with

559

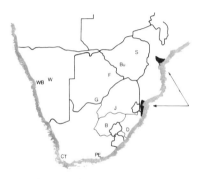

conspicuous raised lenticels. **Leaves:** elliptic to ovate, 5 to 19 × 2,3 to 8 cm, but usually about 7 to 12 cm long, thinly textured, shiny dark green above, rather dull with pale green veining conspicuous below; the young leaves with sparse hairs which are lost by maturity, except for some which persist along the midrib; apex narrowly tapering, sometimes slightly notched; base rounded to shallowly lobed, asymmetric; margin scalloped to finely toothed; petiole up to 5 mm long. Stipules triangular, pointed, up to 10 mm long, sparsely hairy, falling early. **Flowers:** small, creamy-white to yellow, in round branched heads about 2 cm in diameter, on long stalks up to 6 cm long; the stalks and buds are covered with soft, creamy-white, short hairs (September to November). **Fruit:** an obscurely 3-lobed capsule, about 10 mm in diameter, tipped with the remains of the old style, belted round the middle by the remains of the calyx, golden-brown when mature (March).

Lasiodiscus usambarensis Engl.

S.A. no: —
Rhod. no: 626   Chirinda lasiodiscus

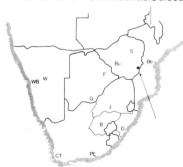

A small tree up to 6 m in height; occurring as part of the under-storey in evergreen forest. **Bark:** dark brown or grey, smooth, with conspicuous lenticels. **Leaves:** elliptic to ovate, 9 to 14 × 5 cm, thinly textured; the veins depressed above; apex narrowly tapering; base tapering; margin scalloped to finely toothed; petiole 3 to 9 mm long. Stipules awl-shaped, finely hairy, about 5 mm long. **Flowers:** small, greenish-white, inconspicuous, in few-flowered axillary clusters without stalks (October to December). **Fruit:** a capsule, about 10 mm in diameter, green, with fine short soft hairs (October to March).

VITACEAE *(The grape-vine family)*

Key to the tree genera:
Flowers with 5 to 6 petals, stamens curved over the ovary .... **1. Rhoicissus**
Flowers with 4 petals, stamens straight (tree species in South West Africa only) **2. Cyphostemma**

1. RHOICISSUS Planchon

Frequently scrambling or climbing shrubs, occasionally small trees. **Leaves:** alternate, with leaf-opposed tendrils, simple or 3-foliolate (occasionally 5-foliolate). Stipules present, or rarely absent.

Flowers: in leaf-opposed, condensed cymes. Bisexual; floral parts in fives to sixes; calyx not toothed; petals thickened or fleshy at their apices; stamens curved over the ovary; ovary immersed in the fleshy disc. **Fruit:** fleshy, indehiscent.

Key to the tree species of *Rhoicissus:*
1 Leaves simple, almost circular or broader than they are long, or kidney-shaped; margin may be 3-lobed .... **R. tomentosa**
  Leaves 3- or 5-foliolate 2
2 Plants with at least some 5-foliolate leaves, although the majority of leaves are 3-foliolate .... **R. digitata**
  Leaves 3-foliolate, never 5-foliolate 3
3 Leaflet margins entire, rarely shallowly lobed .... **R. revoilii**
  Leaflet margins always toothed or lobed 4
4 Leaflet apex square to rounded, margin toothed, each tooth with a short point, 0,5 mm long . ... **R. tridentata**
  Leaflet apex tapering, margin toothed, each tooth tipped with a longer point, at least 1 mm long .. .. **R. rhomboidea**

Rhoicissus digitata (L.f.) Gilg & Brandt
S.A. no: 456,2   Baboon grape. Bobbejaandruif
Rhod. no: —

Usually a climber, occasionally a small bushy tree, 3 to 4 m in height; occurring on coastal dunes and as a common canopy climber in dry sand forest. **Bark:** greyish; the branchlets covered with bright reddish-brown hairs. **Leaves:** 3- to 5-foliolate; leaflets elliptic, 3,5 to 9 × 1,2 to 2,8 cm, upper surface dark green, under surface with fine soft rusty hairs; apex tapering, rounded to square, usually notched; base narrowly tapering; margin entire, rolled under; petiolules short, petiole up to 2,5 cm long, reddish. **Flowers:** greenish-yellow, in short, rather lax, axillary heads, on short stalks about 5 mm long (November to January). **Fruit:** oval, fleshy, about 1,5 × 1,2 cm, purplish-black when mature (January to February).

Rhoicissus revoilii Planchon   Illust. 178
[*R. schlechteri* Gilg & Brandt]
S.A. no: 456,3   Bushveld grape. Bosvelddruif
Rhod. no: 631   Warty grape

Usually a pliant shrub with a strong tendency to scramble, or a small tree up to 7 m in height; occurring in mixed woodland, on rocky hills and koppies, over a wide range of altitudes from sea level to 2 000 m. **Bark:** grey and scaly in the larger specimens; all young parts with dense, tawny or rusty-red, woolly hairs. **Leaves:** 3-foliolate; leaflets very variable in size and shape, from narrowly lanceolate (much of the South African material) to ovate (much of the Rhodesian material) to rhomboid or almost quadrangular, upper surface glossy deep green, may be without hairs or with very fine greyish soft hairs, under surface usually densely covered with rusty to grey-green, short soft hairs, often sickle-shaped; apex tapering to rounded; base tapering, often so markedly asymmetric as to appear lobed on one side; margin entire, rarely shallowly lobed, sometimes slightly rolled under; petiolule up to 2 cm long, petioles up to 4 cm long. **Flowers:** yellowish-green, the stalks and calyces

561

densely covered with rusty or tawny, woolly hairs; produced in small dense axillary branched heads, with a short stalk about 4 cm long (November to February). **Fruit:** 2-lobed, 1 to 1,5 cm in diameter, fleshy, often with a warty or scabby surface, black when mature (June to October).

Galls, which can be mistaken for fruits, are frequently produced and one of these is shown in the illustration. The stem contains a thin rather acid juice which, in times of drought, has been used instead of drinking water and also as an additive to palm wine.

Rhoicissus rhomboidea (E. Meyer ex Harvey) Planchon
S.A. no: 456,4   Bastard forest grape. Basterbosdruif
Rhod. no: 632   Rope-wood grape

Frequently a vigorous climber, only occasionally a small tree, 3 to 6 m in height; occurring at the margins of evergreen forests and at the edge of clearings often in the depths of the forest. **Bark:** dark brown; the stem much-branched; climbing by means of thick tough tendrils; all young parts covered with rusty, short, soft hairs. **Leaves:** 3-foliolate; the terminal leaf obovate to broadly obovate, the lateral leaflets markedly asymmetric, almost square, leathery, glossy dark green above, frequently with the under surface furry with pale rusty hairs; the older leaves may be light green below, with the rusty hairs confined to the veins especially near the base, sometimes almost absent and represented only as long, rusty hairs on the young stems; apex broadly tapering; base narrowly tapering; margin very characteristic, with about 6 tooth-like projections each tipped with a thin point about 1 mm long; petiolules 1 to 4 mm long, petiole up to 2,3 cm long. **Flowers:** small, greenish-yellow, in rather lax branched axillary heads on stalks up to 10 mm long; the flowers without hairs, but the common stalk, or peduncle, with long red hairs (October to December). **Fruit:** grape-like, almost spherical, about 10 mm in diameter, in clusters, becoming dark wine-red to purple when mature; edible (January to April and even on to August and October).

Rhoicissus tomentosa (Lam.) Wild & R. B. Drumm.
[*R. capensis* Planchon]
S.A. no: 456,5   Common forest grape. Gewone bosdruif
Rhod. no: 633   Simple-leaved grape

Usually a woody climber, or liane, reaching the tops of 20 m high trees, but it can occasionally form a small tree, 3 to 7 m in height; occurring in riverine fringes, clambering over trees and bushes and almost always associated with forest. **Bark:** greyish; young branches with thick rusty hairs, most of which are lost by maturity. **Leaves:** simple, large, almost circular, or broader than long, up to 20 ×

562

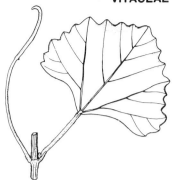

16 cm, but usually about 9 × 7 cm, heavily veined, conspicuously 3-veined from the base, but with the central one obviously the midrib; upper surface deep green and without hairs, under surface with dense rusty soft hairs, occasionally confined to the veins; apex rounded; base deeply lobed; margin may be entire, or more often shallowly toothed, slightly wavy (much of the South African material shows the whole leaf as quite conspicuously 3-lobed, but not deeply divided); petiole up to 6 cm long. **Flowers:** small, creamy-green, in dense heads on a stalk up to 2 cm long, densely furry with rusty hairs when in bud (October to December). **Fruit:** almost spherical, about 2 cm in diameter, fleshy, becoming red and finally purplish-black when mature (January to April).

The fruits are grape-like in appearance and edible, although, according to Swynnerton, 'not up to much'. When boiled with plenty of sugar they are said to make a delicious conserve and an excellent jelly. The split branches have been used as a rope for tying down thatch and also in basket-making. The roots boiled in milk are given to calves as an anthelmintic.

Rhoicissus tridentata (L.f.) Wild & R. B. Drumm.
[*R. cuneifolia* (Ecklon & Zeyher) Planchon]
S.A. no: 456,6   Bitter grape. Bitterdruif
Rhod. no: 634   Bitter grape

Usually a tendril climber up to 10 m in height, sometimes a small bushy shrub, 1 to 2 m high, and very occasionally a small tree up to 4 m; occurring in a wide range of habitats, often associated with boulders on rocky koppies or stony hillsides, also in bush clumps in open grassy woodland and at the margins of evergreen forest in high-rainfall areas. **Bark:** light brown, soft and rather powdery; branchlets with greyish or yellowish hairs, sometimes densely covered with rusty woolly hairs. **Leaves:** 3-foliolate, leaflets narrowly to broadly obovate, up to 9 × 5,5 cm, leathery, dark green above, the under surface with or without dense rusty, yellowish to grey hairs, turning an attractive red in autumn; apex square to rounded; base tapering; margin toothed, with 3 to 18 teeth towards the apex each tipped with a minute thin point (in some South African material the teeth are much reduced and the margin is almost entire); petiolules short, petiole up to 4 cm long. Stipules very small, falling early. **Flowers:** small, greenish-yellow, in small tight heads, on slender peduncles up to 3 cm long, densely furry with rusty, tawny or greyish hairs, especially in bud (November to April). **Fruit:** almost spherical, 1 to 1,8 cm in diameter, fleshy, becoming red and finally black when mature (April to December).

The fruits are eaten by children and the plant is used by the southern Sotho chiefs as a charm when **563** establishing a new village. Zulu women prepare a decoction from the decorticated root as an enema to ease painful menstruation, to facilitate childbirth, and to induce labour if this is delayed; it is also used as a remedy for impotence and barrenness.

2. CYPHOSTEMMA (Planchon) Alston

Usually prostrate, or erect, often climbing, perennial herbs or shrubs; 3 species in South West Africa reach tree size. **Leaves:** rarely simple, usually compound, with 3 leaflets (sometimes up to 9). Stipules present. **Flowers:** in terminal, axillary, or leaf-opposed, flat-topped corymbose cymes. Bisexual; all floral parts in fours; flower buds cylindric or urn-shaped; calyx may have 4 teeth; petals spoon-shaped at the tip, falling very early; stamens straight; ovary more or less attached to the 4 rather fleshy, basal glands. **Fruit:** fleshy, indehiscent.

Key to the three tree species (all occurring in South West Africa and northwards):
1 Petiolules or petiole winged; juvenile leaves often simple, mature leaves 3-foliolate   **C. juttae**
 Petiolules or petiole not winged; leaves at no time simple 2
2 Occurring, in general, north of a line between Walvis Bay and Windhoek; a succulent tree up to
  7 m, bark yellowish to pale brown with a creamy-pink papery peel .... **C. currorii**
 Occurring, in general, south of a line between Walvis Bay and Windhoek; a dwarf succulent tree,
  frequently only 1 m in height or less, bark yellowish-orange with a creamy papery peel ....
  .... **C. bainesii**

Cyphostemma bainesii (J. D. Hook.) Descoings
[*Vitis bainesii* J. D. Hook.; *Cissus bainesii* (J. D. Hook.) Gilg & Brandt]
S.A. no: Gouty vine
Rhod. no: —

A succulent shrub or small tree, seldom exceeding 1 m in height, frequently less, sometimes only 30 cm in height when growing under harsh conditions; occurring in hot, dry rocky areas. **Bark:** smooth, yellowish-orange with a creamy papery peel. **Leaves:** 3-foliolate; leaflet oval or oblong, up to 27 × 11 cm, bright green to bluish-green often with a red margin, thick, fleshy; apex somewhat rounded; base tapering; margin coarsely toothed; petiole short, thickset, up to 3,5 cm long. **Flowers:** small, green, in flat, spreading, terminal sprays, on a succulent stalk, or peduncle, about 15 cm long (December). **Fruit:** oval, about 10 cm long, fleshy, orange when mature (January to May).

Cyphostemma currorii (J. D. Hook.) Descoings
[*Cissus currorii* J. D. Hook.; *C. crameranus* Schinz; *Cyphostemma crameranus* (Schinz) Descoings]
S.A. no: 456   Cobas. Kobas
Rhod. no: —

A thickset, succulent tree up to 7 m in height; occurring in dry, stony areas, and on rocky hillsides. **Bark:** yellowish to pale brown, smooth, with a creamy-pink, papery peel, revealing the whitish to pinkish smooth underbark. **Leaves:** 3-foliolate, large; leaflets broadly elliptic, up to 30 × 20 cm, thick, fleshy, light green, velvety when young; apex more or less rounded; base rounded; margin

 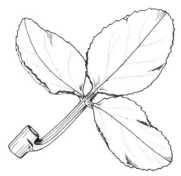

irregularly toothed; petiolules up to 2 cm long or absent, petiole up to 6 cm long, thick, succulent. **Flowers:** small, yellowish-green, succulent, in terminal, flat-topped, spreading, branched heads, about 15 to 18 cm in diameter, on a common stalk, or peduncle, up to 8 cm long, appearing with the young leaves (September to November). **Fruit:** almost spherical, about 10 mm in diameter, in grape-like bunches, red when mature; they contain oxalic acid and are consequently toxic (January to March).

Cyphostemma juttae (Dinter & Gilg) Descoings   Illust. 177
[*Cissus juttae* Dinter & Gilg]
S.A. no: 456,1   Bastard cobas. Basterkobas
Rhod. no: —

A short, thickset, succulent tree, frequently not exceeding 2 m in height, but occasionally reaching 4 m; occurring in desert regions. **Bark:** pale green, smooth, peeling in short, curling, creamy, papery flakes. **Leaves:** often simple and deeply lobed when juvenile, 3-foliolate when mature; leaflets large, broadly elliptic to ovate, 12 to 35 × 5 to 15 cm, the lateral leaflets somewhat smaller, blue-green, fleshy; the midrib on the under surface bears scattered prickles; apex tapering to rounded; base of the terminal leaflet symmetric, those of the lateral leaflets asymmetric, the leaflet bases running into the petiolules forming conspicuous wings; margin coarsely toothed; petiole present. Stipules conspicuous, narrow, falling early. **Flowers:** small, greenish-cream, in branched axillary and terminal flat-topped heads, the main stalk, or peduncle, being thick and armed with prickles (November). **Fruit:** ovoid to almost spherical, about 12 × 7 mm, becoming red and finally purplish-black when mature (December to January).
The photograph was taken in the Pretoria Botanic Garden.

TILIACEAE *(The jute and linden family)*

Key to the tree genera:
1 Fruits 2- to 3-lobed, each lobe with 2 large velvety membranous wings up to 5 × 2 cm ....
.... **1. Carpodiptera**

Fruits without large wings, although a very narrow wing may be present 2   **565**

TILIACEAE

2 Fruits dehiscent, or if indehiscent, then densely bristly .... **3. Sparrmannia**

   Fruits indehiscent, either woody or thinly fleshy, not bristly 3

3 Fruits woody, narrowly ovoid, with conspicuous longitudinal ridges, almost resembling pleats .... **2. Glyphaea**

   Fruits thinly fleshy 1- to 4-lobed berries .... **4. Grewia**

1. CARPODIPTERA Griseb.

Carpodiptera africana Mast.
S.A. no: —
Rhod. no: —   Carpodiptera

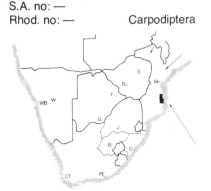
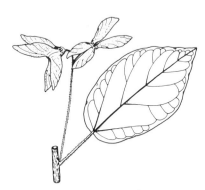

A small tree up to 8 m in height; occurring in coastal woodland and thicket. **Bark:** grey to brown, rather rough. **Leaves:** alternate, simple, ovate to oblong, up to 20 × 13 cm, but usually considerably smaller; apex tapering; base rounded to lobed; margin entire; petiole velvety, usually 1 to 2 cm long, but may reach 6 cm. Stipules long, slender, up to 8 mm, falling very early. **Flowers:** small, white, in branched, hairy, axillary heads, or cymes, with the secondary stalks, or peduncles, up to 3,5 cm long. Usually bisexual; calyx bell-shaped, 2- to 3-lobed; petals 5, up to 6 mm long; stamens many, joined at the base; ovary 2- to 3-lobed (November to December). **Fruit:** an ellipsoidal, 2- to 3-lobed, dehiscent capsule, up to 1,5 cm long; each lobe has 2 leaf-like wings covered with short soft hairs, up to 5 × 2 cm, each spreading sideways (June).

2. GLYPHAEA J. D. Hook. ex Planchon

Glyphaea tomentosa Mast.
S.A. no: —
Rhod. no: —   Glyphaea

A small tree about 4 m in height; occurring in deciduous woodland, and apparently confined to Moçambique. **Bark:** grey to brown. **Leaves:** alternate, simple, oblong, 4 to 9 × 2 to 4 cm, with stellate hairs on both surfaces, conspicuously 3-veined from the base on the under surface, with small pockets of hairs in the axils of the veins; apex tapering; base rounded or slightly lobed, often asymmetric; margin scalloped to toothed; petiole 1 to 1,5 cm long, hairy. Stipules fall very early.

Flowers: yellow, about 4,5 cm in diameter, solitary or in branched, 2- to 3-flowered heads, or cymes, opposite the leaves. Bisexual; all floral parts in fives; sepals narrowly oblong, green-backed and yellow within; petals narrowly oblong, golden-yellow; stamens many, all fertile, forming a central mass; ovary 6- to 10-chambered (January). **Fruit:** unusual, hard, woody, oblong-cylindric, up to 8 × 3 cm, conspicuously ridged, almost with a pleated appearance, sharp-tipped, velvety, containing many small brown seeds (May).
This tree is very similar to *Grewia* except for the distinctive fruit.

3. SPARRMANNIA L.f.

Sparrmannia africana L.f.
S.A. no: 457   Cape stock-rose. Kaapse stokroos
Rhod. no: —

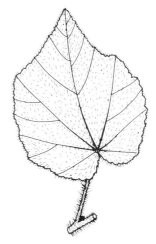

A large shrub or small tree up to 7 m in height; occurring on rocky hillsides and as a rampant weed along the margins of evergreen forest. **Bark:** greenish-grey to light brown, smooth. **Leaves:** alternate, simple, large, broadly ovate, up to 15 × 10 cm, 3- to 9-veined from the base, softly textured, hairy, the upper surface bright green with sunken veins, the under surface dull light green with prominent veins; apex broadly tapering; base deeply lobed; margin toothed, often with 3 to 9 large lobes; petiole up to 15 cm long. **Flowers:** showy, white, up to 3,5 cm in diameter, with a central mass of golden stamens flecked with purple, in about 20-flowered axillary heads, or pedunculate umbels, produced towards the ends of the branches. Bisexual; all floral parts in fours; sepals narrowly lanceolate; petals obovate, white; stamens many, free, forming the central mass, sterile stamens yellow, fertile stamens with purple anthers; ovary 4- to 5-chambered (June to November). **Fruit:** an almost spherical dehiscent capsule, covered with long spiny bristles, about 2 cm in diameter including the bristles (November to May).
In 1886 it was discovered that this plant could provide a fibre which for a number of years was used commercially but it proved to be of indifferent quality. The hairs on the leaves can irritate the skin and cause a rash. The plants grow easily and quickly and have been cultivated for their handsome flowers. Another species *S. ricinocarpa* (Ecklon & Zeyher) Kuntze, occurs from the Cape to north of the Zambezi along mountain ranges and at the margins of moist evergreen forests; it rarely exceeds 2 m in height and is not tree-like in habit. The flowers resemble those of *S. africana,* but are less striking.

4. GREWIA L.

Shrubs or trees. **Leaves:** alternate or fascicled, simple, 3 to 7-veined from the base. **Flowers:** axillary, leaf-opposed or terminal, solitary or in branched heads, cymes or umbels. Bisexual; all floral parts in fives; sepals often coloured within and petalloid; petals shorter than the sepals, with a hairy appendage at the base; stamens many, all fertile, forming a central mass, arising from an androgynophore; ovary 2- to 4-chambered. **Fruit:** a 1- to 4-lobed berry.

Key to the tree species of *Grewia:*
567

2 Under surface of the leaves markedly pale green or even silvery, often with dense whitish or rusty hairs 3

Under surface may be paler than the upper surface, and, if hairy, then the hairs are green   4

3 Under surface whitish to cream, frequently rusty, with dense, woolly hairs; net-veining very prominent and conspicuous .... **G. villosa**

Under surface almost silvery-white, with dense, fine hairs; net-veining not visible   **G. bicolor**

4 Leaves broadly elliptic, ovate to almost circular 5

Leaves lanceolate, elliptic to ovate 7

5 Leaves small, up to 3 × 3 cm, but frequently only 1,5 × 1 cm .... **G. tenax**

Leaves larger than 3 cm long, up to 12 cm long 6

6 Flowers pink; leaves very broadly ovate to almost circular .... **G. lasiocarpa**

Flowers yellow; leaves oblanceolate to obovate .... **G. flavescens**

7 Fruits usually simple, rarely 2-lobed 8

Fruits markedly 2- to 4-lobed 13

8 Fruits spherical 9

Fruits pear-shaped 12

9 Fruits with remains of the style markedly on one side .... **G. flava**

Fruits with the old style terminal 10

10 Leaf apex rounded to broadly tapering; older branches cylindric, although they tend to have grooves on 2 sides .... **G. retinervis**

Leaf apex tapering; older stems becoming 4-angled 11

11 Tip of stalk, or pedicel, with a dense ring of short white hairs immediately below the fruit and, below this, the top 2 to 4 mm of the fruiting stalk without hairs (10x lens); under surface of leaves with or without very sparse simple hairs; occurring in Rhodesia, the extreme northern Transvaal and Moçambique .... **G. gracillima**

Tip of the stalk, or pedicel, without a ring of white hairs, and the top 2 to 4 mm of the stalk immediately below the fruit with dense short hairs (10x lens); under surface of leaves with few to many stellate hairs, especially along the veins (10x lens); occurring in Natal, the Transvaal and Moçambique, only just entering the extreme south-east of Rhodesia .... **G. caffra**

12 Flowers creamy-white to pale yellow; occurring in Natal, the Transvaal (no further north than Soutpansberg) and Moçambique (no further north than Inhambane) .... **G. microthyrsa**

Flowers white; occurring in Moçambique, no further south than Inhambane .... **G. transzambesica**

13 Fruits may be 2-lobed (usually simple) .... **G. flava**

Fruits 2- to 4-lobed (usually 4) 14

14 Flowers appearing with the young leaves; stipules persistent and becoming dark brown and awl-shaped .... **G. praecox**

Flowers appearing with the mature leaves; stipules either not conspicuous, falling early or absent 15

15 Flowers with the inside of sepals and petals mauve, pink, or deep pink 16

Flowers white to pale yellow 17

16 Leaves conspicuously small, 1,3 to 2,5 cm long, clustered on dwarf, twiggy, lateral branchlets; generally favouring dry scrub and confined to the eastern Cape and the Cape midlands..... .... **G. robusta**

Leaves not conspicuously small, 2,5 to 7,5 cm long, alternate, not clustered on dwarf shoots; generally favouring moist localities, widely distributed .... **G. occidentalis**

17 Petals small, greenish-white, triangular, erect; stamens barely spreading .... **G. stolzii**

Petals more or less circular, crinkled 18

18 Sepals thick and chunky, 3,5 mm wide or more, up to 2 cm long .... **G. pachycalyx**

Sepals slender and rather thin, less than 3 mm wide and up to 1,5 cm long   **G. lepidopetala**

19 Flowers terminal or more or less leaf-opposed, white to cream, sometimes mauve; fruits deeply 4-lobed 20

Flowers axillary, yellow; fruits usually shallowly 2-lobed, sometimes 1- to 4-lobed (or 2-lobed so deeply divided as to appear as twinned single lobes) 21

20 Leaves obovate to oblong; apex rounded to broadly tapering, base rounded to shallowly lobed; flowers usually in groups of 3 crowded near the ends of the branches, mostly terminal .... **G. sulcata**

568

Leaves ovate to elliptic-oblong; apex abruptly tapering, base broadly tapering to rounded; flowers usually in groups of 3 to 9, leaf-opposed or sometimes terminal .... **G. lepidopetala**

21 Fruits always simple, not 2- to 4-lobed .... **G. gracillima**
   Fruits usually 2-lobed, sometimes 4-lobed, or simple 22

22 The under surface of the leaves not markedly pale, but velvety green; may have greyish hairs below especially along the veins 23
   The under surface of the leaves markedly pale, with whitish, greyish or yellowish hairs . 24

23 Flowers up to 3 cm in diameter; leaves with fine greyish hairs along the veins on the under surface .... **G. inaequilatera**
   Flowers 1 to 1,5 cm in diameter; leaves without greyish hairs, even along the veins .... **G. microcarpa**

24 Veins on the under surface clearly differentiated from the pale hairy surface, being either without hairs themselves, or with long brownish hairs standing away from the white leaf surface .. 25
   Veins on the under surface with pale hairs, blending in with the leaf surface 28

25 Sepals more than 2 cm long; under surface of leaves with very dense, yellowish-white, woolly hairs .... **G. hexamita**
   Sepals less than 2 cm long; hairs on the under surface fine, lying flattened against the leaf, not woolly 26

26 Leaves obliquely oblong to broadly obovate-oblong up to 14 cm long, with a velvety sheen, the veins on the under surface with conspicuous rusty-red stellate hairs; backs of the sepals with distinctive shaggy, yellowish woolly hairs .... **G. schinzii**
   Leaves oblong, oblong-obovate to elliptic, up to 9 cm or 18 cm long, without a velvety sheen, the veins on the under surface with grey or brown simple hairs, but without rusty-red stellate hairs; backs of the sepals without shaggy hairs 27

27 Leaves oblong to oblong-obovate, up to 18 cm long, veins on the under surface with fine greyish hairs, without longer tufts of brownish hairs in their axils; young branches with soft, woolly hairs .... **G. inaequilatera**
   Leaves oblong to elliptic, up to 9 cm long; veining on the under surface conspicuous brown, and with tufts of long, brownish hairs in their axils; young branches without soft, woolly hairs .. .. **G. micrantha**

28 Veins on the under surface covered with the white hairs, but with odd conspicuous tufts of long brown hairs in their axils .... **G. hornbyi**
   Under surface without brown hairs 29

29 Leaves elliptic, elliptic-oblong or lanceolate; base broadly tapering to rounded ... **G. bicolor**
   Leaves oblong, ovate to broadly obovate-oblong; base lobed 30

30 Leaves thinly textured, upper surface not wrinkled; margin regularly serrate **G. subspathulata**
   Leaves leathery, upper surface sometimes wrinkled or puckered; margin irregularly and coarsely toothed .... **G. monticola**

Grewia bicolor Juss.

[*G. kwebensis* N. E. Brown]
S.A. no: 458   Bastard brandybush. Basterrosyntjie
Rhod. no: 646   False brandybush

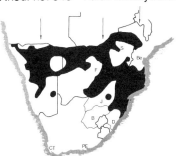
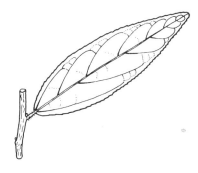

Usually a many-stemmed shrub, occasionally a small tree up to 7 m in height; occurring most frequently in dry deciduous woodland at low altitudes, on sandy flats and rocky mountain slopes; also **569**

at medium altitudes in high-rainfall areas, often associated with termite mounds and frequently in riverine fringes. **Bark:** dark grey, deeply fissured and peeling away in strips in old specimens, grey to reddish-grey and smooth when young. **Leaves:** elliptic to elliptic-oblong or lanceolate, 1,5 to 7 × 1 to 3,2 cm, dark dull green above, almost silvery-white with fine hairs below; the leaves are held horizontally or slightly drooping; apex tapering to rounded; base broadly tapering to rounded, asymmetric, or almost symmetric; margin finely toothed, occasionally almost entire; petiole very short. **Flowers:** yellow, 1,5 cm in diameter, axillary, often produced in profusion; the central mass of stamens characteristic of the genus (October to January). **Fruit:** single, or 2-lobed, each lobe about 6 mm in diameter, reddish-brown when mature, edible, sweetish but astringent. Fruits are frequently parasitised and develop a shaggy, bearded appearance (March to June).

In the Kruger National Park this species forms a distinct shrub layer below the tree canopy. The plant provides fibre for ropes and the root is used to treat chest complaints.

Grewia caffra Meissner
S.A. no: 459 Climbing raisin. Rankrosyntjie
Rhod. no: 647 Climbing grewia

Almost always a scrambling, many-stemmed shrub, sprawling over trees and bushes, very occasionally forming a small tree 2 to 4 m in height; occurring at low altitudes in bush clumps, in riverine fringes or at the margins of coastal dune forest; it can become locally sub-dominant and thicket forming. **Bark:** dark brown, rough; the stems are conspicuously square; the branchlets can become stout and spine-like. **Leaves:** oblong-ovate, 2,5 to 6 × 1,5 to 2,5 cm, the upper surface rather shiny green and without hairs, the under surface only slightly paler green with few to many stellate hairs especially along the veins; apex tapering; base tapering to rounded, usually almost symmetric; margin finely toothed; petiole up to 3 mm long. **Flowers:** yellow, sometimes pinkish, nearly 2 cm in diameter, in short, branched, axillary heads, on short stalks up to 7 mm long; the central mass of stamens characteristic of the genus (November to May). **Fruit:** almost spherical, up to 10 mm in diameter, yellow-brown to red when mature, the pedicel without hairs and the upper 2 to 4 mm of the stalk, immediately below the fruit, with dense, short hairs, visible with a 10x lens; edible (February to July).

Grewia flava DC.
S.A. no: 459,1 Brandybush. Wilderosyntjie
Rhod. no: 649 Brandybush

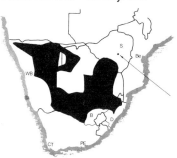

A compact shrub or small tree up to 4 m in height; occurring in dry, deciduous woodland and bushveld. **Bark:** dark grey-brown. **Leaves:** elliptic or oblanceolate, 1,4 to 7 × 0,7 to 2,5 cm, greyish-green and very finely hairy above, more densely hairy and quite markedly paler green below, the net-veining more or less conspicuous; apex rounded; base tapering, almost symmetric; margin finely to rather coarsely toothed; petiole up to 2 mm long. **Flowers:** yellow, about 1,5 cm in diameter, in short branched axillary heads; the sepals are yellow and contribute largely towards the colour of the flowers; stamens yellow in the central mass characteristic of the genus (October to March). **Fruit:** almost spherical, usually 2-lobed, about 8 mm in diameter, or, if single, then the old style is placed markedly on one side, red-brown when mature (December to April).

The leaves are very similar to those of *G. bicolor* but are held upright and not horizontally or slightly drooping as are those of the latter species. The bark provides a fibre from which baskets are woven and the frayed ends of small branches are used as toothbrushes. The fruits, which have only a thin layer of flesh, are edible and sweet although slightly astringent; they are dried, ground and made into porridge and also into beer and a potent alcoholic drink. Stamped and mixed with dried locusts, they are greatly esteemed by the Tswana as a delicacy while the leaves are heavily browsed on by game and stock, especially when grass is scarce. Pegs made from the wood of this tree are driven into the ground as a protection against lightning and in the death rites of the Kgakgadi peoples a small piece of the inner bark is tied to the right arm of the dead man and to that of each of his children.

Grewia flavescens Juss.

S.A. no: 459,2   Rough-leaved raisin. Skurweblaarrosyntjie
Rhod. no: 650   Donkeyberry

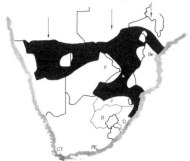

A shrub with a tendency to scramble, or a small shrubby tree up to 5 m in height; occurring at medium to low altitudes, in open woodland, frequently on termite mounds, on rocky koppies, in riverine fringes and at the margins of forest patches. **Bark:** dark grey-brown, with fluted ridges; the trunk and larger branches are square. **Leaves:** oblanceolate to obovate, 4 to 12 × 2 to 8,5 cm, but usually about 7 × 3 cm, or smaller, light green, stellate hairs on both surfaces, but especially on the under surface which is markedly rough to the touch; apex tapering; base rounded to lobed, almost symmetric; margin irregularly but markedly toothed; petiole up to 7 mm long, hairy. Stipules up to 10 mm long, oblong, hairy, but falling early. **Flowers:** yellow, about 2 cm in diameter, sometimes fragrant, axillary, usually in threes on short stalks, or peduncles, up to 1,5 cm long; sepals yellowish-green flushed with pink on the outside, yellow inside; petals yellow, about half the size of the sepals; stamens bright yellow in the central mass characteristic of the genus (December to March). **Fruit:** shallowly furrowed, 2-lobed, occasionally single, or 4-lobed; each lobe 8 to 14 mm in diameter, rather shiny yellowish-brown when mature, with sparse long, white hairs (July to August).

This species has been divided into two varieties:

var. *flavescens* – with narrower leaves, oblanceolate, oblong-lanceolate to obovate, with the base rounded or square; the single stalk, or peduncle, supporting the flower head is usually less than 10 mm long. Widespread.

var. *olukondae* (Schinz) Wild – the leaves are broader, almost circular, the base rounded but often lobed, and the peduncles often more than 10 mm long. Scattered through the Transvaal, Rhodesia, Botswana and South West Africa.

571

TILIACEAE

Grewia gracillima Wild
S.A. no: Silver square-stemmed raisin
Rhod. no: 651   Silver square-stemmed grewia

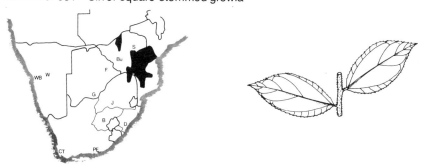

Usually a straggling shrub about 2 m in height with a tendency to scramble, but it may become a small tree up to 5 m; occurring in low altitude woodland, usually in sheltered places along stream banks or on densely wooded, rocky hillsides. **Bark:** grey to silvery-grey; stems frequently 4-angled. **Leaves:** generally rather small, lanceolate, 1,5 to 6 × 0,8 to 2,5 cm, light green, upper surface without hairs, lower surface with or without very sparse, simple hairs; apex tapering; base very broadly tapering, rounded to lobed, almost symmetric to asymmetric; margin toothed to scalloped; petiole 2 to 5 mm long. Stipules small, falling early. **Flowers:** yellow, about 1,3 cm in diameter, in 2- to 3-flowered, axillary heads; petals about half the length of the sepals, the stamens forming a central cone characteristic of the genus (October to February). **Fruit:** spherical, not lobed, about 8 mm in diameter, yellowish when mature; the top 2 to 4 mm of the stalk without hairs, but with a dense ring of short white hairs immediately below the fruit (February to June).

Grewia hexamita Burret
[*G. messinica* Burtt Davy & Greenway]
S.A. no: 460   Giant raisin. Reuserosyntjie
Rhod. no: 652   Large-flowered yellow grewia

A large shrub or small tree up to 5 m in height; occurring at low altitudes in deciduous woodland and in river valleys. **Bark:** reddish-brown, smooth, with conspicuous lenticels; branchlets covered with rusty woolly hairs. **Leaves:** elliptic or oblong-elliptic, up to 10 × 6 cm, but usually 4 to 6 cm long, upper surface shiny green, under surface with very dense, yellowish-white woolly hairs, the veins either white or yellowish-white with scattered brownish hairs, and very conspicuous; apex tapering to rounded; base markedly asymmetric, the one side tapering, the other deeply lobed; margin toothed, somewhat rolled under; petiole up to 3 mm long. **Flowers:** golden-yellow, 4 to 5 cm in diameter, axillary, 2 to 3 together on a short stalk; sepals golden-yellow, velvety on the back and smooth yellow inside; stamens forming a large central mass, the form characteristic of the genus; often produced in profusion (September to November). **Fruit:** deeply divided to almost completely divided into 2 berry-like lobes, occasionally only a single lobe, each lobe up to 1,5 cm in diameter, becoming yellowish-brown to reddish when mature (December to June).

Although the fruit has only a thin fleshy layer round the seed it is edible. This is a most attractive species with large, handsome flowers. It also occurs in Tanzania.

572

Grewia hornbyi Wild
S.A. no: —
Rhod. no: 653   Yellow and pink grewia

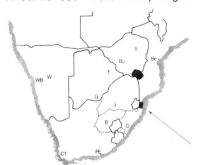 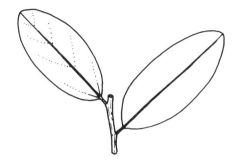

A shrub or small tree up to 4 m in height; occurring at low altitudes in deciduous woodland. **Bark:** grey to brown; young branchlets furry with short white hairs interspersed with scattered tufts of longer rusty hairs. **Leaves:** oblong-elliptic, 1,2 to 4 × 0,7 to 2,2 cm, shiny green above, furry below with dense white hairs which cover the veins as well, but often there are conspicuous tufts of longer brown hairs dotted in the axils of the veins; apex rounded; base rounded or shallowly lobed, asymmetric; margin toothed; petiole 2 to 3 mm long. **Flowers:** about 1 to 2 cm in diameter, yellow; or with the inside of the sepals yellow flushed with pink, the petals, about half the length of the sepals, salmon-pink to rose-pink and the stamens butter-yellow in the central mass characteristic of the genus; axillary (October). **Fruit:** deeply 2-lobed, each lobe about 4 mm in diameter, bright yellow when mature (February).

Grewia inaequilatera Garcke
S.A. no: 460,1   Bastard silver raisin. Bastervaalrosyntjie
Rhod. no: 654   Large-leaved yellow grewia

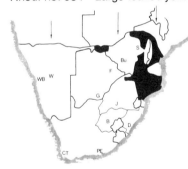 

A shrub or small tree up to 7 m in height; occurring at low altitudes in riverine forest and thicket, also in open mixed woodland. **Bark:** pale grey, smooth; branchlets with soft woolly hairs. **Leaves:** oblong to oblong-obovate, 5 to 18 × 2,5 to 7,5 cm, usually about 10 × 4 cm, uniformly green on both surfaces but with fine greyish hairs along the veins below; apex rounded, often abruptly attenuate; base rounded, markedly asymmetric; margin toothed, becoming almost entire near the base; petiole up to 10 mm long, hairy. Stipules very slender, up to 10 mm long, falling very early. **Flowers:** yellow, up to 3 cm in diameter, axillary, in groups of 2 to 3 together on a short stalk up to 10 mm long; sepals long and slender, yellow on the inside; stamens orange-yellow, forming a conspicuous central mass characteristic of the genus. The backs of the sepals and the flower stalks are conspicuously dotted with rusty, tufted hairs giving them a crusty appearance; the flowers are often borne in beautiful profusion (October to February). **Fruit:** deeply divided, almost forming 2 separate spherical berry-like lobes, each about 1,3 cm in diameter, yellow when mature, edible (April to July).

Grewia lasiocarpa E. Meyer ex Harvey   Illust. 181
S.A. no: 461   Forest raisin. Bosrosyntjie
Rhod. no: —

573

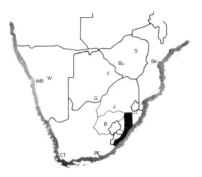 

A straggling bush or small tree up to 3 m in height; occurring at the margins of evergreen forests. **Bark:** grey, smooth; branchlets brown and rough with lenticels. **Leaves:** broadly ovate to almost circular, 4 to 12 × 4 to 12 cm, frequently about 8 × 6 cm, finely and harshly hairy above, slightly paler and softly hairy below; apex broadly tapering to rounded; base rounded, almost symmetric; margin finely toothed or scalloped; petiole 5 to 6 mm long, densely covered with tawny hairs. **Flowers:** attractive pink, up to 3,5 cm in diameter, axillary, in groups of 2 to 3 on slender stalks 1,5 cm long; the stalks and buds are covered with golden hairs; stamens in the central mass characteristic of the genus (January). **Fruit:** deeply furrowed forming twin lobes, each lobe about 1,5 cm in diameter, reddish when mature, with woolly hairs (June).

Grewia lepidopetala Garcke

S.A. no: —
Rhod. no: 655   Green-haired cross-berry

A scrambling shrub or small tree up to 4 m in height; occurring at low altitudes in riverine fringe forest, occasionally on termite mounds, and in river valleys in low rainfall areas. **Bark:** grey, smooth. **Leaves:** ovate, elliptic to oblong, 2,5 to 11 × 1,6 to 5, but usually about 7,5 × 3,5 cm, upper surface without hairs, the under surface with dense, fine, pale green hairs; apex abruptly tapering; base broadly tapering to rounded, almost symmetric to asymmetric; margin finely toothed; petiolate. **Flowers:** white to cream, 2,5 to 3 cm in diameter, the petals wrinkled, about one-third the length of the sepals, in groups of 3 to 9 on short stalks, 1,2 to 1,5 cm long, terminal or leaf-opposed; the central mass of stamens is characteristic of the genus (November to January). **Fruit:** deeply 4-lobed, about 1,5 cm in diameter, probably reddish-brown when mature (February to May).

Grewia micrantha Bojer

[*G. aurantiaca* Weimarck]
S.A. no: Golden raisin
Rhod. no: 656   Gold-fruited grewia

A shrubby tree, 2 to 5 m in height, often with drooping branches; occurring at medium to low altitudes in open woodland. **Bark:** dark grey, rough. **Leaves:** oblong to elliptic, 2,5 to 9 × 1,2 to 4,8 cm, usually about 5 to 6 cm long, the upper surface with or without sparse hairs, the under surface with dense white hairs together with sparse brown hairs along the veins and conspicuous pockets of long brown hairs in their axils; apex tapering to rounded; base rounded, asymmetric; margin toothed;

petiole up to 7 mm long. **Flowers:** yellow, about 2 cm in diameter, axillary, in groups of 2 to 3 on stalks up to 1,5 cm long, with coarse brown hairs; sepals yellow, petalloid; petals deeper yellow, about half the length of the sepals; the stamens forming a central mass characteristic of the genus (November to December). **Fruit:** almost spherical, deeply 2-lobed, almost forming separate fruits, each about 7 mm in diameter, velvety, yellow when mature, edible and pleasant tasting (January to June).

Grewia microcarpa K. Schum.
S.A. no: —
Rhod. no: 657   Northern pink grewia

A much-branched, many-stemmed shrub or small, dense tree up to 4 m in height; occurring in riverine fringes and open woodland where it can become thicket-forming. **Bark:** brown; the stems square, even fluted in older specimens. **Leaves:** elliptic to lanceolate, 1,5 to 6 × 0,7 to 3 cm, usually about 4 × 2,5 cm, glossy bright green and very finely hairy above, dull green and more densely hairy below, net-veining very fine and not conspicuous; apex tapering; base rounded, asymmetric; margin finely toothed; petiole 1 to 2 mm long. **Flowers:** small, but showy in profusion, bright golden-yellow, 1 to 1,5 cm in diameter, in axillary groups of 2 to 3 on a slender stalk up to 10 mm long; sepals petalloid; petals about one-third of the length of the sepals; stamens forming a central mass characteristic of the genus (October to November). **Fruit:** deeply 2-lobed, each lobe about 4 mm in diameter, reddish-brown when mature (February to March).

Grewia microthyrsa K. Schum. ex Burret
S.A. no: 461,1   Lebombo raisin. Lebomborosyntjie
Rhod. no: —

A shrub or small tree up to 4 m in height; occurring at low altitudes in areas of dry bush or woodland. **Bark:** pale grey. **Leaves:** oblong, 2 to 5,5 × 1,2 to 2,5 cm, both surfaces almost without hairs and the under surface only slightly paler green; apex rounded; base rounded, almost symmetric; margin obscurely toothed over the upper half, or almost entire; petiole about 5 mm long. **Flowers:** creamy-white to pale yellow, about 1 to 1,5 cm in diameter, in small terminal clusters; stamens in a central mass characteristic of the genus (October to January). **Fruit:** always single, narrowly pear-shaped, up to 1,3 × 0,7 cm, reddish-brown when mature, pendulous on distinctive, long, slender, curved pedicels (February to March).

575

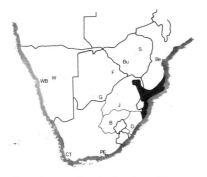

Grewia monticola Sonder   Illust. 179
[*G. obliqua* Weimarck]
S.A. no: 462   Silver raisin. Vaalrosyntjie
Rhod. no: 658   Grey grewia

A shrub or small tree sometimes reaching 8 m in height; occurring over a wide range of altitudes, in riverine fringes and in open woodland, often on termite mounds. **Bark:** dark brown or grey, rough; branchlets inclined to be drooping and densely covered with creamy or rusty woolly hairs. **Leaves:** obliquely elliptic-oblong, 2,5 to 9 × 1 to 5 cm, usually about 5 × 3 cm, leathery, bright green above, greyish to almost white below, finely hairy on both surfaces; veining pale yellow; apex tapering; base rounded or lobed, asymmetric; margin irregularly toothed; petiole 2 to 5 mm long. Stipules fall very early. **Flowers:** yellow, about 2 cm in diameter, in axillary groups of 2 to 3 on short stalks, sometimes 2 to 3 heads together in the single leaf axil; sepals and petals bright yellow, the petals about half the length of the sepals, very showy when the trees are covered with bloom; stamens forming a central mass characteristic of the genus (October to January). **Fruit:** single, or deeply 2-lobed, each lobe about 8 mm in diameter, reddish when mature (February to August).

The wood is red and handsome but the pieces are so small that they can be used only for objects such as walking sticks and assegai handles.

Grewia occidentalis L.   Illust. 180
[*G. chirindae* E. G. Baker; *G. microphylla* Weimarck; *G. rudatisii* Burret]
S.A. no: 463   Cross-berry. Kruisbessie
Rhod. no: 659   Cross-berry

A shrub with a tendency to scramble or a small tree up to 6 m in height, often with slender, drooping or trailing branches; occurring as a climber in closed evergreen forest, or a small tree or shrub at forest margins, in dry, open woodland or bush. **Bark:** pale, grey, smooth. **Leaves:** lanceolate to ovate, 2,5 to 7,5 × 1,5 to 4 cm, light green, the under surface only slightly paler green, thinly textured, with or without sparse hairs on both surfaces; apex tapering to rounded; base tapering, rounded or slightly lobed, almost symmetric; margin finely toothed to scalloped; petiole up to 1,3 cm long. **Flowers:** usually mauve, about 3,5 cm in diameter, in 1- to 3-flowered, leaf-opposed clusters on a stalk up to 1,5 cm long; the inner surface of the sepals and the petals pink, mauve, pale lavender, occasionally almost white, the stamens yellow in a tight central mass characteristic of the genus (October to January). **Fruit:** 4-lobed, characteristically square in shape, about 2,5 cm in diameter, reddish-brown to purplish when mature (January to May).

This species has been divided into two varieties, all the material in Rhodesia and South Africa being placed in the typical variety, var. *occidentalis;* the other variety, var. *littoralis* Wild, is a semi-prostrate shrub, confined to coastal sand dunes between Inhambane and Maputo in Moçambique. The Zulus dress wounds with the bruised bark which has been soaked in hot water and a decoction of the plant is taken to facilitate childbirth and also to remedy impotence and barrenness. The wood is made into assegai handles by the Xhosa while Bushmen use it to fashion their bows.

Grewia pachycalyx K. Schum.   Illust. 183

S.A. no: Large-flowered white cross-berry
Rhod. no: 660   Large-flowered white cross-berry

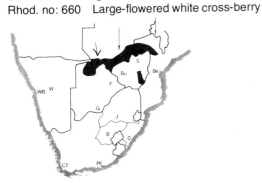

A many-stemmed shrub with a tendency to scramble, or a small bushy tree up to 6 m in height; occurring at low altitudes, often in river valleys where it may become thicket-forming. **Bark:** grey-brown; the branches often drooping. **Leaves:** oblong-lanceolate, 6 to 19 × 2,5 to 9 cm, most often about 8 × 3,5 cm, bright green on both surfaces, the veining prominent below, with fine hairs when young which are lost by maturity; apex tapering; base tapering to rounded, almost symmetric; margin finely toothed to scalloped; petioles up to 8 mm long, hairy. Stipules long, narrow, up to 1,4 cm, persisting for some time but falling eventually. **Flowers:** showy, white, 3 to 4 cm in diameter, in leaf-opposed groups of 3 to 9 on very short stalks; sepals thick, rather fleshy, green-backed, pure white within, curving slightly backwards but the very tip remaining thick and slightly curled forwards; petals broad, rather fragile, frilled and crinkled and, after the first 2 mm, curving sharply backwards to lie against the base of the sepals, this being the most conspicuous difference between this species and *G. stolzii;* stamens white, forming a central mass characteristic of the genus (January to March). **Fruit:** 4-lobed almost to the base, each lobe about 10 mm in diameter, shiny orange-red when mature (March to July).

Grewia praecox K. Schum.

[*G. congesta* Weimarck]
S.A. no: —
Rhod. no: 661   Rolled-leaf grewia

A shrub or small tree up to 4 m in height; occurring at low altitudes in dry types of woodland, frequently associated with termite mounds in riverine fringe thicket and on rocky koppies. **Bark:** light grey and smooth in young specimens, becoming dark brownish-grey and rough. **Leaves:** still half rolled at flowering time, mature leaves oblong to ovate-oblong, 5 to 6 × 2 to 5 cm, both surfaces

577

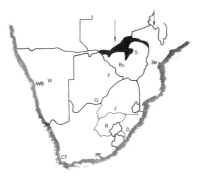
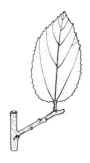

uniformly green and slightly velvety; apex tapering; base broadly tapering to rounded, almost symmetric; margin markedly and irregularly toothed; petiole 1 to 4 mm long. Stipules short, persistent, becoming dark brown and awl-shaped by the second year. **Flowers:** white, occasionally cream, up to 3,5 cm in diameter, faintly sweet-scented, axillary, usually solitary, rarely 2-flowered on very short stalks; sepals green and densely velvety outside, pure white within; petals less than half the length of the sepals; stamens white forming the central mass characteristic of the genus (September to December). **Fruit:** deeply 2- to 4-lobed, each lobe about 7 mm in diameter, becoming reddish when mature with scattered hairs (February to March).

The single seed in each lobe is surrounded by a thin layer of rather dry flesh which is said to be sweet and pleasantly flavoured.

Grewia retinervis Burret

S.A. no: 463,1   Kalahari sand raisin. Basterskurwerosyntjie
Rhod. no: 662   Kalahari sand grewia

A spreading shrub or small, bushy tree up to 4 m in height; occurring in open woodland, frequently associated with areas of Kalahari sand. **Bark:** brownish; the older branches do not become square, but tend to have grooves on two sides. **Leaves:** elliptic-oblong, 2,5 to 5 × 1 to 3 cm, stiffly textured with rather sparse but harsh hairs on both surfaces, most of which are lost by maturity, and which give a scabrid feel; net-veining above and below, sometimes very conspicuous; apex broadly tapering to rounded; base rounded, almost symmetric; margin toothed; petiole 1 to 3 mm long, hairy. Stipules up to 2,5 mm long, falling early. **Flowers:** bright yellow, about 1,5 cm in diameter, in axillary groups of 2 to 3 on short stalks about 6 mm long; sepals green and hairy on the outside, yellow within; petals almost as long as the sepals; stamens form a central mass characteristic of the genus (October to March). **Fruit:** always single, spherical, about 9 mm in diameter, orange-red to reddish-brown when mature, edible (February to May).

Grewia robusta Burch.

[*G. krebsiana* Kuntze]

S.A. no: Karoo cross-berry. Karookruisbessie
Rhod. no: —

Usually a dense rounded shrub, or a small tree up to 4 m in height; occurring in arid Karoo areas, often on stony hill slopes. **Bark:** grey; the branchlets rigidly twiggy and often spiny. **Leaves:** clustered on

578

dwarf, twiggy, lateral branchlets; broadly elliptic to ovate, 1,3 to 2,5 × 1 to 2 cm, leathery, shiny dark green above, rather paler blue-green below, with short hairs; apex broadly tapering; base rounded, sometimes lobed, almost symmetric; margin bluntly toothed to scalloped; petiole very short. **Flowers:** attractive, pink or purplish, up to 2,5 cm in diameter, sweetly scented, solitary, leaf-opposed or in groups of 2 to 3 on the dwarf side shoots; stamens in a central mass characteristic of the genus (August to December). **Fruit:** deeply 4-lobed, 1 to 2 cm in diameter, reddish-brown when mature (March to August).

This is a valuable fodder plant, both the leaves and the fruit being eaten by stock. It is easily cultivated and would be a worthwhile addition to any garden.

Grewia schinzii K. Schum.
S.A. no: Zambezi raisin. Zambezirosyntjie
Rhod. no: 663   Shaggy grewia

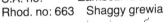

A many-stemmed shrub or small tree up to 5 m in height; occurring in open woodland, often associated with termite mounds, and along riverine fringe forest and thicket. **Bark:** dark brown, smooth, dotted with pale lenticels; branchlets covered with most conspicuous, tangled, shaggy, creamy-rusty, woolly hairs. **Leaves:** obliquely oblong to broadly obovate-oblong, 4 to 14 × 2,5 to 9 cm, but usually about 7 × 4 cm, leathery, mid-green above with a velvety sheen, densely white and velvety below, the lateral veins conspicuous with their rusty stellate hairs; apex tapering to rounded; base round to shallowly lobed, asymmetric; margin coarsely and irregularly toothed; petiole up to 10 mm long. **Flowers:** yellow, about 2,5 cm in diameter, in 2- to 3-flowered, axillary groups, on stalks up to 1,5 cm long; the backs of the sepals and the flower stalks are covered with characteristic shaggy, yellowish, woolly hairs; petals about two-thirds the length of the sepals; stamens in the central mass characteristic of the genus (November to January). **Fruit:** almost completely divided, forming twin berries joined only at the base, each about 10 mm in diameter, glossy yellow when mature with sparse long yellowish hairs; edible, but the flesh is rather dry and not palatable (April to June).

Grewia stolzii Ulbr.
[*G. hopkinsii* Suesseng.]
S.A. no: —
Rhod. no: 664   Green-petalled cross-berry

A straggling shrub or small tree, 3 to 4 m in height; occurring among rocks, in open woodland, frequently on termite mounds and at the margins of evergreen forest. **Bark:** dark grey-brown, with

579

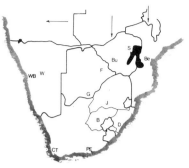 

pale lenticels. **Leaves:** elliptic-oblong, up to 12 × 5,5 cm, but usually about 8 × 4 cm, dark green on both surfaces, with sparse rough stellate hairs on the upper surface giving a scabrid feel, more densely so below; apex tapering; base broadly tapering to square, almost symmetric; margin irregularly and sharply toothed; petiole up to 7 mm long. Stipules short, falling early. **Flowers:** white to pale yellow, about 3 cm in diameter, in 2- to 5-flowered groups, on stalks up to 1,5 cm long, leaf-opposed or terminal; the colour is provided entirely by the inner surface of the sepals; petals small, greenish, triangular and upstanding; stamens in the characteristic central column barely spreading, white with yellow anthers (October to March). **Fruit:** markedly 4-lobed, each lobe about 10 mm in diameter, reddish when mature, slightly hairy, but with long russet hairs in the clefts between the lobes; edible (February to July).

Grewia subspathulata N. E. Brown
S.A. no: Hybrid raisin
Rhod. no: 665 Hybrid grewia

 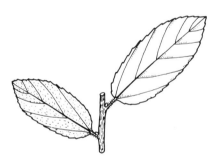

In all respects this plant appears to represent a hybrid between *G. monticola* and *G. bicolor;* its leaves are similar in shape to the former but it has the short soft grey hairs of the latter. Its leaves are not as thin as those of *G. bicolor,* but not as leathery as those of *G. monticola.* So far as is known, no one has attempted to hybridise the two parent species experimentally and until this is done the exact status of *G. subspathulata* must remain in doubt. Generally it occurs together with the two supposed parents, and apparently is not found on its own.

Grewia sulcata Mast.
S.A. no: Stellar cross-berry
Rhod. no: 666 Stellar cross-berry

A vigorous many-stemmed shrub 2 to 3 m in height, or a small tree reaching 5 m; occurring at low altitudes, in riverine fringes, along the sandy banks of the larger lowveld rivers and on coastal dunes. **Bark:** dark reddish-brown, speckled with conspicuous lenticels. **Leaves:** obovate to oblong, 2 to 7 × 1,5 to 4,5 cm, dull green above, only slightly paler green below, with scattered stellate hairs on both surfaces making them rough and harsh to the touch; lateral veins rather prominent below; apex broadly tapering to rounded; base rounded to shallowly lobed, asymmetric; margin scalloped to toothed; petiole up to 5 mm long. Stipules small, falling early. **Flowers:** usually white, but may be cream to almost yellow, up to 3,5 cm in diameter, in axillary and terminal groups of 3, on stalks up to 1,5 cm

580

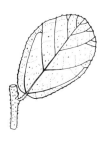

long with creamy-yellow rusty hairs, crowded at the ends of the branches; sepals white inside, pale green with rusty woolly hairs on the back; petals white up to 1,3 cm long; stamens forming the characteristic central column and only slightly spreading (May to August). **Fruit:** usually deeply divided into 4 lobes, sometimes only 2, each lobe about 8 mm in diameter; quite frequently the dry stamens remain round the base of the fruit giving it a wispy look; becoming reddish-brown and slightly fleshy when mature (June to September).

Africans drink a weak, tea-like infusion of the fruits.

Grewia tenax (Forsk.) Fiori

S.A. no: Small-leaved white cross-berry
Rhod. no: 667 Small-leaved white cross-berry

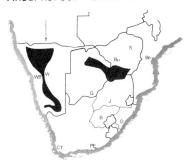

A shrub or small tree, 1 to 3 m in height; occurring in very dry woodland or semi-desert scrub. **Bark:** pale reddish-brown, very finely fissured, lenticellate. **Leaves:** small, broadly oval to obovate, up to 3 × 3 cm, but frequently 1,5 × 1 cm, grey-green, leathery, slightly hairy particularly on the under surface; apex rounded; base broadly tapering to rounded, almost symmetric; margin coarsely toothed; petiole up to 10 mm long. Stipules very small, falling early. **Flowers:** white, 2 to 3 cm in diameter, solitary, leaf-opposed; the inside of the sepals and the petals white, petals narrow; stamens form a short central cone characteristic of the genus (December to May). **Fruit:** so deeply 4-lobed as to give the impression of a tight cluster of 4 berries, each about 10 mm in diameter, shiny bright orange-red when mature; edible (February to June).

Grewia transzambesica Wild

S.A. no: —
Rhod. no: — Coastal-plain grewia

A shrub or small tree up to 7 m in height; occurring in open *Brachystegia* woodland on the coastal plain. **Bark:** brown to grey-brown. **Leaves:** lanceolate to almost ovate, 4 to 10 × 2 to 6 cm, the upper surface with minute scattered hairs especially along the veins, the lower surface more densely hairy, with 3 conspicuous veins; apex tapering to broadly so; base rounded or slightly lobed, almost symmetric; margin shallowly toothed or scalloped; petiole up to 6 mm long, finely hairy. **Flowers:** white, about 1 to 1,5 cm in diameter, in short axillary or terminal branched heads; stamens form the characteristic central mass (February to March). **Fruit:** single-lobed, pear-shaped, finely velvety, about 10 × 7 mm, pendulous on slender stalks (February to April).

581

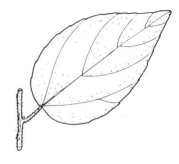

Grewia villosa Willd.
S.A. no: 463,2   Mallow raisin. Malvarosyntjie
Rhod. no: 668   Mallow-leaved cross-berry

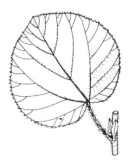

A much-branched shrub to small tree up to 4 m in height; occurring in low altitude mixed woodland. **Bark:** grey; branchlets covered with yellowish silky hairs. **Leaves:** almost circular, up to 12 cm in diameter but usually about 6 × 6 cm, grey-green, the upper surface rather puckered, the lower surface markedly paler with rough, grey, whitish to cream or rusty hairs and conspicuous net-veining; apex rounded; base slightly lobed, almost symmetric; margin toothed; petiole up to 4 cm long, hairy. Stipules ovate, up to 10 mm long, membraneous, persisting for some time. **Flowers:** yellow, about 2 cm in diameter, in very close, tight clusters, on a short stalk, or peduncle, about 5 mm long; the petals are about half the length of the sepals and both are yellow inside, turning pink very soon; the backs of the sepals have long silky brownish-green hairs making the flowers, which seldom open out fully, appear a dull brownish-yellow; the stamens form the central mass characteristic of the genus (November to March). **Fruit:** very shallowly 4-lobed, 1 to 1,5 cm in diameter, reddish when mature, with sparse long silky hairs; edible (April to May).

MALVACEAE *(The hibiscus and mallow family)*

Key to the genera:

1 Fruits indehiscent, rather fleshy .... **3. Thespesia**

　Fruits dehiscent 2

2 Ovary and fruit made up of 18 to 24 carpels opening by apical slits, joined to form a flattened, disc-shaped ring .... **1. Abutilon**

　Ovary and fruits spherical to ovoid; fruit a capsule 3

3 Fruits ovoid and narrowly tapering to the apex, about 3 × 2 cm; if almost spherical then small, about 1,3 × 1,2 cm. Sepals persistent, and conspicuous, up to 3 cm long, strap-shaped, partially surrounding the fruit; fruit and calyx lobes covered with shaggy or velvety golden hairs ....
.... **2. Hibiscus**

　Fruits spherical, about 4 × 3 cm; calyx base persistent, short, cup-shaped; fruit covered with short, dull green, felted hairs .... **4. Azanza**

582

1. ABUTILON Miller

Abutilon matopense Gibbs
S.A. no: Wild abutilon
Rhod. no: 671   Wild abutilon

A bushy shrub, or small tree up to 3 m frequently much-branched from the base; occurring on rocky slopes and among boulders, occasionally in riverine fringes, when the leaves tend to become larger and softer. **Bark:** greyish-brown, smooth. **Leaves:** alternate, simple, often crowded near the tips of the branches, broadly ovate, 2 to 10 × 1,5 to 9 cm, thinly textured and softly velvety, grey-green above, paler green below; 5- to 7-veined from the base; apex broadly tapering to almost rounded; base lobed to deeply lobed; margin obscurely toothed to scalloped; petiole slender, 0,5 to 6 cm long. **Flowers:** attractive, pale apricot to bright yellow, 2 to 4 cm in diameter, in clusters of 1 to 4 on short, leafy shoots. Bisexual; all floral parts in fives; calyx tube bell-shaped, usually hairy, 5-lobed; petals broad, longer than the calyx, joined at the base and attached to the staminal tube which separates at the apex into many filaments; ovary of up to 24 carpels, joined to form a ring round a central raised cushion. The flowers open in the afternoon and evening (October to May). **Fruit:** separating into greenish to blackish flattened, rather disc-shaped mericarps, about 1,4 cm in diameter, which open by apical slits when mature (May to August).

2. HIBISCUS L.

Herbs, shrubs, or trees, sometimes shooting from an underground woody root stock. **Leaves:** alternate, simple, 3- to 7-veined from the base. Stipules small, narrow and hair-like or broad, falling early. **Flowers:** large, attractive, axillary, solitary or in few-flowered heads, or racemes. Bisexual; all floral parts in fives; epicalyx with 5 to 20 segments, calyx tube bell-shaped; separating into 5 lanceolate lobes; petals large, spreading, showy; stamens joined to form a tube; ovary of 4 to 5 fused carpels. **Fruit:** a 4- to 5-valved dehiscent capsule surrounded by the remains of the persistent calyx lobes.

Key to the tree species of *Hibiscus:*
1 Flowers, fruits and young leaves with short velvety hairs; leaves almost circular, margin usually
   entire or minutely toothed, not lobed (except basally) .... **H. tiliaceus**
  Flowers, fruits and all young parts with very conspicuous, long, shaggy, golden hairs; leaves
   usually deeply 3- to 5-lobed; margin toothed 2
2 Branchlets densely covered with sharp prickles; leaves 3- to 7-lobed, broadly ovate to almost
   circular .... **H. diversifolius**
  Branchlets not covered with prickles; leaves usually deeply 3-lobed, occasionally obscurely
   5-lobed .... **H. burtt-davyi**

Hibiscus burtt-davyi Dunkley
S.A. no: —
Rhod. no: 674   Chimanimani tree hibiscus

A shrub or small tree up to 7 m in height; occurring on rocky hillsides, at the margins of *Widdring-tonia/Podocarpus* forest between altitudes of 1 500 and 2 100 m. **Bark:** grey to brown; the stems with dense yellowish hairs, sometimes sticky. **Leaves:** broadly elliptic to almost circular, up to 10 ×

583

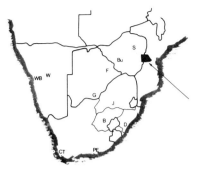

8 cm, usually deeply 3-lobed, occasionally obscurely 5-lobed, with stellate hairs on both surfaces; apex tapering; base rounded to square; margin irregularly to coarsely toothed; petiole up to 5 cm long, with yellowish hairs. **Flowers:** pink or white, up to 5 cm in diameter, axillary, solitary or in short 3- to 5-flowered heads (July). **Fruit:** a silky capsule, with long, shaggy golden hairs; almost spherical, 1,3 × 1,2 cm (August to September).

Hibiscus diversifolius Jacq.
S.A. no: Prickly tree hibiscus
Rhod. no: 676   Prickly tree hibiscus

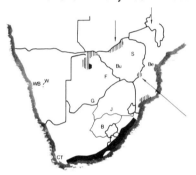

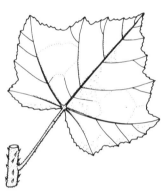

A shrub, often scrambling, or a small to medium sized tree up to 10 m in height; occurring in damp places, along rivers or lining lakes, and in thickets. **Bark:** brownish-grey; young branches hairy and densely covered with prickles. **Leaves:** broadly ovate to almost circular, up to 16 × 16 cm, with 3 to 7 distinct lobes, the upper surface with short stellate hairs, the under surface with longer stellate hairs and a gland near the base of the midrib; apex broadly tapering to rounded; base square to lobed; margin irregularly toothed to scalloped; petiole up to 12 cm long, hairy. **Flowers:** yellow or purplish with a dark red or purple centre, up to 8 cm long, calyx lobes with long, shaggy golden hairs; axillary, solitary, but occasionally giving the impression of a spray at the ends of the branches (July to October). **Fruit:** an ovoid capsule, about 2 cm long, sharply pointed, densely covered with silky golden hairs (August to December).
This species has been divided into two subspecies:

subsp. *diversifolius* – (refer to the black area on the map) stems sparsely hairy and flowers yellow with a maroon centre.

subsp. *rivularis* (Bremek. & Oberm.) Exell – (refer to the vertical lines on the map) stems more densely hairy, leaves with dense, short to long hairs and flowers reddish to purple with darker purple centres.

Hibiscus tiliaceus L.   Illust. 182
S.A. no: 464   Coast hibiscus. Wildekatoenboom
Rhod. no: —

A stout shrub or small tree up to 6 m in height; occurring along the coast often fringing estuaries and tidal rivers. **Bark:** pale greyish-brown, smooth; young branches, leaves and flower buds densely

covered with short soft hairs. **Leaves:** almost circular, or broader than long, up to 15 × 15 cm, paler green below than above, with short soft hairs on both surfaces; apex abruptly pointed; base deeply lobed; margin entire or minutely toothed; petiole up to 12 cm long. Stipules broad, sheathing, up to 3 × 1,5 cm, falling early. **Flowers:** large, showy, yellow aging to apricot, up to 12 cm in diameter, with a deep maroon or blackish centre (September to February). **Fruit:** ovoid, 2 to 2,5 cm long, tapering to the apex, covered with short, yellowish hairs (September to March).

The stems and the branches are long and flexuous and are valued by Africans for their fibre which makes excellent string and rope. This species of *Hibiscus* forms a strong link with the genus *Azanza*.

3. THESPESIA Solander ex Corr.

Shrubs or trees. **Leaves:** alternate, simple, 5- or more veined from the base. Stipules small, hair-like, falling early. **Flowers:** large, showy, yellow, axillary; solitary or in pairs. Bisexual; all floral parts in fives; epicalyx of 3 to 8 small segments, often falling early; calyx saucer-shaped, sometimes minutely toothed; petals large, overlapping; stamens joined to form a tube, with filaments partially free over almost the whole length of the tube; ovary of 5 fused carpels. **Fruit:** a large, semi-woody or rather fleshy, almost spherical capsule, indehiscent.

Key to the tree species of *Thespesia:*
Leaves usually 3-lobed, up to 7 × 6 cm; flowers up to 6 cm in diameter; buds scale-dotted and finely
  hairy .... **T. acutiloba**
Leaves usually entire, up to 15 × 12 cm; flowers up to 8 cm in diameter; buds scale-dotted but
  without the fine hairs .... **T. populnea**

Thespesia acutiloba (E. G. Baker) Exell & Mendonça
S.A. no: 465   Wild tulip tree. Wildetulpboom
Rhod. no: —

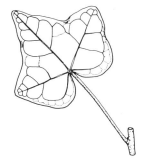

A shrub or small tree usually 3 to 4 m in height, but sometimes reaching 6 m; occurring in coastal dune forest and at the fringes of mangrove swamps. **Bark:** grey, deeply longitudinally furrowed; branchlets grey and scale-dotted. **Leaves:** almost spherical, tending to be 3-lobed, up to 7 × 6 cm, with small, white scales on both surfaces; apex tapering and the apices of the lobes also tapering; base square to lobed; margin of the lobes entire; petiole up to 4,5 cm long. **Flowers:** showy, yellow, up to 6 cm in diameter, with no dark central spot, axillary, solitary or in pairs, often resembling a terminal

585

spray, appearing when the tree is leafless; the buds scale-dotted and finely hairy (January to April). **Fruit:** almost spherical, smooth, about 1,5 to 2 cm in diameter, conspicuous, somewhat fleshy, bright red when mature (February to June).

The heartwood is dark and becomes hard and durable when seasoned; it has been used for carving, to make spears, sticks and musical instruments. The roots soaked in water provide a refreshing bath which is believed to dispel troublesome spirits. The tree is easily cultivated and would make a good garden subject.

Thespesia populnea (L.) Solander ex Corr.

S.A. no: —
Rhod. no: —   Large-leaved tulip tree

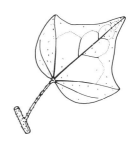

A shrub or small tree 3 to 4 m in height; occurring at the edge of mangrove swamps and along tidal waters. **Bark:** brown. **Leaves:** ovate, up to 15 × 12 cm, densely dotted with small whitish scales on both surfaces; apex abruptly pointed; base lobed; margin entire; petiole up to 9 cm long, scale-dotted. **Flowers:** yellow, with no dark central spot, up to 8 cm in diameter, axillary, solitary; buds scale-dotted, without fine hairs (February to March). **Fruit:** almost spherical, about 2 cm in diameter, yellowish to brownish-green when mature (March to June).

4. AZANZA Alef.

Azanza garckeana (F. Hoffm.) Exell & Hillcoat   Illust. 184
[*Thespesia garckeana* F. Hoffm.]
S.A. no: 466   Snot apple. Snotappel
Rhod. no: 682   Azanza

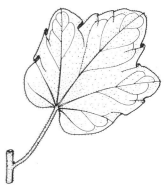

A bushy shrub or small to medium sized tree 3 to 10 m in height; occurring in almost all types of woodland from sea level to about 1 700 m, scattered and never dominant. **Bark:** brown, rough; branchlets with shaggy, woolly hairs. **Leaves:** alternate, simple, 3- to 5-lobed, up to 20 × 20 cm, but usually about 8 to 12 cm long, the upper surface with harsh stellate hairs, the under surface with soft hairs; 3- or more veined from the base; apex of the lobes bluntly tapering to rounded; base lobed; margin entire; petiole up to 13 cm long. Stipules up to 7 mm long, very slender or sickle-shaped, falling early. **Flowers:** showy, yellow, aging to orange-red, with a maroon patch at the base of each petal; up to 6 cm in diameter but not expanding fully, axillary, solitary. Bisexual; all floral parts in fives; epicalyx fused with the calyx which is cup-shaped, short, almost without lobes; petals large,

586

crinkly, overlapping; stamens joined to form a tube, the free filaments arising near the tip of the tube; ovary 5-chambered (December to May). **Fruit:** an almost spherical, woody capsule, 2,5 to 4 cm in diameter, with dense short hairs, clearly divided into 5 sections, yellowish to brownish-green when mature, rather tardily dehiscent (February to September).

Despite their hard woody nature, the fruits are edible. The whole fruit, except the seeds, is chewed like chewing gum and a sweet glutinous slime is produced; the Ndebele name *uxhakhuxhaku* represents the noise made when chewing the fruit. The wood has little value, but has been used for making implement handles and the inner bark provides a fibre. The tree is a host to the cotton stainer, a red and black bug, and is therefore unpopular in cotton producing areas.

BOMBACACEAE *(The baobab family)*

Key to the genera (exotic species marked*):

1 Flowers small, up to 3 cm in diameter; stamens 15 only, united into 5 groups, each resembling a single stamen .... **3. *Ceiba**

   Flowers large, 4,5 to 15 cm in diameter; stamens many 2

2 Fruits indehiscent, with floury, acid pulp; calyx deeply 5-lobed, not continuing growth with the fruit .... **1. Adansonia**

   Fruits dehiscent, full of silky woolly hairs; calyx only shortly lobed, continuing growth with the fruit .... **2. Rhodognaphalon**

1. ADANSONIA L.

Adansonia digitata L.   Illust. 185
S.A. no: 467   Baobab. Kremetartboom
Rhod. no: 684   Baobab

A comparatively short, but grotesquely fat tree, about 10 to 15 m in height, the bole in large specimens being about 28 m in circumference; occurring at low altitudes, in hot dry woodland. **Bark:** pinkish-grey or coppery, smooth, heavily folded. **Leaves:** alternate, digitately 3- to 9-foliolate; leaflets oblong to ovate, 5 to 15 × 3 to 7 cm, the lower leaflets being the smallest, the terminal leaflet the largest, dark green, with short soft hairs; lateral veins looping; apex and base tapering; margin entire; petiolules absent, or almost so, petiole up to 12 cm long. **Flowers:** waxy white, up to 20 cm in diameter, axillary, solitary, pendulous. Bisexual; all floral parts in fives; calyx deeply lobed, with white silky hairs inside; petals large, crinkly, spreading, stamens many, on a central column which is shed with the petals; ovary 5- to 10-chambered. The petals bruise easily and become brown, and the flowers have an unpleasant scent; it seems likely that they are pollinated by bats (October to December). **Fruit:** ovoid, 12 cm or more in length, with a hard woody shell, covered with yellowish-grey velvety hairs, indehiscent (April to May).

The seeds are embedded in a whitish powdery pulp which contains appreciable quantities of tartaric acid and potassium bitartrate; they are refreshing to suck, and when soaked in water make a palatable drink which has been used to treat fevers and scorbutic complaints. Recent work with carbon-dating and the examination of core samples from the stems indicate that there may be annular rings of a sort, **587** and that very large specimens – those with a diameter of 8 m – may well be over 3 000 years old. Indeed, some Africans believe that there is no longer any such thing as a young baobab. The bark is soft and fibrous and, after pounding, makes excellent rope and floor mats. It would also prove suitable for paper manufacture but other sources are more plentiful and easier to obtain. The vitality of these trees is remarkable: even when the interior has been burnt out they continue to flourish and on occasion the hollow trunks have served as houses, prisons, storage barns and even places of refuge from marauding wild animals. Old trees collapse into mounds of fibrous pulp and after the great frost of 1968 had killed many specimens in Rhodesia there were several authentic reports of dead trees bursting into flame by spontaneous combustion. In fact there are those who maintain that all old baobabs are consumed by fire in this dramatic manner but there is little substance to the story. Nevertheless, it is small wonder that these extraordinary trees are surrounded by a wealth of African legend and superstition. There is a well-known tale that God planted them upside down and another that a lion will devour anyone rash enough to pluck a flower from a baobab tree for the blossoms are believed to be inhabited by spirits. It is said that a draught of water in which the seeds have been soaked and stirred about will act as protection against attack by a crocodile, and that a man who drinks an infusion of the bark will become mighty and strong. Seeds of the baobab germinate fairly easily and, given good treatment, plants reach 7 m in 20 years. These trees are protected in South Africa.

2. RHODOGNAPHALON (Ulbr.) Roberty emend. A. Robyns

A. Robyns, in *Bull. Jard. Bot. Brux.* **33** : 253-272 (1963) separates *Rhodognaphalon* from *Bombax* by its persistent calyx which continues to grow with the fruit, and by differences in the pollen.

Rhodognaphalon schumannianum A. Robyns
S.A. no: —
Rhod. no: —   Fleece-fruit

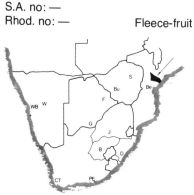

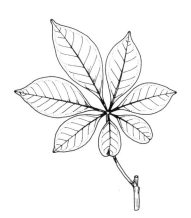

A medium to large tree 15 to 35 m tall; occurring in dry open woodland. **Bark:** greenish-yellow, smooth. **Leaves:** alternate to scattered, digitately 3- to 7-foliolate; leaflets oblong-elliptic, up to 7 × 1,8 cm; apex broadly tapering, abruptly attenuate forming a short slender tip; base tapering; margin entire; petiolule about 10 mm long, petiole up to 7 cm long. **Flowers:** striking, pale yellow to apricot, up to 18 cm in diameter with red stamens, axillary, solitary or in groups of 2 to 5. Bisexual; all floral parts in fives; calyx very shortly lobed, persistent, continuing growth with the fruit; petals narrow, strap-like; stamens many, straight, protruding for about 6 cm from the mouth of the flower; ovary 5-chambered (July to October). **Fruit:** an oval, 5-valved, woody capsule, about 6 × 3 cm, splitting to release numerous smooth brown seeds, all embedded in a fleecy pile of pale reddish-brown silky hairs or wool (September to December).

The specimens seen, which were gathered south of the Zambezi River, were sterile, but it seems likely that they would be *R. schumannianum* A. Robyns; the latter species includes the material previously identified as *Bombax rhodognaphalon* K. Schum. var. *rhodognaphalon*. The other variety, var. *tomentosum* A. Robyns, is probably a synonym of *Rhodognaphalon stolzii* (Ulbr.) A. Robyns, which does not occur south of the Zambezi River.

3. *CEIBA Miller

*Ceiba pentandra (L.) Gaertn.

The kapok tree from tropical America, Africa and India, now widely cultivated throughout the tropics for its kapok fibre, was introduced into southern Africa and there are several records of its having escaped in the Manica e Sofala and Sul do Save provinces of Moçambique.

STERCULIACEAE *(The cacao family)*

Key to the genera:

1 Leaves broadly ovate to almost circular; width more than half the length; may be lobed, occasionally completely divided to form 3 to 7 digitate leaflets 2

   Leaves elliptic, lanceolate to oblanceolate, width always less than half the length; not lobed . 4

2 Leaves with shallow lobes or without lobes, although the margins may be jaggedly toothed; petals less than 2 cm long, persistent, becoming papery; fruit an ovoid to almost spherical capsule, not more than 10 mm in diameter .... **1. Dombeya**

   Leaves markedly and deeply 3- to 9-lobed, occasionally the division becoming complete and so forming separate digitate leaflets; petals about 3,5 × 2,5 cm, or absent; fruit either a large, woody capsule always more than 3 cm long, or a conspicuous capsule with a large wing up to 9 × 3,5 cm 3

3 Flowers without petals; fruits made up of boat-shaped carpels in clusters of 2 to 5, splitting down one side only .... **3. Sterculia**

   Flowers with large petals about 3,5 × 2,5 cm; fruits a cluster of 4 to 5 carpels, indehiscent, each with a wing up to 9 × 3,5 cm .... **2. Triplochiton**

4 A tree of evergreen forest and sand forest; fruiting carpels not strongly keeled .... **4. Cola**

   A tree of mangrove swamps; fruits strongly keeled .... **5. Heritiera**

1. DOMBEYA Cav.

Shrubs or trees. **Leaves:** alternate, simple. Stipules may be conspicuous. **Flowers:** in axillary or terminal cymes or panicles. Bisexual; bracts 3, free, sometimes large, falling early; all floral parts in fives; calyx lobed, the lobes bent back in the mature flowers; petals showy, obliquely asymmetric, persistent, becoming papery; stamens united at the base, in groups of 2 to 3, alternating with 5 narrow staminodes; ovary 3- to 5-chambered. **Fruit:** a small capsule, dehiscent, up to 10 mm in diameter.

Key to the tree species of *Dombeya:*

1 Leaves small, up to 5 cm long 2
   Leaves more than 5 cm long, often large, up to 20 cm long 4
2 Flowers large, 3 to 4,5 cm or more in diameter; bark dark and rough .... **D. tiliacea**
   Flowers small, less than 1,3 cm in diameter; bark pale, smooth 3
3 Leaves ovate, apex tapering to attenuate; bark pale whitish, cream to brown and smooth. Occurring from the eastern Cape to the eastern Transvaal and southern Moçambique ...... **D. cymosa**
   Leaves almost circular; bark grey and smooth. Restricted to a small area near Lydenburg and Letaba in the eastern Transvaal. .... **D. autumnalis**
4 Flowers small, about 1,3 cm in diameter 5
   Flowers more than 1,3 cm in diameter 6
5 Leaves harshly hairy above, with soft rather sparse hairs below .... **D. kirkii**
   Leaves almost without hairs .... **D. cymosa**
6 Flowers usually 1,3 to 2 cm in diameter 7
   Flowers usually 2,5 cm or more in diameter 8

589

7 Ovary with hairs (10x lens). Occurring in open woodland, grassland and bush in areas of medium to low rainfall .... **D. rotundifolia**

Ovary without hairs, but covered with minute brown protuberances which are thickened towards the end. Occurring in woodland and at the margin of evergreen forest in areas of high rainfall .... **D. shupangae**

8 Leaves usually about 3,5 × 2,5 cm, but may reach 8 × 5,5 cm; bark dark grey and rough ... . **D. tiliacea**

Leaves 10 to 12 cm in diameter or may reach 20 cm; bark reddish-brown and smooth tending to become warty with age 9

9 Under surface of the leaves conspicuously pale, often white; flowers always white, although they may have a rose-pink centre .... **D. pulchra**

Under surface of the leaves not conspicuously pale, may be rusty; flowers white to pale or deep pink .... **D. burgessiae**

Dombeya autumnalis Verdoorn
S.A. no: 468   Autumn dombeya. Rotsdrolpeer
Rhod. no: —

A shrub or small tree up to 5 m in height; occurring on rocky, wooded hillsides and in riverine fringes. This species closely resembles *D. rotundifolia,* from which it differs in the following respects: The flowers are smaller and are produced in late summer and autumn among the leaves (the specific name refers to this) and not in spring before the leaves; it does not develop a rough bark and the under surface of the leaves lack the clear net-veining seen in *D. rotundifolia.*

Dombeya burgessiae Gerr. ex Harvey   Illust. 186
[*D. rosea* E. G. Baker]
S.A. no: 468,1   Pink dombeya. Persdrolpeer
Rhod. no: 685   Pink dombeya

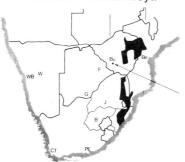 

A large bushy shrub or small tree up to 5 m in height; occurring on rocky koppies, along streams where the tree cover is not thick, in open woodland and at the margin of evergreen forest. **Bark:** reddish-brown, smooth, tending to become warty with age. **Leaves:** conspicuously large, ovate, 5 to 18 × 5 to 18 cm, usually about 10 to 12 cm in diameter, bluntly 3- to 5-lobed, darkish green above, under surface not conspicuously paler but may be rusty; sparsely hairy on both surfaces; apex broadly tapering; base lobed; margin scalloped or entire; petiole up to 12 cm long. Stipules up to 1,5 cm long,

590

falling early. **Flowers:** rose-pink, pale pink, sometimes white, up to 3 to 5 cm in diameter, very showy, in many-flowered axillary heads (April to July). **Fruit:** a small capsule, 7 to 10 mm in diameter, velvety, covered with tawny hairs, splitting to release dark brown seeds (June to October). This is a very variable species; it is most striking and attractive and is widely cultivated. The bark provides a useful fibre. White-flowered forms of this species closely resemble *D. pulchra*, but the leaves of the latter have very pale under surfaces.

Dombeya cymosa Harvey
S.A. no: 469   Natal dombeya. Nataldrolpeer
Rhod. no: —

A shrub to small tree usually up to 8 m in height, only occasionally reaching 10 m; occurring in coastal bush or, further inland, along river and stream banks. **Bark:** pale whitish, cream to brown, smooth. **Leaves:** ovate, 3 to 10 × 2 to 7,5 cm, usually about 4,5 × 3,5 cm, almost without hairs; apex tapering to attenuate; base square to shallowly lobed; margin scalloped; petiole slender, 1,5 to 4 cm long. **Flowers:** white, about 1 to 1,3 cm in diameter, in axillary heads, often produced in profusion, sweetly scented (March to September). **Fruit:** a small capsule, about 3 to 4 mm in diameter, covered with short soft whitish hairs (May to September).

Dombeya kirkii Mast.
S.A. no: 470   River dombeya. Rivierdrolpeer
Rhod. no: 686   River dombeya

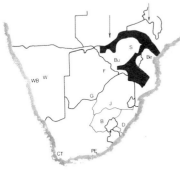
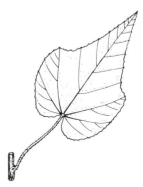

A much-branched shrub or small tree usually 3 to 5 m in height, but reaching 9 m under favourable conditions; occurring at altitudes of up to 1 000 m in riverine thicket. **Bark:** light grey, greyish-brown to dark brown, smooth; young branchlets densely hairy. **Leaves:** broadly ovate, 5 to 13 × 4 to 10 cm, usually about 8 × 6 cm, occasionally shallowly 3-lobed, the upper surface harshly hairy, the under surface with rather sparse soft hairs; apex tapering, usually attenuate; base lobed; margin scalloped or toothed; petiole up to 5,5 cm long. **Flowers:** white, about 1,3 cm in diameter, produced in striking profusion, in many-flowered axillary heads near the tips of the branches, giving the impression of large terminal clusters (March to June). **Fruit:** a small silky hairy capsule, somewhat 3-lobed, about 5 mm in diameter (April to August).
This species somewhat resembles *D. cymosa* but the leaves and calyces are larger, and these and the flower stalks are much more hairy, having a mixture of long and short hairs.

591

STERCULIACEAE

Dombeya pulchra N. E. Brown
S.A. no: 470,1   Silver dombeya. Blombos
Rhod. no: —

A shrub or small tree up to 5 m in height; occurring in wooded river valleys and along stream banks, also on mountainsides at high altitudes. This species strongly resembles the white-flowered forms of *D. burgessiae* but the flowers are always white, although sometimes they have a deep rose centre, and the under surface of the leaves is conspicuously pale, very often white and covered with close short soft hairs. **Flowers:** (December to May). **Fruit:** a small capsule covered with yellowish hairs, about 7 mm in diameter (March to June).

Dombeya rotundifolia (Hochst.) Planchon   Illust. 187
S.A. no: 471   Wild pear. Gewone drolpeer
Rhod. no: 687   Wild pear

A shapely small tree usually 4 to 5 m in height but occasionally reaching 8 m; occurring over a wide range of altitudes, in woodland and wooded grassland, often on termite mounds. **Bark:** dark brown, deeply longitudinally furrowed. **Leaves:** broadly ovate to almost circular, 3 to 15 cm in diameter, strongly 5-veined from the base, upper surface rather rough and dark green, under surface paler green with soft rather long hairs; leathery; apex broadly tapering to rounded; base lobed; margin irregularly toothed to almost entire; petiole up to 8 cm long. **Flowers:** white, rarely pale pink, 1,5 to 2 cm in diameter, in many-flowered axillary branched heads, about 7 × 6 cm, appearing before the leaves; sweetly scented (July to October). **Fruit:** an almost spherical capsule, about 6 mm in diameter, with silky hairs, dark when mature (October to December).

This species closely resembles *D. autumnalis* and the differences are discussed under that species. There is a variety, var. *velutina* Verdoorn, in which the ovary is covered with short stellate hairs instead of silky ones; it is a tall several-stemmed shrub occurring only in one river valley in the Naukluft mountains near Rehoboth in South West Africa.

The wood is blue-grey, heavy, strong, very tough and cross-grained; it has some potential as a general purpose timber, but the pieces are usually too small and twisted to be of any value; however, Africans make bows and implement handles from it. The Zulus use an infusion of the bark or wood to treat intestinal ulcers and Shangaan women drink a decoction of the bark to hasten the onset of labour. This is one of the earliest of the spring flowering trees, forming conspicuous patches of snowy white. It is easily raised from seed, which should be planted in September, and is quite fast-growing under garden conditions. It is hardy, being able to withstand several degrees of frost and is fire-resistant.

592

Dombeya shupangae K. Schum.
S.A. no: —
Rhod. no: —   Large-leaved dombeya

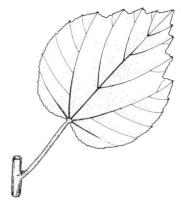

A small tree rarely reaching 10 m in height; occurring in high-rainfall areas, in open woodland and at the margin of evergreen forest.

This species closely resembles *D. rotundifolia,* but its leaves are considerably larger, often 8 to 20 × 8 to 20 cm, and bear short rather than long hairs; the most important difference, apparent only with a 10x lens, is that the ovary is not hairy, but is instead covered with minute brown protuberances which are thickened towards the end.

Dombeya tiliacea (Endl.) Planchon
S.A. no: 472   Forest dombeya. Bosdrolpeer
Rhod. no: —

A shrub or small tree up to 4 m in height; occurring in mixed scrub on hillsides, or at the margin of evergreen forest. **Bark:** dark grey, rough. **Leaves:** small, heart-shaped, up to 8 × 5,5 cm, but frequently 3,5 × 2,5 cm, the upper surface with sparse but harsh hairs, the lower surface with short soft hairs and rather paler green; apex tapering; base lobed; margin scalloped or toothed, sometimes roughly toothed; petiole slender, 1,5 to 3 cm long. **Flowers:** white, 3 to 4,5 cm in diameter, in few-flowered axillary clusters, but crowded near the ends of the branches (February to May). **Fruit:** a capsule, 8 × 5 mm, covered with soft pale tawny hairs (May to June).

2. TRIPLOCHITON K. Schum.

Triplochiton zambesiacus Milne-Redh.
S.A. no: —
Rhod. no: 688   Wine-cup

A large spreading tree up to 18 m in height, with a rather short bole and a densely foliaged crown; occurring along river banks, on alluvial flood-plains, often associated with termite mounds and endemic to the Zambezi valley and the lower reaches of its tributaries. **Bark:** light grey, flaking, revealing whitish patches giving a mottled appearance. **Leaves:** alternate, simple, palmately 5- to 9-lobed, in general outline almost circular, wider than they are long, up to 17 × 20 cm but usually about 10 × 12 cm, medium green, with soft hairs which are lost by maturity; often galled; apices of **593**

STERCULIACEAE

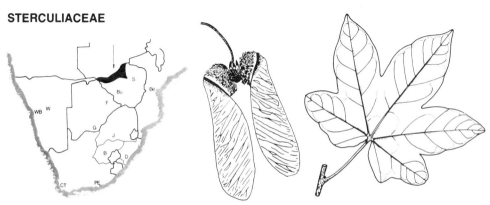

the lobes tapering; base of the leaf square or lobed; margin of the lobes entire; petiole 5 to 7 cm long. **Flowers:** showy, white or yellowish, with a conspicuous deep red centre, about 5 to 7 cm in diameter, axillary or terminal, solitary or in groups of 2 to 4 on short stalks. Bisexual; all floral parts in fives; calyx bell-shaped, lobed; petals broad and furry, overlapping; stamens many, rising from a conspicuous androphore; ovary of 5 carpels, joined. The flowers are open only in the mornings (December to April). **Fruit:** made up of 4 to 5 carpels, each with a large, stiff, membraneous wing, up to 9 × 3,5 cm, pale straw-coloured when mature with brownish markings, usually finely furry, like a moth's wing; the fruits remain on the tree for some months, even into the next flowering season (May to September onwards).

The leaves are cooked and eaten as a vegetable by Africans. The wood is hard and has been used for yokes for oxen.

3. STERCULIA L.

Trees. **Leaves:** alternate, simple or digitately compound. Exstipulate. **Flowers:** in axillary or terminal panicles, before or with the leaves. Sexes separate, either on the same tree or on different trees. Frequently the flowers appear bisexual, but in some the anthers abort, making these flowers functionally female; calyx with 4 to 5 lobes, petalloid; petals absent; stamens 10 to 20 in a central cluster on a slender androphore, sterile in female flowers; ovary of 4 to 5 carpels, attached at first, separating later, vestigial in male flowers. **Fruit:** made up of woody or leathery follicular carpels, splitting down one side only, becoming boat-shaped.

Key to the species of *Sterculia:*
1 Leaves simple, lobed 2
  Leaves compound, with 5 to 9 leaflets arising together at the apex of the petiole (digitate) . 5
2 Leaves small, up to 6 × 5 cm, with rather short whitish hairs on the under surface; fruits smallish, creamy-grey, about 5 cm long (up to 7,5 cm), with a pronounced beak .... **S. rogersii**
  Leaves large to very large, 6 to 40 cm long and broad, without whitish hairs below, but may be grey-green or yellow 3
3 Fruits scarcely beaked, with brown velvety hairs on the outside; seeds brown with a yellow aril and surrounded by a dry powdery pulp .... **S. appendiculata**
  Fruits strongly beaked, with golden to yellowish-fawn, velvety hairs; seeds blackish to blue-grey, the aril not yellow; powdery pulp absent 4
4 Fruits seldom less than 10 cm long, often single, but may be in groups of 3 to 5 carpels; flowers up to 2,5 cm in diameter .... **S. africana**
  Fruits rather small, up to 6 × 3 cm, usually in groups of 5; flowers up to 5 mm in diameter .... **S. quinqueloba**
5 Leaflets oblong, stiff and leathery; fruits up to 9 cm long, the outer surface covered with warty to horned protuberances. Occurring in a small area in the eastern Cape only ..... **S. alexandri**
  The leaflets lanceolate, softly textured with velvety hairs; fruits very large, up to 20 cm long, covered with blunt, thickset spines. Occurring in a relatively small area in the south-eastern Transvaal and Swaziland only .... **S. murex**

Sterculia africana (Lour.) Fiori   Illust. 188
[*S. guerichii* K. Schum.]
S.A. no: 474   African star-chestnut. Afrikaanse sterkastaiing
Rhod. no: 689   Tick tree

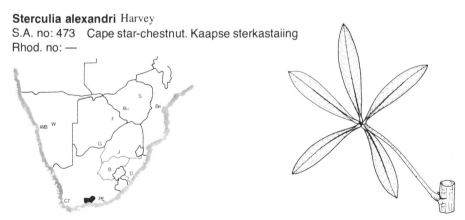

A thick-stemmed tree 5 to 12 m in height, but sometimes reaching 25 m; occurring at low altitudes in hot dry areas, often in or at the margin of mopane bush, frequently on rocky koppies and hillsides. **Bark:** smooth, often silver to white, sometimes greenish-brown to liver-coloured, and peeling or flaking to reveal a beautiful pastel-coloured and marbled underbark; branches soft and brittle. **Leaves:** crowded near the ends of the branches, almost circular, or deeply divided into 3 to 5 lobes, 6 to 15 × 4 to 13 cm, olive-green, veins conspicuous, thinly to densely furry, sometimes harsh to the touch; apices of the lobes tapering; base of the leaf lobed; margins of the leaf and the lobes entire; petiole up to 10 cm long, coarsely hairy. **Flowers:** greenish-yellow with reddish guide lines, up to 2,5 cm in diameter, in compact, terminal, branched, spike-like racemes, up to 9 cm long, appearing before the leaves; sexes separate on the same tree (September to November). **Fruit:** made up of 1 or 3 to 5 carpels each up to 15 cm long, strongly beaked, splitting down one side only, boat-shaped, golden velvety on the outside; mouth fringed with bristly, intensely irritating hairs; the fat blue-grey seeds resembling engorged ticks are attached only round the edge of the opening; there is a small white aril at the base (January to June).

The trees produce a gum resembling gum tragacanth, but not in quantities sufficient for commercial exploitation. The wood is very soft; the fibrous bark is used for making ropes and mats.

Sterculia alexandri Harvey
S.A. no: 473   Cape star-chestnut. Kaapse sterkastaiing
Rhod. no: —

A small tree usually 3 to 4 m in height, occasionally reaching 8 m, sometimes prostrate, throwing up vertical shoots (characteristic of the population in the Van Staaden River gorge); occurring in forest or scrub in precipitous gorges or on steep mountainsides. **Bark:** pale grey, smooth, rather mottled with small raised dots. **Leaves:** compound, completely divided to form 3 to 7 digitate leaflets (usually 5); leaflets oblong, up to 10 × 2,5 cm, stiff, leathery, the upper surface dark green, the under surface paler greyish-green with the yellow veins prominent below; apex tapering, notched; base tapering; margin entire; petiole yellow, up to 10 cm long. **Flowers:** varying from yellow with a rich claret throat, to pale greenish-cream with only occasional red flecks, up to 2 cm in diameter, in sparse axillary branched sprays, about 8 cm long, usually appearing when the tree is bare; the first flowers

595

produced are mostly male (with the female organs aborted), the later flowers are bisexual (May to August). **Fruit:** made up of 1 to 5 carpels joined at the base and densely covered with short golden-brown hairs; each carpel up to 9 × 2,5 cm, with a marked beak, splitting along the upper surface, covered with warty projections, tipped with tufts of brown, bristly hairs which are easily rubbed off (July to October).

The plants are easily propagated from cuttings, and naturally produce off-shoots from underground stems. The seeds are edible and have a pleasant nutty flavour. This is a protected plant in South Africa.

Sterculia appendiculata K. Schum.
S.A. no: —
Rhod. no: 690   Tall sterculia

A tall tree up to 40 m in height, with a straight trunk, the large specimens bearing no branches for 15 to 20 m; occurring in coastal and riverine forest. **Bark:** pale yellow, smooth, conspicuous; branchlets woolly with dense rusty-yellow hairs. **Leaves:** crowded towards the ends of the branches; broadly ovate, large, 14 to 30 × 14 to 30 cm, green, blade occasionally entire but usually divided into 3 to 7 lobes (usually 5); young leaves densely woolly with rusty-yellow hairs, losing these by maturity; apex broadly tapering; base lobed; margin entire; petiole 6 to 11 cm long, densely woolly with rusty-yellow hairs, losing these with age. **Flowers:** greenish or yellowish-brown, up to 2,8 cm in diameter, in terminal hairy few-flowered sprays, up to 12 cm long, before the new leaves (June to July). **Fruit:** made up of 2 to 3 carpels, each up to 9 × 6 cm, covered with short soft brown hairs on the outside; the seeds, which line the opening, are up to 2 cm long, brown with a yellow aril at the base, and are surrounded by dry powdery pulp (August to December).

Sterculia murex Hemsley
S.A. no: 475   Lowveld chestnut. Laeveldkastaiing
Rhod. no: —

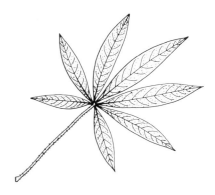

A well-foliaged tree up to 10 m in height; confined to dry, rocky ridges and koppies. **Bark:** grey to black, rough. **Leaves:** compound, digitately 5- to 7-foliolate (occasionally 9); leaflets oblong to lanceolate, up to 15 × 4 cm, dark green; both surfaces with soft hairs, the under surface more densely so; young leaves softly velvety, older leaves becoming harsh to the touch; veins conspicuous; apex and base tapering; margin entire; petiole conspicuously long and slender, 10 to 23 cm in length. **Flowers:** dull yellow-brown, rather waxy, saucer-shaped, 2 to 2,5 cm in diameter, produced near the ends of the branches in axillary sprays, up to 10 cm long, before the leaves (July to October). **Fruit:**

596

made up of conspicuous carpels, each 9 to 20 × 7 to 13 cm, solitary or in groups of 2 to 5, splitting along the upper surface to form a boat-shaped structure which is covered with thickset, spiny protuberances, resembling very short, squat snakes; the carpels are produced on short thickset stalks, and the openings are fringed with irritating hairs (October to January and later).

The empty fruiting carpels are often picked up by visitors to the Kruger National Park and are sometimes used as ashtrays. The seeds are large, being up to 2,5 cm long, black and rich in oil; they are highly esteemed by the local Africans as food. This tree would make an attractive and unusual addition to any garden; the seeds germinate easily and the young trees are fast-growing but sensitive to frost.

Sterculia quinqueloba (Garcke) K. Schum.   Illust. 189
S.A. no: 476   Large-leaved star-chestnut. Grootblaarsterkastaiing
Rhod. no: 691   Large-leaved sterculia

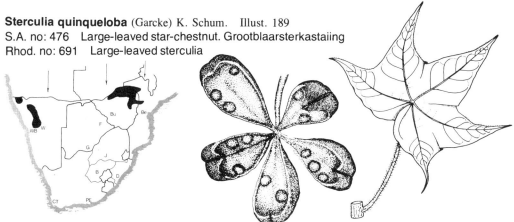

Usually a thickset tree 5 to 12 m in height, but sometimes reaching 25 m; occurring at medium to low altitudes, on rocky koppies and hill slopes, in deciduous woodland and dry bush. **Bark:** cream to pinkish-brown, conspicuously smooth and rather shiny, sometimes flaking in large specimens. **Leaves:** crowded near the ends of the branches, large, conspicuously 5-lobed, very broadly ovate, 15 to 40 × 15 to 40 cm, dark yellowish-green above, greyish to yellowish below with rather woolly hairs, the veins and net-veining prominent and conspicuous; producing spectacular yellow and gold autumn colours; apices of the lobes tapering; base of the leaf lobed; margin of the lobes entire; petiole up to 27 cm long. **Flowers:** yellow, about 5 mm in diameter, in terminal, many-flowered, branched heads, 9 to 30 cm long, produced with the leaves (January to April). **Fruit:** made up of 5 separate carpels, each up to 6 × 3 cm, covered with short golden hairs; the carpels have a short but marked point and split along one side, and the seeds are attached to the rim of the opening among very irritating long hairs; the seeds are black with a small inconspicuous aril (May to September).

The wood is reddish-brown and has been used as a mining timber, in general construction work and for furniture. The tree exudes a good quality gum, but as the flow tends to be seasonal and is not easily tapped, the species is not exploited commercially.

Sterculia rogersii N. E. Brown   Illust. 190
S.A. no: 477   Common star-chestnut. Gewone sterkastaiing
Rhod. no: 692   Squat sterculia

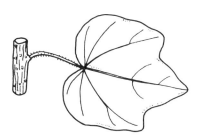

STERCULIACEAE

A small tree up to 5 m in height, often branching from low down, with a characteristic swollen trunk; occurring at low altitudes, in dry woodland and bush, often on rocky outcrops. **Bark:** pale greyish with pink and purplish patches producing a distinctive mottled appearance. **Leaves:** small, almost entire to fairly deeply 3-lobed, broadly ovate, 3 to 6 × 2 to 5 cm, light greyish-green, softly velvety, falling very early in autumn leaving the tree to stand bare for several months; veins are conspicuous; apex broadly tapering; base lobed; margin entire; petiole slender, up to 7,5 cm long. **Flowers:** greenish-yellow flushed with pink and with conspicuous deep pink or red streaks and lines, saucer-shaped, about 2 cm in diamter, each sepal tapering to a long point; axillary, solitary or in small clusters of 2 to 3, produced on the old wood and on the young branches, often in profusion, usually before the leaves (July to January). **Fruit:** made up of 3 to 5 carpels, each up to 7,5 cm long, but usually about 5 cm, with a pronounced beak, and covered with short creamy to pale golden hairs; the seeds, produced round the margin of the opening among irritating long hairs, are about 10 mm long, and black with a small whitish aril. The fruits and flowers are frequently found on the tree at the same time (September to March and later).

The wood is soft, brittle and whitish-cream. The bark provides a good quality fibre which Africans use to weave fishing nets and as a thread to sew sleeping mats.

4. COLA Schott & Endl.

Trees. **Leaves:** alternate, simple, the petiole with a conspicuous swelling or pulvinus, just below the leaf blade. **Flowers:** in clusters on the old wood, or in short axillary racemes or panicles; sexes separate on the same tree or on different trees; floral parts in fours to fives; calyx lobed, usually with dense, short, soft hairs; petals absent; stamens 5 to 12, in an unusual tight ring at the tip of a conspicuous androphore, vestigial in female flowers; ovary of 3 to 4 joined carpels, vestigial in male flowers. **Fruit:** made up of 3 to 4 leathery or woody follicular carpels, splitting longitudinally when mature.

Key to the species of *Cola:*

1 Swelling, or pulvinus, on the petiole just below the leaf, dark and without hairs; fruiting carpels up to 4 cm long .... **C. natalensis**
  Pulvinus with fine short hairs; fruiting carpels not more than 2 cm long 2
2 Hairs on the outside of the flowers dark rusty-brown; flowers and fruit stalks, or pedicels, jointed above the base .... **C. greenwayi**
  Hairs on the outside of the flowers pale rusty-brown; pedicels not jointed . **C. mossambicensis**

Cola greenwayi Brenan
[*C. microcarpa* Brenan]
S.A. no: 478,1   Hairy cola. Basterknuppelhout
Rhod. no: 693   Hairy cola

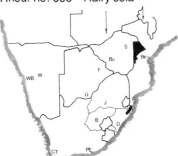

Usually a small under-storey tree 5 to 7 m in height, but reaching 15 to 25 m on occasions; occurring in evergreen forest and sand forest. **Bark:** grey-brown, rather smooth, the stem in large specimens may become fluted; young branches russet. **Leaves:** elliptic to oblanceolate, up to 15 × 7 cm, leathery, dark green above, paler green below; veining prominent on both surfaces; apex tapering, finally attenuate; base tapering to narrowly rounded; margin entire; petiole up to 5,5 cm long, with dark brown, persistent furry hairs on the swelling, or pulvinus, up to 10 mm below the blade,

598

frequently angled at this point. **Flowers:** about 5 mm long and 10 mm in diameter, coloured dark rusty-brown by the soft dense hairs; in tight clusters along the stems, pedicels jointed near the base (October to November). **Fruit:** made up of 3 to 4 carpels, each up to 1,8 × 2 cm, covered with short, soft, rusty-red hairs (November to January).

This species closely resembles *C. natalensis* but differs in that the young branches are densely and persistently hairy, and that the swelling on the petiole and the inner surface of the calyx lobes are also persistently hairy.

Cola mossambicensis Wild

S.A. no: —
Rhod. no: —   Moçambique cola

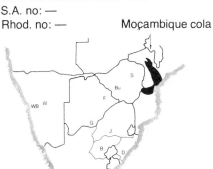

A large tree up to 27 m in height; occurring in evergreen forest, from sea level to about 600 m; apparently endemic to Moçambique and Malawi. **Bark:** ash-grey; young branches and young leaves with soft rusty hairs. **Leaves:** obovate to elliptic, up to 22 × 9,5 cm, leathery, both surfaces finely velvety at first, losing these hairs later, but the pulvinus on the petiole, up to 10 mm below the blade, remaining persistently hairy; veins very conspicuous; apex abruptly attenuate; base broadly tapering to almost rounded; margin entire or sinuate; petiole up to 6 cm long, finely hairy. **Flowers:** up to 8 mm long, coloured pale rusty-brown by the dense hairs; in few- to many-flowered groups on the old wood, the pedicels not jointed (June). **Fruit:** made up of 1 to 2 follicles, each 1,5 × 1,7 cm, with short pale rusty-brown hairs (September to October).

Cola natalensis Oliver

S.A. no: 478   Common cola. Knuppelhout
Rhod. no: —

A small to medium sized tree 7 to 10 m in height; occurring in evergreen forest. **Bark:** grey, smooth, peeling in small flakes in larger specimens; the young branchlets with hairs at first but these are soon lost. **Leaves:** elliptic, 6 to 20 × 1,5 to 6 cm, dark green, the young leaves finely hairy, but all hairs are lost by maturity; midrib and lateral veins conspicuous on the under surface; apex and base tapering; margin entire; petiole up to 2,5 cm long, the pulvinus, just below the blade, conspicuously dark-coloured, almost black, without hairs. **Flowers:** in small axillary clusters, sepals about 6 mm long, coloured reddish-brown by the short, soft, rusty hairs on the outside (October). **Fruit:** made up of 2 to 4 carpels, each up to 4 × 2,7 cm, leathery, with the surface warty and covered with short yellowish to rusty-orange hairs (February).

599

The wood is hard and durable, but the pieces are usually small; it is used mainly for making walking sticks, which are often beautifully carved.

5. HERITIERA Aiton

Heritiera littoralis Aiton
S.A. no: —
Rhod. no: —   Moçambique mangrove

Often a small tree 4 to 5 m in height; but it can reach 20 to 25 m; occurring on the landward side of mangrove swamps where fresh water mingles with and probably predominates over the sea water. **Bark:** light grey, smooth; in large specimens the trunk is buttressed; there are apparently no pneumatophores. **Leaves:** alternate, simple, elliptic, 9 to 30 × 4 to 15 cm, thickly leathery; upper surface green and without hairs, lower surface conspicuously covered in silvery scales with occasional dotted brown scales; apex and base broadly tapering to rounded; margin entire, inclined to be wavy; petiole 0,5 to 1,5 cm long, stout. **Flowers:** white or yellowish-green, bell-shaped, about 5 to 6 mm long, in much-branched, axillary, hairy panicles, about 5 cm long, near the ends of the branches. Sexes separate on different trees; calyx 5-lobed; petals absent; stamens 5, at the tip of a short androphore, vestigial in female flowers; ovary of 5 joined carpels (June). **Fruit:** made up of 5, joined, woody, oblong carpels, each 6 to 8 × 3 to 4 cm and with a distinct keel along the back; the carpels float in water and are distributed in this way (September).

In East Africa the stems are used to make dhow masts; the bark contains 14% tannin.

OCHNACEAE *(The ochna family)*

Key to the genera:
Conspicuous yellow pigment present just under the bark (this shows up well in a slash); flower petals white to cream or pink; stipules persistent on first year branchlets and deeply divided into narrow segments, markedly longitudinally striate .... **2. Brackenridgea**

Yellow pigment absent below the bark; flower petals yellow, very rarely white; stipules fall early, not deeply divided and not striate .... **1. Ochna**

1. OCHNA L.

Shrublets, shrubs or trees, usually completely without hairs. **Leaves:** alternate, simple, margin usually toothed. Stipules entire, or with a fringed margin, or 2-lobed but not deeply so; falling early. **Flowers:** solitary, or in a terminal or branched spray, a raceme or panicle, often produced on a short, lateral shoot. Bisexual; all floral parts in fives; sepals persistent, becoming enlarged, brightly coloured and petalloid; petals 5 to 10, larger than sepals, but falling very early, often within hours of opening; stamens 12 to many, free, filaments partially persistent; ovary of 3, 5 or more distinct carpels, each developing on the very swollen red receptacle. **Fruit:** thinly fleshy, narrowly ovoid, almost spherical or kidney-shaped, joined either laterally or at the base.

Key to the tree species of *Ochna:*
1 Branchlets with conspicuous raised dots, pustules or lenticels 2
   Branchlets without conspicuous lenticels, raised dots or pustules 13

2 Bark smooth, may be peeling in thin membraneous stripes 3
   Bark roughish to rough 9
3 Leaf petiole more than 2 mm long 4
   Leaf petiole less than 2 mm long 5
4 Leaves oblong-elliptic to almost circular, up to 4,5 × 2,5 cm, metallic blue-green **O. glauca**
   Leaves elliptic-oblong, up to 6 × 2,6 cm, green .... **O. barbosae**
5 Flowers and fruits in branched heads .... **O. natalitia**
   Flowers and fruits solitary, or in clusters of up to 4 6
6 Persistent sepals in the fruits more than 2 cm long .... **O. rovumensis**
   Persistent sepals less than 2 cm long 7
7 The very young stems and new growth covered with dense but very fine hairs **O. puberula**
   Young stems and new shoots without hairs 8
8 Bark pale, whitish or brownish .... **O. inermis**
   Bark brown .... **O. serrulata**
9 Persistent sepals in the fruit small, seldom more than 1,2 cm long 10
   Persistent sepals in the fruit usually up to 1,5 cm long, or more 11
10 Bark whitish, rough; fruit with the separate carpels almost spherical, about 6 mm in diameter;
    flowers with yellow anthers .... **O. angustata**
   Bark grey-brown to brown; fruit with the separate carpels ovoid, 5 to 10 mm long; flowers often
    with orange anthers .... **O. natalitia**
11 Mature leaves distinctly bronze-tinged .... **O. polyneura**
   Mature leaves not bronze-tinged 12
12 Persistent sepals in the fruits narrow, up to 1,5 × 0,5 cm, spreading; occurring from the eastern
    Cape to Rhodesia and Moçambique at higher altitudes .... **O. holstii**
   Persistent sepals broad, 1,8 × 1 cm, curved over the fruits; essentially a coastal species found
    near Beira and northwards .... **O. beirensis**
13 Bark rough 14
   Bark smooth, may be flaking in thin pieces 16
14 Persistent sepals in the fruit large, up to 2,5 cm long .... **O. gambleoides**
   Persistent sepals in the fruit not more than 1,5 cm long 15
15 Bark pale whitish-brown, roughish; flowers many, in lax branched heads, or panicles; leaves
    usually large, 23 × 8 cm, margin with dense fine teeth .... **O. atropurpurea**
   Bark dark grey, vertically and horizontally fissured forming thick, square, 'crocodile' segments;
    flowers 4 to 10 in very short sprays, or condensed racemes; leaves not larger than 13,5 ×
    5,5 cm, usually about 10 cm long, margin bluntly toothed, almost scalloped ....
    .... **O. schweinfurthiana**
16 Occurring in the Cape, Natal, Transvaal and extreme south of Moçambique and the east of
    Rhodesia; usually a forest species .... **O. arborea**
   Occurring no further south than the Transvaal; a woodland species found at medium to low
    altitudes .... **O. pulchra**

Ochna angustata N. K. B. Robson
S.A. no: —
Rhod. no: —   Orange-red Moçambique ochna

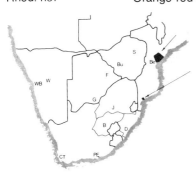

OCHNACEAE

A shrub or small tree up to 5 m in height; occurring in deciduous woodland and coastal scrub. **Bark:** whitish, rough; branchlets with a few lenticels. **Leaves:** elliptic, 4 to 9,5 × 1,5 to 3 cm, thinly leathery; veining not very conspicuous; apex rounded; base narrowly to broadly tapering; margin almost entire to scalloped or finely toothed; petiole slender, up to 6 mm long. **Flowers:** bright yellow, about 2 cm in diameter, in clusters of 3 to 4, on dwarf lateral shoots (September). **Fruit:** usually 5 carpels, each about 6 × 6 mm, almost spherical, attached near the base, the enlarged persistent sepals up to 1,1 cm long, orange-red, flat and spreading (October to November).

Ochna arborea Burch. ex DC.   Illust. 191 and 192
[*O. oconnorii* Phillips]
S.A. no: 479 and 482   Cape plane. Kaapse rooihout
Rhod. no: 703   Cape plane

A shrub or small to medium sized tree 2 to 12 m in height; occurring over a wide range of altitudes, in evergreen forest and bush, and along streams. **Bark:** pale grey, very smooth, peeling in thin papery layers, revealing a beautiful and distinctive reddish to olive green underbark; branchlets without lenticels. **Leaves:** oblong, usually 4 to 5 × 1,5 to 2 cm, but may be up to 14 × 3 cm, leathery, shiny green, young leaves bronze, net-veining conspicuous on both surfaces; apex broadly tapering to rounded, often with a hair-like tip; base tapering to rounded; margin toothed, occasionally entire, sometimes very conspicuously wavy; petiole 2 to 3 mm long. **Flowers:** yellow, up to 2 cm in diameter, the petals broad and crinkled, falling very early; in 2- to many-flowered sprays, on a very short common stalk, usually terminal on short side branches; sweetly scented (August to November). **Fruit:** 1 to 5 separate carpels, each about 10 × 7 mm, kidney-shaped, attached laterally, dark brownish-black when mature; the enlarged persistent sepals, 6 to 9 mm long, become bright orange-red to red (November to February).

The wood is heavy, hard and strong, and is suitable for making implement handles and carved sticks; it is also regarded as a charm to drive evil spirits away from the home and cattle kraals. The bark contains 8% tannin and has been used as snuff to cure headaches.

O. oconnorii now becomes *O. arborea* var. *oconnorii* (Phillips) Du Toit.

Ochna atropurpurea DC.
[*O. mossambicensis* Klotzsch]
S.A. no: —
Rhod. no: 701   Large-flowered ochna

A bushy shrub or small tree seldom more than 3 m in height; occurring on sandy soils, in open woodland and among rocks. **Bark:** pale whitish-brown, rather rough; branchlets stout; without conspicuous lenticels. **Leaves:** obovate to oblanceolate, 7 to 23 × 3 to 8 cm, leathery; net-veining dense, more prominent above than below; apex broadly tapering to rounded, occasionally with a fine hair-like tip; base tapering; margin densely and finely toothed; petiole rather stout and swollen, up to 8 mm long. **Flowers:** bright yellow, 2,5 to 3,5 cm in diameter, in loose branched heads, arising from short lateral shoots (September to November). **Fruit:** usually 4 to 5 carpels, occasionally more, each almost spherical, attached near the base, purplish when mature; the enlarged persistent sepals, 1,2 to 1,4 cm long, become bright red (September to November).

Ochna barbosae N. K. B. Robson
S.A. no: 479,2   Sand plane. Sandrooihout
Rhod. no: 694   Sand ochna

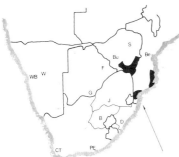

A shrub or small tree up to 4 m in height; occurring in well-drained sandy soils and on dunes. **Bark:** grey, smooth, later becoming dark brown and finely fissured; branchlets with lenticels. **Leaves:** elliptic-oblong, up to 6 × 2,6 cm, rather leathery, green, net-veining dense, clearly defined but not prominent; apex tapering to rounded; base rounded; margin finely toothed or occasionally almost entire; petiole 2 to 4 mm long, slender. **Flowers:** yellow, about 2 cm in diameter, sweetly scented, axillary, solitary, at the tips of short axillary shoots (August to September). **Fruit:** usually 5 separate carpels, each up to 1,2 × 1 cm, slightly flattened, attached near the base, dark brownish-black when mature; the enlarged persistent sepals, up to 2 cm long, become pink to pinkish-red (October to December).

Ochna beirensis N. K. B. Robson
S.A. no: —
Rhod. no: —   Beira ochna

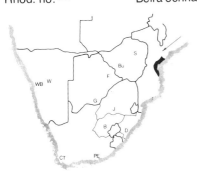

A shrub or small tree up to 5 m in height; occurring near sea level, in littoral scrub or deciduous woodland. **Bark:** brown, roughish; branchlets lenticellate. **Leaves:** rhomboid-elliptic to oblong, 3 to 8 × 1 to 3 cm, thinly leathery; net-veining dense, clearly defined above and below; apex tapering to broadly so, occasionally shortly attenuate; base narrowly tapering and running into the petiole; margin sharply toothed; petiole slender, 2 to 4 mm long. **Flowers:** petals not seen; produced in axillary clusters of 3 to 5 (August to September). **Fruit:** usually 5 separate carpels, each ovoid-cylindric, 11 ×

7 mm, attached at the base; the enlarged persistent sepals, up to 1,8 cm long and curving over the fruits, become carmine-pink (October).

Ochna gambleoides N. K. B. Robson
S.A. no: —
Rhod. no: 696   Large-leaved ochna

A small tree 3 to 7m in height; occurring in *Brachystegia* woodland, often on stony hillsides. **Bark:** silver-grey, rough with deep wide vertical fissures and narrow transverse cracks, producing rectangular flakes; branchlets pale brown, without lenticels. **Leaves:** large, oblong-elliptic to obovate, 8,5 to 20 × 5 to 10 cm, bluish-green, the midrib broad and prominent, the lateral veins slender, somewhat submerged, at right angles to the midrib; apex very broadly tapering to rounded; base broadly tapering to square; margin finely toothed or scalloped; petiole stout, up to 3 cm in diameter. **Flowers:** yellow, rather fragile, about 2 cm in diameter, falling very early; in short dense clusters of 7 to 16 (August to September). **Fruit:** conspicuously large, usually 5 separate carpels, each ovoid, up to 2,5 cm long, attached at the base, black when mature; the enlarged persistent sepals are concave, up to 2,5 cm long and become orange-red to scarlet (October to March).

Ochna glauca Verdoorn
S.A. no: Blue plane
Rhod. no: 697   Blue-leaved ochna

Often a straggling shrub, occasionally a small tree, 2 to 3 m in height; occurring on granite hills and koppies, often growing from cracks in the rocks. **Bark:** dark grey, smooth; the branchlets have scattered lenticels. **Leaves:** oblong-elliptic to almost circular, up to 4,5 × 2,5 cm but usually rather smaller, metallic blue-green (the specific name refers to this), often folded along the midrib and tending to droop; net-veining fine, equally prominent on both surfaces; apex rounded, sometimes notched; base tapering; margin finely toothed; petiole slender, 3 to 4 mm long. **Flowers:** bright yellow, conspicuous, with fragile petals about 6 to 8 × 4 to 6 mm with a small claw at the tip, falling very soon; axillary, solitary (September to November). **Fruit:** usually 2 separate carpels, each about 9 × 6 mm, somewhat flattened and slightly curved, attached near the base, purplish-black when mature; the enlarged persistent sepals, up to 10 mm long, become red to reddish-brown and curve sharply backwards (October to December).

604   The small blue-green leaves distinguish this from other single-flowered species.

Ochna holstii Engl.
[*O. chirindica* E. G. Baker]
S.A. no: 480   Red ironwood. Rooiysterhout
Rhod. no: 698   Common forest ochna

A shrub or small tree, usually 3 to 7 m in height, but sometimes reaching 18 m; occurring in evergreen forest and in forested ravines, but frequently in more open dry areas, often among rocks. **Bark:** grey-brown, rather rough, not flaking; branchlets with many small lenticels; branches, branchlets and leaves spreading horizontally. **Leaves:** obovate to elliptic, up to 12 × 4 cm, light green; lateral veins forming right angles with the midrib; net-veining conspicuous above, not below; apex tapering, sometimes finely notched; base tapering; margin finely toothed and wavy; petiole up to 3 mm. **Flowers:** bright yellow, 2 to 3 cm in diameter, in dense axillary clusters of 7 to 14, either when the tree is leafless or with the new, shiny leaves; the petals remain at least long enough to make a conspicuous show (September to November). **Fruit:** 1 to 9 separate carpels, each up to 1,2 × 0,7 cm, attached near the base, black when mature; the enlarged persistent spreading sepals, up to 1,5 cm long, becoming pinkish-red to deep red (October to January).

This is a very variable species, but all characters grade so completely into each other that it is not possible to subdivide it; the trees in the Chirinda and Vumba mountain forests in Rhodesia have particularly large leaves and unusually long flower stalks, or pedicels, and these characters make it similar to the mountain specimens from east Africa; the Transvaal specimens often have rather densely hairy young shoots and white branches, characters which make them similar to specimens from southern Tanzania and also to *O. puberula*.

Ochna inermis (Forsk.) Schweinf.
S.A. no: 480,1   Lowveld plane. Laveldrooihout
Rhod. no: 699   Boat-fruit ochna

Usually a shrub, but it can become a small tree up to 7 m in height; occurring at low altitudes often in dry mopane scrub or thornveld grassland, often among rocks or in stony or sandy soil. **Bark:** pale, whitish or brownish, smooth; branchlets lenticellate. **Leaves:** elliptic, oblong or almost circular, up to 5 to 6 × 1 to 3 cm, apple-green and glossy; net-veining clearly defined on both surfaces; apex broadly tapering to rounded; base tapering to square; margin wavy, very finely but sharply toothed; petiole slender but conspicuously short, up to 2 mm long. **Flowers:** golden-yellow, 1 to 2 cm in diameter, solitary or occasionally in pairs at the tips of short axillary shoots; petals with a short claw at the tip, falling very early (October to November). **Fruit:** usually 1 to 3 separate carpels, each up to 10 ×   **605**

7 mm, attached near the base, purplish-black when mature; the enlarged persistent sepals, up to 1,6 cm long and boat-shaped, become crimson-red (December to February).

This species is sometimes confused with *O. pretoriensis* Phillips, but the latter is a low-growing bushy shrub up to 3,5 m, occurring round Pretoria and extending into the southern end of the Kruger National Park.

Ochna natalitia (Meissner) Walp.
S.A. no: 481   Natal plane. Natalrooihout
Rhod. no: 702   Showy ochna

A shrub or small to medium sized tree up to 10 m in height; occurring in open wooded grassland, frequently in shallow soil among rocks when it seldom reaches 2 m, or forming part of the under-storey in forested kloofs and at the margins of evergreen forests. **Bark:** grey-brown or brown, finely fissured to rough or flaking, revealing an attractive, smooth, reddish underbark; the branchlets lenticellate, often galled. **Leaves:** oblong to elliptic-oblong, 3 to 13 × 1 to 4 cm, young leaves attractively copper-coloured, maturing to green, the mature leaves vary considerably in size and shape according to their habitat, forest trees having larger and more acutely tapering leaves, while bushes on open stony ground have smaller, more rounded leaves, but there is complete intergrading between the two extremes; net-veining is rather obscure above and below; apex and base tapering to rounded; margin toothed to finely toothed; petiole slender, 1 to 2 mm long. **Flowers:** yellow to golden-yellow, 1,5 to 3 cm in diameter, stamens often orange and conspicuous; produced in branched heads, terminal or on short lateral shoots; the flowers often last long enough to make an attractive show (September to December). **Fruit:** usually 2 to 3 separate carpels, each ovoid, 5 to 10 mm long, attached near the base, black when mature; the enlarged persistent sepals, 0,8 to 1,2 cm long, become pink or red and also make an attractive show (September to December).

Ochna polyneura Gilg
S.A. no: —
Rhod. no: 704   Bronze ochna

 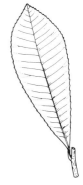

A shrublet, shrub or small tree, sometimes reaching 8 m in height; occurring at medium to low altitudes in open woodland. **Bark:** pale grey, vertically fissured, rough; branchlets with numerous inconspicuous lenticels. **Leaves:** obovate to oblanceolate, 4,5 to 11 × 1,6 to 3,6 cm, conspicuously tinged with bronze; many lateral veins form right angles with the midrib, the tertiary veins forming dense net-veining; apex broadly tapering to rounded; base narrowly tapering; margin densely but

606

shallowly toothed; petiole stout, 1 to 2 mm long. **Flowers:** pale yellow, 1,4 to 1,8 cm in diameter, in a simple axillary raceme up to 2,5 cm long; the petals with a hooked apex, falling early (September to November). **Fruit:** usually 2 to 4 carpels, each ovoid, up to 10 mm long, attached near the base, blackish when mature; the enlarged persistent sepals, 1 to 1,5 cm long, become bronze to deep red (November to January).

This is a striking species noteworthy for its bronze-tinged leaves and fruiting sepals.

Ochna puberula N. K. B. Robson
S.A. no:
Rhod. no: 705   Granite ochna

A shrub or small tree 2 to 4 m in height; occurring in open woodland and wooded grassland, frequently on rocky outcrops. **Bark:** grey, rather smooth; the young stems and new growth are densely covered with very short hairs, and later develop raised brown lenticels. **Leaves:** obovate or oblanceolate, 3,7 to 7 × 1 to 2,5 cm, lateral veins numerous; apex broadly tapering to rounded; base narrowly tapering; margin densely toothed; petiole slender, barely 1,5 mm long. **Flowers:** bright yellow, 1,4 to 2 cm in diameter, in short, rather few-flowered axillary clusters; petals rather narrow, falling very early (October to December). **Fruit:** usually 4 to 7 separate carpels; each ovoid, up to 10 mm long, attached at the base, black when mature; the enlarged persistent sepals, about 10 mm long, become bright red, at first folding over the developing fruits – an unusual feature – and later opening back (November to February).

Ochna pulchra Hook.   Illust. 193
S.A. no: 483   Lekkerbreek. Lekkerbreek
Rhod. no: 706   Peeling-bark ochna

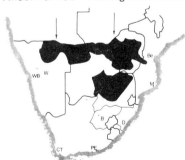 

A small tree usually 3 to 7 m in height; occurring at medium to low altitudes in open woodland; very characteristic of granite sandstone areas. **Bark:** pale grey, sometimes roughish near the base, otherwise peeling thinly to reveal a beautiful, creamy, opalescent underbark; branchlets without lenticels. **Leaves:** elliptic to oblanceolate, 3,5 to 18,5 × 1,3 to 5,7 cm, usually about 7 to 8 × 2,7 cm, fresh light green to yellowish-green, many-veined; net-veining not conspicuous but more clearly defined above than below: apex broadly tapering to almost rounded; base narrowly tapering to almost square; margin usually entire, but may be very slightly toothed towards the apex; petiole rather stout, up to 6 mm long. **Flowers:** pale yellow or greenish-yellow, occasionally darker, on long slender stalks in a terminal raceme about 2 cm long; sweetly scented, petals conspicuously narrow, falling

607

very early (August to November). **Fruit:** usually 1 to 3 separate kidney-shaped carpels, each up to 1,4 cm long, attached laterally, black when mature; the enlarged persistent sepals, 1 to 2 cm long, become showy pink to coral-red (October to January).

This species has been divided into two subspecies: all the material south of the Zambezi River is placed in the typical subspecies, subsp. *pulchra;* in countries to the north this is replaced by subsp. *hoffmanni-ottonis* (Engl.) N. K. B. Robson.

The wood is tough and close-grained but is liable to crack and apparently has little use; the branches are brittle. The unpleasant-smelling greenish-brown oil yielded by the seeds has been reported to be poisonous but in Zambia it is regarded as edible and is much esteemed. The possibility of using the residue as a stock feed has been considered. A man seeking work may slip a root into his pocket as a talisman and hunters sometimes carry a piece as a lucky charm. Bushmen of the southern Kalahari use it to grease their heads and it makes a fair quality soap.

Ochna rovumensis Gilg
S.A. no: —
Rhod. no: 707   Closed-fruit ochna

A shrub or small tree 1 to 4 m in height; occurring at low altitudes, in shaded areas of dense woodland or jesse bush and in riverine fringe thicket, especially among rocks. **Bark:** grey to grey-brown, smooth, frequently somewhat mottled; branchlets with small lenticels. **Leaves:** elliptic, 3 to 6,5 × 1,3 to 3,5 cm; the midrib, lateral veins and net-veining are conspicuous; apex tapering; base tapering to rather rounded; margin finely toothed, frequently wavy; petiole slender, up to 2 mm long. **Flowers:** unusually shaped, the sepals, green at first, do not open back but remain closed, forming an urn-shaped structure about 1,3 cm long from which the bright yellow petals, up to 2,6 cm long, protrude at the mouth; solitary, at the ends of short axillary branchlets (November to December). **Fruit:** usually 5 separate carpels, each ovoid, about 10 mm in diameter, attached at the base, black when mature; the enlarged persistent sepals, 2 to 3 cm long, become showy red, usually remaining closed over the fruits, but occasionally finally opening back (December to February).

Ochna schweinfurthiana F. Hoffm.
[*O. cyanophylla* N. K. B. Robson]
S.A. no: —
Rhod. no: 708   Brick-red ochna

A small tree 3 to 7 m in height; occurring over a considerable range of altitudes in open deciduous woodland. **Bark:** dark grey, thick, fissured and cracked, separating into conspicuous square segments; branchlets without lenticels. **Leaves:** elliptic, 5 to 13,5 × 1,7 to 5,5 cm, but usually about 10 to 11 cm long, rather olive-green; net-veining conspicuous on the upper surface; apex somewhat rounded; base narrowly tapering into the petiole; margin bluntly toothed, sometimes almost scalloped; petiole stout, up to 1,2 cm long. **Flowers:** bright yellow, up to 1,5 cm in diameter, sweetly scented, in a condensed raceme with 4 to 10 flowers on a very short central stem, appearing before or with the young coppery leaves; the petals fall very early (September to November). **Fruit:** usually 2 to 4 separate carpels, each ovoid, up to 9 × 7 mm, attached at the base, black when mature; the enlarged persistent sepals, up to 1,5 cm long, become cherry-red or orange to brick-red (October to January).

Ochna serrulata (Hochst.) Walp.

[*O. atropurpurea* auct. non DC.]
S.A. no: 479,1   Carnival bush. Fynblaarrooihout
Rhod. no: —

A shrub or small tree, usually 2 to 3 m in height, very occasionally reaching 6 m; occurring at the margin of forest, in scrub and on rocky hill slopes. **Bark:** brown, smooth; branchlets densely covered with rough lenticels. **Leaves:** elliptic, up to 5 × 0,7 cm, usually smaller, glossy dark green above, slightly paler green below; apex and base shortly tapering to rounded; margin finely toothed; petiole 1 to 1,5 mm long. **Flowers:** showy yellow, about 2 cm in diameter, sweetly scented, solitary, on short, leafless, side branches; the petals fall early but they make a fine show when the flowers first open (September to November, occasionally on to March). **Fruit:** usually 5 to 6 separate carpels, almost spherical, attached near the base, black when mature; the enlarged persistent sepals, less than 2 cm long, turn red (January to February onwards).

This is a most decorative shrub or small tree both in flower and fruit. The wood is reddish. The Zulus use a decoction of the root to treat children suffering from bone diseases or gangrenous rectitis.

2. BRACKENRIDGEA A. Gray

Brackenridgea zanguebarica Oliver

S.A. no: —
Rhod. no: 709   Brackenridgea

A shrub or small tree, 3 to 5 m in height, occasionally taller; occurring at the margins of evergreen forest, but also at low altitudes in open woodland and coastal bush. **Bark:** dark brown to black, very rough, with knobby protuberances which are yellow inside when broken off; under the bark there is a yellow pigment which can be exposed by slashing. **Leaves:** alternate, simple, elliptic to obovate, rather small, usually 4 to 5 × 1,5 to 2 cm, glossy green above, dull green below, without hairs; with distinctive veining, the fine and numerous lateral veins form an angle of 45° with the midrib, while the tertiary veins are conspicuously cross-hatched and clearly defined above like a fine etching; apex broadly tapering to rounded; base tapering; margin finely toothed, the teeth having glands which are not visible to the naked eye; petiole up to 2,5 mm long. Stipules markedly striate, sometimes divided into linear segments, persistent on first year shoots. **Flowers:** very *Ochna*-like, white to cream or pink, 8 to 10 mm in diameter, faintly scented, fascicled in groups of 2 to 4, terminal or at the base of the new growth. Bisexual; floral parts in fours to fives; sepals bent right back; petals narrow, up to 5 mm long, falling early; stamens 10 to 20, free, falling early; ovary of 5 to 10 separate carpels (October to November). **Fruit:** also very *Ochna*-like, usually 1 to 3 separate ovoid carpels, each about 6 × 6 mm, black when mature; the enlarged persistent sepals become crimson, are slender, up to 8 mm long, and return to horizontal from their curved back position (November to February).

CLUSIACEAE (nom. altern. **Guttiferae**) *(The St John's wort family)*

Key to the genera:

1 Petals large; flowers up to 5 cm in diameter, showy, yellow, without hairs; fruit a small dehiscent capsule .... **1. Hypericum**

Petals small; flowers not more than 1,5 cm in diameter, greenish-yellow, white to cream, with hairs; fruits fleshy 2

2 Young leaves and the under surface of mature leaves without dense rusty hairs; leaves narrowly to somewhat broadly elliptic, with the margin often conspicuously wavy; fruits large, 1,3 to 2,5 cm long .... **4. Garcinia**

Young leaves and under surface of mature leaves with dense, brown to rusty hairs; leaves broadly ovate; margin not conspicuously wavy; fruits small, berry-like, up to 6 mm in diameter 3

3 Young leaves remain pressed together until 2,5 cm long, or more, forming conspicuous tips to the branchlets; petiole up to 3 cm long. Confined to areas of medium to low altitude forest or riverine forest .... **3. Harungana**

Young leaves soon separate, petiole very short to almost absent; widespread over a wide range of altitudes, in open woodland and wooded grassland .... **2. Psorospermum**

1. HYPERICUM L.

Herbs, shrubs or trees. **Leaves:** opposite, simple, with translucent glands or streaks. **Flowers:** terminal, solitary, or in dense branched heads, cymes or panicles. Bisexual; all floral parts in fives; petals yellow, large, conspicuous; stamens many in 5 clusters, collectively forming a characteristic central mass. **Fruit:** a small dehiscent capsule.

St John's wort is a name loosely applied to almost all species of this genus, that most often encountered in gardens being the east Asian *H. chinense* L. These species have long been known for their medicinal properties, hence the name 'wort' which is the Old English term for a plant used as medicine. In medieval times monks dedicated this genus to St John the Baptist.

Key to the indigenous tree species of *Hypericum:*

Leaves small, usually about 2 × 0,5 cm, in opposite pairs crowded along the stems   **H. revolutum**

Leaves much larger, 3 to 8 × 1 to 3 cm, more widely spaced along the stems   **H. roeperanum**

Hypericum revolutum Vahl   Illust. 194

[*H. lanceolatum* Lam.; *H. leucoptychodes* Steudel ex A. Rich.]

S.A. no: 484   Curry bush. Kerriebos

Rhod. no: 710   Curry bush

A shrub or small tree 1 to 3 m in height; occurring at high altitudes in open mountain grassland, along streams and at the margin of evergreen forest; often a pioneer to forest in plant succession and therefore it is ecologically important. **Bark:** brown to reddish-brown, scaly. **Leaves:** small, narrow, usually about 2 × 0,5 cm, in opposite pairs crowded along the stems; fresh green to slightly bluish-green; veins not conspicuous; apex tapering; base clasping the stem; margin entire; petiole absent. **Flowers:** bright yellow, up to 5 cm in diameter, solitary, terminal; petals large, ovate; stamens forming a conspicuous central mass (sporadically at most times of the year). **Fruit:** a reddish-brown capsule, 1 to 1,3 × 0,7 to 1 cm (at most times of the year).

This is a beautiful shrub for the garden; it does well under a wide range of conditions, suckering from roots and propagating easily from cuttings. It gives off a distinct smell of curry.

Hypericum roeperanum Schimper ex A. Rich.
S.A. no: Large-leaved hypericum. Grootblaarkerriebos
Rhod. no: 711   Large-leaved St John's wort

A shrub or small tree up to 5 m in height; occurring at medium to high altitudes, at the margins of evergreen forest, in mountain grassland, moist bamboo thickets and often along stream banks. This resembles the previous species, but is easily distinguished by the much larger leaves, 3 to 8 × 1 to 3 cm, which are more widely spaced along the stems.

2. PSOROSPERMUM Spach

Psorospermum febrifugum Spach   Illust. 195
S.A. no: —
Rhod. no: 712   Christmas berry

A shrub or small tree 3 to 4 m in height, occasionally reaching 7 m; occurring over a wide range of altitudes, scattered through open woodland. **Bark:** grey to brown, rough, rather corky, flaking or peeling in strips. **Leaves:** simple, strictly opposite, with each pair at right angles to the next, elliptic to almost circular, up to 11 × 8 cm, but usually about 4 to 6 cm long, dark green and rather shiny above, with dense rusty hairs below; net-veining conspicuous, particularly on the upper surface; apex broadly tapering to rounded; base rounded to shallowly lobed; margin entire; petioles almost absent. **Flowers:** creamy-white, about 8 mm in diameter, inconspicuous, sweetly scented, in branched, rather compact, terminal heads, or panicles, up to 4 × 4 cm, the stalks and the backs of the calyces densely

611

covered with rusty hairs. Bisexual; all floral parts in fives; sepals glandular; petals with hairs on the inside; stamens many in clusters of 5; ovary 5-chambered (October to December). **Fruit:** a small berry, about 6 mm in diameter, bright red to dark red when mature (November to March).

The bright red berries are sometimes used as decorations at Christmas time in place of the traditional holly. The roots, pounded and mixed with goat's fat, provide a remedy for eczema in African medicine, and are considered to be effective in the treatment of skin diseases and insect bites. There is a superstition that a person wearing a piece of the plant in his hair will be invisible to wild animals.

3. HARUNGANA Lam.

Harungana madagascariensis Lam. ex Poiret   Illust. 196
S.A. no: —
Rhod. no: 713   Orange-milk tree

A small to medium sized bushy tree 4 to 7 m in height, but sometimes reaching 10 to 15 m; occurring at medium to low altitudes in evergreen forest, at forest margins and along river and stream banks; it is one of the earliest colonisers in cleared forest. **Bark:** brown, rather rough and scaly, frequently vertically fissured. A distinctive feature is the bright orange paint-like sap which exudes if leaves are snapped off or if branches are broken. **Leaves:** opposite, simple, elliptic, 6 to 20 × 3 to 10 cm, glossy dark green above with prominent veining, the under surface with dense rusty hairs which may be partially lost by maturity but usually persist; the young leaves at the ends of the branches are distinctive and remain tightly pressed together until quite large; apex tapering; base broadly tapering to rounded; margin entire; petiole up to 3 cm long. **Flowers:** cream, about 5 mm in diameter, sweetly almond scented, in dense many-flowered flat terminal heads (corymbose panicles), 8 to 20 cm in diameter, the stalks and calyces covered with short rusty hairs. Bisexual; all floral parts in fives; sepals glandular; petals with hairs on the inside; stamens in 5 clusters, each cluster made up of a few stamens joined for most of their length, with a sterile cluster, or fasciclode, between each fertile cluster; ovary 5-chambered (January to April). **Fruit:** berry-like, 2 to 4 mm in diameter, greenish-orange becoming deep red when mature, in heavy, massed, terminal heads up to 25 to 30 cm in diameter (April to October).

These trees, with their general browny-yellow appearance, are distinctive in the field. The wood is pinkish-yellow and rather light; the sap has been employed as a dye and in the treatment of scabies and tapeworm. The leaf is used as a remedy for haemorrhages, diarrhoea, gonorrhoea, sore throats and fevers, while the resin from the flower stalks is believed to ease colic and to check infection after childbirth.

4. GARCINIA L.

Shrubs or trees, secreting a yellow sap. **Leaves:** opposite, occasionally whorled,' simple, often with glandular canals and brownish resin canals. **Flowers:** terminal or axillary, solitary or in few- to many-flowered cymes. Sexes usually separate, either on different trees or on the same tree; floral parts in fours to fives; sepals free; petals greenish-white to yellow; stamens in 4 to 5 clusters, alternating with clusters of sterile staminodes, or fasciclodes, the latter persisting in female flowers; ovary 2- to 5-chambered, vestigial or absent in male flowers. **Fruit:** a tough, fleshy berry.

Key to the tree species of *Garcinia:*
1 Leaf apex generally rounded, with or without a short sharp tip, but not narrowly tapering to attenuate; sometimes notched 2
  Leaf apex narrowly tapering or attenuate 3
2 Occurring in evergreen forest and on mountain rocky outcrops; endemic to South Africa and Swaziland; with leathery, pliable leaves .... **G. gerrardii**
  Occurring at low altitudes, along rivers and in thornveld; with hard, stiff leaves ....
  .... **G. livingstonei**
3 Apex usually tapering, may tend to be attenuate but without a conspicuous long narrow tip; lateral veins leave the midrib almost at right angles and then run parallel and close together; leaves bluish to grey-green, dull above .... **G. kingäensis**
  Apex narrowly and conspicuously attenuate; lateral veins leave the midrib at a more acute angle, and are more widely spaced than in the preceding species; leaves shiny dark green above ..
  .... **G. buchananii**

Garcinia gerrardii Harvey ex T. R. Sim
[*G. natalensis* Schlechter; *G. transvaalensis* Burtt Davy]
S.A. no: 485   Forest garcinia. Bosgeelmelkhout
Rhod. no: —

A large shrub or small tree 4 to 5 m in height, but sometimes reaching 10 to 13 m; occurring in evergreen forest, at forest margins and on cliff faces. **Bark:** dark grey to brown, sometimes vertically ridged and frequently with pale patches of lichen; branchlets acutely and conspicuously angled. All parts contain a yellow sap. **Leaves:** oval to elliptic, 4 to 10 × 2,5 to 7 cm, leathery, shiny green above, rather paler green and sometimes brownish tinged below; apex broadly tapering to rounded; base broadly tapering; margin entire, rolled under, often wavy; petiole furrowed, 0,5 to 1,5 cm long. **Flowers:** white or cream, up to 1,5 cm in diameter, in 3- to 9-flowered terminal heads, 4 to 6 cm long (November to January). **Fruit:** berry-like, ovoid, up to 2 cm long, rather fleshy, yellow when mature, produced in profusion; apparently not eaten (March to June).
This species closely resembles *G. volkensii* Engl. which occurs north of the Zambezi River.

Garcinia buchananii Baker   Illust. 197
S.A. no: —
Rhod. no: 714   Granite garcinia

A small tree 4 to 8 m in height, often densely branched; occurring on granite koppies and rocky formations generally, also in riverine fringe forest. **Bark:** greyish-brown, rather rough; all parts contain a rather sticky, yellow sap. **Leaves:** distinctive, oblong or elliptic, 5 to 11 × 3 to 5 cm, thickly

613

leathery, shiny dark green above, paler green below, with many lateral veins conspicuously and finely etched on both leaf surfaces; apex tapering, attenuate into a conspicuous narrow tip; base tapering; margin entire, tightly rolled under and conspicuously wavy; petiole about 5 mm long, channelled above, often tinged with red. **Flowers:** greenish-yellow, 1 to 1,5 cm in diameter, axillary, usually solitary, shortly stalked so that the flower lies close against the stem, or in 2- to 3-flowered clusters; the petals fall very early (September to November). **Fruit:** almost spherical, up to 2,5 cm in diameter, fleshy, yellow to orange when mature, edible (March to June).

The wood is hard and yellow. An infusion of the bark is considered to be an aphrodisiac and is also used as a lotion for septic and venereal sores. The fruit contains ascorbic acid (vitamin C).

Garcinia kingäensis Engl.

[*G. mlanjiensis* Dunkley]
S.A. no: —
Rhod. no: 715   Northern forest garcinia

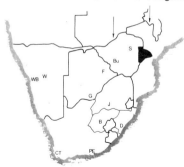

A small to medium sized tree, 4 to 13 m in height, often slender with numerous, regularly formed, horizontal branches; occurring as an under-storey tree in evergreen forest and in forested ravines. **Bark:** brown, smooth; young branches grooved and square in section. **Leaves:** narrowly elliptic to almost oblong, 6 to 16 × 3 to 6 cm but usually about 11 to 12 cm long, leathery, bluish to grey-green, dull above, paler green below, the young leaves very pale green with many conspicuous, fine, almost parallel veins on both surfaces, the veining on the under surface being sometimes almost masked by the darker longitudinal glandular canals; apex and base tapering; margin entire, wavy; petiole channelled above, about 10 mm long, transversely wrinkled (like a stocking slipping down). The leaves yield a yellow latex. **Flowers:** white to yellowish-green, about 10 mm in diameter, solitary or in small groups of 2 to 7 on stout stalks, or pedicels, produced on dwarf spurs arising on older branches in the axils of fallen leaves; often produced in profusion, but falling easily (September to October). **Fruit:** almost spherical, up to 2,5 cm in diameter, becoming yellow-orange when mature, edible (December to January).

Garcinia livingstonei T. Anders.

S.A. no: 486   African mangosteen. Laeveldse geelmelkhout

Rhod. no: 716   African mangosteen

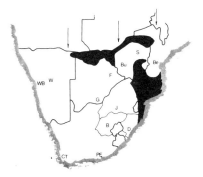
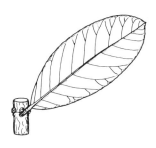

A small to medium sized tree 2 to 10 m in height; it has a distinctive habit, being stiff with rigid branches rising at an acute angle; occurring at low altitudes, in riverine fringes, and in open woodland, often found growing under the shelter of larger trees. **Bark:** grey to grey-black, rough; all parts exude a pale yellow sticky sap. **Leaves:** usually in whorls of 3 (occasionally 4, or opposite), elliptic, oblong to ovate, 4 to 14 × 1,5 to 11 cm, but usually about 9 to 11 cm long, leathery, glossy dark green above, paler green below, the young leaves bright red; apex very broadly tapering to rounded, sometimes notched; base tapering to rounded; margin usually entire, occasionally shallowly scalloped, tightly rolled under and wavy; petiole stout, 4 to 8 mm long. **Flowers:** cream to greenish-yellow, 6 to 14 mm in diameter, on slender stalks in groups of 5 to 15 on short knobby side spurs clustered along the older stems; sweetly scented (August to September). **Fruit:** almost spherical, up to 2,5 cm in diameter, yellow to orange when mature (November to December).

The fruits are produced in profusion and are edible, having a refreshing acid-sweet flesh. In Moçambique they are used to prepare a pleasant alcoholic beverage. Extracts of the leaves and flowers have been tested and show antibiotic properties. The wood is yellowish-white and of medium weight, but is susceptible to borers; nevertheless it is used as a general purpose timber. This species resembles *G. buchanaii* but is larger and with leaves and branchlets which are conspicuously 3-whorled (occasionally 2 to 4); in addition the leaves are wider and lack the dark longitudinal streaks of the glandular canals.

DIPTEROCARPACEAE

MONOTES A.DC.

Shrubs or trees. **Leaves:** alternate, simple, with an extra-floral nectary at the base of the midrib, distinctive as a small spot. **Flowers:** in axillary clusters. Bisexual; all floral parts in fives; sepals with fine hairs, persistent, increasing in size as they grow older so that, in fruit, they resemble large membraneous petals; petals narrow with fine hairs; stamens many, forming a central mass; ovary 3-chambered. **Fruit:** almost spherical, indehiscent, dry, hard, surrounded by the five large calyx lobes, resembling a dry, brittle, star-like flower.

Key to the tree species of *Monotes:*
1 Upper surface of leaves scaberulous, harsh to the touch .... **M. katangensis**
  Upper surface of leaves not harsh to the touch 2
2 Field impression of the tree green; upper surface of leaves dark green, under surface pale greyish
    with silvery hairs .... **M. engleri**
  Field impression of the tree brownish yellow-green; upper surface of the leaves yellow-green,
    under surface the same colour but dull or brownish, especially along the veins ....
    .... **M. glaber**

Monotes engleri Gilg
[*M. tomentellus* Hutch.]
S.A. no: —
Rhod. no: 717   Pink-fruited monotes

615

Usually a small tree about 3 m in height, but occasionally reaching 10 m; occurring at medium altitudes in mixed woodland. **Bark:** grey to dark grey, smooth to rather rough. **Leaves:** broadly elliptic to oblong, 4 to 11 × 2,5 to 6 cm, dark green above, whitish to grey with silvery hairs below; apex rounded, often notched; base rounded or lobed; margin entire; petiole slender, 1 to 2 cm long. Stipules about 10 mm long, slender, persisting for a short time but falling rather early. **Flowers:** yellowish, the petals finely tipped with pale orange, about 10 mm in diameter, in short, axillary heads, 2 to 3 cm long, the stems and calyces covered with fine grey or yellowish hairs (November to February). **Fruit:** almost spherical, 1 to 1,5 cm in diameter; the persistent sepals, 4 to 5 × 2 to 2,5 cm, have conspicuous net-veining and are pink to reddish when young but become pale brown when mature and dry (February to June).

The leaves of this species somewhat resemble those of *Parinari curatellifolia,* but the flowers and fruits and general shape of the tree, are definitive. The wood is used for roofing poles and for the floor poles of granaries; it makes good charcoal.

Monotes glaber Sprague   Illust. 198
S.A. no: —
Rhod. no: 718   Pale-fruited monotes

A small to medium sized tree 4 to 10 m in height; occurring in open woodland, often on sandveld. **Bark:** brown to dark brown, rough, especially on the lower parts of the trunk, tending to become smooth higher up; branches brittle. **Leaves:** elliptic to oblong, 4 to 11 × 1,5 to 6 cm, but usually about 5 to 7 cm long, shiny yellowish-green above, the same colour but dull or brownish below, especially along the veins; new leaves very glossy and rather sticky; apex and base broadly tapering to rounded; margin entire; petioles 5 to 15 mm long. Stipules 5 to 10 × 0,5 to 1 mm, tending to persist and often giving the young branchlets an almost whiskery appearance which is very characteristic. **Flowers:** pale greenish-yellow, star-like, 1 to 1,5 cm in diameter, in slender, 4- to 10-flowered, lax, axillary heads, 2 to 4 cm long, the stalks and the backs of the calyces with fine golden brown hairs (November to March). **Fruit:** almost spherical, ridged, about 10 mm in diameter; the persistent sepals are greenish-yellow sometimes tinged with pink at first, but later become dry and straw-coloured, up to 3 × 1,2 cm (February to July).

The heartwood is light in colour with dark streaks, and although it is difficult to work it takes a good polish; potentially it is a timber suitable for furniture, but the pieces are usually too small to be of any use. The root bark is dried, powdered and sprinkled on food twice daily to treat heart ailments.

616

Monotes katangensis (De Wild.) De Wild.
S.A. no: —
Rhod. no: 719   Red-fruited monotes

A small to medium sized tree, 5 to 13 m in height; occurring in *Brachystegia* woodland, on hillsides and sometimes on rocky koppies. **Bark:** grey, smooth to rather rough with vertical fissures. **Leaves:** elliptic to oblong, 6 to 10 × 3 to 6 cm, leathery, the upper surface green and rather harsh to the touch due to minute rough hairs, the under surface yellowish and velvety with the midrib and lateral veins prominent and conspicuous; apex broadly tapering to rounded, sometimes notched; base broadly tapering, square to slightly lobed; margin entire, tending to roll under; petiole thick, 1 to 2 cm long. Stipules resemble those of the other two species, but fall early and are not conspicuous. **Flowers:** creamy-white, up to 2 cm in diameter, with dense silky hairs, in dense many-flowered axillary clusters, forming shortly branched spike-like racemes up to 15 cm long (January to June). **Fruit:** almost spherical, about 10 mm in diameter, in crowded terminal clusters; with persistent sepals, distinctive bright pinkish-red to reddish-purple, up to 4 × 2 cm, very showy and most conspicuous (July to December).

TAMARICACEAE *(The tamarisk family)*

TAMARIX L.

A genus of some 90 species found from Europe to North China. *T. mannifera* is attacked by a small insect, *Coccus manniparus*, which causes a white substance to fall from holes in the stem; this is the *manna* of the Bedouins living between Egypt and Afghanastan and is said to be the manna which fed the children of Israel. One species is indigenous in southern Africa.

Tamarix usneoides E. Meyer ex Bunge   Illust. 199
[*T. austro-africana* Schinz; *T. articulata* auct. non Vahl]
S.A. no: 487   Wild tamarisk. Abiekwasgeelhout
Rhod. no: —

A shrub or small to medium sized tree, very occasionally reaching 10 m in height; occurring in and fringing desert areas, along brackish shore lines, river banks and frequently in dry river beds. **Bark:**   **617**

dark to almost black, rough. **Leaves:** specially adapted to harsh conditions, very small, scale-like, closely overlapping along the branchlets, yellowish grey-green. **Flowers:** very small, pale whitish-cream, in delicate feathery axillary sprays, or racemes. Bisexual; floral parts in fours to fives; sepals free; petals free or slightly joined at the base; disc glandular, angled or lobed; stamens 4 to 10, rarely 12, in 2 whorls, free; ovary 1-chambered (January to March). **Fruit:** a very small capsule, shedding fine light seeds usually distributed by seasonal river water (February to April).

The leaves provide a valuable fodder in areas where little else exists and the wood is used as a fuel, but is not particularly good. One or more exotic species is cultivated as an ornamental tree and it seems that the population round the mouth of the Swakop river in South West Africa is made up of hybrids between the indigenous species and one of the exotics, *T. ramosissima* Ledb.

CANELLACEAE

WARBURGIA Engl.

Warburgia salutaris (Bertol. f.) Chiov.
[*Chibaca salutaris* Bertol. f.; *Warburgia ugandensis* Sprague; *W. breyeri* Pott]
S.A. no: 488   Pepper-bark tree. Peperbasboom
Rhod. no: 720   Pepper-bark tree

A slender tree usually 5 to 10 m in height, but reaching 20 m in some areas; occurring in evergreen forest and wooded ravines. **Bark:** rich brown, rough. **Leaves:** alternate, simple, aromatic, elliptic to lanceolate, 4,5 to 11 × 1 to 3 cm, glossy dark green above, paler green and dull below; midrib frequently slightly off-centre; apex and base tapering; margin entire; petiole 1 to 3 mm long. **Flowers:** white or greenish, up to 7 mm in diameter, solitary, axillary, or in tight few-flowered heads, or cymes. Bisexual; sepals 3; petals 10 in 2 whorls, obovate, gland-dotted, overlapping; stamens 10, joined to form a tube which is a prominent structure in the centre of the flower, enveloping the ovary and also most of the style; ovary elongate-oblong (April). **Fruit:** a berry, spherical, up to 4 cm in diameter; skin leathery, glandular, black when mature (October to January).

This tree has been used medicinally from early times; the specific name means 'salutary' or 'health giving'. The inner bark is reddish, bitter and peppery and has a variety of applications. It provides a treatment for the common cold; dried and ground to a snuff it is used to clear the sinuses; it is chewed, or smoke from the burning bark is inhaled as a remedy for chest complaints and boiled in water with the roots it is considered effective against malaria. A small piece of bark fetches up to R$1,00 (or SA R1,00) among the African peoples, and is so much in demand that many trees in southern Africa, particularly the larger specimens, have been destroyed. The heartwood is pale or greenish, darkening on exposure to the air. It is oily and aromatic when freshly cut and although it saws, planes and polishes well it is not durable. *Warburgia* also occurs in countries to the north of Zambia and Malawi.

VIOLACEAE *(The violet family)*

RINOREA Aubl.

Shrubs or small trees. **Leaves:** alternate (in all the species dealt with here), rarely opposite or whorled, simple. Stipules usually present, sometimes persisting for a while and quite conspicuous, although

618

very slender. **Flowers:** in axillary or terminal racemes or panicles. Bisexual; all floral parts in fives; sepals small; petals free, but overlapping to form a bell-shape, or spreading and curling back, the upper petal often spurred; stamens free or joined to form a ring or tube; ovary 1-chambered, without a stalk. **Fruit:** a dehiscent capsule.

Key to the tree species of *Rinorea:*
1 Leaves usually less than 9 cm long 2
  Leaves usually more than 9 cm long 3
2 Flowers tend to be produced in profusion; stamens free. Occurring in central Moçambique and the east and south of Rhodesia, not in South Africa .... **R. convallarioides**
  Tends to be few-flowered; stamens joined to form a tube. Occurring in South Africa, near Beira in Moçambique, and northwards .... **R. angustifolia**
3 Leaf margins jaggedly toothed, each tooth being spine-tipped, the spines 2 mm long or more 4
  Leaf margins rather sparsely toothed or scalloped, not usually spine-tipped, but if the teeth tend to be spiny then the spines are less than 2 mm long 5
4 Leaf margins with the teeth set regularly and closely together; flowers up to 10 mm in diameter, in loose, well-branched, terminal heads up to 12 cm long; fruits up to 2,5 cm long **R. arborea**
  Leaf margins with the teeth more widely spaced, but the teeth larger and more spinous, holly-like; flowers rarely more than 5 mm in diameter, in short, dense, very shortly branched, terminal heads up to 8 cm long, but usually less; fruits up to 1,5 cm long .... **R. ilicifolia**
5 Under surface of the leaves with net-veining clear and conspicuous; leaves tend to be narrowly elliptic to oblanceolate .... **R. ferruginea**
  Under surface of the leaves without conspicuous net-veining; leaves tend to be broadly elliptic to ovate .... **R. elliptica**

Rinorea angustifolia (Thouars) Baillon
[*R. holtzii* Engl.; *R. natalensis* Engl.]
S.A. no: 489   White violet-bush. Witviooltjiebos
Rhod. no: —

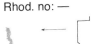

A shrub or much-branched tree, 3 to 6 m in height; occurring as part of the under-storey in evergreen forest, also in woodland where it can be thicket forming. **Bark:** pale grey to brown, smooth. **Leaves:** narrowly elliptic to oblong, 2 to 7 × 1 to 2,5 cm, glossy dark green above, slightly paler below, thinly textured; veining prominent on both surfaces, hairs may be present along the midrib only; apex tapering, abruptly attenuate; base rounded; margin shallowly toothed to scalloped; petiole 2 to 3 mm long. Stipules narrow, 2 to 3 mm long, finely hairy, falling rather early. **Flowers:** white to greenish, about 10 mm in diameter, the petals narrow and curling backwards, inconspicuous, sweetly scented, in 1- to 8-flowered, short, axillary sprays 2 to 4 cm long; the anthers, joined to form a tube, have a small, reddish-purple, lance-shaped appendage (October to November). **Fruit:** a 3-lobed ovoid capsule, 1 to 1,5 cm long, reddish-brown when mature (November to January).

Rinorea arborea Thouars
S.A. no: —
Rhod. no: 721/1   Large-fruited rinorea

A shrub or small tree 3 to 7 m in height; occurring at low altitudes in evergreen forest and open woodland. **Bark:** greyish-brown to brown, rather scaly. **Leaves:** elliptic to oblong, up to 24 × 9 cm

619

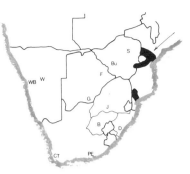

but usually about 15 to 16 cm long, rather leathery, shiny green, with prominent veins, without hairs on either surface; apex and base tapering; margin with jagged, closely and regularly set, spine-tipped teeth; petiole 1,5 to 5 cm long, without hairs. Stipules falling very early. **Flowers:** white to cream, about 10 mm in diameter, widely bell-shaped, the stamens joined to form a tube; in loose, well-branched heads, or compound terminal panicles, 7 to 12 cm long, near the ends of the branches (October to January). **Fruit:** an ovoid, roughly wrinkled, woody capsule, up to 2,5 cm long, brown when mature (January to March).

Rinorea convallarioides (E. G. Baker) Eyles
S.A. no: —
Rhod. no: 721   Heath rinorea

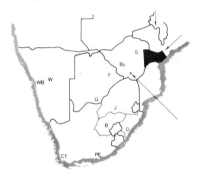

A shrub or small tree 2 to 5 m in height; occurring as part of the under-storey in evergreen forest. **Bark:** light grey to brown, smooth. **Leaves:** oblong to elliptic, 4 to 7 × 1,5 to 4 cm, thinly textured, dark shiny green to greyish-green on both surfaces, with hairs on the main veins only; apex tapering; base tapering to rounded; margin conspicuously toothed; petiole channelled above, 2 to 4 mm long. Stipules triangular, 3 to 4 mm long, falling rather early. **Flowers:** greenish-white to cream, bell-shaped, about 6 mm long, stamens free, sweetly scented, in few- to many-flowered, axillary, spike-like racemes, up to 5 cm long, may be insignificant or, when in profusion, very attractive, resembling a heath (July to September). **Fruit:** a 3-lobed, ovoid capsule, 1 to 1,5 cm long, yellowish-green when mature (October).
This species resembles *R. angustifolia* but it tends to be more floriferous and the stamens are free and not joined as they are in the latter species.

Rinorea elliptica (Oliver) Kuntze
S.A. no: —
Rhod. no: 722   Red-fruited rinorea

A small spreading tree rarely more than 3 to 8 m in height; occurring at low altitudes in evergreen forest and riverine fringe forest. **Bark:** brown to brownish-green, smooth to rather rough. **Leaves:** narrowly to broadly elliptic or ovate, 5 to 10 × 1,4 to 5 cm, bright green, without hairs; apex tapering; base broadly tapering to rounded; margin finely toothed; petiole up to 10 mm long, with or without minute hairs. Stipules up to 10 mm long, thread-like, persisting for a short while. **Flowers:** white, white flushed with pink or entirely salmon, 1 to 1,5 cm in diameter, petals curling back, the stamens

joined to form a tube, sweetly scented, stalks up to 1,5 cm, in loose, axillary spike-like racemes, 1 to 6 cm long (October to November). **Fruit:** an almost spherical capsule, about 6 mm in diameter, drawn into an abrupt sharp point, bright red when mature, splitting into 3 curled segments (November to January).

Rinorea ferruginea Engl.

[*R. gazensis* (E. G. Baker) Brandt]
S.A. no: —
Rhod. no: 723   Hairy-leaved rinorea

A shrub or small tree 2 to 6 m in height; occurring as a fairly common constituent of the under-storey in evergreen forest. **Bark:** pale greyish-brown, rather smooth. **Leaves:** narrowly elliptic to oblanceolate, 12 to 20 × 4,5 to 8 cm, shiny green above, paler green below, net-veining pale and conspicuous on the under surface; the midrib and lateral veins covered with woolly rusty hairs; apex abruptly tapering, finally attenuate into a conspicuous slender tip; base tapering; margin with conspicuous rather slender teeth almost at right angles to the margin; petiole slender, up to 3,5 cm long, with or without woolly rusty hairs. Stipules fall very early. **Flowers:** pale waxy yellow, the petals not curving back, widely bell-shaped about 10 mm long, in short erect terminal heads, about 5 cm long, inconspicuous; the stamens are joined to form a tube and the anthers have orange-brown lanceolate appendages (October to December). **Fruit:** an almost spherical woody capsule, 1 to 1,3 cm in diameter, dark brown when mature; when they have split and have shed the seeds the old capsules drop from the tree at the slightest touch (January to February).

Rinorea ilicifolia (Welw. ex Oliver) Kuntze

S.A. no: 490   Yellow violet-bush. Geelviooltjiebos
Rhod. no: 724   Holly-leaved rinorea

A shrub or small tree 1 to 4 m in height; occurring as part of the under-storey in evergreen forest. **Bark:** grey to brown. **Leaves:** elliptic, broadly elliptic to ovate, 7 to 20 × 3 to 8 cm, glossy bright green or bluish-green above, pale green and sometimes with hairs along the main veins below; apex tapering, broadly tapering to rounded; base tapering to rounded; margin spine-toothed; petiole up to 3 cm long, finely hairy. Stipules up to 10 mm long, falling very early. **Flowers:** pale yellow, aging to deep yellow, about 10 mm in diameter, the petals tending to curl back, sweetly scented, the stamens forming a tube, in rather dense, shortly branched terminal heads up to 8 cm long (September

621

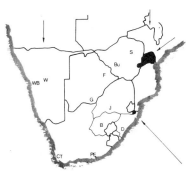

to December). **Fruit:** a 3-lobed, ovoid, wrinkled, woody capsule, about 1,5 cm long, purplish to brown when mature (December).

FLACOURTIACEAE *(The kei-apple family)*

Key to the genera:

1 Fruits indehiscent	2
Fruits dehiscent	10
2 Leaf apices attenuate or shortly so	3
Leaf apices tapering to rounded, not attenuate	5
3 Fruit a fleshy, almost spherical berry, up to 2 cm in diameter	**5. Scolopia**
Fruit hard shelled or slightly fleshy, 2,5 to 4 cm in diameter	4

4 Leaves oblong, 7 to 16 × 2 to 6 cm; margins spiny-toothed, the sharp teeth characteristically curving forward; flowers up to 2 cm in diameter, the central mass of stamens white; fruits thinly fleshy at first, reluctantly dehiscent at maturity, up to 4 cm in diameter; branches unarmed .... **1. Rawsonia**

Leaves ovate-elliptic, 3 to 12 × 1,5 to 6 cm; margins coarsely and bluntly toothed to scalloped, sometimes obscurely so, the teeth not spine-tipped nor curving forward; flowers up to 9 cm in diameter, the central mass of stamens golden yellow; fruits up to 6 cm in diameter, hard shelled, indehiscent; branches spiny .... **2. Oncoba**

5 Flowers usually with petals	6
Flowers always without petals	7
6 Stamens numerous; fruits fleshy	**5. Scolopia**
Stamens 5 only; fruits dry or thinly fleshy	**7. Gerrardina**
7 Leaves narrowly elliptic to oblanceolate; fruits about 10 mm in diameter, white when mature	**12. Aphloia**
Leaves elliptic to obovate or almost circular; fruits not white when mature	8
8 Fruits about 10 mm in diameter, warty	**11. Ludia**
Fruits smooth	9

9 Leaf margin toothed or scalloped; fruits more than 2 cm in diameter; ovary 4-chambered, flowers bisexual, occasionally sexes separate on the same tree .... **13. Flacourtia**

Leaf margins entire, occasionally obscurely toothed, but if so then the fruits are less than 2 cm in diameter; ovary 1- to 2-chambered (rarely 3), flowers with sexes separate on different trees .... **14. Dovyalis**

10 Leaves opposite .... **6. Pseudoscolopia**

   Leaves alternate or somewhat crowded on dwarf shoots 11

11 Leaf margins jaggedly toothed, the teeth curving forwards and spine-tipped, more than 2 mm long .... **1. Rawsonia**

   Leaf margins entire or may be toothed or scalloped, but not jaggedly so 12

12 Flowers white, large and showy, up to 10 cm in diameter; fruit oval, up to 5 cm long .... **3. Xylotheca**

   Flowers small, less than 10 mm in diameter; fruits less than 2 cm in diameter 13

13 Fruits about 1,5 cm (up to 2 cm) in diameter, grey-green or yellowish-green, rough and warty; seeds enveloped in a bright orange-red sticky coating .... **4. Kiggelaria**

   Fruits usually less than 1,5 cm in diameter, seeds without the sticky orange-red coating (although in one species the fruits may reach 2 cm in diameter and the seeds are enveloped for about half their length in a fleshy red aril) 14

14 Fruits about 5 mm long, splitting to release a few seeds covered with long white silky hairs .... **9. Bivinia**

   Seeds without long silky hairs 15

15 Margins of mature leaves entire (may be obscurely and very finely toothed when young), leaves with pellucid glandular dots or streaks .... **15. Casearia**

   Margins of mature leaves toothed or scalloped, at least in part, without pellucid glands .. 16

16 Leaves with 3 to 9 veins from the base, seed with a bright orange to red aril .... **10. Trimeria**

   Leaves with a midrib and lateral veins arising from it; seeds brown, without an aril .... **8. Homalium**

1. RAWSONIA Harvey & Sonder

Rawsonia lucida Harvey & Sonder
S.A. no: 491   Rawsonia. Bosperske
Rhod. no: 725   Rawsonia

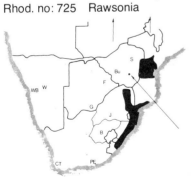

A shrub or small tree 3 to 5 m in height, very occasionally reaching 11 m; occurring as part of the under-storey in evergreen forest. **Bark:** brown, smooth; branches spreading and inclined to droop. **Leaves:** alternate, simple, oblong, 7 to 16 × 2 to 6 cm, leathery, glossy vivid green above (the specific name means shiny), paler green and dull below, the veins standing out clearly on both surfaces, but particularly on the under surface; apex tapering, finally attenuate; base broadly tapering; margin spine-toothed, with the sharp teeth curved, pointing – even arching– forward; petiole up to 1,2 cm long. Stipules narrow, up to 7 mm long, falling very early. **Flowers:** attractive, creamy-white to pale yellow, 1,5 to 2 cm in diameter, axillary, solitary or in few-flowered racemes, only 1 to 2 cm

623

long, shortly stalked so that the flowers are clustered closely along the young stems. Bisexual (very occasionally unisexual by abortion); floral parts in fours to fives; sepals free, overlapping, concave, persistent; petals similar in size and shape to the sepals but each with a petalloid scale opposite it, nearly twice as long as the petal and with a fleshy gland at the base; stamens white, many, forming a central mass; ovary 1-chambered, on a convex receptacle; sweetly scented (September to November). **Fruit:** a fleshy berry-like capsule, yellow to yellowish-brown, rather resembling a miniature orange, up to 4 cm in diameter, later becoming dry and reluctantly splitting from apex to base into 5 valves (November to February).

This species can be confused with *Rinorea ilicifolia*, but the spiny teeth on the leaves point forward, frequently arching; the large axillary flowers and the large yellow fruits also distinguish it from the small flowers, in terminal heads, and the pale brown capsules, 1 to 1,5 cm in diameter, of *Rinorea ilicifolia*. It may also be confused with *Drypetes natalensis* but in that species the leaf base is markedly asymmetric and the flowers and fruits are produced on the main trunk.

The wood is pale pink to reddish and is very hard, heavy, and tough; it is highly esteemed by the Zulus for making sticks.

2. ONCOBA Forsk.

Oncoba spinosa Forsk.   Illust. 200
S.A. no: 492   Snuff-box tree. Snuifkalbassie
Rhod. no: 726   Fried-egg flower

An often spiny shrub or small tree 3 to 5 m in height, occasionally reaching 8 m; occurring over a wide range of altitudes, in open woodland, among rocks and along river and stream banks; it can become thicket-forming. **Bark:** grey, mottled, rather smooth; the young branches are conspicuously greyish and speckled with lenticels; the axillary spines are straight and up to 5 cm long. **Leaves:** alternate, simple, ovate-elliptic, 3 to 12 × 1,5 to 6 cm, but usually about 7 × 3,5 cm, dark green, rather glossy, leathery; apex tapering, somewhat attenuate; base very broadly tapering to rounded; margin coarsely toothed to scalloped, occasionally obscurely so; petiole up to 6 mm long. **Flowers:** white, showy, up to 9 cm in diameter, with the central mass of golden stamens very conspicuous; solitary, axillary or terminal. Bisexual; sepals 3 to 4, free or joined at the base, overlapping; petals 5 to 20, obovate, up to 4 cm long, overlapping; stamens many; ovary 1-chambered; sweetly scented (September to January). **Fruit:** spherical, up to 6 cm in diameter, becoming dark reddish-brown when mature, hard-shelled, faintly ridged longitudinally, indehiscent; the small, shiny brown seeds, about 6 × 4 mm, are embedded in a dry, yellow, sour pulp, edible but not often eaten (April to July).

The seeds contain a drying oil which would be suitable for varnishes but it is too difficult to extract to be a commercial proposition. Snuff boxes are made from the hard-shelled fruits which, when the seeds inside them are dry, make amusing rattles for children and anklets and armlets to add rhythm to the movements of dancers. The root provides a remedy in African medicine for treating dysentery and bladder complaints; the wood is light brown and takes a good polish but the pieces are seldom large enough to be of any value.

3. XYLOTHECA Hochst.

Shrubs or small trees. **Leaves:** alternate, or clustered, simple. **Flowers:** rather large, showy, axillary or terminal, solitary or in branched heads, cymes or umbels. Bisexual, or may be male only by abortion; sepals 3 to 4, free or very shortly joined at the base, very concave; petals 7 to 14, white, resembling those of *Oncoba,* but narrower, free, overlapping; stamens many, free, forming a central mass; ovary 1-chambered, without a stalk. **Fruit:** a tough, woody capsule, splitting into 8 valves.

Key to the species of *Xylotheca:*
Leaves elliptic; seeds with a bright red aril covering the lower half .... **X. kraussiana**
Leaves obovate to broadly oblong; seeds without an aril, but embedded in a thin golden or scarlet pulp
.... **X. tettensis**

Xylotheca kraussiana Hochst.   Illust. 201
S.A. no: 493   African dog-rose. Afrikaanse hondsroos
Rhod. no: —

A handsome unarmed shrub or small tree, frequently 0,5 to 2 m, but sometimes reaching 5 m in height; occurring on coastal dunes, in dune forest and scrub. **Bark:** light grey, rough. **Leaves:** elliptic, 6 to 10 × 2 to 5 cm, dark green above, markedly paler green below, with or without fine soft hairs on both surfaces; apex tapering, broadly tapering to rounded; base tapering; margin entire, somewhat rolled under; petiole about 10 mm long. **Flowers:** white, up to 7 cm in diameter, the stamens forming a conspicuous yellow central mass, sweetly scented, in axillary or terminal groups of 2 to 3, or solitary; the trees are conspicuous for several months (September to November). **Fruit:** an ovoid woody capsule, 3 to 4 cm long, with the apex pointed, becoming brown when mature, often with longitudinal ridges, with or without short soft hairs, finally splitting into 8 valves to expose russet-brown seeds each of which has a conspicuous bright red aril over its lower half (January to May).

Xylotheca tettensis (Klotzsch) Gilg
S.A. no: —
Rhod. no: 727   Northern African dog-rose

A shrub or small tree reaching 5 m in height; occurring at low altitudes in open woodland. **Bark:** greyish; the young branches with or without long yellowish hairs. **Leaves:** alternate or clustered on dwarf lateral shoots; obovate to broadly oblong, 1,5 to 10 × 0,8 to 7,5 cm, paler green below than above, both surfaces with or without fine soft hairs; net-veining rather conspicuous below; apex broadly tapering to rounded; base tapering to square or even slightly lobed; margin entire, wavy; petiole up to 1,5 cm long. **Flowers:** satiny white, 5 to 10 cm in diameter, the stamens forming a

625

conspicuous yellow central mass, solitary, axillary, or in groups of 2 to 3 (August to January). **Fruit:** an ovoid woody capsule, 3 to 4 cm in diameter, with a conspicuous hard tip, finally splitting into 8 valves, the numerous yellowish-brown seeds embedded in a thin golden or scarlet pulp (February to April).

This species is divided into three varieties:

var. *tettensis* – with smaller leaves, usually less than 3 cm long, which are only sparsely hairy; occurring in Moçambique and northwards only;

var. *macrophylla* (Klotzsch) Wild – with larger leaves, more than 3 cm long, which are densely furry; in Moçambique and northwards, only just extending into Rhodesia;

var. *kirkii* (Oliver) Wild – leaves without hairs and not occurring south of the Zambezi River.

4. KIGGELARIA L.

Kiggelaria africana L.   Illust. 202
S.A. no: 494   Wild peach. Wildeperske
Rhod. no: 728   Pink-wood

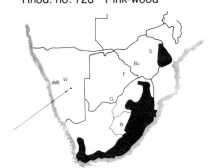

A small to medium sized tree 4 to 13 m in height; occurring in evergreen forest, frequently among rocks and on mountain grasslands. **Bark:** pale grey, smooth, darkening with age and becoming flaky; young branches yellowish-brown. **Leaves:** alternate, simple, oblong to elliptic, 3,5 to 9 × 2 to 5 cm, fresh green above, markedly paler green below, with dense yellowish or greyish soft hairs on both surfaces when young, losing most of these on the upper surface by maturity; apex and base tapering to broadly so; margin entire or rather obscurely toothed, wavy; petiole up to 1,5 cm long. **Flowers:** pale yellow to greenish-white, about 10 mm in diameter, axillary, solitary, on slender stalks about 1,5 cm long (female flowers), or in very sparse, few-branched heads (male flowers). Sexes separate on different trees; sepals 5, almost free; petals 5, each with a small somewhat fleshy scale attached to the base; stamens 8 to 12, free, absent in female flowers; ovary 1-chambered, absent in male flowers (August to January). **Fruit:** a spherical capsule, 1 to 2 cm in diameter, rough, warty, greyish to yellowish-green when mature, splitting into 4 valves to reveal the black seeds which are completely enveloped in a bright orange-red, sticky coating (February to July).

The Tembu people believe that the tree should not be touched as it attracts lightning, but the South Sotho use parts of it for a potion to protect their kraals. The wood is pink and semi-hard, and is suitable for making boards, rafters, agricultural implements and furniture. The Afrikaans name, *speekhout*, refers to its early use for the spokes of wagon wheels. It also provides a pink dye and hydrocyanic acid has been isolated from various parts of the tree, especially the leaves. The fruits are eaten by birds. Trees can be raised from seed or cuttings, and are quite fast-growing.

5. SCOLOPIA Schreber

Shrubs or small trees, armed or unarmed. **Leaves:** alternate, simple. **Flowers:** small, solitary, clustered, or in short axillary racemes. Bisexual; floral parts in fours to sixes; calyx often hairy; petals resembling the sepals; disc fleshy, glandular; stamens many, free, embedded in the disc, often surrounded at the base with long hairs; ovary 1-chambered. **Fruit:** spherical, fleshy, indehiscent.

Key to the tree species of *Scolopia:*

1 Leaves small, not more than 2,5 × 0,8 to 1,9 cm; petiole 1 to 2 mm long, or absent, with decurrent
  leaf base 2

  Leaves usually longer than 2,5 cm; petiole 3 to 10 mm long 3

2 Leaves with apex tapering, 5 to 6 pairs of lateral veins, petioles often reddish; flowers solitary,
  without stalks .... **S. oreophila**

  Leaves with apex broadly tapering to rounded, 7 to 13 pairs of lateral veins, petioles green; flowers
  stalked, in axillary groups of 2 to 3 .... **S. flanaganii**

3 Leaf apex tapering to broadly so .... **S. zeyheri**

  Leaf apex narrowly tapering to attenuate 4

4 Leaf margin conspicuously and regularly toothed; flowers in short, dense, branched heads, or
  racemes; fruit about 10 mm in diameter .... **S. mundii**

  Leaf margin obscurely, bluntly and irregularly toothed; flowers solitary; fruits about 2 cm in
  diameter .... **S. stolzii**

Scolopia flanaganii (H. Bolus) T. R. Sim
S.A. no: 495   Small-leaved thornpear. Fynblaardoringpeer
Rhod. no: —

A compact shrub or small densely leafy tree 5 to 8 m in height; in wooded valleys, high altitude forest
and in open scrub; it can become thicket-forming. The young branches bear slender axillary spines.
Leaves: small, elliptic to obovate, up to 2,5 × 0,8 (to 1,9) cm; apex broadly tapering to rounded;
lateral veins in 7 to 13 pairs; base narrowly tapering; margin widely toothed, with 3 to 5 rather large,
blunt teeth on each side; petiole green, 1 to 2 mm long, or absent. **Flowers:** very small, greenish,
inconspicuous, stalked; in small axillary clusters, or fascicles, of 2 to 3 (January to May). **Fruit:**
almost spherical, about 5 mm in diameter, velvety, yellowish when mature (March to June).

Scolopia mundii (Ecklon & Zeyher) Warb.
S.A. no: 496   Red pear. Rooipeer
Rhod. no: 729   Red pear

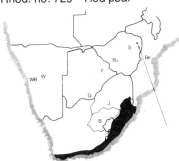

Frequently a small to medium sized tree 3 to 10 m in height, but occasionally up to 20 m; probably
occurring at medium to high altitudes in evergreen forest and at forest margins. **Bark:** grey to brown,
rather smooth to flaking; branchlets may be spiny. **Leaves:** ovate to narrowly ovate, 3,5 to 7 × 2 to
4 cm, shiny green above, dull green below, without hairs; apex tapering, attenuate into a long slender

627

tip; base broadly tapering; margin regularly and conspicuously toothed; petiole about 3 mm long. **Flowers:** greenish, 4 to 8 mm in diameter, in dense axillary branched heads up to 2 cm long, inconspicuous (May to August). **Fruit:** almost spherical, sharply tipped, about 10 mm in diameter, bright yellow to orange when mature, produced in conspicuous profusion (October to January).

Once a fine large tree of considerable economic importance, few specimens over 7 m are left today. The wood is hard, heavy and close-grained; it polishes well and is suitable for furniture; in past years it was used for wagon construction.

Scolopia oreophila (Sleumer) Killick

[*S. flanaganii* (H. Bolus) T. R. Sim var. *oreophila* Sleumer]
S.A. no: 496,1 Bastard small-leaved thorn pear. Basterfynblaardoringpeer
Rhod. no: —

A shrub or small tree sometimes reaching 12 m in height; occurring at high altitudes at the margins of *Podocarpus* forest. The tips of young branchlets have fine hairs; spines may be present. **Leaves:** ovate, ovate-elliptic to oblong, 1,5 to 2,5 × 1 to 2 cm, leathery, shiny green, without hairs; lateral veins in 5 to 6 pairs, net-veining visible; apex tapering; base narrowly tapering; margin toothed to scalloped; petiole 1 to 2 mm long, often reddish. **Flowers:** very small, greenish, without stalks; axillary, solitary (January to March). **Fruit:** almost spherical, about 5 mm in diameter, yellowish when mature (March to April).

Scolopia stolzii Gilg

S.A. no: 496,2 Water thorn pear. Waterdoringpeer
Rhod. no: 730 Large-fruited scolopia

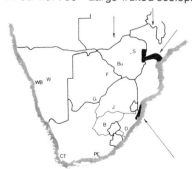 

An unarmed small to medium sized tree up to 10 m in height; occurring at medium to low altitudes, in riverine fringe forest, and at the margin of forests. **Bark:** grey, rather smooth, becoming dark grey to blackish and scaling. **Leaves:** elliptic to ovate-elliptic, 5 to 12 − 2 to 6 cm, leathery, deep green on both surfaces, the young leaves reddish; apex frequently attenuate; base broadly tapering; margin entire or obscurely toothed with widely and irregularly spaced rounded teeth; petiole up to 7 mm long. **Flowers:** greenish-white, about 7 mm long, inconspicuous, solitary, without a stalk, pressed tightly against the stem in the axils of the leaves (September to October). **Fruit:** almost spherical, sharply tipped, 1,5 to 2 cm in diameter, fleshy, yellow when mature (December to March).

A heavily armed trunk of the thorn-pear, Scolopia zeyheri.

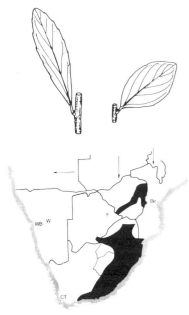

Scolopia zeyheri (Nees) Harvey   Illust. 203
[*S. ecklonii* (Nees) Szyszyl.; *S. gerrardii* Harvey; *S. thorncroftii* Phillips]
S.A. no: 498   Thorn pear. Doringpeer
Rhod. no: 731   Thorn pear

A spiny shrub or small tree usually about 7 m in height, but not infrequently reaching 10 m and sometimes even 23 m; occurring from sea level to about 2 000 m, at the margins of evergreen forest and in open woodland and bush, often associated with termite mounds. **Bark:** light grey, smooth, becoming dark brownish-grey with age, rough and peeling in flakes; axillary spines are usually present on the branchlets and may form large branched masses on the main trunk; when present these spines are distinctive although similar to those produced by several other members of this family. **Leaves:** variable in size and shape, from lanceolate to almost circular, 2 to 8 × 1 to 3,5 cm, leathery, dark green above, paler green below, with 4 to 6 pairs of fairly prominent veins on both surfaces, forming narrow angles with the midrib; young leaves reddish; apex tapering to broadly so; base tapering; margin entire or obscurely and bluntly toothed; petiole up to 10 mm long. In some areas the leaves have a thin, white, wax-like coating, but this is not always present. **Flowers:** small, white or cream to yellow, fading to brown, the central mass of stamens, about 3 to 4 mm long, being the most conspicuous part; in axillary spike-like racemes, 1 to 3 cm long (April to September). **Fruit:** an almost spherical berry tipped with the remains of the persistent style, about 5 to 10 mm in diameter, red when mature (July to September).
The wood is very heavy, hard and difficult to work.

6. PSEUDOSCOLOPIA Gilg

Pseudoscolopia polyantha Gilg
S.A. no: 499   False red pear. Valsrooipeer
Rhod. no: —

A rare shrub or small tree 2 to 5 m in height; occurring in evergreen coastal forest, at the margins of forest and in riverine fringes. **Bark:** grey-brown, rather smooth but becoming rough and flaking. **Leaves:** opposite, simple, oval to lanceolate, about 6,5 × 2 cm or slightly smaller; veins conspicuously looping on the under surface; apex tapering, attenuate; base tapering; margin irregularly and   **629**

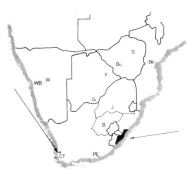

bluntly toothed; petiole short, rather thickset. Stipules absent. **Flowers:** white, about 10 mm in diameter, solitary, axillary or terminal, or in small, branched, 2- to 3-flowered heads, or cymes, often produced in conspicuous profusion. Bisexual; all floral parts in fours; sepals and petals persistent; stamens many; ovary 1-chambered (October). **Fruit:** an almost spherical 2-valved capsule, tapering to a sharp point, about 8 × 6 mm, dark brown tinged with red when mature, with the remains of the persistent sepals and petals round the base, dehiscent (January).

7. GERRARDINA Oliver

Gerrardina foliosa Oliver Illust. 204
S.A. no: 500 Krantz berry. Kransbessie
Rhod. no: —

A small densely leafy tree usually 3 to 5 m in height, occasionally reaching 10 m; occurring in forested ravines, at the margins of evergreen forest and at high altitudes in mist-belt forest. **Bark:** dark grey to brown, rather rough. **Leaves:** alternate, simple, oval to oblanceolate or elliptic, 3 to 7 × 1 to 2,5 cm, with or without sparse short hairs; apex rounded, sometimes notched; base narrowly tapering into the petiole; margin obscurely toothed, inclined to roll under; petiole short and obscured by the decurrent leaf base, up to 3 mm long. **Flowers:** greenish or creamy-white, occasionally slightly pink, about 5 mm in diameter, on long slender stalks up to 3 cm long, axillary, solitary or in 2- to 3-flowered heads, up to 5 cm long. Bisexual; all floral parts in fives; calyx bell-shaped; petals shorter than the calyx lobes, attached to the margin of the basin-shaped disc; stamens opposite the petals; ovary 1-chambered (January to July). **Fruit:** almost spherical, up to 8 mm in diameter, thinly fleshy or dry, indehiscent, red when mature, with the remains of the persistent calyx round the base (probably March to September).
The leaves resemble those of *Myrica serrata*, but lack the distinctive smell of the latter.

8. HOMALIUM Jacq.

Shrubs or trees. **Leaves:** alternate, simple. **Flowers:** in few-flowered heads, or cymes, on a long stalk, or peduncle. Bisexual; floral parts in sevens to nines; calyx tube persistent, sometimes enlarging in the fruit; petals attached at the mouth of the calyx tube, persistent; stamens attached at the base of the calyx lobes, opposite the petals and alternating with glands; ovary 1-chambered, the lower half attached to the base of the calyx tube. **Fruit:** a leathery capsule, opening at the apex by 2 to 5 valves; seeds brown, without arils.

630

Key to the tree species of *Homalium:*

1 Leaves elliptic-oblong, up to 7 × 4 cm but frequently about 4 × 1,7 cm, margins entire, sometimes very obsurely toothed or scalloped; flowers and fruits in rather sparse shortly branched spike-like racemes, about 3,5 cm long .... **H. rufescens**
 Leaves ovate, broadly ovate to almost circular, usually more than 4 cm long 2
2 A medium to tall tree 10 to 20 m in height; flowers and fruits in well-branched, widely spreading heads, up to 10 × 8 cm .:.. **H. dentatum**
 Small to medium sized trees, 5 to 10 m in height; flowers and fruits in narrowly and shortly branched, spike-like racemes 3
3 Known only from near Umtali in the east of Rhodesia .... **H. chasei**
 Only just extending south of the Zambezi River in the Caprivi Strip, Botswana and extreme west of Rhodesia, and north of Beira in Moçambique .... **H. abdessammadii**

Homalium abdessammadii Aschers. & Schweinf.

[*H. wildemanianum* Gilg]

S.A. no: 501,1   Northern homalium. Afrikaanse bastermoerbei
Rhod. no: 733   Northern homalium

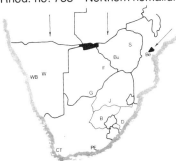

A small to medium sized tree 5 to 10 m in height; occurring at low altitudes, always at the margins of riverine fringe forest. **Bark:** brown; the young branches may be purplish-brown with conspicuous pale lenticels. **Leaves:** ovate to almost circular, 5 to 10 × 3,5 to 6 cm, the lateral veins and open net-veining rather conspicuous on the under surface, somewhat submerged above; with or without hairs on either surface; apex tapering, rounded to abruptly attenuate, may be notched; base broadly tapering to square; margin coarsely and bluntly toothed to scalloped; petiole runs into the midrib, up to 1,5 cm long, frequently pink to red or purplish. **Flowers:** greenish-white, about 10 mm in diameter in shortly branched spike-like heads, up to 12 cm long, terminal or in the axils of the leaves; the anthers are conspicuously reddish (August to November). **Fruit:** a conical woody capsule, about 5 mm in diameter, broadly based and tapering to the sharp point of the persistent style, the remains of the persistent sepals and petals round the base (December to February).

Homalium chasei Wild

S.A. no: —
Rhod. no: 734   Umtali homalium

FLACOURTIACEAE

A rare small tree up to 8 m in height; occurring among rocks in sheltered positions on granite hills. **Bark:** pale grey, smooth; young branches densely covered with yellowish short soft hairs. **Leaves:** ovate, broadly ovate to almost circular, 4 to 7 × 2,5 to 4,2 cm, with short soft yellowish hairs on both surfaces, veining prominent below; apex very broadly tapering to rounded, notched; base broadly tapering to square, sometimes asymmetric; margin shallowly scalloped over the upper two-thirds, entire towards the base; petiole up to 10 mm long, densely hairy. **Flowers:** greenish, 5 to 7 mm in diameter, in dense axillary heads, about 5 cm long (May). **Fruit:** a conical woody capsule, about 6 mm in diameter at the base, sharply tipped with the persistent style, and with the remains of the persistent sepals and petals round the base (June).

Homalium dentatum (Harvey) Warb.
S.A. no: 501   Forest homalium. Bosbastermoerbei
Rhod. no: 735   Common homalium

A medium to tall tree 10 to 20 m in height; occurring in evergreen forest and also in sheltered areas on rocky hillsides. **Bark:** grey, rather smooth, the boles frequently straight with almost horizontal or drooping branches; young branches dark brown with many conspicuous pale lenticels. **Leaves:** broadly ovate, obovate to almost circular, 4 to 13 × 3 to 8 cm, but usually about 7 to 10 × 4 to 6 cm, shiny light to deep green on both surfaces, thinly textured; the veins slightly raised above and prominent below, net-veining rather obscure; apex abruptly tapering to attenuate; base broadly tapering to square; margin conspicuously toothed to scalloped; petiole up to 2,5 cm long. **Flowers:** dull greenish-yellow to creamy-green, up to 5 mm in diameter, unpleasantly smelling, in rather loose many-flowered branched heads up to 10 cm long, in the axils of the leaves near the ends of the branches; the flower stalks and buds are covered with greyish short soft hairs (January to May). **Fruit:** a conical capsule, about 3 mm in diameter at the base, the ovary scarcely increasing in size, with dense short soft hairs; the persistent sepals and petals at the base give the fruiting branch a shaggy appearance and could be mistaken for the flowers themselves (February to June).
The wood is cream with brown streaks; it is hard and takes a good polish.

Homalium rufescens Benth.
S.A. no: 502   River bastard mulberry. Rivierbastermoerbei
Rhod. no: —

A much-branched shrub often with a tendency to scramble, or a small tree up to 7 m in height; occurring in coastal bush and forest and dry thorn scrub. **Bark:** grey to brown; branches dark brown with conspicuous pale lenticels. **Leaves:** elliptic-oblong, 2 to 7 × 1,3 to 4 cm, thinly leathery, shiny dark green above, dull green below, without hairs; apex broadly tapering to rounded; base tapering; margin irregularly and obscurely toothed, may be entire near the base; petiole reddish, up to 4 mm long. **Flowers:** white, sweetly scented, about 5 mm in diameter, in loose heads, axillary near the ends of the branches; produced in showy profusion (September to November). **Fruit:** a small capsule, with the reddish remains of the persistent sepals and petals round the base (November to January).

The wood is hard and dense and has potential value; however, it is uneconomic because of its small size.

9. BIVINIA Jaub. ex Tul.

Bivinia jalbertii Tul.
S.A. no: —
Rhod. no: 736   Cobweb seed

A tall tree up to 30 m in height; occurring in evergreen forest and forested ravines, in areas of locally high rainfall with some winter mist or drizzle. **Bark:** pale grey, smooth; branches rather brittle. **Leaves:** alternate, simple, ovate to broadly elliptic, 4,5 to 10 × 2,5 to 6 cm, dark green, slightly hairy especially along the midrib and lateral veins which are not prominent; apex attenuate into a conspicuous long slender tip; base broadly tapering; margin toothed to scalloped; petiole up to 1,5 cm long. Stipules absent. **Flowers:** greenish-yellow, about 3 mm in diameter, densely crowded along spike-like racemes up to 12 cm long. Bisexual; sepals 5 to 6, each with a broad velvety gland attached to the base; petals absent; receptacle very shallow; stamens about 4 mm long and conspicuous, in bundles of 9 to 10, alternating with the sepals; ovary 1-chambered (January to March). **Fruit:** a woody capsule, about 5 mm long, splitting into 4 to 6 valves to expose the dark reddish-brown seeds covered with long silvery silky hairs which give the fruiting spikes a cobwebby look (November to May).

The wood is borer-proof and has been used for building purposes. This is now a rare species and is specially protected in Rhodesia.

10. TRIMERIA Harvey

Shrubs or trees. **Leaves:** alternate, simple, 3- to 9-veined from the base. Stipules may be leaf-like but fall very early. **Flowers:** sexes separate on different trees; male flowers in branched axillary sprays, or panicles, female flowers in spike-like racemes; sepals 6 to 10 in 2 whorls, the inner sepals larger, with disc glands opposite the sepals in the outer whorl; petals absent; stamens 9 to 12, in bundles of 3 to 4, alternating with the disc glands, absent in female flowers; ovary 1-chambered, absent in male flowers. **Fruit:** a small 3-valved capsule opening at the tip.

Key to the species of *Trimeria:*
Leaves 5- to 9-veined from the base, usually about 10 × 9 cm .... **T. grandifolia**
Leaves usually conspicuously 3-veined from the base, occasionally 5-veined, but if so the outer 2 veins are usually much smaller; leaf size usually about 4 × 2,5 cm .... **T. trinervis**

Trimeria grandifolia (Hochst.) Warb.
[*T. rotundifolia* (Hochst.) Gilg]
S.A. no: 503   Mulberry-leaf trimeria. Wildemoerbei
Rhod. no: 737   Mulberry-leaf trimeria

633

FLACOURTIACEAE

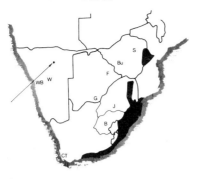 

A small to medium sized tree up to 10 m in height; occurring at medium to high altitudes in well wooded gullies, at the margins of evergreen forest and forming part of the under-storey in evergreen forest. **Bark:** greenish-brown, smooth. **Leaves:** large, obovate to almost circular, up to 13 × 13 cm, conspicuously 5- to 9-veined from the base, especially on the under surface, the young leaves velvety, most of these hairs being lost and the mature leaves becoming shiny and dark green; apex rounded, notched, occasionally abruptly attenuate; base square to shallowly lobed; margin toothed; petiole up to 3 cm long. Stipules leaf-like, up to 6 × 6 mm, but falling very early. **Flowers:** very small, greenish, the male flowers in axillary, usually branched heads, up to 7 cm long, the female flowers in unbranched spike-like racemes, up to 3 cm long (November to February). **Fruit:** an ovoid thinly woody capsule, about 5 × 2,5 mm, yellow when mature and finally splitting over the upper third into 3 segments, releasing 1 to 2 small dark grey seeds each having a conspicuous honeycomb pattern on its surface and a red aril on one side (February to April).

This species has been divided into two subspecies:

subsp. *tropica* (Burkill) Sleumer – occurring as far south as Rhodesia and Moçambique;

subsp. *grandifolia* – occurring in South Africa and Moçambique.

Intermediates between these two do occur in Rhodesia, Moçambique and southern Tanzania.

Trimeria trinervis Harvey
S.A. no: 504   Small-leaved trimeria. Fynblaarbastermoerbei
Rhod. no: —

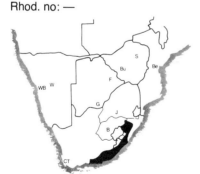 

A shrub or small tree 1 to 5 m in height; scattered in evergreen and scrub forest. **Bark:** grey. **Leaves:** ovate to lanceolate, 2 to 5 × 1,3 to 2,5 cm, but usually about 4 × 2,5 cm, dark green, conspicuously 3-veined from the base (occasionally 5-veined), thinly textured, without hairs; apex tapering; base rounded; margin bluntly toothed; petiole up to 6 mm long. **Flowers:** very small, greenish-white, in short sprays or spike-like racemes, axillary, up to 2 cm long; apparently with two flowering seasons in the year (June to July and November to January). **Fruit:** a 3-lobed sharply tipped capsule, up to 5 × 3 mm, yellow when mature; each seed has a bright orange aril (January to April).

11. LUDIA Commerson ex Juss.

Ludia mauritiana J. F. Gmelin
[*Ludia sessiliflora* Lam.]
S.A. no: —
Rhod. no: —   Ludia

A shrub or small tree 2 to 3 m in height; occurring in dense dune bush. **Bark:** pale grey, mottled. **Leaves:** alternate, simple, obovate, up to 9 × 5 cm, shiny green above, dull and paler green below, leathery, with conspicuous net-veining on both surfaces; apex broadly tapering to rounded, base tapering; margin entire, conspicuously wavy; petiole short. **Flowers:** greenish, about 6 mm in diameter, axillary, solitary or 2 to 3 together, without stalks. Bisexual; sepals 5 to 7, overlapping; petals absent; stamens many, very slender; ovary 1-chambered (October). **Fruit:** almost spherical, fleshy, about 10 mm in diameter, warty, with the remains of the persistent calyx round the base (probably December).

12. APHLOIA (DC.) Benn.

Aphloia theiformis (Vahl) Benn.   Illust. 205
S.A. no: 505   Albino berry. Helderblaar
Rhod. no: 738   Albino berry

A shrub or small tree up to 8 m in height, but occasionally reaching 13 m; occurring at medium to high altitudes in evergreen forest, forested ravines and at forest margins. **Bark:** brown, smooth. **Leaves:** alternate, simple, narrowly elliptic to oblanceolate, 3 to 8 × 1,2 to 3 cm, but usually about 6 to 7 cm long, inclined to droop, glossy dark green above, dull and paler green below; apex and base tapering; margin finely toothed and inclined to roll under; petiole up to 3 mm long. **Flowers:** white, turning cream and aging to deep butter-yellow, about 10 mm in diameter, with a conspicuous central mass of yellow stamens, sweetly scented; on slender stalks 1 to 1,5 cm long, axillary, solitary or in groups of 2 to 3, often produced in profusion along the younger branches. Bisexual; sepals 4 to 6, petalloid, persistent; petals absent; stamens many; ovary 1-chambered, style persistent (September to November). **Fruit:** ovoid, soft, fleshy, about 10 mm in diameter, white when mature, with the persistent remains of the sepals and stamens round the base, and tipped with the persistent style; containing about 6 orange seeds (November to January).

635

13. FLACOURTIA L'Hérit.

Flacourtia indica (N. L. Burm.) Merr.   Illust. 206
[*F. hirtiuscula* Oliver]
S.A. no: 506   Flacourtia. Goewerneurspruim
Rhod. no: 739   Flacourtia

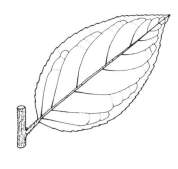

A shrub or small tree, usually 3 to 5 m in height, but sometimes reaching 10 m; occurring in woodland, from sea level to about 1 600 m. **Bark:** usually pale grey and rather smooth, but may become brown or dark grey and flaking revealing pale orange patches which give a mottled appearance; the branches may be unarmed or armed with large spines, which may also form distinctive branched masses on the main trunk; the leaves and branches may be with or without dense soft short hairs. **Leaves:** alternate, simple, elliptic, ovate to almost circular, 2,5 to 12 × 1,3 to 7,5 cm, thinly textured to leathery, light to dark green, starting to colour early for autumn, finally becoming brilliant red, plum-coloured, and purple to purplish-black; apex broadly tapering to rounded; base tapering, occasionally rounded; margin almost entire to scalloped or toothed; petiole up to 1,3 cm long. **Flowers:** greenish-yellow flushed with dull red, about 5 mm in diameter, axillary or terminal, occasionally solitary in the female flowers, or in short sprays, or racemes, or in branched heads, or panicles, up to 2,5 cm long. Bisexual or with occasional unisexual flowers on the same tree; sepals 4 to 7, free or occasionally joined at the base; petals absent; stamens many, forming a central mass; ovary 4- to 8-chambered, surrounded by the disc either as an entire ring or broken into separate parts; styles 4 to 8, persistent; in unisexual flowers the parts of the opposite sex are either reduced or absent (September to December). **Fruit:** berry-like, fleshy, up to 2,5 cm in diameter, dark red or purplish when mature, edible but acid; the persistent styles often set asymmetrically, even well down one side of the fruit (January to June).

Decoctions are prepared from the leaves and roots, the former to treat screw-worm in cattle and the latter to relieve body pains generally. Sufferers from sore throats and hoarseness gargle with an infusion of the bark and this also forms the basis of a linament for soothing rheumatic conditions. A tonic is made from the dry leaves which also provide a remedy for asthma and many other ailments.

14. DOVYALIS E. Meyer ex Arn.

Shrubs or small trees, often spiny. **Leaves:** alternate or fascicled, simple. **Flowers:** axillary; solitary (female flowers), or in small groups, or clusters (male flowers). Sexes separate on different trees; calyx with 4 to 7 lobes; petals absent; stamens 10 to 20, longer than the calyx lobes, often arising from a disc composed of separate, often hairy glands, absent in female flowers; ovary 1- to 2-chambered; styles 2 to 8, absent in male flowers. **Fruit:** ovoid to almost spherical, fleshy, indehiscent.

Key to the tree species of *Dovyalis:*

1 Leaves fascicled, or clustered, on very dwarf lateral shoots; 4 to 8 styles on the ovary; male flowers in dense clusters; fruits up to 4 cm in diameter .... **D. caffra**
  Leaves alternate; 2 to 3 styles on the ovary; male flowers in sparse clusters of 1 to 4; fruits up to 2 cm in diameter 2
2 Calyx much enlarged, almost enveloping the fruit, the calyx lobes fringed with long shaggy hairs .... **D. macrocalyx**
  Calyx may be enlarged but not almost enveloping the fruit, and without shaggy hairs 3

636

3 Calyx lobes becoming enlarged, slender and contorted at the base of the fruit; young branches often speckled with small wart-like glands; fresh mature fruit red with very small whitish spots .... **D. longispina**

Calyx lobes do not greatly enlarge; young branches may have lenticels but not small wart-like glands; fruits without white flecks 4

4 Leaves usually more than 4 cm long 5

Leaves usually less than 4 cm long 6

5 Trees usually without spines; stamens relatively few, about 15; calyx in female flower spreading, not bent back; fruit spherical orange-red, densely covered with very short hairs .... **D. lucida**

Trees usually very spiny; stamens about 40; calyx in the female flower bent back; fruits ellipsoidal, golden-yellow, densely covered with longish hairs .... **D. zeyheri**

6 Occurring in Rhodesia and the central areas of Moçambique, and northwards, not recorded from South Africa; outer surface of the enlarged calyx lobes and the fruit with short sparse, rough or bristly hairs .... **D. hispidula**

Occurring in South Africa and, if in Moçambique, then in the extreme south only 7

7 Leaves thickly and rigidly leathery, usually obovate to almost circular, apex rounded, often notched, margin flat, not wavy; generally a coastal species, confined to a small area in the eastern Cape and, again, in the south of Moçambique .... **D. rotundifolia**

Leaves thinly textured, usually ovate, only occasionally broadly so, apex tapering, margin wavy; occurring in coastal and inland forest, occurring from the Cape to the Transvaal .... **D. rhamnoides**

Dovyalis caffra (J. D. Hook. & Harvey) Warb.   Illust. 207
S.A. no: 507   Kei-apple. Kei-appel
Rhod. no: 740   Kei-apple

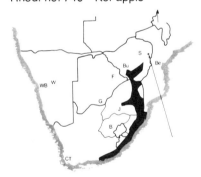

A shrub or small tree, usually 3 to 5 m in height, but sometimes reaching 8 m; occurring in open bush and wooded grassland, often in *Acacia* woodland and frequently associated with termite mounds. **Bark:** grey, smooth, later flaking into square sections; branches armed with stout spines up to 6 cm long. **Leaves:** often in tight clusters, or fascicles, on dwarf lateral branches; narrowly obovate to broadly obovate-elliptic, 2 to 5,5 × 0,5 to 3 cm; apex rounded, occasionally notched; base tapering to narrowly rounded; margin entire, slightly rolled under; petiole up to 5 mm long. **Flowers:** creamy-green, small, in dense clusters, usually on the dwarf lateral shoots, seen more as masses of stamens; inconspicuous (November to January). **Fruit:** almost spherical, up to 4 cm in diameter, fleshy, apricot-coloured when mature (November to January).

The fruits are pleasantly flavoured and make excellent jelly and jam. They are widely cultivated, both for their fruits and as a hedge, even as far afield as Australia, California and the Mediterranean countries. In many areas of southern Africa the plants have escaped and become naturalised. Seed germinates easily but it must be fresh, and the seedlings transplant well. The young plants are generally hardy but they have been reported to be sensitive to frost.

Dovyalis hispidula Wild
S.A. no: —
Rhod. no: 741   Bristly dovyalis

637

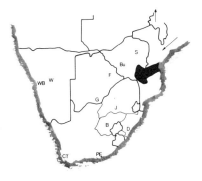

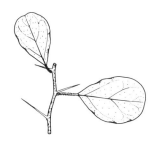

A shrub or small tree 2 to 4 m in height; occurring at low altitudes in mixed woodland. **Bark:** greyish, the stem frequently very spiny to the base; branches have scattered pale lenticels and bear axillary spines up to 7 to 8 cm long. **Leaves:** small, broadly elliptic to obovate, 0,8 to 3,5 × 0,6 to 2,3 cm but frequently only 2 cm long, dull green, with sparse bristly or hispid hairs on both surfaces; apex rounded, notched; base tapering; margin entire or scalloped; petiole up to 8 mm long. **Flowers:** small, greenish, axillary, solitary or in clusters of 2 to 4, on slender stalks 2 to 3 mm long; very inconspicuous (October to November). **Fruit:** almost spherical, fleshy, up to 1 to 2 cm in diameter, bright red when mature, with short harsh bristly hairs; edible (November to January).

Dovyalis longispina (Harvey) Warb.
S.A. no: 510,1   Natal dovyalis. Natalappelkoos
Rhod. no: —

A small to medium sized tree up to 15 m in height; occurring in coastal and dune forest and in open woodland. **Bark:** grey to yellowish-brown, smooth, developing fine vertical fissures with age; young branches armed with slender straight spines up to 8 cm long, the spines and branchlets often with very small wart-like glands which are difficult to see. **Leaves:** elliptic to ovate or nearly circular, 2 to 9 × 1,3 to 6 cm, but usually about 5 to 7 × 2 to 3 cm, 3-veined from the base; apex broadly tapering, often rounded, sometimes notched; base narrowly tapering; margin entire, rolled under; petiole stout, about 2 mm long. **Flowers:** very small, white to pale yellow, inconspicuous, in axillary clusters of 2 to 6 (August to October). **Fruit:** ovoid to almost spherical, up to 1,5 cm long, fleshy, bright orange to red flecked with white when mature; the persistent calyx lobes become enlarged, slender and contorted at the base of the fruit; often produced in profusion (September to November).
The fruits are edible, pleasantly flavoured but slightly acid.

Dovyalis lucida T. R. Sim
S.A. no: 508   Glossy dovyalis. Blinkblaarsuurbessie
Rhod. no: 742   Glossy dovyalis

Usually a shrub or small tree up to 7 m in height, but sometimes reaching 15 m; occurring at medium altitudes in evergreen forest, and at sea level in the eastern Cape. **Bark:** grey, finely fissured, thin; branches usually without spines. **Leaves:** broadly elliptic to almost circular, 2,5 to 8 × 2 to 5 cm, dark green and very glossy above (the specific name refers to this), dull and paler green below; apex broadly tapering to rounded; base tapering; margin entire or rarely irregularly toothed; petiole up to

3 mm long. **Flowers:** very small, inconspicuous, greenish-yellow, solitary or in groups of 2 to 7; they have a short flowering season and are often difficult to find (July to October). **Fruit:** spherical, fleshy, 1 to 1,5 cm in diameter, densely covered with very short hairs, bright orange-red when mature, produced on the older branches, edible but sour (November to December).

Dovyalis macrocalyx (Oliver) Warb.
S.A. no: Shaggy-fruited dovyalis
Rhod. no: 743   Shaggy-fruited dovyalis

A shrub or small tree up to 7 m in height; occurring at the margins of evergreen forest and in riverine fringe forest. **Bark:** grey; young branches slender, bearing straight spines up to 5 cm long. **Leaves:** ovate, up to 10 × 5,5 cm, but usually about 4 to 5 cm long, light green, thinly textured, occasionally rather leathery, the midrib sometimes set to one side, the surface sometimes puckered; apex tapering to broadly so; base rounded or very broadly tapering; margin usually entire but sometimes obscurely toothed; petiole up to 3 mm long. **Flowers:** yellowish, greenish-yellow or pale purplish-pink, in small axillary clusters of 1 to 4, on short stalks; male flowers with 10 to 20 stamens, female flowers with 2 conspicuous styles about 3 mm long; calyx densely covered with stalked glandular hairs, and fringed with long shaggy hairs, persistent and growing with the fruit (September to November). **Fruit:** ovoid, fleshy, 1,5 to 2 cm long, bright red when mature, almost completely enveloped by the persistent enlarged calyx with its hair-fringed margin, reddish and still covered with shaggy glandular hairs; the latter character is distinctive (September to November).
The fruits are edible and make an excellent preserve.

Dovyalis rhamnoides (Burch. ex DC.) Burch. & Harvey
S.A. no: 509   Common dovyalis. Gewone suurbessie
Rhod. no: —

A shrub or small tree reaching 7 m in height; occurring in forested areas near the coast and, inland, in mountain evergreen forest. **Bark:** light grey, rather smooth; branches with straight spines up to 8 cm long. **Leaves:** small, ovate, 1,3 to 3 × 1,3 to 2 cm, usually 3-veined from the base, thinly textured, roughly hairy when young; apex broadly tapering; base rounded or shallowly lobed; margin entire or obscurely toothed, wavy; petiole short. **Flowers:** very small and inconspicuous, greenish to greenish-white, solitary or in small axillary clusters; sepals persistent (June to September). **Fruit:** ovoid, about 1,3 × 0,8 cm, fleshy, bright red when mature, with the enlarged, persistent, slender calyx lobes round the base, and tipped with the remains of the persistent styles (January to February).

639

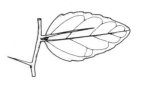

The fruits are pleasantly acid-flavoured and much sought after. The wood is pale yellow, close-grained, heavy, hard and tough, but usually knotted and crooked. The plants are easily propagated from seed and the seedlings transplant well.

Dovyalis rotundifolia (Thunb.) Thunb. & Harvey
S.A. no: 510   Dune dovyalis. Duinesuurbessie
Rhod. no: —

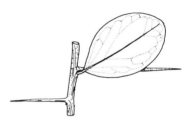

A small tree reaching 7 m in height; occurring in coastal scrub and dune forest, confined to the coastal belt. **Bark:** grey, rather smooth. **Leaves:** obovate, often almost circular, 1,3 to 4 × 0,8 to 3 cm, dark glossy green, leathery, without hairs; apex rounded, notched; base tapering; margin entire; petiole rather stout, up to 5 mm long. **Flowers:** small, inconspicuous, greenish, in clusters, often on the older branches (June to September). **Fruit:** ovoid, fleshy, about 1,3 × 0,8 cm, tipped with the remains of the persistent style, bright red when mature, edible and pleasantly acid-flavoured (January to March). This species has been confused with *D. rhamnoides*, but it differs in having larger, obovate leaves which have rounded apices and are wider above the midline; it is more tree-like and is more strictly confined to the coastal belt.

Dovyalis zeyheri (Sonder) Warb.   Illust. 208
[*D. tristis* (Sonder) Warb.; *D. revoluta* Thom]
S.A. no: 511   Oval kei apple. Wilde-appelkoos
Rhod. no: 744   Oval kei-apple

A shrub or small to medium sized slender tree up to 10 m in height; occurring in open woodland or at the margins of evergreen forest, frequently associated with termite mounds. **Bark:** pale grey to dark grey, usually smooth or flaking, occasionally rough in old specimens; the young branches may be unarmed or armed with paired spines up to 3 cm long. **Leaves:** obovate to broadly elliptic, 1,5 to 7 × 1 to 3,5 cm, light to dark green depending to some extent on the age, but always conspicuously glossy above, dull and paler green below, with or without hairs; apex rounded; base tapering; margin scalloped, sometimes rather obscurely so; petiole up to 8 mm long. **Flowers:** small, inconspicuous, greenish-yellow, about 10 mm in diameter including the central mass of yellow stamens, axillary, solitary or in groups of 2 to 4 (September to December). **Fruit:** ovoid, fleshy, 1 to 2 cm long, bright orange when mature, velvety, the persistent sepals forming a frilled cup at the base; often produced in conspicuous profusion (November to May).

The fruits are edible and pleasantly flavoured, although they are sometimes rather sour and they make a good jelly. Eve Palmer records that the tree occasionally gives off an obnoxious smell of carrion.

15. CASEARIA Jacq.

Shrubs or trees, sometimes very tall. **Leaves:** alternate, simple, in 2 vertical ranks, the branchlets often zigzag, the leaf blades dotted or streaked with pellucid glands. Stipules falling early (they may be persistent in some species). **Flowers:** axillary, in clusters or tight dense almost spherical heads. Bisexual; calyx tube short, dividing into 4 to 5 almost circular, concave, overlapping lobes; petals absent; stamens 6 to 15, occasionally more, alternating with staminodes; ovary ovoid, 1-chambered. **Fruit:** a capsule, fleshy at first, becoming dry when mature and splitting into 2 to 4 valves; the seeds are enveloped in a membraneous, coloured aril.

Key to the species of *Casearia:*

Shrub or small tree usually about 8 m in height, occasionally 12 to 15 m; leaves lanceolate to narrowly ovate; occurring in coastal bush and woodland, not recorded from Rhodesia .... **C. gladiiformis**
Large trees up to 40 m in height; leaves oblong to narrowly oblong; occurring in medium to high altitude evergreen forest, not recorded from South Africa .... **C. battiscombei**

Casearia battiscombei R. E. Fries
S.A. no: —
Rhod. no: 745   Forest sword-leaf

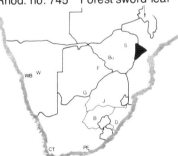

A large tree up to 40 m in height; occurring at altitudes between 1 000 and 2 000 m, in evergreen forest and at forest margins. **Bark:** pale grey to brownish, smooth to scaly and rough, sometimes marked with bosses and scars; the branches are usually long and, in saplings, almost silver. **Leaves:** tend to be crowded near the ends of the branches, oblong, 8 to 22 × 3 to 6 cm, deep green, without hairs on either surface; apex broadly tapering, finally abruptly attenuate; base broadly tapering; margin entire, wavy, sometimes widely and obscurely toothed when young; petiole up to 6 mm long. Stipules very small, triangular, 2 mm long, falling very early. **Flowers:** greenish, about 3 mm in diameter, in small, dense, axillary clusters, tight against the branchlets, inconspicuous (October). **Fruit:** an ovoid capsule, 10 × 5 mm, yellow when mature splitting into 2 to 4 valves, produced in groups of 2 to 4 or in dense clusters along the branchlets; seeds few, pale in colour, more or less enveloped in a fleshy pale whitish aril (January).
The wood is white and is said to provide a good soft timber.

641

Casearia gladiiformis Mast.
S.A. no: 512   Sword-leaf. Swaardblaar
Rhod. no: —

Usually a small tree up to 8 m in height, only occasionally reaching 12 to 15 m; occurring at low altitudes in dry thicket and woodland, in riverine fringe forest, in coastal scrub and dune forest. **Bark:** grey, smooth. **Leaves:** lanceolate or narrowly ovate, 5 to 16 × 4 to 6,5 cm, sword-like (the specific name refers to this), glossy dark green, without hairs; apex tapering; base tapering, frequently asymmetric; margin entire, wavy, sometimes finely toothed; petiole channelled above, up to 1,3 cm long, with or without fine hairs. **Flowers:** small, creamy or greenish-white, in tight axillary clusters along the stem, inconspicuous (August to October). **Fruit:** an ovoid capsule, up to 2 cm long, thinly woody, yellow-orange when mature, finally splitting into 3 to 4 valves, releasing numerous seeds, each half covered with a fleshy aril (October to December).
The ash from the bark is used as snuff.

CACTACEAE *(The prickly pear family)*

*OPUNTIA J. Miller

A number of species of *Opuntia,* the prickly pears, introduced from America, have become naturalised and are now widespread and extremely troublesome in areas of the Cape and Natal. Many plants, including species of *Euphorbia,* are popularly referred to as cacti, but this is incorrect as there is only one member of the family Cactaceae indigenous in Africa: this is *Rhipsalis baccifera* (J. Miller) Stearn, a small plant growing as an epiphyte in evergreen forest. However, many genera and species of Cactaceae have been introduced and are grown in gardens.

PASSIFLORACEAE *(The passion flower family)*

ADENIA Forsk.

Adenia karibaensis De Wilde
S.A. no: —
Rhod. no: 749   Cat-o'-nine-tails

A soft-wooded rather succulent small tree of unusual appearance, 1 to 4,5 m in height; occurring at low altitudes, in dry, rocky woodland and in cracks in rock faces, apparently endemic to this area. **Bark:** grey-green, smooth, the thickset stem tapering rapidly into the long, whip-like, drooping red-brown branches which have a strong tendency to clamber. **Leaves:** alternate, 5-lobed to the base, or very nearly so, almost circular in general outline, up to 11 × 6 cm, leathery, pale greyish-green, sometimes tinged with purple, conspicuous net-veining and lobed basal glands; apex of the leaf lobes tapering; base rounded; margin entire; petiolate. The leaves may be modified to form tendrils up to 12 cm long. **Flowers:** small, greenish-white, 1,5 cm long, narrow, in clusters of 2 to 3 (female flowers), or in short branched heads, 1 to 2 cm in diameter (male flowers), in the axils of the leaves or tendrils. Sexes separate; all floral parts in fives; calyx tube short, calyx lobes alternating with the

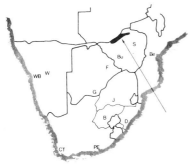

petals; glandular bracts small and yellow. Flowers produced before the leaves or with the very young leaves (October to November). **Fruit:** an ovoid capsule up to 2 cm long, green mottled with white (October to November).

OLINIACEAE

OLINIA Thunb.

Shrubs or trees, the branchlets 4-angled. **Leaves:** opposite, simple. Stipules absent. **Flowers:** in short, axillary, trichotomous cymes, arranged in lax sprays, or racemes, shorter than the subtending leaf. Bisexual; floral parts in fours to fives; calyx tube fused with the ovary, lanceolate or obscurely lobed; petals usually 5, shorter than the calyx tube; stamens 5, filaments very short; ovary 3- to 5-chambered, with opposite bracts which may be as long as the flower. **Fruit:** dry or thinly fleshy.

Key to the species of *Olinia:*
1 Under surface of leaves with conspicuous fine net-veining 2
  Under surface of leaves without conspicuous net-veining 3
2 Occurring in Rhodesia only .... **O. vanguerioides**
  Occurring in the Transvaal and countries to the north of the Zambezi River ... **O. rochetiana**
3 Petal lobes obovate .... **O. ventosa**
  Petal lobes slender, linear 4
4 Flowers in loose heads, rather more than half as long as the leaves .... **O. emarginata**
  Flowers in compact heads, less than half as long as the leaves, and densely clustered round the petiole .... **O. radiata**

Olinia emarginata Burtt Davy
S.A. no: 514   Mountain olinia. Berghardepeer
Rhod. no: —

A shrub or small tree 1 to 5 m, or large tree to 20 m in height; occurring at high altitudes in evergreen forest, wooded ravines, riverine fringes and also among rocks and on mountain crags. **Bark:** grey, mottled, smooth to rough in larger specimens. **Leaves:** oblong to oblanceolate, 2 to 5 × 0,7 to 2 cm, **643**

glossy dark green above, paler green and dull below; apex rounded, notched; base tapering; margin entire, slightly rolled under; petiole very short. **Flowers:** very small, pink, faintly sweet-scented, in axillary many-flowered loose heads, 1 to 3 cm long (October to January). **Fruit:** berry-like, thinly fleshy, about 10 mm in diameter, in dense clusters among the leaves, red when mature (March to June).

Olinia radiata J. Hofmeyr & Phillips
S.A. no: 515   Natal olinia. Natalhardepeer
Rhod. no: —

A medium to large tree up to 21 m in height; occurring in evergreen forest. **Bark:** dark purplish-brown to reddish, smooth. **Leaves:** oblanceolate to elliptic, 5 to 9 × 1,8 to 3,8 cm, glossy dark green above, dull and somewhat paler below; apex broadly tapering to rounded; base tapering; margin entire, wavy; petiole short. **Flowers:** very small, white tinged with purple, in dense axillary many-flowered heads, tightly clustered round the base of the leaf against the stem (October to January). **Fruit:** berry-like, thinly fleshy, up to 1,8 cm in diameter, reddish-purple when mature (April to September).
The bark smells strongly of sweet almonds. This is a protected plant in South Africa.

Olinia rochetiana A. Juss.
[*O. usambarensis* Gilg & Engl.]
S.A. no: 516   Transvaal olinia. Transvaalhardepeer
Rhod. no: —

Frequently a shrub or small tree about 4 m in height, but sometimes reaching 20 m; occurring in patches of evergreen forest and riverine fringe forest. **Bark:** grey or light grey to brown, smooth or finely longitudinally fissured. **Leaves:** elliptic to obovate, 1,3 to 6 × 0,8 to 2,5 cm, green to dark green or yellowish-green, glossy above, rather blue-green and paler below; net-veining conspicuous below; young leaves bright red; apex broadly tapering, finely notched; base tapering, often running into the petiole; margin entire, rolled under; petiole often runs into the midrib, very short to almost absent, purple tinged. **Flowers:** large for the genus, 5 to 8 mm long, white fading to pale pink or rosy-pink, or cream fading to yellow, in short dense branched axillary cymes, about a third the length of the subtending leaf (October to March). **Fruit:** spherical, thinly fleshy, about 6 to 8 mm in diameter, red-brown when mature, often produced in profusion (April to May).

644   *O. rochetiana* is a species of tropical Africa, also occurring in the mountains of the eastern Transvaal.

It seems strange that it has not been recorded in Rhodesia, where it is replaced by *O. vanguerioides* which occurs nowhere else. The Rhodesian material differs in certain floral characters, especially in the size and shape of the petals, and seems to justify separation. It is possible that some of the sterile material collected in Rhodesia may prove to be *O. rochetiana,* and this would close the unlikely geographical gap.

Olinia vanguerioides E. G. Baker
S.A. no: —
Rhod. no: 756   Rhodesian olinia

A medium to large tree 6 to 25 m in height; occurring in evergreen forest, riverine fringe forest and among rocks. **Bark:** greyish to pale brown, smooth but scaling in almost circular thin flakes, exposing yellowish underbark, producing a mottled appearance; the trunks of very small trees may be shallowly buttressed. **Leaves:** lanceolate to elliptic, 5 to 10 × 1,5 to 3 cm, light to dark green, conspicuously blue-green and net-veined below; apex tapering to rounded, may be notched; base tapering; margin entire; petiole short. **Flowers:** large for the genus, 5 to 6 mm long, white to creamy-yellow, in dense axillary branched cymes, about a third the length of the subtending leaf (December to March). **Fruit:** spherical, thinly fleshy, 5 to 6 mm in diameter, pale yellow to reddish when mature, produced in dense clusters (March to June).

This species, apparently endemic to Rhodesia, closely resembles *O. rochetiana;* a note on this is included under the latter species.

Olinia ventosa (L.) Cufod.   Illust. 209
[*O. cymosa* Thunb.; *Plectronia ventosa* L.]
S.A. no: 513   Hard pear. Hardepeer
Rhod. no: —

A medium to large tree 10 to 20 m in height; occurring in evergreen forest, at forest margins, in coastal scrub and on rocky hillsides. **Bark:** pale grey, smooth. **Leaves:** ovate to elliptic, 2,5 to 8 × 1 to 5 cm, glossy dark green above, paler green and dull below; apex and base tapering; margin entire; petiole thickset, about 5 mm long. **Flowers:** very small, whitish sometimes tinged with pink, sweetly scented, in dense axillary branched heads, 5 to 6 cm long (August to October). **Fruit:** berry-like, spherical, about 10 mm in diameter, thinly fleshy, red when mature (December to June).

The crushed leaves and newly cut wood smell strongly of almonds. The wood is hard, heavy and strong and has been used for fencing and telegraph poles and other heavy work. These trees make excellent, fast-growing, evergreen subjects for the garden, although the seed is difficult to germinate.

THYMELAEACEAE *(The dais family)*

Key to the genera:
1 Leaves alternate .... **1. Peddiea**

    Leaves opposite or crowded at the ends of the branches, rarely sub-opposite to scattered 2

2 Leaves seldom more than 15 × 1,5 mm, needle-like .... **3. Passerina**

    Leaves not conspicuously small and needle-like 3

3 Leaf base rounded to lobed; flowers white or yellow with 8 petals, in few-flowered heads or clusters
    .... **2. Englerodaphne**

    Leaf base tapering; flowers pink, petals absent but the calyx lobes petalloid, in dense many-flowered heads .... **4. Dais**

1. PEDDIEA Harvey

Shrubs or trees. **Leaves:** alternate, simple. **Flowers:** in few-flowered terminal branched flat-topped heads, or umbels. Bisexual; the receptacle forming a cylindric tube, often termed the 'calyx tube', with 4 to 5 very small sepals round the mouth; petals absent; stamens 8 to 10 in 2 whorls; ovary usually 2-chambered, surrounded at the base by the cup-shaped disc. **Fruit:** small, fleshy, indehiscent.

Peddiea africana Harvey   Illust. 210
[including **P. fischeri** Engl.]
S.A. no: 517   Green flower tree. Gifolyf
Rhod. no: 757   Green flower tree

A shrub or small tree 3 to 5 m in height, occasionally reaching 7 m; occurring in evergreen forest, at forest margins, in riverine fringe forest, in dense coastal forest just behind the sand dunes and in coastal scrub. **Bark:** pale grey to brown, smooth, thin, fibrous and very tough, stripping all the way down the branchlets rather than breaking. **Leaves:** elliptic, sometimes obovate to oblanceolate, 2,5 to 10 × 1 to 5 cm, but usually 7 to 9 × 3 to 3,5 cm, thinly textured, glossy deep green; apex tapering, finally narrowly rounded, sometimes finely notched; base tapering, running into the petiole; margin entire, slightly rolled under; petiole very short because of the decurrent leaf base, or absent. **Flowers:** receptacle tube 1 to 2 cm long, without hairs, emerald-green to yellowish tinged with red-brown or maroon, in small clusters of 3 to 9, each shortly stalked, 2 to 6 mm long, arising from the same stalk, or peduncle, up to 5 mm long (September to February). **Fruit:** ovoid, about 10 × 7 mm, drawn into a slender point, reddish-purple to black when mature (February to October).

The bark yields a good fibre and makes an excellent rope. It is said to be poisonous. Some populations have the ovaries tipped with a conspicuous but small tuft of creamy hairs which persists in the fruit. Specimens that possess this character are sometimes regarded as being a separate species, namely *P. fischeri,* and their distribution is shown by vertical lines on the map. The distribution of typical *P. africana,* which lacks the tuft of hair, is shown by the black areas on the map. All specimens from north of the Zambezi have tufts of hair on the ovary.

2. ENGLERODAPHNE Gilg

Shrubs or small trees. **Leaves:** opposite, simple. **Flowers:** in few-flowered axillary umbels. Bisexual; calyx tube cylindric, persistent, later enclosing the small fruits; petals 8, almost as long as the calyx lobes; stamens 8 in 2 whorls, the upper whorl attached in the throat of the calyx tube, the lower whorl attached further down; ovary 1-chambered. **Fruit:** a small nut, indehiscent.

Key to the tree species of *Englerodaphne:*
Leaves up to 3 × 1,8 cm, without hairs .... **E. subcordata**
Leaves 2,5 to 8 × 1,3 to 4 cm, with short soft hairs and rather long whitish hairs .... **E. pilosa**

Englerodaphne pilosa Burtt Davy   Illust. 211
S.A. no: 518   Silky fibre-bush. Syhaarveselbos
Rhod. no: —

An undershrub or small to medium sized tree, usually 2 to 3 m in height, reaching 5 to 6 m in dense forest and very occasionally up to 12 m; occurring in high altitude evergreen forest and riverine fringe forest. **Bark:** light creamy-brown to grey, smooth; young branchlets with long, sparse, white, rather shaggy spreading hairs. **Leaves:** ovate to lanceolate, 2,5 to 8 × 1,3 to 4 cm, thinly textured, characteristically pale green making the trees conspicuous in the forest as light patches against the dark background; upper surface of the leaves finely hairy, under surface with dense long whitish hairs; apex tapering; base shallowly lobed; margin entire; petiole very short. **Flowers:** pale orange-yellow, about 10 mm in diameter, pendulous on slender peduncles so that they hang characteristically below the leaves; axillary, solitary or in 2- to 5-flowered groups (January to April). **Fruit:** very small, inconspicuous, enclosed at the base of the persistent calyx tube which is scarcely enlarged (February to May).

Englerodaphne subcordata (Meissner) Engl.
[*E. leiosiphon* Gilg]
S.A. no: 519   Smooth fibre-bush. Gladde veselbos
Rhod. no: —

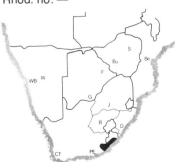

Usually a shrub, occasionally a small tree up to 4 m in height; occurring at forest margins, in coastal thornveld and in riverine thicket. **Bark:** grey, smooth. **Leaves:** small, oval to oblong, up to 3 × 1,8 cm, without hairs; apex broadly tapering; base rounded to shallowly lobed; margin entire, slightly rolled under; petiole rather thick, short. **Flowers:** white, tubular, in terminal clusters of 1 to 7, the calyx tubes up to 1,2 cm long, the petals inserted in the yellow throat (November to May). **Fruit:** small, enclosed at the base of the persistent calyx tube which is scarcely enlarged (March to April and later).

The bark yields a strong fibre. The fruits are said to be poisonous but are reputed to be eaten in Zululand.

3. PASSERINA L.

Ericoid shrubs or small trees with slender branchlets covered in fine to woolly hairs, especially when young. **Leaves:** opposite decussate, simple, small and narrow, lined with woolly hairs. **Flowers:** in spike-like racemes. Bisexual; calyx tube flask-shaped, separating into 4 lobes over half its length; petals absent; stamens 8, equal to or shorter than the calyx lobes; ovary 1-chambered. **Fruit:** a small dry nut enclosed in the persistent calyx tube; seeds black, with a fine sharp beak.

Key to the tree species of *Passerina:*
1 Leaves usually less than 4 mm long; occurring primarily on coastal sand dunes ..... **P. rigida**
   Leaves usually more than 4 mm long; not occurring on coastal sand dunes 2
2 Occurring only in the southern Cape, in forest clearings and at forest margins; branchlets without creamy-white woolly hairs .... **P. falcifolia**
   Occurring from the south-western Cape to Swaziland, in scrub, grassland and on rocky slopes; branchlets with conspicuous creamy-white woolly hairs between the leaves ... **P. filiformis**

Passerina falcifolia (Meissner) C. H. Wright
S.A. no: 520   Outeniqua gonna. Outeniekwagonna
Rhod. no: —

A bushy shrub or small tree, occasionally reaching 5 to 7 m in height, with the branches often drooping; occurring at high altitudes, at the margin of evergreen forest, along stream banks, or in open mountain grassland. **Bark:** dark grey, very tough; branchlets without long white hairs. **Leaves:** closely arranged along the branches, needle-like, 6 to 15 × 1 to 1,5 mm, slightly sickle-shaped (the specific name refers to this), but hardly more so than in *P. filiformis*. **Flowers:** about 3 to 4 mm in diameter, pale reddish-brown, axillary, clustered towards the ends of the branches, each flower between conspicuous bracts (September to November). **Fruit:** a small, dry nut, at the base of slightly enlarged bracts, developing rapidly so that flowers and fruits can be on the plant at the same time (September to November).

Passerina filiformis L.
S.A. no: Brown gonna. Bruingonna
Rhod. no: —

Usually a shrub about 2 m in height, occasionally a small tree up to 3 to 4 m; occurring in hills and mountains, on grassy or rocky mountain slopes, along streams or watercourses and in scrub. **Bark:** greyish-brown; young branchlets between the leaves covered with dense creamy woolly hairs. **Leaves:** closely ranked along the young branches, needle-like, about 10 mm long and barely 1 mm wide, bright green, straight or slightly curved, with an inconspicuous tuft of apical hairs. **Flowers:**

pale yellow to brownish-yellow, solitary in the axils of the leaves near the tips of the branches giving the impression of a small spike; each flower is on a short stalk between two almost ensheathing bracts; may be produced in profusion (September to December). **Fruit:** about 2 × 1 mm, finely hairy, at the base of the subtending bracts which barely increase in size after flowering; the fruits develop rapidly and may be found on the tree with the flowers (October to December).

The bark provides a very strong fibre.

Passerina rigida Wikstr.
S.A. no: Dune gonna. Seekoppiesgonna
Rhod. no: —

Usually a shrub about 2 m in height, occasionally becoming a small tree up to 4 m; occurring on coastal dunes and in dune bush and extending inland along river valleys. **Bark:** greyish-brown; young branchlets closely covered with white velvety hairs, but not as shaggy as those of *P. filiformis*. **Leaves:** very small, ericoid, only 1 to 2 mm long, closely packed along the branchlets, often in 4 distinct rows. **Flowers:** small, tubular, cream to mauve or dark reddish, with 2 bracts at the base of each flower; axillary, solitary, near the ends of the branches, together forming a spike-like structure (October to December). **Fruit:** up to 3 mm in diameter, extending just beyond the margin of the subtending bracts; orange-yellow when mature, flowers and fruits often borne at the same time (November to December).

4. DAIS L.

Dais cotinifolia L.   Illust. 212
S.A. no: 521   Pompon tree. Basboom
Rhod. no: 760 Pompon tree

A shrub or small tree 3 to 7 m in height, very occasionally reaching 13 m; occurring at the margins of evergreen forest, in riverine fringe forest and in bush on steep rocky mountainsides. **Bark:** brown, smooth. **Leaves:** opposite or often crowded near the ends of the branchlets, rarely sub-opposite to scattered, simple, oblong-elliptic to obovate, 7 to 9 × 3,5 to 5 cm; midrib and veining conspicuously pale green, almost translucent, prominent below, without hairs; young leaves pale green, maturing to dark olive-green; apex and base tapering; margin entire, sometimes rolled under; petiole up to 5 mm long. **Flowers:** very attractive, shell-pink to pinkish-mauve, tubular, up to 3 cm long, in dense **649**

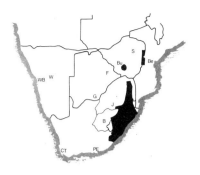

terminal almost spherical heads up to 4 cm in diameter, the whole head having 4 conspicuous, green, shield-like bracts round the base which dry to reddish-brown and become thinly woody. Bisexual; calyx tube cylindric, finely hairy, with 5 petalloid lobes; petals absent; stamens 10, of different lengths, arising from the sides of the calyx tube; ovary 1-chambered, surrounded at the base by the cup-shaped disc (November to February). **Fruit:** a very small reddish-brown nutlet, the ovary having barely increased in size, enclosed at the base of the persistent calyx tube which dries and droops, often still tinged with pink (January to April).

This tree is freely destroyed for the sake of its bark which provides an excellent quality rope. It is most attractive and is becoming widely cultivated, appearing on the lists of many nurseries; it has been cultivated in Europe since 1764.

LYTHRACEAE *(The pride-of-India family)*

Key to the genera:

Leaves with a very conspicuous gland which terminates the midrib before it reaches the apex, always visible on the under surface, often on the upper surface as well; fruit an almost spherical capsule partly enveloped by the persistent calyx; in the flower bud the calyx lacks a long beak ... **1. Galpinia**

Leaves without a gland near the apex; fruit a 2-lobed, more or less flattened, capsule; in the flower bud the calyx forms a long beaked tip .... **2. Rhynchocalyx**

1. GALPINIA N. E. Brown

Galpinia transvaalica N. E. Brown
S.A. no: 523   Wild pride-of-India. Transvaalliguster
Rhod. no: 761   Wild pride-of-India

A many-stemmed shrub or small tree up to 6 m in height; occurring at medium to low altitudes in woodland and thicket. **Bark:** pale, rather smooth. **Leaves:** opposite, simple, 2,5 to 9 × 1,8 to 4 cm, glossy dark green to almost blackish, leathery, with a conspicuous gland which terminates the midrib before it reaches the apex, always visible on the under surface and often on the upper surface as well; apex rounded, often notched; base tapering; margin entire, conspicuously wavy; petioles very short and thickset. Stipules fall early. **Flowers:** white, up to 1,3 cm in diameter, in dense terminal and

650

axillary panicles, somewhat resembling the flowers of *Lagerstroemia indica,* the pride-of-India. Bisexual, floral parts in fives to sixes; calyx bell-shaped, dividing into ovate lobes for half their length; petals crinkly; stamens attached to the mouth of the calyx tube; ovary 2-chambered. The flowers are short-lived but the tree is showy and attractive when in flower (November to May). **Fruit:** a small almost spherical capsule, 3 to 4 mm in diameter, reddish-brown when mature, partially enveloped in the remains of the persistent calyx, produced in dense clusters (June to July).

2. RHYNCHOCALYX Oliver

Rhynchocalyx lawsonioides Oliver
S.A. no: 523,1   Natal privet. Natalliguster
Rhod. no: —

A small tree up to 6 m in height; occurring at the margin of evergreen forest and along rivers. **Bark:** pale grey with a pinkish tinge, finely longitudinally striated, later flaking. **Leaves:** opposite, simple, oval, 3,5 to 6 × 1,3 to 2,5 cm, leathery, with fine net-veining distinguishable on both surfaces; apex tapering to narrowly rounded; base tapering; margin entire, markedly rolled under; petiole short and thickset. **Flowers:** creamy-white, very small, in fine, delicate, axillary and terminal heads, or panicles, 3 to 8 cm in diameter. Bisexual; all floral parts in sixes; in bud the calyx forms a conical beak (the generic name refers to this) which later becomes deeply divided; petals narrowly clawed, lobed at the base; stamens opposite the petals; ovary 2-chambered (March). **Fruit:** a flattened capsule, about 5 to 10 mm in diameter, 2-lobed, splitting at the top to open like a purse, reddish-brown when mature (August, but the old fruits may be still on the tree in March). This is a protected plant in South Africa.

SONNERATIACEAE

SONNERATIA L.f.

Sonneratia alba Smith
S.A. no: —
Rhod. no: —   Sonneratia

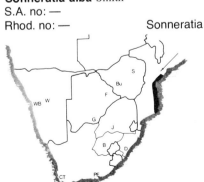 

A small tree up to 8 m in height; often growing in shallow sea water, frequently a common constituent of mangrove swamps in deep mud; producing many small vertical pneumatophores. **Bark:** dark grey

651

to greyish-brown, rather smooth. **Leaves:** opposite, simple, obovate to almost circular, about 10 cm long, yellow-green; apex square, occasionally notched; base narrowly tapering; margin entire; petiole up to 10 mm long, stout. **Flowers:** calyx green, petals white, strap-like, inconspicuous and falling early, stamens many and long forming dense showy white heads, about 4 cm in diameter, solitary or 3 together near the ends of the branches (June to October). **Fruit:** conical, up to 3 × 4 cm, tipped with the persistent style and with the remains of the persistent calyx round the base, green when mature; the fruits rot in the water and so release the seeds (October to December).

LECYTHIDACEAE

BARRINGTONIA J. R. & G. Forster

Barringtonia racemosa (L.) Sprengel   Illust. 213
S.A. no: 524   Powder-puff tree. Poeierkwasboom
Rhod. no: —

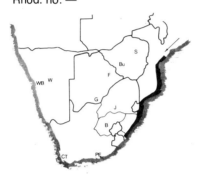

Usually a small tree 4 to 8 m in height, but occasionally reaching 15 m; occurring always near water, along the banks of rivers, in fresh water swamps and occasionally in the less saline areas of mangrove swamps, under which conditions it may develop pneumatophores. **Bark:** greyish, yellowish or brownish, mottled, rather smooth to fissured. **Leaves:** alternate, simple, crowded at the ends of the branches, large, obovate-oblong to oblanceolate, 8 to 35 × 4 to 13 cm, deep green; apex broadly tapering; base narrowly tapering, running into the petiole; margin entire or very shallowly toothed or scalloped; petiole very short, without hairs. **Flowers:** very attractive, white to pale pink, in many-flowered pendulous sprays up to 60 cm in length, or even more. Bisexual; all floral parts in fours; sepals joined at the base, separating into 3 to 4 lobes, green flushed with pink, about 10 × 7,5 mm; petals white, often tinged with pink, elliptic, up to 3 × 1 cm, attached to the staminal tube; stamens many, long, white or pinkish, forming a large central mass 3,5 cm in diameter; ovary 2- to 4-chambered, style red (November to June). **Fruit:** conical to ovate, about 3 × 2 cm, crowned by the remains of the persistent calyx and style, fleshy at first, becoming hard, fibrous and yellowish-brown when mature, the fibrous coat giving it buoyancy in the water so that it may be carried great distances (July to October).
The bark contains tannin and, when powdered, has been used as a fish poison, and extracts have proved effective as an insecticide. The fruit provides a remedy for malaria. This is a most decorative tree which grows easily and rapidly, but it will not stand frost.

RHIZOPHORACEAE *(The mangrove family)*

The term *mangrove* generally refers to plants, frequently not related, which have become adapted for growth in the mud and silt of tidal estuaries and lagoons. Most of these plants prefer still waters and do not favour the turbulence of the open sea. A mangrove swamp forest is often a belt of dark green, rather low-growing trees. Its humid atmosphere and deep mud, alternately inundated and left bare by the tides, provide a unique ecosystem with its own specially adapted forms of animal and plant life. The strangely shaped roots produced by these trees, some elbow-angled and others pencil- and snake-like, are in fact 'breathing roots' or pneumatophores, necessary to the plant because of the scarcity of oxygen in the water-logged substrate. Some of the trees, such as members of *Rhizophora*, have stilt-roots equal in length to the distance between the tides, so that at high tide the trees seem to be floating on the surface, while at low water they are seen perched on their spreading stilts. Some species prefer deep mud and these form the inner zone of a mangrove swamp; others favour a better drained soil and grow on the outer extremeties where the ground is slightly higher. Tap roots are absent, and those on the surface spread over a wide area to anchor the plant in the unstable ground. Some of the fruits are also specially adapted to this environment: in certain species the seed germinates while still on the tree in which case the hypocotyl of the seedling is often thick and torpedo-shaped so that it drops, already growing, like a spear into the mud where it develops roots within a few hours. There are also seeds and fruits that have developed resistant coatings allowing them to remain viable after long periods of immersion in sea water; they are thus able to float long distances before germinating.

Paradoxically, these trees in certain respects resemble plants growing in arid areas where water conservation is essential, as they too face the problem of water loss. Winds increase transpiration and, when the mud starts to dry, the salt concentration becomes so high that they cannot take in any more water and may even start losing it (exosmosis). They are therefore xerophytes living in perpetually water-logged conditions. The trees are provided with ample water-storage organs, and, in order to reduce water loss, their leaves are thick and leathery, even fleshy, and covered with a waxy cuticle.

In southern Africa nine genera are involved, all of them contributing, in one area or another, to the mangrove belts: *Xylocarpus* (Meliaceae), *Heritiera* (Sterculiaceae), *Sonneratia* (Sonneratiaceae), *Barringtonia* (Lecythidaceae), *Bruguiera*, *Ceriops* and *Rhizophora* (Rhizophoraceae), *Lumnitzera* (Combretaceae) and *Avicennia* (Verbenaceae).

Key to the genera in *Rhizophoraceae:*

1 An inland genus, never a constituent of mangrove swamp forest; without stilt-roots or breathing roots; seeds not germinating while still on the plant .... **4. Cassipourea**

Coastal genera of tidal estuaries; developing breathing roots and sometimes stilt-roots; seeds germinate while still on the plant 2

2 Leaves with a conspicuous, bristle-like tip; stilt-roots many-branched and arching over, sometimes growing from the branches as well; calyx 4-lobed .... **2. Rhizophora**

Leaves without a conspicuous bristle-tip; prop-roots more thickset and shorter, seldom branching; calyx 4 to 14 lobed 3

3 Aerial roots conspicuously elbow-angled and large; calyx 8- to 14-lobed; hypocotyl of seedling shallowly or bluntly ridged .... **3. Bruguiera**

Aerial roots not conspicuously elbow-angled, although elbows do sometimes just protrude above the mud; calyx 5- to 6-lobed; hypocotyl of seedling conspicuously and sharply vertically ridged .... **1. Ceriops**

1. CERIOPS Arn.

Ceriops tagal (Perrottet) C. B. Robinson
S.A. no: 525   Indian mangrove. Indiese wortelboom
Rhod. no: —

A shrub or small tree up to 7 m in height; occurring on tidal mud flats, usually growing on the landward side of mangrove swamp forests. **Bark:** light grey-brown, smooth; the base of the stem often with wide buttresses, sometimes with short contorted stilt-roots at the base of the stem, these are more like deeply defined buttress roots but generally this is not a stilt-root species; thin, inconspicuous, elbow-shaped pneumatophores, 20 to 30 cm high, are produced just protruding above the mud. **Leaves:** opposite, simple, all parts without hairs, broadly elliptic, obovate to broadly so, 3 to 9 × 1,5 to 5 cm, yellow-green, thickly leathery to almost fleshy; apex rounded; base tapering; margin entire, **653**

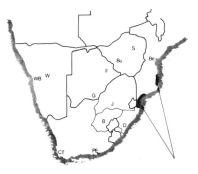

sometimes wavy; petiole 1 to 2,5 cm long. Stipules inter-petiolar, falling early. **Flowers:** small, white, leathery, inconspicuous, in small heads of 4 to 8, on stalks, or peduncles, up to 10 cm long, axillary among the terminal leaves. Bisexual; floral parts in fours to sixes; sepals pale green, equalling the petals in length, not opening out; petals white, rather square, about 3 mm long, with 2 to 3 club-shaped, claw-like hooks on the blunt apex; stamens 10 to 12, arising from a lobed disc; ovary 2-chambered. The flower rests in a reddish-brown cup formed by two bracteoles (August to March). **Fruit:** a green rather leathery ovoid berry up to 2,5 cm long, from which the seedling grows while still on the tree, until the hypocotyl, which is sharply longitudinally ridged, projects some 30 cm (December to March).

The wood is a good fuel and, of all the mangroves, probably the best timber. The bark has a high tannin content and also provides a red dye which is used in the batik industry. This is a protected plant in South Africa.

2. RHIZOPHORA L.

Rhizophora mucronata Lam.

S.A. no: 526   Red mangrove. Rooiwortelboom
Rhod. no: —

A medium sized compact tree up to 10 m in height; occurring on inter-tidal mud flats, most frequently mingling with *Avicennia* on the seaward side of mangrove swamp forests. **Bark:** reddish-brown, dark brown to almost black; the branches are characteristically soft, brittle and thick; younger branches light grey with large conspicuous leaf scars; very characteristic branched stilt-roots up to 2 m long are produced (see introductory note to this family on mangrove swamp forests). **Leaves:** opposite, simple, elliptic, up to 15 × 8 cm, thickly leathery, dark green with cork-like dots on the under surface; apex abruptly tapering, with a distinctive hair-like tip up to 5 mm long; base tapering; margin entire, often rolled under; petiole about 2 cm long. Stipules inter-petiolar, elongate, falling early. **Flowers:** creamy-white, leathery, in few-flowered thick-stalked axillary heads, or cymes. Bisexual; all floral parts in fours; sepals slightly longer than the petals; petals white, hairy, narrow, tapering to a slender point; stamens 8, filaments very short, conspicuous, brownish; ovary 2-chambered (February to October). **Fruit:** a leathery green berry up to 7 cm long from which the germinating seedling grows, reaching a length of 45 × 2 cm, being longer and thicker than those of either *Ceriops* or *Bruguiera;* calyx lobes persistent round the base (August to December).

The red mangrove,
Rhizophora mucronata, *perched
on its characteristic stilt-roots.*

Poles from these trees are used by Africans for building purposes and the wood makes a good fuel and charcoal. The bark, which is rich in tannin, provides a deep brown or blackish dye which toughens fibre fishing lines, although that obtained from *Ceriops* is said to be preferable.

3. BRUGUIERA Lam.

Bruguiera gymnorrhiza (L.) Lam.   Illust. 214
S.A. no: 527   Black mangrove. Swartwortelboom
Rhod. no: —

A rather conical tree up to 10 m in height or more; occurring on the seaward side of mangrove swamps, often intermingled with *Rhizophora*. **Bark:** reddish-brown, fibrous, rough; all parts without hairs; short prop-roots grow at the base of the main stem, but true stilt-roots are not developed; elbow-angled pneumatophores are produced. **Leaves:** opposite, simple, elliptic, up to 23 × 7 cm, dark green, without hairs, resembling the leaves of *Rhizophora* but lacking the conspicuous hair-like tip; apex and base tapering; margin entire, inclined to roll under; petiole up to 3 cm long. Stipules inter-petiolar, falling early. **Flowers:** creamy-white, soon turning brown, up to 4 cm long, solitary, axillary. Bisexual; floral parts in eights to fourteens; the sepals are the most conspicuous feature of the

655

The already growing fruits of the black mangrove, Bruguiera gymnorrhiza, *pierce the mud and develop roots within hours.*

flower and consist of 10 to 18 lobes which separate away at the mouth of the calyx tube, each lobe being very narrow and finely tapered; petals about 3 cm long, as many as the calyx lobes, attached in the mouth of the calyx tube; stamens in pairs opposite each petal; ovary 2- to 4-chambered, stiffly hairy (July to March). **Fruit:** a leathery green top-shaped berry up to 2,5 cm long, remaining within the fringed cup formed by the persistent sepals; the seedling grows from this, the hypocotyl being cigar-shaped, up to 11 cm long, and shallowly or bluntly ridged (about September).

The poles are used by Africans for building huts. The bark has a high tannin content and yields a black dye, which, with treatment, can be made to produce the colours orange, red, brown or violet. This species has been used to stabilise dunes and has been cultivated with success in fresh water swamps, tolerating even complete shade. It is probably the longest-lived of all the mangrove species.

4. CASSIPOUREA Aubl.

Shrubs or trees. **Leaves:** opposite, each pair at right angles to the next, or 3-whorled, simple. Stipules fall early. **Flowers:** solitary, or clustered together in leaf axils, with jointed stalks, or pedicels. Bisexual; all floral parts in fours to sevens; calyx leathery, bell-shaped, dividing into separate lanceolate to ovate lobes for half its length; petals as long as the calyx lobes, narrowly to broadly spathulate, the apex divided into a number of fringe-like segments; stamens 8 to 40, all arising on or outside the toothed disc; ovary 2- to 4-chambered. **Fruit:** a capsule, fleshy at first but splitting later; seeds dark brown to black with reddish arils.

None of the species in this genus occurs in mangrove swamp forests.

Key to the tree species of *Cassipourea:*
1 Leaves usually more than 7 cm long, up to 14 to 19 cm long 2
  Leaves usually less than 7 cm long 3

2 Leaves opposite or frequently arising 3 together at each node, elliptic, apex broadly tapering, finally abruptly and shortly attenuate .... **C. gummiflua**

 Leaves always opposite and never in threes, broadly elliptic to almost circular, apex broadly tapering to rounded, not attenuate .... **C. congoensis**

3 Leaf margin toothed, markedly or obscurely so 4

 Leaf margin entire 5

4 Confined to the extreme north of Rhodesia and northwards; under surface of the leaves covered with short soft hairs .... **C. sp. no.1**

 Confined to the eastern Cape; without hairs on the under surface of the leaves .... **C. flanaganii**

5 Under surface of the leaf covered with short soft hairs; occurring in the extreme north of Zululand and in Moçambique, apparently not recorded from Swaziland .... **C. mossambicensis**

 Under surface of the leaf without hairs except along the midrib; recorded from Swaziland only .... **C. swaziensis**

Cassipourea congoensis DC.

[*C. gerrardii* (Schinz) Alston; *C. malosana* (Baker) Alston]

S.A. no: 529   Bastard onion wood. Basteruiehout

Rhod. no: 762   Lesser onionwood

Often a shrub or small tree 3 to 4 m in height, but sometimes reaching 20 m; occurring at the margins of and in evergreen forest. **Bark:** light grey to grey-brown, rather smooth, becoming dark grey and rough with age; the trunk straight and slender with tiers of flatly spreading branches which give a symmetric appearance. **Leaves:** very variable in size and shape, even on the same tree, obovate to almost circular, 2 to 3 cm long, but usually elliptic, up to 14 cm long; light green when young, becoming glossy dark green and leathery when mature, midrib prominent below, lateral veins somewhat immersed on both surfaces, without hairs; apex broadly tapering to rounded; base tapering to rounded; margin with conspicuously slightly hooked teeth, wavy, occasionally more or less entire; petiole up to 8 mm long. **Flowers:** yellowish, greenish or cream, about 10 mm in diameter, in tight axillary clusters along the stem among the leaves; the slender style, up to 5 mm in length, is conspicuous (September to January). **Fruit:** a berry-like capsule, ovoid, about 10 mm long, with a thin layer of orange flesh when young, becoming black when dry (January to May).

Cassipourea flanaganii (Schinz) Alston

S.A. no: 528   Small-leaved bastard onionwood

Rhod. no: —

657

RHIZOPHORACEAE

A small tree up to 7 m in height; occurring in woodland and at the margins of evergreen forest. Branches brown; branchlets hairy. **Leaves:** obovate to oblong, 2,5 to 4 × 1,2 to 2 cm, glossy dark green, midrib and lateral veins conspicuous on the under surface, without hairs; apex broadly tapering to rounded, notched; base tapering, asymmetric; margin widely toothed; petiole 2 to 4 mm long. **Flowers:** white to cream, up to 8 mm in diameter, solitary on short stalks up to 5 mm long, inconspicuous (June to December). **Fruit:** a capsule, berry-like at first, about 10 × 6 mm, sharply tipped with the remains of the old style and with the persistent sepals round the base (July to February).

Cassipourea gummiflua Tul.   Illust. 215
[*C. verticillata* N. E. Brown]
S.A. no: 530   Onionwood. Uiehout
Rhod. no: 763   Onionwood

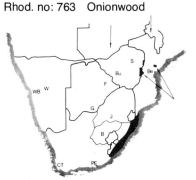

A small to large densely foliaged tree 6 to 20 m in height, often with long branches; occurring in evergreen forest and in riverine woodland. **Bark:** brownish-grey, rather smooth, often lichen-mottled; young branches often with scattered lenticels. **Leaves:** opposite or frequently in whorls of 3, large, elliptic, 8 to 19 × 3,5 to 7,5 cm, leathery, yellowish-green to dark green above, paler green below, midrib and lateral veins yellowish, prominent on the under surface, looping near the margin, without hairs; apex broadly tapering, finally abruptly and shortly attenuate forming a channel-tip; base tapering to square; margin entire or sometimes markedly toothed; petiole rather short; the petioles, young leaves and branchlets reddish, particularly in the flowering branches. **Flowers:** greenish-cream, about 6 mm in diameter, in more or less dense clusters, shortly stalked, axillary, along the stems; stamens up to 14, conspicuous (December to April). **Fruit:** a spherical capsule, about 7 mm in diameter, yellowish-green when mature (April to May).

This species has been divided into three varieties, var. *verticillata* (N. E. Brown) J. Lewis being the only one to extend south of the Zambezi River. The flowers attract bees and ants and the cut wood has a strong smell of onion.

Cassipourea mossambicensis (V. Brehmer) Alston
S.A. no: 531   Sand onionwood. Sanduiehout
Rhod. no: —

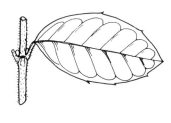

A shrub or small bushy tree up to 6 m in height; occurring in sand forest, at the margins of evergreen forest and as an under-storey tree in evergreen forest. **Bark:** grey to brown. **Leaves:** obovate-oblong, 3 to 8 × 2 to 5 cm, leathery, glossy green above, paler green and finely hairy below; the midrib and lateral veins conspicuous on the under surface, looping near the margin, net-veining usually clearly visible; apex broadly tapering to rounded; base tapering to rounded; margin entire, conspicuously rolled under; petiole short. **Flowers:** small, green in axillary groups of 1 to 3, each on a short pedicel about 3 mm long (November to December). **Fruit:** a small green capsule containing a yellowish juice, the aril completely enveloping the seed (March to April).

Cassipourea swaziensis Compton
S.A. no: 531,1   Swazi onionwood. Swazi-uiehout
Rhod. no: —

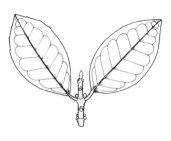

A small many-branched tree 3 to 4 m in height; occurring at altitudes of over 900 m, on rocky outcrops. **Bark:** grey, fissured. **Leaves:** lanceolate, oblong to ovate, up to 7 × 3 cm, without hairs except along the midrib, net-veining conspicuous below; apex and base tapering; margin entire; petiole short, densely hairy. **Flowers:** small, white, with a central mass of stamens, in axillary clusters (October). **Fruit:** apparently not yet collected or described, but likely to be similar to its close allies.

Cassipourea sp. no. 1
S.A. no: —
Rhod. no: 764   Urungwe onionwood

A shrub or small slender tree about 4 m in height; occurring at low altitudes, in thicket. **Bark:** pale grey, with lenticellate streaks of paler grey. **Leaves:** clustered at the ends of spur-shoots, broadly ovate to almost circular, 3 to 5 × 1,5 to 5 cm, very bright green above, softly hairy below with conspicuous veins; apex and base broadly tapering; margin entire to markedly toothed; petiole short. **Flowers:** small, greenish, in inconspicuous axillary clusters (October to December). **Fruit:** an ovoid capsule, about 8 × 4 mm, pale green when mature with short white hairs (December to January). This is a rare tree, having been collected once only; however, it is obviously similar to *C. sp. 1* of White in *Forest Flora of Northern Rhodesia*. At the time of going to press it was learned that this species is *C. gossweileri* Exell.

COMBRETACEAE *(The combretum family)*

Key to the genera:

1 A constituent of mangrove swamps; fruits oval, urn-shaped, without wings, crowned with the remains of the persistent calyx and style; leaves succulent, spirally arranged .... **6. Lumnitzera**

Not occurring in mangrove swamps; fruits with 2 to 5 wings, or obsolete wings like ridges, leaves not succulent, opposite, alternate, sometimes spirally arranged 2

2 Leaves usually opposite or whorled (very rarely alternate) 3

Leaves usually alternate, scattered, spirally arranged or fascicled on dwarf lateral shoots 6

3 Fruits frequently 2- to 3-winged (occasionally 4, rarely 5), bases of the wings tapering and running into the stalk .... **3. Pteleopsis**

Fruits usually 4- to 5-winged (sometimes 6), bases of the winges lobed or square (in one species the wings are obsolete and represented as ridges) 4

4 Fruits long and narrow, about 3 × 1,5 cm; calyx produced into a long slender tube above the ovary, densely covered with soft golden-brown hairs .... **4. Quisqualis**

Fruits more or less spherical in outline; calyx tube bell-shaped or cup-shaped 5

5 Stamens 8 to 10; petals usually attached near the apex of the upper receptacle .... **1. Combretum**

Stamens 4; petals attached near the edge of the disc .... **2. Meiostemon**

6 Petals present; fruits 4- to 5-winged (occasionally 6) .... **1. Combretum**

Petals absent; fruits 2-winged .... **5. Terminalia**

1. COMBRETUM Loefl.

Shrubs, climbers or trees; with hairs, multi-cellular stalked glands and possibly microscopic multi-cellular scales. **Leaves:** opposite (rarely alternate or whorled), simple. Stipules absent. **Flowers:** in elongate or almost spherical spikes, or racemes, or in panicles, axillary and/or terminal. Bisexual; floral parts in fours to fives; calyx tube cup-shaped or bell-shaped, dividing into lobes; petals small and inconspicuous, or large and showy; stamens 8 to 10 in 2 whorls; disc with or without hairs; ovary below all the other floral parts. **Fruit:** 4- or 5-winged (sometimes 6), indehiscent, or occasionally tardily dehiscent.

Key to the tree species of *Combretum:*
Note: with only leaves and fruits, *Meiostemon tetrandrus* would certainly be taken for a species of *Combretum* and would key out at No. 3 (however, it is a small tree, being 3 to 4 m in height, and differs from *C. engleri* in having much smaller fruits) or, depending upon its leaf size, at No. 23 (but it differs from *C. celastroides* in that the wings of its fruits are only 5 mm wide); if flowers are available, it will be noted that those of the *Combretum* species have 8 to 10 stamens, while those of *Meiostemon* have only 4.

1 Leaves conspicuously small, usually not exceeding 4 cm in length 2
Leaves usually longer than 4 cm 7
2 Leaves generally without hairs (although there may be minute pockets of hairs in the axils of the veins on the under surface) 3
Upper and/or under surface of leaves remaining softly velvety to maturity 4
3 Usually a small to large tree 7 to 15 m in height; leaves grey-green giving the tree a characteristic greyish appearance; fruits seldom more than 1,5 × 1,5 cm, conspicuously pale yellowish when young .... **C. imberbe**
Usually a shrub to small tree 3 to 4 m in height, with a tendency to scramble; leaves shiny green; fruits up to 4 × 4 cm, green when young .... **C. engleri**

4 Leaf base tapering; under surface of leaves usually with dense, brown, short, soft hairs, giving the tree a characteristic brownish appearance; fruits rich dark red-brown with the wings golden-edged .... **C. hereroense**

Leaf base rounded to lobed; hairs on the leaves not brown 5

5 Leaves almost circular, about 4 × 4 cm. Occurring in the north-west of South West Africa only .... **C. wattii**

Leaves obovate to elliptic. Not occurring in South West Africa 6

6 Leaves among the flowers become silvery-white and very showy; fruits 5-winged, up to 4 cm long. Reaching its southern limit in the north of Rhodesia and adjacent areas in Moçambique .... **C. obovatum**

Leaves among the flowers do not become silvery-white; fruits 4-winged, up to 2,5 cm long. Occurring only in the north and central areas of Moçambique and northwards .... **C. pisoniiflorum**

7 Fruits with obsolete wings, only 4- to 5-angled .... **C. bracteosum**

Fruits clearly winged 8

8 Leaves retaining hairs either above and/or below to maturity 9

Leaves without hairs at maturity 20

9 Fruits small, usually 2 cm long or less 10

Fruits medium to large, 2 to 5 cm long 15

10 Flowers spectacular red; usually a strong climber or scrambler .... **C. paniculatum**

Flowers greenish-yellow, yellow or white, not red 11

11 Leaf apex very broadly tapering to rounded. At high altitudes in the Transvaal only .... **C. moggii**

Leaf apex tapering to attenuate. Not confined to the Transvaal 12

12 Leaf apex attenuate .... **C. celastroides**

Leaf apex tapering but not attenuate 13

13 Leaf base rounded to shallowly lobed; blade with dense grey velvety hairs on both surfaces .... **C. molle**

Leaf base tapering; blade without dense velvety hairs above 14

14 A shrub or small tree, frequently using its long drooping branches to support itself and scramble into adjacent trees; flowers usually December to February .... **C. padoides**

A medium sized rounded tree, almost always along river banks .... **C. erythrophyllum**

15 Fruits 3 to 5 cm long 16

Fruits 2 to 3 cm long 18

16 Usually a scrambling shrub, occurring in low altitude valleys and along escarpments; fruits 5-winged .... **C. obovatum**

Small to medium sized trees; fruits 4-winged 17

17 Fruits yellow-green when young, becoming light yellow-brown later, up to 3,5 cm long; leaves in whorls of 3 to 4, occasionally opposite, developing beautiful autumn colours .... **C. fragrans**

Fruits rust-red when young, becoming rich chocolate-brown or deep golden-brown with a metallic sheen, up to 4,5 cm long; leaves opposite to alternate, not conspicuous in autumn .... **C. collinum**

18 Fruits brilliant red when freshly mature, drying to tan-brown; leaves usually with silvery, silky hairs; bark peeling .... **C. psidioides**

Fruits yellowish-green, sometimes flushed with pink or reddish-brown when freshly mature, drying to pale brown; leaves without silky hairs 19

19 Occurring in a restricted area in southern Natal only .... **C. edwardsii**

Occurring no further south than the Caprivi Strip, Botswana and the north of Rhodesia .... **C. albopunctatum**

20 Fruits small, usually less than 2 cm long 21

Fruits medium to large, 2 to 6 cm long 24

21 Leaves characteristically grey-green, giving the tree a greyish appearance; usually medium to large trees .... **C. imberbe**

Leaves green, not grey-green; shrubs or medium sized trees 22

22 Mature leaves dark shiny green above, pale to whitish below .... **C. kraussii**

Mature leaves may be paler below but not conspicuously so 23

23 Leaves narrowly elliptic; mature fruits reddish-brown, giving the whole tree a reddish-brown appearance .... **C. caffrum**

Leaves elliptic to broadly ovate; mature fruits individually attractive, the wings becoming bright red while the body remains green, drying to golden-brown but not produced in such profusion as to colour the tree .... **C. celastroides**

24 Mature fruits red to red-brown 25

Mature fruits straw-coloured to light brown 27

25 Leaves frequently with under surface usually, but not always, silvery-white; fruit up to 4,5 cm long, rusty-red when young, becoming rich chocolate-brown to deep golden-brown with a metallic sheen .... **C. collinum**

Leaves never have a silvery-white under surface; fruits up to 3 cm long, greenish when young 26

26 Fruits reddish-brown when freshly mature and the same colour when dry; leaf apex abruptly attenuate, the slender tip often twisting .... **C. apiculatum**

Fruits a striking brilliant red when freshly mature, but drying to a tan-brown; leaf apex rounded, shallowly notched, often with a hair-like tip .... **C. psidioides**

27 Small to medium sized trees 28

Usually climbers, occasionally small trees 29

28 Fruits large, up to 6 cm long; flowers in axillary spikes 3 to 7 cm long, stamens with distinctive orange anthers; branchlets drooping. Widespread .... **C. zeyheri**

Fruits up to 3,5 cm long; flowers in axillary spikes up to 2,5 cm long, stamens with pale yellow anthers; branchlets not drooping. Confined to low altitude dry woodland, the Zambezi Valley and adjacent areas .... **C. elaeagnoides**

29 Flowers a spectacular crimson or purplish-red 30

Flowers yellowish to white, or tinged with pink 31

30 Red stamens 8 mm long (occasionally longer). Widespread .... **C. paniculatum**

Red stamens 18 mm long. Occurring in restricted areas in Moçambique and northwards .... **C. holstii**

31 Stamens whitish, 6 mm long. Occurring in a very confined area on the northern Natal border, otherwise north of the Zambezi River .... **C. xanthothyrsum**

Stamens white, large, conspicuous, 17 mm long. Widespread .... **C. mossambicense**

Combretum albopunctatum Suesseng.

S.A. no: 531,2   Silver-dot bushwillow. Okavangoboswilg
Rhod. no: 765   Silver-dot combretum

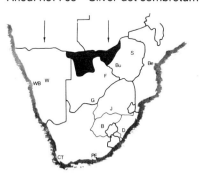
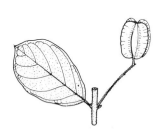

A shrub with a tendency to scramble, or a small tree 3 to 5 m in height; occurring at low altitudes, in dry woodland and on alluvial soils in riverine thicket. **Bark:** grey to brownish-grey, sometimes mottled, smooth. **Leaves:** opposite to sub-opposite, ovate to oblong, 4 to 10 × 2 to 5,5 cm, thinly textured to leathery, young leaves densely covered with brownish hairs, most of which are lost from the upper surface by maturity but persist on the under surface which also has microscopic glistening scales; apex broadly tapering to rounded; base tapering; margin entire; petiole 2 to 4 mm long. **Flowers:** yellow, sweetly scented, in short axillary spikes up to 3 × 1 cm (October to November). **Fruit:** 4-winged, up to 2 to 3 × 1,8 to 2,5 cm, reddish-brown, satiny, minutely spotted with almost microscopic, circular, dish-shaped, silvery scales (January to May).

Combretum apiculatum Sonder
[*C. apiculatum* subsp. *leutweinii* (Schinz) Exell]
S.A. no: 532 and 532,1   Red bushwillow. Rooibos
Rhod. no: 766   Red bushwillow

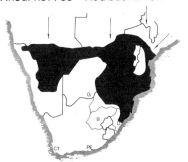 

A small to medium sized tree, 3 to 10 m in height, occasionally bushy and shrub-like; occurring at medium to low altitudes in dry open woodland. **Bark:** grey to dark grey or brownish-grey, smooth becoming scaly and rough with age. **Leaves:** opposite, narrowly to broadly obovate-elliptic, oblong or broadly ovate, 3 to 13 × 1,5 to 8 cm, thinly leathery, young leaves sticky and glutinous with a varnished shine, without hairs or with dense to sparse hairs on both surfaces, sometimes with rusty hairs along the veins, or with pockets of hairs in the axils of the veins on the under surface, with microscopic, transparent, thin-walled scales present; apex abruptly attenuate, forming a slender tip, often twisted; base rounded to slightly lobed; margin entire, wavy; petiole up to 10 mm long. **Flowers:** yellow to creamy-green, heavily scented, in axillary spikes up to 7 × 1,5 cm (September to February). **Fruit:** 4-winged, 2 to 2,8 × 1,5 to 2,5 cm, reddish-brown when mature (January to May), with a satiny sheen and possibly soft hairs, at least on the body. Old fruits present until October.
The Zulus use a decoction of the leaves as a steam bath and as an enema to relieve stomach disorders. The ash from the burnt stem is mixed with white clay and water and the face is covered with this several times to treat conjunctivitis. The wood is hard and heavy, but the pieces are usually too small to be of any use; however, it is resistant to borers and termites and provides useful fencing posts; it also makes a good firewood.

Combretum bracteosum (Hochst.) Brandis
S.A. no: 532,2   Hiccup nut. Hikklimop
Rhod. no: —

A shrub with a tendency to scramble, or a small tree up to 8 m in height; occurring in dune forest, or at the margins of evergreen forest, seldom far from the sea. **Bark:** light brown; the long slender branches clamber into the surrounding trees using the leaf petioles as grappling hooks. **Leaves:** opposite to sub-opposite, broadly elliptic, 4 to 10 × 1,7 to 5 cm; pale green on both surfaces or slightly darker and without hairs on the upper surface, the lower surface finely hairy; apex broadly tapering, often attenuate; base broadly tapering to narrowly rounded; margin entire, rolled under; petiole slender, up to 10 mm long. **Flowers:** deep orange to scarlet, about 6 mm in diameter, on stalks about 6 mm long, in dense compact racemes at the tips of the branches, the stamens and style protruding from the flower giving a spiky appearance; 2 conspicuous leaf-like bracts occur at the base of each flower stalk, or

663

pedicel (September to October). **Fruit:** without wings, ovoid, about 10 mm long, frequently with 4 to 5 vertical ridges, pale brown when mature (December to March or later).

The source of the common name, hiccup-nut, is somewhat obscure; while Medley Wood said that the edible fruits produced hiccups, C. A. Smith held that they were used in treating the complaint. Whatever the derivation, the name has been in use for over 100 years.

Combretum caffrum (Ecklon & Zeyher) Kuntze
S.A. no: 533   Cape bushwillow. Kaapse vaderlandswilg
Rhod. no: —

A small to medium sized tree up to 10 m in height; occurring along river and stream banks and in moist areas. **Bark:** pale grey to greyish-brown. **Leaves:** opposite to sub-opposite, narrowly elliptic, 4 to 10 × 1 to 2,5 cm, drooping, shiny green when mature, but may be finely velvety when young; apex and base tapering; margin entire; petiole 5 to 8 mm long. **Flowers:** greenish-yellow, in short thick almost spherical axillary heads, about 1,5 cm in diameter (October). **Fruit:** 4-winged, 1,3 to 1,8 cm long, reddish-brown, produced in profusion giving the whole tree a reddish-brown appearance (January to May).

This species very closely resembles *C. erythrophyllum.* The Zulus regard the root bark as a charm which ensures the downfall of their enemies. The timber is suitable for rough farm use and is useful as a fuel.

Combretum celastroides Welw. ex C. Lawson
S.A. no: 534   Savanna bushwillow. Savanneboswilg
Rhod. no: 767   Jesse-bush combretum

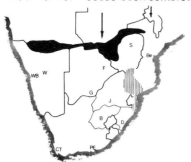

A dense, straggling bush about 4 m in height, or a small tree up to 7 m; occurring in dry woodland, on rocky hillsides, frequently on Kalahari sand. **Bark:** grey, rather smooth. **Leaves:** opposite to sub-opposite, rarely alternate, elliptic to broadly ovate, 2,5 to 14 × 1 to 8, but usually about 8 cm long, thinly leathery, green, the upper surface without hairs, the lower surface hairy especially along the veins and in their axils; becoming beautiful deep red to plum-coloured in autumn; apex attenuate; base tapering to rounded; margin entire; petiole up to 8 mm long. **Flowers:** greenish to yellow, in rather sparse axillary spikes, usually about 5 to 8 cm long, but may reach 12 cm (December to March). **Fruit:** 4-winged, 1 to 2 cm long, the wings becoming bright red while the body of the fruit still remains greenish-yellow, drying to golden-brown with a satiny sheen (February to June).

664   This is a thicket-forming species and is one of the main constituents of the almost impenetrable 'jesse bush'. The species has been divided into three subspecies, two of which occur south of the Zambezi River:

subsp. *celastroides* (refer to black areas on the map) – with larger flowers, the disc measuring up to 4 mm in diameter; the leaves are finely velvety below.

subsp. *orientale* Exell (refer to the vertical lines on the map) – with smaller flowers, the disc measuring 2 to 2,5 mm in diameter; the leaves are without hairs or nearly so.

subsp. *laxiflorum* (Welw. ex C. Lawson) Exell does not extend further south than western Zambia.

Combretum collinum Fresen.   Illust. 216
[*C. cognatum* Diels; *C. eylesii* Exell; *C. mechowianum* O. Hoffm.]

S.A. no: 541, 541,1, 541,2 and 541,3   Bushwillow. Boswilg
Rhod. no: 768   Variable combretum

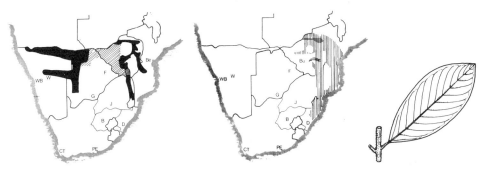

A small to medium sized tree 4 to 12 m in height; ocurring at medium to low altitudes in open woodland. **Bark:** light grey, rather rough. **Leaves:** opposite to alternate, narrowly elliptic to broadly ovate or obovate, up to 19 × 8 cm but usually about half this size, rather dark green above, paler green to silvery below, with or without dense woolly hairs; apex broadly tapering, tapering to attenuate; base broadly tapering; margin entire; petiole usually up to 3 cm long. **Flowers:** cream to yellow, up to 5 mm in diameter, sweetly scented, in axillary spikes usually about 5 to 6 cm long but which may reach 10 cm, conspicuous when the tree is in full flower; often produced with the previous season's leaves (August to October). **Fruit:** 4-winged, 3 to 4,5 cm long, rusty-red when young, becoming dark chocolate-brown or deep golden-brown when mature, with a marked metallic sheen caused by scales; old fruits may be found on the tree for most of the year (January to August).

Recent revision of this species has resulted in the combination of many previously maintained species, and in the formation of 4 subspecies which occur south of the Zambezi River:

1 Leaves with long, spreading hairs and prominent veining (refer to the black areas on the map)
   .... subsp. *gazense* (Swynnerton & E. G. Baker) Okafor
   Leaves without hairs, or nearly so 2
2 Fruits densely hairy; under surface of leaves green to yellowish (refer to the vertical lines on the
   map) .... subsp. *suluense* (Engl. & Diels) Okafor
   Fruits without hairs 3
3 Leaf apex tapering to attenuate; under surface silvery-white (refer to the horizontal lines on the
   map) .... subsp. *taborense* (Engl.) Okafor
   Leaf apex rounded to broadly tapering; under surface yellowish-green (refer to the oblique lines on
   the map) .... subsp. *ondongense* (Engl. & Diels) Okafor

The wood is hard and durable and makes good fencing posts. The roots provide a fibre used in basket work.

Combretum edwardsii Exell
S.A. no: 534,1   Natal combretum. Natalklimop
Rhod. no: —

Usually a strong, climbing shrub with trailing branches, occasionally a small tree up to 5 m in height; occurring in evergreen forest. **Bark:** grey to brown; young branches with brown woolly hairs, most of   **665**

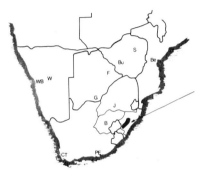

which are lost later. **Leaves:** opposite, elliptic to oblong-elliptic, up to 9 × 5 cm, covered at first with conspicuous brown hairs, most of which are lost by maturity; but some hairs are still retained, especially on the under surface; apex tapering; base rounded to shallowly lobed; margin entire; petiole up to 1,2 cm long. **Flowers:** with minute yellow petals concealed by short soft brownish hairs, produced in short axillary spikes, about 3 to 4 cm long (September to October). **Fruit:** 4-winged, 2 to 2,5 cm long, greenish-yellow tinged with pink, becoming pale brown when dry (January to July).

Combretum elaeagnoides Klotzsch
S.A. no: 534,2   Oleaster bushwillow. Oleasterboswilg
Rhod. no: 769   Large-fruited jesse-bush combretum

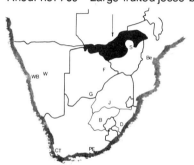

A small tree about 5 m in height with a tendency to clamber; occurring at low altitudes, in hot dry areas, in mixed woodland and on rocky hillsides. **Bark:** light grey to grey-brown, smooth to peeling or flaking, occasionally becoming dark and rather rough with age. **Leaves:** opposite to sub-opposite, rarely 3-whorled, narrowly elliptic, 3,5 to 13 × 1 to 6 cm, usually about 7 to 11 × 1,8 to 3 cm, paler green below than above, usually without hairs but with silvery scales on both surfaces, visible with a 20× lens; apex broadly tapering; base rounded to shallowly lobed; margin entire, sometimes wavy; petiole 3 to 10 mm long. **Flowers:** creamy-white to yellow, in dense axillary spikes up to 2,5 cm long, but often forming almost spherical heads, appearing before or with the young leaves; frequently in conspicuous profusion (September to January). **Fruit:** 4-winged, 2 to 3,5 cm long, creamy-green becoming brown when dry, the old fruits still on the tree with the next season's flowers (January to October).
This is a conspicuous constituent of 'jesse bush' at low altitudes. The wood is used for the handles of fish spears and for poles to support huts. It is often troublesome because of its rapid re-growth and consequent invasion of disturbed areas.

Combretum engleri Schinz
S.A. no: 535   Sand bushwillow. Sandboswilg
Rhod no: 780/1

A shrub or tree 3 to 4 m in height with a tendency to scramble; occurring at medium altitudes in mixed woodland and thicket, frequently on Kalahari sand and on rocky outcrops. **Bark:** grey to brownish. **Leaves:** opposite, conspicuously small, ovate to obovate or narrowly elliptic, 2 to 4 × 0,7 to 2 cm, shiny green, without hairs except for tufts in the axils of the veins on the under surface; apex broadly

666

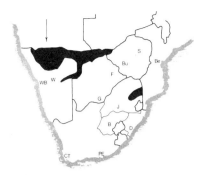

tapering to rounded; base tapering to rounded; margin entire; petiole slender, 2 to 3 mm long. **Flowers:** pale yellow, in short, rather few-flowered spikes up to 1,3 cm long, resembling a small axillary cluster with no common stalk or peduncle; glutinous and sticky, produced before or with the very young leaves (October to November). **Fruit:** 4-winged, up to 4 × 4 cm, green with reddish-brown microscopic scales producing a satiny sheen (March onwards).

Combretum erythrophyllum (Burch.) Sonder   Illust. 217
S.A. no: 536   River bushwillow. Riviervaderlandswilg
Rhod. no: 770   River combretum

A medium sized, spreading, densely foliaged tree up to 12 m in height, rarely a shrub; occurring along river banks where it can form thick stands; often several stemmed from the base, with the trunks reclining and overhanging the water, as a result of annual torrential flooding. **Bark:** pale, usually grey, smooth, flaking with age to expose paler grey patches which thus give it a mottled appearance. **Leaves:** sub-opposite, occasionally 3-whorled, elliptic, up to 10 × 5 cm but usually about 5 × 2 cm, upper surface usually without hairs and with the veining immersed, the under surface finely velvety, frequently with yellowish-rusty hairs, the midrib and lateral veins very conspicuous, the young leaves yellowish, shiny and viscous, maturing to fresh mid-green; apex and base tapering; margin entire; petiole 1 to 4 mm long. **Flowers:** cream to pale yellow, in dense axillary spikes, frequently almost spherical, about 10 mm in diameter, or may be more elongate, but still short, 1,5 to 2 × 1 cm, appearing just after the first young leaves (September to November). **Fruit:** 4-winged, 1 to 1,5 cm long, with a well-formed apical peg usually present; the very young fruits shiny and viscous, drying to a pale honey-brown; old fruits remain on the tree until the next flowering season (January to October). Sometimes the leaves turn red in autumn, and the specific name refers to this. The wood is yellow, tough and easily worked, and has been used as a general purpose timber. The seed germinates easily and the plants are fast growing; it is surprisingly drought-resistant and does well in gardens. This species is very similar to *C. caffrum*.

Combretum fragrans F. Hoffm.
[*C. ghasalense* Engl. & Diels; *C. ternifolium* Engl. & Diels; *C. tetraphyllum* Diels]
S.A. no: —
Rhod. no: 771   Four-leaved combretum

A small to medium sized tree 4 to 10 m in height; occurring at medium to low altitudes in dry woodland, often fringing vleis or pans and frequently found on termite mounds. **Bark:** grey, smooth

667

to rather rough, with irregular longitudinal fissures. **Leaves:** in whorls of 3 to 4, or opposite, ovate to ovate-oblong, up to 18 × 9 cm but usually about 11 to 13 cm long, shiny and glutinous when very young, becoming rather dark green when mature, the younger leaves velvety with golden-brown hairs which persist on the under surface, but most of which are lost on the upper surface by maturity; apex tapering to rounded; base usually broadly tapering; margin entire; petiole may be up to 10 mm long, but is usually almost absent. **Flowers:** greenish-white, cream to yellow, in dense, usually branched, spikes up to 4 cm long, rising from a thickset golden-brown velvety main axis, 1 to 2 cm long, appearing before or with the new leaves (August to October). **Fruit:** 4-winged, ovoid, up to 3,5 × 2,5 cm, viscid when young, maturing rapidly, at first yellow-green flushed with reddish-brown, drying to light yellow-brown, may be produced in profusion, sometimes remaining on the tree into the next flowering season, but fruits may also fall early while still green (September to November, sometimes remaining until the following October).

The leaves become beautifully coloured in autumn so that the tree could be confused with *Faurea speciosa*. An infusion of the roots is used in African medicine to bathe children suffering from convulsions.

Combretum hereroense Schinz   Illust. 218

[*C. transvaalense* Schinz; *C. hereroense* var. *villosissimum* Engl. & Diels; *C. rhodesicum* E. G. Baker]

S.A. no: 538   Russet bushwillow. Kierieklapper
Rhod. no: 772   Mouse-eared combretum

A small tree 3 to 5 m in height, but sometimes reaching 10 m; occurring at medium to low altitudes in open wooded grassland, sometimes at vlei margins and frequently on termite-mounds. **Bark:** dark grey, rough and flaking. **Leaves:** opposite to sub-opposite, oval to heart-shaped, 2 to 7 × 1 to 4,5 cm, but usually about 3 × 2 cm, deep green to grey-green above, densely covered with brown velvety hairs below, giving the whole tree a characteristic brown look, sometimes without hairs; the lateral veins are prominent on the under surface; apex rounded, notched, rarely tapering, may be apiculate; base tapering; margin entire; petiole about 5 mm long. **Flowers:** white, cream to yellow, in dense axillary and terminal spikes up to 6 cm long, occasionally almost spherical, about 10 mm in diameter, often produced in the axils of conspicuous scars left by old leaves, usually scented, produced before or with the new flush of leaves (September to November). **Fruit:** 4-winged, about 2 × 2 cm, conspicuous, rich dark reddish-brown from an early age, becoming rich brown with golden-edged wings (January to June).

The leaves are browsed on by cattle and can provide a useful fodder.

668

Combretum holstii Engl.

S.A. no: —
Rhod. no: — Moçambique burning bush

Often a woody climber, occasionally a small tree 3 to 5 m in height; occurring in low altitude woodland and in riverine fringe forest. **Bark:** grey to brownish. **Leaves:** opposite to sub-opposite, oblong-elliptic, up to 20 × 8,5 cm, thinly textured, without hairs, minutely glandular; apex tapering; base rounded to lobed; margin entire; petiole up to 10 mm long, the basal section persisting after the leaf falls and forming a curved spine. **Flowers:** conspicuous, crimson to purplish-red, up to 6 × 3 mm long, red stamens up to 1,8 cm long, in axillary spikes up to 14 cm long, usually appearing when the tree is bare (August to November). **Fruit:** 5-winged, up to 3,5 × 3 cm, with a satiny sheen, pale brown when dry (October to January).
This species is closely related to *C. mossambicense*.

Combretum imberbe Wawra   Illust. 219

S.A. no: 539   Leadwood. Hardekool
Rhod. no: 773   Leadwood

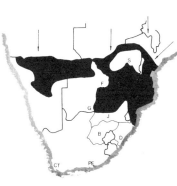

The distinctive bark of the leadwood,
Combretum imberbe.

Sometimes a shrub, but most frequently a small to large tree 7 to 15 m in height; occurring at medium to low altitudes, in mixed woodland, often along rivers or dry watercourses, particularly on alluvial soils. **Bark:** sometimes pale grey, smoothish and cracked in rectangular flakes, but most often dark grey to almost black and rough with characteristic deep longitudinal furrows and irregular transverse cracks. **Leaves:** small, obovate to oval, 2,5 to 8 × 1 to 3 cm, very characteristically grey-green, giving the whole tree a greyish appearance (except when in heavy fruit), often produced on short spinescent lateral shoots, thinly textured to rather leathery, without hairs, but with silvery, microscopic scales densely covering both surfaces; apex broadly tapering to rounded, often with a fine hair-like tip; base broadly tapering to narrowly tapering; margin entire, often wavy; petiole 4 to 10 mm long. **Flowers:** cream to yellow, sweetly scented, in rather slender spikes, 4 to 8 cm long, in the axils of the leaves, or sometimes forming a terminal head, or panicle (November to March). **Fruit:** 4-winged, seldom exceeding 1,5 × 1,5 cm, densely covered with silvery scales, characteristically pale yellowish-green even when mature (see Illust. 219), giving the tree a distinctive appearance, drying to a light brown; sometimes persisting into the next flowering season (February to June or on to December).

The heartwood is dark in colour and extremely hard, heavy and durable. It is difficult to work, rapidly blunting and breaking tools, and is therefore not suitable for furniture; however, it turns well and has been used for ornaments. It makes fine fencing standards, mine props and railway sleepers, and many of the finest specimens have been exploited for these purposes. The wood is so hard that Africans made blades for their hoes from it before metal became available. The wood provides an excellent fuel as it burns slowly; the ash has a high lime content and the Matabeles use it as a toothpaste and also as substitute for whitewash. The Hereros never destroy these trees as it is believed that they are the ancestors of all their peoples. Smoke from the burning leaf is inhaled to relieve coughs and colds. This tree is protected in South West Africa.

Combretum kraussii Hochst.

[*C. nelsonii* Dümmer; *C. woodii* Dümmer]
S.A. no: 540   Forest bushwillow. Bosvaderlandswilg
Rhod. no: —

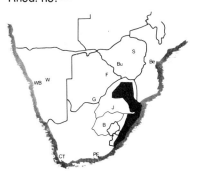

A shrub or small to medium sized tree up to 12 m in height; occurring from medium altitudes to sea level, in evergreen forest, wooded valleys and open woodland; also on rocky hillsides and mountain grassland. **Bark:** dark grey and furrowed on large specimens; young stems greenish, smooth. **Leaves:** opposite, obovate to elliptic, up to 9 × 5 cm. This species has the distinctive habit, in Natal if not over its whole range, of producing fresh green young leaves in spring which after about a month become streaked with white, frequently entirely losing their colour so that the tree appears to be covered in snowy blossom; then they slowly turn green again, their original colour being fully restored by mid-summer; the leaves turn red in autumn and fall in winter. The mature leaves are dark glossy green above and silvery-white below; apex tapering to rounded; base tapering; margin entire; petiole 2 to 7 mm long. **Flowers:** creamy-white, in dense axillary heads 1 to 3 cm long, appearing with the new leaves (August to November). **Fruit:** 4-winged, up to 2 × 1,7 cm, becoming light to dark red or russet-red when mature, drying to a mid-brown (February to June).

Dust from the sawn wood can prove irritating to the skin. The trees are fast-growing and would make good garden subjects.

Combretum moggii Exell
S.A. no: 540,2   Rock bushwillow. Rotsboswilg
Rhod. no: —

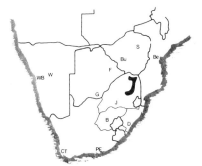

Usually a shrub, occasionally a small tree up to 5 m in height; occurring at high altitudes on steep rocky banks and hillsides, usually among rocks. **Bark:** greyish-brown, flaking and rough. **Leaves:** opposite, elliptic, usually about 5 to 7 × 1,5 to 2 cm, thinly leathery, finely velvety with microscopic silvery scales; apex very broadly tapering to rounded; base tapering to square; margin entire; petiole squat, up to 9 mm long. **Flowers:** greenish-yellow, in rather dense rounded clusters, about 1,5 cm in diameter (October). **Fruit:** 4-winged, up to 2 × 2 cm, greenish tinged with red, drying to brown (December to April).

Combretum molle R. Br. ex G. Don   Illust. 220
[*C. atelanthum* Diels; *C. gueinzii* Sonder; *C. holosericeum* Sonder]
S.A. no: 537   Velvet bushwillow. Basterrooibos
Rhod. no: 775   Velvet-leaved combretum

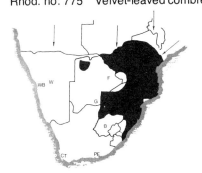

A small to medium sized spreading tree up to 10 m in height; occurring over a wide range of altitudes, from sea level to about 1 500 m, in open woodland. **Bark:** grey, grey-brown to almost black, rough and fissured, inclined to be flaky. **Leaves:** opposite, narrowly elliptic, broadly ovate-elliptic to almost circular, up to 14 × 9 cm but usually about 6 to 10 × 4 to 6 cm, with dense grey velvety hairs on both surfaces, especially below; some forms are almost without hairs; net-veining conspicuous especially on the under surface; apex tapering, often with a fine hair-like tip; base rounded to shallowly lobed; margin entire: petiole thickset, only 2 to 3 mm long. **Flowers:** greenish-yellow to yellow, in dense axillary spikes, often branched, 4 to 9 cm long, heavily scented, attracting insects; produced in profusion before or with the very new leaves (September to November). **Fruit:** 4-winged, 1,5 to 2 cm (rarely up to 2,5) × 1,5 to 2 cm, yellowish-green flushed with red, drying to golden reddish-brown, some of the old fruits remaining on the tree into the next flowering season (January to June and later).
This is a large and diverse species, some of its forms having been given specific names in the past. With its great variation it may be tempting to start to subdivide it once again but, to quote Exell and Garçia, *Contra. Conhec. Fl. Moçamb.* **2** : 106 (1954), 'in the long history of synonyms cited, they (those who might wish to subdivide the species) will find names for nearly all the diverse combinations of characters but, once they abandon the sheet anchor of *C. molle* R. Br. ex G. Don, they will find themselves sailing in very troubled water.'
In African medicine, the leaves – either fresh or dry and moistened – provide dressings for wounds; the   **671**

leaf and root together are believed to be an antidote for snakebite while the root alone is used to treat both abortion and constipation. A feverish child is bathed in a decoction of the dried leaves to reduce its temperature, while an infusion of the inner bark is taken orally or as an enema to relieve various stomach complaints. The wood is hard and yellow; it is suitable for implement handles and fencing posts and is said to be reasonably termite-proof. The seed germinates easily and the trees are quite fast-growing.

Combretum mossambicense (Klotzsch) Engl.

[*C. cataractarum* Diels; *C. detinens* Dinter; *C. armatum* Phillips]
S.A. no: 540,3   Knobbly combretum. Knoppiesklimop
Rhod. no: 776   Shaving-brush combretum

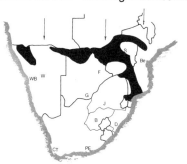

Usually a scrambling or climbing shrub with long trailing branches, but sometimes a small tree about 5 m in height; occurring at low altitudes in hot dry areas, common along the outer fringe of riverine thicket and forest, found also on koppies and associated with termite mounds. **Bark:** grey to brownish, smooth; the persistent petiole bases sometimes develop into spines. **Leaves:** opposite to sub-opposite, elliptic to elliptic-oblong, up to 15 to 20 × 7 to 9 cm, but usually about 6 × 3 cm, young leaves usually with fine hairs, losing these by maturity; apex tapering to rounded; base broadly tapering, often rounded, sometimes shallowly lobed; margin entire, inclined to be wavy; petiole with the lower 2 mm persistent forming a blunt woody peg after the leaf has fallen which may develop into a curved spine up to 2 cm long. **Flowers:** showy, sweetly scented, with conspicuous petals up to 9 × 4 mm, white or tinged with pink, with large prominent heads of stamens bearing pink or orange to red anthers; produced in dense axillary spikes up to 6 × 4 cm, these held horizontally along the upper side of long slender trailing branches; frequently produced before the leaves (August to November). **Fruit:** usually 5-winged (occasionally 4), up to 3 × 2,5 cm, with the wings papery thin and pale straw-coloured (October to January).

Combretum obovatum F. Hoffm.

S.A. no: —
Rhod. no: 777   Spiny combretum

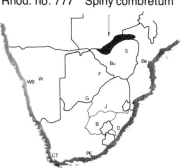

A scrambling shrub, very occasionally a small tree 3 to 7 m tall; occurring at low altitudes in river valleys and along escarpments. **Bark:** light brown, branches armed with hard curved spines formed from the petiole bases. **Leaves:** opposite or 3-whorled, obovate to broadly so, up to 6,5 × 3 to 4 cm, with dense short soft hairs, markedly paler green below than above, many of the leaves among and

672

below the flowers becoming silvery-white, showy and easily mistaken for flowers themselves; apex rounded with a hair-like tip; base rounded to shallowly lobed; margin entire; petiole up to 1,2 cm long, the lower 3 mm remaining after the leaf has dropped and developing into a curved spine. **Flowers:** brownish, anthers white, in almost spherical, axillary heads, 1 to 1,5 cm in diameter, near the ends of the branchlets (November). **Fruit:** 5-winged, up to 4 cm long, whitish when young, drying to a pale straw colour (January to June).

Combretum padoides Engl. & Diels

S.A. no:　　　Thicket bushwillow
Rhod. no: 778　Thicket combretum

A shrub or small tree 3 to 5 m in height, often using its long trailing branches to scramble into adjacent trees; occurring at low altitudes in hot dry areas, in riverine fringes, on rocky hills and along escarpments and in mixed woodland; it is often thicket-forming. **Bark:** dark brownish grey, rough. **Leaves:** opposite to sub-opposite, rarely alternate, elliptic to narrowly so, 3 to 10 × 3 to 4,5 cm, thinly textured, dull green; veining yellowish and conspicuous with hairs along the veins below; apex and base tapering; margin entire; petiole slender, up to 10 mm long. **Flowers:** cream to pale yellow in simple or branched, axillary or terminal, rather loose spikes up to 10 cm long, often produced in profusion (December to February). **Fruit:** 4-winged, 1 to 1,5 cm long, pale yellowish-green when young drying to light brown, on very slender stalks about 3 mm long, often produced in masses (March to June).

This species can be difficult to separate from *C. celastroides;* however, it differs in that the fruits are smaller and the apical peg is shorter or absent; in addition, the two species are different in habit.

Combretum paniculatum Vent.　Illust. 221

[*C. microphyllum* Klotzsch]
S.A. no: 540,1　Flame combretum. Vlamklimop
Rhod. no: 779　Burning-bush combretum

Usually a vigorous climber or scrambling shrub, occasionally a small tree 3 to 4 m in height; occurring in areas of high rainfall at the margins of evergreen forest and in forested ravines, and also at low altitudes in dry types of woodland and along river banks where it can become thicket-forming. **Bark:** grey to pale brown, inclined to become flaking in larger specimens. **Leaves:** opposite, ovate, oblong-elliptic to almost circular, up to 18 × 9,5 cm, thinly leathery, mid-green to glossy dark green, slightly paler green below; midrib and lateral veins yellowish and conspicuous; with marked net-

673

veining, especially above; apex broadly tapering to rounded; base square to shallowly lobed; margin entire, inclined to be wavy; petiole up to 3 cm long, the lower 2 to 5 mm may be persistent, remaining after the leaf falls to form a blunt square spine. **Flowers:** showy, crimson-red, the crimson stamens being the most conspicuous feature; petals about 2,5 × 2,5 mm, stamens up to 1,5 cm long; in individually small axillary clusters, but the massed effect along the trailing branches is one of large, curving sprays (August to November). **Fruit:** usually 4-winged (occasionally 5), usually 2 × 2 cm, occasionally up to 2,5 cm, greenish-pink to red when young, drying to a pale straw colour, the wings thin and papery; fruits mature very rapidly so that they may be found with the flowers (September to January).

There are two subspecies distinguished as follows:

Occurring in evergreen forest; leaves oblong-elliptic, up to 18 × 9,5 cm, usually without hairs, and with 4 to 8 pairs of lateral veins; flowering with the leaves; fruits usually 2 × 2 cm, occasionally up to 2,5 cm (refer to the vertical lines on the map) ....subsp. *paniculatum*

Occurring in low altitude, hot dry woodland, often along river banks; leaves ovate-oblong to almost circular, smaller than those of the preceding subspecies, usually about 4,5 × 4 cm (up to 11 × 6 cm), usually with greyish hairs and 5 to 6 pairs of lateral veins, flowering before the leaves; fruits usually 2 × 2 cm, occasionally up to 5 × 3 cm (refer to the black areas on the map) .... subsp. *microphyllum* (Klotzsch) Wickens

This plant is becoming increasingly popular in gardens; it grows rapidly but is frost-tender. In African medicine the crushed root and stem scrapings are mixed with dog faeces, dried and powdered and then sprinkled on food to treat madness.

Combretum pisoniiflorum (Klotzsch) Engl.

S.A. no: —
Rhod. no: —   Moçambique wingless combretum

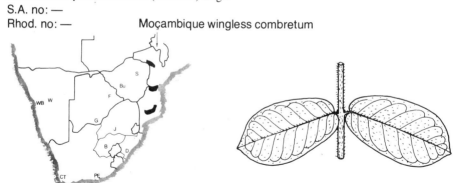

A scrambling shrub or liane, occasionally a small tree about 4 m in height; occurring at low altitudes in open woodland and thicket. **Bark:** grey to brown. **Leaves:** opposite, broadly elliptic, usually about 4 × 2,5 cm, shiny green above, velvety below; apex very broadly tapering to rounded; base rounded to shallowly lobed; margin entire; petiole velvety, up to 5 mm long. **Flowers:** cream aging to yellow, in short dense axillary spikes, 3 to 5 cm long (October). **Fruit:** 4-angled, ridged, or very narrowly 4-winged, 2 to 2,5 × 1 to 1,5 cm, drying to pale brown (December to January).

Combretum psidioides Welw.

S.A. no: 543,1   Silver bushwillow. Silwerboswilg
Rhod. no: 780   Peeling-twig combretum

A shrub or small to medium sized tree up to 10 m in height; occurring at low altitudes in dry areas, in mixed woodland, frequently on Kalahari sand. **Bark:** grey to dark grey, rough, corky and flaking in square sections; the bark of young branches always peels. **Leaves:** opposite, narrowly elliptic to oblong, sometimes almost circular, up to 26 × 16 cm, but usually about 6 to 10 × 3 to 6 cm, characteristically silvery silky (except in subsp. *glabrum);* veining prominent above and below, with net-veining conspicuous especially below; young leaves flushed with orange-red; apex rounded, shallowly notched, often with a hair-like tip; base rounded to shallowly lobed; margin entire, frequently rolled under; petiole stout, up to 10 mm long. **Flowers:** greenish-yellow to yellow, in

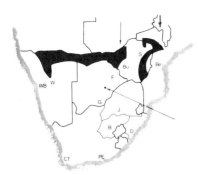

rather dense axillary spikes, up to 10 cm long, usually 4 to 6 cm, appearing just before or with the very young leaves, sweetly scented, the stalks densely covered with short grey hairs and with a tuft at the tips of the small petals (September to October). **Fruit:** 4-winged, 2 to 3 × 2 to 3 cm, viscous when young, maturing to brilliant red and drying to tan-brown (January to May).

This species has been divided into 4 subspecies, 3 of which occur south of the Zambezi River (treated as one on the map):

1 Leaves shiny green, without hairs; tips of petals without hairs .... subsp. *glabrum* Exell
  Leaves with hairs; tips of petals fringed with hairs 2
2 Lower surface of leaf densely covered with hairs .... subsp. *dinteri* (Schinz) Exell
  Lower surface of leaf with conspicuous hairs almost confined to the veins ....
  .... subsp. *psidioides*

The fourth subspecies, subsp. *kwinkiti* (De Wild.) Exell, occurs in northern Angola and Zaire.

The tree produces an edible gum. The fibrous roots are used in basket weaving and also provide an infusion used to treat coughs. The specific name means 'like *Psidium*' (the guava), and probably refers to the peeling bark on the branches, which also distinguishes this species from *C. molle*.

Combretum wattii Exell

S.A. no: 544   Round-leaved bushwillow. Waterboswilg
Rhod. no: —

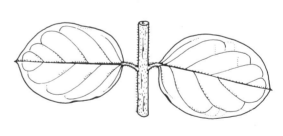

A dense much-branched shrub or small tree 4 to 6 m in height; occurring along dry gravelly watercourses. **Bark:** grey, thinly flaking in narrow longitudinal strips; the branches are long and trailing, arching over and sometimes almost scrambling; branchlets densely covered with yellowish woolly hairs. **Leaves:** opposite to sub-opposite, small, almost circular, about 4 × 4 cm, rather leathery, grey-green, with short hairs; apex rounded, shallowly notched; base rounded; margin entire; petiole about 8 mm long, with woolly hairs. **Flowers:** up to 1,5 cm in diameter, fleshy, with large anthers to the stamens, in short axillary spikes, all parts densely covered with pale yellowish-brown woolly hairs (August to September). **Fruit:** 4- to 5-winged, 3 to 4 × 3 to 4 cm, the wings softly velvety, pinkish-brown, the margin frilled, drying to a pale straw colour (November to January).

Combretum xanthothyrsum Engl. & Diels

S.A. no: Sand-forest bushwillow
Rhod. no: —

675

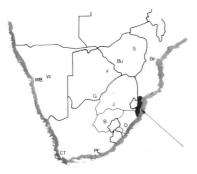

A scrambling shrub or small tree up to 4 m in height; occurring in secondary forest; in Zululand it is characteristic of degraded sand forest. **Bark:** pale creamy-brown, finely vertically striated; branches long and slender. **Leaves:** opposite, oval to elliptic, up to 13 × 7 cm, glossy green above, paler green below, without hairs, the veining rather conspicuous on both surfaces; apex broadly tapering to slightly attenuate; base broadly tapering; margin entire; petiole up to 1,5 cm long. **Flowers:** yellow, with conspicuous white stamens up to 6 mm long, in dense branched heads, or paniculate racemes, on very short lateral branchlets, along the trailing branches; showy when in flower (August). **Fruit:** 4-winged, up to 5 × 5 cm, resembling the fruits of *C. zeyheri,* drying to pale brown (April).
A decoction of the roots is used as an aphrodisiac, to treat venereal diseases and also to rid patients of intestinal worms.

Combretum zeyheri Sonder   Illust. 222
S.A. no: 546   Large-fruited bushwillow. Raasblaar
Rhod. no: 781   Large-fruited combretum

Occasionally a shrub, usually a small to medium sized tree up to 10 m in height; occurring at medium to low altitudes, in open woodland, on rocky hillsides and sometimes along rivers, tolerating a wide range of soils including those that are fairly heavily mineralised. **Bark:** brownish-grey to grey, smooth to finely fissured and flaking in small pieces, giving a mottled appearance; branchlets very slender and pliant, seeming to droop under the 'weight' of the large leaves; branchlets often reddish. **Leaves:** opposite or 3-whorled, clustered towards the ends of the branches, elliptic to oblong, up to 14 × 9 cm, but usually about 7 to 10 × 3 to 5 cm, dark green, finely hairy when young, losing these by maturity; net-veining conspicuous below; apex broadly tapering to rounded; base rounded; margin entire, often wavy; petiole up to 10 mm long. **Flowers:** greenish-yellow to yellow with orange anthers, in axillary spikes about 3 to 7 cm long, appearing before the leaves or with the first flush, sweetly scented, quite showy when in profusion (September to November). **Fruit:** 4-winged, probably the largest of the fruits in this genus, up to 6 × 6 cm, pale green when fresh, drying to a pale brown, conspicuous, remaining on the tree until the leaves have fallen (February to May, on to October).
This tree is said to indicate 'sour bushveld' carrying poor grasses which are not usually palatable to stock and game. The Afrikaans name *raasblaar* is onomatopoeic and echoes the rustling sound made by the leaves and fruits in the wind. The roots are fibrous and are woven into baskets and fishing traps. The crushed leaves combined with oil are used as an embrocation to ease backache, and when mixed with water provide an eye lotion. The roots, together with other ingredients, are regarded as a

remedy for nose-bleeding and when pounded and mixed to a paste with fat, form an ointment to relieve haemorrhoids. The wood is yellow, termite- and borer-proof, and is a useful general purpose timber; it is easy to work but not durable unless thoroughly seasoned.

2. MEIOSTEMON Exell & Stace

Meiostemon tetrandrus (Exell) Exell & Stace
S.A. no: —
Rhod. no: 782   False combretum

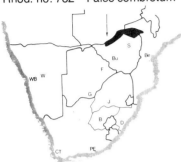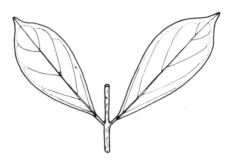

A straggling shrub or small tree up to 5 m in height; occurring at low altitudes, frequently a constituent of 'jesse bush', often thicket-forming, also occurring on rocky koppies. **Bark:** grey or brownish-grey; branchlets reddish-brown. **Leaves:** opposite, simple, elliptic, up to 6 × 3 cm, thinly textured, green, finely hairy when young but soon losing these hairs; apex tapering; base rounded; margin entire; petiole slender, up to 5 mm long. **Flowers:** greenish-yellow to yellow, occasionally tinged with pink or brown, in sparse axillary spikes, up to 9 cm long, but usually 2 to 5 cm. Resembling the flowers of *Combretum,* but with 4 stamens instead of 8 to 10 (December to January). **Fruit:** small, *Combretum-*like, 4-winged, 8 to 10 mm long, reddish-brown drying to a very pale straw colour (February to April).
All the material south of the Zambezi River is placed in subsp. *australis* Exell; the typical subspecies, subsp. *tetrandrus,* does not extend further south than Zambia. This genus differs from *Combretum* only in the number of stamens; otherwise the two genera are inseparable.

3. PTELEOPSIS Engl.

Shrubs or small to medium sized trees, without scales or stalked glands. **Leaves:** opposite to sub-opposite, simple. **Flowers:** in small, terminal, axillary or extra-axillary, rounded heads. Flowers male or bisexual in the same spike; receptacle 2-tiered, the lower receptacle somewhat flattened, the upper bell-shaped; sepals very small; petals 4 to 5, joined; stamens 8 to 10 in 2 whorls. Male flowers, with the ovary absent, usually towards the base of the spike. **Fruit:** 2- to 5-winged, the wings often running down on to the stalk; frequently produced in profusion.

Key to the tree species of *Pteleopsis:*
Fruits frequently 4-winged (occasionally 5), up to 10 mm long, usually with a distinct apical peg; leaves usually dull green, apex rounded or notched; petiole usually less than 6 mm long........
.... **P. anisoptera**
Fruits usually 2- to 3-winged (rarely 4), up to 1,5 cm long, usually lacking an apical peg; leaves often shiny green, with the apex (of some leaves) narrowly tapering; petiole up to 10 mm long ......
.... **P. myrtifolia**

Pteleopsis anisoptera (Welw. ex C. Lawson) Engl. & Diels
S.A. no: —
Rhod. no: 783   Four-winged pteleopsis

A bushy densely leafy shrub or tree 3 to 12 m in height; occurring at medium altitudes in mixed woodland and thicket, and on rocky hillsides and stony outcrops. **Bark:** grey to dark grey, rather smooth in smaller specimens becoming striated to rough with age. **Leaves:** opposite to sub-opposite, **677**

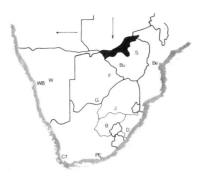

rarely alternate, elliptic, up to 7 × 3 cm, usually 2 to 5 × 1 to 2,3 cm, usually dull matt green above when mature, with short soft hairs when young, tending to retain the hairs on the under surface; apex rounded, often notched; base tapering; margin entire inclined to roll under; petiole 2 to 6 mm long; rather conspicuous conical leaf buds, 2,5 mm long, arise in the axils of leaves or fallen leaves. **Flowers:** white, cream to yellow, about 5 mm in diameter, strongly and unpleasantly scented; in short, axillary, few-flowered heads, often almost spherical, on stalks about 1,5 cm long (November to April). **Fruit:** frequently 4-winged (occasionally 5), about 10 mm long; greenish-yellow drying to light brown, usually with a distinct apical peg (February to June).

Pteleopsis myrtifolia (Welw. ex C. Lawson) Engl. & Diels
S.A. no: 547 Pteleopsis. Mirteboswilg
Rhod. no: 784 Two-winged pteleopsis

A bushy densely leafy shrub or tree 3 to 12 m in height; occurring at medium to low altitudes in mixed woodland, thickets and riverine fringe forest, and on rocky hillsides and stony outcrops. **Bark:** grey to dark grey, rather smooth in smaller specimens becoming striated to rough with age. **Leaves:** opposite to sub-opposite, rarely alternate, elliptic, up to 7 × 3 cm, usually 2 to 5 × 1 to 2,3 cm, usually shiny green above when mature, with short soft hairs when young, tending to retain these hairs on the under surface; apex usually narrowly tapering (sometimes only on some leaves), occasionally rather rounded; base tapering; margin entire, tending to roll under; petiole up to 10 mm long, somewhat slender; rather conspicuous leaf buds sometimes present in the axils of leaves or fallen leaves. **Flowers:** white or cream to yellow, about 5 mm in diameter, strongly and rather unpleasantly scented; in short, axillary, few-flowered heads, often almost spherical, on stalks up to 1,5 cm long (November to April). **Fruit:** usually 2- to 3-winged (rarely 4), about 1,5 cm long, greenish-yellow drying to light brown, usually lacking an apical peg (February to June).

4. QUISQUALIS L.

Quisqualis parviflora Gerrard ex Harvey
S.A. no: 547,1 Hoedanig
Rhod. no: —

A robust liane, climber or small tree, up to 5 m in height; occurring in evergreen forest, wooded ravines and sand forest, from sea level to about 1 500 m. **Bark:** light brown, smooth; young

678

 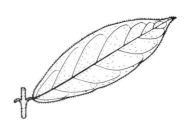

branchlets with fine golden-brown to chocolate coloured hairs; milky or watery sap is present. **Leaves:** sometimes arising, unexpectedly, from the very tip of a spinescent lateral or alternate (rarely opposite) branch; elliptic to oval, 4,5 to 11 × 2 to 5 cm, the upper surface shiny green with sparse long hairs, the lower surface without hairs except for fine brown hairs along the veins; apex tapering, finally attenuate, sometimes narrowly so; base tapering to shortly rounded; margin entire; petiole sharply curled or hooked enabling the plant to climb. **Flowers:** small, yellowish, in axillary and terminal spikes about 1,5 cm long. Bisexual; all floral parts in fives; sepals joined to form a long tube above the ovary, separating into 5 lobes round the mouth, densely covered with golden-brown soft hairs; petals rounded; stamens 10 in 2 whorls; ovary with the style partly joined to the calyx tube (April). **Fruit:** rather long and narrow, 3 × 1,5 cm, with 5 narrow wings, indehiscent (June).

There is an interesting play of words on the name of this plant. *Quisqualis* is the Latin translation of the Dutch *hoedanig,* meaning 'how' or 'what' and this, in turn, is a pun on the plant's Malayan name, *udani.*

5. TERMINALIA L.

Small to medium sized trees. **Leaves:** spirally arranged or clusterd at the ends of the dwarf lateral branchlets, simple, often crowded near the ends of the branches. **Flowers:** in axillary spikes, with male and bisexual flowers in the same spike, the male flowers usually nearer the apex; stalked, the stalk corresponding to the lower receptacle present in the other genera in this family; the upper receptacle shallowly cup-shaped with the calyx lobes round the lip; petals absent; stamens 10; ovary below all the other floral parts. **Fruit:** hard, flattened, 2-winged (except in *T. boivinii* which is without a wing), indehiscent.

Key to the species of *Terminalia:*
```
1 Fruits not winged, only with obscure, obsolete ridges ............................... T. boivinii
  Fruits 2-winged ............................................................................. 2
2 Fruits up to 3 cm long, barely more ................................................... 3
  Fruits 3 to 6 cm long, and larger ...................................................... 7
3 Leaf margin with a hair-like fringe ...................................... T. gazensis
  Leaf margin without conspicuous hairs ............................................. 4
4 Leaves comparatively broad, broadly obovate ............................. T. phanerophlebia
  Leaves comparatively narrow, narrowly ovate, obovate to elliptic ............................ 5
5 Leaves more than 5,5 cm long, with conspicuous, long, silvery, silky hairs ....... T. sericea
  Leaves less than 5,5 cm long, may have hairs but these are not silvery ...................... 6
6 Lateral veins prominent on the leaf upper surface; leaves usually 3,5 to 4 × 1,5 cm, not
  conspicuously plum-coloured in autumn ......................................... T. stuhlmannii
  Lateral veins not prominent on the leaf upper surface; leaves up to 2,5 × 1,2 cm, turning
  plum-coloured in autumn ............................................. T. randii
7 Leaves usually 2 to 3 × 1,5 cm, (occasionally up to 7 × 3 cm); heart-shaped, clustered on dwarf
  spinescent lateral branchlets ....................................... T. prunioides
  Leaves more than 7 cm long ............................................................. 8
8 Petiole very short, 2 to 4 mm long, or absent ............................. T. brachystemma
  Petiole more than 10 mm long ........................................................ 9
```

679

9 Branchlets becoming corky in the second year; leaves very large, frequently 20 × 11 cm, and up to 32 × 13 cm; fruits up to 8 × 5,5 cm, remaining yellowish-green when mature, not becoming red, though they may be occasionally faintly tinged with pink .... **T. mollis**

    Branchlets remaining smooth or fibrous for several years, not becoming corky; leaves usually about 7 to 15 × 3 to 7 cm, occasionally up to 18 × 7,5 cm but not larger; fruits bright showy red, rose-pink, greenish-red to red-brown 10

10 A tree of low altitude riverine forest, sometimes reaching heights of 25 m, but usually 4 to 5 m; bark grey, smoothish .... **T. sambesiaca**

    A tree of medium to low altitude open woodland, not exceeding 10 m in height 11

11 Leaves usually comparatively narrow, oblanceolate, occasionally broader, base narrowly tapering; veining not conspicuous above, fairly clear net-veining below, often with rather long shaggy coarse brown hairs .... **T. trichopoda**

    Leaves usually comparatively broad, oval to elliptic, base rounded or very broadly tapering; upper surface finely but conspicuously puckered, heavy and prominent net-veining below, also with yellowish or brownish hairs .... **T. stenostachya**

Terminalia boivinii Tul.
S.A. no: —
Rhod. no: —   Wingless terminalia

A shrub or small tree, usually 5 to 8 m in height, but sometimes reaching 10 m; occurring in coastal scrub, always near the sea. **Bark:** grey-brown, smooth; branchlets with 4 to 6 spur-shoots, each 2 to 5 mm long; further spurs may be borne directly on the long shoots. **Leaves:** on the spur shoots, narrowly elliptic to heart-shaped, 2,5 to 6 × 1 to 3 cm, thinly textured, shiny green above, yellowish-green below, without hairs; apex very broadly tapering to rounded; base narrowly tapering and running into the petiole; margin entire; petiole very short due to the decurrent leaf base, may be up to 5 mm long. **Flowers:** small, white to cream in lateral spikes barely more than 1,5 cm long (November). **Fruit:** narrowly ellipsoidal, about 10 × 4 mm, with obsolete wings represented by obscure ridges, greenish-yellow, drying to brown (January to May).

This unusual species of *Terminalia* occurs from Kenya southwards to Moçambique; other closely related species are found in the Malagasy Republic.

Terminalia brachystemma Welw.
S.A. no: 548   Kalahari sand terminalia. Bastertrosblaar
Rhod. no: 785   Kalahari sand terminalia

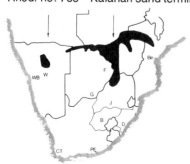 

A small bushy tree usually 3 to 5 m in height, but sometimes reaching 10 m, with the branches often horizontal and conspicuously layered; occurring in open woodland, on Kalahari sand and often round vleis. **Bark:** pale brownish-grey to grey, smoothish to longitudinally fissured and rather stringy; bark on the branchlets dark and peeling to reveal pale brown under bark. **Leaves:** clustered near the ends of the branches, elliptic, obovate to broadly obovate, 9 to 15 × 5 to 7 cm, leathery, green above, bluish-green and with or without sparse hairs especially along the midrib below; midrib fairly prominent below; apex very broadly tapering to rounded; base narrowly tapering and often overrunning the petiole; margin entire; petiole 2 to 4 mm long or often absent due to the decurrent leaf base. **Flowers:** small, cream to pale yellow, in axillary spikes, 6 to 11 cm long (October to February). **Fruit:** up to 5 × 3,5 cm, with an almost circular wing, bright crimson when mature, drying to reddish or purplish-brown (January to April, sometimes on to June).

This species hybridises easily with *T. sericea* and hybrids are widespread over the range of *T. brachystemma*. The wood is used to make axe handles and a decoction of the roots provides a remedy for stomach ache.

Terminalia gazensis E. G. Baker
S.A. no: —
Rhod. no: 786   Fringe-leaved terminalia

A small to large tree often 5 to 7 m in height, but sometimes reaching 20 m; occurring in medium altitude evergreen forest, and at medium to low altitudes in open woodland and riverine fringes. **Bark:** pale brown or grey and smooth in smaller specimens, becoming very dark grey or brown and rough, flaking in small squares. **Leaves:** elliptic to obovate, 5 to 8 × 3 to 5 cm, but sometimes up to 14 × 7 cm, usually velvety and covered with short soft yellowish or greyish hairs which are mostly lost by maturity; thinly textured, midrib and lateral veins rather prominent below; apex and base tapering; margin finely scalloped, very occasionally entire, with a distinct velvet fringe round the edge (a ciliate margin); petiole about 3 mm long, slender. **Flowers:** small, white to yellow, in slender rather loose axillary spikes, 4 to 10 cm long, often produced in profusion, but strongly and usually unpleasantly scented (December to February). **Fruit:** rather long and narrow, up to 3 × 1,5 to 2 cm, the central body markedly high-domed and the wing rather narrow, yellowish-green tinged with red when mature (March to June).

Typical *T. gazensis* has mature leaves almost without hairs and with finely scalloped margins. The latter feature is very unusual in this family; however, some material collected in the Belingwe district of Rhodesia appears to have thicker, very hairy leaves, with entire margins.

Terminalia mollis C. Lawson   Illust. 223
S.A. no: —
Rhod. no: 787   Large-leaved terminalia

A medium to large well-shaped tree 8 to 15 m in height, commonly 10 m and frequently larger; occurring at medium altitudes in open woodland, especially on the edges of vleis. **Bark:** grey and very rough; the branchlets are corky. **Leaves:** large, elliptic to oblong, 16 to 32 × 7 to 13 cm, frequently with short soft hairs on the upper surface most of which are lost by maturity, but always densely covered with pale to slightly brownish matted hairs on the under surface; conspicuous net-veining below but often almost masked by the dense hairs, veining rather obscure on the upper surface; apex very broadly tapering to rounded; base rounded or shallowly lobed; margin entire, often with a

681

conspicuous fringe of long hairs; petiole thickset, up to 4 cm long. **Flowers:** greenish-white, larger than is usual in this genus, up to 12 mm in diameter, in strong axillary spikes 8 to 18 cm long, strongly scented, the sepals covered with hairs on the outside and densely bearded within (October to December). **Fruit:** large, up to 8 × 5,5 cm, with a stout finely hairy wing, ribbed and wavy, characteristically yellowish-green when mature and hanging in heavy conspicuous masses; these fruits never turn red though they may occasionally be slightly pink-tinged; they always become pale brown when dry (January to June).

This species resembles *T. stenostachya* under which the differences are given.

Terminalia phanerophlebia Engl. & Diels
S.A. no: 549   Lebombo terminalia. Lebombotrosblaar
Rhod. no: —

A shrub or small tree up to 6 m in height; occurring at low altitudes in open woodland and scrub, on stony hillsides, along rocky watercourses and at the margins of forest. **Bark:** brownish-grey; branchlets shiny purplish-brown with very fine appressed hairs and peeling in small rings. **Leaves:** broadly obovate, 3 to 10 × 1,5 to 4,5 cm, light green, grey-green to dark green, with sparse soft hairs when young, losing most of these by maturity, the midrib and net-veining immersed above, prominent below; apex broadly tapering; base tapering; margin entire; petiole 1 to 2 cm. **Flowers:** white, cream, sometimes tinged with pink, in axillary spikes 4 to 10 cm long (October to February). **Fruit:** usually 2 to 3 × 1,5 to 2,5 cm, though occasionally up to 4 × 2,7 cm, characteritically greenish-yellow when mature, rarely turning pink, minutely hairy (January to June).

Terminalia prunioides C. Lawson   Illust. 224
S.A. no: 550   Purple-pod terminalia. Sterkbos
Rhod. no: 788   Purple-pod terminalia

A shrub or small to medium sized tree, usually 3 to 7 m in height, but sometimes reaching 13 m; occurring in low altitude open woodland and scrub, on rocky hill slopes and in the deep alluvial soils of low altitude rivers. **Bark:** brownish to grey, rough, vertically striated to fluted, fibrous; branches frequently long, thin, drooping and often somewhat tangled; branchlets spine-tipped. **Leaves:** clustered at the ends of dwarf spinescent lateral branchlets; broadly obovate or heart-shaped, usually 2 to 3 × 1,5 cm, but sometimes reaching 7 × 3 cm, thinly textured, dark green, often with short soft hairs when young, losing most of these by maturity; apex rounded or notched; base tapering; margin

682

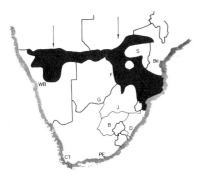
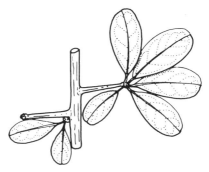

entire; petiole almost obscured by the decurrent leaf base. **Flowers:** white or cream to pale yellow with a strong rather unpleasant smell, in slender axillary spikes, 4 to 8 cm long, clustered at the tips of the spines (October to January, occasionally later). **Fruit:** very striking, 4 to 6 × 2 to 3 cm, bright plum-red or purple-red, making the trees conspicuous in autumn and winter (January to July). The wood is hard and tough and is used in the building of huts and to make implement handles; it makes a good fuel.

Terminalia randii E. G. Baker
S.A. no: 550,1   Small-leaved terminalia. Doringtrosblaar
Rhod. no: 789   Small-leaved terminalia

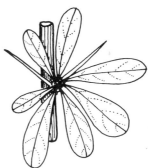

A rigid spiny shrub or small tree 5 to 10 m in height; occurring at low altitudes in dry areas, frequently on barren stony ground or black soils, in woodland or thornveld, often on rocky hill slopes. **Bark:** dark grey or brownish-grey, longitudinally cracked and fissured; branches with short, hard, woody, boss-like dwarf branches in the axils of short sharp stipular spines about 10 mm long. **Leaves:** clustered on the short dwarfed branches, small, narrowly obovate, 1 to 2,5 × 0,7 to 1,2 cm, pale green to slightly bluish-green, turning plum-coloured in autumn, may be sparsely hairy when young, losing these hairs by maturity; lateral veins inconspicuous on both surfaces; apex very broadly tapering to rounded; base narrowly tapering; margin entire; petiole slender, 2 to 5 mm long. **Flowers:** white to cream, occasionally slightly pink-tinged, in sparse spikes up to 3 cm long, clustered among the leaves, frequently forming almost sub-spherical heads of 6 to 12 flowers only (November to March). **Fruit:** 1 to 2,5 × 0,6 to 1,2 cm with a marked notch at the apex, purple to purplish-red, drying to a light straw-brown, produced in profusion on very slender stalks which snap easily so the fruits fall readily, some, however, remaining on the tree for the whole year (usually February to July). When in the leaf only, this tree strongly resembles the cultivated species of *Pyracantha* or 'hawthorn' in appearance. The wood is hard and yellow.

Terminalia sambesiaca Engl. & Diels
S.A. no: —
Rhod. no: 790   River terminalia

A small to large tree often 4 to 5 m in height but sometimes reaching 25 m; occurring at low altitudes in riverine fringes and occasionally on rocky hills. **Bark:** grey, smooth, with dark patches giving a mottled appearance, becoming roughish in large specimens. **Leaves:** crowded at the ends of the **683**

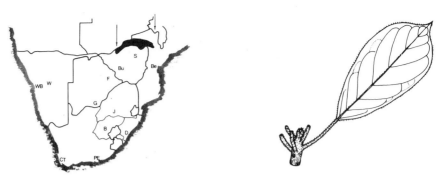

branches, elliptic to broadly obovate, usually about 7 × 3 cm, but reaching 18 × 13 cm, green, thinly textured with soft hairs along the net-veining which is visible below; apex rounded; base tapering; margin entire or sometimes obscurely scalloped; petiole up to 3 cm long, slender in the smaller leaves becoming stout in the large leaves. **Flowers:** creamy-white sometimes tinged with pink, with an unpleasant smell; in axillary spikes, which are usually 6 to 8 cm long but may reach 15 cm (December to January). **Fruit:** frequently 4 to 5 cm long but may be very large, up to 9 × 5 cm, elliptic, green flushed with pink, drying to red-brown (January to May).

Terminalia sericea Burch. ex DC.   Illust. 225
[*T. silozensis* Gibbs]
S.A. no: 551   Silver terminalia. Vaalboom
Rhod. no: 791   Silver terminalia, Mangwe

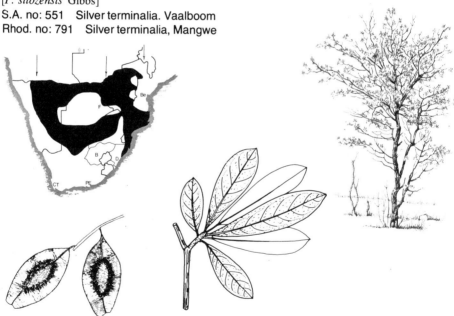

A small to medium sized well-shaped tree, usually 4 to 6 m in height but occasionally reaching 10 m; occurring in open woodland, frequently on şandy soils and often at vlei margins, locally very common, even dominant or co-dominant. **Bark:** dark grey or brownish and deeply vertically fissured; the slender branchlets dark brown or purplish, peeling and flaking in rings and strips exposing light brown underbark; young stems are often parasitised and, as a result, bear round galls often up to 2 to 3 cm in diameter frequently with leaves growing from them. **Leaves:** clustered towards the tips of the slender branchlets; narrowly obovate-elliptic, 5,5 to 12 × 1,5 to 4,5 cm, pale green covered with silvery silky hairs which give a characteristic sheen, lateral veins obscure; apex broadly tapering to rounded; base narrowly tapering; margin entire; petiole up to 10 mm long. **Flowers:** small, cream to pale yellow, heavily and rather unpleasantly scented, in axillary spikes up to 7 cm long (September to January). **Fruit:** 2,5 to 3,5 × 1,5 to 2,5 cm, pink to rose-red when mature, drying to reddish-brown (January to May but they remain on the tree almost until the next flowering season).

684

The fruit may be parasitised and develop into deformed tangled masses of twisted, rusty-hairy structures. This species hybridises freely with *T. trichopoda* and other species. The silvery silky leaves, to which the specific name refers, are very attractive and the early pioneers to Rhodesia, travelling through the Mangwe pass, thought this was the famous silver-leaf tree of the Cape Peninsula *(Leucadendron argenteum)*. However, although they are beautiful, the leaves of *Terminalia sericea* cannot compare with those of the silver tree. Among African peoples this tree has a wide variety of uses. A decoction of the roots, which has a very bitter taste, is not only taken to cure diarrhoea and to relieve colic but is also applied as an eyewash, while a hot infusion of the roots' outer layers makes a fomentation for treating pneumonia. The silky, silvery leaf hairs are used by Tswana potters for glazing their wares. Good crops are ensured at harvest and planting times by thrusting a stick into the floor of a shrine in homage to ancestral spirits, but to cut down an entire tree is believed to bring hail-storms. A glucoside, nerifolin, has been isolated from parts of the plant and this has been found to have an effect on the heart and pulse rate. The wood is yellow and hard; it provides a useful general purpose timber and is suitable for furniture; fencing posts cut from these trees will last for many years.

Terminalia stenostachya Engl. & Diels   Illust. 226

S.A. no: —
Rhod. no: 792   Rosette-leaved terminalia

A small to medium sized tree ususlly 3 to 5 m in height; but sometimes reaching 10 m; occurring mainly at low altitudes in open woodland. **Bark:** grey, rough with deep vertical furrows. **Leaves:** conspicuously clustered into terminal rosettes, oval to broadly elliptic, 11 to 18 × 4,5 to 7,5 cm, dark green; upper surface without hairs, conspicuously net-veined and puckered; lower surface markedly and heavily net-veined with yellowish to brownish hairs; apex very broadly tapering to rounded; base broadly tapering to rounded; margin entire, slightly wavy; petiole 1,5 to 3 cm long. **Flowers:** creamy-white, heavily but unpleasantly scented, sepals bearded within and their backs very sparsely hairy, in rather slender delicate axillary spikes up to 14 cm long (October to January). **Fruit:** 3 to 5 × 2 to 3 cm, with very fine short hairs, showy bright red when mature, drying to reddish-brown, nestling in the centre of the leaf rosette, somewhat resembling eggs in a bird's nest, never produced in the large pendulous trusses found in *T. mollis* (January to June).

This species has been confused with *T. mollis* which, however, is a larger tree reaching 15 m in height. It differs also in that its fruits are yellowish-green, never bright red, are larger (up to 8 × 5,5 cm) and form heavy pendulous conspicuous clusters. Its leaves do not form rosettes, they are much larger than those of *T. stenostachya*, and their upper surface is not puckered; the backs of its sepals are heavily hairy, which is distinctive, and the bark of its branchlets is corky.

Terminalia stuhlmannii Engl.

S.A. no: 551,1   Zig-zag terminalia. Stompiestrosblaar
Rhod. no: 793   Zig-zag terminalia

A small tree, usually 3 to 4 m in height, occasionally up to 12 m, tending to form a flat crown; occurring at low altitudes in dry wooded grassland. **Bark:** grey to brownish, smooth; branches usually produced in layers; dwarf stubby, boss-like, woody, lateral shoots are produced, sometimes with spines at their bases. **Leaves:** clustered on the dwarf lateral shoots; narrowly obovate, 1,5 to 6 × 1 to 2 cm, leathery, lateral veins fairly prominent on both surfaces, bluish-green above, yellowish-green below, with fine hairs when young, losing most of these by maturity; apex rounded; base narrowly tapering; margin entire, slightly and very tightly rolled under; petiole slender, 1 to 3 mm long.

685

Flowers: white to cream; stamens long for the genus, up to 4 mm; the male flowers are produced at the base of rather sparse axillary spikes, 3 to 8 cm long, with bisexual flowers above them (April). **Fruit:** elliptic, 2 to 3 × 1,5 to 1,8 cm, yellowish-red becoming reddish-purple when mature, drying to light brown (January to April).

The poles are used in hut building.

Terminalia trichopoda Diels
S.A. no: —
Rhod. no: 794   Hybrid terminalia

A medium sized tree up to 10 m in height; occurring at medium altitudes in open woodland. **Bark:** grey and roughish with longitudinal fissures; the young branchlets peel and flake as in *T. sericea*. **Leaves:** tending to crowd near the ends of the branches; obovate or narrowly obovate, up to 18 × 7 cm, but usually about 13 to 15 × 4 to 6 cm, leathery, the upper surface usually without hairs, the lower surface always hairy; often with long shaggy coarse brown hairs, veining obscure; apex broadly tapering; base narrowly tapering; margin entire; petiole thickset, up to 2 cm long. **Flowers:** greenish-white, cream to pale yellow, strongly but rather unpleasantly scented, in dense axillary spikes up to 14 cm long (November to January). **Fruit:** up to 7,5 × 4,2 cm, hanging in heavy clusters and so resembling *T. mollis*, but turning dull pink when mature, although seldom becoming red, drying to pale brown (February to June).

This species hybridises freely with *T. mollis* and *T. sericea*. It has also been suggested that *T. trichopoda* itself may be a hybrid between *T. sericea* and *T. stenostachya*.

6. LUMNITZERA Willd.

Lumnitzera racemosa Willd.
S.A. no: 552   Spring-tide mangrove. Tongawortelboom
Rhod. no: —

A low spreading succulent shrub or small tree, 5 to 6 m in height; frequently fringing mangrove swamps but rarely submerged by sea water except perhaps by the highest spring tides, being better adapted to equally marshy but less saline conditions; also occurring on sand dunes. **Bark:** reddish brown to dark brown, rough; pneumatophores absent. **Leaves:** alternate, simple, clustered at the ends of the branches, narrowly obovate to elliptic, usually about 5 × 2 cm, but may reach 9 × 2,5 cm, succulent, light green; apex rounded, often notched; base very narrowly tapering, almost forming a

686

winged petiole; margin very shallowly scalloped, slightly rolled under and often inclined to be wavy; petiole absent, obscured by the decurrent leaf base. **Flowers:** creamy white, about 10 mm long, urn-shaped, with the petals curling out of the mouth, in axillary spikes 2 to 4 cm long. Bisexual; all floral parts in fives; calyx tube persistent, ultimately dividing into 5 sepals, 2 persistent bracteoles present; petals fall early; stamens usually 10 in 2 whorls; ovary below the other floral parts (February to October). **Fruit:** ovoid to oblong, 1 to 1,5 cm long, tipped with the persistent calyx, style and stigma, woody, 1-seeded, dispersed by the sea water (April to January).

All the South African material belongs to the typical variety, var. *racemosa;* a yellow-flowered variety, var. *lutea* (Gaudich) Exell, occurs on Timor. The wood makes a good fuel.

MYRTACEAE *(The eucalyptus and guava family)*

Key to the genera (naturalised exotic species marked*):

1 Leaves long and narrow, linear, usually about 5 to 8 mm wide, seldom more than 10 mm wide 2

Leaves elliptic, ovate to obovate, usually more than 10 mm wide 3

2 Confined to the south-western Cape; flowers creamy-white to pale yellow, in fluffy branched heads, axillary, near the ends of the branches .... **4. Metrosideros**

An introduced exotic, usually encountered in gardens but escaped in some areas in Rhodesia; flowers forming the well-known fluffy, cylindric, crimson head, or 'bottlebrush' ....
.... **6. *Callistemon**

3 Fruit a capsule, small, up to 4 × 2,5 mm .... **5. Heteropyxis**

Fruit a fleshy berry, not less than 10 mm long 4

4 Fruits with many small seeds .... **1. *Psidium**

Fruits 1- to 2-seeded 5

5 Calyx tube almost spherical, sharply differentiated from the stalk, or pedicel; flowers 5 to 15 mm in diameter, often solitary or in axillary clusters, or fascicles, not forming branched heads .... **2. Eugenia**

Calyx tube gradually tapering into the stalk; flowers larger, 1 to 2,5 cm in diameter, in branched heads, cymes or corymbs, axillary and terminal .... **3. Syzygium**

Species of *Eucalyptus* are planted extensively and have become part of the African landscape, but there is no evidence that these trees have become naturalised. Even an apparently isolated population can be traced back to some early habitation.

1. *PSIDIUM L.

*Psidium guajava L.

The guava, originally introduced from tropical America, has become naturalised in Rhodesia (Rhod. no: 795) and in areas of the Transvaal, including the Kruger National Park, and is now widespread along the Natal coast and in Zululand.

687

MYRTACEAE

*Psidium cattleianum Sabine

The strawberry-gauva, said to be the most delectable of all the guavas, was introduced from South America, and has now escaped and become established along areas of the Natal coast.

2. EUGENIA L.

Shrubs, sometimes dwarfs rising from a woody rootstock, or trees. **Leaves:** opposite, sub-opposite or in whorls of 3, simple, gland-dotted. **Flowers:** solitary, occasionally fascicled, or in axillary or terminal cymose racemes. Usually bisexual, but the sexes may be separate on different trees; all floral parts in fours; calyx tube almost spherical, sharply differentiated from the stalk or pedicel; petals longer than the calyx tube; stamens usually 16, in 4 whorls; ovary 2-chambered. **Fruit:** ovoid to almost spherical, fleshy, indehiscent.

Key to the tree species of *Eugenia:*
Young leaves and shoots distinctly reddish with dense whitish hairs; confined to a very limited area in the eastern Cape and southern Natal .... **E. erythrophylla**
Young leaves and shoots without dense withish hairs .... **E. capensis**

Eugenia capensis (Ecklon & Zeyher) Harvey & Sonder

 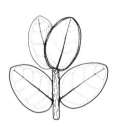

A shrub or dwarf tree up to 1,5 m in height but reaching 10 m or more in some of the subspecies; occurring in coastal dune scrub, sometimes associated with mangrove swamps, may be found in open woodland, riverine bush, evergreen forest or among rocks on mountain slopes. **Bark:** pale creamy-brown or grey, finely vertically fissured, sometimes flaking. **Leaves:** elliptic, oblong-elliptic to almost circular, usually about 4 × 2,5 to 4 cm but may be larger, thinly textured to leathery, without hairs, shiny dark green above, the under surface pale green, gland-dotted, with the midrib and lateral veins prominent; the very young leaves may be reddish but lack the dense whitish hairs of *E. erythrophylla*, often becoming yellowish-green before assuming their mature colour; usually aromatic when crushed; apex rounded, or broadly tapering and abruptly attenuate or forming a long narrow tapering tip; base broadly tapering to rounded or shallowly lobed; margin entire, rolled under; petiole 2 to 6 mm long, sometimes darkly coloured and wrinkled or channelled. **Flowers:** white, up to 1,2 cm in diameter, solitary or in axillary clusters of 2 to 8 (often on the old wood in the axils of fallen leaves), on slender stalks 0,2 to 1,5 cm long; the central mass of stamens is prominent. **Fruit:** ovoid to almost spherical, fleshy, about 1 to 1,5 cm long, yellowish becoming cherry-red and finally purplish-red when mature, tipped with the remains of the old calyx; edible and pleasantly flavoured but sometimes rather acid.

This is one of the most variable species in the whole of Africa. At one extreme it is a rhizomatous suffrutex; at the other a tall forest tree. F. White, in *Flora Zambesiaca* and in *Kirkia* Vol. 10, recognises nine subspecies as occurring in southern Africa, five of which are included in the present work:

subsp. *capensis*
S.A. no: 553,1   Dune myrtle. Duinemirt
Rhod. no: —
A shrub or small tree sometimes reaching 4 m in height. Leaves ovate to almost circular with a rounded apex; flowers appear from July to April, fruits from April to December. Occurs in coastal

dune scrub, sometimes associated with mangrove swamps, occasionally found in open woodland and riverine bush seldom far from the coast, from Port Elizabeth to the Zambezi delta. The trees can become very floriferous and attractive, resembling cherry trees. Africans boil the leaves and use these as a poultice to treat pneumonia.

subsp. *natalitia* (Sonder) F. White
[*E. woodii* Dümmer; *E. zuluensis* Dümmer; *E. natalitia* Sonder]
S.A. no: 553,2   Natal myrtle. Natalmirt
Rhod. no: —

A shrub or small tree up to 8 m in height but occasionally much taller. Leaves elliptic to broadly elliptic with the apex broadly tapering or attenuate forming a long narrowly tapering tip; flowers appear from July to December, fruits from November to September, but may be found at most times of the year. Occurring in open woodland or evergreen forest, from the eastern Transkei through Natal to the mountains of the eastern Transvaal.

subsp. *nyassensis* (Engl.) F. White   Illust. 227
[*E. bukobensis* auct.; *E. chirindensis* E. G. Baker; *E. nyassensis* Engl.]
S.A. no: —
Rhod. no: 796   Northern wild myrtle

A shrub or small tree, usually from 3 to 5 m in height but sometimes reaching 13 m. Leaves elliptic to oblong elliptic and larger than those of the other subspecies, being usually about 6 × 3 cm, but even reaching 11 × 5 cm; flowers appear from October to April, fruits from June to December. Occurring in medium altitude evergreen forest, in the mountains of eastern Rhodesia and northwards.

subsp. *simii* (Dümmer) F. White
[*E. simii* Dümmer]

A shrub or small tree with elliptic to oblanceolate leaves about 5 × 1,3 cm, was named in 1912 *E. simii* by Dümmer from material collected by Gerrard and said to be from Natal; the locality is not known and no further collections appear to have been made.

subsp. *zeyheri* (Harvey) F. White
[*E. zeyheri* (Harvey) Harvey ex Sonder]
S.A. no: 553   Wild myrtle. Wildemirt
Rhod. no: —

A shrub or small densely foliaged tree 3 to 10 m in height. Leaves narrowly elliptic to lanceolate or oblanceolate; flowers appear from August to November, fruits from January to March. Occurring in somewhat open evergreen forest, coastal bush and sand forest, riverine thicket and along streams, from Port Elizabeth eastwards through Natal to Zululand. The wood is white, fine-grained, hard and heavy, taking a fine polish and mellowing to an attractive yellow-brown, but its small size limits its use; it has been found satisfactory for implement handles and other small articles.

Eugenia erythrophylla Strey
S.A. no: 553,3   Large-leaved myrtle. Grootblaarmirt
Rhod. no: —

An erect small to medium sized tree 3 to 10 m in height; occurring in coastal and mountain forest. **Bark:** light grey, with fine striations, scaling. **Leaves:** ovate to narrowly ovate, 6 to 12 × 3 to 7 cm, thickly leathery, shiny dark green above, paler green below; the very young leaves and shoots are distinctly pink or reddish with dense whitish hairs, losing these and becoming green by maturity; apex broadly tapering, abruptly and shortly attenuate; base broadly tapering; margin entire and markedly rolled under; petiole thickset, 2 to 6 mm long, blackish and wrinkled. **Flowers:** white, with the conspicuous central mass of stamens 9 to 11 mm in diameter; bisexual or male only; male flowers congested on short lateral shoots which sometimes continue growth thus forming leafy shoots;

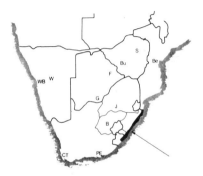 

bisexual flowers axillary, usually solitary, on stalks up to 8 mm long (November to December). **Fruit:** ovoid to almost spherical, up to 2,5 cm long, almost smooth, red when mature, crowned with the persistent calyx lobes (November to March).

3. SYZYGIUM Gaertn.

Shrubs or trees. **Leaves:** opposite, simple. **Flowers:** in axillary and terminal heads, cymes or corymbs; in several species, if not most, the flower heads are often parasitised and become sterile deformed clusters. Bisexual; floral parts in fours to fives; calyx tube obovate, tapering into the stalk or pedicel; petals more or less joined but falling early; stamens many in multiple whorls giving the conspicuous eucalyptus-like central mass; ovary 2-chambered. **Fruit:** fleshy, 1-seeded, indehiscent.

Key to the tree species of *Syzygium:*
1 Leaf base tapering; petiole distinct, at least 6 mm long .... **S. guineense**
  Leaf base square to lobed, usually clasping the stem; petiole, if present, very short 2
2 Occurring at low to medium altitudes, always along river or stream banks .... **S. cordatum**
  Occurring at high altitudes among mountain quartzite crags, or in evergreen forest where it can become dominant .... **S. masukuense**

Syzygium cordatum Hochst.   Illust. 228
S.A. no: 555   Umdoni. Waterbessie
Rhod. no: 798   Water berry

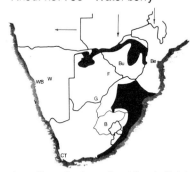 

A medium sized tree 8 to 15 m in height, but sometimes flowering as a dwarf shrub; occurring along stream banks, in riverine thicket and forest, always near water or along watercourses, and in Natal and Moçambique forming stands of almost pure swamp forest. **Bark:** dark brown, rough and fissured. **Leaves:** near the ends of the branches, the successive pairs being set at marked right angles to each other; elliptic, oblong to almost circular, up to 8 × 6 cm, bluish-green above, paler green below, the young leaves reddish; apex broadly tapering to rounded; base deeply lobed (the specific name refers to this); margin entire; petiole absent or extremely short. **Flowers:** creamy-white to pinkish, the stamens being the most conspicuous feature, about 2 to 2,5 cm in diameter in dense heads up to 10 cm in diameter at the ends of the branches; sweetly scented, producing abundant nectar (August to November). **Fruit:** ovoid, fleshy, about 1,5 cm long, deep purple when mature; edible but acid (November to March).

690

The wood is light reddish-brown to greyish, medium hard and heavy; it works well but should be water-seasoned; it has been used for beams and rafters and, being durable in water, is especially suitable for boat-building. An alcoholic drink is made from the fruits, and milk gourds are seasoned by the pleasantly aromatic wood smoke. This species hybridises freely with the typical subspecies of *S. guineense*, these hybrid forms are frequently being encountered where both species occur.

*Syzygium cumini (L.) Skeels

The jambolan-plum, introduced from India and tropical Asia for its edible and attractive purple-red fruits, has escaped to a limited extent near Mount Selinda in the east of Rhodesia (Rhod. no: 799), and also near Vilanculos and in the Zambezi valley below Tete.

Syzygium guineense (Willd.) DC.

A small to large tree, usually up to 10 m in height but sometimes reaching 20 m; the various subspecies occur either in open deciduous woodland at medium to low altitudes, frequently fringing vleis and sometimes growing along river banks, or in evergreen and mountain mist-belt forest. **Bark:** varying in the subspecies from pale ashen-grey and smooth to grey-brown or dark grey and rather rough, becoming heavily buttressed in large specimens. **Leaves:** elliptic, 3,5 to 12 × 1,5 to 5 cm, but usually about 5 to 8 × 3,5 to 4 cm, yellowish-green to shiny dark green above, rather paler green and dull below, young leaves may be purplish-red when this colour tends to persist for some time on the under surface but is entirely lost by maturity; apex tapering to abruplty attenuate when it forms a narrowly rounded tip; base tapering; margin entire, slightly rolled under; petiole 0,5 to 2 cm long, slender. **Flowers:** creamy-white, sweetly scented, about 1,5 cm in diameter, axillary and terminal, forming heads up to 10 × 10 cm, or with 4 to 8 rather widely spaced flowers in branched heads up to 3 cm in diameter. **Fruit:** ovoid to almost spherical, fleshy, 1 to 3 × 1 to 3 cm, usually dark purple when mature but occasionally white or marked with white, edible.

This species is even more variable than *Eugenia capensis* and is probably the most variable woody species in the whole of Africa. F. White, in *Flora Zambesiaca* and in *Kirkia* Vol. 10 recognises five subspecies as occurring in southern Africa, four of which are included in the present work.

subsp. **guineense**   Illust. 229
S.A. no: 557   Woodland waterberry. Waterpeer
Rhod. no: 801   Woodland waterberry

A small to medium sized tree usually up to 10 m in height. Leaves elliptic, usually about 8 to 9×3 to 4 cm, with the apex tapering; flowers appearing from August to December, fruit from December to April; a rare form of this subspecies produces more spherical fruits which are almost totally white or purple and white in colour. Occurring in open deciduous woodland at medium to low altitudes, frequently fringing vleis, sometimes along river banks; widespread from Natal, through the Transvaal to Rhodesia and northern Botswana, Caprivi and Moçambique. In some of the evergreen forests in the east of Rhodesia and adjacent areas of Moçambique there are populations which, growing in swampy and perennially wet areas of high rainfall forest, display a marked tendency to produce elbow-angled roots. An infusion of the roots is used in African medicine to bathe a patient if an illness has become serious; the bark is also used as a medicine, but is poisonous and deaths from its use have been recorded. The wood is pale red, hard, strong and easy to work and is said to be durable; it has been used to make dug-out canoes.

subsp. **barotsense** F. White
S.A. no: Bi-coloured waterberry
Rhod. no: 801   Bi-coloured waterberry

A small to medium sized tree, usually up to 8 m in height, but may be taller; it is characteristic of low altitude river banks. The bark is markedly pale grey, its roots often bare and conspicuous, its fruits large, almost spherical and about 3 cm in diameter, the lower half being white, the upper half purple; flowers appearing from August to December, fruits from December to April. It occurs along some of the major rivers in the west, east and south of Rhodesia, Caprivi, Botswana and northwards.

subsp. **gerrardii** (Harvey ex J. D. Hook.) F. White   Illust. 230
[*S. gerrardii* (Harvey ex J. D. Hook.) Burtt Davy]
S.A. no: 556   Forest waterberry. Boswaterhout
Rhod. no: 800   Forest waterberry.

A medium to large tree 10 to 20 m in height. Leaves elliptic, 3,5 to 12×1,5 to 5 cm, but usually about 5×3,5 cm, young leaves purplish-red and this colour tends to persist for some time on the under surface but is lost entirely by maturity; the apex is abruptly attenuate ultimately forming a narrowly rounded tip; flowers appear from June to October, sometimes on to December or January, fruits from July to December or later. Occurring in evergreen and mountain mist-belt forest; from Transkei, through Natal, Zululand, Swaziland and the eastern Transvaal mountains to the mountains in the east of Rhodesia and adjacent Mocambique, and northwards. The wood is pale brown, often with an irregular dark brown graining; it is medium-hard and saws easily but is difficult to plane; it finishes and polishes well and is suitable for panelling, flooring and furniture; it is durable and at one time was widely used in housing. An infusion of the bark provides a remedy for chest complaints in African medicine.

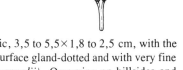

subsp. **legatii** (Burtt Davy & Greenway) F. White
[*S. legatii* Burtt Davy & Greenway]
S.A. no: 558   Mountain waterberry. Bergwaterhout
Rhod. no: —

A small to medium sized tree. Leaves elliptic to oblong-elliptic, 3,5 to 5,5×1,8 to 2,5 cm, with the apex very broadly tapering to almost rounded, and the under surface gland-dotted and with very fine but distinct net-veining (which separates this from subsp. *gerrardii*). Occurring on hillsides and mountain slopes in the eastern and northern Transvaal.

*Syzygium jambos (L.) Alston

The rose-apple, originally from the east Indies but now widespread throughout the tropics, has become naturalised in the Chirinda forest (Rhod. no: 802). The flowers are conspicuously large and showy, up to 6 cm in diameter, with oval petals 2 cm long, and occur in branched axillary heads up to 8×8 cm; the edible yellowish fruits are large, oval or spherical, 2,5 to 5 cm in diameter, and make an excellent preserve.

Syzygium masukuense (Baker) R. E. Fries
S.A. no: —
Rhod. no: 803   Small-fruited waterberry

Variable in size, ranging from a small bushy shrub 1,5 m in height when growing in exposed places among rocks, to a large tree 25 m in height; occurring at high altitudes, among mountain quartzite crags, or in evergreen forest when it can become dominant. **Bark:** pale brown, smooth to peeling. **Leaves:** elliptic to almost circular, usually about 2,5 × 2 cm but may reach 9 × 3 cm, the larger leaves are more characteristic in the evergreen forests while the smaller leaves are mostly found on small shrubs in open exposed places; young leaves are often bright red; apex may be rounded but often

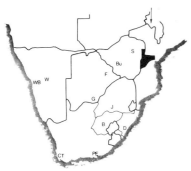
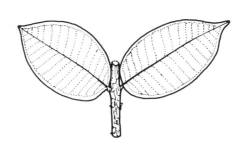

more or less abruptly attenuate into a slender point; base square to slightly lobed, sometimes slightly clasping the stem; margin entire, inclined to be wavy; petiole almost absent, or squat and 1 to 3 mm long. **Flowers:** conspicuous, cream, 1 to 1,5 cm in diameter, with the characteristic central mass of stamens, the calyx tube mauve to purplish-red; produced in rather sparse terminal heads (September to February). **Fruit:** ovoid to almost spherical, fleshy, about 10 mm in diameter, deep bluish-purple when mature, tipped with the remains of the 4 persistent calyx lobes (April to May).

4. METROSIDEROS Banks ex Gaertn.

Metrosideros angustifolia (L.) Smith   Illust. 231
S.A. no: 559   Lance-leaf myrtle. Smalblaarmirt
Rhod. no: —

A shrub or small tree up to 4 m in height, occasionally reaching 7 m; occurring in mountainous areas, along watercourses and river banks where it can become locally common. **Bark:** grey to brown, rather flaky. **Leaves:** opposite to sub-opposite, simple, long and narrow, 3,5 to 8 × 0,4 to 1 cm, thinly leathery, without hairs; apex and base tapering; margin entire; petiole slender, about 1 to 3 mm long, but rather obscured by the decurrent leaf base. **Flowers:** white, cream to pale yellow, about 6 mm in diameter, with a central mass of stamens, in many-flowered axillary heads, or cymes, up to 2,5 × 2 cm, near the tips of the branches and rather lost among the leaves. Bisexual; all floral parts in fives; calyx short, bell-shaped; petals spreading, longer than the sepals; stamens 20 to 30 or more, in 1 to many whorls, much longer than the petals; ovary usually 3-chambered (October to December). **Fruit:** a pale brown many-seeded capsule, broader than it is long, about 3 × 4 mm, partially protruding from the persistent calyx tube, produced in short stalked axillary clusters along the branchlets, often in profusion (November to March).

5. HETEROPYXIS Harvey

Trees. **Leaves:** alternate, simple, gland-dotted. Stipules absent. **Flowers:** small, in terminal branched heads, or panicles. Bisexual; all floral parts in fives; calyx cup-shaped, shortly lobed; petals attached to the calyx tube; stamens 4 to 10, the outer whorl opposite and equalling, or shorter than, the petals; ovary 2- to 3-chambered. **Fruit:** a small capsule.

693

MYRTACEAE

Key to the species of *Heteropyxis:*

Leaves with lateral veins prominent below, forming an acute angle with the midrib, with grey hairs on the under surface persisting to maturity; capsules spherical, about 3 × 3 mm, barely protruding from the persistent calyx .... **H. canescens**

Leaves with the lateral veins not very prominent below, forming a more open angle with the midrib, with the hairs on the young leaves being lost by maturity; capsule ellipsoidal, up to 4 × 2,5 mm, with more than half of its length protruding from the persistent calyx .... **H. natalensis**

Heteropyxis canescens Oliver
S.A. no: 454   Bastard lavender tree. Basterlaventelboom
Rhod. no: —

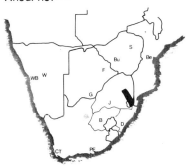

A small tree 3 to 8 m in height, rarely to 20 m; occurring in forested ravines and riverine forest. **Bark:** grey. **Leaves:** narrowly elliptic, up to 15 × 3,5 cm, the under surface with grey hairs which persist to maturity and with prominent lateral veins forming an acute angle with the midrib; apex and base narrowly tapering; margin entire; petiolate. **Flowers:** greenish-yellow, about 3 mm long, in short, dense, branched terminal heads, each about 2 cm long; the flower stalks and young branches with short soft grey hairs (September to March). **Fruit:** an almost spherical pale brown capsule about 3 × 3 mm, barely protruding beyond the persistent calyx (March to July).

Heteropyxis natalensis Harvey   Illust. 232
[*H. dehniae* Suesseng.]
S.A. no: 455   Lavender tree. Laventelboom
Rhod. no: 805   Lavender tree

Usually a small well-foliaged tree 5 to 7 m in height, sometimes crooked and twisted, occasionally reaching 10 m; occurring on stony koppies and hills, also on termite mounds in bush clumps and at the margins of evergreen forest. **Bark:** distinctively pale grey, often almost white, thinly flaking. **Leaves:** narrowly elliptic, ovate to obovate, 3 to 14 × 1 to 4 cm, shiny light green above, dull below with the veins not very prominent and forming a more open angle with the midrib, with lateral veins bearing hairs which are lost by maturity; apex and base narrowly tapering; margin entire; petiole 0,8 to 2,5 cm long, slender, pink over the lower half. **Flowers:** yellowish-green, cream to pale yellow, fragrant, about 3 mm in diameter in branched spreading axillary and terminal heads, each about 3 to 4 cm long, which may be produced in conspicuous profusion (December to March). **Fruit:** an ellipsoidal capsule, up to 4 × 2,5 mm, more than half its length protruding beyond the persistent calyx, straw-coloured, finally splitting into 2 to 3 valves releasing the seeds after which the old capsules may remain on the tree for many months (March to May).

The crushed twigs and leaves are strongly aromatic, often smelling of lavender. In African medicine nose-bleeding is checked by inhaling the steam from a decoction of the roots; the leaves are reputedly used to scent tobacco and, in powdered form, are dosed to stock to eradicate intestinal worms. The wood is brownish-purple, tough and suitable for use as fencing posts and charcoal. The seed germinates readily but the plants, which are probably frost-sensitive, appear to be slow-growing. The leaves develop rich red autumn colours.

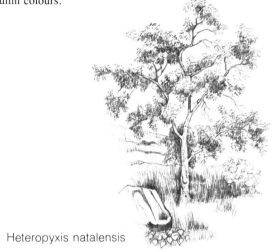

Heteropyxis natalensis

6. *CALLISTEMON R. Br.

*Callistemon viminalis (Salisb. ex Gaertn.) Don ex Loudon

The bottlebrush, introduced from Australia as an ornamental tree, has escaped in some areas of central Rhodesia (Rhod. no: 806).

MELASTOMATACEAE *(The dissotis and tibouchina family)*

MEMECYLON L.

Shrubs or trees, without hairs. **Leaves:** opposite, simple. **Flowers:** in axillary clusters, or cymes, panicles or umbels. Bisexual; all floral parts in fours; calyx somewhat fleshy, joined to form a tube, bell- or saucer-shaped, divided for about half way, forming 4 lobes; petals longer than the calyx lobes; stamens 8, longer than the petals, the anthers conspicuously hatchet-shaped with the connective often spurred or horned; ovary 1-chambered. **Fruit:** spherical, fleshy, indehiscent.

Key to the tree species of *Memecylon:*
1 Leaves very conspicuously 3-veined from the base .... **M. sansibaricum**
  Leaves sometimes obscurely 3-veined from the base, the veins usually immersed 2
2 Leaf apex attenuate to a fine point; blade broadly ovate, 3 to 5 × 2 to 3 cm ... **M. natalense**
  Leaf apex rounded, finally very abruptly and shortly pointed; blade almost circular to broadly
    ovate, up to 9 × 7 cm .... **M. grandiflorum**

Memecylon erythranthum Gilg

The inclusion of this species is based on one collection by Swynnerton from Melsetter. As only a single sterile specimen was collected, some doubt must surround this record. Apart from this, it occurs only in Tanzania where it is a shrub or small tree up to 8 m in height with leaves which are dark glossy green, ovate to oblong and 9 to 18 × 3 to 7 cm. (Rhod. No: 809/1.)

695

MELASTOMATACEAE

Memecylon grandiflorum R. & A. Fernandes
S.A. no: 560,1   Pondo rose-apple. Pondoroosappel
Rhod. no: —

A shrub or small tree up to 7 m in height; occurring in ravine forest. **Bark:** pale grey. **Leaves:** broadly ovate to almost circular, up to 9 × 7 cm, shiny green above, dull green below; may be obscurely 3-veined from the base, veins immersed; the pink from the petiole running into the midrib; apex rounded, abruptly and shortly pointed; base rounded to shallowly lobed; margin entire and tightly rolled under; petiole 2 to 5 mm long. **Flowers:** greenish-yellow, about 3 to 5 mm in diameter, shortly stalked, axillary, solitary or in clusters of 2 to 4 (November). **Fruit:** ovoid, about 10 mm in diameter, tightly clustered along the stem in the leaf axils, becoming bright yellow-orange when mature, crowned by the dry persistent calyx lobes; edible (April to August).

Memecylon natalense Markgraf
S.A. no: 560   Natal rose-apple. Natalroosappel
Rhod. no: —

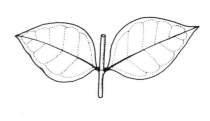

A small tree up to 6 m in height; occurring at the margins of evergreen forest and also as a constituent of the under-storey where it can become locally common. **Bark:** dark grey or greyish-brown, smooth or finely longitudinally striated. **Leaves:** arranged horizontally along the twigs, broadly ovate, 3 to 5 × 2 to 3 cm, shiny bright green above, dull paler green below, veining immersed on both surfaces, even the midrib not very prominent below, may be obscurely 3-veined from the base; apex attenuate; base rounded; margin entire, rolled under; petiole 2 to 3 mm long. **Flowers:** white, inconspicuous, 5 to 7 mm in diameter, on very short stalks, axillary, solitary or in small clusters of 2 to 4 (October to December). **Fruit:** ovoid to almost spherical, up to 10 mm in diameter, fleshy, dark blackish-purple when mature, crowned with the dry persistent calyx lobes; the jointed stalk up to 10 mm long (February to August).

This species resembles *Eugenia capensis* subsp. *natalitia,* but the latter has aromatic leaves.

Memecylon sansibaricum Taub.
[*M. buchananii Gilg; M. sousae* R. & A. Fernandes]
S.A. no: Mottled-bark rose-apple
Rhod. no: 809/2   Mottled-bark memecylon

A shrub or small tree 3 to 7 m in height; occurring in evergreen forest, riverine forest and dense

woodland. **Bark:** grey to olive-grey, smooth, sometimes peeling to reveal a pale brown underbark and

thus giving a mottled appearance; branchlets often with thickened swellings at the nodes and junctions of the young branchlets. **Leaves:** elliptic to ovate, 6 to 9 × 2,5 to 4,5 cm, dark green above, paler green below, markedly 3-veined from the base; apex broadly attenuate, or narrowly so, sometimes sharply pointed; base tapering; margin entire, rolled under; petiole 3 to 4 mm long. **Flowers:** small, greenish-yellow, in dense axillary clusters about 2 cm in diameter on slender stalks up to 6 mm long (October to January). **Fruit:** ovoid to almost spherical, about 7 mm in diameter, white when young, dark blue to purplish when mature, crowned by the dry persistent calyx lobes (December to March).

ARALIACEAE *(The ivy and cussonia family)*

Key to the genera:

1 Leaves simple, palmately lobed or deeply to almost completely divided 2

   Leaves compound 3

2 Leaves palmately lobed, shallowly to rather deeply divided; fruits dry, winged ....
   .... **4. Seemannaralia**

   Leaves deeply divided; fruits fleshy .... **3. Cussonia**

3 Leaves pinnately compound .... **2. Polyscias**

   Leaves digitately compound, the leaflets arising together at the apex of the petiole 4

4 Flowers and fruits in terminal umbellate panicles or clusters; leaf margins entire or toothed
   ....,. **1. Schefflera**

   Flowers and fruits in groups of distinctive spikes; leaf margins entire or variously toothed
   .... **3. Cussonia**

1. SCHEFFLERA J. R. & G. Forster

Schefflera umbellifera (Sonder) Baillon
[*Cussonia umbellifera* Sonder; *C. chartacea* Schinz]
S.A. no: 566   Bastard cabbage tree. Basterkiepersol
Rhod. no: 811   Forest false cabbage tree

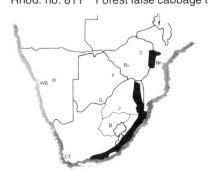

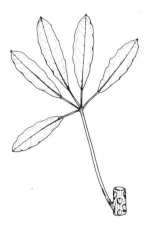

ARALIACEAE

A small to medium sized tree up to 10 m in height; occurring at the margin of forest and in bush clumps from the coast to high altitudes. **Bark:** grey, smooth, resinous. **Leaves:** crowded at the ends of the branches, compound, digitately 3- to 5-foliolate; leaflets oblong to elliptic, 7,5 to 15 × 2,5 to 5 cm, leathery, glossy dark green above, paler green below; apex broadly tapering; base tapering; margin entire, or sometimes toothed, often conspicuously wavy; petiolules slender, petiole 15 to 30 cm long. **Flowers:** small, greenish-cream to yellowish, in loose terminal heads, panicles or umbels, up to 18 cm in diameter. Bisexual. All floral parts in fives; calyx margin toothed or almost entire; petals 5, or 10 in 2 whorls; stamens equal the petals in number; ovary 5- to 8-chambered (January). **Fruit:** almost spherical, about 2 to 3 mm in diameter, greyish-green becoming dark red when mature, in loose clusters (April to August).

The branches are brittle and the wood which is white is moderately soft and suitable for fruit boxes and matches. Seed is scarce as the fruits are eaten by birds; germination is difficult and growth is slow. The seedlings have simple leaves. *S. goetzenii* Harms (Rhod. no: 810), is a liane of the eastern mountain forests in Rhodesia.

2. POLYSCIAS J. R. & G. Forster

Polyscias fulva (Hiern) Harms
S.A. no: —
Rhod. no: 812   Parasol tree

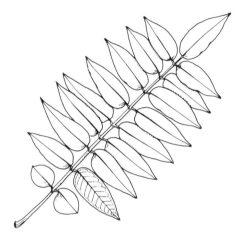

A large tree up to 25 m in height, characteristically with a clear straight bole, with branches developing high up, forming a narrow crown; occurring in evergreen forest. **Bark:** grey. **Leaves:** alternate, compound, once-pinnate, very large, up to 80 cm long, usually with 9 to 13 pairs plus a terminal leaflet; leaflets ovate, sometimes narrowly so, 9 to 16 × 4,5 to 8 cm, leathery, dark green and without hairs above, under surface densely velvety with creamy-rusty stellate hairs; apex tapering, often attenuate; base lobed and clasping the rachis; margin entire; petiolules very short, thickset, almost obscured by the lobed base of the leaflets; petiolate. **Flowers:** small, greenish-yellow to cream, honey-scented, in loose axillary heads, or panicles, branching in a symmetric manner, up to 36 × 12 cm. Bisexual; all floral parts in fives; disc nearly flat; ovary 2-chambered (February to April). **Fruit:** ovoid to almost spherical, 3 to 6 × 3 to 4 mm, often ribbed, crowned with 2 persistent styles, closely clustered along the side branches of the main head (August).

3. CUSSONIA Thunb.

Shrubs arising from underground stems, or trees. **Leaves:** scattered, digitately compound with leaflets either simple or completely divided into a series of vertical sections or vertebrae, sometimes with lateral leaflets arising at the points of articulation. **Flowers:** sessile or shortly stalked, bracteate, with a single bract at the base, or with 3 bracts which persist round the fruit; in terminal spikes, or racemes or umbels, in groups of up to 12 or more. Bisexual; all floral parts in fives; calyx much reduced to almost absent; petals somewhat fleshy; stamens spreading, falling rather early; ovary 2-chambered. **Fruit:** fleshy, almost spherical or laterally compressed, the spikes equalling the flower spikes in size.

Key to the tree species of *Cussonia:*
1 Leaves simple 2
  Leaves compound 3

Polyscias fulva *standing above the forest canopy.*

2 Leaves 7 to 20 cm in diameter .... **C. natalensis**
  Leaves 25 to 50 cm in diameter .... **C. arborea**
3 Leaflets toothed, lobed to deeply lobed, but never vertebrate 4
  Leaflets vertebrate 6
4 Leaflets characteristically blue-green; margin shallowly to deeply lobed; inflorescence a branched
    panicle .... **C. paniculata**
  Leaflets green, margin entire or toothed, but not lobed 5
5 Leaflets small, 5 to 8 × 2 to 4 cm, margin entire or only slightly toothed. Occurring only in the
    Cape .... **C. thyrsiflora**
  Leaflets large, 15 to 25 × 5 to 10 cm, margin conspicuously toothed or scalloped. Does not occur
    in South Africa .... **C. arborea**
6 Racemes or spikes in unbranched umbellate heads; floral bracts, single, free, awl-shaped ... 7
  Racemes or spikes in double umbels; floral bracts clasping the fruits; flowers and fruits sessile
    8
7 Fruits round; pedicels or flower stalks 5 to 20 mm long .... **C. zuluensis**
  Fruits angular-sided; flower stalk almost absent .... **C. nicholsonii**
8 A small tree 3 to 4 m in height, several stemmed from the base. Confined to the Gamtoos River
    valley west of Port Elizabeth .... **C. gamtoosensis**
  Usually taller than 4 m, single stemmed. Occurring north of Port Elizabeth 9
9 A tall growing sparsely branched tree up to 25 m in height; inflorescences and leaves form
    conspicuous globose heads .... **C. sphaerocephala**
  Much lower-growing and more thickset than the previous species, with a single, rather short and
    somewhat massive stem (except in high forest); inflorescences and leaves forming irregular
    heads .... **C. spicata**

Cussonia arborea Hochst. ex A. Rich.
[*C. kirkii* Seem.]
S.A. no: —
Rhod. no: 813   Octopus cabbage tree

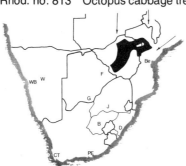

A small to medium sized tree, 3 to 10 m in height; occurring in *Brachystegia* woodland often among rocks. **Bark:** light brown, corky. **Leaves:** compound with 5 or more leaflets, or sometimes simple with various degrees of division into lobes (especially on suckers and young plants); leaflets obovate-elliptic to elliptic, 15 to 25 × 5 to 10 cm, with or without very fine hairs; apex tapering to attenuate; base tapering; margin scalloped, toothed to jaggedly toothed; petiolules absent, petiole up to 30 cm long. **Flowers:** yellowish-green, rather fleshy, without stalks, in 6 to 15 terminal slender medusoid spikes, up to 30 to 35 cm long (September to November). **Fruit:** almost spherical, thinly fleshy, 5 to 7 mm in diameter, dark purple when mature; closely clustered along the axes (November to January).

The wood is of little value as timber, but in Malawi it is used to make xylophone keys. These are fixed to two pieces of wood secured to a sounding board and, when struck with a small piece of wood about the size of a pencil, produce beautiful liquid notes.

Cussonia gamtoosensis Strey
S.A. no: 565,2   Gamtoos cabbage tree. Gamtooskiepersol

Rhod. no:—

Flowers of the octopus cabbage tree, Cussonia arborea.

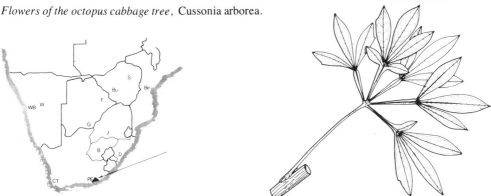

A many-stemmed tree up to 4 m in height; occurring in dry euphorbia scrub on stony hillsides. **Bark:** pale grey, smooth. **Leaves:** comparatively small, up to 30 cm in diameter, digitately compound with 3 to 7 leaflets; leaflets vertebrate but only sparingly so; lanceolate, 4 to 10 × 1,5 to 2,5 cm, thickly leathery, dull greyish olive-green; tapering to apex and base; margin entire or with 1 to 2 teeth, rolled under; petiolules 2 to 6 cm long, petiole ribbed, up to 30 cm long. **Flowers:** spirally arranged in small almost spherical spikes only 2 to 3 × 2 to 2,5 cm, with 4 to 8 spikes per umbel, the full inflorescence taking two seasons to develop. **Fruit:** about 8 mm long, conical, fleshy, purplish when mature, with bracts clasping the fruit; closely crowded along the axes.

Cussonia natalensis Sonder
S.A. no: 562   Simple-leaved cabbage tree. Rotskiepersol
Rhod. no: 814   Simple-leaved cabbage tree

A small thickset round-crowned tree up to 8 m in height; occurring on rocky hills and hillsides. **Bark:** dark grey, deeply fissured and corky. **Leaves:** simple, deeply 5-lobed but not completely divided, small for the genus, 7 to 12 × 7 to 20 cm; margin bluntly toothed; petiole up to 30 cm long, slender. **Flowers:** greenish-yellow in rather thickset, cylindric spikes, up to 15 × 1,5 cm about 12 spikes   **701**

radiating from the end of a branch (April to October). **Fruit:** fleshy, about 4 mm in diameter, purple when mature, closely crowded along the axes (September to December).

Cussonia nicholsonii Strey
S.A. no: —   Wedge-fruited cabbage tree
Rhod. no: —

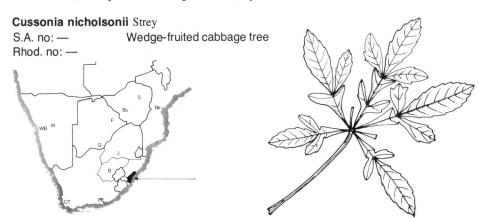

A small several-stemmed but rarely branched tree up to 3 m in height; occurring in a variety of habitats, from hillsides to dry scrub and riverine thicket. **Bark:** reddish-grey to grey, smooth to flaking. **Leaves:** twice compound, the first division digitate, the leaflets 7 to 9 in number, spreading fan-like, up to 30 cm in diameter; the leaflets are vertebrately divided into the secondary leaflets with 1 to 3 articulations, secondary leaflets up to 10 cm long, oblong, glossy dark green above, dull dark green below, leathery; apex and base tapering; margin sparsely to distinctly toothed (occasionally entire); petiolules 3 to 5 cm long, petiole 20 to 30 cm long, the rachillae bearing triangular wings. **Flowers:** greenish-yellow, almost without stalks, in 8 to 30 dense cylindric spikes, 5 to 12 × 3 to 4 cm, forming unbranched terminal umbellate heads taking two seasons to develop. **Fruit:** more or less spherical, angular-sided, rather wedge-shaped, up to 1,5 cm long, pale purplish when mature, closely clustered along the spikes.

Cussonia paniculata Ecklon & Zeyher
S.A. no: 563   Mountain cabbage tree. Bergkiepersol
Rhod. no: —

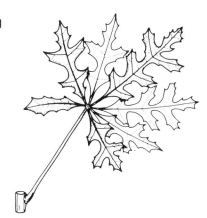

Leaves and fruits of the mountain cabbage tree, Cussonia paniculata.

A short thickset tree rarely exceeding 5 m in height; occurring on dry stony hills; this is the common *Cussonia* found near Johannesburg and Pretoria in suitable habitats. **Bark:** grey, longitudinally fissured, thick and corky; trunk thick and squat. **Leaves:** up to 60 cm in diameter, characteristically coarsely lacy in appearance, compound, with 7 to 9 leaflets arranged fan-wise; leaflets entire, shallowly to deeply lobed and constricted forming segments, separated by narrow waist-like sections; each leaflet 10 to 30 × 2 to 6 cm, very characteristically pale blue-grey-green, although occasionally green; apex and base tapering; margin toothed; petiolules 1,5 to 3 cm long, petiole 20 to 30 cm long, slender. **Flowers:** small, green, stalked; in short densely flowered spikes, 2,5 to 5 cm long, branched, forming panicles (January to April). **Fruit:** fleshy, up to 6 cm in diameter, purple when mature, closely crowded along the axes (May to June).
The leaves provide good fodder for stock. The wood is greyish white, soft and light, and was used for making brake-blocks on wagons.

Cussonia sphaerocephala Strey
S.A. no: 561,1   Forest cabbage tree. Boskiepersol
Rhod. no: —

A tall slender sparsely branched tree up to 25 m in height; occurring in coastal dune forest and moist wooded mountain ravines. **Bark:** reddish-grey when young becoming dark grey, smooth or slightly fissured to rather corky. **Leaves:** compound, the first and second divisions forming a complex geometric pattern of triangularly winged rachillae and lateral pinnules. The 6 to 12 leaflets all arise fan-wise from the top of the 90 cm long petiole; the whole fan of leaflets may measure up to 40 cm in diameter; leaflets rarely single, usually vertebrate with 1 to 5 joints; leathery, shiny dark green above, dull dark green below; apex tapering; base decurrent, forming a winged petiolule; margin entire to coarsely toothed; petiole ribbed; the characteristic head of leaves forms an almost spherical crown – hence the specific name. According to Strey the stem is initially single, straight and tall, bearing one round head of leaves; in the first season of flowering an umbel of leafy branches is produced at the

703

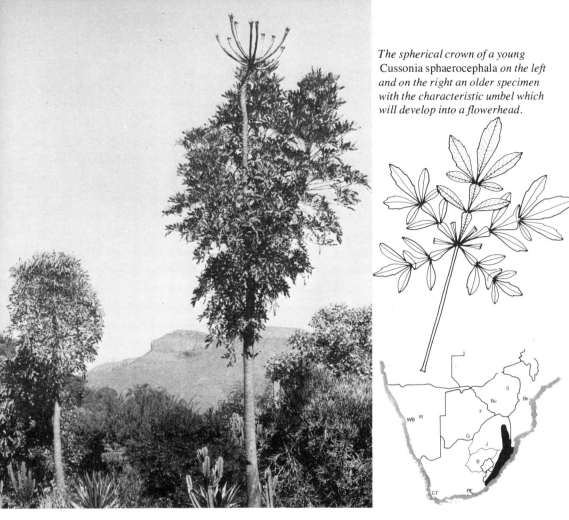

The spherical crown of a young Cussonia sphaerocephala *on the left and on the right an older specimen with the characteristic umbel which will develop into a flowerhead.*

apex of the trunk, each of these branches having a knob-like thickening covered with large bracts at its tip. Only during the following season are inflorescences produced at the tips of these inflorescene branches. Since the leaves produced in the first year have by now fallen, the structure resembles a 'compound' or double umbel. These floral structures are therefore produced over two years, as in *C. spicata* and *C. gamtoosensis,* instead of every year, as is the case in the single umbel species of *Cussonia.* The tips of the stems which have fruited are now more or less truncated, and they dry out and eventually the stems produce one or two side shoots which grow into lateral branches. **Flowers:** greenish-cream, densely arranged in short thickset squat spikes forming a compact double umbel, each spike 8 to 14 × 4 to 6 cm. **Fruit:** fleshy, about 6 mm in diameter, purple when mature, with the floral bracts clasping the fruit; densely crowded along the axes (July to September).

The relationship between this species and *C. spicata* is insufficiently understood.

Cussonia spicata Thunb.
[*C. kraussii* Hochst.]
S.A. no: 564   Cabbage tree. Gewone kiepersol
Rhod. no: 815   Cabbage tree

A thickset tree 3 to 10 m in height; in South Africa it occurs both on mountain slopes and in the dry lowveld; in Rhodesia it is more a tree of high altitudes, on mountainsides and stony outcrops. **Bark:** yellowish-grey, thick and corky. **Leaves:** crowded at the ends of the branches; compound, up to 70 cm in diameter, with 5 to 9 leaflets arising from the end of a stout petiole up to 40 cm long; leaflets dark green to bluish-green, lobed and dissected, vertebrate, twice compound with lateral leaflets

704

The candle-like inflorescence of the cabbage tree, Cussonia spicata.

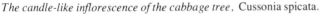

adding to the pattern given by the winged rachillae; apex and base tapering; margin entire to sharply toothed; petiolules absent or up to 5 cm long. **Flowers:** greenish-yellow, closely packed along 8 to 12 thick spikes, 5 to 15 × 1,5 to 4 cm (November to May). **Fruit:** almost angular, 4 to 6 mm in diameter, purple when mature, closely clustered along the spikes and with the floral bracts clasping the fruits (June to September).

In South Africa five forms of this species are known to occur. The wood is whitish, light, soft and coarse. The succulent roots are eaten in times of need and, macerated, are used by Zulus to treat malaria. The leaves are said to provide a valuable fodder for stock. The trees are apparently fairly fast-growing but they may be frost-tender.

705

ARALIACEAE

Cussonia thyrsiflora Thunb.
S.A. no: 565   Coast cabbage tree. Kuskiepersol
Rhod. no: —

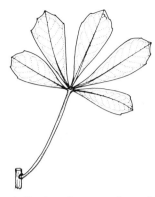

A shrub or small tree up to 5 m in height; occurring in dry coastal scrub. **Bark:** pale grey, rather corky, the branches marked with prominent leaf scars. **Leaves:** compound, with 6 to 8 leaflets arising together, fan-like, at the end of the petiole; leaflets obovate, 5 to 8 × 2 to 4 cm; apex broadly tapering; base tapering; margin entire or slightly toothed, rolled under; petiolules absent, petiole 5 to 15 cm long, may be winged. **Flowers:** greenish-yellow, in 6 to 12 short spikes, 4 to 6 × 1 to 2 cm (November to January). **Fruit:** fleshy, about 4 mm in diameter, purple when mature, closely crowded along the axes (April to June).

Cussonia zuluensis Strey
S.A. no: 561   Zulu cabbage tree. Zoeloekiepersol
Rhod. no: —

A small several-stemmed tree up to 4 m in height; occurring in dry coastal scrub and forest, also along river valleys and sometimes farther inland. **Bark:** grey-green, smooth to flaking. **Leaves:** twice compound, with 8 to 12 leaflets arranged fan-wise at the apex of the petiole, each leaflet up to 15 cm long, much dissected, with lateral leaflets; glossy dark green above, dull green below; apex tapering with a hair-like tip; base tapering; margin sparsely to distinctly toothed; petiolules and rachillae are winged, petiole up to 10 cm long. **Flowers:** greenish-yellow, closely packed along 8 to 26 spikes, each 20 to 30 × 3 to 5 cm, on distinctive long slender stalks up to 35 cm long. **Fruit:** goblet-shaped, fleshy, up to 8 × 5 mm, pale purplish when mature and closely crowded along the axes.

4. SEEMANNARALIA R. Viguier

Seemannaralia gerrardii (Seem.) Viguier
S.A. no: 567   Wild maple. Wilde-ahorn
Rhod. no: —

A small to medium sized tree 5 to 10 m in height, occasionally taller; occurring in coastal and mountain ravine forests and on rocky hills. **Bark:** grey; the branches thick and brittle with vertical striations, resinous. **Leaves:** crowded near the ends of the branches, simple, almost circular, 7 to 16 cm in diameter, pale to medium green, soft and thinly textured, sometimes with hairs when young but usually losing these by maturity; shallowly to rather deeply divided to form 5 to 7 lobes; apex of

706

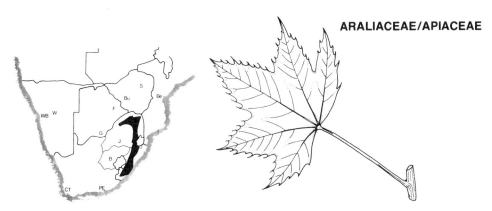

lobes finely pointed; base of the leaf lobed; margin toothed, the teeth drawn out into glandular hairs giving a shaggy appearance; petiole up to 12 cm long. **Flowers:** small, green, in dense heads, or many-flowered paniculate umbels, 2 to 3 cm in diameter. Bisexual; all floral parts in fives; much resembling the flowers of *Cussonia,* but the calyx tube is saucer-shaped and not cup-shaped (March to April). **Fruit:** ovoid, flattened, almost winged, about 10 × 8 mm, ribbed, in dense spherical heads 3 to 4 cm in diameter, but many of these together can give the effect of large heads, purple when mature; the flat membraneous seeds are distinctive (June to September).

APIACEAE (nom. altern. **Umbelliferae**) *(The carrot and parsley family)*

Key to the tree genera:
Leaflets arranged in 2 to 3 regular pairs plus a terminal leaflet, margins jaggedly toothed, each tooth hair-tipped .... **2. Steganotaenia**

Leaflets 7 to 9, arising as a group of 4 leaflets (2 opposite pairs) at the junction of the petiole and the rachis with a group of 3 leaflets at the end of the rachis (occasionally there is an additional pair of leaflets between these two groups); sometimes the upper group only may be present and the leaf thus becomes 3-foliolate; margins entire or obscurely scalloped .... **1. Heteromorpha**

1. HETEROMORPHA Cham. & Schlecht.

Heteromorpha arborescens (Sprengel) Cham. & Schlecht.   Illust. 233
[*H. trifoliata* (Wendl.) Ecklon & Zeyher]
S.A. no: 568   Parsley tree. Wildepieterseliebos
Rhod. no: 816   Parsnip tree

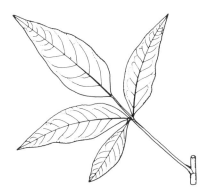

A straggling open-branched shrub or small tree up to 7 m in height; occurring over a wide range of altitudes, frequently fringing evergreen forest (where it reaches its greatest size), and found in wooded ravines, on hillsides and rocky outcrops. **Bark:** reddish-brown to purplish-brown, smooth, somewhat waxy in appearance, characteristically peeling in almost papery flakes. **Leaves:** alternate, compound, elliptic, glossy light green or grey-green, becoming yellow to red in autumn; sometimes with a single leaflet (mainly Eastern Cape) but usually with the 3 to 9 leaflets arranged in an unusual and variable manner; frequently with 4 arising at the junction of the petiole and rachis, this group comprising 2 large upper leaflets about 5 to 7 × 1 to 2 cm, and 2 smaller lower leaflets, 3,5 to 5,5 × 1 to 1,5 cm,   **707**

often each with short petiolules usually arising from the same point and producing a fan effect, or there may be 2 leaflets on each side, one large and the other small, both on a common short petiolule; the final 3 leaflets consist of a terminal cluster of 2 small lateral leaflets without petiolules and a large terminal leaflet up to 8 cm long. The group of 4 is quite often absent, leaving only the terminal group of 3, and the leaf then appears trifoliolate; or all except the terminal leaflet may be absent thus giving the impression of a simple leaf; or sometimes there are more than 7 leaflets; aromatic when crushed, smelling of parsnips hence the common name. **Flowers:** small, greenish-white or yellowish, often strong-smelling, in dense round heads or compound umbels, up to 5 cm in diameter, with all the flower stalks rising from the same point at the tip of the flowering branch; appearing with the leaves. Bisexual; all floral parts in fives; calyx 5-toothed; petals inflexed at the apex, keeled on the inner surface; stamens slightly longer than the petals; ovary with 2 chambers which later split away from each other, each with very short styles (December to January). **Fruit:** formed from the 2 carpels, or mericarps, of the ovary, which split away from each other, marked with longitudinal ridges, flattened, rather heart-shaped, 5 to 7 mm long, drying to a creamy-brown (April onwards).

In African medicine an infusion of the leaves is prepared as an enema to treat abdominal disorders and is given as a remedy for mental and nervous conditions. Another leaf-preparation is given to children for intestinal worms. The smoke from the burning wood is inhaled to relieve headaches, and a decoction of the decorticated root is used to treat breathlessness, coughs and dysentery. The fruits contain a volatile aromatic oil.

2. STEGANOTAENIA Hochst.

Steganotaenia araliacea Hochst.   Illust. 234
S.A. no: 569   Carrot tree. Geelwortelboom
Rhod. no: 817   Carrot tree. Pop-gun tree

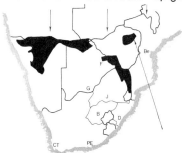

A small erect sparsely branched shrub or small tree 2 to 7 m in height; occurring over a wide range of altitudes but more characteristic of low altitude woodland, also on rocky outcrops in sheltered areas. **Bark:** green or yellowish grey-green, rather waxy in appearance, inclined to peel in papery strips and rectangles; slender stemmed, shortly branched near the top only. **Leaves:** crowded at the ends of the branches, compound, with 2 to 3 pairs of leaflets plus a terminal leaflet; leaflets broadly ovate, 3 to 5 × 2 to 3,5 cm, widely spaced along the rachis, fresh green; apex tapering to a fine point; base broadly tapering to truncate; margin conspicuously and jaggedly toothed, each tooth ending in a fine hair-like point; petiolules 5 to 10 mm long, petiole up to 10 cm long. **Flowers:** small, green to greenish-white, in tight clusters, or compound umbels, with all the stalks rising from the same point at the tip of the flowering branchlet, heads up to 8 cm in diameter; 3 to 7 heads may be produced together on a branching common axis forming a large cluster, 11 to 20 cm in diameter. Bisexual or male only; all floral parts in fives; calyx toothed; petals with long inflexed apices, keeled on the inner surface; disc flat; stamens longer than the petals; ovary heart-shaped, styles about half as long as the stamens, absent in the male flowers (August to October). **Fruit:** flattened, heart-shaped, formed from 2 mericarps separating away, each about 7 to 12 × 5 to 7 mm, produced in large untidy clusters, pale creamy-brown with a conspicuous papery wing, eventually splitting to release the seeds (November onwards, remaining dry on the trees for months).

The wood is soft and brittle. Children make pop-guns from this tree by slipping the bark off a length of stem; this bark comes away easily in late winter. The roots are chewed to relieve sore throats and the bark to alleviate asthma. The Shona believe that the plant produces abortion in goats. All parts of the tree smell strongly of carrots.

ALANGIACEAE

ALANGIUM Lam.

Alangium chinense (Lour.) Harms
S.A. no: —
Rhod. no: 818   Alangium

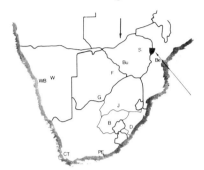

A slender sparsely branched tree up to 10 m in height, but sometimes reaching 20 m; occurring in moist evergreen forest. **Bark:** grey, smooth. **Leaves:** alternate, simple, varying from narrowly elliptic to ovate and broadly ovate, 4 to 19 × 2,5 to 10 cm, young leaves tending to be palmately lobed and large with fine soft hairs most of which are lost by maturity, conspicuously 4- to 5-veined from the base, the midrib prominent and sometimes branching once or twice; apex tapering to broadly tapering; base markedly asymmetric, tapering on one side, square on the other; margin entire in adult leaves, petiole up to 2,5 cm long, finely hairy. **Flowers:** with golden hairs; the petals creamy white to pale yellow, about 1,5 cm long, narrow, curling back; sweetly scented; in small axillary branched heads, or cymes. Bisexual; floral parts in fours to tens; calyx short, truncate; petals may be very shortly joined at the extreme base; stamens alternating with the petals; ovary 1- to 2-chambered (November to March). **Fruit:** fleshy, flattened, broadly tapering to the apex, about 10 × 6 mm, crowned with the remains of the old calyx (February to June).
This is a widespread pan-tropical species, collected only a few times in Rhodesia and in adjacent areas in Moçambique.

CORNACEAE *(The dogwood family)*

Key to the tree genera:
Leaf margins roughly to jaggedly toothed; apex broadly tapering to rounded, finally abruptly sharply pointed; blade broadly elliptic to almost circular, under surface with pale woolly hairs, usually grey, rusty or brown along the main veins .... **1. Curtisia**

Leaf margins entire; apex narrowly tapering into a long point, blade elliptic to narrowly elliptic, without dense woolly hairs .... **2. Afrocrania**

1. CURTISIA Aiton

Curtisia dentata (N. L. Burm.) C. A. Smith
[*C. faginea* Aiton]
S.A. no: 570   Assegai tree. Assegaai
Rhod. no: 819   Assegai tree

A medium to large tree, frequently 6 to 12 m in height, but specimens up to 20 m are not uncommon; occurring over a wide range of altitudes, in evergreen forest, on grassy mountain slopes and as a small bushy tree in coastal scrub forest. **Bark:** brown and smooth in younger trees becoming dark brown and square-fissured. **Leaves:** opposite, simple, oval, broadly elliptic to almost circular, 2,5 to 10 × 2,5 to 7,5 cm, but usually about 7 × 4 cm, leathery, the upper surface shiny dark green, without hairs and with conspicuous pale veins, the under surface light green with woolly hairs, and very prominent veins which are covered with short soft grey, rusty or brown hairs; the young leaves and the leaf buds **709**

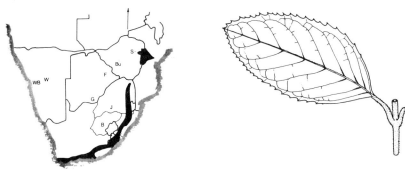

are covered with dense woolly grey or rusty hairs; apex broadly tapering to rounded, finally abruptly sharply pointed; base broadly tapering to square; margin strongly and coarsely toothed, with the teeth often curved back or reflexed; petiole up to 1,5 cm long. **Flowers:** small, inconspicuous, cream, with all parts covered with light grey soft hairs, in branched terminal heads, or panicles, up to 12 cm long. Bisexual; all floral parts in fours; calyx joined to form a twisted tube, separating into 4 lobes; petals twice as long as the calyx tube; stamens alternating with the petals and equal to them in length; ovary 4-chambered (October to March). **Fruit:** almost spherical, fleshy, about 10 mm in diameter, 4-seeded, crowned with the remains of the persistent calyx, white at first becoming red when mature (frequently sporadic, six to ten months after flowering, about May to October).

The fruits are bitter but are sought after and distributed by birds, wild pigs, monkeys and baboons. The bark has been used for tanning; the wood is reddish, fine-grained, hard, strong, elastic, tough and heavy but not very durable as it tends to split on seasoning and the heartwood is liable to rot. Nevertheless, it was found to be suitable for various parts of wagons and also for tool handles and at one time was so heavily exploited that fine specimens are now rare. The trees are fast-growing but are not easily propagated from seed and are tender to frost; they are frequently heavily parasitised, the leaves by a black fungus, and the flowers by galls, and frequently therefore little fruit is set. The Assegaibos gave its name to a small town in the Cape Province.

2. AFROCRANIA (Harms) Hutch.

Afrocrania volkensii (Harms) Hutch.
S.A. no: —
Rhod. no: 820   Afrocrania

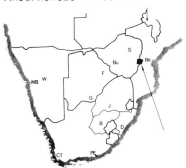

A tall tree up to 17 m in height, often with a straight bole and a wide spreading crown; occurring in high altitude rain forest, where the light green leaves are conspicuous against the dark green of the forest background and often clearly mark the course of forest streams. **Bark:** grey to dark grey, striated and flaking. **Leaves:** alternate or opposite, simple, large, elliptic to narrowly elliptic, 5 to 17,5 × 2,5 to 6,3 cm, light green, thinly textured, finely covered with silvery hairs when young but losing most of these by maturity; veins depressed above, prominent below; apex tapering into a long point; base broadly tapering; margin entire; petiole up to 2 cm long. **Flowers:** very small, greenish-yellow, in dense terminal heads. Sexes separate on different trees; floral parts in fours to fives; calyx joined to form a tube, attached to the ovary, lobes minute; petals about 3 mm long, attached to the expanded section of the calyx tube; stamens alternating with the petals; ovary 2-chambered. The buds

710

are completely enveloped in an involucre of 4 bracts (August to December). **Fruit:** ellipsoidal, fleshy, 13 × 6 mm, dark purple when mature (November to January).
This tree tolerates cold and heavy rainfall.

ERICACEAE *(The erica and heather family)*

Key to the tree genera:
1 Leaves broad, lanceolate, serrate; fruits fleshy .... **1. Vaccinium**

   Leaves very small, needle-like; fruits dry, dehiscent capsules 2

2 Bracts on the stalk below the flower 3, very rarely 1 or absent; calyx lobes equal ... **2. Erica**

   Bracts absent; calyx lobes unequal .... **3. Philippia**

1. VACCINIUM L.

Vaccinium exul Bolus
S.A. no: 571   African cranberry. Bosbessiebos
Rhod. no: —

A shrub or small tree usually 2 to 4 m in height, but sometimes reaching 7 m; occurring at high altitudes, on rocky outcrops and steep mountain grassland, in clumps of bush and fringing forest. **Bark:** light brown, striated. **Leaves:** alternate, simple, lanceolate to elliptic, 4 to 6 × 1 to 2 cm, leathery, green above, rather blue-green below; apex tapering; base broadly tapering; margin toothed; petiole up to 5 mm long. **Flowers:** greenish to creamy-white, occasionally pale pink, bell-shaped, about 7 mm long, in axillary sprays, or racemes, up to 4 cm long; although attractive in themselves, they are rather lost among the leaves. Bisexual; floral parts in fours to fives; calyx tube attached to the ovary; stamens 5 to 10 attached to the corolla tube; ovary 4- to 5-chambered (August to October). **Fruit:** almost spherical, about 7 mm in diameter, becoming red and finally black when mature, crowned with the remains of the persistent calyx (April to May).
The genus *Vaccinium* contains such well-known plants as the bilberry and the cranberry, and is confined largely to the northern hemisphere. This species, at one time the only one known from the African continent, was named *exul,* meaning 'the exile'. The red fleshy fruits are edible and make a good jam.

2. ERICA L.

Frequently low-growing shrubs, rarely small trees. **Leaves:** usually 3- to 6-whorled, rarely alternate, small, rigid, needle-like or linear, so far rolled under that they almost form a cylinder. **Flowers:** solitary, in clusters or, rarely, in racemes. Bisexual; all floral parts in fours; the calyx 4-lobed, small (flowers corolline), or prominent and almost equalling the petals in length (flowers calycine); petals joined, bell-shaped or urn-shaped; stamens usually 8, free; ovary usually 4-chambered. **Fruit:** a small dehiscent capsule, hidden in the withered remains of the old flower; seed extremely fine.
The Scots heather, renowned bringer of good luck, belongs to a closely related genus, *Calluna* Salisb. **711**

ERICACEAE

Key to the tree species of *Erica:*

1 Occurring in Moçambique and Rhodesia .... **E. pleiotricha**
  Occurring in South Africa 2
2 Leaves in whorls of 4 3
  Leaves in whorls of 3 4
3 Leaves up to 5 mm long, ascending, often lying pressed against the branchlets; flowers with
    conspicuous calyx lobes about 3 mm long, almost three-quarters the length of the flower. Does
    not occur further west than Uitenhage .... **E. caffrorum**
  Leaves up to 9 mm long, may be somewhat spreading, not lying pressed against the branchlets;
    flowers with very small calyx lobes, less than 2 mm long. Does not occur further east than
    Swellendam .... **E. caterviflora**
4 Leaves very small, up to 4 mm long, less than 1 mm wide; flowers small, white ....
    .... **E. inconstans**
  Leaves 4 to 10 mm long, 1 mm or more wide; flowers white or pink, 4 to 7 mm long 5
5 Flowers rose-pink, about 4 mm long .... **E. canaliculata**
  Flowers white or cream, 5 to 7 mm long 6
6 Calyx small; flowers up to 7 mm long, larger than those of the other tree species. Widespread
    .... **E. caffra**
  Calyx conspicuous; flowers up to 5 mm long. Confined to the south-western Cape only ....
    .... **E. triflora**

Erica caffra L.
S.A. no: 572   Water tree erica. Waterheide
Rhod. no: —

Characteristic Ericaceae
needle-like leaves.

A shrub or small tree, often low and twisted, but sometimes reaching 4 m in height; occurring in
mountain ravines, on cliffs, generally in damp situations. **Bark:** dull greyish. **Leaves:** in whorls of 3,
about 10 mm long, greyish-green, with fine short grey hairs; margin rolled under giving a needle-like
appearance. **Flowers:** attractive, white or cream, bell-shaped or urn-shaped, 4 to 7 mm long,
corolline; solitary or in small groups of 2 to 3 among the leaves and clustered towards the ends of the
branches (July to October). **Fruit:** a many-seeded capsule, about 3 mm long (October to January).

Erica caffrorum Bolus
S.A. no: 573   Mountain tree erica. Bergboomheide
Rhod. no: —

Usually a shrub, even a sub-shrub, occasionally a small tree up to 4 m in height; occurring in mountainous areas, often among the rocky cliffs, but also in gullies, at the margins of evergreen forest and on grassy mountain slopes. **Bark:** grey-brown, rather rough. **Leaves:** in whorls of 4, thickly packed along the slender branchlets, about 5 mm long, slightly curved, with or without hairs. **Flowers:** pink or whitish, in clusters at the ends of the branches; calycine, the calyx lobes almost obscuring the corolla and giving the flower a spiky, rather unkempt appearance (November to February). **Fruit:** a small, 4-lobed, many-seeded capsule (March onwards).

Erica canaliculata Andr   Illust. 235
S.A. no: Grooved-bark tree erica
Rhod. no: —

A shrub or small tree up to 4 m in height; occurring in the dry mesophytic forests where, in protected valleys, it reaches its greatest size; frequently seen as a low shrub along roadsides. **Bark:** greyish to greyish-brown, finely longitudinally grooved (the specific name refers to this), narrowly flaking; branches with fine greyish hairs. **Leaves:** in whorls of 3, needle-like, 4 to 10 mm long, dark green. **Flowers:** very attractive rose-pink, 4 to 5 mm long, in groups of 3, produced in heavy profusion; corolline, with the calyx up to 2 mm long, pale backed, red within (October to March but at most times of the year). **Fruit:** a very small capsule, about 2 to 3 mm long (throughout the year).

Erica caterviflora Salisb.
S.A. no: 574   Honey tree erica. Heuningboomheide
Rhod. no: —

A shrub or small tree reaching 5 m in height; occurring on mountainsides. **Bark:** greyish-brown. **Leaves:** in whorls of 4, 5 to 9 mm long, slightly curved, with or without hairs. **Flowers:** beautiful, pink, tubular, about 5 mm long, corolline; produced in such profusion that the leaves are hidden (December to March). **Fruit:** a very small lobed capsule (February to May).
The flowers have a strong smell of honey but apparently attract few insects.

Erica inconstans Zahlbr.
S.A. no: 574,1   Uitenhage tree erica. Uitenhage boomheide
Rhod. no: —

An upright shrub or small tree reaching 6 m in height; occurring on mountainsides and in evergreen forest. **Bark:** grey. **Leaves:** in whorls of 3, up to 4 mm long by less than 1 mm wide. **Flowers:** white,   **713**

small, corolline, with the corolla much larger than the calyx (June). **Fruit:** a very small capsule (July to October).

This rare plant is not often collected; it is confined to mountainous areas within its range.

Erica pleiotricha S. Moore
[E. thryptomenoides S. Moore; *E. eylesii* L. Bolus]
S.A. no: —
Rhod. no: 821   Northern tree erica

A shrub or small tree 1 to 4 m in height; occurring at high altitudes on mountainsides and in gullies among rocks. **Bark:** grey. **Leaves:** ovate to needle-like, 2 to 4 × 0,5 to 1,5 mm, paler green below than above, but the margin may be so rolled under that it almost completely obscures the under surface. **Flowers:** corolline, pink, lavender or lilac, bell-shaped, 3 to 5 mm long, with distinctive brown to maroon anthers on the stamens (April to November). **Fruit:** a very small capsule (shortly after flowering). The variety involved here is var. *blaerioides* (Wild) Ross.

Seven further *Erica* species occur in Rhodesia but none of them reaches tree proportions; all have small flowers varying from pink to purplish in colour.

Erica triflora L.
S.A. no: 575   Bearded tree erica. Baardboomheide
Rhod. no: —

Usually a shrub 1 to 2 m in height; occasionally becoming tree-like reaching 4 m; occurring at high altitudes in mountainous areas. **Bark:** grey-brown, scaly; branchlets pale with whitish hairs. **Leaves:** in whorls of 3 crowded along the branchlets, about 10 mm long, slightly curved inwards, without hairs. **Flowers:** white, urn-shaped, about 5 mm long, calycine; in clusters at the ends of the branches, the calyx almost obscuring the corolla (July to February). **Fruit:** a very small 4-lobed capsule (December to January or later).

3. PHILIPPIA Klotzsch

Shrubs or small trees. **Leaves:** very small, rolled under, ericoid. **Flowers:** very small, in terminal clusters; bract absent. Bisexual; floral parts in threes to fours; calyx lobes unequal, one larger than the others; corolla very small, its lobes bent inwards; stamens 6 or 8 in 2 whorls; ovary 4-chambered, the style and stigma often protruding well beyond the mouth of the flower, the stigma saucer-shaped. **Fruit:** a capsule, dehiscent.

Key to the tree species of *Philippia* (a 10x lens is required for identification of these species):
1 Anthers joined 2
  Anthers free 4
2 Leaves and calyces glandular and often sticky .... **P. chamissonis**
  Leaves and calyces without glands 3
3 Stigma protruding beyond the mouth of the flower; lobes of the calyx sepals shortly joined at the base only .... **P. hexandra**
  Stigma included within the petals; lobes of the calyx joined for half their length or more ......
  .... **P. benguelensis**
4 Lobes of the calyx joined for at least half their length.................................... **P. evansii**
  Lobes of the calyx shortly joined at the base only 5
5 Branchlets more or less covered with extremely short white hairs, often resembling a scaly layer
  .... **P. simii**
  Branchlets covered with dense, unusually branched, long hairs.......................... **P. mannii**

Philippia benguelensis (Welw. ex Engl.) Britten
S.A. No: —
Rhod. no: 822   Common tree philippia

A shrub or small tree up to 6 m in height; occurring at medium altitudes in open woodland, especially on rocky hills, and at high altitudes among rocks and in mountain grassland. **Bark:** grey to brown, rather rough. **Leaves:** closely crowded along the slender branchlets, needle-like, about 2 mm long, dull dark green to grey-green. **Flowers:** brownish-pink, 2 to 3 mm long, often produced in profusion among the leaves towards the ends of the branches; anthers joined (February to May). **Fruit:** an almost spherical capsule, about 2 mm in diameter, dull red when mature (May to September).
In Rhodesia this is the most widespread of the species.

Philippia chamissonis Klotzsch
S.A. no: 575,1   Cape tree philippia. Kaapse basterboomheide
Rhod. no: —

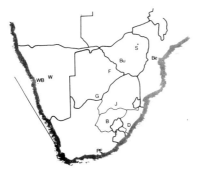

Usually a robust shrub 1 to 2 m in height, sometimes a small dense tree reaching 4 m with the stem up to 30 cm in diameter; occurring on flats and hills, also among rocks. **Bark:** grey to brownish, fissured. **Leaves:** glandular and often sticky, crowded along the branchlets; needle-like, 1 to 2 mm long, grey-green. **Flowers:** yellowish-green, white or pale pink, 1 to 1,5 mm long, produced in profusion; anthers joined, at least when young (February to April). **Fruit:** a small round capsule (appearing somewhat later than the flowering).
This species has been used for cabinet work.

Philippia evansii N. E. Br.
S.A. no: —
Rhod. no: 822/1   Early-flowering philippia

A shrub or small tree up to 6 m in height; confined to high altitudes in moist short grass on mountain slopes, or at the edge of forest, in ravines and along mountain streams. **Bark:** grey to brown, rather rough. **Leaves:** crowded along the branches, 1 to 2 mm long, needle-like. **Flowers:** pink to reddish, 1 to 1,5 mm long, often in profusion among the leaves (June to February). **Fruit:** an ovoid capsule, 1,5 mm in diameter, brownish when mature (September).

Philippia hexandra S. Moore
S.A. no: —
Rhod. no: 823   Petrolbush

A shrub or small tree up to 5 m in height; usually confined to high altitude mountainsides, often near streams and among rocks. **Bark:** grey, fissured and inclined to be flaky. **Leaves:** crowded along the branches, needle-like, 1 to 2 mm long, dull dark green. **Flowers:** rather inconspicuous, greenish to reddish-brown, 1 to 2 mm long, often produced in profusion and frequently in spherical heads about 10 mm in diameter at the ends of the branches; stamens joined (December to July). **Fruit:** a very small spherical capsule (shortly after flowering).

This and *P. benguelensis* are the most generally encountered species in Rhodesia, although *P. hexandra* is less widespread. The flowers produce clouds of pollen when the bushes are shaken and the dry wood burns easily and rapidly.

Philippia mannii (J. D. Hook.) Alm & Fries
[*P. pallidiflora* Engl.]
S.A. no: —
Rhod. no: 824　Hook-bristle philippia

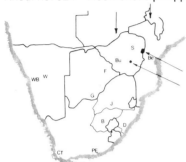

A shrub or small tree up to 4 m in height; occurring at high altitudes on mountainsides and among rocks. **Bark:** dark grey, striated; branchlets covered with dense, unusually branched (barbellate), long hairs. **Leaves:** densely crowded along the stems, slightly larger than those of the other species described here, even up to 6 mm long, needle-like. **Flowers:** small, yellowish, reddish to purplish, in clusters near the ends of the branches (September to June). **Fruit:** a capsule, 2 to 4 mm in diameter (shortly after flowering).

Only subspecies, subsp. *pallidiflora* (Engl.) R. Ross, reaches its southern limit in eastern and central Rhodesia; subsp. *usambarensis* (Alm & Fries) R. Ross does not extend further south than Tanzania.

Philippia simii S. Moore
S.A. no: 576　Transvaal tree philippia. Transvaalse basterboomheide
Rhod. no: 826/1　White-velvet philippia

This species resembles *P. mannii* but lacks the long branched hairs, having instead such short close white hairs that they appear as a white coating on the branches.

MYRSINACEAE

Key to the genera:

1 Fruits crowned by remains of the persistent calyx, many-seeded; all floral parts arise above the ovary .... **1. Maesa**

Fruits not crowned by the persistent calyx but frequently sharp-tipped with the remains of the style, single-seeded; all floral parts arise below the ovary 2

717

2 Often a liane, or a vigorous climber; petals free; stamens with the filaments up to 2 mm long
.... **2. Embelia**

Usually a shrub or tree, not tending to climb; petals joined 3

3 Leaves usually less than 4 cm long; twigs thin and woody; stamens with very short filaments joined
at the base .... **3. Myrsine**

Leaves 5 to 13 cm long; twigs rather thick and soft; stamens with filaments absent or very nearly so
.... **4. Rapanea**

1. MAESA Forsk.

Maesa lanceolata Forsk.　Illust. 236
S.A. no: 577　Maesa. Bruinsapblaar
Rhod. no: 827　Maesa

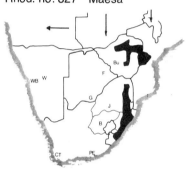

A straggling shrub or small lax tree 5 to 10 m in height; occurring at the margins of evergreen forest, almost always along rivers and streams, occasionally in open mountain grassland. **Bark:** grey, greyish-brown to reddish-brown, rather rough; young branches smooth and occasionally covered with short, soft, rusty hairs. **Leaves:** alternate, simple, elliptic to ovate-elliptic to broadly so, usually about 5 to 10 × 3 to 10 cm but may reach 15 cm long, gland-dotted, thick, leathery, the upper surface glossy green and without hairs, the under surface pale green and finely hairy, often with rusty hairs especially along the prominent veins; apex and base tapering; margin usually coarsely toothed, occasionally entire in forest specimens; petiole 2 to 3 cm long. **Flowers:** very small, white to deep cream, sweet smelling, in axillary or terminal many-flowered heads, or panicles, up to 10 × 5 cm, with the stalks and the backs of the calyces finely but densely covered with rusty hairs. Bisexual; floral parts in fours to fives; calyx persistent, with 2 bracts at the base; the lobes of the corolla joined to form a tube at the base; stamens joined to the corolla tube; ovary below all the other floral parts, 1-chambered (November to August). **Fruit:** spherical, thinly fleshy, 3 to 6 mm in diameter, white when mature, crowned with the persistent calyx and style, containing many small black seeds; produced in bunches about 10 cm in diameter (March to December, often with the flowers).
Although this plant is said to be toxic it has a number of uses in African folk-medicine. Slightly warmed leaves are rubbed on wounds and sprains; the Zulus make a decoction of the decorticated root as an emetic to treat biliousness and from the powdered fruit or seeds they prepare a remedy reputed to rid both humans and stock of intestinal worms. The fruit is also used to relieve stomach pains and sore throats – in which it apparently produces a burning sensation. Jaundice is treated with a preparation from the root, and the bark, which has a sharp taste, is an ingredient in a stimulating beverage.

2. EMBELIA N. L. Burm.

Embelia ruminata (E. Meyer ex A. DC.) Mez
S.A. no:　Embelia
Rhod. no: —

A brittle-stemmed climbing shrub, occasionally becoming tree-like and reaching 7 m in height; occurring in scrub forest, evergreen forest, in riverine fringes and on coastal sand flats. **Bark:** greyish.
718　**Leaves:** alternate, crowded at the ends of the branchlets, simple, obovate to oblong, 1 to 5 × 1 to

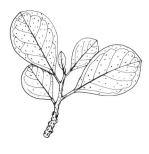

2,5 cm, fleshy, shiny dark green, pellucid gland-dotted although not always conspicuously so; apex broadly tapering to rounded; base tapering; margin entire, rolled under; petiole up to 10 mm long, sometimes slightly winged. **Flowers:** small, inconspicuous, green to brownish, in short wispy spikes about 1,5 to 2 cm long, produced below the leaves and occasionally on older wood. Bisexual, or with the sexes separate, usually on the same tree; floral parts in fours to fives; sepals joined, occasionally almost free; petals free, spreading, sometimes curved back; stamens joined to the petals; ovary ovoid, 1-chambered (July to December). **Fruit:** a spherical capsule, green and fleshy at first, dehiscent when mature, about 7 mm in diameter, sharply tipped with the remains of the old style which is up to 2 to 3 mm long (February to May).

3. MYRSINE L.

Shrubs or small trees, often much-branched. **Leaves:** alternate, simple, with glands and sometimes with glandular hairs. **Flowers:** very small, in axillary clusters. Bisexual; floral parts in fours to fives; calyx glandular; petals joined, longer than the calyx; stamens joined to the petals; ovary 1-chambered. **Fruit:** spherical, thinly fleshy, 1-seeded, indehiscent.

Key to the tree species of *Myrsine:*
Leaves small, usually less than 2 × 1 cm; stamens with pink, red or purplish anthers protruding beyond the petals. Widespread .... **M. africana**
Leaves up to 5 × 2,5 cm; stamens brown, shorter than the petals. Very rare .... **M. pillansii**

Myrsine africana L.
S.A. no: 577,2   Cape myrtle. Mirting
Rhod. no: 829   Myrsine

A small shrub or rarely a tree up to 3 m in height; occurring among rocks, in open woodland, at the margins of evergreen forest, over a wide range of altitudes; often a pioneer species. **Bark:** reddish to brown, scabrous. **Leaves:** small, lanceolate, elliptic to almost circular, 0,5 to 2 × 0,5 to 1 cm, leathery, glossy green, without hairs, gland-dotted but often these are not conspicuous; apex tapering to rounded, often notched; base tapering; margin entire or with very small teeth over the upper half, finely rolled under; petiole up to 1,5 mm long. **Flowers:** small, pinkish; stamens with pink or red to purplish anthers protruding beyond the petals (October to May). **Fruit:** thinly fleshy, up to 4 mm in diameter, pink when mature (January to July).
This is often cultivated as an ornamental shrub; it is easily propagated from seed.

719

MYRSINACEAE

Myrsine pillansii Adamson
S.A. no: 577,1　Large Cape myrtle. Grootmirting
Rhod. no: —

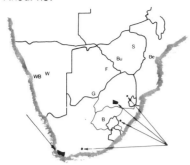 

Usually a much-branched shrub, occasionally a small tree up to 4 m in height; a rare species occurring in low scrub or bush, or along streams at the margins of evergreen forest. **Bark:** grey to greyish-brown. **Leaves:** ovate to elliptic, 2 to 5 × 0,7 to 2 cm, glossy dark green above, paler green below, thickly textured; apex narrowly rounded, occasionally notched; base tapering; margin entire, sometimes with a few very scattered irregular teeth; petiole about 5 mm long and covered with glandular hairs which may extend for a short way up the midrib. **Flowers:** small, greenish, axillary, solitary or in small clusters of 2 to 4, inconspicous; stamens with brown anthers (November). **Fruit:** about the size and shape of peppercorns, 1,5 to 3 mm in diameter, purple when ripe. This is a protected plant in South Africa.

4. RAPANEA Aubl.

Shrubs or trees. **Leaves:** alternate, simple, gland-dotted with glandular scales when young. **Flowers:** in small axillary clusters or on the older branches. Bisexual, or with the sexes separate, usually on the same tree but may be on different trees; floral parts in fours to fives; calyx lobes scarcely joined, often gland-dotted; corolla longer than the calyx, with a short tube; stamens joined to, and shorter than, the corolla; ovary spherical, 1-chambered. **Fruit:** thinly fleshy, 1-seeded, indehiscent.

Key to the tree species of *Rapanea:*
Leaves oblong or oblong-lanceolate, flat, 5 to 13 cm long, the gland-dots usually inconspicuous; fruits spherical, up to 5 mm in diameter .... **R. melanophloeos**
Leaves oblanceolate, the apex and margins curved down, 3 to 4 cm long, gland-dots conspicuous; fruits ellipsoidal, up to 9 cm long .... **R. gilliana**

Rapanea gilliana (Sonder) Mez
S.A. no: 578,1　Dwarf Cape beech. Dwergboekenhout
Rhod. no: —

A densely foliaged shrub or small tree up to 4 m in height; locally frequent in coastal scrub on dunes and on rocky outcrops near the sea. **Bark:** brown; young branchlets covered with short soft hairs which are lost later. **Leaves:** oblanceolate, up to 6 × 1,7 cm, leathery; apex broadly tapering to rounded; base tapering; margin entire, wavy, rolled under, minutely but conspicuously gland-dotted; petiole almost absent. **Flowers:** greenish, 3 to 5 mm long, in groups of 4 to 7 in the axils of the leaves or fallen leaves, or they may be borne on very dwarfed lateral shoots. **Fruit:** ellipsoidal, thinly fleshy, 7 to 9 mm long, crowned with the persistent style.

Rapanea melanophloeos (L.) Mez   Illust. 237
S.A. no: 578   Cape beech. Kaapse boekenhout
Rhod. no: 830   Rapanea

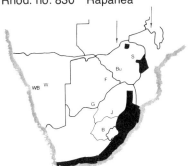

A medium to tall tree usually 4 to 10 m in height, but sometimes reaching 20 m; occurring in evergreen forest, in riverine fringes and sometimes in the drier coastal and mountain forests. **Bark:** light grey, smooth to flaking; the stem is frequently fluted in large specimens and the young branches are square in section. **Leaves:** clustered near the ends of the branches, oblong to oblong-lanceolate, 5 to 13 × 0,8 to 5 cm, thickly leathery, dull dark green above, paler green below, with many inconspicuous gland-dots which may be seen when the leaf is held up to the light, young leaves red and shiny; apex broadly tapering, sometimes notched; base narrowly tapering; margin entire, rolled under; petiole up to 1,5 cm long, red, grooved above. **Flowers:** small, greenish or whitish, inconspicuous, in few-flowered clusters, or fascicles, axillary and also arising below the leaves where the old leaves have fallen (June to August, continuing on to December). **Fruit:** spherical, thinly fleshy, up to 5 mm in diameter, on short stalks, massed along the branchlets just below the leaves, green becoming white and finally purple; the fruits first appear about 3 months after the flowers and therefore flowers and fruits may be found on the tree at the same time (September to March).

The Zulus use a decoction of the bark as an expectorant and an emetic. The wood is fine-grained, very attractive and durable; it works well and takes a fine polish. It has been much prized for cabinet work and, in recent years, has been used in the making of violins. The tree is hardy and attractive in the garden, but is so easily cultivated that, given ideal conditions, it is apt to take over and become difficult to eradicate.

SAPOTACEAE *(The stamvrug family)*

Key to the tree genera:

1 Floral parts in fives to sixes; sepals in one whorl; the corolla lobes without lateral appendages (except in *Inhambanella* in which each corolla lobe has a pair of dorsal appendages) 2

   Floral parts in threes to fours; sepals in 2 whorls; corolla lobes with 2 petalloid lateral appendages 8

2 Corolla lobes with appendages; fruit large, about 4 × 2 cm .... **10. Inhambanella**

   Corolla lobes without appendages; fruit usually less than 4 × 2 cm 3

3 Fruits spherical or nearly so 4

   Fruits ovoid or ellipsoidal 5

4 Fruits up to 1,2 cm in diameter; 1-seeded .... **1. Sideroxylon**

   Fruits 2 to 3 cm in diameter; containing 3 to 5 seeds, which give the fruit a segmented appearance
   .... **5. Chrysophyllum**

721

5 Leaves with pellucid dots when viewed against a bright light; fruits with a pronounced beak, up to 10 mm long .... **3. Aningeria**

Leaves without pellucid dots; fruits without a beak .... **5. Chrysophyllum**

6 Lateral veins in the leaves arching close to the margin, but not looping or running parallel .... **4. Afrosersalisia.**

Lateral veins not arching, but running parallel 7

7 Lateral veins many, running closely parallel, somewhat submerged but clearly visible above, not prominent below; under surface with short dense appressed hairs ..... **6. Bequaertiodendron**

Under surface of the leaves with prominent well-spaced parallel lateral veins and scattered hairs .... **2. Pachystela**

8 Floral parts in threes .... **8. Manilkara**

Floral parts in fours 9

9 Seeds basally attached, laterally flattened with a hard shiny coat .... **7. Mimusops**

Seeds laterally attached, ellipsoidal or only slightly flattened, with a parchment-like or rough coat .... **9. Vitellariopsis**

1. SIDEROXYLON L.

Sideroxylon inerme L.
S.A. no: 579   White milkwood. Witmelkhout
Rhod. no: 832   White milkwood

A dense leafy shrub or small tree up to 10 m in height; the stem and branches often gnarled and twisted; this is almost always a tree of coastal woodland and littoral forest where it forms dense thickets; it also occurs further inland in Rhodesia and the Transvaal, along rivers, in open woodland and frequently on termite mounds. **Bark:** brown, becoming thick and dark to almost black; young branches covered with fine soft grey to rusty hairs. Milky latex present. **Leaves:** alternate, simple, elliptic to obovate-oblong, 4 to 12 × 2 to 5 cm, shiny dark green above, paler green below, often with rusty hairs which rub off with age, leaving untidy-looking patches, until all the hairs have finally fallen; thickly leathery, with net-veining visible but inconspicuous; apex broadly tapering to rounded; base tapering; margin entire, rolled under; petiole up to 1,5 cm in length, with long rusty hairs when young which are lost by maturity. **Flowers:** greenish to white, up to 3 to 4 mm long, solitary or in few- to many-flowered congested clusters, or fascicles, in the leaf axils or sometimes on the older wood. Bisexual; all floral parts in fives; calyx lobes may be very shortly joined at the base; corolla lobes joined at the base into a well-developed tube; stamens equalling the corolla in length, with staminodes which may be petalloid and strap-like; ovary spherical or conical, covered with silky hairs, 5-chambered (January to July). **Fruit:** spherical, fleshy, up to 1,2 cm in diameter, shortly stalked, solitary or in clusters consisting of few to many fruits along the stem, smooth, purplish-black when mature, containing a milky latex; 1-seeded, the seed almost spherical, faintly angled or ribbed (July to January).

722 This species is protected in South Africa where three specimens have been proclaimed National

White milkwoods, Sideroxylon inerme, *characteristically growing near the sea.*

Monuments. One of these is the famous 'Post Office Tree' in Mossel Bay to which, in 1500, passing Portuguese sailors tied a shoe containing a letter describing the drowning at sea of the famous explorer, Bartholomew Diaz. Over a year later the message was discovered by Commander Joao da Nova to whom it had been addressed. If this tale is true, the Post Office Tree must be as least 600 years old and certainly its twisted and gnarled appearance gives the impression of great age. Another renowned specimen of *Sideroxylon inerme* is the 'Treaty Tree' in Woodstock, Cape Town, next to which stood the small house where the commander of local defences formally handed over the Cape to the British after the Battle of Blaauwberg in 1806. The third National Monument is the 'Fingo Milkwood Tree' near Peddie in the eastern Cape. Here, in 1835, the Fingo people affirmed their loyalty to God and the British king after English soldiers had led them to safety when they were relentlessly pursued by Chief Hintza and his warriors. The wood of this species is heavy, hard, strong and durable, even in damp conditions. It has been used as a general purpose timber, and for building boats, bridges and mills. In African medicine a preparation is made from a mixture of oil yielded by the seeds of *Trichilia emetica* and the roasted powdered roots of *Sideroxylon;* this is rubbed into incisions over a fractured limb to aid healing. An infusion of the bark is reputed to dispel nightmares.

Only the typical subspecies, subsp. *inerme,* occurs in South Africa; subsp. *diospyroides* (Baker) J. H. Hemsley reaches its southern limit in the south of Rhodesia, while subsp. *cryptophlebium* (Baker) J. H. Hemsley occurs on Aldabra Island.

2. PACHYSTELA Pierre ex Radlk.

Pachystela brevipes (Baker) Engl.
S.A. no: —
Rhod. no: 833   Pachystela

A medium to large tree 12 to 20 m in height; occurring in riverine forest and low altitude closed canopy forest. **Bark:** brown, grey-brown to dark grey, smooth to rather rough; the bole is characteristically deeply fluted and the young shoots and petioles are covered with short appressed brownish hairs. All parts contain milky latex. **Leaves:** crowded near the ends of the branchlets, simple,

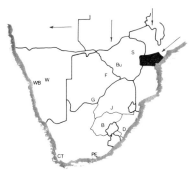

oblanceolate to obovate, 9 to 20 × 3 to 8 cm, green above, with sparse silvery hairs below and conspicuous well-spaced parallel veins; apex broadly tapering to almost rounded; base narrowly tapering, running into the petiole; margin entire, finely rolled under; petiole up to 1,3 cm long, brownish, channelled above. Stipules slender, hairy, persistent. **Flowers:** greenish to creamy-white, up to 4,5 mm long, sweetly scented, in 2- to many-flowered clusters on dwarf warty lateral protuberances, closely clustered along the branchlets. Bisexual; all floral parts in fives; sepals shortly joined at the base, or free; corolla with a short tube, otherwise with free, overlapping lobes; stamens attached to the throat of the tube; ovary ovoid, 5-chambered (January to May). **Fruit:** ovoid, fleshy, up to 2,5 × 1,5 cm, yellow to orange when mature, indehiscent, tipped with the remains of the persistent style, with the rather fleshy persistent calyx lobes round the base; the single seed is smooth, shiny and nut-brown. The fruits are edible having a small amount of mucilaginous sweet tasting flesh (July to October).

3. ANINGERIA Aubrév. & Pellegrin

Aningeria adolfi-friedericii (Engl.) Robyns & Gilbert
S.A. no: —
Rhod. no: 834   Aningeria

A large tree up to 50 m in height; occurring in evergreen rain forest. **Bark:** brownish, rather smooth although shallowly and longitudinally fissured; the bole develops broad buttresses; the young shoots and emerging leaves are densely covered with dark brown hairs which are lost later. All parts contain milky latex. **Leaves:** elliptic to oblong, usually large, 4 to 22 × 2 to 8,5 cm, dark green above, rather paler green below, with conspicuous net-veining and rather tangled brownish hairs which wear away, remaining only along the midrib and perhaps the lateral veins when fully mature, with pellucid dots seen when the leaf is viewed against the light; apex broadly tapering to rounded; base tapering; margin entire, sometimes rolled under; petiole up to 2 cm long, with short soft brown hairs. **Flowers:** creamy-green, up to 6 mm long, in clusters, or fascicles, in the axils of leaves or fallen leaves (July to January). **Fruit:** narrowly ellipsoidal, greenish, up to 4 × 1 cm, indehiscent, with a pronounced beak up to 10 mm long (January to April).

In East Africa the wood is highly esteemed for furniture. This species may occur alongside *Chrysophyllum gorungosanum;* although the leaves of both species closely resemble each other in general appearance, they differ in that the under surface of the leaves of *Aningeria* has tangled

724

spreading hairs, whereas on the under surface of the leaves of *Chrysophyllum* there are appressed hairs which produce a satiny sheen.

In East Africa this species has been divided into five subspecies, but on the evidence of the single sterile collection in Rhodesia it is not possible to say with certainty to which of these it belongs.

4. AFROSERSALISIA A. Chev.

Afrosersalisia kassneri (Engl.) J. H. Hemsley
[*Tulestea kassneri* (Engl.) Aubrév.]
S.A. no: —
Rhod. no: 835   Afrosersalisia

A shrub or small tree up to 4 m in height, with slender branches; apparently a rare tree of low altitude rain forest. **Bark:** brown, very finely fissured. All parts contain milky latex. **Leaves:** alternate, simple, oblanceolate to lanceolate, 5 to 10 × 1,5 to 2,5 cm, without hairs, the lateral veins arching near the margin but not looping or running parallel; apex tapering, finally attenuate; base very narrowly tapering and running into the petiole; margin entire; petiole 1,5 to 2,5 cm long. **Flowers:** white, 2 to 3 mm long, axillary, solitary or fascicled. Bisexual; all floral parts in fives; sepals finely hairy; corolla with a short tube about 1,5 mm long, and lobes about 2 mm long; stamens attached at the base of the corolla lobes, staminodes very small; ovary 5-chambered (October to December). **Fruit:** ovoid, fleshy, about 1 to 1,5 cm long, tapering to a point, indehiscent, red when mature; single-seeded (December).

5. CHRYSOPHYLLUM L.

Shrubs or trees, all parts containing milky latex. **Leaves:** alternate or scattered, simple. Stipules absent. **Flowers:** in axillary clusters or fascicles or in the axils of fallen leaves. Bisexual; all floral parts in fives; sepals free; corolla with a bell-shaped tube as long as the lobes; stamens attached in the throat of the tube, opposite the corolla lobes, staminodes normally absent; ovary 5-chambered. **Fruit:** spherical to ellipsoidal, fleshy, indehiscent; usually 3- to 5-seeded, the seeds rather flattened.

Key to the tree species of *Chrysophyllum:*
Leaves with the lateral veins distinct, not closely parallel, fairly well spaced ....
.... **C. gorungosanum**
Leaves with the lateral veins closely parallel giving a characteristic streaked appearance to the under
surface .... **C. viridifolium**

Chrysophyllum gorungosanum Engl.
[*C. boivinianum* auct.; *C. fulvum* S. Moore]
S.A. no: —
Rhod. no: 836   Brown-berry fluted milkwood

A large tree up to 40 m in height; occurring in evergreen forest. **Bark:** light greyish-brown; bole rather slender, strongly fluted near the base. **Leaves:** alternate, narrowly to broadly elliptic to oblong-elliptic, 7 to 15 × 2 to 6 cm, upper surface deep green without hairs, lower surface with a satiny sheen formed by rusty to golden-brown or silvery-brown very fine soft appressed hairs, especially over the prominent midrib and lateral veins; apex broadly tapering, often abruptly attenuate to a slender point; **725**

base tapering; margin entire, very finely rolled under; petiole up to 2,5 cm long. **Flowers:** small, whitish, in short axillary clusters, the stalks and sepals densely covered with short rusty hairs (December to January). **Fruit:** almost spherical or ellipsoidal, up to 4 × 2,5 cm, covered with short dense chocolate-brown hairs; usually 3- to 5-seeded (July to October).

Possible confusion with *Aningeria* is discussed under that genus.

Chrysophyllum viridifolium J. M. Wood & Franks
S.A. no: 580   Fluted milkwood. Bosstamvrug
Rhod. no: 837   Fluted milkwood

A medium to large tree 10 to 40 m in height; occurring in evergreen forest and a common canopy and emergent tree in coastal forests. **Bark:** grey to grey-brown, mottled with light grey, smoothish; the bole long and clear, strongly fluted near the base in large specimens, the branches rather slender and supporting a massive crown; the young twigs and new leaves densely covered with short rusty red hairs. **Leaves:** scattered, oblong or ovate-oblong, 3,8 to 11 × 2 to 5 cm, glossy dark green above, paler green below; lateral veins form very distinctive parallel multi-striations which join just before the margin forming a distinct submarginal vein; apex broadly tapering; base rounded; margin entire but very wavy; petiole up to 10 mm long, with fine rusty hairs, especially when young, which persist on the midrib on the under surface even when the mature leaves are otherwise lacking hairs. **Flowers:** yellowish, about 2 mm long, with the stalks and calyx lobes covered with dense rusty hairs, produced in axillary clusters of up to 20, and also arising on warty lateral protuberances on older branchlets (January to February). **Fruit:** almost spherical, about 2 to 3 cm in diameter, yellow when mature, containing about 4 large shiny brownish-black seeds which shape the fruit into partial segments; edible, with a pleasant taste. The flowers and fruits are often on the tree together (February to March).

6. BEQUAERTIODENDRON De Wild.

Shrubs or trees. All parts contain a milky latex. **Leaves:** alternate or spirally arranged, simple, the veins closely parallel. Stipules may be present. **Flowers:** axillary, solitary or in congested clusters or fascicles, or in the axils of fallen leaves. Bisexual; all floral parts in fives; sepals free; corolla tube as long as the lobes; stamens attached to the corolla tube; staminodes may be present; ovary 5-chambered. **Fruit:** ellipsoidal, fleshy, indehiscent, with a persistent style.

Key to the tree species of *Bequaertiodendron:*

Leaf apex broadly to narrowly tapering, may be rather attenuate; flowers solitary or 2 to 3 only in each cluster; stipules absent .... **B. natalense**

Leaf apex usually rounded, sometimes notched, frequently with a hair-like tip, very rarely shortly tapering; flowers fascicled, several to many in each cluster; stipules slender, inclined to persist . ... **B. magalismontanum**

Bequaertiodendron magalismontanum (Sonder) Heine & J. H. Hemsley   Illust. 238 and 239

[*Chrysophyllum magalismontanum* Sonder; *C. argyrophyllum* Hiern; *Pouteria magalismontanum* (Sonder) A. Meeuse]

S.A. no: 581   Stamvrug. Stamvrug

Rhod. no: 838   Stem-fruit

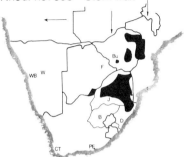

A small to medium sized tree 3 to 10 m in height; in South Africa these trees are characteristic of rocky outcrops and hills, where they are low-growing, dense and often with distinctive grey-green, small leaves; in Rhodesia they can be locally common in evergreen forest and wooded ravines, and along river banks, especially among rocks in sandy soil. **Bark:** grey, smooth, slightly scaly. **Leaves:** alternate, often crowded near the ends of the branchlets; oblanceolate to obovate-elliptic, usually 7 to 14 × 2 to 3 cm, glossy dark green above, or with a conspicuous grey bloom which is easily rubbed off, with beautiful silvery to golden-brown silky appressed hairs below, young leaves and twigs densely covered with russet-brown hairs; midrib very prominent below, all other veins somewhat submerged, running closely parallel but clearly visible; apex rounded, sometimes notched and frequently with a hair-like tip, very rarely shortly tapering; base narrowly tapering, running into the petiole; margin entire, tightly rolled under; petiole rather stout, about 10 mm long. Stipules slender, inclined to persist. **Flowers:** brownish-pink, about 10 mm long, strongly scented, in few- to many-flowered clusters, in the axils of fallen leaves (June to December). **Fruit:** ovoid, fleshy, 1,5 to 2,5 × 1 to 1,8 cm, red when mature, sharply tipped with the remains of the persistent style; densely crowded along the old wood (December to February).

The fruits are edible and have a high vitamin C content; they have a sweet but rather astringent flavour and may be used to make wine, brandy, syrup and a good tart jelly. An infusion of the finely stamped fruit and roots is regarded as a treatment for epilepsy. To relieve headaches the powdered roots are rubbed into incisions made on the forehead and the head of the patient is then held over a pot of smouldering root ashes. In gardens its evergreen foliage and brightly coloured fruits are decorative; the seed germinates easily when fresh and trees may also be propagated from cuttings. It is quite fast-growing and hardy.

Bequaertiodendron natalense (Sonder) Heine & J. H. Hemsley

[*Chrysophyllum natalense* Sonder; *Pouteria natalensis* (Sonder) A. Meeuse]

S.A. no: 582   Natal milkplum. Natalmelkpruim

Rhod. no: 839   Forest stem-fruit

A small to medium sized tree 6 to 15 m in height, rarely taller; occurring in mixed evergreen forest, ravine forest and in coastal forest, where it often grows gregariously at margins and in clearings. **Bark:** brown, flaking or scaling, with the bole sometimes showing a tendency to fluting. The stem is straight, with horizontal branches; the young twigs, leaf petioles and floral parts are densely covered with dark brown hairs. **Leaves:** alternate or spirally arranged but tending to be crowded at the ends of the branches; obovate-lanceolate, 6 to 15 × 2 to 5 cm, glossy green above, without hairs, the under

727

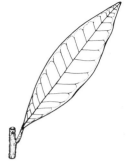

surface with greyish silvery appressed hairs giving a silky appearance which may wear away in old leaves; midrib prominent below, immersed above, with the lateral veins closely parallel, immersed but clearly visible; apex broadly tapering, sometimes attenuate; base tapering; margin entire, slightly rolled under and wavy; petiole often brown or blackish, rough, up to 1,4 cm long. Stipules absent. **Flowers:** white to cream, about 5 mm long, without stalks, tightly clustered in groups of 1 to 3 in the axils of the leaves (December to March). **Fruit:** ovoid, fleshy, about 2 × 1,5 cm, red when mature, tipped with the remains of the persistent style and with the fleshy remains of the persistent calyx lobes round the base; densely crowded along the old wood (September to December).

The fruits are edible. The wood is tough and durable and is suitable for fencing poles and implement handles and also for hut building. The Zulus use it to make milking buckets.

7. MIMUSOPS L.

Shrubs or trees; all parts contain milky latex. **Leaves:** alternate or scattered, simple, not conspicuously crowded near the tips of the branches. Stipules absent. **Flowers:** axillary, solitary or fascicled in clusters of 2 to 4. Bisexual; all floral parts in fours; calyx 8-lobed, in 2 dissimilar whorls, persistent as rather fleshy lobes at the base of the fruit; corolla lobes 8, each with 2 petalloid lateral appendages; stamens joined to the corolla lobes and alternating with staminodes; ovary usually 8-chambered. **Fruit:** fleshy to rather leathery, indehiscent, tipped with the remains of the old style; seeds laterally flattened, with a hard shiny coat, attached basally.

Key to the tree species of *Mimusops:*

1 Leaves with silky white, occasionally yellowish, hairs which persist to maturity; margin strongly
    rolled under .... **M. caffra**
  Leaves frequently with brownish hairs, but these are lost by maturity; margin may be slightly, but
    not strongly, rolled under 2
2 Petiole usually less than 1 cm long .... **M. obovata**
  Petiole usually 1 to 2,5 cm long 3
3 Fruits almost spherical, about 1 to 2 cm in diameter. In dry evergreen bush and low altitude riverine
    fringes. In the extreme south-east of Rhodesia and fairly widespread in Moçambique, but not
    recorded from South Africa .... **M. obtusifolia**
  Fruits ovoid, 2 to 3 × 1 to 2,5 cm. In moist evergreen forest and mixed woodland. Widespread in
    Rhodesia, except for the extreme south-east, and the Transvaal; just entering Zululand and
    Moçambique .... **M. zeyheri**

Mimusops caffra E. Meyer ex. A.DC.   Illust. 240
S.A. no: 583   Coast red-milkwood. Kusrooimelkhout
Rhod. no: —

A shrub or small to medium sized tree up to 15 m in height; this is a coastal species, being a major constituent of the dune vegetation, frequently growing right down to the high tide mark, fully exposed to the sea winds and salt spray; such exposed specimens are usually small shrubs, the larger trees growing in more sheltered areas. **Bark:** dark grey, thin, wrinkled longitudinally; the boles are seldom straight, more often gnarled and twisted; the young stems, petioles and flower heads are all densely covered with long rusty hairs. **Leaves:** obovate to obovate-oblong, 3 to 7 × 1,5 to 4 cm, stiffly leathery, without hairs and blue-green above, paler green with white, silvery or yellowish silky hairs

below; apex rounded, frequently notched; base tapering; margin entire and strongly rolled under; petiole up to 1,5 cm long. **Flowers:** sepals with rusty hairs, petals white to cream, star-like, about 10 mm in diameter, on slender stalks in axillary groups of 2 to 4, drying to a conspicuous red-brown (September to March). **Fruit:** ovoid, fleshy, about 2 × 1,3 cm, bright orange-red when mature; edible and pleasantly sweet (April to September).

The wood is reddish, close-grained, heavy, hard, strong and elastic; it is durable when exposed to water and is therefore suitable for boat-building; it is considered a 'royal timber' in Zululand. The seeds are dispersed by water and are often washed up in quantities on the beaches. It is valuable in consolidating sand and dunes.

Mimusops obovata Sonder
S.A. no: 584   Red-milkwood. Rooimelkhout

Rhod. no: —

A medium to large tree usually up to 15 m, sometimes reaching 20 m in height; occurring at low altitudes in dense evergreen coastal forest, riverine fringes and open woodland. **Bark:** pale greyish, rough. **Leaves:** scattered along the branches, variable in size and shape, usually obovate to oblong or elliptic, 2 to 7 × 1 to 4 cm, shiny dark green above, dull green below; fine net-veining is visible; apex very broadly tapering to rounded; base tapering; margin entire, may be slightly rolled under; petiole up to 10 mm long. Trees which grow in open rocky places tend to have thicker and narrower leaves. **Flowers:** calyx with rusty hairs, corolla lobes white to cream, star-like, about 10 mm in diameter, sweetly scented, on slender stalks up to 3 cm long and covered with fine rusty hairs, in small axillary groups of 1 to 3 (August to November). **Fruit:** ovoid, fleshy, 2 to 3 × 1 to 2,5 cm, bright orange-red when mature; frequently 1-seeded (November to March).

The edible fruits are pleasant tasting and are used to make jellies and wine. The wood is close-grained, pink or reddish, hard and heavy; when seasoned it is durable and said to be termite-proof; it was formerly used in wagon construction.

Mimusops obtusifolia Lam.
[*M. kirkii* Baker; *M. fruticosa* A.DC.]
S.A. no: —
Rhod. no: 840   Round-fruited red-milkwood

A shrub or small to medium sized, much-branched, densely leafy tree up to 10 m in height; occurring   **729**

from coastal evergreen thicket to low altitude forest, along river banks, sometimes dominant in the riverine fringe, also in mixed woodland and occasionally on termite mounds. **Bark:** grey to blackish, becoming very rough and deeply fissured. **Leaves:** elliptic to obovate, 3,5 to 8 × 1,5 to 5,5 cm, leathery to fleshy, without hairs, glossy dark green above, dull green below, with fine net-veining visible; apex rounded, frequently notched; base tapering to broadly tapering; margin entire, not rolled under; petiole up to 2,5 cm long and covered with short brownish hairs. **Flowers:** cream, about 10 mm in diameter, star-like, calyx covered with brownish short hairs, in axillary clusters of 2 to 6 (March to September). **Fruit:** almost spherical, about 1 to 2 cm in diameter, yellow to orange when mature, 1- to 5-seeded (May to January).

This is a very variable species which is closely related to *M. zeyheri*.

Mimusops zeyheri Sonder   Illust. 241
[*M. monroi* S. Moore]
S.A. no: 585   Transvaal red-milkwood. Moepel
Rhod. no: 841   Common red milkwood

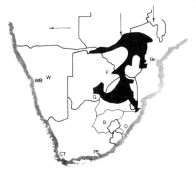 

Occasionally a large shrub, but usually a small to medium sized tree up to 15 m in height, sometimes taller, with a round well-shaped crown; occurring at low altitudes in hot areas with an adequate rainfall, frequent on well-wooded rocky hillsides, in riverine fringes, at the margins of evergreen forest and in dry open woodland. **Bark:** grey, dark brown to blackish, rather smooth in young specimens, becoming rough. **Leaves:** scattered, ovate, lanceolate to oblong, 4 to 11 × 2 to 5 cm, thickly leathery, shiny dark green above, paler green below, the young leaves and twigs covered with dense appressed rusty hairs which are lost by maturity; apex broadly tapering to rounded, often notched; base tapering; margin entire, slightly thickened; petiole up to 3 cm long. **Flowers:** sepals with greyish hairs, petals creamy-white, star-shaped, about 10 mm in diameter, on slender stalks up to 3 cm long, clustered in axillary groups of 3 or more, often in profusion (October to March). **Fruit:** ovoid, fleshy, 2 to 3 × 1 to 2,5 cm, yellow when mature; 1- to 4-seeded (April to October).

The fruits are pleasant tasting and have a fairly high vitamin C content which provides an important supplement to the diet of the local people. The wood is light brown; it is not very strong or durable, but it works easily and could be a useful general purpose timber. This tree could be an attractive garden subject if situated in a well-drained area which has summer rainfall and a mild winter climate; however, it is generally considered to be slow-growing.

8. MANILKARA Adans.

Shrubs or more usually trees; all parts contain milky latex, a feature which is often not readily evident in large specimens. **Leaves:** alternate, usually crowded at the ends of the branches, simple. **Flowers:** usually many, fascicled and crowded in the leaf axils or in the axils of fallen leaves. Bisexual; all floral parts in sixes; calyx in 2 dissimilar whorls of 3; corolla forming a short tube, each corolla lobe divided into 3 segments; stamens joined to the corolla lobes and alternating with staminodes; ovary with 6 to 16 compartments. **Fruit:** fleshy or rather dry, indehiscent, tipped with the short remains of the style.

Key to the tree species of *Manilkara:*
1 Leaves in terminal rosettes, usually on short thick much-scarred lateral branchlets . **M. mochisia**
  Leaves may be crowded near the ends of branchlets, but not in rosettes and not strictly terminal   2
2 Mature leaves without hairs .... **M. concolor**
  Mature leaves with the under surface silver-grey with dense closely appressed hairs **M. discolor**

Manilkara concolor (Harvey ex C. H. Wr.) Gerstner
S.A. no: 586   Zulu milkberry. Zoeloemelkbessie
Rhod. no: 842/1

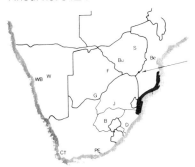

A shrub or small much-branched tree 3 to 7 m in height; occurring in low altitude forest. **Bark:** grey, brown or black, rather corky and deeply longitudinally fissured; branches grey and fissured. **Leaves:** tend to be produced at the ends of the branches but not in crowded rosettes, as in *M. mochisia;* obovate-oblong to narrowly spathulate-oblong, up to 8,5 × 1 to 3,5 cm, but usually smaller; thickly leathery, without hairs, dark green; apex rounded and notched; base tapering; margin entire, rolled under; petiole rather stout, up to 8 mm long. **Flowers:** small, greenish-white, on slender stalks up to 2,5 cm long, in several- to many-flowered clusters, in the axils of leaves and fallen leaves, often produced in profusion near the ends of the branchlets (August to October). **Fruit:** ovoid, fleshy, 1 to 1,5 × 0,8 to 1,5 cm, pale yellow to orange or red when mature; edible; 1- to 2-seeded (October to November).

Manilkara discolor (Sonder) J. H. Hemsley
[*Labourdonnaisia discolor* Sonder; *Muriea discolor* (Sonder) Hartog]
S.A. no: 592   Forest milkberry. Bosmelkbessie
Rhod. no: 842   Forest milkberry

SAPOTACEAE

A medium to large tree 5 to 17 m in height, sometimes reaching 40 m; occurring over a wide range of altitudes, from sea level to about 2 000 m in evergreen forest. **Bark:** brown to dark grey, longitudinally fissured with rough patches and the lower bole shallowly fluted in very large specimens. The younger parts are covered with fine cinnamon hairs. **Leaves:** crowded at the ends of the branches, obovate-oblong, 3,5 to 10 × 1,5 to 4 cm, upper surface deep green, under surface with silvery silky hairs; apex very broadly tapering to rounded; base tapering; margin entire, rolled under; petiole up to 1,5 cm long. **Flowers:** calyx with rusty hairs, corolla creamy-yellow, about 7 mm in diameter, on short stalks up to 10 mm long, solitary or in small axillary groups of about 3 (June to September). **Fruit:** almost spherical, fleshy, up to 1,2 cm in diameter, yellow to red when mature, shortly tipped with the remains of the persistent style; 1-seeded (December to March).

The fruits are said to be delicious. The wood is hard and valuable and is used by the Chopi to make xylophone keys.

Manilkara mochisia (Baker) Dubard
[*M. macaulayae* Hutch. & Corbishley; *M. umbraculigera* Hutch. & Corbishley; *Mimusops mochisia* Baker]
S.A. no: 588   Lowveld milkberry. Laeveldmelkbessie
Rhod. no: 843 Lowveld milkberry

A shrub or spreading tree up to 15 m in height with the branches arching downwards; locally common at low and medium altitudes in hot dry woodland. **Bark:** dark blackish, rough; branchlets short, thick, heavily marked with leaf scars. **Leaves:** in very characteristic tight rosettes at the tips of the branches and on dwarf knobby lateral shoots; narrowly elliptic-ovate to narrowly spathulate, 1,5 to 6 × 0,7 to 2,7 cm; the young leaves are covered with pale cinnamon hairs which are soon lost; the mature leaves are green; apex rounded, notched; base tapering; margin entire, rolled under; petiole up to 4 mm long.

The rosettes of leaves of Manilkara mochisia.

Flowers: greenish-yellow, up to 10 mm long, with a strange but not unpleasant scent, on slender stalks about 1,2 cm long, in dense axillary clusters among and just below the leaves, often appearing before or with the first flush of leaves (October to December). **Fruit:** ovoid, fleshy, about 1 to 1,2 cm long, yellow when mature, with red flesh which is edible and milky; 1- to 3-seeded (January to March).

The flowers are extremely attractive to insects. The wood provides termite-proof fencing poles.

9. VITELLARIOPSIS (Baillon) Dubard

Shrubs or small trees; all parts contain milky latex. **Leaves:** alternate, crowded at the ends of the branchlets, simple. Stipules sometimes persistent and bristle-like. **Flowers:** fascicled in axillary groups of 2 to 3. Bisexual; all floral parts in eights; sepals shortly joined at the base, in 2 dissimilar whorls of 4; corolla with a short tube, each of the 8 corolla lobes usually divided into 3 segments, stamens 8, alternating with 8 broad staminodes; ovary 8-chambered. **Fruit:** thinly fleshy, rather leathery; with 1 large seed, ellipsoidal or only slightly flattened, with a parchment-like or rough coat, laterally attached.

Key to the tree species of *Vitellariopsis:*
1 Leaves usually more than 7 cm long, petiole usually more than 10 mm long .. **V. marginata**
  Leaves usually less than 7 cm long, petiole usually less than 10 mm 2
2 Fruit ovoid, shortly tipped with the remains of the style, yellow when ripe. Occurring only in the midlands of Natal .... **V. dispar**
  Fruit resembles a miniature gourd as the apex is drawn out into a curved beak. Occurring only in Rhodesia.. **V. ferruginea**

Vitellariopsis dispar (N. E. Brown) Aubrév.
[*Austromimusops dispar* (N. E. Brown) A. Meeuse]
S.A. no: 589   Tugela milkwood. Tugelabastermelkhout
Rhod. no: —

A large shrub or medium sized tree up to 10 m in height; occurring in woodland and bush, confined to a small area. **Bark:** grey, rough; branchlets marked with leaf scars. **Leaves:** oblanceolate, 2 to 6 × 0,7 to 2 cm, dark green to yellowish-green, paler below than above, midrib distinct above, prominent below; apex broadly tapering; base tapering and running into the petiole; margin entire, curved back; petiole slender, 3 to 8 mm long. **Flowers:** yellowish, up to 6 mm long, on slender stalks up to 2 cm long, densely crowded in axillary clusters (September to December). **Fruit:** ovoid, 2 to 3 × 1,5 to 2,5 cm, with fine soft hairs, yellow when mature, shortly tipped with the persistent remains of the style (January to March).

Vitellariopsis ferruginea Kupicha
S.A. no: —
Rhod. no: 844   Gourd Milkwood

A shrub or small tree up to 8 m in height; occurring on rocky hills and in wooded ravines. **Bark:** grey, smooth. **Leaves:** clustered near the ends of the branches, obovate-oblong to elliptic, 4,5 to 7 × 2 to 3 cm, leathery, young branchlets, leaves and petioles covered with long dark reddish-brown

733

hairs, upper surface of mature leaves without hairs, lower surface losing most of the hairs by maturity; apex rounded, notched; base tapering; margin entire, rolled under; petiole 2 to 5 mm long. **Flowers:** corolla white or tinged with pink, calyx backed with reddish-brown hairs; about 1,5 cm in diameter, on slender stalks up to 2 cm long covered with dark reddish-brown hairs, pleasantly scented; in axillary groups of 2 to 4 (November to January). **Fruit:** strangely shaped, mainly ovoid, but with the apex drawn out into a curved beak, thus they rather resemble miniature gourds, the whole fruit about 3,5 × 1,7 cm, edible, covered with reddish-brown woolly hairs (December to March).

Apparently there was a solitary record made near Beira in Moçambique of the closely related species *V. sylvestris* (S. Moore) Aubrév.

Vitellariopsis marginata (N. E. Brown) Aubrév.

[*Austromimusops marginata* (N. E. Brown) A. Meeuse]

S.A. no: 590   Bush milkwood. Bosbastermelkhout
Rhod. no: —

A medium to tall tree usually 8 to 10 m in height, but sometimes reaching 20 m; occurring in low altitude and coastal forest, ravine forest, along streams, in thickets, woodland and coastal scrub. **Bark:** light brown to grey, vertically fissured and flaking in small strips. **Leaves:** crowded at the ends of the branches, obovate-elliptic-oblong, 6 to 13 × 2 to 5 cm, rather glossy green above, dull and paler green below; midrib prominent below and pale yellow; apex broadly tapering to rounded; base tapering; margin entire, rolled under; petiole 1 to 2 cm long, reddish. **Flowers:** calyx with short soft brownish-green hairs, petals creamy-white, about 10 mm long, on slender stalks 2 to 5 cm long, clustered in axillary groups of 4 near the ends of the branches (August to January). **Fruit:** ovoid, fleshy, up to 5 × 3,5 cm, purplish-red when mature, with the apex tapering in the mature fruit, much attenuate when young (January to March).

The fruit is evidently not eaten. The wood is reddish and is regarded as a 'royal timber' in Zululand.

10. INHAMBANELLA (Engl.) Dubard

Inhambanella henriquesii (Engl. & Warb.) Dubard

[*Lecomtedoxa henriquesii* (Engl. & Warb.) Dubard]

S.A. no: 591   Inhambanella. Melkpeer
Rhod. no: 845   Inhambanella

A medium to large tree 10 to 40 m in height; characteristic of coastal and low altitude evergreen forest. **Bark:** grey, mottled, finely scaly to rather rough. All parts contain milky latex. **Leaves:** spirally

arranged or crowded at the ends of the branches, oblanceolate to broadly elliptic, 5 to 17 × 2,7 to 8 cm, leathery, distinctive dark green above, paler green below, in some years developing fine and striking coppery-black spring colours; apex rounded and slightly notched; base tapering; margin entire, wavy; petiole up to 5 cm long. Stipules fall early. **Flowers:** corolla yellow or creamy-white, honey-scented, about 1,5 cm in diameter, on stalks up to 2 cm long, in few- to many-flowered axillary clusters, or fascicles; although produced in profusion they are not conspicuous. Bisexual; floral parts in fives to sixes; sepals free; corolla lobes longer than the calyx, each with a pair of dorsal appendages; stamens attached to the petals, alternating with petalloid staminodes; ovary 5-chambered (August). **Fruit:** spherical, 2 to 3 cm in diameter, yellow to red when mature, with milky flesh (October to November).

EBENACEAE *(The ebony family)*

Key to the genera:
Leaves alternate, but may be opposite, sub-opposite or whorled; calyx not enlarging, not conspicuous in the fruit; fruit usually 1-seeded .... **1. Euclea**

Leaves nearly always alternate; calyx enlarging and becoming conspicuous at the base of the fruit; fruit usually with 2 or more seeds .... **2. Diospyros**

1. EUCLEA Murray

Sub-shrubs, shrubs or trees, sometimes suffrutices. **Leaves:** alternate, opposite, sub-opposite or whorled, simple. Stipules absent. **Flowers:** solitary or in racemes, pseudo-racemes, pseudo-cymes or panicles. Sexes separate on different trees; floral parts in fours to fives; calyx not enlarging in the fruit but persistent; corolla with an urn-shaped or almost spherical tube, separating into very fine lobes only round the rim; stamens 10 to 30, free or joined in pairs or groups, absent or reduced to staminodes in female flowers; ovary 2- to 6-chambered on a fringed, somewhat fleshy disc. **Fruit:** a spherical, usually 1-seeded berry; seeds divided into 3 parts by a curved line linked by a shallow groove, rather resembling the markings on a tennis ball.

Key to the tree species of *Euclea:*
1 Leaves and all young parts without hairs... 2
  Some or all of the leaves, young shoots and flowering branches are hairy at somes stage 10
2 Leaves conspicuously narrow,1 to 8 × 0,2 to 0,4 cm .... **E. linearis**
  Leaves may be rather narrow but are usually more than 4 mm wide 3
3 Leaves usually widest above the middle, somewhat broadly tapering or rounded at the apex, narrowly tapering to the base 4
  Leaves usually widest at the middle, or sometimes below the middle, tapering almost equally to apex and base 6
4 Leaves and branchlets covered with rusty peltate hairs .... **E. undulata**
  Young parts without rusty peltate hairs 5
5 In the extreme south of South West Africa, the western, north-western and southern Cape only; leaves small, usually about 2,5 × 1,3 cm, margins not wavy .... **E. racemosa**
  From east tropical Africa south to Humansdorp but no further west; leaves usually about 6 × 2,5 cm, margins often wavy and curled down almost from the midrib ...... **E. schimperi**   **735**

6 Leaf margins markedly wavy 7
  Leaf margins not wavy 9
7 Leaves usually 2 to 4 × 0,5 to 1,5 cm, the leaves and young parts covered with glands producing a rust-coloured exudate .... **E. undulata**
  Leaves larger than 4 × 1,5 cm, up to 10 × 4 cm, leaves and young parts without a rust-coloured exudate, but may have rusty granules on the flower stalks 8
8 Flower stalks with rusty granules .... **E. divinorum**
  Flower stalks without rusty granules .... **E. crispa**
9 Fruits in raceme-like sprays more than 1,2 cm long; ovary densely covered with short bristles . ... **E. crispa**
  Fruits in very short sprays, less than 1,2 cm long; ovary without hairs, but may have scale-like glands .... **E. undulata**
10 Branchlets long, very slender and hanging down; leaves very narrow; fruits usually solitary . ... **E. pseudebenus**
  Branchlets not conspicuously slender and drooping; leaves not normally very narrow; fruits may be solitary but are usually in small groups or sprays up to 3,5 cm long 11
11 Fruits somewhat beaked to ovoid-conical (if spherical then more than 10 mm in diameter); densely covered with long hairs when young 12
  Fruits spherical (less than 10 mm in diameter); almost without hairs 13
12 Fruits less than 10 mm in diameter; leaf margin not wavy and covered with hoary white hairs . ... **E. tomentosa**
  Fruits up to 1,5 cm in diameter; leaf margin very wavy, without hairs .... **E. coriacea**
13. Leaves blue-green, thickly leathery, densely hairy when young, almost without hairs when mature .... **E. crispa**
  Leaves not blue-green, or if so then distinctly hairy, at least on the under surface 14
14 Fruits in a spike-like spray 1,2 to 2 cm long .... **E. crispa**
  Fruits in a branched spray up to 3,5 cm long .... **E. natalensis**

Euclea coriacea A. DC.

S.A. no: 593   Mountain guarri. Bergghwarrie
Rhod. no: —

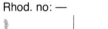

A shrub under 3 m in height or a tree up to 10 m depending upon conditions; occurring on rocky mountain slopes or along stream banks. **Bark:** greenish-brown, wrinkled; branchlets dark brown with coarse hairs. **Leaves:** alternate, occasionally sub-opposite, ovate to oblong, 2 to 5 × 1 to 3 cm, stiff and leathery, green above and without hairs, but with both dense rusty fine hairs and coarse spreading hairs on the under surface; apex tapering with a hair-like tip; base rounded to slightly lobed; margin entire or minutely scalloped, heavily wavy, distinctly thickened; petiole 2 to 5 mm long. **Flowers:** creamy-white, about 7 mm long, in small axillary sprays about 1,5 to 2 cm long, with up to 7 flowers (September to October). **Fruit:** almost spherical, about 1,5 cm in diameter, yellow to red when mature, in short sprays about 2 cm long with 2 to 7 fruits; 1- to 3-seeded (November to December).
The roots provide a violent purgative. The Southern Sotho doctors wash their divining bones in a decoction made from the fruits as this is believed to give them greater accuracy.

Euclea crispa (Thunb.) Sonder ex Gürke

S.A. no: 594 and 594,1   Blue guarri. Bloughwarrie
736 Rhod. no: 846   Blue-leaved euclea

A shrub 1 to 2 m in height or a small tree up to 8 m; occurring in open woodland, among rocks and at forest margins; often forming almost pure stands over a small area. **Bark:** grey, smooth to slightly rough in large specimens; branchlets and young parts often have a rusty appearance, produced by brown granules, but this soon disappears. **Leaves:** sub-opposite, rarely alternate, lanceolate, oblanceolate to elliptic, 1,5 to 5 × 0,5 to 1,5 cm, occasionally up to 10 × 4 cm, dark green to light green or bluish-green above, with or without short hairs which are lost by maturity, paler green below; apex broadly tapering to rounded, notched; base tapering; margin entire or sometimes minutely scalloped, flat, or in larger leaves wavy, tending to roll under; petiole slender, 1,5 to 2 mm long. **Flowers:** very small, inconspicuous, greenish to yellow, in 3- to 10-flowered axillary sprays, or pseudo-racemes, up to 2 cm long; ovary densely covered with short bristle-like hairs (October to February). **Fruit:** spherical, about 4 to 5 mm in diameter, reddish-brown becoming finally black when mature, in sprays about 2 cm long, usually with few hairs but sometimes very hairy (April to December).
This species is divided into two varieties:

var. *crispa* – leaves variable in shape, generally rather smaller and narrower; very widespread.

var. *ovata* (Burch.) De Winter – leaves much more ovate, densely hairy especially when young, the margin conspicuously wavy and frequently minutely scalloped; a restricted distribution in the southern Orange Free State and neighbouring districts extends down to Cradock and Middelburg in the Cape and northwards to the northern Cape, Kimberley and Kuruman.

The var. *ovata* overlaps *E. coriacea* and resembles it so closely vegetatively that sterile material is frequently difficult to distinguish. However, differences in the floral structure of the two appear to be definitive, the corolla tube of *E. coriacea* being slightly lobed at the mouth only, while that of *E. crispa* var. *ovata* is divided into lobes for at least half its length.

Euclea divinorum Hiern   Illust. 242
S.A. no: 595   Magic guarri. Towerghwarrie
Rhod. no: 847   Diamond-leaved euclea

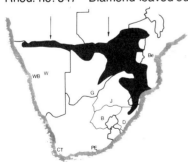

A shrub or small tree up to 8 m in height; occuring in thorn scrub, on hillsides, along river banks and in woodland; in Rhodesia it is a feature of the vegetation on termite mounds. **Bark:** grey, smooth, dark and flaking into square segments with age. **Leaves:** sub-opposite, opposite, rarely alternate, elliptic, 3,5 to 8 × 1 to 2,5 cm, leathery, dark green, grey-green to bluish-green above, without hairs, frequently finely wrinkled, much paler green below; apex rounded; base tapering; **737**

margin entire and characteristically very wavy; petiole up to 5 mm long. **Flowers:** very small, white to creamy-yellow, in short dense branched axillary heads, frequently almost spherical, up to 1,5 cm in diameter, with 2 to 3 heads per leaf axil; the flower stalks are dotted with rusty-brown granules, and from the base of the stalks arise two deciduous bracts, oblong and curved (July to January). **Fruit:** spherical, rather fleshy, about 5 to 7 mm in diameter, purplish-black when mature (October to December but may be as late as May). The fruits, which are edible though not very pleasant to taste, are taken as an aperient and can have strong purgative action. They have also been used to make a purple ink and in the brewing of beer, while the bark produces a brown dye. The Ovambos hang small branches of the tree at the doors of their huts as good luck charms and because of its reputed supernatural powers the wood is never used as fuel. The frayed ends of twigs provide effective toothbrushes and the wood, which is dark brown, hard and close-grained, is used to make small pieces of furniture and implements. The plants are fairly fast-growing and hardy.

Euclea linearis Zeyher ex Hiern
S.A. no: 596   Lance-leaf guarri. Smalblaarghwarrie
Rhod. no: 848   Lance-leaved euclea

Usually a shrub up to 1 m in height, occasionally a small tree reaching 4 m; occurring on rocky hillsides, grassy ridges and dry wooded slopes; often gregarious, it can cover areas about 27 × 8 m; in Rhodesia it is usually associated with serpentine derived, or heavily mineralised, soils. **Bark:** grey, smooth; the young branches reddish-brown. **Leaves:** closely resembling the narrow leaved form of *E. crispa;* linear, frequently slightly sickle-shaped, 1 to 8 × 0,2 to 0,4 cm, without hairs, hard and leathery, grey-green or yellowish-green, uniformly coloured above and below; apex abruptly tapering to rounded; base tapering and running into the petiole; margin entire; petiole barely 1 mm long. **Flowers:** very small, creamy-white, in 3- to 7-flowered compact sprays up to 1,5 cm long, the stalks dotted with a reddish-brown exudate (August to December). **Fruit:** spherical, thinly fleshy, up to 8 mm in diameter, becoming red and finally black when mature, the purplish flesh being sweet-tasting (February to June).

Euclea natalensis A. DC.   Illust. 243
[*E. multiflora* Hiern]
S.A. no: 597   Large-leaved guarri. Natalghwarrie
Rhod. no: 849   Large-leaved euclea

A shrub to medium sized tree up to 12 m in height, often with a spreading crown and a somewhat drooping habit; occurring from coastal dune bush to about 1 000 m, in a variety of habitats from dry arid areas to open woodland and riverine fringes, also common among rocks and on koppies. **Bark:** grey to dark grey, smooth to rough. **Leaves:** alternate, elliptic to obovate-oblong, 3 to 10 × 0,8 to 4 cm, glossy dark green above, the under surface paler green and covered with dense pale rusty woolly hairs; apex broadly tapering to rounded; base tapering; margin entire, wavy; petiole up to 10 mm long. **Flowers:** small, greenish-white to cream, sweetly or rather unpleasantly scented, in dense branched axillary heads up to 3,5 cm long, often produced in profusion; all parts except the petals covered with dense rusty woolly hairs (May to January). **Fruit:** spherical, 7 to 10 mm in diameter, almost without hairs, red becoming black when mature; in branched sprays up to 3,5 cm long (October to June).

The roots have a number of uses: when pounded and boiled they produce a black dye; the Zulus prepare a purgative from them; the Shangaans apply them, charred and ground, to the skin in cases of leprosy and in a powdered form they are taken to relieve headache and toothache. The wood is white marked with brown and is heavy, hard and strong.

Euclea pseudebenus E. Meyer ex A. DC.
S.A. no: 598   Ebony tree. Ebbeboom
Rhod. no: —

A shrub to medium sized slender tree 3 to 10 m in height with drooping branches; occurring in the arid areas of stony and sandy desert where few trees can survive. **Bark:** dark and rough; branchlets very slender, hanging straight down; finely hairy. **Leaves:** very narrow and slender, 1,3 to 5 × 0,2 to 0,5 cm, slightly curved, leathery, grey-green to yellowish-green, may be finely hairy when young; apex and base tapering; margins entire; petiole up to 3 mm long. **Flowers:** small, greenish yellow, in small axillary clusters (August to September). **Fruit:** almost spherical, thinly fleshy, about 5 to 8 mm in diameter, usually solitary, black when mature (February to May).

The fruit is edible but is not particularly pleasant-tasting. The wood is reported to be beautiful, hard, durable and fine-grained and the heartwood is black. It is very suitable for carving and inlay work, but because it grows in inaccessible situations and is comparatively scarce, it is unlikely to be commercially exploited.

In South West Africa the Namas call this tree the *tsawib* – a reference to its ebony-like wood – and the place, Tsawisis, is named after them.

Euclea racemosa Murray
S.A. no: 599   Sea guarri. Seeghwarrie
Rhod. no: —

A low shrub or small tree up to 6 m in height; occurring in coastal dune scrub and low coastal forest. **Bark:** grey, smooth. **Leaves:** alternate, opposite or sub-opposite, oblanceolate to obovate, 1,5 to 5 × 0,7 to 1,5 cm, but usually about 2,5 × 1,3 cm, thickly leathery, paler green below than above, without hairs; apex rounded, notched; base tapering; margin entire, thickened, rolled under, not wavy; petiole 1 to 4 mm long, wrinkled. **Flowers:** small, creamy-white, in short axillary spikes up to 4 cm long (December to March). **Fruit:** spherical, thinly fleshy, about 7 mm in diameter, black when mature (February to May).

The seeds often fail to germinate as they are parasitised by the larva of a fly.

739

Euclea schimperi (A. DC.) Dandy
S.A. no: 600 and 600,1   Bush guarri. Bosghwarrie
Rhod. no: 850   Bush guarri

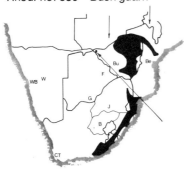

A shrub or small tree 3 to 8 m in height; occurring in coastal scrub and low altitude bush and forest; in Rhodesia in medium to low altitude woodland in areas of moderate rainfall. **Bark:** grey to blackish, rather smooth. **Leaves:** resemble those of *E. divinorum,* alternate, sub-opposite or in pseudo-whorls of 3 to 4 at the ends of the branches; obovate to linear-oblanceolate, 3 to 9 × 0,5 to 3 cm, but usually about 6 × 2,5 cm, leathery, shiny light green above, dull and rather paler green below, without hairs; apex broadly tapering to almost rounded; base tapering; margin entire, thickened, curled under from almost the midrib, usually wavy; petiole 2 to 6 mm long. **Flowers:** small, creamy-white, sweetly scented, in short axillary sprays up to 4 cm long (December to May). **Fruit:** almost spherical, about 8 mm in diameter, thinly fleshy, rich red to purplish when mature (February to September).
The wood is heavy and hard and was previously used to make wagon wheels; today it is used mainly for fuel, although it is said to split and crackle when burned.

Euclea tomentosa E. Meyer ex A. DC.
S.A. no: 600,2   Honey guarri. Heuningghwarrie
Rhod. no: —

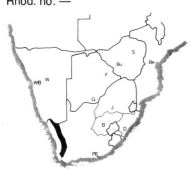

A shrub or small tree 3 to 4 m in height; occurring in arid areas, on rocky mountain slopes and in
ravines along watercourses. **Bark:** blackish-grey. **Leaves:** obovate to ovate-oblong, 3 to 7 × 1,3 cm,

stiffly leathery, dull green to grey above and below, with hoary white hairs at least below; apex tapering to rounded; base tapering to almost square; margin entire, thickened and flat with long white hairs; petiole almost absent. **Flowers:** small, in few-flowered axillary sprays up to 2,5 cm long; the whole spray is covered with crisped white hairs and there are conspicuous bracts at the base of the flowers which fall very early (September to October). **Fruit:** conical, up to 9 mm in diameter, thinly fleshy, occasionally 2 to 3 together producing an almost triangular effect, red to purplish-black when mature (October to November).

Euclea undulata Thunb.

S.A. no: 601 and 601,1   Common guarri. Gewone ghwarrie

Rhod. no: 851   Thicket euclea

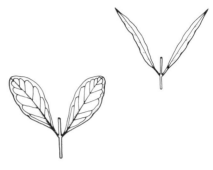

A dense twiggy shrub or small tree up to 7 m in height; common and widespread, occurring on open rocky slopes, in open mopane/acacia woodland, along watercourses and on termite mounds; it may form almost impenetrable thickets. **Bark:** grey, scaly; branchlets twiggy, angular and densely leafy; leaves and all young parts with glands which cover the surface with a granular rust-coloured exudate. **Leaves:** alternate or in psuedo-whorls, crowded at the ends of the branches, small, obovate to narrowly elliptic, 2 to 4 × 0,5 to 1,5 cm, leathery, yellowish-green to dark green or blue-green above, paler green below, sometimes rust-brown, caused by rust-brown glands dotted over the surface; apex broadly tapering or rounded to abruptly attenuate; base tapering; margin entire, finely rolled under, conspicuously wavy or almost flat; petiole 1 to 3 mm long. **Flowers:** small, whitish, in axillary raceme-like sprays up to 2 cm long; ovary without hairs but may have scale-like glands (December to April). **Fruit:** spherical, thinly fleshy, 4 to 6 mm in diameter, reddish-brown becoming black when mature, in very short sprays less than 1,2 cm long (April to October).

This species often closely resembles *E. divinorum*, but it can be distinguished by its much smaller leaves and fruits and its inflorescences which are unbranched and less dense. The fruits are edible but not very pleasant-tasting. The leaves make a useful fodder for stock and the wood, which is brown, hard, heavy, close-grained and durable, is suitable for fencing posts and for joinery. The powdered root is a drastic purgative; the bark contains tannin and is used to ease headaches while the root provides a remedy for toothache and heart ailments.

2. DIOSPYROS L.

Sub-shrubs, shrubs or trees, sometimes suffrutices. **Leaves:** alternate, simple. Stipules absent. **Flowers:** axillary, solitary or in clusters, cymes or pseudo-racemes. Sexes separate on different trees, occasionally apparently bisexual but functionally male; floral parts in threes to fives; calyx joined at the base and deeply lobed, or cup-shaped and toothed round the rim, persistent and enlarging in the fruit: corolla urn-shaped, 3- to 5-lobed; stamens 3 to 15, in 1 or more whorls, free or joined in pairs; ovary 2- to 16-chambered, on a somewhat fleshy disc, without hairs. **Fruit:** berry-like, becoming dry and sometimes reluctantly dehiscent, with the characteristic calyx lobes round the base; usually with 2 or more seeds.

Diospyros comes from the Greek and can be freely translated as 'celestial pear', a reference to those species with delectable fruits, such as the persimmon. Unfortunately, the southern African species do not have these delicious fruits, but some are pleasantly flavoured.

741

EBENACEAE

Key to the tree species of *Diospyros:*

1 Fruits narrowly ellipsoidal, calyx lobes 3 .... **D. inhacaënsis**
  Fruits ovoid, spherical or even narrowly elliptic; if narrowly elliptic there are always 4 or more
    enlarged calyx lobes 2
2 Calyx lobes up to half the length of the fruit 3
  Calyx lobes almost or equal to the length of the fruit, and sometimes enveloping it 15
3 Leaves usually less than 3,6 × 2 cm 4
  Leaves usually larger than 4 × 1,5 cm 8
4 Occurring in a coastal belt from East London to Moçambique, and inland from Rhodesia
    northwards .... **D. natalensis**
  Occurring inland, from the southern Cape to the Transvaal and also from the western Cape to
    South West Africa 5
5 Leaves densely felted with fine interwoven stellate hairs mixed with stiff appressed bristle-like
    hairs .... **D. austro-africana**
  Leaves variously hairy but not densely grey-felted below 6
6 Mature leaves not exceeding 1,3 cm in length .... **D. ramulosa**
  Mature leaves usually exceeding 1,3 cm in length 7
7 Calyx lobes in fruit 4 (all floral parts in fours) .... **D. acocksii**
  Calyx lobes in fruit 5 (all foral parts in fives) .... **D. glabra**
8 Under surface of leaves and calyces and flower stalks densely covered with creamy-pink woolly
    hairs .... **D. kirkii**
  Leaves and floral parts without creamy-pink woolly hairs 9
9 Bark with vertical and horizontal fissures producing a very conspicuous 'crocodile bark' .....
    .... **D. quiloensis**
  Bark not conspicuously square flaked 10
10 Small trees rarely reaching 10 m in height 11
   Medium to large trees 10 to 40 m in height 13
11 Leaves dull green or grey-green, small, 1,5 to 8 × 0,5 to 3 cm, usually about 5 × 1,5 cm; fruits
     broadly ovoid, up to 2 cm long .... **D. lycioides**
   Leaves dark green, or glossy dark green, usually more than 7 × 2 cm; fruits ovoid to spherical,
     2 to 4 cm in diameter 12
12 Bark dark blackish, deeply fissured and rough; leaves dark glossy green above, greyish-green
     below; fruits large, up to 4 cm in diameter; persistent calyx 5-lobed, small . **D. batocana**
   Bark grey, peeling to reveal patches of smooth cream underbark; leaves shiny dark green above,
     paler green below; fruits 1,8 to 2,5 cm long, persistent calyx up to 12-lobed, covering almost
     half the fruit .... **D. senensis**
13 Bark grey, finely longitudinally fissured; branchlets, leaf petioles, flower stalks and calyces
     covered with short rusty hairs .... **D. ferrea**
   Bark dark grey or brown and conspicuously rough; young parts without rusty hairs 14
14 Fruits up to 1,5 cm in diameter, yellowish-green becoming blue-black when mature; petiole 2 to
     5 mm long; a very large forest tree up to 40 m in height, with a great girth but an unusually
     small, sparse, shortly branched crown. In southern Africa occurring only in eastern Rhodesia
     and adjacent areas in Moçambique .... **D. abyssinica**
   Fruits up to 2,5 cm in diameter, yellow to purplish when mature; 10 mm long; usually 10 to 15 m
     in height, occasionally up to 25 m, with a dense dark rounded crown, in woodland and in
     riverine fringes. Widespread .... **D. mespiliformis**
15 Calyx lobes bladder-like, completely enclosing the fruit, reddish-brown .... **D. whyteana**
   Calyx lobes not forming a bladder-like structure, although they may be large 16
16 Calyx lobes spreading or bending back, not clasping or loosely enveloping the fruit 17
   Calyx lobes firmly clasping or loosely enveloping the fruit 19
17 Calyx lobes large, almost leaf-like, thinly textured .... **D. squarrosa**
   Calyx lobes slender, narrow 18
18 Often a scandent shrub, only occasionally a small tree, with branches spreading at almost
     right-angles; leaves thinly leathery .... **D. simii**
   Always a dense erect shrub or medium sized tree up to 13 m in height, with erect, ascending
     branches; leaves leathery .... **D. dichrophylla**

19 Fruit almost spherical, strongly 5-angled, covered with long thick pale yellow to golden bristly hairs .... **D. villosa**

Fruit not strongly 5-angled, not covered with long golden hairs, although it may bear short soft hairs 20

20 Mature fruits about 10 mm long; under surface of the leaves harsh to the touch **D. scabrida**

Mature fruits more than 10 mm long; leaves not harsh to the touch 21

21 Strictly a coastal species, occurring in dune scrub and dune forest, extending no further south than Tongaland; leaves obovate to almost circular .... **D. rotundifolia**

Not confined to coastal regions; leaves obovate to elliptic or narrowly so 22

22 Occurring in the Cape, Natal and Transvaal only; calyx lobes slender ...... **D. dichrophylla**

Occurring in the east and south of Rhodesia and adjacent areas in Moçambique, not in South Africa; calyx lobes large, expanded, leaf-like .... **D. usambarensis**

Diospyros abyssinica (Hiern) F. White

S.A. no: —

Rhod. no: 852   Giant diospyros

A large tree, one of the tallest in Chirinda forest, reaching 40 m in height, with a great girth and, proportionately, a strangely small, sparse, shortly branched crown; occurring in evergreen forest. **Bark:** dark brown to black, conspicuously rough, fibrous. **Leaves:** elliptic to oblong-elliptic, 5 to 12 × 2 to 4,5 cm, young leaves red becoming glossy dark green above, dull green below; apex rather attenuate into an ultimately narrowly rounded tip; base broadly tapering to square; margin entire, conspicuously wavy; petiole 2 to 5 mm long, channelled. **Flowers:** creamy-white to yellow, about 5 mm long, corolla lobes as long as the tube, fragrant, solitary or in axillary clusters of 2 to 4 near the ends of the branchlets (October to January). **Fruit:** spherical, fleshy, about 1,5 cm in diameter, yellowish-green becoming blue-black when mature; the lobed basal cup covers about one quarter to one third of the fruit (March to October).

The wood is white and very hard, although not durable in the ground or in wet places; it works well but is difficult to finish.

Diospyros acocksii (De Winter) De Winter

S.A. no: 602   Namaqua jackal-berry. Namakwajakkalsbessie

Rhod. no: —

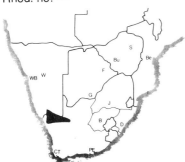
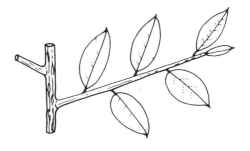

EBENACEAE

A rigidly branched shrub or small tree up to 5 m in height, with the branches at right-angles to the stem; occurring along dry watercourses in desert areas. **Bark:** ash-grey with blackish markings, or grey with a reddish tinge, smooth to finely warty; young branches deep mahogany red. **Leaves:** small, elliptic to obovate-elliptic, 1,3 to 2,3 × 0,5 to 1 cm, leathery, glossy green above, the under surface often with sharp hairs; apex and base tapering; margin entire, often slightly wavy, rolled under; petiole very short but distinct, 0,5 to 1,5 mm long. **Flowers:** creamy-white, urn-shaped, up to 10 mm long, axillary, solitary, pendulous, on stalks up to 5 to 7 mm long. **Fruit:** ovoid, slightly 4-angled, 1 to 1,3 cm long, the persistent calyx disc 4-lobed, forming a cup-shaped base covering the lower one-third of the fruit.

Diospyros austro-africana De Winter

S.A. no: Fire-sticks. Kritikom
Rhod. no: —

A much-branched shrub 2 to 3 m in height, or a small tree sometimes reaching 10 m; occurring in a wide variety of habitats. **Bark:** dark, blistering and peeling in long narrow strips. **Leaves:** narrowly obovate, up to 3 × 0,2 to 0,5 cm, stiff and thickly leathery, densely grey felted and interwoven with stellate and bristle-like hairs on both surfaces, giving the tree a grey appearance; apex broadly tapering to rounded; base tapering; margin entire, flat; petiole very short or absent. **Flowers:** creamy-white to pink or even red, 4 to 9 mm long, axillary, solitary, pendulous on stalks up to 2 cm long, clasped by conspicuous rust-coloured boat-shaped bracts which fall early and leave scars (August to November). **Fruit:** spherical, fleshy, up to 1,5 cm in diameter, covered with short soft hairs, red to black when mature, with the 4- to 5-lobed cup clasping the base for almost half of its length (January to June). This species is divided into four varieties:

1 Mature leaves not exceeding 1,5 cm in length, with dark coloured hairs; flowers pink or cream. Occurring in the dry summer-rainfall areas of the Cape, Orange Free State and the Transvaal .... var. *microphylla* (Burch.) De Winter
  Mature leaves 1,5 to 3 cm long, with pale grey hairs 2
2 Upper surface of the leaves almost without hairs, wrinkled. Occurring in the winter-rainfall areas of the Cape .... var. *rugosa* (E. Meyer ex A.DC.) De Winter
  Upper surface of the leaves with short soft pale grey hairs 3
3 Flowers deep pink to red. Occurring in Lesotho, the Orange Free State and Natal ....var. *rubriflora* (De Winter) De Winter
  Flowers cream to white. Occurring in the winter-rainfall areas of the Cape and north to Namaqualand .... var. *austro-africana*
  The wood is used to make fire by friction.

Diospyros batocana Hiern

S.A. no: 602,1   Sand jackal-berry. Sandjakkalsbessie
Rhod. no: 853   Batoka diospyros

A small tree, often twisted and crooked, up to 7 m in height; occurring at low altitudes in hot woodland. **Bark:** dark blackish, rough and deeply fissured. **Leaves:** narrowly to broadly elliptic, 5 to 10 × 2,2 to 4,5 cm, but usually about 7 × 3 cm, hard, leathery, glossy dark green above, pale greyish-green below; apex and base rather rounded; margin entire, broadly rolled under; petiole 3 to 8 cm long. **Flowers:** creamy-white sometimes tinged with violet, about 1,5 cm long, sweetly

scented, the sepals and backs of the petals covered with dark upward-pointing bristly hairs; flowers without stalks, in clusters on the old wood, often on knobby lateral growths, seldom in the axils of the current year's leaves (June to September). **Fruit:** ovoid to almost spherical, fleshy, up to 4 cm in diameter, with short, soft, dark brown hairs when young, orange when mature; the 5 small persistent calyx lobes do not extend far along the fruit (September to February).

The fruits are eaten by children and, as a famine food only, by adults. A cold water infusion of the leaves is used as an enema to clear the lower bowel, but it seems that an overdose may prove fatal. The leaves are laid upon millet as a cover in preparation for beer making, this process reputedly improving the flavour. The whole tree is generally dark green in appearance, and the wood, which is hard, is suitable for making spoons and small carvings.

Diospyros dichrophylla (Gand.) De Winter

S.A. no: 603   Poison-peach. Tolbos

Rhod. no: —

A shrub 2 to 3 m in height, or a small to medium sized densely leafy tree up to 13 m; occurring in coastal scrub and on sandy flats, in open grassland, at the margins of evergreen forest, in wooded ravines and on wooded rocky hillsides. **Bark:** grey to brown, rather smooth. **Leaves:** oblanceolate to narrowly ovate, 1,5 to 6 × 0,6 to 1,5 cm, leathery, glossy dark green and without hairs above, with or without rather paler green sparse to dense hairs below; apex broadly tapering to rounded; base tapering; margin entire, tightly rolled under; petiole 3 to 6 mm long. **Flowers:** creamy-white, about 10 mm long, axillary, solitary, pendulous, on stalks up to 2,5 cm long (November to March). **Fruit:** almost spherical, about 2 to 2,5 cm in diameter, densely golden velvety, occasionally reluctantly splitting into 5 valves; the 4 to 5 narrow persistent calyx lobes, up to 2,5 cm long, are usually curved backwards but occasionally loosely clasp the base of the fruit (April to October).

This species resembles *D. simii* and the differences are discussed under the latter species. The wood is hard, black and ebony-like, but is of little value except as fuel. The fruits are said to be poisonous.

Diospyros ferrea (Willd.) Bakh.

S.A. no: —

Rhod. no: 854   Bristle-fruited diospyros

A rather slender tree 10 to 20 m in height; occurring in moist evergreen forest and coastal forest. **Bark:** grey, finely longitudinally fissured; young branches tend to zigzag and, together with the **745**

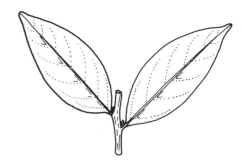

petioles and flower stalks and sepals, are covered with fine rusty hairs. **Leaves:** elliptic, may be 3 to 7 × 1 to 3 cm but usually about 4,5 to 6 × 2 cm, thinly textured, glossy green above, paler shiny green below without hairs; midrib depressed above, fairly prominent below; lateral veining almost immersed on both sides but fine net-veining is visible; apex broadly tapering to somewhat attenuate, terminating in a short, narrowly rounded and minutely notched tip; base broadly tapering; margin entire, slightly thickened, wavy; petiole slender, up to 2 to 5 mm long. **Flowers:** white fading to yellow, about 5 mm long, axillary, solitary, in 3- to 5-flowered shortly stalked clusters, inconspicuous (November to December). **Fruit:** narrowly ovoid, brownish when mature, tipped by the remains of the persistent style and with a few bristly hairs near the apex; the persistent 4-lobed calyx cup at the base envelops about one quarter of the fruit (January to March).

Diospyros glabra (L.) De Winter
S.A. no: 603,1   Blueberry bush. Bloubessiebos
Rhod. no: —

An erect dense shrub or small tree up to 5 m in height; occurring on mountain slopes, at the margins of evergreen forest and also in open grassland and on sandy flats. **Bark:** dark grey, mottled. **Leaves:** small, narrowly to broadly elliptic, 1,5 to 3 × 0,4 to 1 cm, leathery, without hairs, glossy dark green above, pale green and shiny below; apex and base tapering; margin entire, not conspicuously wavy; petiole barely more than 1 mm long. **Flowers:** white, up to 6 mm long, the petals curling back, in 2- to 5-flowered sprays, up to 1,5 cm long, axillary, solitary, pendulous, in the axils of bracts which fall early (October to December). **Fruit:** ovoid to almost spherical, about 10 mm in diameter, reddish to purplish when mature; the 5 persistent calyx lobes narrow, small, curling back, not clasping the base of the fruit (January to March).

Diospyros inhacaënsis F. White
S.A. no: 604   Zulu jackal-berry. Zoeloejakkalsbessie
Rhod. no: —

A small to medium sized tree 5 to 15 m in height; occurring in evergreen coastal forest and littoral scrub. **Bark:** greyish, slightly rough. **Leaves:** usually borne in one plane, elliptic, 2,5 to 6,5 × 1,5 to 3,5 cm, leathery, without hairs, glossy dark green; apex rounded to attenuate into an abrupt slender point; base tapering; margin entire, tightly wavy; petiole up to 5 mm long. **Flowers:** white, in small axillary 2- to 3-flowered clusters (November to March). **Fruit:** narrowly ellipsoidal, sharply pointed, about 1,5 × 0,8 cm, purplish-black when mature, with 3 persistent calyx lobes (June to July).

746

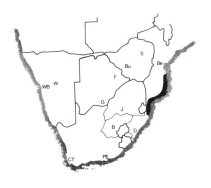

Diospyros kirkii Hiern
S.A. no: —
Rhod. no: 855   Pink diospyros

A small tree up to 7 m in height; occurring in open woodland on sandveld and often gregarious on rocky ridges and stony outcrops. **Bark:** dark grey, very rough, often flaking in square sections. **Leaves:** broadly elliptic to almost circular, up to 15 × 8,5 cm, the young leaves, stems, petioles and the under surface of mature leaves covered with dense woolly pinkish hairs, the older leaves losing these to some extent; apex rounded; base broadly tapering to square and even slightly lobed; margin entire; petiole thickset, 5 to 12 mm long. **Flowers:** pinkish, the backs of the sepals, petals and stalks all densely covered with pinkish woolly hairs, in few-flowered axillary heads, about 2 cm long, sometimes on last season's wood (September to November). **Fruit:** almost spherical, 3,5 to 4 cm in diameter, yellowish when mature; the 5 to 6 persistent calyx lobes are narrow, up to 1,5 cm long, tightly pressed to the fruit (April to August).
The fruits are highly esteemed by Africans. This species hybridises naturally with *D. mespiliformis*.

Diospyros lycioides Desf.   Illust. 244
S.A. no: 605, 605,1 and 605,2   Bluebush. Bloubos
Rhod. no: 856   Red star-apple

A shrub 2 to 3 m in height, sometimes a small tree up to 7 m; occurring in almost all types of habitat. **Bark:** dark grey, rather smooth. **Leaves:** crowded at the tips of the branches, oblanceolate, 1,5 to 8 ×

747

0,5 to 3 cm, usually about 5 × 1,2 cm, rather leathery, dull green or grey-green, the young leaves with silky hairs which may persist in the adult leaves; midrib and lateral veins may be distinctly raised on the under surface; apex broadly tapering to rounded; base tapering; margin entire; petiole short but distinct, 0,3 to 1,5 mm long. **Flowers:** creamy-white, 0,8 to 1,5 cm in diameter, sweetly scented, the sepals conspicuously long and slender; solitary in the axils of the leaves, each flower pendulous on a slender stalk up to 3 cm (September to December). **Fruit:** broadly ovoid, up to 2 cm long, sharp-tipped, covered with short soft hairs when young but losing these and becoming hard and reddish-brown to red when mature; the 4 to 5 persistent calyx lobes, up to 10 mm long, curve strongly backwards (January to May, old fruits remaining on the tree into the next flowering season).

Little use is made of the wood; the tough black roots rapidly blunt ploughs and other farming implements. Roots are chewed after a meal, turning the mouth red, and their frayed ends are used as toothbrushes.

Diospyros mespiliformis Hochst. ex A. DC. Illust. 245
S.A. no: 606   Jakkalsbessie . Jakkalsbessie
Rhod. no: 857   Ebony diospyros

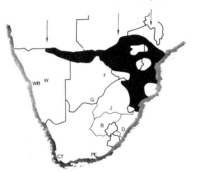

Usually a medium sized tree 10 to 15 m in height, occasionally reaching 25 m, with a dense dark rounded crown, giving excellent shade; occurring at low to medium altitudes, in woodland, frequently on termite mounds, also along rivers and in riverine fringes, more rarely on rocky hill slopes and koppies. **Bark:** dark blackish-grey, rough with deep longitudinal furrows. **Leaves:** elliptic to obovate-oblong, 4,5 to 14 × 1 to 3 cm, glossy dark green above, rather paler green below, almost without hairs and turning yellow in autumn; the new spring flush is an attractive red; apex broadly taper-ing to rounded; base tapering, sometimes square; margin entire, frequently closely wavy; petiole up to 10 mm long. **Flowers:** these are given a generally creamy-grey appearance by the almost woolly hairs on the calyx and flower stalks, but the corolla is cream to pale yellow, up to 1,2 cm long; solitary in the axils of the leaves (October to November). **Fruit:** ovoid to almost spherical, fleshy, up to 2,5 cm in diameter, with very short soft hairs when young, losing these by maturity and becoming hard-skinned and yellow to purplish. The 4 to 5 wavy persistent lobes of the calyx extend over about one-third of the fruit, the tips curling back and so not fully clasping the fruit (April to September).

The fruits are edible and held in high esteem by Africans who often leave a tree standing in their cultivated lands in order to reap the fruits; they are either eaten fresh or stored as a fruit preserve, and are also used to make beer. In African folk-medicine the leaves, twigs and bark provide remedies for ringworm, leprosy, fevers and dysentery and for treating wounds. In the northern Transvaal the people, fearing that they might become possessed by spirits, will not eat the fruit when away from home. The wood becomes dark brown to almost black on drying and provides a good timber, being close-grained, strong, hard, durable, and almost termite-proof. It works well but becomes rough when planed; it has been used to make canoes, stamping blocks and pestles, and is suitable for furniture and flooring. This species hybridises with *D. kirkii*. The seeds have been found in jackal dung, hence one of the common names, *jakkalsbessie*.

Diospyros natalensis (Harvey) Brenan   Illust. 246
[*D. nummularia* Brenan]
S.A. no: 607 and 607,1   Small-leaved jackal-berry. Fynblaarjakkalsbessie
Rhod. no: 858   Acorn diospyros

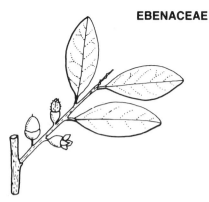

A much-branched shrub or small tree up to 6 m in height, occasionally slightly taller; occurring in dune forest or dune scrub along the coastal belt, or in riverine fringes, at the edge of evergreen forest and among boulders on rocky koppies. **Bark:** pale grey, rather smooth. **Leaves:** borne horizontally along the very slender branchlets; elliptic to ovate, 1 to 3,6 × 0,5 to 2 cm, glossy dark green above, rather paler green below, with hairs when young; apex very broadly tapering to rounded; base square; margin entire, with hairs when young but these are soon lost; petiole slender, 1 to 2 mm long. **Flowers:** small, white, solitary or in 2- to 3-flowered axillary heads, up to 7 mm long (July to November). **Fruit:** resembling miniature acorns, slender, up to 1,2 × 0,6 cm, sharply tipped, yellowish when mature; the persistent calyx cup-shaped and covering almost half the fruit (November to May).

Diospyros quiloensis (Hiern) F. White
S.A. no: —
Rhod. no: 859   Crocodile-bark diospyros

A small to medium sized tree up to 10 m in height with a graceful shape and rounded crown; occurring in hot arid river valleys. **Bark:** grey to dark grey, characteristically deeply longitudinally and transversally fissured, forming a conspicuous 'crocodile bark'. **Leaves:** may be scattered along the shoots or crowded near the ends of very short, slow-growing, knobby lateral shoots, oblanceolate to narrowly obovate, or spathulate, up to 6 × 2 cm, usually about 4 to 5 × 1,5 cm, dark green and very glossy above, rather paler green below; fine hairs may be present on the under surface, especially along the midrib; apex very broadly tapering; base narrowly tapering; margin entire, slightly rolled under, wavy; petiole slender, 1 to 5 mm long. **Flowers:** creamy-white to pale yellow, sweetly scented; the male flowers up to 8 mm long in loose 2- to 12-flowered clusters in the axils of fallen leaves, the female flowers larger, up to 10 mm long, in axillary groups of 2 to 3 (October to December). **Fruit:** resembling slender acorns, up to 2,5 × 1 cm, yellowish when mature, sharply tipped, the persistent calyx obscurely 4-lobed, cupping the base for barely one quarter of the length of the fruit (January to July).

The fruits are edible but not much sought after. The wood is hard and yellow with a black heartwood; it is much esteemed for carving and as a very durable general purpose timber.

Diospyros ramulosa (E. Meyer ex A. DC.) De Winter
S.A. no: 607,2   Namaqua fire-sticks. Namakwakritikom
Rhod. no: —

A dense rigidly branched shrub or small tree up to 5 m in height; occurring in hot arid areas. **Bark:** ashy-grey to brown, tending to flake in very narrow strips. **Leaves:** crowded at the ends of the branches or may be spaced along longer branchlets; very small, elliptic to obovate, 0,5 to 1,3 × 0,2 to 0,5 cm, finely but densely hairy on both surfaces; apex broadly tapering to rounded; base tapering; margin entire, may be slightly rolled under; petiole extremely short or absent. **Flowers:** greenish-white to cream, 0,5 to 1 cm long, axillary, solitary, the stalks very short with narrow bracts at the base. **Fruit:** almost spherical, fleshy, 1 to 1,5 cm in diameter, smooth and without hairs, yellowish when mature; the 4 to 5 persistent calyx lobes, up to 5 mm long, tend to curl back and therefore do not fully clasp the base.

This species resembles *D. austro-africana* var. *microphylla* but differs in having fruits without hairs, calyx lobes which curve backwards and bracts at the base of the flowers which are narrow or leaf-like and not boat-shaped.

Diospyros rotundifolia Hiern
S.A. no: 608   Dune jackal-berry. Duinejakkalsbessie
Rhod. no: —

 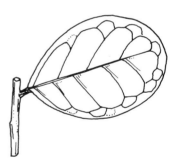

A small to medium sized tree 4 to 9 m in height; essentially a coastal species and an important constituent of dune scrub and low coastal forest. **Bark:** dark brownish-black. **Leaves:** obovate to almost circular, 3 to 6 × 2 to 6 cm, thickly leathery, olive-green to grey-green and glossy above, paler green below; apex rounded, often notched; base broadly tapering to square; margin entire, often rolled under; petiole up to 5 mm long. **Flowers:** creamy-white, up to 8 × 8 mm, axillary, solitary (October to November). **Fruit:** ovoid, fleshy, up to 2,5 × 1,5 cm, smooth, glossy red to purplish when mature; the persistent calyx lobes, up to 2,5 cm long, form a rimmed cup-shaped base, which firmly clasps the fruit and then separates into 4 to 5 lobes, each up to 10 mm long, which curl back (April to September).

Diospyros scabrida (Harvey ex Hiern) De Winter
S.A. no: 608,1   Hard-leaved monkey plum. Hardeblaartolbos
Rhod. no: —

Usually a shrub 2 to 3 m in height, occasionally a tree up to 10 m; occurring in rocky situations, also in ravines and at the margins of evergreen forest. **Bark:** ash-grey, smooth. **Leaves:** elliptic, broadly oblong to almost circular, up to 7 × 3 cm, thickly leathery, glossy green, with occasional sparse hairs

750

above, densely hairy below and harsh to the touch; apex broadly tapering to rounded; base square to lobed; margin entire, hairy; petiole 1 mm long. **Flowers:** white to cream, about 10 mm long, axillary, sometimes solitary, usually in 2- to 4-flowered clusters, on stalks up to 2 cm long, the leaf-like bracts at the base falling early (November to April). **Fruit:** ovoid, fleshy, about 10 mm long, red when mature, tipped with the remains of the old style; the 4 to 5 persistent calyx lobes remarkably large, wing-like, up to 2,5 cm long, separate but completely enveloping the fruit (March to April).
This species has been divided into two varieties:

var. *scabrida* – leaves elliptic, 3 to 8 cm long; occurring mainly in Natal

var. *cordata* (E. Meyer ex A. DC.) De Winter – leaves broadly ovate to almost circular, seldom exceeding 4 cm long, usually 3 cm or less. Occurring mainly in the coastal areas of the eastern Cape.

This species, with its large calyx lobes, bears some resemblance to *D. whyteana* but in that species the calyx lobes are joined to form an inflated structure.

Diospyros senensis Klotzsch
S.A. no: —
Rhod. no: 860   Peeling-bark diospyros

A rigidly spiky shrub or small tree 3 to 5 m in height; occurring in hot dry areas, at the edges of pans and in riverine fringes. **Bark:** grey, peeling to reveal smooth cream underbark; bole occasionally fluted. **Leaves:** obovate, oblong to almost circular, 7 to 14 × 4 to 8,5 cm, leathery, shiny dark green above, paler green below, sparsely hairy to more or less densely covered with short soft hairs on both surfaces, losing most of these by maturity; the midrib and veins form a conspicuous yellowish net-work on the under surface; apex broadly tapering to rounded, often notched; base broadly to narrowly tapering, ultimately narrowly to broadly square; margin entire, with a fringe of hairs especially when young, losing most of these by maturity; petiole 3 to 10 mm long. **Flowers:** creamy-white to yellowish, on stalks up to 7 mm long, in 3- to 5-flowered clusters, in or above the axils of the leaves (November to December). **Fruit:** ovoid to almost spherical, 1,8 to 2,5 cm long, yellowish when mature; the persistent calyx, up to 12-lobed, forms a cup covering almost half the fruit (January to September).
The wood is tough and is used for implement handles and in building. An infusion of the roots is rubbed on to children's chests to ward off colds.

751

EBENACEAE

Diospyros simii (Kuntze) De Winter
S.A. no: 609   Star-apple. Ranktolbos
Rhod. no: —

A shrub tending to scramble, or an erect small tree up to 5 m in height; occurring in forests and at the margin of evergreen forest. **Bark:** grey to brown, rather smooth; branches at right-angles to the stem. **Leaves:** oblanceolate to obovate, 3 to 5 × 1 to 2 cm, thinly leathery, with or without sparse hairs, glossy dark green above, paler geen below; apex broadly tapering to rounded; base narrowly tapering; margin entire; petiole 5 to 8 mm long. **Flowers:** white to cream, up to 10 mm long, on stalks up to 2,5 cm long, axillary, solitary or in 2- to 3-flowered clusters. **Fruit:** almost spherical, fleshy, up to 1,5 cm in diameter, covered with dense, short, soft golden hairs; the 4 to 5 persistent calyx lobes slender, as long as, or longer than the fruit, not clasping the base but tending to spread out sideways, not curling back.

This species resembles *D. dichrophylla,* and the fruits are almost identical; however, the latter species is an erect shrub or tree up to 13 m in height, its branches are erect or ascending, and its leaves leathery and usually densely hairy (although specimens without hairs may occur).

Diospyros squarrosa Klotzsch
S.A. no: —
Rhod. no: 861   Rigid-star berry

A shrub or a rather straggling small tree up to 8 m in height; occurring on stream banks and in riverine fringe forest, also common on stony hillsides and at the foot of rocky koppies. **Bark:** grey to brown, roughish. **Leaves:** obovate, 5 to 9 × 3 to 5 cm, thinly textured, pale dull green on both surfaces, sparsely hairy below, especially along the midrib; net venation conspicuous below; apex broadly tapering to rounded; base rather narrowly tapering; margin entire, conspicuously wavy; petiole up to 10 mm long. **Flowers:** creamy-white, fragrant, up to 10 mm long, axillary, solitary or in 2- to 3-flowered clusters, or very short stalked cymes (November to December). **Fruit:** almost spherical, slightly flattened at the tip, fleshy, about 2 cm in diameter, with or without sparse hairs, yellow and pleasantly flavoured when mature; the 4 persistent calyx lobes about 1,8 × 0,5 to 0,8 cm, velvety, rigidly leaf-like (the specific name refers to this), bending back from directly beneath the fruit, not clasping the base at all (February to July).

752

Diospyros usambarensis F. White
S.A. no: —
Rhod. no: 862   Dye diospyros

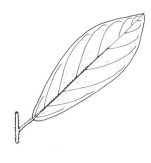

A shrub or small tree 4 to 5 m in height, occasionally reaching 10 m; occurring on rocky hill slopes, in open woodland, along river banks and in riverine fringes at low altitudes. **Bark:** grey to blackish, rough. **Leaves:** tending to crowd at the ends of the branches, obovate to elliptic, 5 to 10 × 2,5 to 5 cm, light to dark green and glossy above, paler green below; apex broadly tapering; base tapering, though finally shortly rounded; margin entire, sometimes finely wavy; petiole about 10 mm long, rather slender. **Flowers:** white, axillary, in short 3- to 4-flowered clusters (October to December). **Fruit:** ovoid, fleshy, up to 2 cm long, yellowish when mature, with short soft golden hairs; the 4 to 5 persistent calyx lobes are large, expanded and leaf-like, up to 3 cm long, joined for about 10 mm forming a cup, light green, conspicuously veined, tending to curve over the fruit (January to June). The wood is hard and white; a black dye is said to be obtained from the bark and roots.

Diospyros villosa (L.) De Winter
S.A. no: 610 and 610,1   Hairy star-apple. Harige ranktolbos
Rhod. no: —

Usually a shrub with a tendency to scramble, occasionally a small tree 3 to 4 m in height; occurring at the margin of evergreen forest, in wooded ravines and river valleys. **Leaves:** obovate-oblong to very broadly oblong, 1 to 13 × 0,5 to 6 cm, thinly leathery, rather stiff, both surfaces hairy when young, losing most of these on the upper surface by maturity, but the lower surface remaining densely shaggy with pale whitish to almost rusty-red woolly hairs; apex broadly tapering to rounded, often notched; base square to lobed; margin entire, rolled under; petiole up to 2 cm long. **Flowers:** pale lemon to yellow, about 10 mm long, densely furry on the outside, sweetly scented, axillary, solitary or in very short 2- to 3-flowered spikes (March to May). **Fruit:** almost spherical, strongly 5-angled, fleshy, 1,5 to 2,5 × 3 cm, densely covered with long thick pale yellowish to golden bristly hairs. The mature fruit splits into 5 woody valves, which is unusual; the 5 persistent calyx lobes are large, wing-like and thinly textured, and loosely envelop the whole fruit (June to October).

Diospyros whyteana (Hiern) F. White   Illust. 247
S.A. no: 611   Bladder-nut. Bostolbos
Rhod. no: 863   Bladder-nut

753

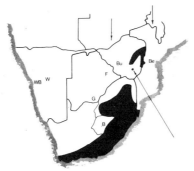 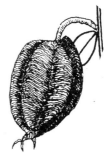 

A shrub or small tree 5 to 7 m in height; occurring in scrub and forest, on mountain slopes and in rocky places. **Bark:** grey to almost black, smooth. **Leaves:** borne alternately in 2 ranks, narrowly elliptic to ovate-oblong, 2,5 to 4,5 × 1 to 2 cm, dark green and strikingly glossy above, paler dull green with sparse hairs below; apex narrowly tapering; base tapering to almost rounded; margin entire, rather wavy with a hair fringe; petiole about 1 to 2 mm long. **Flowers:** white, cream to pale yellow, fragrant, 5 to 10 mm long, almost pendulous on hairy stalks up to 2 cm long, in short axillary sprays which later develop into leafy twigs (August to November). **Fruit:** very distinctive, ovoid to almost spherical, 1 to 1,5 cm long, occasionally 2 cm, red when mature; the persistent sepals become large, joined, inflated, bladder-like, up to 3 cm long, drying to a reddish-brown, completely but loosely, enveloping the fruit (January to May, but the sepals may remain on the tree for months after the fruits have fallen and so may be found on the tree at almost any time of the year).

The seeds germinate readily and the plants grow quite rapidly so this would make an attractive garden subject.

Diospyros sp. no. 1
S.A. no: —
Rhod. no: 863/1   Gaza diospyros

A tree 5 to 12 m in height; occurring in evergreen forest at medium to high altitudes. **Bark:** brown, fissured to slightly rough. **Leaves:** elliptic, 5 to 10 × 1,5 to 3,5 cm, dark green, without hairs; apex broadly to narrowly attenuate; base tapering; margin entire, wavy; petiole 1 to 3 mm long. Mature **flowers** and **fruits** apparently not yet collected, but flower buds are known to be produced on the older wood.

This species differs from *D. abyssinica* in that it lacks the very marked parallel veining and from *D. ferrea* in having duller green leaves.

OLEACEAE *(The olive family)*

Key to the genera:
1 Fruit a woody capsule; corolla with a well-defined tube, corolla lobes spreading with a group of brownish to purplish hairs at their bases .... **1. Schrebera**

Fruit fleshy, never woody; corolla lobes without a group of brownish to purplish hairs at their bases 2

754

2 Leaves with small pockets (acarodomatia), in the axils of the veins on the under surface; calyx tube deeply lobed almost to the base; corolla tube very short or absent; flowers in few-flowered heads, axillary or on the older wood ....**2. Chionanthus**

Leaves without pockets in the axils of the veins on the under surface; calyx cup-shaped, toothed or shortly 4-lobed; corolla with a very short but distinct tube; flowers in many-flowered heads, axillary or terminal .... **3. Olea**

1. SCHREBERA Roxb.

Shrubs or trees. **Leaves:** opposite, compound or simple, the rachis sometimes winged. **Flowers:** bisexual, in paniculate cymes; calyx bell-shaped, obscurely lobed; corolla tube well defined, with 6 large spreading lobes, each with a group of swollen brownish to purplish hairs at the base; stamens 2, inserted in or just below the throat of the corolla tube; ovary 2-chambered, small, 2-lobed at the apex. **Fruit:** a 2-valved woody capsule, dehiscent.

Key to the tree species of *Schrebera:*
Leaves simple .... **S. trichoclada**
Leaves compound, rachis usually winged .... **S. alata**

Schrebera alata (Hochst.) Welw.   Illust. 248
[*S. gilgiana* Lingelsh.; *S. mazoensis* S. Moore; *S. argyrotricha* Gilg]
S.A. no: 612   Wing-leaved wooden-pear. Wildejasmyn
Rhod. no: 864   Wing-leaved wooden-pear

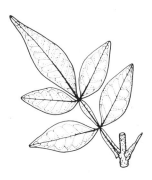

Usually a small tree about 8 m in height, but sometimes reaching 15 m; occurring in evergreen forest or open woodland. **Bark:** grey or brown. **Leaves:** compound, with 1 to 2 pairs of leaflets plus a terminal leaflet; leaflets elliptic to oblong, 3 to 7 × 1 to 4 cm, shiny dark green above, somewhat paler green below, velvety when young; apex broadly tapering, sometimes attenuate forming a slender tip, or rounded and notched; base tapering, asymmetric; margin entire; petiolules very short or absent except on the terminal leaflet which as a petiolule about 10 mm long, petiole 1 to 5 cm long, the petiole and rachis both winged. **Flowers:** white sometimes flushed with pink, the corolla tube about 1,5 cm long with spreading lobes, about 1,5 cm in diameter, with clusters of reddish-brown swollen hairs near the mouth of the corolla tube, sweetly scented, in terminal heads 6 to 11 cm long (December to February). **Fruit:** a woody pear-shaped capsule, 2,5 to 3 × 1 cm, light brown when mature, splitting into 2 valves to release about 8 flattish seeds each with a light brown papery wing up to 1,1 cm long (March to July).
The wood is pale brown with dark striations, hard, heavy and durable; it makes a good fuel. One particular tree at Waddilove Mission in the Marandellas area in Rhodesia is called *muti-usina-zita,* meaning 'tree without a name'. The Rev. Brandon Graaf says that it is so named because it was thought not to occur elsewhere in that area and to have been introduced by the ancients who worked gold deposits there; it is also believed that it was through this specimen that God talked to his people in the days gone by. It should be noted that the name *muti-usina-zita* is also applied to *Cleistanthus schlechteri* but by the peoples in the Buhera district of Rhodesia. This fast-growing shapely tree would make a good garden subject.
In *Flora South Africa* the species *S. argyrotricha* is upheld as distinct from *S. alata.*

755

OLEACEAE

Schrebera trichoclada Welw.　Illust. 249
S.A. no: 613　Wooden-pear. Sandjasmyn
Rhod. no: 865　Wooden-pear

A shrubby bush or small to medium sized tree 6 to 10 m in height, with a rounded or spreading crown; occurring at medium to low altitudes, in deciduous woodland, along rivers, on stony hillsides, rocky koppies and Kalahari sand. **Bark:** yellowish-grey, flaking in circular patches, becoming dark grey and deeply furrowed with age; branchlets with conspicuous circular corky lenticels. **Leaves:** simple, elliptic to oblong-elliptic, up to 12 × 7 cm but usually rather smaller; apex broadly tapering to almost rounded, often abruptly attenuate into a sharp point; base broadly tapering to square; margin entire; petiole usually up to 8 mm long. **Flowers:** creamy-white to yellow, with patches of sepia or purplish-brown hairs at the throat of the corolla tube at the base of the lobes; corolla tube up to 1,2 cm long, with spreading lobes, 1 to 1,6 cm in diameter, axillary or terminal, solitary on a stalk up to 4 cm long, or in 2- to 7-flowered heads, the flower stalks about 1,5 cm long, the common stalk up to 4 cm long (November to January). **Fruit:** a woody pear-shaped capsule up to 6 × 3 cm, very pale creamy-brown when mature, splitting longitudinally into 2 valves to release winged seeds (May to July).

An infusion of the roots is used by the Tonga as an eye lotion.

2. CHIONANTHUS Gaertn.

Trees: **Leaves:** opposite, simple, with small pockets (acarodomatia) said to house mites, in the axils of the veins on the under surface of the leaves. **Flowers:** bisexual, in the branched heads, or paniculate cymes, occasionally without common stalks, axillary or on the older wood; all floral parts in fours; calyx deeply lobed almost to the base, lobes rounded; corolla with a very short tube, or with the lobes separating to the base or joined in pairs; stamens 2 (rarely 4); ovary almost spherical, narrowing into a short style. **Fruit:** thinly fleshy, indehiscent.

Key to the species of *Chionanthus:*
1 Flowers in tight axillary clusters, almost without stalks .... **C. battiscombei**
　Flowers in stalked and branched paniculate cymes 2
2 Leaves up to 7 cm long .... **C. foveolata**
　Leaves on the flowering branches 8 to 13 cm long .... **C. peglerae**

Chionanthus battiscombei (Hutch.) Stearn
[*Linociera battiscombei* Hutch,; *Dekindtia africana* Gilg]
S.A. no: 614　Small-fruited ironwood. Waterpokysterhout
Rhod. no: 866　Small-fruited ironwood

A small tree 4 to 8 m in height, occasionally reaching 10 m; occurring on the banks of mountain streams, most frequently in riverine fringes and forested ravines. **Bark:** grey to brown, smooth. **Leaves:** narrowly or broadly elliptic to obovate, 5 to 10,5 × 2 to 3,8 cm, thickly leathery, glossy dark green above, rather paler green and dull below; apex broadly tapering, sometimes abruptly attenuate into a short slender point; base tapering; margin entire and markedly curled back; petiole up to 9 mm long. **Flowers:** white, cream to yellowish, about 7 to 10 mm long, fragrant, in dense compact rounded axillary heads, 1 to 2 cm in diameter; the corolla lobes, although separate almost from the

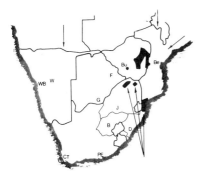 

base, do not spread, and thus the flower is tubular in shape (September to February). **Fruit:** ovoid, fleshy, about 1,8 × 1 cm, tipped with the very short persistent remains of the old style; purplish-black when mature (February to August).

Chionanthus foveolata (E. Meyer) Stearn
[*Linociera foveolata* (E. Meyer) Knobl.]
S.A. no: 615, 615,1 and 615,2   Fine-leaved ironwood. Gewone fynblaarysterhout
Rhod. no: 867   Fine-leaved ironwood

Very variable in size ranging from 5 to 30 m in height; occurring at medium to high altitudes, on hillsides in bush, rocky places, wooded ravines and mountain evergreen forests, also in coastal scrub forest and dune bush. **Bark:** light to dark grey, finely scaly. **Leaves:** ovate-oblong, 2 to 7 × 1,3 to 3,7 cm, glossy dark green; apex attenuate; base rounded or nearly so; margin entire, rolled under; petiole 2 to 7 mm long. **Flowers:** white to cream sometimes tinged with pink, about 5 to 7 mm long, sweetly scented, in short lax sprays, about 2 cm long in the axils of the leaves and also on the old wood (September to December). **Fruit:** ovoid, fleshy, 1,5 to 3 cm long, purplish-black when mature (November to July).

This species is divided into three subspecies:
1 Ultimate branchlets with velvety hairs, the leaves usually less than twice as long as they are broad. Occurring from the Cape Peninsula to Zululand; not in Rhodesia .... subsp. *tomentella* (Verdoorn) Stearn
  Ultimate branchlets without hairs, or if slightly hairy then the leaves more than twice as long as they are broad 2
2 A small tree up to 10 m in height; fruits about 2 cm long; leaves narrow. Occurring form Port Elizabeth to the Transvaal; not in Rhodesia .... subsp. *foveolata*
  A large forest tree up to 30 m in height; fruits up to 3 cm long. Occurring in the Transvaal, Rhodesia and Moçambique .... subsp. *major* (Verdoorn) Stearn

The wood of subsp. *foveolata* is pale brown, strong and heavy.

Chionanthus peglerae (C. H. Wright) Stearn
[*Linociera peglerae* (C. H. Wright) Gilg & Schellenb.]
S.A. no: 616   Large-leaved ironwood. Reusepokysterhout
Rhod. no:—
A medium to tall tree up to 18 m in height; occurring from sea level to medium and high altitudes, in evergreen forest. **Bark:** grey. **Leaves:** oblong to oblong-elliptic, 8 to 13 × 3 to 6,5 cm, the upper half   **757**

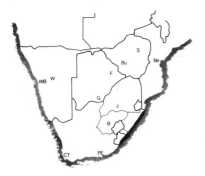

generally widest, glossy dark green; apex tapering, sometimes shortly attenuate; base tapering, running into the petiole; margin entire, thickened; petiole about 10 mm long. **Flowers:** white or cream, about 6 mm long, inconspicuous, in rather loose axillary sprays, or cymose panicles (August to February). **Fruit:** ovoid, fleshy, up to 2,5 × 1,5 cm, black when mature (November to May). This tree is rather rare; the wood appears to be little used.

3. OLEA L.

Shrubs or trees. **Leaves:** opposite, simple. **Flowers:** bisexual, in many-flowered axillary or terminal panicles; all floral parts in fours; calyx cup-shaped, shortly 4-lobed; petals joined to form a short tube, ultimately 4-lobed; stamens 2, joined to the corolla tube; ovary almost spherical, 2-lobed at the apex. **Fruit:** thinly fleshy, indehiscent.

Key to the species of *Olea:*
1 Leaves usually less than 1,5 cm in width 2
  Leaves usually more than 1,5 cm in width 3
2 Undersurface of the leaves densely covered with small silvery, golden or brown scales, (a 10x lens may be necessary to see these), which give a brownish colour and sheen to the leaves; flower heads usually axillary, occasionally also terminal ....**O. europaea**
  Under surface of the leaves without brownish scales or sheen, but may be minutely pitted; flower heads always terminal .... **O. exasperata**
3 Fruits about 10 × 5 mm; trees without a gum-like exudate; usually medium to large forest trees up to 18 m in height .... **O. woodiana**
  Fruits up to 2 × 1 cm; trees with a characteristic gum-like exudate; usually small to medium sized trees .... **O. capensis**

Olea capensis L.   Illust. 251
S.A. no: 618, 618,1 and 618,2   Ironwood. Ysterhout
Rhod. no: 869   Ironwood olive

Often a bushy shrub or a small to medium sized tree up to 10 m in height, but it may be much larger, occasionally reaching 40 m; occurring in bush, littoral scrub and evergreen forest. **Bark:** light grey, becoming dark grey and vertically fissured with age; a characteristic blackish gum is exuded from bark wounds. **Leaves:** lanceolate-oblong to almost circular, 3 to 10 × 1,5 to 5 cm, light to dark green and glossy above, rather paler green below although sometimes almost unicoloured, occasionally purplish-tinged, without hairs or scales; apex broadly tapering to almost rounded; base tapering; margin entire, thickened and often very wavy; petiole often purplish, 0,3 to 1,7 cm long. **Flowers:** very small, white or cream, sweetly scented, in many-flowered axillary or terminal heads, 3 to 8 cm long (August to February, or later). **Fruit:** ovoid, fleshy, up to 2 × 1 cm, purple when mature, said to be pleasant tasting (February to September).

This species has been divided into three subspecies:

1 Fruits oblong-elliptic, up to 2 × 1 cm; flowers in lax heads ....
.... subsp. *macrocarpa* (C. H. Wright) Verdoorn
  Fruits almost spherical to oblong elliptic, up to 1 cm long; flowers in dense heads 2
2 Leaves very variable, apex often rounded; branchlets grey to greyish-brown ....
.... subsp. *capensis*
  Leaves usually broadly elliptic, apex tapering; branchlets grey to whitish ....
.... subsp. *enervis* (Harvey ex C. H. Wright) Verdoorn

The wood of the subspecies *capensis* and *enervis* is rarely used, but that of subsp. *macrocarpa* makes a fine timber. It has dark brown heartwood and is attractively figured, fine-grained, hard and heavy and although it is difficult to work it has been widely used as railway sleepers, in bridge construction and for flooring blocks. It can also produce beautiful furniture. Fresh, mature healthy seed germinates well and the plants can be reasonably fast growing.

Olea europaea L.   Illust. 250
[*O. africana* Miller; *O. chrysophylla* Lam.]
S.A. no: 617   Wild olive. Swartolienhout
Rhod. no: 868   Wild olive

A shrub or small to medium sized tree, 5 to 10 m in height, occasionally reaching 18 m; occurring in a variety of habitats, usually near water, on stream banks, in riverine fringes, but also in open woodland, among rocks and in mountain ravines. **Bark:** grey to brown or blackish, smooth to rough when old. **Leaves:** narrowly oblong-elliptic, 2 to 10 × 0,7 to 1,7 cm, grey-green to shiny dark green above, greyish or yellowish with a dense covering of silvery, golden or brown scales on the under surface; apex and base narrowly tapering, apex sharp-tipped; margin entire, rolled under and curved back from the midrib; petiole slender, up to 10 mm long, so the leaves tend to droop. **Flowers:** greenish-white, white or cream, 6 to 10 mm long, sweetly scented, in loose axillary or occasionally terminal heads, 5 to 6 cm long (October to February). **Fruit:** ovoid, thinly fleshy, about 10 × 8 mm, tapering to a sharp tip, dark brown or black when mature (March to July).

The wood is close-grained, strong and very hard; the sapwood is whitish to pale brown but the heartwood is very handsome, dark reddish-brown or golden-brown with beautiful dark figuring. It works well, takes a fine finish and is most suitable for high class furniture and cabinet work; it is also very durable, makes good fencing posts and, in addition, provides an excellent, pleasant-smelling fuel. The plants are drought-resistant and frost-tolerant, but are slow-growing; the commercial olive has been grafted on to wild stock with success. Africans drink an infusion of fresh bark to relieve colic; they use an infusion of the leaves as an eye lotion for both humans and animals, while a decoction of the leaves provides a gargle for sore throats. The plants are much browsed on by stock, but the leaves are said to be astringent. Although rather bitter, the fruit is edible and widely sought after.

Subsp. *africana* (Miller) P. S. Green is the only subspecies which occurs south of the Zambezi river.

759

OLEACEAE

Olea exasperata Jacq.
S.A. no: 619   Coast olive. Basterolienhout
Rhod. no: —

A bushy or straggling shrub or a small rounded tree 1 to 7 m in height; occurring on sand dunes in coastal bush, but also on hillsides, in open grassland and in valleys. **Bark:** greyish-brown; the young branchlets conspicuously rough with raised lenticels. **Leaves:** linear-oblong, 3 to 7 × 0,3 to 1 cm, thinly leathery, may be minutely pitted, sometimes slightly rough to the touch; apex tapering to rounded, ultimately with a finely pointed tip; base narrowly tapering; margin entire, tending to curve under; petiole 4 to 7 mm long. **Flowers:** small, white, in short broad many-flowered terminal heads. **Fruit:** ovoid, thinly fleshy, up to 10 × 8 mm, yellowish-purple when mature.
In the 17th century the root was considered to be an antidote for snakebite.

Olea woodiana Knobl.
S.A. no: 620   Forest olive. Bosolienhout
Rhod. no: —

A small to medium sized tree up to 10 m in height, occasionally reaching 20 m; occurring in evergreen forest, woodland and coastal bush. **Bark:** pale grey, smooth. **Leaves:** elliptic, 4 to 8 × 1 to 3,5 cm, shiny green above, dull paler green below with minute scales resembling pits, with or without hairs, the midrib prominent and the lateral veins looping near the margin; apex narrowly tapering to rounded, sometimes notched; base tapering; margin entire, rolled under and irregularly wavy; petiole up to 10 mm long. **Flowers:** white, about 5 mm long, in loose axillary or terminal heads 2 to 4 cm long (November). **Fruit:** ovoid, thinly fleshy, about 10 × 5 mm, greenish-yellow when mature (March to April).
The wood is pale to dark brown, very hard and heavy, and has been described as 'steel-like'.

4. *LIGUSTRUM L.

*Ligustrum lucidum Ait.

This large leaved privet from eastern Asia, widely planted as a hedge or as an ornamental tree, has become naturalised in some areas of central Rhodesia (Rhod. no: 870).

SALVADORACEAE *(The mustard tree family)*

Key to the genera:
Axillary spines present; sexes separate on different trees; ovary 2-chambered, with the stigma clearly defined .... **1. Azima**

Spines absent; flowers usually bisexual; ovary 1-chambered, with the stigma obscure . **2. Salvadora**

1. AZIMA Lam.

Azima tetracantha Lam.
[*A. tetracantha* var. *laxior* C. H. Wright; *A. spinosissima* Engl.]
S.A. no: 622,1   Needle bush. Speldedoring
Rhod. no: 876   Bee-sting bush

Usually a spiny shrub with a tendency to scramble, or a small tree up to 8 m in height; occurring at low altitudes in bush, scrub, woodland and thornveld, frequently along watercourses and in riverine thicket. **Bark:** green to brown; branchlets sometimes square in section, often densely hairy, with sharp axillary paired spines, up to 0,5 to 5 cm long, producing 4 spines at each pair of leaves, 1 or more of the spines sometimes developing into a leafy branch. **Leaves:** opposite or sub-opposite, each pair set at right-angles to the next, simple, elliptic-oblong to almost circular, 1,3 to 5,5 × 0,7 to 4,5 cm, leathery, pale green, may be without hairs but frequently hairy to densely hairy on both surfaces; apex and base broadly tapering to rounded; margin entire; petiole squat, about 1 mm long. **Flowers:** greenish or greenish-yellow, 2 to 5 mm long, in loose axillary heads, or cymes, up to 3 cm long. Sexes separate on different trees; all floral parts in fours; calyx bell-shaped; petals free, curving backwards; stamens alternating with the petals, vestigial in female flowers; ovary 2-chambered with a short squat stigma, vestigial in male flowers (September to March). **Fruit:** spherical, thinly fleshy, about 10 mm in diameter, yellowish to white when mature (January to July).
Stock browse on the leaves and as a result their milk and butter may have a pronounced flavour. The leaves and the roots together are considered an effective antidote for snakebite, and the sap, which is used as a disinfectant, provides not only a remedy for toothache but treatment for bleeding gums after extraction. A prick from a thorn from this tree produces an unpleasant burning sensation.

2. SALVADORA Garcin ex L.

Shrubs or trees, sometimes with a tendency to scramble. **Leaves:** opposite, simple, with minute oil glands. Stipules vestigial or opposite. **Flowers:** usually bisexual, in terminal and axillary long branched panicles; calyx bell-shaped, shortly 4-lobed or divided for about half its length; corolla shortly joined at the base, with 4 lobes spreading and curling back; stamens attached to the corolla tube; glandular disc 4-lobed, alternating with the stamens; ovary 1-chambered, stigma obscure. **Fruit:** thinly fleshy, indehiscent.

Key to the tree species of *Salvadora:*
Leaves oblong-elliptic, broadly tapering to apex and base, with or without rather loose but dense hairs; flowers in terminal panicles longer than the leaves; inconspicuous glands alternating with the stamens .... **S. persica**

761

SALVADORACEAE

Leaves narrow, linear-oblong, apex rounded, base narrowly tapering, densely covered with very short soft grey hairs; flowers in terminal panicles as long as, or shorter than the leaves; conspicuous glands alternating with the stamens .... **S. angustifolia**

Salvadora angustifolia Turrill
[*S. australis* Schweick.]
S.A. no: 621   Transvaal mustard tree. Transvaalse mosterdboom
Rhod. no: 877   Narrow-leaved mustard tree

A shrub or small tree 3 to 6 m in height; occurring at low altitudes in hot areas, along river banks, on flood plains, koppies, brackish sandy flats and often on termite mounds. **Bark:** greyish-brown, scaling and rough near the base, becoming grey and flaking in rectangular sections when old; young branchlets covered with short soft grey hairs. **Leaves:** linear-oblong, 2 to 7 × 0,3 to 1,7 cm, rather succulent, greyish-green or bluish-green, covered with fine soft grey hairs; apex rounded, finally sharp-tipped; base narrowly tapering, running into the very short petiole; margin entire; petiole barely 1 mm long. **Flowers:** greenish-white, very small, in loose terminal or axillary heads, 2 to 5 cm long, towards the ends of the branches (May to November). **Fruit:** ovoid, 5 to 10 mm long, greenish or purplish with a white bloom when mature; the dry calyx and petals persist at the base but are not conspicuous (November to March).

This species is divided into 2 varieties, with all the African material being placed in var. *australis* (Schweick.) Verdoorn; the typical variety, var. *angustifolia,* lacks hairs on the leaves and occurs only in the Malagasy Republic.

This plant is said to emit an unpleasant odour; nevertheless, the fruit is regarded as edible although the leaves are inclined to taint the milk and butter of animals browsing on them. A lotion for treating sore eyes is prepared from a leaf infusion.

Salvadora persica L.
S.A. no: 622   Mustard tree. Regte mosterdboom
Rhod. no: 878   Mustard tree

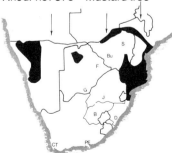 

Frequently a trailing and scrambling shrub, occasionally a small tree 3 to 5 m in height; occurring at low altitudes in hot areas, in river and stream bank vegetation, also in dry open woodland often on termite mounds; it can become thicket-forming. **Bark:** brown, slightly rough; the young branches green. **Leaves:** oblong-elliptic to almost circular, 2,5 to 5 × 1 to 4 cm, light to dark green, rather fleshy, sometimes with wart-like glandular dots and dense rather loose hairs; apex broadly tapering to

762

rounded, sharp-tipped; base broadly tapering; margin entire; petiole up to 10 mm long. **Flowers:** greenish to yellowish, very small, in loose slender-branched axillary or terminal sprays, 2 to 6 cm long (June to September). **Fruit:** spherical, fleshy, 5 to 10 mm in diameter, pink to scarlet when mature (September to February).

Although the plants are said to emit an unpleasant odour, the fruit is believed to be edible and has an agreeable sweet, aromatic, slightly pungent and peppery taste. The roots are used for cleaning teeth and to relieve toothache.

LOGANIACEAE (including **Strychnaceae, Potaliaceae** and **Buddlejaceae**)
(The strychnos family)

Key to the genera:

1 Tall straight-stemmed trees, unbranched for most of their height, finally a few branches form a rather sparse crown; leaves very large, about 95 × 40 cm or more; flowers large and handsome, up to 4 cm in diameter, in heads up to 45 cm wide .... **2. Anthocleista**

Trees not clean-stemmed and very tall, usually well-branched from rather low down; leaves not very large; flowers small 2

2 Leaves usually conspicuously 3- to 5-veined from the base; fruit spherical, woody or fleshy, but not dehiscent .... **1. Strychnos**

Leaves never 3-veined or more from the base; fruit a dehiscent capsule, less than 5 mm in diameter 3

3 Leaves usually in whorls of 3, if opposite then not densely scaly or hairy on the under surface; calyx leathery, usually hairy within .... **3. Nuxia**

Leaves opposite or sub-opposite, the under surface usually much paler to whitish with dense scales or woolly hairs; calyx softly textured, without hairs within .... **4. Buddleja**

Strychnos spinosa p769

1. STRYCHNOS L.

Armed or unarmed shrubs or trees, sometimes with a tendency to scramble. **Leaves:** opposite, decussate, 3- to 5-veined from the base. Stipules reduced to an interpetiolar ridge. **Flowers:** bisexual, in axillary or terminal, simple or compound cymes. Floral parts in fours to fives; calyx dividing into lobes for about half its length; corolla with the inner surface of the lobes often bearded; stamens

763

attached to the corolla tube; ovary 1- to 2-chambered. **Fruit:** almost spherical, may be fleshy or with a thickly woody shell, indehiscent, 1 to many seeds embedded in a fleshy pulp.

The poison, curare, is obtained from the South American species *S. toxifera* Schomb., and *S. nux-vomica* L. from India provides strychnine.

Key to the tree species of *Strychnos:*

1 Fruits small, usually less than 5 cm in diameter, softly fleshy to leathery, 1- to 2-seeded . 2
  Fruits large, usually more than 5 cm in diameter, with a thick woody shell, many-seeded . 7
2 Leaves leathery, usually less than 6 cm in length 3
  Leaves rather thinly textured, usually more than 6 cm long 5
3 Leaves broadest below the middle, apex usually narrowly tapering to attenuate; fruits narrowed
    into a neck before joining the stalk (i.e. with a stipe) .... **S. usambarensis**
  Leaves broadest at or above the middle, apex rounded or shortly tapered; fruits without a stipe at
    the base 4
4 Leaves obscurely 3- to 5-veined from the base, net-veining not visible, apex rounded; flowers
    often appear before the leaves; seeds not grooved .... **S. decussata**
  Leaves strongly 3-veined from the base, clearly net-veined, apex distinctly tapering; flowers in
    the axils of current leaves; seeds deeply grooved .... **S. henningsii**
5 Leaves with all lateral veins equally prominent, not distinctly 3- to 5-veined from the base or near
    the base .... **S. mellodora**
  Leaves markedly 3- to 5-veined from the base or near the base 6
6 Calyx lobes petalloid; leaves sometimes have small pockets (acarodomatia) in the axils of the
    veins and a pair of reduced leaves at the base of the lateral branchlet tends to persist **S. mitis**
  Calyx lobes not petalloid; leaves without acarodomatia, and the pair of reduced leaves falls early
    leaving a ring-like scar near the base of the lateral branchlet .... **S. potatorum**
7 Leaves with apex abruptly narrowed and tipped with a conspicuous straight spine **S. pungens**
  Leaves not spine-tipped 8
8 Flower heads axillary, occasionally also terminal; calyx lobes short and broad, usually less than
    half the length of the corolla tube; lateral branchlets never forming spines 9
  Flower heads terminal; calyx lobes long and narrow, often equalling the corolla in length; lateral
    branchlets often forming spines 10
9 Leaves dull green, almost the same colour below as above, with conspicuous pale net-veining on
    both surfaces; dwarf lateral shoots absent .... **S. innocua**
  Leaves shiny dark green above, distinctly paler green below; net-veining not conspicuous; hard
    rigid dwarf lateral branches present .... **S. madagascariensis**
10 Bark thickly and persistently corky, deeply longitudinally fissured; ultimate branchlets rather
    thick, purplish, with longish hairs .... **S. cocculoides**
  Bark not thickly corky, tending rather to flake in rectangular segments; ultimate branchlets thin,
    rather pale coloured, with or without very short hairs .... **S. spinosa**

Strychnos cocculoides Baker   Illust. 252
S.A. no: 623   Corky-bark monkey orange. Geelklapper
Rhod. no: 881   Corky-bark monkey orange

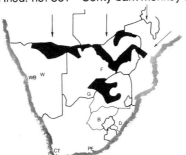

A small tree 2 to 8 m in height, with a compact rounded crown; occurring in woodland on sandveld and on rocky hill slopes. **Bark:** creamy-brown, deeply corky and ridged longitudinally; the branchlets thick, purplish, with longish hairs, and armed with strong curved spines and often ending in a terminal spine. **Leaves:** broadly ovate-oblong to almost circular, 2,5 to 5 × 1,5 to 4 cm, dark green, the upper surface either roughly hairy or without hairs and shiny, the under surface paler green and dull, conspicuously 5-veined from the base; apex and base very broadly tapering to rounded; margin entire; petiole 2 to 6 mm long. **Flowers:** small, greenish-white, in dense compact heads, up to 3,5 cm in diameter, terminal on short lateral branchlets; calyx lobes slender and almost equalling the corolla in length (September to November). **Fruit:** hard, woody-shelled, about 7 cm in diameter, dark green speckled with white, yellowish when mature (April to August).

The edible fruits are much sought after and the confusion regarding the relative merits of the two species, *S. cocculoides* and *S. spinosa,* may well be deliberate. *S. spinosa* is generally claimed to have the more delicious fruit, but this is a fallacy cunningly encouraged by the local peoples who know that, in fact, *S. cocculoides* has unquestionably the more delectable flavour and hope, in this manner, to safeguard it and enjoy its fruit themselves. The specific name means 'like a small grain' and refers to the unusually small fruits of the type specimen. In South West Africa the pulp is said to liquefy completely, and people in the north of the country often pick the fruit green, bury it in the sand and return to it later by which time a refreshing liquid, which is very acceptable in these arid areas, will have been formed. The wood is white and, though tough, is rather soft and pliable; it is used to make implement handles. This species can be distinguished from *S. spinosa* as the latter lacks a corky bark.

Strychnos decussata (Pappe) Gilg
S.A. no: 624   Cape teak. Kaapse kiaat
Rhod. no: 882   Cape teak

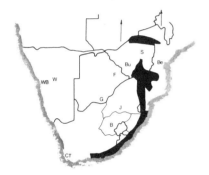

A small slender tree 3 to 12 m in height, often with drooping densely leafy branches; occurring at low altitudes in bush, along rocky dry watercourses, in sandveld, often on termite mounds, and in coastal thicket. **Bark:** dark grey, rather smooth, but with conspicuous lenticular light brown dots; the branchlets also have many small lenticels and a thin waxy layer which splits longitudinally and peels away. Spines not present. **Leaves:** obovate to elliptic, broadest at or above the middle, 1,5 to 5 × 1 to 3 cm, rather leathery, glossy dark green, without hairs; somewhat obscurely 3- to 5-veined from the base, net-veining not visible; apex rounded; base broadly tapering; margin entire; petiole 3 to 6 mm long. **Flowers:** small, white to greenish-white, fragrant, in small loose branched heads, about 3,5 × 2 cm, in the axils of the leaves or on old wood (October to December). **Fruit:** almost spherical but somewhat oblique, fleshy with a crusty rind, about 1,5 cm in diameter, orange or red when mature, containing 1 to 2 smooth seeds (March to September).

The wood is dark brown, heavy and handsome. It works easily and polishes well, and although the small size of the pieces prevents it from being generally used as timber, it has been found suitable for musical instruments. The bark and fruit are reputedly poisonous especially when green, but the root bark, scraped and ground, is favoured as snuff and an infusion prepared from it provides a remedy for stomach disorders. The tough, pliant sticks from this tree are made into laths and are believed to protect huts against lightning; in the 19th century they provided Zulu chiefs with their sticks of ceremony and gave the plant its local name of 'king's tree'.

Strychnos henningsii Gilg
S.A. no: 625   Coffee-bean strychnos. Rooibitterbessie
Rhod. no: 883   Coffee-bean strychnos

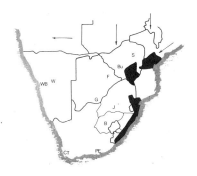

Ranging from a small often shrubby tree 3 m in height, to a large tree up to 21 m; occurring from low altitude dry areas along river banks, in riverine fringes, in scrub, on termite mounds, to coastal and mist-belt evergreen forest. **Bark:** pale grey, rough in smaller specimens becoming dark brown, mottled and scaling to reveal pale grey patches; the branchlets have a waxy coating which splits longitudinally, peeling away; unarmed. **Leaves:** elliptic to broadly ovate, broadest at or above the middle, 2,5 to 6,5 × 0,8 to 4,4 cm, rather leathery, glossy light green, without hairs; 5-veined from the base, but the outer 2 veins rather indistinct, appearing strongly 3-veined; net-veining clearly visible; apex and base broadly tapering; margin entire; petiole 2 to 5 mm long. **Flowers:** small, greenish-cream, sometimes fading to darker yellow, in dense broad flat axillary heads, about 1,5 cm in diameter, in the axils of the current leaves (June to October). **Fruit:** almost spherical, fleshy, about 1,2 cm in diameter, yellow-orange and finally purplish-black when mature; 1- to 2-seeded, each seed with a deep groove down one side and resembling a coffee-bean (December to March).

The wood is pale to dark brown and heavy; the heartwood is very durable and valued as fencing posts and implement handles. Bitter alkaloids, known to be poisonous, have been isolated from the bark and fruits; the bark is used in African medicine as a purgative, as a remedy for colic, to relieve nausea and to treat syphilis. The root provides a remedy for rheumatic pains.

Strychnos innocua Delile
S.A. no: —
Rhod. no: 884   Dull-leaved mukwakwa

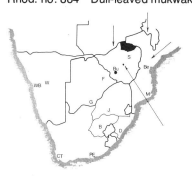

A small straight-stemmed tree 3 to 6 m in height; occurring in open woodland and on rocky koppies. **Bark:** light grey, smooth; branches pale grey-brown, unarmed. **Leaves:** elliptic to obovate, 4 to 10 × 2 to 7 cm, leathery, dull bluish-green or pale green, only slightly green below, with or without hairs; 3- to 5-veined from the base, with net-veining on both surfaces; apex rounded; base tapering to almost rounded; margin entire; petiole 2 to 6 mm long. **Flowers:** greenish-yellow to cream, up to 8 mm long, in 2- to 4-flowered axillary clusters, on short stalks about 2 to 5 mm long; calyx lobes short and broad (October to December). **Fruit:** almost spherical, up to 7,5 cm in diameter, deep yellow when mature, with a thick woody shell and an edible pulp (February to June).

This species hybridises with *S. pungens*.

766

Strychnos madagascariensis Poiret   Illust. 253
[*S. innocua* Delile subsp. *dysophylla* (Benth.) Verdoorn; *S. innocua* Delile subsp. *gerrardii* (N. E. Brown) Verdoorn]
S.A. no: 626   Black monkey orange. Swartklapper
Rhod. no: 886   Shiny-leaved mukwakwa

A small shrubby tree about 6 m in height, often many-stemmed from the base, sometimes reaching 15 m; occurring in open woodland, on rocky koppies, in riverine fringes and coastal forest. **Bark:** light grey, smooth; the branches are unarmed but frequently produce hard rigid knobby dwarf lateral shoots from 1 to 3 cm long which give the impression of spines. **Leaves:** elliptic to almost circular, 2 to 10 × 1 to 6 cm, shiny dark green above, conspicuously paler green below, rather leathery; 3- to 5-veined, with the 1 to 2 pairs of distinct secondary veins curving to run parallel to the margin; net-veining not conspicuous; apex tapering to attenuate; base tapering to rounded; margin entire, with or without a hair fringe; petiole 1 to 5 mm long. **Flowers:** small, greenish-yellow, in 1- to 4-flowered clusters on short stalks, with several clustered together in the axils of the leaves or on the old wood; calyx lobes short and broad (August to December). **Fruit:** almost spherical, up to 8 cm in diameter, distinctive bluish-green when young, yellow when mature, with a thick woody shell (February to November, often overlapping into the next flowering season).
The fruit is edible and the pulp is dried and kept for several weeks; if fire-dried it is said to increase in sweetness. The wood is whitish; the seed germinates readily and the plants are fairly fast-growing.

Strychnos mellodora S. Moore
S.A. no: —
Rhod. no: 888   Forest strychnos

A large tree reaching 40 m in height; occurring in moist evergreen forest. **Bark:** dark grey-brown, cracking into small rectangular sections; the branchlets are smooth, without hairs or spines. **Leaves:** elliptic, 6 to 12 × 2 to 5 cm, thinly leathery, dull green above, paler green below, not distinctly 3- to 5-veined from the base, but with 5 to 8 secondary veins on each side, all equally prominent; apex attenuate into a slender tip; base tapering; margin entire; petiole up to 8 mm long. **Flowers:** small, white, honey-scented (the specific name refers to this), in showy, many-flowered axillary heads up to 12 cm long near the tips of the branches (October to November). **Fruit:** spherical, fleshy, 1 to 1,5 cm in diameter, yellowish when mature (January).
The fruits have a bitter taste and are apparently not eaten.

767

LOGANIACEAE

Strychnos mitis S. Moore
S.A. no: 627   Pitted-leaf strychnos. Geelbitterbessie
Rhod. no: 889   Pitted-leaf strychnos

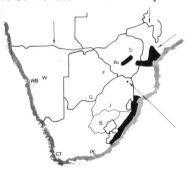 

A medium to large tree, 7 to 50 m in height, with a rounded crown; occurring in medium altitude moist evergreen forests and coastal bush. **Bark:** pale grey to greenish and very thin; branchlets slender, pale grey to creamy-brown, unarmed, may be finely hairy. **Leaves:** elliptic to ovate, 5 to 11,5 × 1,5 to 5 cm, glossy dark green above, paler green below, conspicuously 3- to 5-veined from the base or near the base, one pair of conspicuous veins arises about 10 mm above the base, small pockets (acarodomatia), which are said to house mites, may be present in the axils of the lateral veins; apex tapering to narrowly tapering; base tapering to rounded; margin entire, often wavy; petiole 2 to 5 cm long. A pair of reduced leaves near the base of the branchlets tends to persist. **Flowers:** small, creamy-white, faintly scented, in short dense branched axillary heads about 2,5 cm long, near the ends of the branchlets, often produced in such profusion that the large dark crowns of the trees are covered with flowers; the sepals are petalloid (February to April). **Fruit:** spherical, rather thin-walled, about 1 to 1,5 cm in diameter, yellow to orange when mature; 1- to 2-seeded (May to July, or on to November).
The wood is whitish, yellow to light brown, hard and heavy; it is difficult to work, does not finish well and seems to be little used other than to make implement handles.

Strychnos potatorum L.f.   Illust. 254
[*S. stuhlmannii* Gilg]
S.A. no: 630   Grape strychnos. Swartbitterbessie
Rhod. no: 890   Grape strychnos

Sometimes a shrub, but usually a small to medium sized heavily foliaged tree 5 to 15 m in height; occurring at medium to low altitudes, in open woodland, along dry watercourses, often on termite mounds, and in riverine fringes. **Bark:** characteristically very pale silvery-grey to yellowish-brown, usually smooth but may become rather rough with age; the branches are often dichotomously branched, pale to dark brown, without spines. **Leaves:** elliptic to ovate, 6 to 15 × 3 to 9 cm, thinly textured, glossy dark green above, paler green and dull below, without hairs on either surface; markedly 3- to 5-veined from the base or near the base, the veins being conspicuously pale green curving towards but not reaching the apex; apex narrowly tapering; base rounded or shallowly lobed; margin entire; petiole 1 to 7 mm long. A reduced pair of leaves near the base of branchlets falls early, leaving a ring scar. **Flowers:** whitish to yellowish-green, about 5 mm long, in 2- to 5-flowered heads on very slender stalks up to 10 mm long, several heads together forming a spiky-looking cluster near the base of the branchlets in the axils of small scales (October to December). **Fruit:** almost spherical, softly fleshy, smooth, about 2 cm in diameter, blue-black when mature, rather grape-like (February to July, or into the next flowering season).

The seeds, if rubbed on the inside of a container, are said to purify drinking water by causing precipitation of impurities. There are conflicting reports on the edibility of the fruits but it appears that the bark and roots are toxic and, when crushed and pounded, are used as a fish poison. However, elephants are said to uproot the trees to obtain the roots and in Botswana the bark is often found deeply scored by the teeth of baboons.

Strychnos pungens Solereder
S.A. no: 628   Spine-leaved monkey orange. Stekelblaarklapper
Rhod. no: 891   Spine-leaved monkey orange

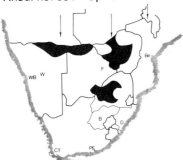

A small tree 3 to 7 m in height; occurring in open woodland, often in stony places and at the base of rocky koppies. **Bark:** grey to brown, smooth in smaller specimens becoming rough and flaking into square sections with age; branchlets conspicuously lenticellate, without spines but with short rigid lateral branchlets. **Leaves:** usually narrowly elliptic, but may be broadly elliptic or even obovate, 3 to 8 × 1,3 to 5 cm, leathery, shiny dark green above, scarcely paler green but dull below, without hairs, 3-veined almost from the base, the outer veins forming a distinctive vein running just inside the margin; apex abruptly drawn into a very distinctive hard sharp spine; base broadly tapering to rounded; margin entire; petiole thick, 1 to 4 mm long. **Flowers:** greenish-white, up to 9 mm long, in tight rounded clusters about 2 cm in diameter, in the axils of the current leaves or on older branches (October). **Fruit:** spherical, woody-shelled, up to 12 cm in diameter, distinctive bluish-green when young, yellow when mature (March to August).

The pulp in the fruit is fragrant and pleasant-tasting, the presence of citric acid making it refreshing; however the unripe fruit sometimes causes headaches, giddiness and vomiting. A decoction of the roots is used to cure stomach ache and to treat bronchitis, while an infusion of the crushed leaves in water provides a lotion for sore eyes. The wood is yellow and apparently has little value.

Strychnos spinosa Lam.
S.A. no: 629   Spiny monkey orange. Groenklapper
Rhod. no: 892   Spiny monkey orange

769

LOGANIACEAE

A shrub or small tree 1 to 7 m in height; occurring from sea level to about 1 500 m, in open woodland and riverine fringes. **Bark:** grey, roughish tending to flake in rectangular segments, but not deeply fissured or corky; branchlets rather pale, thin, with or without very short hairs, with hooked thorns. **Leaves:** elliptic, ovate to almost circular, 1,5 to 9 × 1,2 to 7,5 cm, light to dark green and glossy above, paler green and dull below, leathery, with or without fine hairs, distinctly 3- to 5-veined from the base, the veins being pale green and curving along the margin; apex tapering to rounded, sometimes notched; base tapering, rounded or slightly lobed; margin entire, inclined to be wavy; petiole 2 to 10 mm long. **Flowers:** creamy-green, up to 6 mm long, in compact heads, about 4 × 3,5 cm, terminal on short lateral twigs, densely crowded together on short stalks about 10 mm long (October to January). **Fruit:** spherical, woody-shelled, up to 12 cm in diameter, deep yellow to yellow-brown when mature (March to August).

The roots or green fruit are used by the Zulus as an antidote to snakebite while the roots alone provide an emetic and also a remedy for fevers and inflamed eyes. An analgesic is made from a decoction of the leaves, and jigger fleas are removed from the feet by an application of a paste in which the grated root is mixed with oil. Sounding-boxes for the musical instrument known as the *mbira* are sometimes made from the shells of the dried fruit; the wood is suitable for fuel.

Strychnos usambarensis Gilg

[*S. micans* S. Moore]
S.A. no: 631   Stipe-fruited strychnos. Bloubitterbessie
Rhod. no: 893   Stipe-fruited strychnos

A shrub or much-branched small to medium sized tree up to 10 m in height; occurring in moist evergreen forest, on the rocky banks of streams and in coastal bush; also in mixed woodland, on rocky koppies and among boulders. **Bark:** medium grey-brown with many lenticels; branchlets without spines. **Leaves:** borne horizontally along the branchlets; ovate to elliptic, often broadest below the middle, 3 to 8 × 1,2 to 3,5 cm, usually 4 to 6 × 1,5 to 2,5 cm, rather glossy dark green above, paler green and dull below, thinly leathery; rather obscurely 3- to 5-veined from the base or near the base; apex narrowly tapering to attenuate; base tapering, rounded or shallowly lobed; margin entire; petiole 2 to 6 mm long. **Flowers:** very small, whitish or yellowish-green, sweetly scented, in compact axillary clusters (January to May). **Fruit:** spherical, softly fleshy, 1 to 1,5 cm in diameter, with the base drawn out into a neck, or stipe, jointed with the stalk, yellow when mature with a waxy bloom; single seeded (May to January).

2. ANTHOCLEISTA Afzel.

Anthocleista grandiflora Gilg

[*A. zambesiaca* Baker]
S.A. no: 632   Forest fever tree. Boskoorsboom
Rhod. no: 894   Big-leaf

A tall slender tree 6 to 30 m in height, with a straight clean stem, comparatively shortly branched high up; characteristic of high rainfall, medium to low altitude forest. **Bark:** pale grey or brown, smooth. **Leaves:** clustered at the ends of the branches, simple, very large, obovate-oblong, 95 × 35 cm, or more; apex broadly rounded; base tapering to rounded; margin entire, thickened, often unevenly crisped; petiole absent or very short. **Flowers:** creamy-white, the tube up to 4 cm long, opening out at

The forest fever tree, Anthocleista grandiflora, *growing in the Salisbury Botanic Gardens.*

the throat into 11 to 13 corolla lobes, about 4 cm in diameter, greenish outside, creamy within, firmly fleshed, jasmine-scented, terminal, in large flat-topped branched heads, or trichotomously branched cymose panicles, up to 45 cm in diameter. Bisexual; calyx leathery, deeply 4-lobed; petals joined to form a tube, separating into spreading lobes; stamens as many as the corolla lobes, joined at the base forming a short ring; ovary 2-chambered on a fleshy disc. Although the flowers are large and attractive, they are usually borne so high up that they escape attention (September to January). **Fruit:** almost spherical, fleshy, up to 3,5 × 2 cm, smooth, drying to brown, with many minute seeds (January to June).

The wood is soft, brittle, white to yellowish and marked with horseshoe-shaped groups of small air-holes. It nails without splitting and could prove useful for such articles as fruit boxes, otherwise it seems to have little value. A decoction of the leaves is used as a remedy for malaria and the bark is chewed to relieve diarrhoea. The plants coppice freely, propagate easily from seed and the growth is rapid although they require plentiful water and are tender to frost.

LOGANIACEAE

3. NUXIA Lam.

Shrubs or trees, with fibrous stringy bark. **Leaves:** whorled, sometimes opposite, very rarely alternate. **Flowers:** bisexual, in terminal or axillary, paniculate or corymbose cymes; calyx bell-shaped, with 4 erect lobes, hairy within; corolla tube rarely protruding beyond the calyx, the 4 lobes only extending beyond the calyx and usually bending backwards; stamens attached in the throat of the corolla tube; ovary 2-chambered, tapering into the style. **Fruit:** a small capsule, not more than 5 mm long and splitting into 2 valves.

Key to the tree species of *Nuxia:*
1 Leaves opposite, not in whorls of 3 .... **N. oppositifolia**
  Leaves in whorls of 3 (very rarely opposite) 2
2 Flowers forming terminal heads projecting well beyond the leaves, the whole inflorescence oblong in outline. Confined to a small area in the Transvaal from Zeerust to Pretoria . **N. glomerulata**
  Flowers in terminal and axillary heads among the leaves, the inflorescence tending to be broader than long. Widespread 3
3 Leaves 5 to 15 cm long, petioles 2,5 to 4,5 cm long; flowers in large, loose panicles ....
  .... **N. floribunda**
  Leaves 1 to 8 cm long, petioles up to 10 mm long only; flowers in dense congested heads ....
  .... **N. congesta**

A fifth species *N. gracilis* Engl., a bushy shrub, 2 to 3 m in height, occurs at low altitudes in dry areas often along watercourses. It occurs in the northern Cape and near Lydenburg; it does not reach tree proportions.

Nuxia congesta R. Br. ex Fresen.   Illust. 255
[*N. viscosa* Gibbs]
S.A. no: 633   Broshout. Wildevlier
Rhod. no: 895   Brittlewood

A shrub or tree, variable in size, from 2 to 20 m in height; occurring from coastal to medium altitude evergreen forest, also in rocky gorges, and in dry areas among boulders. **Bark:** dark brown, shredding in longitudinal strips. **Leaves:** in whorls of 3, crowded at the ends of the branches, elliptic to almost circular, 1 to 8 × 0,6 to 3,8 cm, rather leathery, scaly or hairy; apex tapering to rounded, with a hair-like tip; base tapering; margin entire or coarsely toothed; petiole 2 to 10 mm long. **Flowers:** white, sometimes tinged with mauve, about 5 mm long, in dense congested heads, mushroom-shaped or flat-topped, at the ends of the branchlets (May to July). **Fruit:** a small many-seeded hairy capsule only just protruding beyond the persistent calyx lobes (August to October).
The wood is whitish-yellow, hard and heavy, but seems to have little use except as fuel.
Dr I. C. Verdoorn, in *Flora of South Africa* XXVI (1963), reduced a number of species to synonymy under *N. congesta;* she then loosely separated this complex into three races:

(a) the eastern race – occurring in the northern and eastern Transvaal, Natal and the eastern Cape;
(b) the central race – occurring in the central Transvaal;
772 (c) the western race – occurring in Botswana, Rhodesia and the extreme western Transvaal.

In Rhodesia only the eastern and western races occur and appear to be distinct in both appearance and habitat. If the Rhodesian material were considered in isolation, one would have no hesitation in separating the populations that occur in more open rocky situations (such as the Shashe koppies between Fort Victoria and Umvuma and in the hills of the Matopos), under *N. viscosa* Gibbs, from the typical *N. congesta* which are sizable trees largely confined to the forests of the eastern mountains.

Nuxia floribunda Benth.   Illust. 256
S.A. no: 634   Forest nuxia. Bosvlier
Rhod. no: 896   Forest nuxia

A small to medium sized tree 3 to 10 m in height, occasionally reaching 15 m; occurring in evergreen forest or at forest margins. **Bark:** pale grey, smooth and rather powdery; the young branchlets purplish at first, becoming pale with prominent raised leaf scars. **Leaves:** in whorls of 3, oblong-elliptic, 5 to 15 × 1 to 5,5 cm, light glossy green, the midrib prominent and purplish in young leaves; apex and base tapering; margin entire, often wavy, sometimes obscurely toothed; petiole slender, 1,5 to 4,5 cm long. **Flowers:** creamy-white, about 3 mm long, in repeatedly branched sprays, 25 to 30 cm long, both terminal and axillary, near the ends of the branchlets, producing a large, conspicuous, fragrant and attractive mass (May to August). **Fruit:** an ovoid capsule, about 4 mm long, protruding about half way beyond the persistent calyx, pale creamy-brown when mature, splitting into 4 lobes, and releasing the very fine seed (June to October).

The large handsome flower heads distinguishes this species from the other species of *Nuxia*. The wood is pale yellowish, hard, heavy and was once employed in wagon construction, but is now little used. These plants may be propagated from cuttings and with difficulty from seed and although they need plenty of water and are frost-tender, would make good garden subjects.

Nuxia glomerulata (C. A. Smith) Verdoorn
[*Lachnopylis glomerulata* C. A. Smith]
S.A. no: 634,1   Rock nuxia. Rotsvlier
Rhod. no: —

A straggling shrub or small tree, 1 to 3 m in height, often gnarled and twisted; occurring on open hillsides, stony slopes or in rocky ravines. **Bark:** greyish to brownish. **Leaves:** usually in whorls of 3, narrowly oblanceolate to oblong, 1,5 to 5 × 0,5 to 1,5 cm, green above, rather paler green below, young leaves with soft short hairs on both surfaces, most of which are lost by maturity, the midrib alone remains hairy especially on the under surface; fine net-veining is clearly visible; apex broadly

773

tapering to rounded, with a hair-like tip; base tapering; margin entire or with few teeth in the upper section; petiolate. **Flowers:** white, about 3 mm long, fragrant, in rather small compact, dichotomously branched terminal heads, standing out clearly above the leaves (February). **Fruit:** a brown capsule, about 3 × 1 mm, scarcely protruding beyond the persistent calyx; opening by 2 apical pores (August).

Nuxia oppositifolia (Hochst.) Benth.
S.A. no: 635   River nuxia. Watervlier
Rhod. no: 897   River nuxia

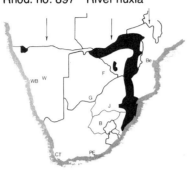

A shrub or small tree up to 7 m in height; occurring along rivers and streams, in riverine thicket, among rocks and reeds. **Bark:** grey. **Leaves:** opposite, narrowly oblong, 4,5 to 9 × 0,5 to 2,4 cm, light green to greyish-green, rather sticky, finely hairy when young but losing most of these by maturity; apex very broadly tapering to rounded; base narrowly tapering and running into the petiole; margin entire, or with shallow blunt teeth; petiole 2 to 10 mm long. **Flowers:** small, white, in terminal and axillary, inconspicuous, dichotomously or trichotomously branched heads (October to January). **Fruit:** a small capsule, about 3 mm long, scarcely protruding beyond the remains of the persistent calyx (January to May).
The wood is reddish-yellow, handsomely marked, dense, close-grained, but it is seldom sound and is little used.

4. BUDDLEJA L.

Shrubs or small trees, with minute scales or stellate hairs. **Leaves:** opposite to sub-opposite. Stipules may be conspicuous, or represented by an interpetiolar ridge, sometimes obscure. **Flowers:** bisexual, in many-flowered terminal and axillary paniculate cymes, sometimes congested into almost spherical heads; all floral parts in fours; calyx shortly joined, with the lobes hairy on the outside, without hairs within, persistent; corolla tube bell-shaped to cylindric, separating into 4 lobes which may be bearded in the throat; stamens inserted in the throat of the corolla tube; ovary 2-chambered. **Fruit:** a small capsule, splitting at the apex.

Key to the species of *Buddleja:*
1 Leaves without a petiole .... **B. salviifolia**
　Leaves petiolate, although may be very short 2
2 Stipules conspicuous, broad and leaf-like .... **B. auriculata**
　Stipules not conspicuous, falling very early, or absent 3
3 Corolla tube cylindric, up to 9 mm long; anthers not protruding from the mouth **B. pulchella**
　Corolla tube bell-shaped, 3 to 4 mm long; anthers protruding from the mouth 4
4 Leaves long and narrow, usually more than 3 times as long as broad 5
　Leaves not conspicuously long and narrow, oblong to ovate, usually less than 3 times as long as
　　broad 6
5 Leaves more or less smooth above; margin entire .... **B. saligna**
　Leaves deeply wrinkled and puckered above; margins distinctly and closely scalloped ....
　　... **B. loricata**

6 Leaves oblong to oblong-ovate, wrinkled and puckered; margins lobed, the lobes sinuate and scalloped, wavy .... **B. glomerata**

Leaves deltoid, or almost triangular, not conspicuously wrinkled; margins irregularly scalloped or toothed, but not sinuate or wavy .... **B. dysophylla**

Buddleja auriculata Benth.
S.A. no: 636,5   Weeping sage. Treursalie
Rhod. no: 899   Eared buddleja

 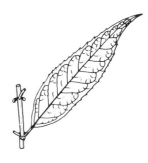

A shrub or small tree, 3 to 4 m in height, with the branches arching almost to the ground; occurring in rocky ravines, on mountain slopes or at the margins of high altitude evergreen forest. **Bark:** light brown, rough and stringy. **Leaves:** ovate-lanceolate to oblong, 3 to 12 × 1 to 5 cm, medium to dark green and rather glossy above, the under surface with whitish-grey hairs; midrib and lateral veins depressed above, prominent below; fine net-veining distinct; apex tapering to a narrow point; base broadly tapering to rounded; margin finely toothed, occasionally entire, rolled under; petioles hairy, 3 to 10 mm long. Stipules large, leaf-like, conspicuous, falling fairly early (the specific name, 'ear-shaped', refers to these). **Flowers:** cream, orange-yellow, lavender or lilac, to flesh-coloured or salmon, sweetly scented, up to 7,5 mm long, in attractive terminal and axillary heads, 4 to 6 cm long (April to August). **Fruit:** a creamy-brown capsule, 3,5 to 6 × 2 to 2,5 mm, protruding for about half its length from the persistent calyx lobes, splitting longitudinally into 2 to 4 valves (June to September).

Buddleja dysophylla (Benth.) Radlk.
S.A. no: 636,3   White climbing sage. Witranksalie
Rhod no: —

 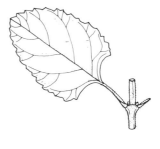

A shrub with a tendency to scramble or a small erect tree up to 4 m in height; occurring at the margins of evergreen forest, in scrub and thickets, in ravines and along the banks of rivers. **Bark:** brown; branches brittle; young parts often densely covered with long rusty hairs. **Leaves:** ovate to broadly ovate, 1 to 10 × 0,7 to 7,5 cm, the upper surface green and sparsely hairy, the under surface markedly paler and densely covered with greyish to creamy or richly rusty stellate hairs and the midrib and lateral veins conspicuous; apex broadly tapering; base square to shallowly lobed or wedge-shaped, making the leaf deltoid; margin irregularly scalloped or toothed; petiole 0,3 to 3 cm long often narrowly winged. Stipules absent, represented by a ridge. **Flowers:** white or cream, sometimes with a maroon throat, about 4 mm long, the anthers protruding from the mouth of the flower; sweetly

775

scented, forming large loose heads at the ends of the branches; stalks and backs of the calyx lobes are densely covered with rusty-yellowish hairs (May to September). **Fruit:** a cylindric capsule, about 4 mm long, covered with brown furry hairs, protruding about two-thirds of its length from the persistent calyx and remains of the corolla, finally splitting into 4 lobes (July to September).

Buddleja glomerata H. L. Wendl.
S.A. no: 636,1   Karoo sage. Karoosalie
Rhod. no: —

A shrub or small tree up to 4 m in height; occurring among rocks on hills and mountains. **Bark:** light brown, covered with a thin layer of bluish scaly hairs, easily rubbed off; the young branchlets are green but densely covered with silvery-white stellate or scaly hairs, as are the petiole, midrib and lateral veins. **Leaves:** oblong to broadly oblong, 1,2 to 6 × 0,2 to 2,6 cm, the upper surface bluish-green, wrinkled and puckered, with sparse short hairs, the under surface rusty to silvery-white with dense scaly hairs, heavily net-veined; apex broadly tapering; base broadly tapering to rounded or shallowly lobed; margin more or less deeply divided into lobes rather than teeth, the lobes themselves being scalloped and sinuate; petiole hairy, 0,2 to 1,3 cm long. Stipules form a prominent interpetiolar ridge. **Flowers:** yellowish to bright yellow, about 3 mm long, the anthers protruding from the mouth of the flower, in terminal almost spherical heads, 8 to 15 cm in diameter (September to March). **Fruit:** a small hairy capsule, about 4 × 2 mm, with the hairs rubbing off in places, protruding for about one-third of its length beyond the persistent calyx lobes (September to March).

The plants grow easily from cuttings, needing a well-drained soil, and are resistent to drought, heat and cold. The flowers are said to smell like cockroaches.

Buddleja loricata Leeuwenberg
[*B. corrugata* (Benth.) Philips]
S.A. no: 636,2   Mountain sage. Bergsalie
Rhod. no: —

A bushy shrub or small tree up to 4 m in height; occurring among rocks or in moist sheltered places on the slopes of high mountains usually above 1 800 m. **Bark:** pale brown. **Leaves:** narrowly oblong-elliptic, 1,5 to 9 × 0,2 to 2 cm, medium to dark green above, wrinkled and puckered (the specific name refers to this), the under surface covered with dense rusty hairs; the midrib and lateral veins depressed above, prominent below; apex tapering to broadly tapering; base tapering to rounded; margin distinctly and closely scalloped; petiole 2 to 10 mm long, with rusty hairs. Stipules absent, represented by a ridge. **Flowers:** cream, sometimes with an orange throat, about 4 mm long, in many-flowered dense terminal heads; the anthers protruding from the mouth of the flower; flower stalks and the backs of the calyx lobes are densely hairy (October to December). **Fruit:** a small ovoid capsule, about 4 × 2 mm, tipped by the persistent style, covered with fine creamy-grey hairs, and splitting when mature into 2 to 4 valves; in dense creamy woolly heads (January to March).

This species resembles *B. salviifolia,* but the latter is more tree-like, its leaves lack the rusty hairs on the lower surface, the apex is rounded and notched and the upper half is more tapering, the stipules are slender, about 8 mm long, and the petiole is absent.

Buddleja pulchella N. E. Brown
S.A. no: 636,4   Red climbing sage. Rooiranksalie
Rhod. no: 900   Climbing buddleja

Usually a shrub, sometimes scrambling, occasionally a small tree up to 7 m in height; occurring at the margins of evergreen forest and round clearings in the forest. **Bark:** brown, stripping in flakes; the young stems are covered with dense woolly hairs. **Leaves:** ovate to oblong, 2,5 to 9 × 1 to 4 cm, the upper surface dark green and rather shiny, the under surface made tawny or rusty with dense stellate hairs; the midrib and lateral veins prominent below; apex tapering to a sharp point; base tapering and running into the petiole; margin entire or shallowly lobed; petiole 0,5 to 1,7 cm long. Stipules absent or represented by a slight ridge. **Flowers:** cream, sometimes with an orange throat, up to 9 mm long, the anthers not protruding from the mouth of the flower; in dense branched terminal and axillary heads (July to August). **Fruit:** an oblong capsule, about 5 mm long, protruding for about half its length from the persistent calyx (August to October).

Buddleja saligna Willd.
S.A. no: 636   Witolienhout. Witolienhout
Rhod. no: 901   Olive buddleja

A shrub or small tree up to 7 m in height; occurring on dry hillsides, in mixed scrub, wooded valleys, at the margins of forest and in coastal thicket. **Bark:** creamy-brown to dark brown, longitudinally furrowed. **Leaves:** linear to oblong, 1,5 to 10 × 0,2 to 1,5 cm, medium to dark green, rather shiny and smooth above, markedly paler green below with dense pale stellate hairs; net-veining is conspicuous on the under surface, rather faint above; apex and base tapering, but the base may be rounded; margin entire, rolled under; petiole 2 to 10 mm long. Stipules absent, sometimes represented by a slight ridge. **Flowers:** white or cream sometimes with a reddish throat, about 4 mm long, honey-scented, with the anthers protruding from the mouth of the flower; in large multi-flowered

The flowers of the witolienhout, Buddleja saligna.

terminal and axillary heads about 12 × 12 cm (August to January). **Fruit:** an ovoid capsule, about 2 mm long, pale yellowish-brown when mature, protruding for about half its length beyond the persistent calyx (September to March).

The wood is tough, hard, heavy, very durable and makes good fencing posts and shafts for assegais; it also provides a good fuel. A decoction of the leaf is used to treat coughs and colds; scrapings of the root are taken as a purgative and to induce vomiting. Plants are easily raised from seeds or cuttings and are fast-growing and hardy; this would make an attractive garden subject.

Buddleja salviifolia (L.) Lam.   Illust. 257
S.A. no: 637   Sagewood. Wildesalie
Rhod. no: 902   Sagewood

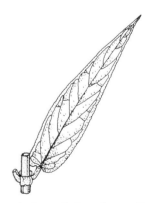

A shrub or small tree, 3 to 8 m in height, often many-stemmed from the base, the branches tending to droop; occurring at the margin of, or in evergreen forest, also on rocky mountain slopes and along watercourses. **Bark:** reddish-brown; the branchlets covered with dense woolly hairs. **Leaves:** broadly or narrowly lanceolate, 3 to 14 × 0,7 to 4 cm, dark green to grey-green, wrinkled and puckered above, the under surface with rusty to whitish hairs; apex narrowly tapering; base deeply lobed; margin finely scalloped, thickened, often rolled under; petiole absent. Stipules slender, interpetiolar, about 6 to 8 mm long. **Flowers:** attractive, white to cream, or lilac to purple, up to 10 mm long, with the anthers not protruding from the mouth of the flower, in large terminal pyramidal heads about 12 cm long (August to October). **Fruit:** an ovoid capsule about 4 to 5 mm long, protruding for about half its length from the persistent calyx (October to December).

778   The heartwood is brown, close-grained, compact, hard and heavy; it was used to make the shafts for assegais and Eve Palmer states that today it makes excellent fishing rods. A decoction of the root provides a remedy for coughs and for the relief of colic while an infusion of the leaves is applied as an eye lotion. The plants strike readily from cuttings, are hardy, and fast-growing but make rather untidy garden subjects which are extremely prone to insect attack.

APOCYNACEAE *(The oleander family)*

Key to the genera (exotic species marked *):

1 Fruit (and ovary) single, not divided into separate carpels 2

  Fruit (and ovary) of 2 separate carpels 3

2 Unarmed shrubs or trees .... **1. Acokanthera**

  Armed shrubs or small trees .... **2. Carissa**

3 Leaves opposite or in whorls of 3 to 5 4

  Leaves alternate or scattered 18

4 Fruits fleshy, spherical to ovoid 5

  Fruits dry, follicular, not fleshy 10

5 Fruit 1- to 2-seeded 6

  Fruit many-seeded 8

6 Leaves large, elliptic to oblong, 12 to 28 × 3 to 6 cm .... **11. Rauvolfia**

  Leaves elliptic up to 11 × 5 cm 7

7 Flower heads usually terminal; stigma sharply pointed; extending only just south of the Zambezi River .... **10. Hunteria**

  Flower heads usually axillary; stigma not sharply pointed; occurring in eastern Rhodesia and in Moçambique .... **3. Pleiocarpa**

8 Calyx joined to form a distinct tube, splitting away horizontally and dropping away from the base .... **9. Voacanga**

  Calyx lobes separated almost to the base 9

9 Fruit of 2 large separate mericarps, each almost spherical .... **7. Tabernaemontana**

  Fruits bi-lobed, the 2 mericarps joined by a distinct saddle .... **8. Ephippiocarpa**

10 Each lobe of the twin fruit less than 5 cm long 11

  Each lobe of the twin fruit more than 5 cm long 12

11 Fruits longitudinally striated, with many seeds in each lobe .... **4. Gonioma**

  Fruits heavily lenticellate, not conspicuously striated, with 2 to 4 seeds in each lobe .... **6. Diplorhynchus**

12 Corolla tube cylindric, not widening appreciably to the mouth 13

  Corolla tube bell-shaped, widening to the mouth 17

13 Fruits very long and slender, up to 32 cm long by no more than 1 cm wide, pendulous .. 14

  Fruits cylindric, to narrowly cigar-shaped, usually about 11 × 2 cm, may be up to 18 cm long, rather sturdy, not pendulous 15

14 Leaves broadly elliptic, dark glossy green above, 7 to 14 × 4 to 7 cm ...... **5. Holarrhena**

  Leaves lanceolate, light clear green, 5 to 8 × 1,5 to 2 cm .... **19. Wrightia**

779

15 Bark thick and corky; leaves usually about 7 × 2,5 cm (up to 11 × 4,5 cm); flowers green, small, petal lobes up to 6 mm long in few-flowered heads .... **16. Oncinotis**

Bark smooth; leaves usually larger than 7 × 2,5 cm (up to 19 cm and 26 cm long); flowers white or creamy-yellow in few to many-flowered heads 16

16 Leaves usually 7 to 9 × 4 to 6,5 cm (up to 19 × 8 cm), light green; flowers white, in small fascicles or few-flowered heads. .... **13. Mascarenhasia**

Leaves usually 14 to 17 × 4 to 6,5 cm (up to 26 × 9,5 cm), dark green; flowers creamy-yellow, in dense, shortly stalked heads .... **12. Funtumia**

17 Petals broad, very showy .... **17. *Nerium**

Petals long, very narrow, strap-like or even thread-like, distinctive and unusual ....
.... **18. Strophanthus**

18 Spines absent; anthers with long, hairy appendages .... **14. Adenium**

Stipules modified into rigid spines; anthers with only a short, terminal appendage................
.... **15. Pachypodium**

1. ACOKANTHERA G. Don

Shrubs or small trees, unarmed. Milky latex is present. **Leaves:** opposite to sub-opposite, simple, axillary glands minute or absent. Stipules absent. **Flowers:** in axillary, many-flowered, usually much contracted corymbs or short racemes. Bisexual; all floral parts in fives; calyx small, divided almost to the base; corolla tube cylindric dividing at the mouth into 5 short lobes, hairy within; stamens enclosed within the corolla tube; ovary not divided, 2-chambered. **Fruit:** single, spherical or ellipsoidal, fleshy, indehiscent. All species are exceptionally poisonous, although it is known that ripe fruits are edible. However, it is not advisable to eat even the 'ripe' fruit because of the likelihood of poisoning.

Key to the tree species of *Acokanthera:*
1 Fruits more than 2 cm long; corolla tube more than 1,2 cm long .... **A. oblongifolia**
  Fruits 0,8 to 2 cm long; corolla tube 0,8 to 1,1 cm long 2
2 Leaves ovate-elliptic, oblong or lanceolate; secondary veins very distinct .... **A. oppositifolia**
  Leaves broadly elliptic to almost circular; secondary veins rather obscure .... **A. schimperi**

Acokanthera oblongifolia (Hochst.) Codd
[*A. spectabilis* (Sonder) J. D. Hook.; *Carissa oblongifolia* Hochst.]
S.A. no: 638   Dune poison-bush. Duinegifboom
Rhod. no: —

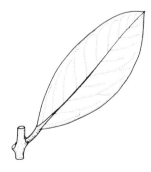

A shrub or small tree up to 7 m in height, occasionally reaching 15 m; occurring in coastal bush and woodland, on sand dunes seldom far from the sea. **Bark:** dark greyish, rough. **Leaves:** broadly elliptic, oblong to lanceolate, 6 to 12 × 2,5 to 6 cm, thickly leathery, glossy dark green above, paler green below, sometimes purple-tinged, without hairs; midrib rather prominent below but lateral veins obscure; apex rounded, with a hair-like tip; base broadly tapering to rounded; margin entire, rolled under; petiole thick, wrinkled, 4 to 10 mm long. **Flowers:** white or slightly tinged with pink; corolla tube slender, 1,3 to 2 cm long, with the lobes each 5 to 7 mm long, sweetly scented; in few-flowered axillary groups, forming masses of flowers along the stems (August to October). **Fruit:** ovoid to almost spherical, fleshy, about 2,5 cm long, purplish-black when mature, 1- to 2-seeded (February to April).

The fruit is said to be highly toxic, especially when unripe. Bushmen dip their arrow-heads into the potent poison yielded by the wood and bark and this has also on occasion been put to use by suicides and would-be murderers, while the Zulus destroy marauding dogs with a preparation from the root. The plants are easy to propagate and would be very beautiful in gardens were it not for their poisonous properties which make them potentially extremely dangerous.

Acokanthera oppositifolia (Lam.) Codd   Illust. 258 and 259
S.A. no: 639   Common poison-bush. Gewone gifboom
Rhod. no: 903   Common poison-bush

A shrub to small tree, 2 to 5 m in height; widespread in a variety of habitats, from rocky places, coastal bush, riverine thicket and forest, to open woodland, often on termite mounds. **Bark:** brown and deeply fissured when old. **Leaves:** ovate-elliptic to oblong, 5 to 10 × 2 to 5 cm, usually about 7 × 3 cm, thickly leathery, medium to dark green and glossy above, paler green and sometimes purple tinged below, the young leaves are reddish, without hairs; lateral veins are distinct; apex broadly tapering, tipped with a sharp almost spine-like point; base broadly tapering; margin entire, rolled under; petiole thickset, wrinkled, 5 to 10 mm long. **Flowers:** white within, pink on the outside, up to 1,1 cm long, the corolla lobes about 2,5 mm long, sweetly scented, in dense axillary clusters (April to December). **Fruit:** ovoid, fleshy, usually about 1 to 1,3 cm long, occasionally up to 2 cm long, red becoming purplish when mature, poisonous (September to February).

All parts of this species – the commonest and most widespread of the genus *Acokanthera* in southern Africa – are highly toxic, with the possible exception of the ripe fruits, and the bark and wood have been used in the preparation of arrow poison. For this, chips are boiled in water until a tar-like substance is obtained and this is then strained and stored, usually in a calabash placed safely in a high tree out of the reach of children. When arrow poison is required, other ingredients such as snakes' heads and the feet of tortoises may be added, but while these have merely a superstitious significance, the toxicity of *Acokanthera* is very real. Experimental work has shown that the injection of the poison into a healthy animal causes death almost immediately while humans inflicted with an arrow wound succumb within thirty minutes to two hours. Meat grilled over a fire kindled from sticks of this tree has proved fatal, and animals which eat the leaves or fruits invariably show dullness, then violent spasms and finally paralysis and death. Paradoxically enough, various parts of the plant have been widely used by Africans as a cure for snakebite.

Acokanthera schimperi (A. DC.) Schweinf.
S.A. no: 640   Round-leaved poison-bush. Rondeblaargifboom
Rhod. no: 904   Round-leaved poison-bush

A shrub or small rather sparsely branched tree up to 6 m in height; occurring in dry woodland, often among rocks. **Bark:** greyish-brown, rather rough. **Leaves:** broadly elliptic to almost circular, 4 to 7 × 3 to 5,5 cm, stiff and leathery, shiny dark green above, paler green and dull below, varying from very scabrid, or harsh to the touch, to only slightly so; lateral veins usually obscure; apex and base very broadly tapering to rounded; margin entire, rolled under; petiole squat, wrinkled, 2 to 6 mm long.

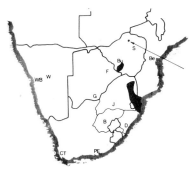

Flowers: white, pink to red, the corolla tube 8 to 9 mm long, the lobes each up to 4 mm long, sweetly scented; in many-flowered axillary clusters (February to May). **Fruit:** almost spherical, fleshy, up to 2 cm in diameter, bright red and finally purple when mature (August to November).

This species is divided into two varieties, of which only var. *rotundata* Codd occurs south of the Zambezi River; the typical variety is known to be very poisonous so it is likely that the local variety is also toxic.

2. CARISSA L.

Shrubs or small trees, much-branched, spiny, often densely so and sometimes scrambling. Spines opposite, simple or forked, often very stout. Milky latex present. **Leaves:** opposite, simple; axillary glands very small or absent. Stipules absent. **Flowers:** terminal or pseudo-axillary, in much contracted umbels or corymbs. Bisexual; all floral parts in fives (rarely fours); calyx small, divided almost to the base; corolla tube cylindric, lobes spreading, sometimes densely hairy in the throat; stamens enclosed within the corolla tube; ovary entire (i.e. not divided), 2-chambered. **Fruit:** single, fleshy, spherical or oblong, indehiscent.

Key to the tree species of *Carissa*:

1 Spines straight, or simple; corolla lobes overlapping to the right .... **C. edulis**
  Spines forked, either once or twice, very rarely simple; corolla lobes overlapping to the left .. 2
2 Fruits large, 3 to 5 cm long, many seeded; corolla lobes 1,5 to 3,5 cm long **C. macrocarpa**
  Fruits rarely more than 1,6 to 2 cm long, 1- to 2-seeded; corolla lobes 0,2 to 1,2 cm long . 3
3 Corolla lobes 9 to 12 mm long, tube 11 to 14 mm long; leaves 5 to 10 cm long .... **C. wyliei**
  Corolla lobes 2 to 5 mm long, tube 6 to 9 mm long; leaves 1 to 7 cm long 4
4 Fruits black when mature; corolla lobes only 2 mm long, and broader than long **C. haematocarpa**
  Fruits red when mature; corolla lobes 3,5 to 5 mm long, and longer than broad **C. bispinosa**

Carissa bispinosa (L.) Desf. ex Brenan   Illust. 260
S.A. no: Num-num. Noemnoem
Rhod. no: 905   Y-thorned carissa

A shrub, sometimes scrambling, or a small tree up to 5 m in height; occurring at medium to low altitudes in dry woodland and coastal scrub; also at the margins of evergreen forest and in forest. **Bark:** grey; the stems and leaves conspicuously green; the spines once or twice forked, very occasionally simple, up to 4,5 cm long. **Leaves:** broadly to narrowly ovate, 1 to 7 × 0,8 to 3,5 cm, leathery or thinly so, glossy dark green above, paler green below, without hairs; the lateral veins obscure; apex broadly tapering to rounded; base rounded, square or lobed; margin entire, rolled under; petiole up to 3 mm long. **Flowers:** white to pinkish, the corolla tube slender, 6 to 9 mm long, with lobes up to 5 mm long, overlapping to the left, sweetly scented; in terminal clusters (October to March). **Fruit:** ovoid, fleshy, about 1,6 cm long, red when mature, edible (March to October). This species is divided into two varieties:

var. *bispinosa* – with stout, Y-shaped thorns, up to 4,5 cm long; leaves thickly leathery, broadly ovate, 1 to 3 cm long, the base square to lobed. Occurring in hot dry karroid scrub at medium to low altitudes and in hot dry woodland.

var. *acuminata* (E. Meyer) Codd – with slender spines, small and rather delicate, seldom more than 3 cm long; the leaves not so thick, much narrower, 2,5 to 7 cm long, the base square to rounded. Occurring as an under-storey plant in evergreen forest.

Intermediates between these two varieties are not uncommon. The var. *bispinosa* closely resembles *C. edulis,* the two obvious features separating them being that *C. edulis* has straight thorns and the corolla lobes overlap to the right. The Y-shaped thorns of *C. bispinosa* might also lead to some confusion with *Balanites maughamii,* but the leaves, flowers and fruits are distinctive. The variety *acuminata* closely resembles *C. wyliei* which is, however, a more lax shrub with bigger leaves; the flowers are quite different. (See key and descriptions).

Carissa edulis Vahl

S.A. no: Simple-spined num-num. Enkeldoringnoemnoem
Rhod. no: 906   Simple-spined carissa

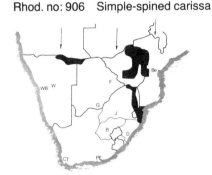 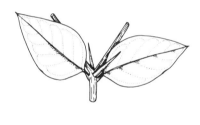

A shrub, with a tendency to scramble, occasionally a small tree up to 5 m in height; occurring in woodland and scrub. **Bark:** grey, smooth; young branchlets with or without hairs; spines simple, straight, up to 4 cm long. **Leaves:** ovate to ovate-elliptic, occasionally almost circular, 2,5 to 6 × 1,8 to 3 cm, leathery, dark green above, paler green below, with or without short soft hairs; lateral veins obscure; apex tapering, often with a bristle-like tip; base rounded to shallowly lobed; margin entire; petiole 1 to 4 mm long. **Flowers:** white tinged with purple, up to 1,8 cm long and about 2 cm in diameter, with corolla lobes overlapping to the right, sweetly scented; in terminal heads about 4 cm in diameter (September to December). **Fruit:** ovoid to almost spherical, up to 1,1 cm in diameter, purplish-black when mature; 2- to 4-seeded (November to January).
The similarity between this species and *C. bispinosa* var. *bispinosa* is mentioned under the latter.

Carissa haematocarpa (Ecklon) A. DC.

S.A. no: 640,2   Karoo num-num. Karoonoemnoem
Rhod. no:—

A shrub or small tree, 2 to 4 m in height; occurring in dry karroid bush. **Bark:** greenish-grey, wrinkled; young branches finely hairy; spines once or twice forked, up to 4,5 cm long. **Leaves:** ovate-elliptic to elliptic, 1,5 to 2,8 × 1 to 1,5 cm, leathery, glossy dark green above, paler green and often wrinkled below; apex tapering to rounded, sometimes with a bristle-like tip; base rounded to square; margin entire; petiole up to 3 mm long. **Flowers:** white, with the corolla tube up to 7 mm

783

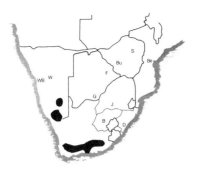

long, and lobes about 5 mm in diameter, overlapping to the left, sweetly scented; in short terminal heads (October to December). **Fruit:** ovoid to almost spherical, fleshy, 6 to 10 mm long, purplish and finally black when mature; 1- to 2-seeded (April to October).

This species is very similar to *C. bispinosa,* but can be separated by the smaller leaves, the small flowers and the black mature fruits.

Carissa macrocarpa (Ecklon) A. DC.
S.A. no: 640,1   Large num-num. Grootnoemnoem
Rhod. no: —

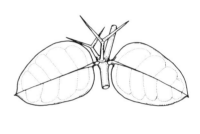

Usually a densely twiggy, branched, spiny shrub or small tree up to 4 m in height; occurring in coastal bush, on sand dunes, seldom far from the sea. **Bark:** grey; the spines are once to twice forked and up to 5 cm long. **Leaves:** broadly ovate, 2 to 6 × 1,7 to 3,5 cm, leathery, glossy dark green above, paler green below, the lateral veins obscure; apex tapering to rather rounded, bristle-tipped; base square to rounded; margin entire; petiole up to 5 mm long; axillary glands conspicuous. **Flowers:** white, sweetly scented, individually quite large, the corolla tube up to 1,4 cm long, the spreading lobes up to 3,5 cm in diameter and overlapping to the left; often produced in clusters at the base of Y-shaped thorns, or terminal (July to November). **Fruit:** ovoid, fleshy, up to 5 cm long, red when mature; many-seeded (September to January).

The fruits make an excellent jam. The bushes are often used as hedges in warm areas; they are rather frost-tender but under suitable conditions grow rapidly.

Carissa wyliei N. E. Brown
S.A. no: Forest num-num. Bosnoemnoem
Rhod. no:—

Usually an under-shrub, sometimes scrambling, occasionally a small tree, 1 to 3 m in height; occurring in low altitude and coastal forest. **Bark:** pale green; the branchlets slender, generally without spines (unusual in this genus), occasionally with very small forked spines, only 3 mm long near the apex of the branchlets. **Leaves:** ovate, 5 to 10 × 2,5 to 4,5 cm, leathery, dull green to bluish-green above, paler green below; the lateral veins indistinct; apex broadly tapering, bristle-tipped; base rounded; margin entire; petiole up to 3 mm long. **Flowers:** white tinged with pink, sweetly scented, with the corolla tube about 11 to 14 mm long, and the spreading lobes about 2,5 cm in diameter (May). **Fruit:** ovoid, fleshy, up to 1,2 cm long, red when mature; 1- to 2-seeded (May).

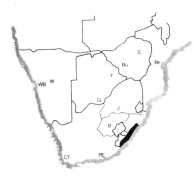

This is said to be an uncommon species with a very limited distribution; however, this could be due to lack of knowledge. The similarity between this species and *C. bispinosa* var. *acuminata* is mentioned under the latter.

3. PLEIOCARPA Benth.

Pleiocarpa pycnantha (K. Schum.) Stapf
[*P. swynnertonii* S. Moore]
S.A. no: —
Rhod. no: 913   Pleiocarpa

A small to large tree, frequently 3 to 5 m in height, but sometimes reaching 30 m; occurring in evergreen forest. **Bark:** grey, smooth in small specimens, becoming rough with irregular longitudinal and horizontal cracks, rather scaly and flaking when old; young branches with conspicuous lenticels; milky latex present, coagulating to become elastic and rubber-like. All parts without hairs. **Leaves:** in whorls of 3 (or occasionally 4), simple, elliptic to oblanceolate, 8 to 12 × 2 to 4 cm, leathery, yellowish-green to shiny dark green above, usually paler green below, with a rather conspicuous marginal vein; apex tapering, often attenuate; base tapering and running into the petiole; margin entire, wavy; petiole slender, up to 1,5 cm long, channelled above. **Flowers:** white often fading to cream or yellow, heavily scented, with the corolla tube about 1,4 cm long; in axillary clusters, usually 3- to 10-flowered, but there may be up to 40 flowers in a cluster. Bisexual; all floral parts in fives; sepals free or only slighlty joined at the base; corolla tube cylindric, the lobes spreading; stamens enclosed within the corolla tube (September to December). **Fruit:** with 2 to 5 separate rounded carpels, or mericarps, each spherical, fleshy, up to 2 cm in diameter, finely wrinkled, becoming yellow-orange and finally red when mature; 1- to 2-seeded (February to April).
This species is divided into two varieties, only the typical variety, var. *pycnantha,* extending south of the Zambezi River.
The wood is hard and durable and is used for huts, implement handles, pestles, and as sharpened stakes in elephant traps. The roots are chewed as a stimulant and also, combined with other ingredients and mixed with palm wine, as a laxative. Among certain peoples the wood is believed to be a charm which brings success to hunters.

APOCYNACEAE

4. GONIOMA E. Meyer

Gonioma kamassi E. Meyer Illust. 261
S.A. no: 641 Kamassi. Kamassie
Rhod. no: —

A shrub or small tree up to 6 m in height, with a slender stem and densely leafy crown; occurring in evergreen forest seldom far from the coast; this is one of the commonest under-storey trees in the Knysna forest. **Bark:** light grey, rather smooth; watery or milky latex is present. **Leaves:** sometimes opposite, usually in whorls of 4 (occasionally 3), simple, oblong to oblanceolate, 4 to 10 × 1 to 2,8 cm, glossy dark green above, light green below; apex tapering; base narrowly tapering and running into the petiole; margin entire, rolled under; petiole short, 2 to 5 mm long. **Flowers:** white to yellowish, fragrant, with the corolla tube hairy within, about 5 mm long, and the lobes spreading, about 7 mm in diameter; in terminal heads. Bisexual; all floral parts in fives; sepals free; stamens enclosed within the corolla tube; ovary made up of 2 free carpels (October to April). **Fruit:** with 2 separate follicular carpels, each oblong, 2,5 to 4 × 1 to 1,5 cm, set at right angles to the stalk, longitudinally striated, light brown when dry and mature; splitting down the upper surface to release numerous papery-winged seeds (December to June).
The wood is light yellow-brown, moderately hard, heavy, very fine-grained and evenly textured; it works easily and has been used for turnery, carving and implement handles. At one time it was an important export, although the pieces of timber were never of any great size.

5. HOLARRHENA R. Br.

Holarrhena pubescens (Buch.-Ham.) Wall. Illust. 262
[*H. febrifuga* Klotzsch]
S.A. no: 642 Jasmine tree. Koorspeul
Rhod. no: 914 Jasmine tree

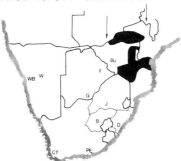 

A shrub or small tree usually 3 to 5 m in height, occasionally reaching 7 m; occurring at low altitudes in rocky places, on koppies, in gorges, and on stony hillsides, often near watercourses and occasionally in open woodland. **Bark:** rather pale grey-brown to dark and almost black, smooth to deeply corky and fissured; young branches finely hairy, green and conspicuously lenticel-dotted; milky latex is present. **Leaves:** opposite, simple, broadly elliptic to oblong, 7 to 14 × 4 to 7 cm, glossy dark green above, pale green below, both surfaces rather sparsely hairy; apex rounded, usually abruplty attenuate; base very broadly tapering to rounded; margin entire, widely wavy; petiole thickset, up to 8 mm long. **Flowers:** pure white, sweetly jasmine-scented, conspicuous, about 1,5 cm long and up to 2 cm in diameter, in large many-flowered dense axillary heads, or congested corymbose racemes, near the ends of the branches; the calyces and flower stalks are usually finely hairy. Bisexual; all floral parts in fives; the calyx lobes may alternate with long glands; corolla tube cylindric with 5 spreading lobes; stamens attached near the base of the corolla tube; ovary of 2 free carpels (November to January). **Fruit:** paired follicular carpels, long and very slender, up to 30 × 0,4 cm, pendulous, dark green and conspicuously dotted with lenticels, drying to pale brown and splitting longitudinally to release many slender seeds about 1 cm long, each with a dense tuft of silky hairs which acts as a parachute as the seeds are carried by the wind (February to June).

The wood is soft. In Moçambique the bark is used to treat fevers.

6. DIPLORHYNCHUS Welw. ex Ficalho & Hiern

Diplorhynchus condylocarpon (Muell. Arg.) Pichon   Illust. 263
S.A. no: 643   Horn-pod tree. Horingpeultjieboom
Rhod. no: 915   Wild rubber

 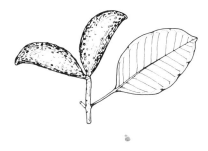

A shrub or small tree, 4 to 10 m in height; occurring on stony hillsides and in open woodland; it is one of the plants which tolerates the serpentine-derived soils of the Great Dyke in Rhodesia, where it often occurs with *Combretum zeyheri*. **Bark:** grey-brown to blackish, flaking in square sections. **Leaves:** opposite, simple, elliptic, 3 to 7 × 2 to 4 cm, yellowish-green, rather shiny above, may be softly hairy when young; apex broadly tapering or abruptly attenuate; base tapering to rounded; margin entire, rather wavy; petiole slender, up to 2,5 cm long, the leaves tending to droop. **Flowers:** white to cream, faintly scented, slender, about 10 mm long and 10 mm in diameter, in rather loose branched axillary comparatively few-flowered heads, or panicles, near the ends of the branches. Bisexual; all floral parts in fives; calyx divided almost to the base; corolla tube cylindric or almost bell-shaped, with 5 slender lobes; stamens enclosed in the corolla tube; ovary of 2 free carpels (September to December). **Fruit:** paired follicular carpels, oblong, up to 4,5 cm long, the tip curved down into a beak, hard and woody, both mericarps standing away at right angles to the branch, dark reddish-brown when dry and heavily dotted with pale lenticels, finally splitting and curving well back to release 2 to 4 seeds, each with a large membraneous wing (March to August).

The tree contains a milky latex, which forms a soft, rubber-like substance which has been used as a bird-lime and, on one occasion, by Fred Eyles, one of Rhodesia's early botanists, to temporarily repair the cracked sump of his car; this held until help could be reached. The latex is also smeared on to the hides of drums to improve their quality and tone. A strong decoction of the root was prepared, in the past, by people of all races to relieve black-water fever, while some Africans take the leaves as a remedy for headaches and stomach disorders and an infusion of the root to treat diarrhoea. The wood has an attractive grain and is suitable for ornaments, for furniture if large enough, and for good fencing posts which often take root. The trees are fire-resistant and will withstand even repeated early burning.

7. TABERNAEMONTANA L.

Shrubs or trees. All parts contain copious milky latex. **Leaves:** opposite, simple. Stipules joined to form a short tubular sheath usually with many resiniferous glands within. **Flowers:** in few-flowered, terminal or pseudo-axillary corymbs or panicles. Bisexual; all floral parts in fives; calyx rather small, divided almost to the base, with several minute glands inside at the base; corolla tube cylindric, ovoid or barrel-shaped with spreading lobes; stamens enclosed within the corolla tube or just protruding from the mouth; ovary of 2 free carpels. **Fruit:** paired mericarps, each ovoid to spherical, leathery, fleshy within, keeled, warty or smooth; many seeded.

Key to the tree species of *Tabernaemontana:*

1 Flowers large, showy; tube up to 3 cm long; lobes spreading up to 4 cm in diameter; twin fruits each remarkably large, up to 20 cm in diameter, surface smooth but flecked with white .... **T. angolensis**
   Flowers much smaller; tube 10 mm long or less; lobes not more than 2,5 cm in diameter; fruits may be smooth or warty, not usually more than 7 cm in diameter 2
2 Flowers showy; tube 8 to 10 × 3,5 mm; lobes 1,2 cm long; fruits smooth, green **T. ventricosa**
   Flowers smaller; tube 6 to 7 × 1,5 mm; lobes about 10 mm long; fruits encrusted and rough with creamy-grey warts .... **T. elegans**

Tabernaemontana angolensis Stapf

[*T. stapfiana* Britten; *Conopharyngia stapfiana* (Britten) Stapf]
S.A. no: —
Rhod. no: 916   Soccer-ball fruit

A medium to tall tree, 10 to 16 m in height; occurring in evergreen forest. **Bark:** yellow-brown, rather smooth, with many large lenticels. **Leaves:** oblong-elliptic, up to 30 × 10 cm, glossy dark green above, pale to greyish-green and dull below; apex broadly tapering to almost rounded; base tapering and tending to run into the petiole; margin entire; petiole sturdy, up to 2,5 cm in the largest leaves. **Flowers:** showy, resembling those of *Plumeria* (frangipani), with the corolla tube greenish-white, the lobes pure white and the throat yellow, up to 3 cm long and 4 cm in diameter, in heads of 6 to 12 flowers on rather long stalks, at the ends of the branches (December to February). **Fruit:** paired, almost spherical, very large, from 18 to 20 cm in diameter; dark green with paler spots, rather melon-like, each with a slight groove down the one side, joined at the base only, indehiscent, falling to the ground and rotting; apparently not edible (March).

Tabernaemontana elegans Stapf   Illust. 264

[*Conopharyngia elegans* (Stapf) Stapf]
S.A. no: 644   Toad tree. Laeveldse paddaboom
Rhod. no: 917   Toad tree

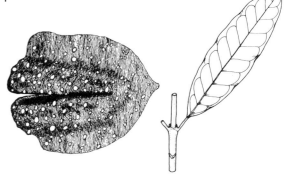

A small tree, 3 to 5 m in height, occasionally reaching 10 m; occurring in evergreen riverine fringes at low altitudes and in coastal scrub forest, often in rocky places. **Bark:** thick, pale creamy brownish-grey, corky, deeply fissured; the branchlets with tough stringy bark; all parts without hairs. **Leaves:** oblong to elliptic, 9 to 20 × 5 to 7 cm, thinly leathery, glossy dark green above, markedly paler below; apex broadly tapering to almost rounded, occasionally attenuate; base narrowly to broadly tapering; margin entire; petiole thickset, up to 2,5 cm long. Stipules united into a distinctive short sheath, falling quite early. **Flowers:** white to cream, up to 2,5 cm in diameter with a short corolla tube up to 7 mm long, and lobes about 10 mm long; in loose axillary or terminal heads, which may be faintly sweetly scented; large ovate bracts are present among the flower heads but fall early (October to February, sometimes on to May). **Fruit:** paired, each mericarp ovoid to almost spherical, joined at the base only, 6 to 7 × 4 to 5 cm, conspicuously ridged with the tip turned down into a beak; dark green dotted with pale grey warts, splitting when mature to expose bright orange pulp containing many brown seeds; the old shrivelled and empty fruits may stay on the tree for months and still be there at the next flowering season (April to September).

The dry shrivelled and gaping fruits are pale brown and warty, resembling a toad's head. The pulp is highly esteemed by certain Africans and is eaten with relish by birds, monkeys and baboons. The coagulated latex, which is rubber-like but of inferior quality, is used as a styptic. The root is taken as a remedy for pulmonary diseases.

Tabernaemontana ventricosa Hochst. ex A. DC.
[*Conopharyngia ventricosa* (Hochst. ex A. DC.) Stapf]
S.A. no: 645   Forest toad tree. Bospaddaboom
Rhod. no: 918   Small-fruited toad tree

A tree, from 4 to 25 m in height; occurring in evergreen forest. **Bark:** grey; all parts without hairs. **Leaves:** oblong to elliptic, 9 to 17 × 3,5 to 6 cm, glossy dark green above, paler green below; apex tapering or attenuate; base broadly tapering to rounded; margin entire; petiole 0,5 to 1,5 cm long. Stipules joined to form a very short sheath about 2 mm long, falling early. **Flowers:** white to cream, sweetly scented, up to 2,5 cm in diameter, with a tube up to 10 mm long; in rather small dense, axillary or terminal heads (October to December). **Fruit:** paired, joined at the base only, each mericarp ellipsoidal to oblong, 4 to 6 × 2,5 to 4 cm, smooth, dark green mottled with paler green, splitting to reveal orange-coloured pulp containing many seeds (April to September).

8. EPHIPPIOCARPA Markgraf

Ephippiocarpa orientalis (S. Moore) Markgraf
S.A. no: 645,1   Dwarf toad tree. Kleinpaddaboom
Rhod. no: —

A shrub or small tree, 1 to 3 m in height; a common under-storey constituent of coastal forest. **Bark:** pale green; branchlets green and slender. No milky latex is present. **Leaves:** opposite, simple, lanceolate to elliptic, 7 to 12 × 2,5 to 3,5 cm, thinly textured; the lateral veins obscure; apex tapering to attenuate; base tapering; margin entire; petiole up to 10 mm long, with tooth-like glands in the leaf axils. Stipules fall early. **Flowers:** white, sweetly scented, up to 1,5 cm long and 2,5 cm in diameter, in few-flowered, sparse terminal heads, on slender stalks. Bisexual; all floral parts in fives; calyx lobes leaf-like, divided almost to the base, with several minute glands inside at the base; corolla tube

789

APOCYNACEAE

cylindric, with spreading lobes; stamens enclosed within the corolla tube, forming a cone; ovary of 2 almost free carpels (October to February). **Fruit:** paired, fleshy, joined by a distinct saddle, each lobe about 2,5 × 2,5 cm, ridged, creamy-green marked with dark green streaks and resembling a pair of short, thickset horns; each lobe contains several brown, ridged seeds (April to May).

9. VOACANGA Thouars

Shrubs or trees; all parts contain milky latex. **Leaves:** opposite, simple; leaf bases united to form a short rim or sheath. Axillary glands present. **Flowers:** in terminal, often paired corymbs or racemes. Bisexual; all floral parts in fives; calyx tubular with glands at the base, splitting horizontally; corolla tube cylindric thickened at the mouth, with spreading lobes; stamens attached near the mouth of the corolla tube; disc annular, fleshy; ovary of 2 free or partly joined carpels. **Fruit:** 2 large spherical or pear-shaped fleshy mericarps with sticky latex.

Key to the species of *Voacanga:*
Leaves oblong to oblanceolate, apex very broadly tapering to rounded, sometimes notched, base narrowly and gradually tapering into the petiole, both surfaces conspicuously scattered with pale coloured dots and pits; the lobes of the fruit up to 7 to 9 cm in diameter .... **V. thouarsii**
Leaves broadly ovate to broadly elliptic, apex broadly tapering to abruptly and broadly attenuate, base tapering, pale coloured dots and pits very sparsely scattered but usually absent; the lobes of the fruit each 5 cm in diameter .... **V. schweinfurthii**

Voacanga schweinfurthii Stapf
S.A. no: —
Rhod. no: —   Small-fruited voacanga

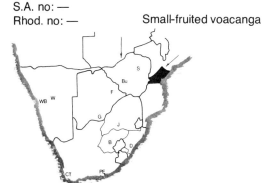 

A small tree up to 8 m in height; occurring in coastal forest, mixed woodland on sand or along river banks. **Bark:** grey or pale brown, smooth to rather rough, irregularly fissured. **Leaves:** broadly ovate to broadly elliptic, up to 17 × 10 cm, glossy dark green above, light pale green and dull, with conspicuous net-veining below; sparsely scattered pale dots and pits may be present; apex broadly tapering, to abruptly and broadly attenuate; base tapering; margin entire; petiole obscured by the decurrent leaf base, up to about 1,5 cm long. **Flowers:** white, with a strong rather foetid scent, about 3 to 4 cm in diameter, petals joined at the base to form a tube; in 10- to 20-flowered terminal and axillary heads (November to January). **Fruit:** paired, the mericarps ovoid to almost spherical, joined at the base only, each up to 5 cm in diameter, shiny dark green with conspicuous pale brownish lenticels, fleshy, becoming pale brown when dry; many seeded (January to August).

Voacanga thouarsii Roemer & J. A. Schultes   Illust. 265
S.A. no: 646   Wild frangipani. Wildefrangipani
Rhod. no: 919   Wild frangipani

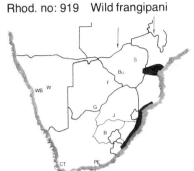

A small to medium sized, well rounded tree, 5 to 15 m in height; at the margins of evergreen forest and in swamp forest. **Bark:** pale grey, smooth becoming rough with age. **Leaves:** crowded near the ends of the branches, oblong to oblanceolate, 8 to 16 × 2,5 to 5,5 cm, thinly leathery, both surfaces with scattered pale coloured patches and pits; apex broadly tapering to rounded, sometimes notched; base narrowly tapering and running into the petiole; margin entire; petiole partially obscured by the decurrent leaf base, 1 to 2 cm long. Stipules small, ensheathing, but falling early. **Flowers:** showy, white fading to yellow, with a strong cloying scent, up to 4,5 cm in diameter; corolla tube about 1,4 cm long; in few-flowered heads, usually in pairs near the tips of the branchlets (August to February). **Fruit:** paired, joined at the base, each mericarp about 7 to 9 cm in diameter, ovoid to almost spherical, thickly leathery, dark green mottled with paler green or whitish-yellow, finally splitting to reveal numerous seeds embedded in a fleshy pulp (December to September).
The latex has been used as bird-lime. When standing in water in swamp forest, the trees can develop air roots which rise above the water level.

10. HUNTERIA Roxb.

Hunteria zeylanica (Retz.) Gardner ex Thwaites
[*H. africana* K. Schum.]
S.A. no: —
Rhod. no: —   Hunteria

A medium to large tree, 10 to 40 m in height; occurring in evergreen forest and riverine fringes. **Bark:** grey, smooth. **Leaves:** opposite, simple, elliptic, up to 11 × 5 cm; apex broadly tapering to abruptly attenuate; base tapering; margin entire; petiole up to 1,5 cm long. Stipules absent. **Flowers:** white to pale yellow, about 1,5 cm in diameter with the corolla tube 8 mm long; in few-flowered, terminal or pseudo-axillary heads, or corymbs. Bisexual; calyx divided almost to the base with scale-like glands between the lobes; corolla tube widest near the middle, with the mouth constricted by a thickened ring, without hairs; stamens enclosed within the tube; ovary of 2 free carpels; stigma sharply pointed

791

(August to December). **Fruit:** paired, fleshy, joined at the base, each mericarp spherical up to 10 mm in diameter, orange when mature; 1- to 2-seeded (November to March).

This species is divided into three subspecies, only the subsp. *africana* (K. Schum.) Pichon occurring on the African continent; the other two subspecies occur in India and the Far East.

11. RAUVOLFIA L.

Rauvolfia caffra Sonder   Illust. 266
[*R. natalensis* Sonder]
S.A. no: 647   Quinine tree. Kinaboom
Rhod. no: 920   Rauvolfia

A small to large tree, 6 to 20 m in height; nearly always associated with available ground water, along wooded stream banks and at the margins of evergreen forest. **Bark:** grey to brown, rough, fissured and rather corky; younger bark distinctively rippled or wrinkled; all parts contain milky latex. **Leaves:** in whorls of 3 to 5, usually 4, simple, oblong to elliptic, 12 to 28 × 3 to 6 cm, thinly leathery, glossy bright green above, dull paler green below; midrib channelled above; the net-veins are almost translucent; apex attenuate; base narrowly tapering and running into the petiole; margin entire; petiole partly obscured by the decurrent leaf base, about 1 to 3 cm long; numerous glands in the leaf axils form a dense fringe, but this is not conspicuous. Stipules absent. **Flowers:** white, sweetly scented, up to 4 mm long and only 2 mm in diameter, in large dense heads, or cymes at the ends of the branches of a large umbel, 12 to 20 cm in diameter. Bisexual; all floral parts in fives; calyx small, divided almost to the base, or joined to form a shallow cup; corolla tube cylindric, thickened round the mouth, with a densely hairy throat; corolla lobes small; stamens attached above the centre of the corolla tube; ovary of 2 partially joined carpels (July to October). **Fruit:** almost spherical paired fleshy mericarps, grooved between the 2 lobes, each lobe about 1,3 cm in diameter, becoming black and wrinkled when mature; sometimes only 1 mericarp develops; 1- to 2-seeded (October to March).

The wood is soft and pale; it nails well, is suitable for fruit boxes, and for spoons, bowls, curios and drums. The latex is thin and bitter, leading, at one time, to its use in the treatment of malaria, but it is now known to be ineffective. However, the bark, especially that of the root, is known to contain reserpine and related alkaloids, obtained commercially from *R. serpentina* Benth., from India and the Far East, and *R. vomitoria* Afzel., from East Africa; this drug is a tranquilliser used in the treatment of high blood pressure. Some Africans use the latex as a remedy for infant diarrhoea and many other ailments, from skin disorders to abdominal complaints, are treated by various parts of the tree. *R. caffra* is an ornamental plant; it germinates readily from seed, transplants well and is comparatively fast-growing.

This species resembles *Breonadia microcephala* Hiern (Rubiaceae), but in the latter the fruit is a dry nutlet, the leaves are leathery, dark green, rather broader, and the veins are not translucent.

12. FUNTUMIA Stapf

Funtumia africana (Benth.) Stapf
[*F. latifolia* (Stapf) Schlechter]
S.A. no: —
792   Rhod. no: 923   Silk rubber

A medium sized tree up to 15 m in height; it frequently becomes common in the under-storey of moist evergreen forest. **Bark:** grey, smooth; the bole slightly buttressed in larger specimens; all parts with milky latex which rapidly becomes sticky on exposure to air. **Leaves:** opposite, simple, oblong-elliptic, up to 26 × 0,5 cm, but usually about 14 to 17 × 4 to 6,5 cm, leathery, dark green above, paler green below with the midrib and lateral veins particularly prominent on the under surface; apex abruptly attenuate; base broadly tapering; margin entire; petiole squat, about 10 mm long in the largest leaves; axillary glands small and numerous. Stipules absent. **Flowers:** creamy-yellow, sweetly scented, about 1,5 cm in diameter, the corolla tube about 5 mm long; in dense shortly stalked axillary clusters, or cymes. Bisexual; all floral parts in fives; calyx small, with flattened glands at the base; corolla tube very thick and fleshy in the upper half, the mouth very narrow, the lobes narrow and without hairs; stamens enclosed within the corolla tube; ovary of 2 free carpels (October to December, but may continue on to April). **Fruit:** paired, each follicular carpel narrowly elliptic, flattened, about 11 × 2 cm, both at right angles to the stalk thus resembling a 2-bladed propeller, pale brown when mature, splitting along the upper surface to release the many small wind-distributed seeds, each with a tuft of silvery silky hairs at one end (November to April).

The latex has been used as bird-lime. The wood is white and even-textured and cheap furniture has been made from it; it burns well and might possibly be suitable for matches.

13. MASCARENHASIA A. DC.

Mascarenhasia arborescens A. DC.   Illust. 267
[*M. variegata* Britten & Rendle]
S.A. no: —
Rhod. no: 924   Mascarenhasia

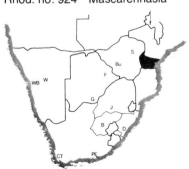

A shrub or small tree up to 8 m in height; occurring in evergreen forest and in riverine fringes. **Bark:** brownish, smooth; all parts contain milky latex. **Leaves:** opposite, simple, oblong-elliptic, 6 to 19 × 2 to 8 cm, usually about 7 to 9 × 4 to 6,5 cm, leathery, glossy light green; net-veining conspicuous below, with the veins looping some distance from the margin; apex abruptly attenuate, the tip finally narrowly rounded and finely notched; base tapering and running into the petiole; margin entire; petiole somewhat obscured by the decurrent leaf base, but about 2 to 5 mm long; axillary glands obscure. Stipules absent. **Flowers:** white, about 10 mm in diameter, in small axillary or terminal clusters, fascicles or cymes. Bisexual; all floral parts in fives; calyx lobes almost free, with many glands at the base; corolla tube cylindric, without hairs; stamens attached in the tube, barely protruding; ovary of 2

793

free carpels (September to December). **Fruit:** paired narrowly elliptic follicular carpels, about 11 × 2 cm, at right angles to the stem, or even slightly bent back, resembling miniature propellers, finally splitting to release seeds, each with a tuft of golden silky hairs at one end (February to July). The trees yield a rubber of inferior quality.

14. ADENIUM Roemer & J. A. Schultes

Adenium obesum (Forsk.) Roemer & J. A. Schultes   Illust. 268
[*A. multiflorum* Klotzsch]
S.A. no: 647,3   Impala lily. Impala-lelie
Rhod. no: 925   Sabi star

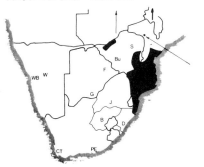

A thickset succulent shrub or small tree, occasionally reaching 3 m in height but usually smaller; occurring at low altitudes in hot dry areas among rocks sometimes in open sandy woodland. **Bark:** grey-green, smooth; all parts contain copious watery sap. Spines absent. **Leaves:** alternate or spiralled, crowded at the ends of the branches, obovate to oblong-obovate, 7 to 12 × 3 to 8 cm, rather fleshy, shiny dark green to bluish-green above, paler green and dull below, without hairs, the midrib prominent on the under surface and often tinged with pink; apex rounded or notched; base tapering and running into the petiole; margin entire, wavy; petiole obscured by the decurrent leaf base, so either absent or up to 5 mm long; axillary glands conspicuous, several in each axil. Stipules minute or absent. **Flowers:** very showy, white or pale pink with a pink to crimson border, the margin crisped, up to 5 cm in diameter, in many-flowered terminal heads, or contracted terminal cymes, flowering in winter when the plants are bare. Bisexual; all floral parts in fives; calyx divided almost to the base; corolla tube funnel-shaped, with broad, spreading lobes; stamens inserted at the base of the expanded section of the tube, the anthers forming a cone and fused with the style, with long thread-like hairy appendages; ovary of 2 free carpels (May to August). **Fruit:** paired cigar-shaped follicular mericarps, covered with pinkish-grey short soft hairs when young, reaching 24 × 2 cm, at right angles to the supporting stem, light brown when mature, splitting to release many long narrow cylindric seeds, each with a tuft of long silky golden-brown hairs at each end so that the seed is blown along the ground like an axle with two wheels (July to January).

The plants are reputed to have toxic properties, and are used to poison fish and on arrow-heads. Nevertheless, all parts are heavily browsed on by game and stock – a reason why the plants seldom exceed 70 cm in height. These shrubs have a thick underground stem and because of this are difficult to transplant successfully; however, seed germinates readily though the plants are sensitive to overwatering and frost.

All the material south of the Zambezi River belongs to var. *multiflorum* (Klotzsch) Codd; this variety probably only just crosses the Zambezi River, giving way further north to the typical variety, var. *obesum,* with paler flowers, less pointed petals, more crisped margins and differences in the venation of the leaves. This is a protected plant in Rhodesia.

15. PACHYPODIUM Lindl.

Succulent shrubs or small trees, the stems usually large and swollen at the base. **Leaves:** alternate or spirally arranged, often crowded near the apex of the branches, simple; axillary glands absent. Stipules modified into rigid, paired spines. **Flowers:** in few- to many-flowered cymes. Bisexual; all floral parts in fives; calyx small, divided almost to the base, without glands; corolla tube cylindric or bell-shaped, the lobes broad, as long as the tube; stamens inserted above the constriction of the corolla tube, joined, the anthers with only a short terminal appendage; ovary of 2 free carpels. **Fruit:** paired cylindric or narrowly oblong follicular mericarps.

Key to the tree species of *Pachypodium:*

Stem usually columnar, but may be sparingly branched; usually 2 to 4 m in height; in the extreme north-western Cape and south of South West Africa only .... **P. namaquanum**
Stem usually with a few branches, up to 6 m in height; in the north of South West Africa and Angola only .... **P. lealii**

Pachypodium lealii Welw.
S.A. no: 648   Bottelboom. Bottelboom
Rhod. no: —

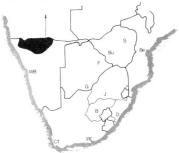

A thickset succulent shrub or small tree up to 6 cm in height, rather bottle-shaped and tapering to the apex with a few upright branches near the top; occurring on arid rocky hillsides. **Bark:** grey to pale brown with darker conspicuous transverse scars, otherwise smooth, with many long slender stipular spines up to 3 cm long on the branches. **Leaves:** few, crowded or fascicled near the tips of young branchlets, or scattered along the larger branchlets, obovate-oblong, 2,5 to 8 × 1,5 to 3,5 cm, with short hairs on both surfaces; apex rounded, sharp pointed; base tapering; margin entire, wavy; petiole absent. **Flowers:** showy, white flushed with purple underneath and down the tube, up to 6 cm in diameter, flowering when the trees are leafless (July to August). **Fruit:** paired follicular mericarps, slender, up to 11 × 1 cm, torpedo-shaped, pale brown when mature splitting to release many seeds, each with a tuft of silvery silky hairs up to 2 cm long at one end (November).

Parts of the tree have been used to prepare arrow poison and it is now known to contain a glucoside, pachypodiin, with an action similar to that of digitalis. This is a protected tree in South Africa and South West Africa.

Pachypodium namaquanum (Wyley ex Harvey) Welw.   Illust. 269
S.A. no: 649   Halfmens. Halfmens
Rhod. no: —

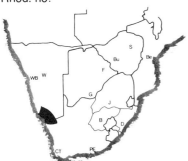

A succulent plant or occasionally a small tree, usually with an unbranched cylindric stem, 1,5 to 2,5 m in height, but not infrequently reaching 4 m and rarely 5 m, occasionally shortly branched near the top; occurring in dry rocky deserts, among boulders and on stony hillsides. The stem, thickset at

795

the base, tapering to the apex, is beset with warty protuberances or tubercles, each one spine-tipped; occasionally branched from near the base, also with a few short branches near the apex. **Leaves:** crowded near the apex of the stem, obovate-oblong, 8 to 12 × 2 to 6 cm, grey-green, densely velvety on both surfaces; apex tapering to rounded; base narrowly tapering to rounded; base narrowly tapering and running into the petiole; margin entire and very wavy; petiole obscured by the decurrent leaf base. **Flowers:** tubular, red inside and green outside, up to 5 cm long and 1 cm in diameter at the mouth, corolla lobes short; produced among the leaves at the tips of the stems (July to September). **Fruit:** paired follicular mericarps, up to 4 cm long, joined at the base, densely covered with short soft grey hairs, tapering to the apex, pale brown when mature splitting to release many seeds about 4 mm long, each with a tuft of long whitish hairs twice the length of the seed (September to December).

According to local African legend, these trees are half man and half plant, and this is easy to understand, for, when seen in the distance against the skyline, they could easily be mistaken for humans. An unusual feature is that the tip of the stem always inclines towards the north at an angle varying between 20° and 30°. This tendency, which is shared by some low-growing species of succulent Euphorbia, has led to their being called 'magnetic plants' but it is unlikely that they are in fact attracted towards the pole by magnetism. It is more probable that these plants, which are strongly phototropic and grow in areas where the sun is in the north for the greater part of the year, curve their tips northwards to protect the growing shoots from excessive heat. This species fascinates gardeners, but while the seed germinates fairly readily, it does not thrive away from its natural desert conditions. It is protected in South Africa and also in South West Africa.

16. ONCINOTIS Benth.

Oncinotis inandensis J. M. Wood & M. S. Evans
[*O. natalensis* Stapf; *O. chirindica* S. Moore]
S.A. no: 647,1   Magic rope. Towertou
Rhod. no: 927   Magic rope

A shrub, often scrambling or a great forest liane up to 30 m in height, occasionally a small tree; occurring in evergreen forest. **Bark:** dull brown with small white lenticels, or pale yellowish, thick and corky. All parts contain milky latex. **Leaves:** opposite, simple, obovate-oblong, 6 to 11 × 1,5 to 4,5 cm, rather leathery, both surfaces with short soft hairs, and small glands near the base of the leaf; apex abruptly and broadly tapering; base tapering; margin entire; petiole up to 6 mm long, velvety. Stipules absent. **Flowers:** green, insignificant, up to 4 mm long with slender corolla lobes, about 6 mm long, curled back, in short sparse axillary sprays, or panicles of few-flowered cymes. Bisexual; all floral parts in fives; calyx small, divided almost to the base, glands minute or absent; corolla tube short, hairy, with 5 narrow spreading lobes, often bent back; stamens attached near the base of the corolla tube, the anthers forming a cone and produced into narrow appendages; ovary of 2 free carpels (October). **Fruit:** paired follicular mericarps, long, slender, cigar-shaped up to 18 × 1 cm, pale brown when mature splitting to release many small seeds, each with a bristly beard at one end and at least initially with a tuft of creamy silky hairs at the other, the tuft of hairs rarely remaining attached until maturity but usually floating away on its own (October).

17. *NERIUM L.

*Nerium oleander L.

The oleander, originally from the Mediterranean countries, is widely cultivated in southern Africa as an ornamental and has escaped in some valleys in the western and south-western Cape. All vegetative parts are extremely poisonous.

18. STROPHANTHUS DC.

Strophanthus speciosus (L. F. Ward & Harvey) Reber   Illust. 270
S.A. no: 647,2   Poison rope. Gewone giftou
Rhod. no: 932   Poison rope

A shrub, usually scrambling, occasionally a small tree up to 3 m in height; occurring at the margins of evergreen forest, in ravine and scrub forest, usually at medium altitudes. **Bark:** greenish, smooth; all parts contain a watery sap. **Leaves:** in whorls of 3, simple, narrowly elliptic, 3 to 10 × 0,8 to 2,5 cm, leathery, glossy green above, paler green and dull below; apex tapering to rounded; base tapering; margin entire; petiole up to 6 mm long, with 3 scale-like overlapping axillary glands but not conspicuous. **Flowers:** quite striking, yellow with a dull reddish patch at the base of each corolla lobe; the corolla tube up to 10 mm long and almost 10 mm wide at the mouth, separating into very slender corolla lobes and almost 10 mm wide at the mouth, separating into very slender corolla lobes up to 3 cm long, sweetly scented; in about 16-flowered heads, or corymbs, at the ends of the branches. Bisexual; all floral parts in fives; calyx divided to the base with few to many glands; corolla bell-shaped with very slender, spirally twisted lobes; stamens inserted deep in the tube, the anthers with apical appendages and forming a cone; ovary of 2 free carpels (September to October). **Fruit:** paired follicular mericarps, slender, up to 18 × 1 to 1,5 cm, each at right angles to the stem or even bent back, smooth, light brown when mature, splitting to release the many seeds, each with a tuft of hairs at one end (February to August).
Specimens from the Cape tend to have smaller leaves than those from Natal and further north. The seeds and foliage are said to be poisonous and are used to prepare arrow poison and for homicidal purposes. The roots are roasted, pounded, and the powder given to cattle to treat snakebite; humans sniff up this powder and swallow some of it for the same purpose. Cardiac glucosides have been isolated from the seeds.

19. WRIGHTIA R. Br.

Wrightia natalensis Stapf
S.A. no: 650   Saddle pod. Saalpeultjie
Rhod. no: 933   Saddle pod

A shrub or small tree up to 8 m in height, occasionally reaching 15 m, with a small crown; occurring in dry woodland, scrub forest, frequently on hillsides. **Bark:** grey, slightly fissured; the bole usually straight. Milky latex is present but not copious, being especially noticeable in green fruits and in the bark. **Leaves:** opposite, simple, lanceolate, 5 to 8 × 1,5 to 2 cm, light clear green; apex tapering to broadly tapering; base tapering to rounded; margin finely toothed to almost entire, sometimes slightly sinuate; petiole 2 to 4 mm long. Stipules absent. **Flowers:** creamy-yellow, with a short tube up to

797

4 mm long, the petal lobes about 1,5 cm long, curling back, sweetly scented, the sparse sub-corymbose pseudo-axillary sprays, the stalks and calyx covered with rusty hairs. Bisexual; all floral parts in fives; calyx divided almost to the base, with small basal glands; corolla tube short, cylindric, with longer lobes; stamens attached to the throat, and anthers joined to form a cone in the mouth of the corolla tube; ovary of 2 separate carpels (October to November). **Fruit:** paired follicular mericarps, very slender, up to 32 × 1 cm, pendulous, dark green speckled with small pale lenticels, pale brown when dry splitting to release many seeds, each with a long plume-like tuft at one end (July to September).

BORAGINACEAE *(The heliotrope and forget-me-not family)*

The two tree genera are difficult to key out, except by differences in the style and stigma:

Style once divided .... **2. Ehretia**

Style twice divided .... **1. Cordia**

1. CORDIA L.

Shrubs or trees. **Leaves:** alternate, rarely sub-opposite, or opposite, simple. **Flowers:** in paniculate cymes with scorpioid branches (the floral branches developed on opposite sides alternately and the flowers 2-ranked). Bisexual and unisexual, often on the same tree; floral parts in fours to fives; calyx funnel-shaped; corolla tube cylindric or funnel-shaped, with the lobes spreading and curving back; stamens attached in the tube; ovary 4-chambered, style long and twice-branched. **Fruit:** fleshy, surrounded by the persistent and enlarged calyx.

Key to the tree species of *Cordia:*
1 Leaf apex tapering to broadly tapering 2
  Leaf apex very broadly tapering to rounded 4
2 Leaf base rounded to lobed, under surface softly hairy, leaf margin entire ...... **C. abyssinica**
  Leaf base tapering, under surface with or without very sparse hairs or scabrid hairs; margins entire
    or toothed 3
3 Leaf margin entire .... **C. goetzei**
  Leaf margin toothed .... **C. caffra**
4 Leaves oblanceolate to oblong, not almost circular; petiole up to 10 mm long .... **C. sinensis**
  Leaves ovate to circular; petiole more than 1,2 cm long 5
5 Leaves 5 to 8 cm long; hairs harsh and scabrid on the upper surface only, with soft yellowish to
    rusty hairs below .... **C. ovalis**
  Leaves 8 to 16 cm long, either with harsh, scabrid hairs on both surfaces or with soft velvety hairs
    below, or on both surfaces 6
6 Leaves densely covered with soft hairs on both surfaces .... **C. pilosissima**
  Leaves with harsh, scabrid hairs at least above, or on both surfaces 7
7 Leaves 8 to 16 cm long, usually about 9 cm, rough on both surfaces; flowers about 1,5 cm in
    diameter .... **C. grandicalyx**
  Leaves up to 30 × 30 cm, usually about 15 cm long, rough on upper surface; flowers up to 2,5 cm
    in diameter .... **C. abyssinica**

Cordia abyssinica R. Br.   Illust. 271
S.A. no: 651   Large-leaved cordia. Grootblaarpieringbessie
Rhod. no: 968   Large-leaved cordia

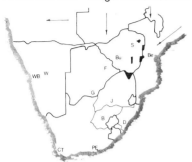 

A small to medium sized tree, 4 to 15 m in height, heavily branched with a rounded crown; occurring at medium to low altitudes in woodland and bush, in warm and moist areas, often along river banks. **Bark:** pale to dark brown, smoothish, finely fissured; the young branchlets with sparse long hairs. **Leaves:** broadly ovate, up to 30 × 30 cm, but usually about 15 × 9 cm, thinly leathery, dark green and rough to the touch above, paler green and velvety below with net-veining clearly defined; apex broadly tapering; base rounded to shallowly lobed; margin entire; petiole slender, up to 7 cm long, sparsely hairy. **Flowers:** showy, white, up to 2,5 cm in diameter, funnel-shaped, sweetly scented, in large dense terminal heads; corolla lobes crinkled; calyx lobes not conspicuously long, the stalks and the backs of the calyx lobes covered with short soft brown hairs (April to June). **Fruit:** spherical, fleshy, about 10 mm in diameter, yellow to orange when mature, with sweet mucilaginous flesh; with short remains of the calyx at the base (July to October).

The heartwood is pinkish brown and durable; it works easily and polishes well. It is used to make grain mortars, would be suitable for furniture and has been found useful as a coffee shade tree. Germination from seed appears to be rather erratic, but when once started, the trees grow fast and well, reaching 7 to 8 m and flowering profusely in 7 years. This is a beautiful tree though frost-tender.

Cordia caffra Sonder
S.A. no: 652   Septee. Septeeboom
Rhod. no: —

A shrub or small to medium sized tree usually up to 7 m in height, the bole frequently leaning, but sometimes reaching 13 m; occurring in coastal evergreen forest and scrub forest. **Bark:** whitish to light brown. **Leaves:** ovate to narrowly ovate, 5 to 10 × 2,5 to 4 cm, but usually about 5 to 7 cm long, densely covered with short soft yellowish hairs when young but losing nearly all of these by maturity, becoming shiny green; apex tapering; base rounded to square; margin irregularly finely to coarsely toothed; petiole very slender, up to 5 cm long. **Flowers:** white, bell-shaped, about 5 × 10 mm, sweetly scented, on slender stalks, in dense many-flowered terminal heads (September). **Fruit:** spherical, fleshy, up to 1,2 cm in diameter, yellow to orange when mature; shortly cupped by the persistent calyx (January).

The wood is soft but tough and makes good fencing posts. This is a small, almost prostrate bush when growing on sand dunes exposed to the full sea-spray and wind. It needs light and therefore is seldom

799

found in dense forest, more often growing round the margin. It is easily cultivated from seed and is fairly fast-growing.

Cordia goetzei Gürke
S.A. no: —
Rhod. no: 969   Blue-bark cordia

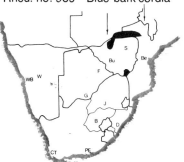

A shrub, often tending to scramble, or a small tree up to 7 m in height; occurring at low altitudes, occasionally in hot dry river valleys, most often in riverine fringes, sometimes on termite mounds and hot rocky slopes. **Bark:** distinctive, the stems being square in section with ridges at the corners; the bark is conspicuous, smooth, green-grey in small specimens, becoming hard blue-grey with dark grey plate-like flakes peeling away to reveal dove-grey patches. **Leaves:** variable in shape, often broadly elliptic, up to 12 × 5 cm, but usually about 7 × 2 cm, thinly textured, rather brittle, with or without a few sparse hairs; the lateral veins not conspicuous; apex and base tapering; margin entire; petiole 0,6 to 3 cm long, channelled above. **Flowers:** white to creamy-yellow, funnel-shaped, about 6 mm in diameter, on slender stalks in few-flowered axillary or terminal heads, about 3 to 6 cm in diameter (September to November). **Fruit:** resembling small sharply pointed acorns, about 1,5 × 1 cm, the basal cup enclosing about one third of the fruit (January to February).

Cordia grandicalyx Oberm.
S.A. no: 653   Round-leaved cordia. Rondeblaarpieringbessie
Rhod. no: 970   Round-leaved cordia

A shrub or small tree up to 5 m in height; occurring at low altitudes in hot dry areas. **Bark:** dark grey-brown, fissured. **Leaves:** very broadly ovate to almost circular, up to 16 × 11 cm, but usually about 9 cm long, both surfaces harsh to the touch, light green or rust-coloured; very conspicuous net-veining below; apex rounded; base rounded to lobed; margin more or less entire, to scalloped or obscurely toothed; petiole up to 2,5 cm long. **Flowers:** whitish-cream, very rapidly fading to yellow, about 1,5 cm in diameter, with large, conspicuous calyces, sweetly scented; in loose rather few-flowered to dense heads, terminal on short new side shoots with the very young leaves (October to December). **Fruit:** distinctive, broadly ovoid, about 2,5 to 3 cm in diameter, tapering into an almost spike-like tip and bedded on the large expanded frilled and sometimes recurved calyx lobes (November to December).

Cordia ovalis R. Br. ex A. DC.   Illust. 272
S.A. no: 654   Snot berry. Snotbessie
Rhod. no: 971   Sandpaper cordia

 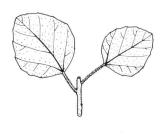

A shrub or small bushy tree, 4 to 7 m in height; occurring at low altitudes in hot woodland, often on dry rocky hillsides or associated with termite mounds. **Bark:** pale grey to grey, smooth, sometimes inclined to be flaky; fibrous. **Leaves:** distinctive, ovate to almost circular, 5 to 8 × 4 to 6 cm, leathery, deep green, very harsh to the touch above, with softer yellowish to rusty hairs below; midrib and lateral veins yellowish and prominent below; apex and base rounded; margin entire or slightly scalloped; petiole 1 to 2 cm long, with rusty hairs. **Flowers:** pale yellow or greenish-yellow, with the corolla tube about 5 mm long, and the lobes spreading to about 10 mm in diameter, fragrant, in dense terminal clusters; the calyx and stalks covered with fine yellowish or rusty soft hairs (October to May). **Fruit:** ovoid, fleshy, up to 2 cm long, orange-red when mature, sharp pointed and bedded in a basal cup with the toothed margin formed from the persistent sepals which covers the lower one-third of the fruit; containing a mucilaginous jelly-like pulp and 1 seed (December to June).

Cordia pilosissima Baker
S.A. no: 655   Woolly cordia. Wollerige pieringbessie
Rhod. no: 972   Woolly cordia

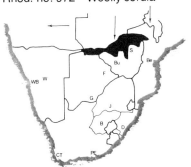 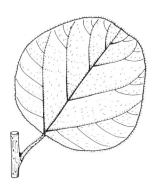

A straggling shrub, 3 to 5 m in height, often with a tendency to scramble, or a small tree occasionally reaching 10 m; occurring at low altitudes in hot areas, especially along the Zambezi valley and its main tributaries. **Bark:** grey and rough; all young parts densely covered with long soft hairs. **Leaves:** ovate to almost circular, 8 to 16 × 7 to 16 cm, light green, both surfaces densely covered with soft hairs, occasionally slightly harsh on the upper surface; veins very conspicuous below showing strong net-veining which is also visible on the upper surface in young leaves but becomes immersed and obscure with age; apex rounded; base rounded to lobed; margin entire or obscurely scalloped; petiole up to 3 cm long. **Flowers:** white, cream or pale yellow, up to 1,5 cm in diameter, in dense terminal heads; the calyces and stalks are densely covered with yellowish hairs and the mature calyx is markedly longitudinally ribbed (October to December). **Fruit:** ovoid, fleshy, up to 2,5 cm long, yellow-orange when mature, sharply tipped and bedded in the much enlarged, frilled and recurved persistent calyx, somewhat resembling that of *C. grandicalyx* (February to May).
The trees may be battered and broken by elephant which browse heavily on the leaves.

BORAGINACEAE

Cordia sinensis Lam.
[*C. rothii* Roemer & J. A. Schultes; *C. gharaf* Ehrenb. ex Aschers.]
S.A. no: Grey-leaved saucer-berry
Rhod. no: 973   Grey-leaved cordia

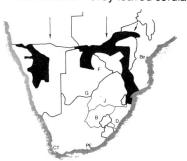 

A shrub or small tree up to 7 m in height, often with slender branches tending to droop; occurring generally at low altitudes in hot dry woodland, frequently along river banks, on termite mounds and in littoral scrub. **Bark:** brown to pale creamy-brown, smooth. The wood is tough. **Leaves:** opposite, sub-opposite or alternate, oblanceolate to oblong, 3 to 9 × 1,3 to 4,5 cm, greyish-green, with long pale hairs on both surfaces; apex rounded, sometimes shallowly notched; base narrowly tapering; margin entire or irregularly and rather widely toothed over the upper half; petiole about 10 mm long, with long pale hairs. **Flowers:** white, about 6 mm long, rather urn-shaped, with the corolla lobes narrow and small, in terminal clusters; the stalks and backs of the calyx lobes are covered with yellowish-brown short soft hairs (December to February; August in South West Africa). **Fruit:** ovoid, up to 2 cm long, orange-red when mature, with a conspicuous long tip, and bedded in the cup-shaped remains of the persistent calyx which has a toothed margin and covers the lower third of the fruit (April to June; December in South West Africa).

2. EHRETIA L.

Shrubs or trees. **Leaves:** alternate, simple. **Flowers:** in many-branched.. dichotomous cymes, with scorpioid branches (the floral branches develop on opposite sides alternately and the flowers are strictly 2-ranked – said to resemble a scorpion's tail). Bisexual or unisexual, usually both on the same tree; floral parts in fours to sevens; calyx small, bell-shaped, usually 5-lobed; corolla tube bell-shaped; stamens attached in or below the throat of the tube; ovary 2- to 4-chambered, the style once-branched. **Fruit:** small, fleshy, indehiscent.

Key to the tree species of *Ehretia:*
1 Leaves rarely longer than 3 cm, petioles up to 2 mm long, or absent; leaves, flowers and fruits,
   borne on short, spiky lateral branches .... **E. rigida**
  Leaves longer than 4 cm, petioles 2 to 8 mm long; without short rigid lateral branches 2
2 Leaves broadly elliptic, up to 18 × 8 cm; a tree up to 20 m in evergreen mountain forest......
  .... **E. cymosa**
  Leaves obovate to almost circular, up to 11 × 6,5 cm; a small tree up to 7 m, in hot dry areas, in
   thicket, woodland and sand forest, often along watercourses and on termite mounds ....
  .... **E. amoena**

Ehretia amoena Klotzsch
[*E. coerulea* Gürke]
S.A. no: 656   Sandpaper bush. Skurweblaarbos
Rhod. no: 974   Stamperwood

A shrub or small tree, 2 to 7 m in height; occurring at medium to low altitudes, often in hot areas, frequently on termite mounds, along the banks of watercourses and in sand forest near the coast. **Bark:** whitish, light brown, light grey to dark grey, smooth, occasionally flaky. **Leaves:** obovate to almost circular, 4 to 11,5 × 2,5 to 6,5 cm, dark green above, paler green below where the midrib and lateral veins are prominent and net-veining is conspicuous; both surfaces with soft short hairs or

802

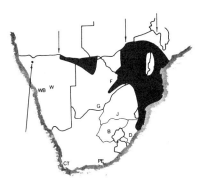

roughly scabrid, especially the upper surface; apex broadly tapering, sometimes abruptly attenuate; base narrowly tapering; margin entire or irregularly and coarsely toothed over the upper third, slightly wavy; petiole 2 to 8 mm long, slender. **Flowers:** white to pale mauve or blue, sweetly scented, about 10 mm in diameter, showy when in profusion, in terminal lax panicles, on new shoots either before or with the new leaves; the flowers are short lived, sometimes lasting one day only (October to February). **Fruit:** spherical, fleshy, about 5 to 7 mm in diameter, red when mature, often produced in profusion (December to February).

Intermediates between this species and *E. rigida* occur, and the hybrids are often difficult to distinguish from the parents.

The wood is used to make pestles for stamping grain.

Ehretia cymosa Thonn.
[*E. divaricata* Baker]
S.A. no: —
Rhod. no: 975   Forest stamperwood

A medium to large tree up to 20 m in height; occurring in evergreen forest and forest patches on steep mountainsides. **Bark:** grey to dark grey, smooth, rather rough to scaly; characteristcally branching from quite low down. **Leaves:** broadly elliptic, up to 18 × 8 cm, glossy dark green above, paler dull green below, with the upper surface finely hairy, and the under surface with or without hairs; apex rather abruptly tapering; base tapering; margin entire; petiole up to 2 cm long.. **Flowers:** white, sweetly scented, about 6 mm in diameter, with hair-like stamens protruding from the mouth; in large terminal heads, produced in such profusion as to cover the tree with white blossoms; the stalks and calyx lobes have fine soft hairs (September to May). **Fruit:** almost spherical, fleshy, up to 10 mm in diameter, reddish when mature (October to December).

The wood is handsome with alternate dark and light bands; it is suitable for cabinet work and furniture but it does not occur in sufficient quantity to exploit. This species has been divided into five varieties, only var. *divaricata* (Baker) Brenan occurring south of the Zambezi River.

Ehretia rigida (Thunb.) Druce   Illust. 273
S.A. no: 657   Puzzle bush. Deurmekaarbos
Rhod. no: 976   Puzzle bush

A rigid twiggy shrub or small tree, 2 to 5 m in height; widespread in a variety of habitats, from the margins of evergreen forest to open woodland, on termite mounds, and in coastal and karroid scrub.   **803**

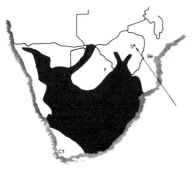 

Bark: greyish, smooth; the branches tend to droop. **Leaves:** frequently produced on short rigid lateral branchlets, small, obovate, rarely more than 2,5 to 3 × 1 cm, with or without soft sparse hairs which occasionally may be scabrid; apex very broadly tapering to rounded; base narrowly tapering; margin entire; petiole up to 2 mm long or absent. **Flowers:** attractive, pale lavender, mauve to blue or white, sweetly scented, about 7 mm in diameter, in dense terminal heads, often produced on short rigid lateral branchlets (August to February). **Fruit:** almost spherical, fleshy, 5 to 7 mm in diameter, bright orange-red when mature; edible (October to January).

The wood is tough and flexible. In African medicine the powdered root is applied to cuts in the skin over the abdomen and chest to relieve pains and is also used to treat gall-sickness in cattle. This tree is fairly widely used as a good-luck charm. Hunters in the Transvaal believe that the strength of their prey will be reduced if a twig is pointed towards it, while a bad-tempered ox is said to become docile if the cattle kraal gate is made from the branches. The powdered root, mixed with hair from a goat's head, is sprinkled over hunters to bring them luck and a branch is dragged round huts and gardens to protect them from a threatening hailstorm.

Intermediates between this species and *E. amoena* occur, and are possibly hybrids.

VERBENACEAE *(The verbena family)*

Key to the genera (exotic genera marked*):

1 Leaves compound, digitately 3- to 7-foliolate .... **3. Vitex**

    Leaves simple 2

2 Trees of mangrove swamps, producing vertical pencil-like roots; fruit a 2-valved capsule .... **6. Avicennia**

    Not mangroves; fruits not 2-valved capsules 3

3 Calyx forming a large, distinctive, papery saucer-shaped structure, 2 to 4 cm in diameter .... **5. Holmskioldia**

    Calyx not forming a papery saucer-shaped structure 4

4 Flowers and fruits in simple racemes or sprays .... **1. *Duranta**

    Flowers and fruits in branched heads, which may be congested and dense 5

5 Flowers with the corolla tube distinctly pouched at the base; fruit with a single stone containing 4 seeds .... **2. Premna**

    Flowers with or without a slight pouch at the base of the corolla tube; fruits with 4 one-seeded stones or 2 two-seeded stones .... **4. Clerodendrum**

1. *DURANTA L.

*Duranta repens L.

The forget-me-not tree (Rhod. no: 981), introduced from Central and South America as an ornamental, has become widely naturalised in Rhodesia, Natal and probably elsewhere in South Africa. It is an attractive shrub or small tree with pale blue or white flowers and small orange berry-like fruits.

2. PREMNA L.

Shrubs or trees. **Leaves:** opposite or in whorls of 3, simple. **Flowers:** in corymbs or panicled cymes. Bisexual or unisexual usually on the same tree; floral parts in fours to fives; calyx bell-shaped, 2- to 5-toothed or lobed; corolla 2-lipped and 5-lobed, with the tube sometimes curved and pouched at the base (gibbous), stamens 4, attached in or near the throat of the tube; ovary 2- to 4-chambered. **Fruit:** fleshy, indehiscent, with a single stone containing 4 seeds.

Key to the tree species of *Premna:*
In South Africa only; leaves 2 to 5 × 1 to 3,5 cm; flowers up to 5 mm long ...... **P. mooiensis**
In Rhodesia, Botswana, the Caprivi Strip, Moçambique and in countries to the north; leaves usually 6 to 9 cm long (up to 12 × 9 cm); flowers up to 2,5 cm long .... **P. senensis**

Premna mooiensis (H. H. W. Pearson) Pieper
S.A. no: 658   Skunk bush. Muishondbos
Rhod. no: —

A shrub or small to medium tree, 2 to 12 m in height; occurring at low altitudes in dry rocky areas. **Bark:** greyish-brown; the branches are rather angular and brittle with prominent leaf scars. **Leaves:** ovate to elliptic, 2 to 5 × 1 to 3,5 cm, thinly textured, with or without scabrid hairs; apex broadly tapering to rounded; base tapering; margin entire or roughly toothed over the upper third; petiole slender, up to 1,2 cm long. **Flowers:** white to cream, up to 5 mm long, with a short corolla tube, the lobes asymmetrically forming a 2-lobed upper lip and a 3-lobed lower lip, in rather sparse terminal clusters (September to November). **Fruit:** ovoid or slightly pear-shaped, about 5 mm long, black when mature, the base loosely surrounded by the persistent calyx lobes (November to December). The crushed leaves have a pungent, unpleasant, foetid smell. The wood is durable in the ground and has been used as fencing poles.

Premna senensis Klotzsch
S.A. no: Northern premna
Rhod. no: 982   Northern premna

A shrub, sometimes scrambling or a small bushy tree up to 7 m in height, the branches often drooping; occurring in riverine fringes, sometimes forming thickets along the river banks; also on termite mounds or on dry rocky hillsides. **Bark:** light brown to grey, smooth to rather rough and flaking, with longitudinal fissures; branches with distinct lenticels and young branchlets densely covered with short soft hairs. **Leaves:** opposite or in whorls of 3, broadly ovate to oblong, up to 12 × 9 cm, but usually about 6 to 9 cm long, pale green, leathery, both surfaces covered with soft hairs; apex attenuate; base broadly tapering to rounded; margin coarsely and bluntly toothed over the upper half; petiole up to

805

3,5 cm in length in the larger leaves, usually about 1,5 cm, rather slender. **Flowers:** white, with the tube up to 2,5 mm long and the corolla lobes spreading to a diameter of about 4 mm, in rather small sparse terminal heads (November to February). **Fruit:** ovoid, fleshy, about 5 × 4 mm, dark blue when mature, produced in profusion often with the flowers (January to February).
Game browse on the leaves and sticks are used to make fire by friction.

3. VITEX L.

Shrubs or trees, often with glandular leaves and flowers. **Leaves:** opposite, rarely in whorls of 3, compound, digitately 3- to 7-foliolate, occasionally 1-foliolate. **Flowers:** in axillary cymes, or terminal panicles, with or without stalks. Bisexual; floral parts in fours to fives; calyx bell-shaped, truncate or 5-lobed, persistent, with glandular hairs; corolla 2-lipped and 5-lobed with a bell-shaped or cylindric tube; stamens 4, attached about half way down the corolla tube; ovary thick walled, incompletely 4-chambered. **Fruit:** fleshy, indehiscent, with the enlarged persistent calyx at the base.

Key to the tree species of *Vitex:*
1 Leaflets less than 5 cm long 2
  Leaflets usually longer than 5 cm 3
2 Apices of leaflets broadly tapering to rounded, margins markedly toothed over the upper third or half; without hairs except for tufts in the axils of the veins below .... **V. harveyana**
  Apices of leaflets rounded with an abruptly pointed tip, margins entire; young leaves densely hairy, even woolly, with the hairs largely confined to the midrib and lateral veins when mature
  .... **V. obovata**
3 Petiole of mature leaves up to 5 cm long 4
  Petiole of mature leaves more than 5 cm long 5
4 Fruits about 3 mm long, completely enveloped in the persistent trumpet-shaped calyx **V. zeyheri**
  Fruits about 6 mm long, persistent calyx with 5 papery lobes at the base of the fruit ....
  .... **V. rehmannii**
5 Mature leaflets without, or nearly without, hairs at least on the upper surface 6
  Mature leaflets with the upper surface hairy or velvety 8
6 Leaflets rather small and narrow, less than 8 × 3 cm .... **V. amboniensis**
  Leaflets usually more than 8 cm long, broad to almost circular 7
7 Flowers blue, violet or white and violet in sparse, branched heads; petiolules usually about 1 cm long, up to 2 cm only in the largest leaflets .... **V. doniana**
  Flowers yellow to whitish in dense heads; petiolules 1,5 to 3 cm long .... **V. sp. no. 1**
8 Fruits up to 8 mm in diameter 9
  Fruits 10 mm in diameter or more 11
9 Fruits surrounded by a distinctive, thin, bright orange-yellow papery layer which flakes away revealing the black fruit beneath .... **V. buchananii**
  Fruits green, brownish to black, without orange-yellow papery layer 10
10 Petiolules of lateral leaflets very short to absent, but that of the terminal leaflet pronounced, up to 2 cm long .... **V. sp. no. 2**
   Petiolules of all leaflets very short or absent .... **V. wilmsii**
11 Upper surface of mature leaflets with rather harsh hairs .... **V. madiensis**
   Upper surface of mature leaflets with soft hairs 12

12 Leaflet margins coarsely and irregularly toothed over the upper third .... **V. isotjensis**
   Leaflet margins entire or almost so, and may be puckered 13
13 Bark grey to brown, roughish; usually a shrub or small tree up to 6 m in height; leaflets up to 8 ×
   4 cm, with very short soft hairs above, densely velvety below .... **V. mombassae**
   Bark dark grey to brown, distinctly deeply vertically fissured; almost always a reasonable
   sized, round crowned tree, 7 to 10 m in height; leaflets up to 11 × 6 cm, the upper surface more
   densely hairy than that in the preceding species with dense almost woolly hairs below......
   .... **V. payos**

Vitex amboniensis Gürke
[*V. swynnertonii* S. Moore]
S.A. no: 659   Large-fruited vitex. Pruimvingerblaar
Rhod. no: 983   Large-fruited vitex

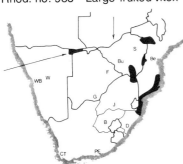 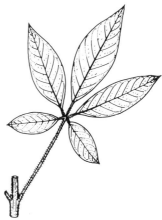

A spreading shrub, often with a tendency to scramble, or a small tree sometimes reaching 10 m in
height; occurring in forest patches, thickets and among rocks, also in open woodland. **Bark:** grey to
dark grey, smooth becoming rather rough with age. **Leaves:** digitately divided into 5 leaflets; leaflets
oblanceolate to elliptic, up to 8 × 3 cm, but usually about 6 × 2 cm, leathery, paler below than above,
with short soft hairs, lost on the upper surface by maturity; midrib and lateral veins prominent; apex
tapering, often slightly attenuate; base tapering; margin entire or very occasionally slightly toothed
over the upper third; petiolules up to 2 cm long, petiole slender up to 6,5 cm long. **Flowers:** blue to
mauve, with a yellow throat, in few- to 12-flowered heads; corolla 2-lipped, the lower lip being rather
paler in colour, the calyx and the stalks with short hairs (November to December). **Fruit:** ellipsoidal,
up to 3,8 cm long, sharp-tipped with the remains of the persistent style, brown to purple when mature,
with a basal frill formed by the persistent calyx (March to May).

Vitex buchananii Baker ex Gürke
[*V. volkensii* Gürke; *V. radula* Mildbr. ex Pieper]
S.A. no: —
Rhod. no: 990   Orange-fruited vitex

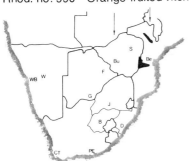 

Frequently a creeper or strong liane, but occasionally a small tree up to 6 m in height; occurring in
patches of evergreen forest and bush clumps. **Bark:** grey to grey-brown with light longitudinal
fissures; the young branchlets conspicuously quadrangular and channelled. **Leaves:** usually
5-foliolate, sometimes 3-foliolate; leaflets broadly elliptic to ovate-lanceolate, up to 11 × 4 cm, with

807

the upper surface finely hairy, often rather scabrid and the lower surface paler green and softly and finely hairy; apex attenuate; base tapering, often markedly asymmetric; margin entire; petiolules up to 2 cm long, petiole up to 11 cm long, slender. **Flowers:** white or slightly flushed with violet, sweetly scented, about 4 to 5 mm long, in large loose terminal and axillary sprays up to 30 cm long (November to February). **Fruit:** spherical, fleshy, about 8 mm in diameter, covered with an unusual and distinctive bright orange-yellow papery layer which flakes away revealing the black fruit beneath; the persistent calyx is saucer-shaped (March to June).

Vitex doniana Sweet
[*V. cuneata* Schumacher & Thonn.]
S.A. no: —
Rhod. no: 984   Black plum

A medium sized round crowned tree, 8 to 14 m in height; occurring in, and at the margins of, evergreen forest, in riverine fringes and also open woodland. **Bark:** dark brown, rather smooth with narrow vertical fissures. **Leaves:** 5-foliolate, the lower 2 leaflets being smaller; leaflets oblong, obovate to almost circular, 6 to 14 × 3 to 8 cm, dark green above, pale greyish-green below, thickly leathery, with only a few scattered stellate hairs present on the upper surface, otherwise without hairs; apex rounded or abruptly attenuate; base tapering; margin entire; petiolules up to 10 mm long and sparsely hairy, petioles distinctly curved, up to 15 cm long. **Flowers:** small, blue or violet to white with the larger lobe blue or violet, in sparse, branched axillary heads, 3 to 12 cm in diameter, with only a few flowers open at a time (August to November). **Fruit:** ovoid, fleshy, up to 3 cm long, purplish-black when mature, edible; the lobes of the persistent calyx curve back resembling small paper plates; the calyces remain on the tree after the fruits have fallen (December to June).
The fruits resemble prunes in taste and are regarded as a remedy for anaemia. The roots are used to treat gonorrhoea.

Vitex harveyana H. H. W. Pearson
[*V. geminata* H. H. W. Pearson]
S.A. no: 660   Three-finger vitex. Krantzvingerblaar
Rhod. no: —

A shrub or small tree, 3 to 7 m in height; occurring in river valleys, on stony hillsides and in coastal bush. **Bark:** grey to brownish. **Leaves:** may be 5-foliolate, although almost always 3-foliolate, with the lower two leaflets undeveloped; leaflets obovate, 3 to 5 × 1 to 2 cm, rather leathery, without hairs except for small tufts in the axils of the conspicuous veins on the under surface; apex broadly tapering to rounded; base tapering; margin markedly toothed in the upper third or half; petiolules absent or very short, up to 0,6 mm on the terminal leaflet; petiole up to 2,5 cm long. **Flowers:** blue or mauve, sweetly scented, up to 10 mm long, with the corolla lobes curved back, in loosely branched few-flowered axillary heads, the common stalk up to 5 cm long and finely velvety (October to November). **Fruit:** almost spherical, fleshy, 8 to 10 mm in diameter, black when mature; the persistent calyx forms a basal cup which does not extend far up the fruit (March).

Vitex isotjensis Gibbs
[*V. patula* E. A. Bruce]
S.A. no: Golden vitex. Rotsvingerblaar
Rhod. no: 985   Golden vitex.

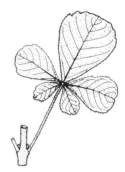

A shrub or small tree, 2 to 7 m in height; occurring in open woodland, on rocky outcrops, in clefts in rocks, riverine fringes and coastal bush. **Bark:** light grey to brown, rather smooth, sometimes with longitudinal striations; all young parts and the leaf buds are densely covered with long golden hairs. **Leaves:** 5-foliolate, the lower 2 being smaller or very small, or not developed at all; leaflets obovate, up to 7,5 × 3,5 cm, the terminal leaflet being the largest, light green, with both surfaces finely covered with soft, often golden hairs, the upper surface often being puckered; veins and net-veining prominent on the under surface; apex rounded; base narrowly tapering; margin coarsely and irregularly toothed over the upper third, rolled under; petiolules absent or very short, up to 6 mm long on the terminal leaflet; petiole up to 6 cm long, slender, covered with golden soft hairs. **Flowers:** pale blue or white, small, obscurely 2-lipped, often with the lower lip purplish or bluish and the upper lip whitish, in rather sparse branched axillary heads, 3 to 7 cm in diameter, on a common stalk up to 5 cm long; the stalks and calyx lobes are covered with golden soft hairs (October to January). **Fruit:** ovoid, fleshy, 1 to 1,5 cm long, purplish-black when mature; the persistent calyx forms a toothed basal cup; edible (January to April).
The leaves are browsed on by elephants; the sticks are used to make fire by friction.

Vitex madiensis Oliver
S.A. no: —
Rhod. no: 986   Rough-leaved vitex

A shrub or small spreading tree, 3 to 4 m in height, occasionally reaching 7 m, or sometimes a suffrutex; occurring in grassland, open woodland and forest. **Bark:** pale whitish-grey; the leaf buds

809

are densely covered with long tawny hairs. **Leaves:** in whorls of 3 or opposite, 5-foliolate; leaflets broadly obovate, up to 15 × 6 cm, the lower two leaflets being markedly smaller, glossy green above and harsh to the touch, paler green and softly hairy below; apex rounded to square or very abruptly and shortly attenuate; base narrowly tapering and running into the petiole; margin almost entire to finely scalloped; petiolules almost absent or very short, up to 8 mm long in the terminal leaflet; petiole sturdy, up to 11 cm long, with soft tawny hairs. **Flowers:** white to pale or deep violet, bright purple or mauve-blue, up to 5 mm long in dense many-flowered branched axillary heads, with the stalks and calyx lobes covered with tawny hairs (September to February). **Fruit:** ovoid, fleshy, up to 3 cm long, pendulous on long stalks; black when mature; the persistent calyx forms a rather small shallow basal cup; edible (April to May).

This species is divided into a number of varieties, but only var. *milanjiensis* (Britten) Pieper extends south of the Zambezi River.

Vitex mombassae Vatke
[*V. pooara* Corbishley]
S.A. no: 663   Smelly-berry vitex. Poerabessie
Rhod. no: 987   Smelly-berry vitex

Frequently a shrub, 2 to 3 m in height, but sometimes a small tree up to 6 m; occurring in hot areas on stony outcrops, and in deciduous woodland, especially on Kalahari sand. **Bark:** grey to brown, rather rough; all young parts densely and heavily covered with long tawny hairs. **Leaves:** usually 5-foliolate, but often with the lower 2 leaflets deformed or not developed at all, so frequently 3-foliolate; leaflets broadly obovate-elliptic, up to 8 × 4 cm, covered with very fine short soft hairs on the upper surface and with dense hairs below, the young leaves covered with dense, long, tawny-gold woolly hairs; veins and net-veining conspicuous on the under surface; apex rounded, frequently abruptly and shortly attenuate; base tapering and running into the petiolule; margin almost entire; petiolules very short, petiole up to 9 cm long, covered with short, soft tawny hairs. **Flowers:** about 5 mm long, obscurely 2-lipped with one lip pale blue or mauve and the other white or cream; in small axillary few-flowered heads, on a slender common stalk up to 5 cm long, among the leaves; the calyx lobes and stalks are covered with long, tawny-golden hairs (October to December). **Fruit:** ovoid to almost spherical, up to 2 cm in diameter, dark brown to black when mature; the lobes of the persistent calyx become quite large, at first enveloping most of the fruit but later opening out and even bending back (January to June).

The fruit is edible, contains vitamin C and the juice stains dark purple or black; it has an unpleasant smell and a persistent taste.

Vitex obovata E. Meyer
S.A. no: 661   White vitex. Keivingerblaar
Rhod. no: —

A small tree up to 4 m in height; occurring in coastal scrub and riverine bush. **Bark:** light grey; all young parts covered with long tawny rather woolly hairs. **Leaves:** 5-foliolate, occasionally 3-foliolate; leaflets obovate, up to 4,5 × 2,5 cm, leathery, with hairs on both surfaces when young but losing most of these by maturity, so that they become confined to the midrib and lateral veins on the under surface; apex rounded with an abruptly pointed tip; base tapering; margin entire; petiolules absent or very nearly so, petiole up to 2,5 cm long. **Flowers:** white, bell-shaped, 6 to 8 mm long, with

5 corolla lobes, in branched axillary heads, on a common stalk up to 5 cm long (November). **Fruit:** pear-shaped, up to 5 mm long, sharply tipped with the remains of the style, brownish to black when mature; the persistent calyx forming a basal cup (April).

Vitex payos (Lour.) Merr.   Illust. 274
[*V. eylesii* S. Moore; *V. hildebrandtii* sensu Garçia, *Contribuiçoes para o Conhecimento da Flora de Moçambique*, 2:172]
S.A. no: —
Rhod. no: 988   Chocolate berry

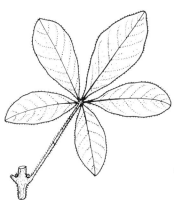

A small to medium sized tree, 4 to 10 m in height with a rounded crown; occurring in open woodland and on rocky outcrops at medium to low altitudes. **Bark:** grey to brown, deeply vertically fissured; all young parts densely covered with tawny woolly hairs. **Leaves:** 5-foliolate, or 3- to 4-foliolate if the basal leaflets do not develop; leaflets obovate to broadly so, up to 11 × 6 cm, bright green and finely hairy above, densely covered with long tawny hairs below, where the veins and net-veining are prominent; apex broadly tapering to rounded; base tapering; margin entire, often thickened, rolled under and somewhat puckered; petiolules almost absent, petiole stout, up to 12 cm long, covered with short tawny hairs. **Flowers:** white to dark mauve or blue, about 6 mm long, obscurely 2-lipped, with the lower lip mauve and the upper lip white, in small axillary few-flowered to dense heads, on a slender common stalk up to 7 cm long (November to February). **Fruit:** ovoid to almost spherical, 1,5 to 2 cm long, black when mature; the persistent calyx forms a large basal plate or shallow cup (February to June).
The fruits have a distinctive coffee-like flavour and are much sought after; they lack vitamin C.

Vitex rehmannii Gürke
S.A. no: 664   Pipe-stem tree. Pypsteelboom
Rhod. no: —

A shrub or small slender tree up to 6 m in height; occurring at low altitudes in open woodland, on stony hillsides and rocky koppies. **Bark:** conspicuously whitish-grey; all young parts covered with fine soft hairs. **Leaves:** 5-foliolate, occasionally 3-foliolate; leaflets narrowly oblong-elliptic, 2 to 10 × 0,5 to 1,5 cm, usually longer than 5 cm, rather leathery, without hairs above, with fine short hairs, especially along the veins, on the under surface; apex and base tapering; margin entire, wavy; petiolules absent or very short, sometimes up to 6 mm long on the terminal leaflet; petiole up to

811

3,5 cm long, with fine short hairs. **Flowers:** white tinged with mauve or purple, bell-shaped, up to 8 mm long, with a widely open throat, in rather loose branched axillary heads, usually longer than the leaves and produced in profusion (December to January). **Fruit:** pear-shaped, up to 6 mm long, blackish when mature; the persistent calyx 5-lobed, papery, considerably enlarged, with the lobes resembling green or brownish papery petals at the base of the fruit (February to April).

An infusion of the leaves is prepared as an enema to relieve stomach-ache. The wood is yellowish-grey, medium hard, fairly strong with a straight grain, working easily and taking a good finish; when fully seasoned it is resistant to termites and is used to make stools and implement handles. The young twigs often have hollow stems which are suitable for the stems of tobacco pipes.

Vitex wilmsii Gürke
[*V. reflexa* H. H. W. Pearson; *V. wilmsii* var. *reflexa* (H. H. W. Pearson) Pieper]
S.A. no: 665   Hairy vitex. Harige vingerblaar
Rhod. no: —

A shrub or small tree up to 8 m in height; occurring in evergreen forest, on wooded hillsides, among rocks and in medium to low altitude bush. **Bark:** grey; branchlets densely hairy. **Leaves:** 5-foliolate, often 3-foliolate, if the basal leaflets do not develop; leaflets broadly elliptic to ovate, 4,5 to 10 × 2 to 5 cm, softly textured, with fine very short hairs above and long pale hairs, especially along the veins, on the under surface; apex and base tapering to somewhat rounded; margin entire, rather wavy and fringed with long pale hairs; petiolules absent or very short, petiole stout up to 5 cm long. **Flowers:** white to pale mauve, up to 8 mm long, in rather loose branched axillary heads, on a common stalk up to 7 cm long, finely hairy (October to November). **Fruit:** pear-shaped, up to 6 mm long, blackish when mature, with the persistent calyx at the base conspicuous, fluted, parchment-like and trumpet-shaped (May to June).

Vitex zeyheri Sonder
S.A. no: 666   Silver pipe-stem tree. Vaalpypsteelboom
Rhod. no: —

A shrub or small tree up to 5 m in height; occurring on stony hills and in rocky valleys. **Bark:** grey or brown, rough, longitudinally fissured; branchlets covered with short pale hairs. **Leaves:** 5-foliolate or 3-foliolate; leaflets oblong to oblong-lanceolate, 3 to 8 × 0,8 to 3 cm, leathery, greyish-green, with or without whitish hairs; apex rounded or abruptly attenuate; base tapering; margin entire; petiolules

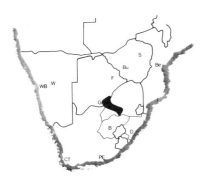

absent or very short, petiole up to 4 cm long. **Flowers:** cream or pale mauve, about 8 mm long, sweetly scented, in loose branched axillary heads, on a common stalk up to 5 cm long, with greyish hairs (November to December). **Fruit:** pear-shaped, about 3 mm long, completely enveloped by the enlarged papery trumpet-shaped persistent calyx (March to April).

This species resembles *V. rehmannii* and intermediates are found grading from one species to the other.

Vitex sp. no. 1
S.A. no: —
Rhod. no: 991   Large-leaved vitex

A large tree up to 20 m in height; occurring in evergreen forest. **Bark:** greyish, smooth. **Leaves:** 5-foliolate; leaflets obovate to oblanceolate, 10 to 19 × 4,5 to 6 cm, without hairs; apex tapering, shortly and narrowly attenuate; base tapering, running into the petiolule; margin entire; petiolules 1,5 to 3 cm long; petiole up to 15 cm long. **Flowers:** whitish to pale yellow, in dense heads on slender common stalks up to 11 cm long (January). **Fruit:** ovoid, about 1,2 cm long, with the persistent calyx forming a pronounced basal cup (April).

Vitex sp. no. 2
S.A. no: —
Rhod. no: 992   Victoria vitex

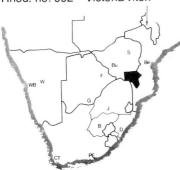

A shrub or small tree up to 4 m in height; occurring in low altitude woodland, often on alluvial flats. **Bark:** brownish-grey; branchlets knobby with conspicuous leaf scars. **Leaves:** often 3-foliolate (or 5-foliolate with the lowermost pair of leaflets small); leaflets broadly elliptic, 7 to 12 × 3 to 4 cm, rather scabrid above, net-veining conspicuous below; apex tapering to attenuate; base tapering; margin entire or with large irregular teeth over the upper third to half; petiolules very short to absent on the lateral leaflets, up to 2 cm long on the terminal leaflet; petiole up to 11 cm long. **Flowers:** whitish, pale mauve or yellowish, densely clustered in short sprays, often below the leaves (October to December). **Fruit:** almost spherical, 4 to 6 mm in diameter, greenish when almost mature (January to April).

4. CLERODENDRUM L.

Shrubs or trees. **Leaves:** opposite or whorled, simple. **Flowers:** in lax axillary cymes near the ends of the branches or in congested terminal panicles. Bisexual; floral parts in fours to fives; calyx 5-lobed, with a bell-shaped or cylindric tube; corolla 5-lobed with a narrowly cylindric tube, which may be slightly pouched at the base; stamens 4, attached to the upper part of the tube and often conspicuous, protruding well out of the mouth of the flower; ovary 4-chambered, style slender, long, protruding with the stamens. **Fruit:** small, fleshy, indehiscent, with 4 one-seeded stones or 2 two-seeded stones.

Key to the tree species of *Clerodendrum:*

Leaf margin entire; blade with or without fine hairs above, often covered with short soft hairs below especially along the midrib and lateral veins; petiole distinct up to 2 cm long; flowers white, about 10 mm in diameter, in dense rounded, terminal heads; fruits not clearly lobed ... **C. glabrum**

Leaf margin coarsely toothed; blade with both surfaces velvety, the under surface occasionally densely hairy and even woolly; petiole frequently obscured by the decurrent leaf base; flowers up to 2 cm in diameter with 5 ovate petals, the upper 4 whitish, the lower petal electric blue to purple; fruits markedly 2- to 4-lobed .... **C. myricoides**

Clerodendrum glabrum E. Meyer   Illust. 275
[*C. rehmannii* Gürke; *C. ovale* Klotzsch]
S.A. no: 667   White cat's whiskers. Harpuisblaar
Rhod. no: 994   White cat's whiskers

A shrub or small to medium sized tree up to 10 m in height; occurring in open woodland, among rocks, often associated with termite mounds, along rivers and on coastal dunes. **Bark:** dark grey to blackish, deeply fissured; with slender straight vertical branches arising from the main horizontal branches; branchlets with fine soft hairs at first, losing these later, and marked with lenticels. **Leaves:** opposite or in whorls of 3 to 4, ovate to elliptic, 2 to 10 × 1 to 7 cm, dark green, with or without fine hairs above, paler green and often covered with soft short hairs below, especially along the midrib and lateral veins; also with sunken gland dots; apex tapering to rounded; base tapering; margin entire; petiole up to 2 cm long. **Flowers:** white, about 10 mm in diameter, with reddish, pink or mauve stamens and style, in dense rounded terminal heads, showy when in profusion (August to July at the coast, December to April inland). **Fruit:** almost spherical, about 10 mm in diameter, not closely lobed, closely packed into round heads, each fruit bedded in the persistent remains of the calyx lobes; the old dry fruits often remain on the tree for months (March to May).

814   The flowers have a sweet scent which may become sharp and unpleasant, though it attracts many insects. The leaves, which have a foetid smell when crushed, are said to repel beetles; they are also added to milk to rid calves of intestinal worms. An infusion is considered a remedy for colic; a decoction is placed on wounds to prevent infection by maggots, and is also used to cure coughs and fevers. The pounded leaves placed in the armpit and the back of the neck are said to induce sleep and provide a remedy for convulsions in children while an infusion of the roots is taken as an antidote to snakebite. This is one of the so-called 'rain trees', a phenonomen caused by a small bug (see *Lonchocarpus capassa*).

Clerodendrum myricoides (Hochst.) R. Br. ex Vatke
[*C. amplifolium* S. Moore; *C. reflexum* H. H. W. Pearson; *C. teaguei* Hutch.]
S.A. no: 667,1   Blue cat's whiskers. Kleinharpuisblaar
Rhod. no: 996   Blue cat's whiskers

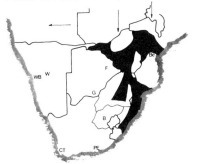

Often a shrub but also frequently a small tree, 3 to 7 m in height; characteristic of rocky places in thickets along streams, also in open woodland often associated with termite mounds. **Bark:** grey, striated, marked with lenticels, becoming rough when old. **Leaves:** opposite or whorled, ovate, 2,5 to 9,5 × 1 to 5,5 cm, usually about 5 × 2,5 cm, softly textured, both surfaces covered with fine dense hairs, paler green below than above, the under surface occasionally densely hairy and even woolly; apex tapering, occasionally attenuate; base tapering, running into the petiole; margin coarsely toothed; petiole somewhat obscured by the tapering leaf base, but may be up to 1,5 cm long. **Flowers:** attractive, up to 2 cm in diameter, with 4 whitish corolla lobes, the fifth lower corolla lobe being an electric blue to purple; in few-flowered axillary and terminal heads (October to January). **Fruit:** 2- to 4-lobed, about 5 × 10 mm becoming reddish and finally black when mature (December to February). The leaves have a foetid smell when crushed. The fruits, which are edible, are taken as a remedy for skin complaints; the root bark provides a treatment for east-coast fever in cattle and diarrhoea in calves, while the root itself is believed to cure spleen ailments.

5. HOLMSKIOLDIA Retz.

Shrubs or small trees. **Leaves:** opposite, simple. **Flowers:** in axillary and terminal cymes. Bisexual; calyx glandular, bell-shaped or plate-like, broad and papery, distinctively coloured, with or without lobes; corolla 2-lipped and 4- to 5-lobed, with a slightly curved cylindric tube; stamens 4, attached to the upper part of the tube and protruding from the mouth; staminodes reduced to a dense hairy ridge; ovary 4-chambered, hairy and glandular, with the style long and slender protruding with the stamens. **Fruit:** 4-lobed, thinly fleshy, enclosed within the much enlarged persistent calyx.

Key to the tree species of *Holmskioldia:*
Occurring in the south-eastern Transvaal and adjacent areas only; leaves usually up to 4 × 2,5 cm, margin conspicuously toothed over the upper half, petiole more or less clearly defined; calyx usually 2 to 2,5 cm in diameter and distinctly 5-lobed .... **H. speciosa**
Occurring along the Zambezi River and in adjacent areas and countries to the north; leaves up to 7 × 3 cm, margin toothed over the upper third or quarter only, or entire, petiole obscured by the decurrent leaf base; calyx large, 3 to 4 cm in diameter .... **H. tettensis**

VERBENACEAE

Holmskioldia speciosa Hutch. & Corbishley
S.A. no: 668   Wild parasol flower. Wildeparasolboom
Rhod. no: —

A rather upright shrub or small tree reaching 6 m in height; occurring in bush and thicket on rocky mountain slopes. **Bark:** grey to brownish. **Leaves:** oblong, ovate to triangular, up to 4 × 2,5 cm, softly textured with short soft hairs; apex and base tapering; margin toothed, often conspicuously so, usually over the upper half; petiole more or less clearly defined, about 10 mm long. **Flowers:** calyx mauve, petals blue; the calyx saucer-shaped, distinctly 5-lobed, 2 to 2,5 cm in diameter (at most times of the year but mainly March to July). **Fruit:** small, 4-lobed, bedded in the large remains of the persistent calyx (with, or only shortly after, the flowers).

Holmskioldia tettensis (Klotzsch) Vatke   Illust. 276
[*H. spinescens* (Klotzsch) Vatke]
S.A. no: —
Rhod. no: 1000   Wild Chinese hats

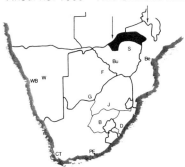 

A much-branched rather upright shrub or small tree reaching 7 m in height; occurring in open woodland, riverine thicket and edging pans at low altitudes. **Bark:** grey or brown, lenticel-dotted, rough in larger specimens. **Leaves:** elliptic to oblanceolate, up to 7 × 3 cm, the lower surface softly and finely hairy; apex broadly tapering; base narrowly tapering and running into the petiole; margin roughly toothed to almost lobed over the upper third to quarter, sometimes entire; petiole obscured by the decurrent leaf base. **Flowers:** the calyx mauve, the corolla bright blue; calyx saucer-shaped, 3 to 4 cm in diameter, papery, scarcely lobed; corolla tube opening into a 5-lobed lip; in loose sprays, often in profusion (October to March). **Fruit:** small, 4-lobed, covered with golden-brown velvety hairs, bedded in the large persistent calyx (with, or very shortly after, the flowers).
The brick-red to orange species, often seen in gardens, is *H. sanguinea* Retz., from the foot-hills of the Himalayas in India.

6. AVICENNIA L.

Avicennia marina (Forsk.) Vierh.
S.A. no: 669   White mangrove. Witseebasboom
Rhod. no: —

816

The breathing roots of the white mangrove, Avicennia marina, *rising out of the tidal mud.*

Often a small tree, 3 to 5 m in height, but it can reach 10 m, with a much-branched rounded crown; a common and often dominant constituent of mangrove swamps, but also away from the sea, encroaching back up the feeder streams, and growing on the banks of fresh water rivers. No prop or stilt roots are produced, but the underground root system is extensive and, in soft mud, throws up a forest of pencil-like pneumatophores, 15 to 38 cm long. The tree is a first colonizer of poor swamp land where little else will grow. Mud and silt accumulate among the pneumatophores and conditions become suitable for the establishment of the other mangroves, *Ceriops* and *Rhizophora*. In mangrove swamp forests *Avicennia* has usually been forced back to the landward side. **Bark:** yellowish-green, inclined to be powdery. **Leaves:** opposite, simple, ovate, lanceolate to elliptic, 3 to 10 × 1,2 to 4 cm, usually about 7 × 2,5 cm, without hairs, green above, pallid grey below; apex and base tapering; margin entire; petiole thickset, about 5 mm long. **Flowers:** white or cream to yellow, sweetly scented, small, in dense spherical terminal or axillary heads, or capitate cymes, on thickset square stalks, about 2 to 3 cm long. Bisexual; floral parts in fours to fives; corolla tube bell-shaped, rather shorter than 4 to 5 petal lobes, somewhat fleshy; stamens 4, enclosed within the tube; ovary 4-chambered (August to January). **Fruit:** a rather flattened capsule, about 2 to 2,5 cm in diameter, dehiscing by 2 valves (March to September).

The seed germinates on the tree before it is liberated but, unlike the other mangroves, *A. marina* does not produce the torpedo-shaped hypocotyl; the fruits are frequently washed up on beaches. The bark is rich in tannin and yields a brown dye; the wood, which is grey to yellowish, fairly dense and evenly grained, is durable and suitable for poles and, in East Africa, for the ribs of dhows. It also provides a highly satisfactory fuel for lime kilns.

817

LAMIACEAE

LAMIACEAE (nom. altern. **Labiatae**) *(The salvia family)*

Key to the genera:
Leaves small, almost circular, 1,5 to 2,5 × 1,3 to 2,3 cm, both surfaces silvery with appressed whitish hairs, veining conspicous and distinctive below, seeming to fan out from the base and along the midrib giving the leaf a shell-like appearance; flowers 1 to 1,5 cm long. This species is endemic to the Chimanimani mountains .... **2. Hemizygia**

Leaves ovate, up to 9 × 8 cm, not silvery white, but with soft velvety green hairs, veining conspicuous below, but normally penni-veined, not fanning out; flowers very small. Widespread .... **1. Iboza**

1. IBOZA N. E. Brown

Iboza riparia (Hochst.) N. E. Brown
S.A. no: Ginger bush
Rhod. no: 1008   Ginger bush

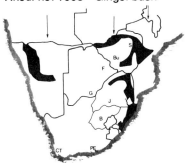 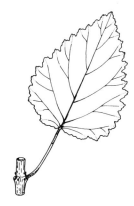

A shrub or occasionally a small tree up to 3 m in height; occurring on rocky outcrops and at the margins of evergreen forest, often near water. **Bark:** light grey to brown, smooth, occasionally peeling with age. **Leaves:** opposite, simple, ovate, up to 9 × 8 cm, usually about 7 × 6 cm, softly textured, with fine dense short soft green hairs on both surfaces; veins conspicuous, penni-veined; apex tapering; base lobed; margin coarsely scalloped to toothed; petiole up to 2 mm long. **Flowers:** very small, mauve, pinkish to white, in large dense much-branched, axillary and terminal panicles, up to 20 cm long, together forming attractive masses. Sexes separate on different plants; floral parts in fours to fives; calyx tube more or less bell-shaped; corolla bell-shaped, shortly lobed; stamens 4, inserted in the throat of the tube, absent in female flowers; ovary 4-lobed, vestigial in male flowers (mainly July to September). **Fruit:** a very small nutlet (shortly after the flowers).

2. HEMIZYGIA Briq.

Hemizygia flabellifolia S. Moore
S.A. no: —
Rhod. no: 1010   Shell-leaf

 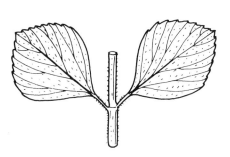

818

A shrub or small tree up to 7 m in height; occurring among rocks on mountain slopes, also in riverine fringe forest, apparently endemic to the Chimanimani mountains. **Bark:** brownish, fissured. **Leaves:** opposite, simple, very distinctive, almost circular, 1,5 to 2,5 × 1,3 to 2,3 cm, both surfaces silvery grey with appressed whitish hairs, the veins very conspicuous below, fanning out from the base and along the midrib, giving the leaf the appearance of a grey-green shell; apex rounded; base abruptly and narrowly running into the petiole; margin finely and regularly toothed; petiole almost obscured by the decurrent leaf base, but may be 5 mm long. **Flowers:** white, lined or tinged with pink or lavender, 1 to 1,5 cm long, aromatic; in terminal sprays. Bisexual; all floral parts in fives; calyx 2-lipped; corolla 2-lipped and 5-lobed; stamens 4, the upper stamen aborted; ovary 4-lobed (September to June). **Fruit:** 4 small nutlets, enclosed in the dry and scarcely enlarged papery remains of the calyx (very shortly after the flowers).

SOLANACEAE *(The potato family)*

Key to the genera (exotics marked*):

1 Fruit a dehiscent capsule .... **4. *Nicotiana**

  Fruit a fleshy berry 2

2 Leaves up to 5 × 1 cm; flowers solitary .... **1. Lycium**

  Leaves up to 14 to 23 cm or more in length 3

3 Plants prickly or spiny; if without spines then fruits small, about 1,5 cm in diameter . **2. Solanum**

  Plants without spines; fruits up to 9 × 5 cm .... **3. *Cyphomandra**

1. LYCIUM L.

Shrubs or trees, the branchlets often spinescent. **Leaves:** alternate or fascicled, simple. **Flowers:** axillary, solitary. Bisexual; floral parts in threes to fives; calyx tube bell-shaped, small; corolla bell- or urn-shaped, with 4 to 5 spreading lobes; stamens 4 to 5, alternating with the corolla lobes and joined to the tube; ovary 2-chambered. **Fruit:** spherical, ovoid to conical, fleshy, indehiscent.

Key to the tree species of *Lycium:*
Leaves very narrow, 1 to 2,5 × 0,1 to 0,3 cm .... **L. afrum**
Leaves narrowly oblong to oblanceolate, 1,3 to 5 × 0,2 to 1 cm .... **L. austrinum**

Lycium afrum L.
S.A. no: 669,2   Kraal honey-thorn. Kraalkariedoring
Rhod. no: —

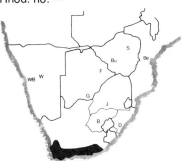

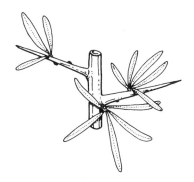

A shrub or occasionally a small tree, 4 to 5 m in height; occurring in dry coastal and karroid scrub. **Bark:** pale creamy-brown; branchlets armed with rigid spines 1 to 4,5 cm long, which often bear leaves and flowers. **Leaves:** alternate or fascicled, very slender, 1 to 2,5 × 0,1 to 0,3 cm, thinly leathery, dark green to bright green; apex rounded; base tapering; margin entire; petiole almost absent. **Flowers:** purple or mauve, tinged with green or brown, with the corolla up to 2 cm long, with very

819

short lobes, only about 3 mm long; axillary, solitary, pendulous on slender stalks up to 8 mm long, sometimes in pairs, on the dwarf spinescent lateral branches (November to May). **Fruit:** spherical, fleshy, about 1,2 cm in diameter, becoming red and finally black when mature (shortly after, or with, the flowers).

This makes a good hedge plant; the seed germinates easily and the plants are fast growing. The wood is tough.

Lycium austrinum Miers
S.A. no: 669,1   Large honey-thorn. Groot kariedoring
Rhod. no: —

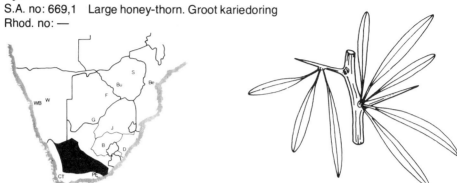

Often a shrub about 2 m in height, or a hard spiny small tree, rarely more than 4,5 m, with rigid branches curving over and down; occurring in hot dry karroid scrub. **Bark:** pale grey to creamy-brown, uneven, lumpy rather than rough. **Leaves:** alternate, but usually fascicled on dwarf lateral spinescent branchlets; oblanceolate, 1,3 to 5 × 0,2 to 1 cm, blue-green to yellowish-green; apex rounded; base tapering and obscuring the petiole; margin entire. **Flowers:** with a slender, tubular corolla up to 2 cm long, cream to mauve sometimes with yellow lobes, axillary, solitary (February to May). **Fruit:** spherical, fleshy, 6 to 9 mm in diameter, orange-red when mature (slightly later than the flowers).

The fruits are eaten by birds and so are seldom seen.

2. SOLANUM L.

Herbs, shrubs or small trees. **Leaves:** alternate or opposite. **Flowers:** in extra-axillary or terminal racemose or umbellate cymes. Bisexual; all floral parts in fives; calyx separating into 5 to 10 lobes; corolla shortly tubular with usually 5 spreading lobes; stamens attached in the throat of the corolla tube, the anthers large and conspicuous; ovary usually 2 chambered. **Fruit:** spherical, fleshy, indehiscent.

Key to the tree species of *Solanum* (exotic species marked*):
1 Leaves deeply 5- to 7-lobed, to almost completely divided; fruits 4 to 5 cm in diameter, yellow to black when mature .... **S. aculeastrum**
　Leaves elliptic to ovate or oblong, margin entire; fruits small red or woolly berries up to 1,5 cm in diameter 2
2 Leaves elliptic, petiole up to 2,5 cm long; branches spiny; fruits up to 10 mm in diameter, shiny red when mature .... **S. giganteum**
　Leaves ovate to ovate-oblong, petiole 2,5 to 5 cm long; branches without spines; fruits up to 1,5 cm in diameter, covered with greyish woolly hairs .... ***S. mauritianum**

Solanum aculeastrum Dunal
S.A. no: 669,3   Poison-apple. Bokappel
Rhod. no: 1013   Poison-apple

A very prickly shrub or small tree up to 4 m in height; occurring in wooded grassland, sometimes forming fairly dense colonies. **Bark:** greyish-brown, with a few prickles; branchlets covered with whitish woolly hairs and beset with many very sharp, curved thorns about 2 cm long. **Leaves:** usually

alternate, very broadly elliptic to almost circular in general outline, 4,5 to 14 × 3 to 11 cm, but deeply to almost completely divided into 5 to 7 lobes; deep green above, almost white and woolly below; apex of the lobes tapering; base of the leaf rounded to shallowly lobed; margin of the lobes entire; petiole up to 3 cm long, frequently spiny, with the spines extending on to the midrib on the under surface of the leaf. **Flowers:** whitish to pale mauve, 2 to 2,5 cm in diameter with the corolla lobes narrow and strap-like; in extra-axillary heads (December to January). **Fruit:** almost spherical, fleshy, 4 to 5 cm in diameter, yellow when mature later becoming brownish to black, smooth (May to June).

The fruit is poisonous at all stages of development, but is used by the Zulus as a remedy for ringworm in cattle and horses; the ash from the fruit is rubbed into cuts above the knee to relieve rheumatism.

Solanum giganteum Jacq.
S.A. no: 669,4   Red bitter-apple. Grootbitterappel
Rhod. no: 1014   Red bitter-apple

A much-branched shrub or small tree, 3 to 5 m in height; occurring in woodland, on mountain slopes, often in deep shade in forest clearings and at the margin of thicket. **Bark:** pale greyish to brownish; branchlets covered with thick white woolly hairs, and beset with short almost straight prickles about 5 mm long. **Leaves:** alternate, elliptic, up to 23 × 9 cm, dark green above, densely covered with whitish woolly hairs below especially when young; apex and base tapering; margin entire; petiole up to 2,5 cm long. **Flowers:** white to violet, about 10 mm in diameter, in many-flowered branched terminal heads; the branches and backs of the calyx lobes are covered with whitish woolly hairs (December to February). **Fruit:** almost spherical, fleshy, about 10 mm in diameter, bright red when mature, resembling small tomatoes, in dense heads up to 20 cm in diameter (March to April).

The leaves provide a remedy for festering ulcers, the lower woolly surface being used to clean the sore while the smooth upper surface is applied as a healing dressing. The fresh juice and leaves are made into an ointment for the same purpose. The fruits, which are apparently edible, are used by the Xhosa and Zulus to curdle milk and to treat throat ulcers.

This species resembles the exotic *S. mauritianum,* but the latter lacks the prickles.

*Solanum mauritianum Scop.

The bug tree, originally introduced from Asia, has become naturalised and is now a troublesome weed in Natal, Zululand and other areas in southern Africa. The fruits are poisonous.

821

3. *CYPHOMANDRA Mart. ex Sendtner

*Cyphomandra betacea (Cav.) Sendtner

The tree tomato (Rhod. no: 1020), from South America, is cultivated for its fruits. It has become naturalised in the east of Rhodesia, parts of the eastern Cape and possibly in Natal.

4. *NICOTIANA L.

*Nicotiana glauca R. J. D. Graham

The blue-green nicotiana, from the Argentine, has become naturalised over much of southern Africa (Rhod. no: 1022); it is especially noticeable in the arid, semi-desert areas of the west and north-western Cape, where it provides welcome shelter and shade where trees are rare.

SCROPHULARIACEAE *(The snapdragon family)*

Key to the genera:
1 Fruit a fleshy berry, indehiscent .... **1. Halleria**

　Fruit a dehiscent capsule 2

2 Leaves usually whorled, rarely opposite, and then with whorls present .... **4. Bowkeria**

　Leaves usually opposite 3

3 In Transkei and Natal, barely extending into the eastern Cape; flowers with the corolla lobes longer than the bell-shaped tube, stamens attached in the mouth of the tube .... **3. Anastrabe**

　In the southern and south-western Cape, in Rhodesia and adjacent areas in Moçambique and one small area in the northern Transvaal; flowers with the corolla lobes much shorter than the cylindric tube, stamens attached about half way down the tube .... **2. Freylinia**

1. HALLERIA L.
Halleria lucida L.　Illust. 277
S.A. no: 670　Tree-fuchsia. Notsung
Rhod. no: 1023　Tree-fuchsia

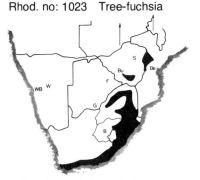
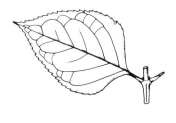

A shrub, often with trailing branches, or a small tree, 2 to 3 m in height, occasionally reaching 12 m; occurring from coastal and karroid scrub to evergreen forest, at the margins of forest, in forested ravines and on rocky mountain slopes. **Bark:** pale grey, rather rough and longitudinally fissured. **Leaves:** opposite, simple, ovate, 2,5 to 7 × 1 to 4 cm, thinly leathery, shiny bright green, without hairs; apex tapering to attenuate; base very broadly tapering to square, often asymmetric; margin finely toothed to scalloped; petiole up to 10 mm long. **Flowers:** brick red and orange, tubular, curved, up to 4 cm long, in axillary clusters, or fascicles, often on the older wood; showy, although usually rather hidden among the leaves. Bisexual; calyx short, cup-shaped, with 3 to 5 lobes; corolla with a

822

long cylindric curved tube widening at the mouth and 4 to 5 short lobes; stamens 4, attached to the lower section of the corolla tube; disc cushion-shaped; ovary 2-chambered (May to December). **Fruit:** broadly ovoid to almost spherical, fleshy, about 10 mm long, black when mature, crowned with the long thread of the persistent style, forming a tail-like wisp (August onwards).

The Zulus soak the dry leaves in water and squeeze drops into the ear to relieve earache. The plant is considered a charm against evil: twigs are burnt when offering sacrifices to ancestral spirits and plants are set alight each year, the ash mixed with fat and smeared on to cuttings of *Rhamnus prinoides* which are driven into the ground around a village to protect the inhabitants from wizards and bad weather. The fruit has a rather sickly sweet taste; it tends to dry the mouth so it is not much sought after except in times of food shortage when the green fruits are buried in sand to hasten their maturing. The wood is yellowish, hard, tough but little used, the pieces seldom being large enough. This is an attractive and unusual garden plant and is easily propagated by layering. It is an extremely attractive tree to a wide variety of birds and thus has additional value in the garden.

2. FREYLINIA Pangella ex Colla

Shrubs or small trees. **Leaves:** usually opposite. **Flowers:** in cymes. Bisexual; floral parts in fours to fives; sepals 5, persistent; corolla with a funnel-shaped to cylindric tube, and 5 short lobes; stamens 4, attached about half way down the corolla tube; ovary 2-chambered. **Fruit:** an ovoid, dehiscent capsule.

Key to the tree species of *Freylinia:*
Leaves long and very narrow, 10 to 13 × 0,4 to 1,3 cm, margins entire; flowers white to cream. Occurring in the southern and south-western Cape only .... **F. lanceolata**
Leaves small, ovate to lanceolate, 1,7 to 4,5 × 0,5 to 1 cm, margins toothed; flowers white, mauve or lilac. Occurring in eastern Rhodesia, central Moçambique and northern Transvaal only .... **F. tropica**

Freylinia lanceolata (L.f.) G. Don
S.A. no: 670,1   Honey bell bush. Heuningklokkiesbos
Rhod. no: —

 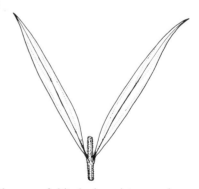

A shrub or small tree up to 5 m in height; occurring over a wide range of altitudes in moist areas, along stream and river banks and fringing vleis. **Bark:** grey, rather smooth; branchlets drooping. **Leaves:** opposite, narrowly elliptic to lanceolate, 10 to 13 × 0,4 to 1,3 cm, slightly curved, dull green, with or without hairs, midrib prominent below; apex and base tapering; margin entire; petiole somewhat obscured by the decurrent leaf base. **Flowers:** white to cream, richly yellow within, cylindric, up to 10 mm long, in terminal heads (sporadically throughout the year). **Fruit:** a small capsule (also throughout the year).
This charming plant, the flowers of which smell strongly of honey, is easily cultivated.

Freylinia tropica S. Moore
S.A. no: Transvaal honey bell bush
Rhod. no: 1024   Inyanga hedge plant

A slender shrub, usually about 2 m in height, but sometimes a small tree up to 7 m, with slender rather loosely spreading branches; occurring at high altitudes, at the margins of evergreen forest, along

823

Honey bell bush, Freylinia lanceolata, *in the Kirstenbosch Gardens, Cape Town.*

streams and on exposed misty mountain slopes; it is frequently a pioneer plant on cleared land. **Bark:** rather pale grey, greenish to dark grey, or light brown, smooth to rather rough. **Leaves:** opposite, narrowly obovate or lanceolate, 1,7 to 4,5 × 0,5 to 1 cm, shiny bright green; apex broadly tapering; base tapering; margin with a few variable teeth over the upper third; petiole 1 to 4 mm long. **Flowers:** white, mauve or lilac, with the corolla tubular, up to 10 mm long, with spreading lobes, each about 6 mm long; in axillary clusters of 1 to 4 near the ends of the branchlets (September to February). **Fruit:** a pale brown ovoid capsule, 3 to 5 mm long, tipped by the remains of the persistent style, dehiscent (October to March).

This has been used as an attractive hedge.

3. ANASTRABE   E. Meyer ex Benth.

Anastrabe integerrima E. Meyer ex Benth.
S.A. no: 671   Pambati tree. Pambatieboom
824   Rhod. no: —

A shrub or small tree, 5 to 10 m in height; occurring at the margins of evergreen forest and in ravine forest. **Bark:** grey. **Leaves:** usually opposite, simple, elliptic to ovate-oblong, 2,5 to 10 × 1 to 3,5 cm, glossy dark green above, creamy-brown below; apex tapering and hair- or bristle-tipped; base tapering to rounded; margin entire, rolled under, or may have very fine teeth; petiole up to 8 mm long. **Flowers:** yellow, with the throat tinged with red, 1 to 1,5 cm long, in few- to many-flowered axillary or terminal heads, or cymes. Bisexual; floral parts in fours to fives; calyx bell-shaped, with lobes as long as the tube; corolla also bell-shaped, with 2 lips, longer than the tube, the upper lip hooded and slightly 3-lobed, the lower slighty 2-lobed; stamens 4 fixed in the mouth of the corolla tube, the 5th rudimentary; ovary 2-chambered (January to May). **Fruit:** an ovoid capsule, up to 8 mm long, splitting into 2 valves (March to July).

4. BOWKERIA Harvey

Shrubs or trees. **Leaves:** usually in whorls of 3 to 4, sometimes opposite, simple. **Flowers:** in racemose cymes, occasionally solitary, or 2 to 3 in the leaf axils, conspicuous bracts at the base of the flower stalks. Bisexual; floral parts in fours to fives; calyx 5-lobed, leathery, ribbed, with fine hairs, sometimes glandular; corolla broadly bell-shaped, or scuttle-shaped and inflated with the lobes forming 2 lips, the upper shallowly divided into 3 segments, the lower into 2 segments; stamens 4, usually attached at the base of the corolla tube and enclosed by the tube, staminodes may be present; ovary 2- to 3-chambered, glandular. **Fruit:** an ovoid capsule, dehiscing into 2 to 3 valves.

Key to the tree species of *Bowkeria:*
1 Usually a much-branched shrub, 1 to 3 m in height, but can become tree-like; flowers bright yellow
.... **B. citrina**
  Shrubs or small trees; flowers white, sometimes streaked with red 2
2 Leaves with fine, short hairs, the upper surface rather shallowly wrinkled; flowers white with
    reddish streaks in the throat. Occurring in the Transvaal and Swaziland .... **B. cymosa**
  Leaves with fine short soft hairs, or densely woolly, the upper surface heavily wrinkled; flowers
    pure white. Occurring from the eastern Cape to Zululand .... **B. verticillata**

Bowkeria citrina Thode   Illust. 278
S.A. no: Yellow shell-flower bush
Rhod. no: —

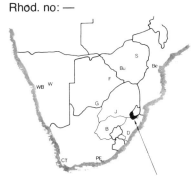

825

SCROPHULARIACEAE

Usually a much-branched shrub, 1 to 3 m in height, but it can become tree-like; occurring at high altitudes, along stream banks and at the margins of evergreen forest. **Bark:** greyish-white; most of the plant golden gland-dotted, and covered with fine soft hairs. **Leaves:** in whorls of 3 to 4, occasionally opposite, narrowly elliptic, up to 7 × 1,1 cm, with or without fine hairs, pleasantly aromatic when crushed; the midrib and veins on the under surface conspicuously golden-yellow and prominent; apex tapering to a fine point; base tapering; margin entire or finely scalloped, markedly so in young plants; petiole up to 6 mm long. **Flowers:** beautiful, scuttle-shaped, bright yellow, almost 2 × 2 cm, axillary, solitary (November to June). **Fruit:** a brown ovoid rather woody capsule, about 9 × 5 mm, splitting into 2 lobed valves, with the remains of the calyx at the base; the flowering and fruiting times frequently overlap; seeds minute (April to June).

Bowkeria cymosa MacOwan
S.A. no: 672   Transvaal shell-flower bush. Transvaalse skulpblombos
Rhod. no: —

 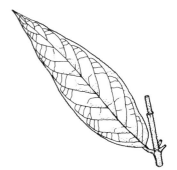

A leafy shrub or small tree, 3 to 4 m in height; occurring on hill slopes and wooded stream banks. **Bark:** brown. **Leaves:** in whorls of 3, lanceolate-oblong, 2,5 to 15 × 1 to 5 cm; upper surface darkish green, puckered, with or without very fine hairs; the under surface paler green and covered with short soft hairs; net-veining is very prominent below and conspicuous although sunken above; apex narrowly tapering; base tapering to narrowly rounded; margin entire or finely toothed, rolled under; petiole up to 6 mm long. **Flowers:** white with reddish to yellowish streaks in the throat, 1 to 1,5 cm in diameter, in axillary, few-flowered branching sprays (November to April). **Fruit:** a narrowly elliptic capsule, about 7 × 3 mm, splitting into 2 to 3 valves, sharply tipped with the remains of the old style and bedded in a papery cup formed from the persistent calyx (March to June).

Bowkeria verticillata (Ecklon & Zeyher) Schinz
[*B. triphylla* Harvey; *B. gerrardiana* Harvey]
S.A. no: 673   Natal shell-flower bush. Natalse skulpblombos
Rhod. no: —

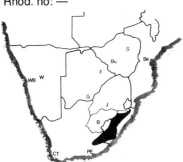 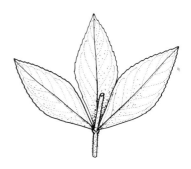

A bushy shrub or small tree usually 3 to 5 m in height, but occasionally reaching 10 m; occurring in mountainous areas above 600 m, in and at the margins of evergreen forest, in valleys and on stony mountain slopes. **Bark:** grey; branchlets reddish with white lenticels. **Leaves:** usually in whorls of 3 (occasionally 4, or opposite), elliptic, ovate to broadly lanceolate, 2,5 to 13 × 0,6 to 6,5 cm; the upper surface dark green and wrinkled; the under surface paler green, sometimes reddish and covered

826

with fine soft short hairs or densely woolly, with the midrib and lateral veins prominent; apex tapering; base tapering to rounded; margin toothed; petiole absent or very short. **Flowers:** white, showy, heavily scented, up to 2 cm long, with the corolla markedly inflated and the lobes forming distinct lips; in axillary pairs on slender stalks (October to April). **Fruit:** an ovoid thinly woody capsule, about 1,6 cm long, splitting into 3 valves at the tip (January to July).

The wood is white, hard but rather brittle. This is a beautiful small tree, fairly fast growing and hardy, but is seldom seen in gardens.

BIGNONIACEAE *(The jacaranda family)*

Key to the genera (exotics marked*):

1 Leaf twice compound, rachis 10 to 15 cm long, leaflets small, about 10 × 2 mm; flowers mauve-blue, in heavy branched heads; fruit an almost circular, flattened, wavy, 2-valved capsule .... **4. *Jacaranda**

Leaves simple, 3-foliolate or once-compound 2

2 Fruits very large sausage-shaped, heavy, fibrous, up to 1 m × 18 cm, indehiscent . **8. Kigelia**

Fruits dehiscent capsules 3

3 Flowers large, about 8 cm long × 9 cm wide at the mouth, not including the spread of the corolla lobes, striking, orange to crimson with a yellow centre .... **7. Fernandoa**

Flowers tubular to bell-shaped, but not more than 5 cm long × 1 to 1,5 cm wide at the throat, not including the spread of the corolla lobes 4

4 Capsules conspicuously long and narrow, 13 to 85 × 1 to 2,5 cm 5

Capsules elliptic, about 8 × 1,5 or 5 × 2,5 cm 7

5 Leaflets 1 to 4,5 × 0,5 to 3 cm, narrowly ovate to ovate elliptic; margins markedly scalloped to toothed; flowers narrowly cylindric, orange to scarlet .... **1. Tecomaria**

Leaflets longer than 4,5 cm, usually about 6 to 9 × 3 to 4 cm; margins entire or sometimes finely toothed 6

6 Bark grey, smooth, flaking in round pieces revealing paler under bark; flowers very showy, pale pink about 3 cm long .... **6. Stereospermum**

Bark grey to brown, smooth to finely vertically striated, not flaking in round pieces; flowers golden-yellow, or mottled yellow and maroon, 2 to 5 cm long .... **5. Markhamia**

7 Leaves simple, markedly greyish, the veining conspicuously sunken above giving a puckered surface; flowers white, large, with a cylindric tube; fruit a thick, woody, warted capsule .... **3. Catophractes**

Leaves simple, 3-foliolate or pinnately compound, veining not deeply sunken so the surface is not puckered; flowers deep yellow, bell-shaped; fruit a smooth, thin-walled capsule **2. Rhigozum**

1. TECOMARIA Spach

Tecomaria capensis (Thunb.) Spach   Illust. 279
S.A. no: 673,1   Cape honeysuckle. Kaapse kamperfoelie
Rhod. no: —

A large many-stemmed shrub or small tree up to 4 m in height; occurring over a wide range of altitudes, at the margins of evergreen forest, in bush, scrub and along stream banks. **Bark:** pale brown, heavily lenticelled. **Leaves:** opposite, compound, with 2 to 5 pairs of leaflets plus a terminal leaflet; leaflets ovate to oblong-ovate, 1 to 4,5 × 0,5 to 3 cm, dark glossy green above, paler green below with small pockets of hairs in the axils of the veins; apex tapering; base rounded, asymmetric;

827

margin scalloped to toothed; petiolules very short, petiole 2 to 3 cm long. **Flowers:** orange to scarlet, showy, up to 5 cm long, in many-flowered terminal sprays, or racemes. Bisexual; floral parts in fours to fives; calyx bell-shaped, short, 5-lobed; corolla narrowly cylindric, widening slightly near the mouth, 2-lobed, with the upper lobe hooded, the lower lipped; stamens 4, protruding from the mouth of the tube; ovary 2-chambered (June to November). **Fruit:** a long slender flat capsule, up to 13 × 1 cm, splitting into 2 valves and releasing large numbers of papery-winged seeds (October to February).

This is a very ornamental plant and is widely cultivated. The species is divided into two subspecies, only the typical subspecies, subsp. *capensis,* occurring south of the Zambezi River.

2. RHIGOZUM Burch.

Spiny shrubs or small trees, sometimes with the branchlets in whorls of 3. **Leaves:** solitary or fascicled on small lateral branchlets which are no more than cushions, simple or compound, 3-foliolate or pinnate. **Flowers:** in fascicles on the lateral cushions. Bisexual; all floral parts in fives; calyx short, may be markedly ribbed, with or without hairs; corolla bell-shaped below the mouth, with broad, showy, spreading lobes; stamens attached to the base of the widened section of the tube; disc thick, saucer-shaped; ovary 2-chambered. **Fruit:** an oblong to elliptic, flattened beaked capsule, splitting to release many papery-winged seeds.

Key to the tree species of *Rhigozum:*
1 Leaves pinnately compound, usually with 3 pairs of leaflets plus a terminal leaflet (very rarely 3-foliolate) .... **R. zambesiacum**
  Leaves simple or 3-foliolate 2
2 Leaves usually simple, up to 2,5 × 0,4 cm, sometimes 3-foliolate; decurrent leaf base obscures the petiole .... **R. brevispinosum**
  Leaves usually 3-foliolate, leaflets usually less than 1,3 cm long; petioles about 5 mm long ......
  .... **R. obovatum**

Rhigozum brevispinosum Kuntze
[*R. spinosum* Burch. ex Sprague; *R. binifolium* S. Moore]
S.A. no: 674   Western Rhigozum. Kortdoringgranaat
Rhod. no: 1027   Western Rhigozum

A rigid erect spiny shrub or small tree, 2 to 4 m in height; occurring in open woodland and on rocky ridges. **Bark:** grey-brown. **Leaves:** fascicled on very short furry knobby dwarf lateral shoots, just below a short straight spine about 10 mm long; simple, (rarely 3-foliolate), slender, oblanceolate, up to 2,5 × 0,4 cm; apex rounded; base narrowly tapering and running into the petiole; margin entire; petiole obscured by the decurrent leaf base. **Flowers:** showy, golden-yellow, sweetly scented; corolla with a tube about 1,5 cm long, and 5 broad, delicate crinkled lobes, about 3,5 cm in diameter, sometimes with reddish streaks in the throat (September to December). **Fruit:** a slender flat smooth thin-walled capsule, about 7 × 1,2 cm, creamy-brown (December to May).

A shrub, *R. trichotomum* Burch., the *driedoring,* with its branches characteristically arising in threes, commonly occurs in the arid northern and north-western Cape, South West Africa, and Botswana, and could be confused with *R. brevispinosum*.

Rhigozum obovatum Burch.
S.A. no: 675   Karoo Rhigozum. Geelberggranaat
Rhod. no: —

Usually a rigid compact shrub, or small tree, 1 to 3 m in height; occurring in dry rocky places and karroid scrub. **Bark:** grey, smooth. **Leaves:** on sharp lateral branchlets; 3-foliolate, but often apparently simple due to one or more of the leaflets not developing; leaflets obovate, 0,5 to 1,3 × 0,2 to 0,5 cm, greyish-green; apex rounded, often finely notched; base narrowly tapering; margin entire, revolute; petiolules about 2 mm long, petiole up to 5 mm long. **Flowers:** showy, bright yellow, up to 3,5 cm in diameter (September to November, and intermittently at other times of the year, usually just after rain). **Fruit:** a flattened, narrow, smooth thin-walled capsule, 6 to 8 × 1 cm, brown, dehiscing along the flat surface (intermittently throughout the year).

This plant is beautiful when in flower; it is heavily browsed on by game and stock so that plants are frequently kept down to a height of about 1 m.

Rhigozum zambesiacum Baker   Illust. 280
S.A. no: 676   Eastern Rhigozum. Mopaniegranaat
Rhod. no: 1028   Eastern Rhigozum

A spiny bushy shrub or small tree up to 7 m in height; occurring at low altitudes in hot dry woodland and on rocky outcrops and hillsides. **Bark:** grey-brown, smooth, with slight longitudinal ridges; the lateral branches are often short arching rigid and spine-tipped, carrying short spines along their length. **Leaves:** clustered on the small knobby bosses above which there is a straight spine, 1 to 1,5 cm long, either on the main stem or on the spinose branchlets; compound, sometimes with one pair of leaflets, but more often with 3 to 5 pairs, plus the terminal leaflet; leaflets obovate, usually about 5 × 3 mm, dark green; apex rounded; base narrowly tapering; margin entire; petiolules absent, petiole up to 5 mm long. **Flowers:** showy, golden-yellow, about 3,5 cm in diameter, with a sweet but transient scent; corolla with a tube 1 to 1,5 cm long and spreading, crinkled and frilled lobes (September to December). **Fruit:** a slender, flat, smooth thin-walled capsule, about 7 × 1,5 cm, pale brown, dehiscing along the flat surface; the remains of the old empty capsules remain on the plant for months (November to January).

Given rather dry conditions, this plant can be successfully grown in a garden.

3. CATOPHRACTES D. Don

Catophractes alexandri D. Don   Illust. 281
S.A. no: Trumpet thorn. Trompetterdoring
Rhod. no: 1029   Trumpet thorn

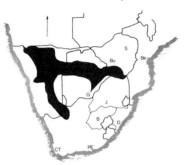

An erect spiny shrub or small tree, 1 to 3 m in height; occurring in very arid country, often on limestone ridges and outcrops, sometimes forming pure communities. **Bark:** brown; the stems shiny brown with slender very sharp spines up to 5 cm long arising above the leaves (the generic name refers to this). **Leaves:** opposite or more often fascicled along the stem, simple, oblong, 2 to 4 × 1 to 2,5 cm, covered with dense grey woolly hairs, giving the whole plant a pale grey appearance; upper surface puckered, the veins sunken; net-veining prominent below; apex rounded; base narrowly rounded; margin coarsely and deeply toothed to scalloped; petiole up to 5 mm long. **Flowers:** showy, pure white sometimes tinged with pink, with a yellow throat; about 5 cm in diameter; axillary, solitary; the sweet scent disappears soon after picking. Bisexual; floral parts in fives to sevens; calyx tube about 2,5 cm long, 5-lobed, ribbed, hairy, conspicuous; corolla tube greenish, up to 5 cm long, with 5 to 7 spreading lobes; stamens as many as the corolla lobes; ovary 2-chambered (the flowers open soon after rain and so may be found intermittently at most times of the year). **Fruit:** a thickly woody elliptic capsule, about 5 × 2,5 cm, rather flattened, becoming grey and finally dark brown when mature, warty, finally dehiscing along the flat faces to release many papery winged seeds (at most times of the year).

4. *JACARANDA Juss.

*Jacaranda mimosifolia D. Don

The jacaranda (Rhod. no: 1030), from Brazil, is widely planted as a street tree and in gardens and has become naturalised to a limited extent in parts of Rhodesia.

5. MARKHAMIA Seem. ex Baillon

Shrubs or trees. **Leaves:** opposite, compound, imparipinnate. **Flowers:** in a terminal or axillary raceme or panicle. Bisexual; floral parts in fives and fours; calyx shorter than the corolla tube, splitting down one side, peaked at the apex giving a boat-shaped outline; corolla funnel-shaped at the base, widening to bell-shaped at the mouth with the 5 lobes forming 2 lips; stamens 4, enclosed within the

830

tube; ovary 2-chambered. **Fruit:** a long narrow flat capsule, splitting to release the papery winged seeds.

Key to the tree species of *Markhamia:*

Leaves with 2 to 3 pairs of leaflets plus a terminal leaflet; leaflets usually about 7 × 3,5 cm; flowers yellow densely flecked with maroon; corolla tube 2 to 3 cm long; lobes spreading, 3 to 4 cm in diameter .... **M. acuminata**

Leaves with usually 5 pairs of leaflets plus a terminal leaflet; leaflets usually about 9 × 4 cm; flowers large, bright yellow, only with reddish streaks on the lower lobes; corolla tube up to 5 cm long; lobes spreading, up to 5 cm in diameter .... **M. obtusifolia**

Markhamia acuminata (Klotzsch) K. Schum.   Illust. 282
S.A. no: 677   Bean tree. Klokkiesboontjieboom
Rhod. no: 1031   Bean tree

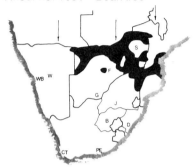

A small often straggling tree up to 7 m in height; occurring at medium to low altitudes, in riverine fringes and often on rocky outcrops and hillsides. **Bark:** grey, smooth to rough and rather vertically and narrowly flaky, giving it a shaggy look; young branchlets with conspicuous lenticels. **Leaves:** with 2 to 3 pairs of leaflets plus a terminal leaflet, the lowermost pair small and the subsequent pairs increasing in size to the terminal leaflet; leaflets obovate to almost circular, 2,5 to 10 × 2 to 6 cm; there may be fine yellowish hairs on both surfaces, with the upper surface losing most of these by maturity, and the under surface remaining finely hairy; both surfaces scaly; apex usually attenuate; base broadly tapering, often asymmetric; margin entire or finely toothed; petiolules almost absent, petiole 4 to 9 cm long. **Flowers:** striking, yellow densely flecked with maroon; corolla tube 2 to 3 cm long, with the lobes spreading to 3 to 4 cm in diameter; in terminal or axillary racemes, or on the old wood (September to January). **Fruit:** a slender capsule, up to 60 × 1 to 1,5 cm, dark brown with pale lenticel dots, splitting longitudinally in 2 valves (January to May).

The flowers are sometimes frequented by large ants. The branches are brittle; the wood, which is yellowish, fine-grained and fairly durable, has been used for roofing timbers and implement handles but is usually not of sufficient size to be of value. The roots are roasted and ground and the powder rubbed into incised skin to relieve backache. These trees can be grown from truncheons.

Markhamia obtusifolia (Baker) Sprague
S.A. no: Golden bean tree
Rhod. no: 1032   Golden bean tree

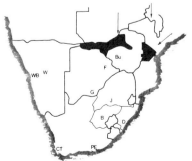

A bushy shrub, 1 to 2 m in height, but it can develop into a small tree up to 5 m in height and even 13 m; occurring at medium to low altitudes in open woodland and at the margins of evergreen forest. **Bark:** light brown to grey, rather smooth, with longitudinal striations in large specimens. **Leaves:** with 5 pairs of leaflets plus a terminal leaflet; leaflets oblong to elliptic, up to 14 × 6 cm, but usually about 9 × 4 cm; the young leaves covered with dense long golden hairs, the upper surface losing most of these by maturity, the under surface remaining densely woolly; apex rounded, sometimes abruptly attenuate or notched; base rounded or square, sometimes asymmetric; margin entire; petiolules absent, petiole up to 8 cm long, covered with fine short golden hairs. **Flowers:** showy, bright yellow with reddish streaks on the lower three corolla lobes; corolla tube up to 5 cm long and the lobes spreading, over 5 cm in diameter; in many-flowered terminal branched panicles up to 20 cm long; the calyx lobes, buds and stalks densely covered with golden hairs (November to June). **Fruit:** a slender flattened capsule, up to 85 × 2,5 cm, but frequently smaller, covered with dense golden soft hairs with a distinct longitudinal ridge down the two flattened sides which mark the lines of dehiscence (January to September).

6. STEREOSPERMUM Cham.

Stereospermum kunthianum Cham.   Illust. 283
S.A. no: —
Rhod. no: 1033   Pink jacaranda

A rounded tree up to 13 m in height; occurring at medium to low altitudes, frequently on rocky outcrops and hillsides, also in open woodland, associated with termite mounds and at margins of evergreen forests. **Bark:** grey, smooth to flaking in round patches revealing paler underbark. **Leaves:** opposite, compound, with 4 pairs of leaflets plus a terminal leaflet; leaflets oblong, about 8 × 3 cm, with short soft hairs; apex broadly tapering, often abruptly attenuate; base tapering; margin entire, occasionally toothed in coppice growth; petiolules almost absent, petiole up to 7 cm long. **Flowers:** showy, delicate pink with red streaks on the lower corolla lobes; corolla with the tube up to 3 cm long, and spreading lobes, 3 to 4 cm in diameter; in large panicles, produced before the leaves. Bisexual; calyx bell-shaped, irregularly 2- to 5-lobed; corolla bell-shaped with 5 spreading lobes partially forming 2 lips; stamens 4, enclosed within the corolla tube; ovary linear-oblong, 2-chambered (August to October). **Fruit:** a slender flat capsule, up to 45 × 1 cm, reddish-brown, splitting into 2 valves to release many winged seeds, the old remnants of the capsule remaining on the tree for months (October to December).

The wood provides a good fuel and the pods, chewed with salt, are used as a cough remedy. These trees make spectacular garden subjects and are becoming increasingly available from nurseries, but at times they appear to be difficult to rear successfully in the garden.

7. FERNANDOA Welw. ex Seem.

Fernandoa magnifica Seem.
S.A. no: —
Rhod. no: 1034   Fernandoa

A small tree, 3 to 4 m in height when growing in dry woodland but reaching 30 m when in moist evergreen forest. **Bark:** pale brown to grey, rough and deeply fissured; bole usually rather slender.

Leaves: opposite, compound, with 4 to 6 pairs of leaflets plus a terminal leaflet; leaflets lanceolate to oblong, 8 to 16 × 3,5 to 5 cm; apex rather attenuate; base broadly tapering to rounded; margin toothed to scalloped or very obscurely so to almost entire, rather wavy; petiolules almost absent, petiole up to 8 cm long. **Flowers:** very striking, bright orange or crimson with a yellow centre, cup-shaped, rather asymmetric, about 8 cm long and 9 cm wide at the mouth, the corolla only shallowly divided into lobes; axillary, usually solitary, appearing before the leaves. Bisexual; calyx bell-shaped, irregularly 3- to 4-lobed; corolla widely bell-shaped, constricted towards the base; stamens 4, slightly protruding from the mouth of the corolla tube; ovary narrow (August to October). **Fruit:** a slender, flattened, spirally twisted capsule, 40 to 70 × 1 to 1,5 cm, pale brown, with a fine ridge along the 2 flattened sides which mark the lines of dehiscence; seeds many, flat, 2-winged; the remains of the capsules remain on the tree for months after the seeds are shed (September to January).

8. KIGELIA DC.

Kigelia africana (Lam.) Benth.   Illust. 284
[*K. pinnata* (Jacq.) DC.]
S.A. no: 678   Sausage tree. Worsboom
Rhod. no: 1035   Sausage tree

 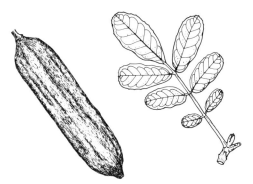

A medium to large tree up to 18 m in height, with a rounded crown; occurring at low altitudes in open woodland and in riverine fringes. **Bark:** grey, generally smooth, flaking in thin round patches in large specimens. **Leaves:** opposite, crowded near the ends of the branches, compound, with 3 to 5 pairs of leaflets plus a terminal leaflet; leaflets oblong, up to 10 × 6 cm, leathery, roughly hairy on both surfaces, rather yellowish-green above, paler green below; apex broadly tapering to rounded; base square, asymmetric in the lateral leaflets, symmetric in the terminal leaflet; margin entire, sometimes obscurely toothed, wavy; the lower leaflets shortly petiolulate, the terminal pair without petiolules; petiole up to 15 cm long. **Flowers:** striking, dark maroon with heavy yellow veining on the outside, cup-shaped, asymmetric, up to 15 cm across the mouth, unpleasant smelling; in 6- to 12-flowered lax pendulous sprays up to 90 cm long. Bisexual; calyx shortly tubular with 2 to 5 ribbed lobes; corolla widely cup-shaped with 5 broad spreading lobes; stamens 4, slightly protruding beyond the mouth of the corolla tube; ovary 1-chambered (August to October). **Fruit:** very unusual, sausage-shaped, up to 1 m × 18 cm, greyish-brown, heavily lenticel-dotted, indehiscent, heavy, weighing up to 10 kg, containing a fibrous pulp in which are embedded many seeds (December to June).

The flowers are visited by bats and, when they fall to the ground, are eaten by game and stock. The   **833** unripe fruits are said to be poisonous but are taken as a remedy for syphilis and rheumatism, and the ripe fruits, which are inedible, are baked and added to beer to aid fermentation. In times of food shortage the seeds are roasted and eaten. A dressing for ulcers and sores is made from the powdered fruit; this is also used to increase lactation and it is rubbed on to the bodies of babies to make them fat, though the head is carefully avoided during this process for it is believed that hydrocephalus might otherwise result! If hung in a hut, the fruits are considered to be a charm against whirlwinds. The fruits and bark, ground and boiled in water, are either taken orally or used as an enema in treating children's stomach ailments. At the time of writing medical investigations are being carried out on the use of the fruit extract in treating skin conditions, including those caused by exposure to the sun, but so far the tests apparently reveal variable results. The wood is whitish or yellow and, although rather soft, is tough and has been used for planking, yokes and boxes and also to make dugout canoes. There is a historic specimen growing at the point where Rhodesia, Zambia and the Caprivi Strip meet. Under this tree Dr David Livingstone pitched camp just before he saw the Victoria Falls for the first time and he is said to have carved his initials on the trunk, though these have been long obliterated. The trees are easily cultivated and grow well in warm areas.

PEDALIACEAE *(The sesame family)*

SESAMOTHAMNUS Welw.

Shrubs or small trees with swollen stems giving rise to numerous erect stiff grey branches armed with spreading spines. **Leaves:** fascicled on short lateral branchlets often no more than cushions, simple. **Flowers:** solitary, terminal or axillary, or in short, few-flowered racemes. Bisexual; floral parts in fours to fives; calyx short, divided almost to the base; corolla with a very long cylindric slender curved tube, often with a slender spur produced at the back, 5-lobed and partially 2-lipped; stamens 4, joined to the throat of the tube; ovary 2-chambered. **Fruit:** an elliptic to oblong or ovate, dehiscent rigid compressed capsule.

Key to the tree species of *Sesamothamnus:*
1 Corolla tube with a slight swelling at the base, without a distinct spur .... **S. guerichii**
  Corolla tube with a distinct spur, about 6 mm to 3,8 cm long 2
2 Not in South West Africa; corolla tube with a spur 6 to 8 mm long .... **S. lugardii**
  Only in northern South West Africa and northwards; corolla tube with a spur up to 3,8 cm long
  .... **S. benguellensis**

Sesamothamnus benguellensis Welw.
S.A. no: 679,1   Kaoko sesame bush. Kaokosesambos
Rhod. no: —

Sesamothamnus guerichii (Engl.) E. A. Bruce
S.A. no: 679   Herero sesame bush. Hererosesambos
Rhod. no: —

These two species, both from the Kaokoveld of South West Africa, closely resemble each other and differ in the following details:

834

S. benguellensis – flowers up to 7 cm long, the corolla tube markedly curved and with a distinctive spur at the base up to 3,8 cm long; the capsule up to 9 cm long, oblong, sharp-tipped; the leaves lanceolate to ovate and narrowly tapering to the base (lines on the map).

S. guerichii – the flowers with the corolla tube up to 10 cm long, almost straight, with a slight swelling at the base; capsule up to 6 cm long, elliptic to ovate, not sharp-tipped; leaves lanceolate to ovate, not conspicuously tapering to the base (black area on the map).

Sesamothamnus lugardii N. E. Brown
S.A. no: 680   Transvaal sesame bush. Transvaalse sesambos
Rhod. no: 1036   Sesame bush

A grotesque succulent shrub or small tree up to 4 m in height, rather resembling a miniature baobab; occurring in hot dry country, often on rocky ridges. **Bark:** grey to yellowish marked with black, finely peeling; branches armed with strong straight or slightly curved spines, 1 to 1,5 cm long, just below

The Transvaal sesame bush, Sesamothamnus lugardii *, in the Pretoria Botanic Gardens.*   **835**

the leaves. **Leaves:** in clusters along the stems, obovate to broadly so, up to 2,5 × 2 cm, frequently smaller, grey to whitish-grey caused by massed flat whitish grey glandular hairs especially on the under surface where the veins, which are without hairs, are prominent; apex rounded, sometimes shallowly notched; base tapering; margin entire; petiole 1 to 3 mm long. **Flowers:** striking, white, corolla with a slender tube up to 8 cm long and 5 broad spreading lobes, about 5 to 6 cm in diameter; there is a conspicuous spur, 6 to 8 mm long, at the base of the tube; axillary, solitary (November to February). **Fruit:** a heart-shaped, flat, woody, pale brown capsule, about 5 × 3,5 cm, dehiscing round the edges to release the papery winged seeds (December to April).

ACANTHACEAE

Key to the tree genera:
1 Leaves small, 2,5 to 6 cm long; flowers rather small, about 2 × 1,2 cm ..... **1. Sclerochiton**

   Leaves large, more than 6 cm long; flowers up to 3 to 7 cm long 2

2 Leaf margins entire, wavy; flowers strongly 2-lipped, the upper lip hooded .... **3. Duvernoia**

   Leaf margins coarsely and irregularly toothed; flowers bell-shaped, only very slightly 2-lipped
.... **2. Mackaya**

1. SCLEROCHITON Harvey

Sclerochiton harveyanus Nees
S.A. no: Blue-lips
Rhod. no: 1045 Blue-lips

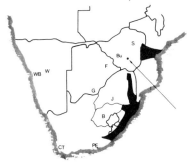

A shrub, often scrambling, or a small tree up to 4 m in height; occurring in and at the margins of evergreen forest where it frequently forms part of the under-storey. **Bark:** brown, smooth, thinly flaking on the branchlets. **Leaves:** opposite, simple, elliptic to oblanceolate, 2,5 to 6 × 1,5 to 2,5 cm, glossy green, with or without very small but dense woolly hairs (a 10x lens required) along the midrib on the under surface; apex and base tapering; margin bluntly and irregularly toothed, sometimes obscurely so; petiole slender, up to 8 mm long. **Flowers:** bluish-mauve to purple, about 2 × 1,2 cm, in short racemes. Bisexual; calyx 5-lobed to the base; corolla with a short tube, then spreading out in a

836

flat upstanding limb; stamens 4, attached about half way down the tube and protruding from the mouth; ovary 2-chambered (December to March). **Fruit:** a thinly woody ellipsoidal beaked capsule, about 10 mm long, splitting into 5 valves (March to May).

2. MACKAYA Harvey

Mackaya bella Harvey

S.A. no: 681,1   Mackaya. Blouklokkiesbos

Rod. no: –

A shrub or small tree, 1 to 4 m in height; occurring in evergreen forest, often along stream and river banks. **Bark:** pale greyish-brown. **Leaves:** opposite, simple, elliptic, up to 14 × 3,5 cm, dark green; apex finely attenuate; base narrowly tapering; margin coarsely and irregularly toothed; petiole slender, about 1,5 cm long. **Flowers:** attractive, delicate pale lavender lined and marked with purple; corolla with tube up to 4 cm long, expanded above, and widely spreading lobes up to 4 to 6 cm in diameter; flowers in lax terminal racemes up to 15 cm long, all produced on the same side of the peduncle. Bisexual; calyx 5-lobed almost to the base; corolla bell-shaped, with 5 spreading lobes slightly 2-lipped; stamens 2, attached at the base of the expanded section of the tube, barely protruding from the mouth; ovary 2-chambered (September to November). **Fruit:** a narrowly club-shaped capsule, up to 3,5 cm long, dark brown when mature, splitting into 2 valves which curl well back and eject the seeds with an ejector mechanism (October to December).

The wood is used to kindle fire by friction. This makes a beautiful garden plant, growing well in partial to complete shade and tolerating some frost; it is easily grown from cuttings and thrives in sheltered positions.

Characteristic leaves of the Mackaya bella.

837

3. DUVERNOIA E. Meyer ex Nees

Duvernoia adhatodoides E. Meyer ex Nees
[*Adhatoda duvernoia* C. B. Clarke]
S.A. no: 681   Pistol bush. Pistoolbossie
Rhod. no: —

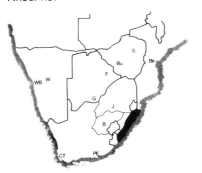

A shrub or small tree, 3 to 7 m in height; occurring in and at the margins of evergreen forest, often along stream banks and in ravines. **Bark:** brown, rough, fissured; the branches and stems are brittle. **Leaves:** opposite, simple, broadly lanceolate, up to 23 × 15 cm, but usually about 15 × 7 cm, shiny dark green, the midrib prominent on both surfaces; apex broadly tapering to abruptly attenuate; base tapering; margin entire, rather wavy; petiole about 2 cm long. **Flowers:** showy, white to mauve and beautifully marked with purple in the throat; densely crowded into short compact axillary racemes, 5 to 8 cm long, on stalks up to 6 cm long. Bisexual; the corolla with a tube about 7 mm long and 2-lipped with 5 unequal lobes, the upper lip about 2,5 cm long and hooded, the lower lip ornately lobed; stamens 2, in the mouth of the tube; ovary 2-chambered. Leaf-like bracts and bracteoles occur among the flowers at the base of the stalks (February to July). **Fruit:** a club-shaped capsule, about 3 × 1 cm, green, dehiscing explosively with a loud crack, an ingenious ejector mechanism throwing the seeds some distance from the parent plant; seeds discoid, about 5 mm in diameter, covered with rough projections (February to July).
The flowers are apparently pollinated by large black and yellow carpenter bees.

RUBIACEAE *(The gardenia family)*

Key to the tree genera:
1 Flowers in spike-like racemes .... **2. Hymenodictyon**

   Flowers solitary or in small groups of 2 to 4 or more 2
   Flowers in branched heads 17

2 Flowers usually more than 10 mm long or in diameter 3

   Flowers usually 10 mm or less in diameter 12

3 Under surface of the leaves reddish-brown with very distinctive, prominent, almost parallel veins; corolla tube widely funnel-shaped and widening round the mouth, less than 2 cm in length and in diameter .... **17. Feretia**

   Under surface of the leaves may have conspicuous veining, but not distinctive reddish-brown; corolla tube, if less than 2 cm long, then cylindric to narrowly so 4

4 Branches and branchlets spiny; flowers less than 2 cm long and in diameter **10. Xeromphis**

   Branches and branchlets may be rigidly twiggy, but not usually spiny; if spiny then the flowers more than 2 cm long and usually more than 3 cm in diameter 5

5 Flowers very conspicuous and showy, more than 2 cm long or in diameter 6

   Flowers not very conspicuous and showy, usually about 2 cm or less long or in diameter 10

6 Calyx 5- to 8-lobed; corolla almost without hairs, 5- to 8-lobed; stamens 5 to 8 .. **13. Gardenia**

  Calyx 5-lobed; corolla 5-lobed, ususally with velvety hairs; stamens 5 to 7 7

7 Corolla tube bell-shaped; not usually hairy outside 8

  Corolla tube slender and narrow; with more or less dense hairs outside 9

8 Fruits with fine but conspicuous longitudinal ridged ribs .... **15. Didymosalpinx**

  Fruits may have obscure longitudinal lobes, but not sharply ridged as above **14. Rothmannia**

9 Corolla lobes long and narrow .... **20. Sericanthe**

  Corolla lobes large and broad .... **21. Heinsia**

10 Leaves almost without hairs, to glossy .... **36. Ancylanthos**

  Leaves hairy to densely so 11

11 Corolla tube bell-shaped, with a widening mouth; silky outside; lobes always 5 **22. Aulacocalyx**

  Corolla tube narrow and slender, not silky outside; lobes usually more than 5, up to 8 **38. Coffea**

12 Rigid shrubs or small trees with the branchlets at right angles to the branches **33. Dinocanthium**

  Branchlets not rigid or set at right angles to the branches 13

13 Leaves up to 7 cm long, ovate, apex conspicuously and narrowly attenuate forming a drip-tip
  .... **28. Rytigynia**

  Leaves usually longer than 7 cm, narrower, elliptic to narrowly so, sometimes attenuate   14

14 Leaves conspicuously long and slender, up to 14 cm long and seldom broader than 1,7 cm;
  flowers and fruits with slender stalks .... **6. Pauridiantha**

  Leaves not conspicuously narrow, up to 5 cm broad 15

15 Flowers and fruits without stalks or almost so .... **42. Lasianthus**

  Flowers and fruits with stalks 16

16 Flowers and fruits on long, slender stalks, usually solitary, sometimes as a tight cluster on a
  slender stalk, or cyme; fruits globose .... **24. Polysphaeria**

  Flowers and fruits on short stalks, always in groups of 3 to 4; fruits ellipsoid **23. Cremaspora**

17 Flowers 1 to 2 cm or more in length or diameter 18

  Individual flowers less than 10 mm long or broad 38

18 Flowers very striking, brownish-pink, orange to crimson 19

  Flowers cream, white, bluish or very pale pink 21

19 Corolla tube very distinctive, up to 8 cm long, slender, pink to brick red, expanding into 4 to 5
  cream, rather short lobes; in lax heads .... **40. Ixora**

  Corolla tube not more than 3 cm long 20

20 A tree of 13 m; flowers in dense heads, tubes narrow, slightly curved, up to 3 cm long. Fruits
  crimson, with two crimson wings .... **25. Alberta**

  Usually a shrub or small tree to 5 m (occasionally 10 m); flowers in few-flowered heads, about 4
  to 8 flowers; tube straight, quite wide, bright orange to orange-red, up to 2,5 cm long. Fruit
  urn-shaped greenish-red to brownish crowned with the 5 persistent calyx lobes   **9. Burchellia**

21 Calyx forming a distinctive saucer-shaped, membraneous structure, almost flat, about 2 ×
  1,5 cm, asymmetric; corolla tube long and slender, up to 4 cm in length ..... **1. Carphalea**

  Calyx not forming a conspicuous flat, plate-like structure, although always tubular 22

839

22 Leaves with dense soft, short, woolly hairs, sometimes with harsh hairs on one or both surfaces 23

Leaves without hairs or rather sparsely hairy 31

23 Leaves usually less than 8 to 10 cm long 24

Leaves usually longer than 8 to 10 cm, up to 20 cm 27

24 Upper surface of the leaves harshly hairy, though they may be sparingly so 25

Leaves densely velvety 26

25 Leaf base tapering .... **21. Heinsia**

Leaf base narrowly rounded to shallowly lobed .... **18. Tricalysia**

26 Corolla greenish-yellow, falling early and frequently not seen; so the flower dominated by the hairy calyx .... **35. Pachystigma**

Corolla white, sometimes flushed with pink, or greenish-white, not falling early; calyx not very conspicuous .... **18. Tricalysia**

27 Fruit not crowned with the remains of the persistent calyx 28

Fruit crowned with the remains of the persistent calyx 29

28 Fruit almost spherical, about 1,5 cm in diameter, green streaked with white, becoming reddish-brown when mature .... **37. Guettarda**

Fruit ovoid, tapering to the base, about 3,5 cm long, green becoming orange-yellow when mature .... **16. Oxyanthus**

29 Flowers with conspicuous club-shaped stigmas, giving the inflorescence a pincushion effect .... **39. Pavetta**

Flowers without conspicuous club-shaped stigmas 30

30 In South Africa and possibly southern Moçambique only .... **35. Pachystigma**

In Rhodesia, Botswana, South West Africa and northwards .... **29. Vangueriopsis**

31 Corolla tube long up to 8 cm 32

Corolla tube rarely more than 2 cm long 33

32 Corolla lobes comparatively short and conspicuously bent back .... **16. Oxyanthus**

Corolla lobes about 3 cm long, broad and spreading .... **7. Leptactina**

33 Corolla tube falling early and so frequently not seen; the flowers are dominated by the narrow green, hairy calyx lobes which form dense clusters along the stem .... **35. Pachystigma**

Corolla not falling very early; calyx not appearing as above 34

34 Flower heads produced on one side of the stem only 35

Flower heads produced on both sides of the stem 36

35 In the east of Rhodesia and adjacent Moçambique, not in South Africa .... **11. Aïdia**

In South Africa not further north than the Transvaal .... **12. Mitriostigma**

36 Flowers in short-stalked, or peduncled, tight, dense axillary clusters or cymes **18. Tricalysia**

Flowers in long peduncled larger heads 37

37 Flowers in compact many-flowered heads; the long, slender styles with club-like stigmas giving a very characteristic pin-cushion appearance to the inflorescence .... **39. Pavetta**

Flowers in lax, rather few-flowered heads, styles not conspicuously long, up to 10 mm, the stigmas not club-like .... **19. Kraussia**

38 Flowers in conspicuous dense, tightly spherical heads on the ends of slender stalks 39

Flowers not in tightly spherical heads 40

39 Leaves up to 5 × 2,5 cm, ovate; apex narrowly attenuate, forming a slender drip-tip ....
.... **5. Cephalanthus**

Leaves 12 to 30 × 2,5 to 6 cm, narrowly elliptic to lanceolate; apex tapering .. **4. Breonadia**

40 Fruits ellipsoidal or pear-shaped 41

Fruits spherical to ovoid 42

41 Flowers 3 to 4 mm in diameter in few-flowered axillary clusters ...... **34. Craterispermum**

Flowers about 10 mm in diameter in dense axillary clusters .... **23. Cremaspora**

42 Flowering or fruiting heads terminal 43

Flowering or fruiting heads axillary 47

43 Leaves with conspicuous net-veining on one or both surfaces 44

Leaves without net-veining 45

44 Upper surface of leaves with rather sparse harsh hairs; stipules slender, falling early; fruit a dry dehiscent capsule with a distinctive ring round the apex; seeds many, winged **3. Crossopteryx**

Upper surface of the leaves without hairs; stipules ovate, or triangular, persisting for some time; fruit fleshy, single-seeded .... **8. Tarenna**

45 Fruit a dry capsule, splitting into 2 valves .... **2. Hymenodictyon**

Fruit fleshy 46

46 Buds long and narrow, the flowers lying close together like bunches of small green sticks; style conspicuous, paddle-shaped .... **8. Tarenna**

Buds either rather thickset and heads few-flowered, or extremely small in many-flowered, rather misty heads; style not conspicuous .... **41. Psychotria**

47 Leaves frequently almost circular; fruits spherical, conspicuously tapering to the base, shortly stalked, light brown to reddish-brown when mature .... **27. Tapiphyllum**

Leaves not almost circular; fruits not conspicuously tapering to the base, may be shortly stalked but usually with long stalks; yellowish-brown, red, purplish to black when mature 48

48 Calyx lobes slender, always conspicuous even if small, often forming characteristic tangled masses 49

Calyx lobes inconspicuous, not long or contorted 50

49 Inflorenscence a racemose cyme; calyx lobes usually shorter than the corolla tube in the bud
.... **26. Vangueria**

Inflorescence a Y-branched cyme; calyx lobes almost as long as, or longer than the corolla tube in the bud .... **30. Lagynias**

50 Floral parts in fours 51

Floral parts in fives 54

51 Corolla tube funnel-shaped or saucer-shaped, stigma not lobed 52

Corolla tube bell-shaped, tubular or urn-shaped; stigma 2- to 3-lobed 53

52 Flowers whitish to greenish-white, in short dense branched cymes on short lateral branchlets; calyx lobes fall early; fruit black when mature .... **8. Tarenna**

Flowers waxy white, in 2- to 8-flowered clusters; calyx lobes do not fall early; fruit purple when mature .... **24. Polysphaeria**

53 Corolla tube bell-shaped; flowers in dense many-flowered heads; stigmas subglobose and 3-lobed .... **32. Plectroniella**

Corolla tube tubular or urn-shaped; flowers in rather sparse, few-flowered heads, or apparently solitary by abortion; stigmas usually 2-lobed .... **31. Canthium**

54 Leaf apex attenuate into a long slender drip-tip 55

Leaf apex tapering, may be attenuate, but not forming a drip-tip 56

55 Calyx lobes shed early; leaf base tapering; petiole 5 to 8 mm long, not obscured by a decurrent leaf base .... **28. Rytigynia**

Calyx lobes not shed early; leaf base running into the petiole; petiole up to 1,5 cm, somewhat obscured by the decurrent leaf base .... **8. Tarenna**

56 Leaves ovate to elliptic, not narrowly elliptic or obovate to lanceolate or oblanceolate .... **31. Canthium**

Leaves narrowly elliptic or obovate, to lanceolate or oblanceolate .... **8. Tarenna**

1. CARPHALEA Juss.

Carphalea pubescens (Klotzsch) Verdc.
[*Dirichletia pubescens* Klotzsch]
S.A. no: Cups and saucers
Rhod. no: 1053   Cups and saucers

A shrub or small tree up to 3 m in height; occurring at low altitudes in open woodland, often on stony soils and rocky outcrops. **Bark:** grey, thick and corky, longitudinally fissured. **Leaves:** opposite, simple, lanceolate to narrowly elliptic, 2 to 7,5 × 0,7 to 2,5 cm, the under surface with sparse hairs and conspicuous pale-coloured ascending veins; apex and base tapering; margin entire; petiole about 5 mm long. **Flowers:** greenish-white to white, about 10 mm in diameter, sweetly scented; in terminal branched heads, or corymbose cymes. Bisexual; all floral parts in fives; calyx forming a conspicuous, expanded, asymmetric, saucer-shaped tube, about 2 × 1,5 cm; corolla tube slender, up to 4 cm long, the lobes spreading, densely bearded with long yellowish hairs in the throat; stamens attached in the mouth of the tube. The flowers resemble those of *Holmskioldia* in shape but not in colour (December to April). **Fruit:** small, hard, ovoid, remaining embedded in the base of the dry persistent calyx (January to June).

2. HYMENODICTYON Wall.

Shrubs, sometimes lianes, or small trees. **Leaves:** opposite, simple. Stipules falling early; leaf-like bracts are conspicuous. **Flowers:** in terminal branched or unbranched spike-like racemes. Bisexual;

all floral parts in fives; calyx tubular; corolla tubular, shortly lobed, stamens attached in the throat of the corolla tube; ovary 2-chambered. **Fruit:** a capsule, splitting into 2 valves; seeds winged.

Key to the species of *Hymenodictyon:*
Leaves up to 24 × 10 cm, seldom less than 9 × 4,5 cm, petiole thickset. Occurring in Rhodesia and adjacent areas of Moçambique, not in South Africa .... **H. floribundum**
Leaves seldom more than 5 × 3 cm, petiole slender. Occurring in the Transvaal, the south of Rhodesia and adjacent areas of Moçambique .... **H. parvifolium**

Hymenodictyon floribundum (Hochst. & Steudel) B. L. Robinson   Illust. 285
S.A. no: —
Rhod. no: 1054   Firebush

A small tree up to 8 m in height; always associated with granite formations, on rocky hills and outcrops. **Bark:** grey, smooth to rough, flaking in small squares. **Leaves:** crowded near the ends of the branches, obovate to oblong-elliptic, up to 24 × 18 cm, but usually about 9 × 4,5 cm, green above, paler green below, thick and brittle, the midrib prominent on the under surface; apex shortly and abruptly attenuate; base tapering; margin entire, wavy; petiole thickset, up to 2 cm long. **Flowers:** small, greenish-white, not conspicuous, in thickset spike-like racemes, up to 15 cm long (September to December). **Fruit:** a reddish-brown capsule, about 1,5 × 0,8 cm, densely clustered along the inflorescence (November to March).
The young leaves are reddish and sticky, very rapidly turning green. The autumn leaves are magnificent crimson and red (see Illust. 285). These trees are thin-barked and very susceptible to fire and therefore frequently found growing in cracks and fissures in rocks, on dwalas and whale-backs, in places inaccessible to fire.

Hymenodictyon parvifolium Oliver
S.A. no: 682   Yellow firebush. Wildebrandbos
Rhod. no: 1055   Yellow firebush

A shrub, sometimes a liane, or a small tree up to 5 m in height; occurring at low altitudes, in open woodland, on sandy soils and rocky ridges. **Bark:** dark grey, smooth, soft-looking, transversely wrinkled. **Leaves:** ovate, up to 5 × 2 cm, but often smaller, glossy green, thick, slightly fleshy and brittle; apex and base tapering; margin entire, wavy; petiole slender, about 5 mm long. **Flowers:** yellowish-green to cream, up to 3 mm long, rather unpleasantly scented, in dense branched terminal

843

spike-like racemes about 12 cm long; the buds are green, the young flowers yellow fading to white then brown (October to January). **Fruit:** a reddish-brown ovoid capsule, up to 2,5 × 1 cm, thinly woody or leathery, with large greyish-brown lenticels, finally splitting into 2 and then 4 valves, releasing the oblong winged seeds (April to October).

The autumn colours in this species are yellow, not red as in *H. floribundum*.

3. CROSSOPTERYX Fenzl

Crossopteryx febrifuga (Afzel. ex G. Don) Benth.   Illust. 286
S.A. no: 683   Crystal-bark. Sandkroonbessie
Rhod. no: 1056   Crystal-bark

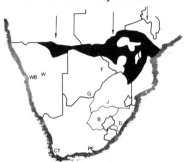 

A shrub or small tree, frequently 4 to 6 m in height but may reach 10 m; occurring in dry woodland on sandy soils. **Bark:** grey, flaking in small squares. **Leaves:** opposite, simple, elliptic to ovate, 4 to 13 × 2 to 6 cm, net-veining conspicuous especially below; the upper surface with rather sparse harsh hairs, the under surface with short soft hairs, young leaves glossy reddish-brown, flushing after the first rains, becoming green and sometimes shiny when mature; apex and base tapering; margin entire; petiole 2 to 10 mm long. Stipules awl-shaped, falling early. **Flowers:** small, creamy-white or tinged with pink, in dense branched terminal heads. Bisexual; floral parts in fours to sixes; the corolla tube much longer than the calyx tube; stamens attached in the throat of the corolla tube; ovary 2-chambered (November to January). **Fruit:** an ovoid brown capsule, about 10 × 7 mm, with a distinctive ring round the apex; splitting into 2 valves to release many small flat oval seeds which have a conspicuously hair-fringed margin (May to August).

If the dry bark is stripped from a branch, glistening crystals can be seen on its inner surface; this bark is said to be poisonous and is used in certain witchcraft ordeals. Parts of the tree provide a remedy for fever (the specific name refers to this). The wood, which is a pale, light brown, often with a pinkish tinge, is handsome, hard and durable and does not shrink or split. It is suitable for building, for wood-work and carving and also makes a good fuel.

4. BREONADIA Ridsd.

Breonadia microcephala (Delile) Ridsd.   Illust. 287
[*Adina microcephala* (Delile) Hiern]
S.A. no: 684   Matumi. Mingerhout
Rhod. no: 1057   Matumi

A medium to large tree, 10 to 40 m in height; occurring at low altitudes along the banks of permanent streams and rivers, in riverine fringe forest. **Bark:** grey to grey-brown, rather rough with longitudinal ridges. **Leaves:** crowded at the ends of the branches, alternate or in whorls of 4; simple, lanceolate to narrowly elliptic, 12 to 30 × 2,5 to 6 cm, tough, leathery, glossy dark green above, paler green below, without hairs; the veins pale yellowish-green and conspicuous; apex and base narrowly tapering; margin entire, rolled under; petiole thickset, up to 2 cm long. Stipules quite large, narrowly triangular, falling early. **Flowers:** small, pale mauve, sweetly scented, in compact round axillary heads up to 4 cm in diameter, on long slender stalks up to 6 cm long, with 2 leaf-like bracts along their length. Bisexual; all floral parts in fives; calyx lobes short; corolla tubular, widening into a funnel-shaped throat, 5-lobed; disc cup-shaped; stamens inserted in the throat of the tube, protruding from the

844

mouth; ovary 2-chambered (December to March). **Fruit:** small, brown, 2-lobed capsules about 2 to 3 mm long, densely clustered into spherical heads, giving a rough, crusty, warty appearance; seeds very small and 2-winged (June to July).

An extract of the bark is used to cure stomach ailments and is given to children as a tonic. The wood is hard, heavy, durable, yellow to light brown and handsomely figured in black; it has an oily consistency and a distinctive smell. Fine furniture is made from it and the tree is in demand for construction work of all kinds. It is also highly prized for dugout canoes in Malawi. The resemblance between this species and *Rauvolfia caffra* (Apocynaceae) is discussed under the latter. This is a protected tree in South Africa.

5. CEPHALANTHUS L.

Cephalanthus natalensis Oliver
S.A. no: 685   Tree strawberry. Witaarbeibos
Rhod. no: 1058   Tree strawberry

A scrambling shrub or a small straggling tree up to 8 m in height or a huge liane; occurring in areas of montane forest, scrub, among rocks and in open mountain grassland. **Bark:** grey to brownish, rather smooth. **Leaves:** opposite, simple, ovate, up to 5 × 2,5 cm, very glossy dark green; apex attenuate forming a slender drip-tip; base very broadly tapering to rounded; margin entire, wavy; petiole slender, up to 5 mm long. Stipules thread-like, persisting for a time, but eventually falling. **Flowers:** greenish-white, about 3 mm long, in dense spherical terminal heads about 3 cm in diameter, on a slender stalk 2 to 3 cm long. Bisexual; all floral parts in fives; calyx small; corolla tubular, with the stamens deep in the throat; ovary 2-chambered (September to February). **Fruit:** a small capsule, fleshy at first, together forming a whitish or reddish spherical head up to 2 cm in diameter; the flesh has a rather pleasant bitter-sweet flavour (February to May).

The fruits are eaten raw or made into a conserve, and are also taken by people of all races as a remedy for fevers, but the treatment is probably not very effective.

6. PAURIDIANTHA J. D. Hook.

Pauridiantha symplocoides (S. Moore) Bremek.
[*Urophyllum symplocoides* S. Moore]
S.A. no: —
Rhod. no: 1060   Pauridiantha

A shrub or small tree, 2 to 5 m in height, occasionally reaching 10 m, with long slender branches tending to droop; a constituent of the under-storey in evergreen forest. **Bark:** brown, finely fissured and cracked, forming square sections. **Leaves:** opposite, simple, narrowly elliptic, 7 to 14 × 0,7 to 1,7 cm, thinly textured, shiny dark green, with pale veins conspicuous on the under surface; apex narrow, attenuate, forming a very slender drip-tip; base tapering; margin entire; petiole slender, 0,5 to 2 cm long. **Flowers:** white to yellowish-white, about 6 mm in diameter, on slender stalks, axillary, solitary or in pairs. Bisexual; all floral parts in fives; calyx shortly tubular; corolla urn-shaped with hairs in the throat, 5-lobed; stamens joined to the throat of the corolla tube; ovary 2-chambered (September to November). **Fruit:** spherical, fleshy, many seeded, about 5 mm in diameter, on slender stalks, black when mature (December to March).

7. LEPTACTINA J. D. Hook.

Leptactina macrophylla (Hiern) Wernh.
[*L. hexamera* K. Schum.]
S.A. no:—
Rhod. no: —

Leptactina

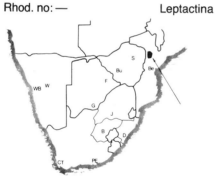

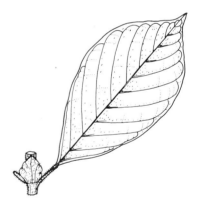

A shrub or slender tree up to 10 m in height; occurring in evergreen forest. **Bark:** brown, rather scaly. **Leaves:** opposite, simple, elliptic, 14 to 30 × 5,5 to 13 cm, dark green, both surfaces rough to the touch with sparse scabrid hairs, apex attenuate forming a drip-tip; base tapering; margin entire; petiole up to 10 mm long. Stipules large, leaf-like, persisting for some time. **Flowers:** white, gardenia-like, the corolla tube up to 6 cm long, spreading lobes up to 3 cm long; in dense terminal cymes, without stalks. Bisexual; all floral parts in fives; calyx shortly tubular; corolla hairy with a slender tube and narrow lobes; stamens fixed in the throat of the tube (September). **Fruit:** probably ovoid and many-seeded.

8. TARENNA Gaertn.

Shrubs or small trees. **Leaves:** opposite, simple. Stipules ovate to slender, usually falling early. **Flowers:** in short dense branched cymes, axillary or terminal on short side branchlets. Bisexual; all floral parts in fives; calyx short, the lobes usually falling early; corolla tube funnel- or salver-shaped; buds long and narrow, like bunches of small green sticks; stamens attached in the throat of the tube; ovary 2-chambered, style paddle-shaped. **Fruit:** fleshy, spherical, 1-seeded.

846

Key to the tree species of *Tarenna:*

1 Leaves mature at the time of flowering 2
  Leaves immature at the time of flowering 5
2 Leaf apex attenuate forming a pronounced drip-tip .... **T. pavettoides**
  Leaf apex not forming a pronounced drip-tip 3
3 Leaf blades membranous; fruits black when mature .... **T. longipedicellata**
  Leaf blades leathery; fruits yellow to yellowish brown when mature 4
4 Leaf apices broadly tapering to rounded, margin rolled under. Usually a costal species
  .... **T. littoralis**
  Leaf apices often abruptly attenuate, margin flat. An inland species .... **T. zimbabwensis**
5 Leaves covered with short soft hairs, especially below .... **T. luteola**
  Leaves without hairs or nearly so 6
6 Leaves usually 3 to 5 cm long, apex more or less rounded, often abruptly and shortly attenuate;
  veining not distinct on upper surface; remaining green on drying .... **T. junodii**
  Leaves usually about 7,5 × 1 to 1,5 cm, generally longer and comparatively narrower than those of
  the preceding species; apex broadly tapering; veining distinct on the upper surface; leaves tend
  to turn black on drying .... **T. neurophylla**

Tarenna junodii (Schinz) Bremek.
S.A. no: Climbing dune tarenna. Klimbasterbruidsbos
Rhod. no:—

A shrub with a strong tendency to climb, or a small tree, 3 to 4 m in height; occurring in dune scrub and sand forest. **Bark:** brown; the branchlets sometimes bent to form climbing hooks. **Leaves:** narrowly obovate, usually about 3 to 5 × 1 to 2 cm, thinly textured, dark green above, markedly paler green below, almost without hairs; veins obscure; apex more or less rounded, often abruptly attenuate; base narrowly tapering; margin entire; petiole slender, 1 to 4 mm long. **Flowers:** small, white, axillary or terminal, in short dense branched heads, about 4 cm in diameter (October to November). **Fruit:** fleshy, spherical, about 5 mm in diameter, in dense heads, black when mature (November to December, but may remain on the tree later).

Tarenna littoralis (Hiern) Bridson
[*Enterospermum littorale* Hiern]
S.A. no: 687   Dune tarenna. Duinebasterlemoenbos
Rhod. no: 1065   Limpopo tarenna

847

A shrub or small tree, 2 to 6 m in height; occurring along the coastal belt where it is a common constituent of dune scrub and forest; sometimes further inland. **Bark:** pale whitish-grey; branchlets inclined to be square in section. **Leaves:** elliptic to obovate, 3 to 9 × 1 to 4,6 cm, leathery, glossy green above, paler green with conspicuous net-veining below; upper surface without hairs; apex broadly tapering to rounded; base tapering; margin entire, tightly rolled under; petiole 2 to 6 mm long. Stipules rather large, triangular, ensheathing the leaf bud and persisting for some time. **Flowers:** white to cream, about 5 mm long, with a prominent slender style protruding from the mouth; in dense terminal heads 3 to 6 cm in diameter (October to November). **Fruit:** spherical, fleshy, about 8 mm in diameter, yellow when mature (March to July).

Tarenna longipedicellata (Garçia) Bridson
S.A. no:—
Rhod. no:— Beira tarenna

A slender tree, 5 to 20 m in height; occurring in evergreen forest, along streams and rivers, often on termite mounds, also in littoral woodland. **Bark:** pale brown, finely fissured; the bole buttressed. **Leaves:** elliptic, up to 13 × 6 cm, without hairs; apex shortly attenuate; base tapering; margin entire; petiole up to 10 mm long. Stipules wispy, about 2 mm long, soon falling. **Flowers:** small, whitish, with the corolla tube about 8 mm long, in small terminal dense heads (December). **Fruit:** fleshy, spherical, about 5 mm in diameter, black when mature, on slender stalks, in dense branched heads (December to May).

Tarenna luteola (Stapf) Bremek.
[*Pavetta luteola* Stapf]
S.A. no: —
Rhod. no: 1062 Velvet-leaved tarenna

A shrub, sometimes scrambling, or a small tree up to 4 m in height; occurring at low altitudes in woodland and thicket, in riverine fringes, on sandy soils. **Bark:** grey to brownish. **Leaves:** often tightly clustered on short lateral branches, obovate to elliptic, up to 7 × 3,5 cm, with fine soft hairs especially below; apex tapering to rounded; base tapering; margin entire; petiole 2 to 4 mm long. **Flowers:** small, cream, in dense terminal and axillary heads about 4 to 6 cm in diameter (November). **Fruit:** fleshy, almost spherical about 7 mm in diameter, black when mature, tipped with the conspicuous whitish hairy remains of the calyx (January to March).

Tarenna neurophylla (S. Moore) Bremek.   Illust. 288
[Pavetta neurophylla S. Moore]
S.A. no: Lowveld tarenna. Laeveldse basterbruidsbos
Rhod. no: 1063   Common tarenna

A much-branched shrub or small tree up to 7 m in height; a constituent of the under-storey in evergreen forest, also along streams in open woodland, in sand forest and on rocky koppies. **Bark:** pale grey to whitish. **Leaves:** well-spaced along the branchlets, lanceolate, 3 to 9 × 1 to 1,5 cm, glossy light green, yellowish-green to deep green, leathery, without hairs; veining distinct on the upper surface, net-veining obscure; apex broadly tapering; base tapering; margin entire, wavy; petiole 2 to 4 mm long. **Flowers:** white to cream, about 7 mm long with conspicuous green stigmas which persist after the petals have fallen, sweetly scented, in axillary and terminal clusters (October to December). **Fruit:** almost spherical, up to 8 mm in diameter, black when mature, tipped with the short remains of the persistent style (December to April or later).
Tarenna barbertonensis (Bremek.) Bremek. is now placed in synonymy under *T. supra-axillaris* (Hemsley) Bremek.

Tarenna pavettoides (Harvey) T. R. Sim
[Kraussia pavettoides Harvey; *Pavetta swynnertonii* S. Moore]
S.A. no: 686   Bastard bride's bush. Basterbruidsbos
Rhod. no: 1064   Large-leaved tarenna

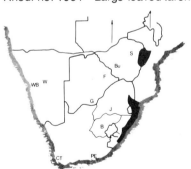 

A shrub or small to medium sized tree up to 10 m in height; occurring at the margins of evergreen forest, as a constituent of the under-storey in forest and also in swamp forest. **Bark:** brown to rusty brown, longitudinally scaly; branchlets 4-angled, dark brownish-green, softly hairy when young. **Leaves:** well-spaced along the branchlets, oblanceolate, 3,8 to 20 × 2 to 5 cm, thinly textured, dark green to bright green, without hairs except for sparse hairs along the midrib on the under surface; net-veining not defined; apex attenuate forming a drip-tip; base tapering, running into the petiole; margin entire; petiole slender, somewhat obscured by the decurrent leaf base, may be up to 1,5 cm long. **Flowers:** small, whitish, sweetly scented, in axillary branched heads, 2 to 4 cm in diameter (September to December). **Fruit:** almost spherical, fleshy, about 8 mm in diameter, black when mature, tipped with the remains of the persistent style (March to May).

849

RUBIACEAE

Tarenna zimbabwensis Bridson
[*Enterospermum rhodesiacum* Bremek.]
S.A. no: 687,1   Mountain tarenna. Bergbasterlemoenbos
Rhod. no: 1066   Zimbabwe tarenna

A large shrub or small tree, 4 to 8 m in height; often occurring among rocks and also at the margins of evergreen forest. **Bark:** light grey, rather smooth. **Leaves:** narrowly to broadly ovate, 4,5 to 10,5 × 2,5 to 6,5 cm, glossy dark green to yellowish-green, the young leaves with a white waxy bloom; upper surface without hairs; conspicuous net-veining particularly below; apex tapering to rounded, often abruptly attenuate; base tapering to rounded; margin entire, flat; petiole up to 10 mm long. Stipules large, conspicuous, ovate, leaf-like, persisting for some time. **Flowers:** greenish-white with conspicuous stigmas; in branched flat-topped terminal heads about 3 to 6 cm in diameter (November to December). **Fruit:** spherical, fleshy, about 8 mm in diameter, in dense heads, yellowish-brown when mature (April to July).

9. BURCHELLIA R. Br.

Burchellia bubalina (L.f.) T. R. Sim   Illust. 289
[*B. capensis* R. Br.]
S.A. no: 688   Wild pomegranate. Wildegranaat
Rhod. no: —

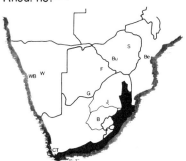 

A shrub or small tree usually 3 to 5 m in height, but occasionally reaching 10 m; occurring in evergreen lowland to montane forest, at the margins of forest, in open woodland, grassland and swamps. **Bark:** grey, mottled, smooth. **Leaves:** opposite, simple, broadly ovate, 5 to 18 × 2,5 to 8 cm, usually about 10 to 13 cm long, glossy dark green, without hairs above, dull green with fine soft hairs especially along the veins below; apex tapering; base rounded to slightly lobed; margin entire, rolled under; petiole thickset, velvety, up to 1,5 cm long. Stipules leathery, toothed, falling early, leaving a conspicuous ridge. **Flowers:** showy, scarlet to orange, tubular, up to 2 to 2,5 cm long, in shortly branched terminal, 4- to 8-flowered heads. Bisexual; all floral parts in fives; calyx tube short; corolla urn-shaped shortly 5-lobed; stamens joined to the upper section of the corolla tube, with no

850

filament; ovary 2-chambered (September to December). **Fruit:** urn-shaped, rather leathery, about 1 to 1,5 cm long, reddish-green to brownish, crowned with the 5 persistent horn-like enlarged calyx lobes (November onwards).

The flowers contain copious nectar and birds often slit the petal tube near the base to obtain the sweet liquid. The roots, which are sometimes worn as an amulet, provide an infusion which is taken as an emetic and used as a body-wash, while combined with the bark they make suitable splints for binding the fractured limbs of animals. The hard, dense and close-grained wood is used for hut-building and for making agricultural implements. This is a very satisfactory tree in the garden for it is attractive at all times and beautiful when in flower. It is easily propagated from seed or cuttings although it is rather slow growing; according to Eve Palmer it thrives even in dense shade. Its somewhat superficial resemblance, when in leaf and flower, to the true pomegranate, has given rise to a common name – 'wild pomegranate' – while both the Afrikaans and specific names refer to the buffalo-like horns of the old calyx lobes on the fruit.

10. XEROMPHIS Rafin.

Shrubs or small trees. Branches armed with spines formed from lateral branchlets. **Leaves:** opposite, or more usually densely clustered on dwarf side branchlets, simple. Stipules short, sometimes toothed, almost joined at the base or attached to the petiole. **Flowers:** 1 to 3 together at the ends of abbreviated lateral shoots. Bisexual; all floral parts in fives; calyx with a short tube; corolla with 5 slender lobes; stamens attached to the walls of the tube; ovary 2-chambered. **Fruit:** a somewhat leathery berry.

Key to the tree species of *Xeromphis:*

Leaves seldom more than 2 cm long, almost without hairs; flowers only about 10 mm in diameter; fruits 5 to 8 mm in diameter .... **X. rudis**
Leaves 2,5 to 3 cm in length or more, usually with dense velvety hairs on both surfaces; flowers up to 2 cm in diameter; fruits up to 2,5 cm long .... **X. obovata**

Xeromphis obovata (Hochst.) Keay   Illust. 290
[*Randia kraussii* Harvey; *R. vestita* S. Moore; *R. dumetorum* auct. non (Retz.) Lam.]
S.A. no: 689   Thorny bone-apple. Doringbeenappel
Rhod. no: 1067   Thicket xeromphis

A spiny shrub or small tree up to 5 m in height, occasionally reaching 10 m; occurring over a wide range of altitudes, on forest margins, in open woodland and scrub, often forming dense thickets. **Bark:** light grey to dark grey, mottled, smooth to rough. **Leaves:** opposite or in clusters on short side branches, oval to obovate, up to 3,8 × 2,5 cm, usually densely velvety on both surfaces, but may be almost without hairs, dark green to grey-green, with conspicuous pale veins; apex rounded; base tapering; margin entire, may be rolled under; petiole 1 to 3 mm long. **Flowers:** attractive, white fading to yellow, up to 2 cm in diameter, resembling a small gardenia, in axillary groups of 2 to 3 (October to November). **Fruit:** almost spherical, up to 2,5 cm long, greenish-brown when mature, becoming very hard when dry; crowned with the persistent remains of the calyx (April to May). The fruits are taken as an emetic. The wood is yellowish-red, heavy, close-grained and might be suitable for engraving but the pieces are usually too small; the slender stems are used in Zululand as laths in building.

RUBIACEAE

Xeromphis rudis (E. Meyer ex Harvey) Codd
[*Randia rudis* E. Meyer ex Harvey]
S.A. no: 689,1   Small bone-apple. Kleinbeenappel
Rhod. no: 1068   Lesser xeromphis

Usually a shrub, 1 to 2 m in height, sometimes inclined to scramble, occasionally becoming a small tree up to 3 to 4 m; occurring in open woodland and scrub, and at the margins of evergreen forest. **Bark:** grey to brown. **Leaves:** in rosettes on dwarf lateral shoots tightly clustered along the stems, broadly obovate, seldom exceeding 2 × 1,5 cm, dark green, almost without hairs; veins prominent below; apex very broadly tapering to rounded; base narrowly tapering; margin entire, wavy; petiole slender, 1 to 3 mm long. **Flowers:** white aging to yellow, about 10 to 15 mm in diameter, in axillary groups of 2 to 3 (October). **Fruit:** almost spherical, 5 to 8 mm in diameter, greenish-brown when mature, crowned with the remains of the old calyx (April to June).

11. AÏDIA Lour.

Aïdia micrantha (K. Schum.) Bullock ex F. White
S.A. no: —
Rhod. no: 1069   Aïdia

A large shrub, sometimes with a tendency to scramble, or a medium sized tree up to 13 m in height; occurring at low altitudes in riverine fringes and evergreen forest. **Bark:** brown to dark brown. **Leaves:** opposite, simple, elliptic to lanceolate, up to 15 × 5 cm, green to yellowish-green, rather glossy and puckered above, dull below with soft hairs; veins depressed above, prominent below; apex attenuate; base tapering; margin entire, wavy; petiole up to 1,5 cm long. **Flowers:** creamy-white, sweetly scented, in short branched axillary heads 1,5 to 2,5 cm long, along the upper side of the branches only. Bisexual; all floral parts in fives; corolla tube about 6 mm long with narrow lobes, about 10 × 3 mm, curving sharply backwards, and the throat of the tube with long dense white silky hairs; the stamens without filaments, with the anthers about 5 mm long, alternating with the corolla lobes, giving the flower a star-like appearance; the ovary with a short style and a bright magenta stigma, producing a small spot of colour in the centre of the flower (October to November). **Fruit:** slightly wider than long, about 8 × 10 mm, orange and possibly becoming brown and finally black when mature, with the usually persistent calyx forming a conspicuous rim-like neck round the apex, but it may fall leaving only a circular scar (October to May).

852 This species has been divided into several varieties, only var. *msonju* (K. Krause) Petit occurring south of the Zambezi River, the other varieties being confined to west and central tropical Africa. The wood is used to make bows and arrows.

12. MITRIOSTIGMA Hochst.

Mitriostigma axillare Hochst.
[*Gardenia citriodora* Hook.]
S.A. no: 689,2   Small false loquat. Basterlukwart
Rhod. no: —

Usually a compact shrub, occasionally a small tree, 3 to 4 m in height; occurring as a constituent of the under-storey in dune and coastal forest, and also in wooded ravines. **Bark:** grey to brown. **Leaves:** opposite, simple, lanceolate to rather narrowly ovate, 5 to 15 × 3,5 to 6 cm, dark green, without hairs; the veins prominent below; apex tapering; base rounded or very broadly tapering; margin entire; petiole stout, up to 10 mm long. Stipules triangular, slender, persisting for some time before falling. **Flowers:** white aging to yellow, about 2 cm in diameter, sweetly scented, axillary, in groups of 3 or more, in few-flowered very shortly branched cymes produced on the upper side of the branches only. Bisexual; all floral parts in fives; calyx velvety, shortly tubular; corolla funnel-shaped, with 5 spreading lobes; stamens 5, not or scarcely protruding from the mouth of the tube; ovary 1- to 2-chambered (September to November). **Fruit:** ovoid, narrowly tapering to the apex, up to 2,5 cm long, orange when mature, crowned with the papery persistent calyx (April to May).
The genus *Mitriostigma* resembles *Oxyanthus,* but in the latter the anthers and the style protrude from the corolla tube which is long and narrowly cylindric.

13. GARDENIA Ellis

Shrubs or trees; the branches frequently produced in whorls of 3, often rigid but seldom spinescent. **Leaves:** opposite or whorled, simple. Stipules present. **Flowers:** usually axillary and solitary. Bisexual; floral parts in fives to eights; calyx shortly tubular; corolla with a long tube, and 5 to 8 broad spreading lobes; stamens 5 to 8, attached in the mouth of the tube; ovary 1- to 2-chambered. **Fruit:** spherical, ovoid to ellipsoidal, tough and leathery, many-seeded.

Key to the tree species of *Gardenia:*
1 Fruits less than 3,5 cm in length 2
  Fruits more than 3,5 cm long 3
2 Leaves without hairs, the corolla tube and backs of the petals flushed with red or pink . **G. amoena**
  Leaves densely velvety, becoming harshly rough when old; flowers pure white   **G. resiniflua**
3 Fruits conspicuously ribbed or ridged 4
  Fruits not conspicuously ribbed or ridged 5
4 Fruits ovoid to almost round, and shallowly ribbed, greyish-green, usually covered with whitish to
     grey encrustations.. **G. volkensii**
  Fruits narrowly ellipsoidal, with very conspicuous ridges .... **G. posoquerioides**
5 Leaves with an average length of 18 to 24 cm; flowers up to 12 cm long × 13 cm in diameter..
  .... **G. imperialis**
  Leaves not more than 14 cm long; flowers not more than 7 cm long 6

853

6 Calyx tube extended beyond the insertion of lobes as a conspicuous ribbed sleeve; fruits bright orange-yellow .... **G. cornuta**

Calyx tube terminating in the lobes, with no projecting sleeve; fruits yellowish-brown or greenish, not becoming orange-yellow 7

7 Occurring in forest occasionally in woodland and bush from the eastern Cape to Zululand, no further north .... **G. thunbergia**

Occurring in woodland from the north and north-eastern Transvaal northwards **G. ternifolia**

Gardenia amoena Sims   Illust. 291

[*G. neuberia* Ecklon & Zeyher; *G. gerrardiana* Harvey & Sonder]
S.A. no: 690   Spiny gardenia. Doringkatjiepiering
Rhod. no: —

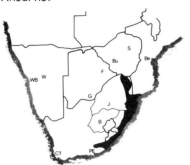 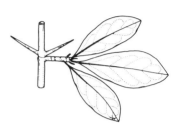

A shrub about 2 m in height, or a small tree reaching 7 m; adapted to a wide range of habitats. **Bark:** ashen grey to grey-brown, smooth when young becoming rough with age; the branches opposite, each pair being produced at right angles to the succeeding pair; the twigs often reduced to stout opposite spines. **Leaves:** opposite or fascicled, crowded on short, knobby, dwarf side shoots, obovate to elliptic, 2,5 to 6 × 1 to 2,3 cm, pinkish-red when young, glossy dark green above when mature, paler green below, without hairs; apex and base tapering; margin entire, wavy; petiole stout, about 2 mm long. Stipules short, pointed, falling early. **Flowers:** attractive, white within, with the corolla tube up to 4 cm long and narrow, about 3 mm in diameter, rose-pink to deep red, the red colour running to the back of the spreading corolla lobes on their outer edge; corolla lobes 5, up to 2,5 cm long × 1,5 cm wide, spreading, rather twisted; sweetly scented (November to March, or later). **Fruit:** almost spherical to ovoid, about 2,5 cm long, dark brown to blackish when mature, crowned by the 5-pronged persistent calyx almost forming a short apical funnel (January to July).

The fruits are said to be edible, but these together with the roots, are taken by the Zulus as an emetic. The wood is heavy and is suitable for fencing stakes and for the framework of fishing baskets.

Gardenia cornuta Hemsley

S.A. no: 690,1   Natal gardenia. Natalkatjiepiering
Rhod. no: —

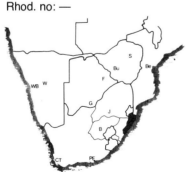 

A small densely branched tree, 4 to 5 m in height; occurring in open woodland and grassland, often forming thickets. **Bark:** pale grey, occasionally flaking. **Leaves:** crowded at the ends of short, almost spinescent lateral branchlets; broadly obovate, 2 to 5 × 1,5 to 2,7 cm, shiny light green above, dull green below, without hairs; apex very broadly tapering to rounded; base narrowly tapering; margin entire, rather wavy; petiole 1 to 3 mm long. **Flowers:** showy, white aging to yellow, with a sweet heavy scent; corolla with a tube up to 6 cm long, and 5 spreading lobes, each about 3 cm long; the calyx has a tube about 1,3 cm long from the base to the point where the six narrow twisting lobes arise, and the calyx then continues for a further 5 mm as an unusual ridged sleeve, so that the calyx lobes seem to rise only part of the way up the tube (November). **Fruit:** distinctive, ovoid, up to 4,5 × 2 cm, tapering to a narrow base, with the apex at first crowned with the calyx which tends to wither away later; a striking bright orange-yellow when mature, often produced in profusion and remaining on the tree for months (April to June).

The Zulus use an infusion of the fruits and roots as an emetic and the sticks for fencing and as a fuel.

Gardenia imperialis K. Schum.
S.A. no: —
Rhod. no: 1070   Large pink gardenia

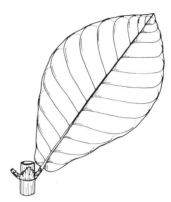

A small slender tree up to 8 m in height; occurring in riverine fringe forest, along mountain streams and in swamp forest. **Bark:** pale grey, smooth. **Leaves:** crowded near the ends of the branches, remarkably large, elliptic to obovate, 10 to 25 × 5 to 14 cm, usually 18 to 24 cm long, dark green, thickly leathery, heavily veined, bearing a considerable resemblance to those of *Uapaca kirkiana;* almost without hairs; young leaves glutinous; apex rounded, may be very abruptly and shortly attenuate; base broadly tapering to rounded; margin entire; petiole thickset, up to 2 cm long. **Flowers:** particularly large, 13 cm in diameter, white, the corolla tube up to 12 cm long, the lobes ovate and spreading; the corolla tube and the backs of the lobes are flushed with pink, greenish-red to red (August to February). **Fruit:** ovoid, about 6 × 3,5 cm, greenish-brown to yellowish when mature; the flower often remains attached to the apex of the developing fruit, which is ultimately crowned by the persistent calyx (December to July).

Gardenia posoquerioides S. Moore
S.A. no: —
Rhod. no: 1072   Forest gardenia

A shrub or small tree, 2 to 4 m in height, with lax branches; occurring as a constituent of the under-storey in evergreen forest. **Bark:** pale grey to brownish, smooth. **Leaves:** opposite, elliptic to slightly oblanceolate, 8 to 24 × 3 to 8,5 cm, thinly textured, rather puckered, shiny green; apex attenuate; base tapering; margin entire; petiole up to 2 cm long. **Flowers:** white, sweetly scented,

855

with a corolla tube 12 to 15 cm long and 5 unusually narrow and sharply pointed corolla lobes, each about 4 × 1 cm; calyx shortly tubular with slender lobes about 4,5 cm long (December to February). **Fruit:** narrowly ellipsoidal, up to 5,5 × 2 cm, pale brown or yellowish-brown when mature, with 5 to 7 distinct longitudinal ridges, and crowned with the remains of the old calyx; the fruits and the next season's flowers are often on the tree at the same time (October to March).
An unusual and distinctive species.

Gardenia resiniflua Hiern
S.A. no: Gummy gardenia
Rhod. no: 1073   Gummy gardenia

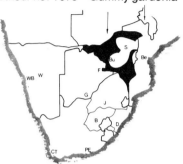

A much-branched shrub or small tree up to 7 m in height; occurring at low altitudes in woodland and thicket, often along rivers. **Bark:** pale grey, smooth. **Leaves:** crowded at the ends of short rigid side branchlets; obovate, up to 5,5 × 4 cm, but may even reach 8 × 5 cm; the young leaves softly velvety, mature leaves with sparse hairs above, densely velvety below, becoming harsh to the touch with age, pale green; the veining conspicuous especially below giving a puckered and wrinkled appearance to the leaf; apex broadly tapering, often very shortly attenuate; base tapering; margin entire; petiole absent. **Flowers:** white, rather slender, up to 3 cm long and 3 cm in diameter, heavily scented (November to December). **Fruit:** ovoid to almost spherical, about 1,3 cm in diameter, with or without short soft hairs, crowned by the remains of the persistent calyx; yellowish to yellowish-brown when mature (February to May).
The wood is suitable for carving and for making spoons and forks. The fruit is soaked in water for a week and the decoction is then used in tattooing.

Gardenia ternifolia Schum. & Thonn.
[*G. jovis-tonantis* (Welw.) Hiern; *G. asperula* Stapf & Hutch]
S.A. no: 690,2   Large-leaved Transvaal gardenia. Geelkatjiepiering
Rhod. no: 1071   Large-leaved common gardenia

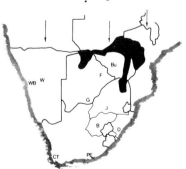
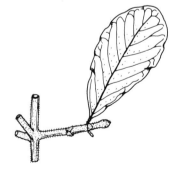

A shrub or small rigid spreading tree up to 7 m in height; occasional in wooded grassland, on koppies along streams and vleis, sometimes associated with termite mounds. **Bark:** grey or yellowish-brown, smooth; branchlets in whorls of 3 at right angles to the branches, covered with a rusty powder. **Leaves:** opposite or in whorls of 3, crowded near the ends of short rigid branchlets; oblanceolate to narrowly obovate, up to 13 × 8 cm, yellowish-green to shiny dark green above, paler green below,

856

with short hairs on both surfaces which are rough to the touch; midrib prominent above and below, lateral veins clearly defined with tufts of hairs in their axils; apex rounded; base tapering; margin entire; wavy; petiole almost absent. Stipules connate, forming a sheath. **Flowers:** white aging to yellow, 4 cm in diameter with a tube up to 4,5 cm long, and spreading corolla lobes, sweetly scented; the calyx about 2 cm long with irregular leafy lobes (September to December). **Fruit:** ovoid, 5 × 3,5 cm, finely velvety, yellowish-brown when mature, crowned with the remains of the calyx lobes (February to June).

The subspecies involved here is subsp. *jovis-tonantis* (Welw.) Verdc. The seeds are said to yield a black dye. The wood is yellow or pink, hard and very fine-grained. In certain areas Africans put branches on their roofs to ward off lightning and for this reason Welwitsch dedicated the tree to Jove, the god of the heavens, whose weapon was the thunderbolt.

Gardenia thunbergia L.f.   Illust. 293
S.A. no: 692   White gardenia. Witkatjiepiering
Rhod. no: —

A shrub or small tree, 2 to 5 m in height; occurring in evergreen forest, occasionally in woodland and bush. **Bark:** pale grey, smooth; branchlets short and rigid. **Leaves:** in whorls of 3 to 4, crowded near the ends of the branchlets, elliptic, up to 14 × 6 cm, although usually smaller, glossy light green, without hairs; the veins conspicuous; apex rounded, tapering to finely attenuate; base tapering; margin entire, wavy; petiole about 10 mm long. **Flowers:** showy, creamy-white, 7 cm in diameter, heavily perfumed; corolla with a tube about 7 cm long, and 8 large spreading lobes (October to February). **Fruit:** ovoid, usually about 7 × 3,5 cm, shallowly furrowed and roughly dotted with whitish encrustations, greyish-green when mature, heavily fibrous within (at almost all times of the year as one fruiting season frequently overlaps the next).

An infusion of the root is used as an emetic to treat biliousness and also skin eruptions in leprosy; the leaf is believed to cure syphilis. The wood is very hard and is suitable for making tools and implement handles but its size limits its use. The plants are easily raised from seed or truncheons and, although rather slow-growing, are hardy and are attractive in a garden.

Gardenia volkensii K. Schum.   Illust. 292
[*G. spatulifolia* Stapf & Hutch.]
S.A. no: 691   Transvaal gardenia. Transvaalkatjiepiering
Rhod. no: 1074   Common gardenia

A small rigid tree, 3 to 7 m in height; occurring at medium to low altitudes in open woodland. **Bark:** pale grey, smooth; the branchlets in whorls of 3 at right angles to the branches. **Leaves:** in whorls of 3, crowded at the ends of short rigid side branchlets; broadly obovate, 3 to 5 × 2,5 to 4 cm, glossy dark green, rarely with scabrid hairs on both surfaces, usually the only hairs present being minute pockets in the axils of the veins on the under surface; apex broadly tapering to rounded; base narrowly tapering and running into the petiole; margin entire; petiole obscured by the decurrent leaf base. **Flowers:** white aging to yellow, 8 cm in diameter; the corolla with a tube up to 8 cm long and with spreading lobes (August to December). **Fruit:** ovoid to almost spherical about 6 × 3 to 5 cm, shallowly ribbed, grey-green usually covered with whitish to grey encrustations (November to May).

All the material from this area belongs to subsp. *spatulifolia* (Stapf & Hutch.) Verdc. The Zulus take an infusion of the fruits and roots as an emetic. The wood is white, fine-grained, hard and heavy and is suitable for carving ornaments, but the small size of the pieces limits their use. These plants are easily propagated from cuttings or from seed; they are quite fast-growing and are attractive in a garden, given a warm situation and well-drained soil. Each individual flower is short-lived, but one follows the other in succession so the flowering season is considerably extended.

Gardenia volkensii

14. ROTHMANNIA Thunb.

Shrubs or trees. **Leaves:** opposite, simple. Stipules ovate, hairy within. **Flowers:** showy, usually solitary, axillary or terminal, or in shortly branched cymes. Bisexual; all floral parts in fives; calyx rather fleshy, 5 lobed; corolla widely bell-shaped, with soft hairs in the throat, and comparatively short but broad and spreading lobes; stamens attached in the mouth of the tube; ovary 1- to 2-chambered. **Fruit:** ovoid to almost spherical, leathery, rather hard-shelled, many-seeded.

Key to the tree species of *Rothmannia:*

1 Flowers about 3,5 cm in diameter, usually in groups of 2 to 4; fruits about 2,5 cm in diameter .. .. **R. globosa**
  Flowers more than 5 cm in diameter, always solitary; fruits 5 cm or more in diameter 2
2 Stem and leaves with short soft hairs .... **R. urcelliformis**
  Stem and leaves without hairs 3
3 Corolla lobes overlapping to the left .... **R. manganjae**
  Corolla lobes overlapping to the right 4
4 From the eastern and western Transvaal southwards to the Cape Peninsula. Maroon or reddish
    streaks and markings inside the throat of the corolla tube .... **R. capensis**
  In Rhodesia, the northern Transvaal and Moçambique. Reddish markings often, if not always, on
    the outside of the throat of the corolla tube .... **R. fischeri**

Rothmannia capensis Thunb.   Illust. 294
S.A. no: 693   Common rothmannia. Wildekatjiepiering
Rhod. no: —

A well-shaped small tree up to 14 m in height, but can reach 20 m; occurring over a wide range of altitudes, from sea level to about 1 600 m, in evergreen forest, wooded ravines and on rocky hillsides. **Bark:** grey-brown, darkish and rather rough or palish grey-brown and finely cracked into crocodile segments. **Leaves:** crowded towards the ends of the branches, elliptic, up to 10 × 4 cm, leathery, glossy dark green above, paler green below, without hairs, with distinctive swellings or pockets, about 4 per leaf, against the midrib in the axils of some of the veins, these are clearly visible on both surfaces; apex tapering to rounded; base tapering; margin entire, wavy; petiole almost absent.

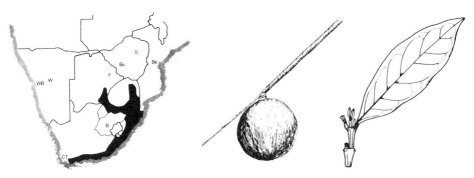

Flowers: white, rich cream to yellow, widely bell-shaped, with maroon or liver-coloured streaks and markings in the throat, sweetly scented, about 8 cm long and 6 to 7 cm in diameter; axillary, solitary (December to February). **Fruit:** spherical, about 7 cm in diameter, leathery, green when mature when they also soften; the juice stains blue (January onwards, at most times of the year).

Juice obtained from the fruits is heated and applied to wounds and burns to hasten healing while the roots are used to treat rheumatism and leprosy. The wood is hard and strong and is suitable for implement handles, poles for huts and for use as a fuel. The seeds germinate easily if removed from the pith before planting and the seedlings must be kept moist. This would make an admirable garden subject: Eve Palmer points out that the flowers keep their scent even when dried.

Rothmannia fischeri (K. Schum.) Bullock
S.A. no: 694   Woodland rothmannia. Rhodesiese katjiepiering
Rhod. no: 1075   Woodland rothmannia

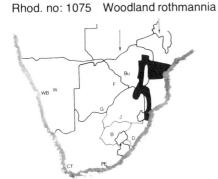

A shrub or small tree up to 8 m in height; occurring in open woodland, frequently among rocks. **Bark:** grey, smooth. **Leaves:** lanceolate to elliptic, 3,5 to 9 × 2 to 5 cm, leathery, dark green, and with hairs only in pockets in the axils of the veins on the under surface; apex and base tapering; margin entire, wavy; petiole up to 10 mm long. **Flowers:** cream with purple markings usually on the outside; corolla tube funnel-shaped, up to 10 cm long × 8 cm in diameter; axillary, solitary (October to December). **Fruit:** spherical, hard, about 5 cm in diameter, shiny green when mature (April onwards, at most times of the year).

The wood is white and hard, but brittle.

Rothmannia globosa (Hochst.) Keay
S.A. no: 695   Small-flowered rothmannia. Klokkieskatjiepiering
Rhod. no: —

A slender tree usually 4 to 7 m but up to 15 m in height; occurring at the margins of evergreen forest, in dune bush and riverine fringes and as a constituent of coastal woodland. **Bark:** brown or dark grey, smoothish when young, becoming rough with age. **Leaves:** elliptic to lanceolate, 4 to 10 × 1 to 3 cm, dark green or mid-green above, paler green below; the midrib and lateral veins pale green, yellow to pinkish, sometimes red to maroon and prominent below, with very small pockets of hairs in the axils; apex broadly tapering to narrowly rounded; base tapering; margin entire; petiole up to about 6 mm long. **Flowers:** bell-shaped, white often marked and flecked with pink in the throat, unusually small

859

for this genus, about 2,5 cm long × 3,5 cm in diameter, axillary, solitary, or occasionally in 2- to 4-flowered congested cymes on short lateral branches (August to November). **Fruit:** spherical, also small for the genus, about 2,5 cm in diameter, brown when mature, becoming rather hard and woody when dry (January to March).

The powdered roots are used to treat leprosy. The wood is pale grey, heavy and hard, but the small size of the pieces limits its value. This tree is easily cultivated and is gaining in popularity as an attractive garden subject as it is fairly fast-growing and tolerates some frost.

Rothmannia manganjae (Hiern) Keay   Illust. 295
S.A. no: —
Rhod. no: 1076   Scented bells

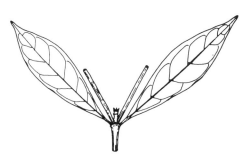

A shrub or small tree, 4 to 6 m in height; occurring in woodland and at the margins of evergreen forest. **Bark:** grey to brown, smooth. **Leaves:** lanceolate, up to 11 × 5 cm, glossy green, without hairs; veins pale green and distinct; apex and base tapering; margin entire, wavy; petiole up to 6 mm long. **Flowers:** creamy-white with dark reddish or purplish markings in the throat, bell-shaped, up to 10 cm long and 8 cm in diameter, sweetly scented, axillary, solitary (September to November). **Fruit:** spherical, hard, about 5 cm in diameter, green when mature becoming blackish when dry (at most times of the year).

Rothmannia urcelliformis (Schweinf. ex Hiern) Bullock ex Robyns
S.A. no: —
Rhod. no: 1077   Forest rothmannia

A medium to large tree, 8 to 20 m in height; occurring in evergreen forest. **Bark:** greyish-brown, sometimes reddish, smooth becoming rough with age; branchlets covered with short soft hairs. **Leaves:** lanceolate to elliptic, up to 13 × 5 cm, dark green and rather glossy, with short soft hairs; veins conspicuous on the under surface; apex and base tapering; margin entire; petiole 6 to 10 mm long. **Flowers:** white to creamy-white with reddish to pink markings in the throat, trumpet-shaped, up to 10 cm long × 10 cm in diameter, the outer surface of the corolla lobes may be greenish; axillary, solitary (October to November). **Fruit:** spherical, up to 7 cm in diameter, brownish-black when mature (at most times of the year).

15. DIDYMOSALPINX Keay

Didymosalpinx norae (Swynnerton) Keay
[*Gardenia norae* Swynnerton]
S.A. no: —
Rhod. no: 1078   Climbing bells

A spiny shrub tending to scramble, or a small tree, 5 to 7 m in height, with long trailing branches; occurring in evergreen forest. **Bark:** pale brown to grey, rather smooth; branchlets with robust opposite spines. **Leaves:** opposite, simple, elliptic to oblanceolate, 6,5 to 14 × 2,5 to 5,5 cm, glossy green; apex attenuate; base tapering; margin entire; petiole about 6 mm long. Stipules joined, intrapetiolar. **Flowers:** white, trumpet-shaped, about 5 cm long and 1,5 to 3 cm in diameter, with rather short spreading lobes, axillary, solitary. Bisexual; floral parts in fives, occasionally fours; calyx tube short; corolla with the tube longitudinally ribbed, with long silky hairs within, and with ovate lobes; anthers joined to the corolla tube, without filaments; ovary 1- to 2-chambered (December to January). **Fruit:** spherical, about 3 cm in diameter, with conspicuous thin longitudinal ribs, and crowned with the remains of the old calyx (June to October).

16. OXYANTHUS DC.

Shrubs or trees. **Leaves:** opposite, simple, often large. Stipules ovate, falling early. **Flowers:** in axillary racemes or panicles. Bisexual; all floral parts in fives; calyx shortly tubular; corolla tubular, 5-lobed; stamens attached in the mouth of the tube, without filaments; ovary 1- to 2-chambered. **Fruit:** an ovoid berry, many-seeded.

Key to the tree species of *Oxyanthus:*
1 Corolla tube seldom longer than 3,5 cm; leaf apex tapering to attenuate forming a long drip-tip, base tapering to rounded .... **O. speciosus**
  Corolla tube 6 to 8 cm long; leaf apex abruptly and shortly attenuate, base square or lobed, asymmetric 2
2 Leaves often scabrid or harshly hairy on both surfaces; occasionally without hairs except for scabrid to soft, yellowish to whitish hairs confined to the midrib and lateral veins on the under surface and to the branchlets .... **O. latifolius**
  Leaves and branchlets without hairs .... **O. pyriformis**

RUBIACEAE

Oxyanthus latifolius Sonder
S.A. no: 696,1   Zulu loquat. Zoeloelukwart
Rhod. no: —

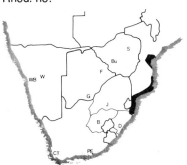 

A shrub or low tree, 4 to 5 m in height; occurring in evergreen forest, at the margins of forest, in dense bush clumps and in sand forest. **Bark:** grey to brown; young branchlets covered with dense soft hairs. **Leaves:** elliptic, 5 to 20 × 4 to 13 cm, often shortly and harshly hairy on both surfaces, occasionally without hairs except for scabrid or soft yellowish or whitish hairs along the midrib and veins below; apex abruptly and shortly attenuate; base lobed, asymmetric; margin entire; petiole thickset, up to 10 mm long. **Flowers:** white, with a conspicuously long and slender tube up to 6 cm in length, and 5 comparatively short corolla lobes which curve back; in condensed racemes which resemble round heads, closely nestled into the leaf axils (November). **Fruit:** ovoid, tapering to the base, about 3,5 cm long, orange-yellow when mature, on stalks about 1,5 cm long (June).

Oxyanthus pyriformis (Hochst.) Skeels   Illust. 296
[*O. natalensis* Sonder]
S.A. no: 696,2   Natal loquat. Natallukwart
Rhod. no: —

Usually a shrub, sometimes a small tree up to 7 m in height, occasionally reaching 10 m; a sub-canopy tree in moist evergreen forest. **Bark:** grey to brown. **Leaves:** ovate, up to 26 × 10 cm, shiny dark green above, paler green below with the veins conspicuous, without hairs; apex tapering to abruptly and shortly attenuate; base square, asymmetric; margin entire; petiole stout, up to 10 mm long. **Flowers:** white, long and slender, with a tube up to 8 cm long, and short corolla lobes, about 7 mm long, bent backwards, on shortly branched stalks forming rather loose axillary clusters (November to February). **Fruit:** oblong, up to 4 × 2,5 cm, rather soft, yellow to pale red when mature (February to April, or later).
This is a most suitable species for warm frost-free gardens, being very attractive at all times with the dark leaves and white flower-heads.

Oxyanthus speciosus DC.
[*O. gerrardii* Sonder]
S.A. no: 696   Wild loquat. Wildelukwart
862   Rhod. no: 1080   Whipstick tree

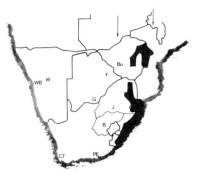 

A shrub or rather slender tree up to 12 m in height; occurring in evergreen forest, on mountain slopes and along streams. **Bark:** pale grey, slightly fissured. **Leaves:** elliptic to narrowly ovate, up to 30 × 15 cm, although often smaller, leathery, glossy dark green, without hairs; apex tapering to narrowly attenuate forming a long drip-tip; base tapering to rounded; margin entire; petiole 1 to 2 cm long. **Flowers:** white, sweetly scented, small for this genus, the corolla tube being 2,5 to 3,5 cm long, and the lobes about 5 mm long and curved back; in very compact racemes giving the appearance of dense clusters in the axils of the leaves (November to January). **Fruit:** urn-shaped, 2 to 5 cm long, yellow when mature (March to May, or later).

All this material is assigned to subsp. *stenocarpus* (K. Schum.) Bridson.

The very slender branches are used to make whipsticks.

17. FERETIA Delile

Feretia aeruginescens Stapf   Illust. 297
S.A. no: Feretia
Rhod. no: 1082   Feretia

A shrub, sometimes scrambling, or a small tree, 3 to 4 m in height; occurring at low altitudes, in riverine fringe forest, and in dense woodland always near water, along rivers, near springs or at the edge of pans. **Bark:** brown to grey-brown, inclined to be scaly, shallowly fissured, longitudinally and transversely cracked; branchlets opposite, covered with short soft hairs and inclined to peel and flake longitudinally. **Leaves:** opposite, simple, on short slender lateral branchlets; obovate to oblanceolate, up to 11 × 7 cm, but usually about 5 to 8 × 2 to 5 cm, glossy dark green with soft to harsh hairs above, the under surface reddish-brown with soft hairs and very prominent, almost parallel veins; apex tapering, sharply tipped; base tapering; margin entire; petiole 1 to 3 mm long. Stipules ovate, falling early. **Flowers:** white, sometimes flushed with pink, the corolla tube up to 1 cm long, separating into slender spreading lobes round the mouth, 1,5 cm in diameter, axillary, solitary or in few-flowered clusters. Bisexual; floral parts in fours to fives; calyx tube short; corolla tube funnel-shaped, the throat velvety on the inside; stamens inserted at the mouth of the tube (October to November). **Fruit:** almost spherical, about 1,5 cm in diameter, pink, red to crimson when mature, crowned with the remains of the old calyx which may fall, leaving a circular scar near the apex (June to September).

863

18. TRICALYSIA A. Rich. ex DC.

Shrubs or small trees. **Leaves:** opposite, simple. Stipules awl-shaped, falling early. **Flowers:** solitary or in several-flowered axillary cymcs, bracts present. Bisexual; floral parts in fours to eights; calyx tube short, often rather flat; corolla tube cylindric, trumpet-shaped or deeply bell-shaped, the mouth of the tube and the throat may be densely hairy; stamens 4 to 8; ovary 2- rarely 3-chambered. **Fruit:** ovoid to spherical, fleshy, many-seeded.

Key to the tree species of *Tricalysia:*

1 Leaf base narrowly rounded to shallowly lobed .... **T. allenii**
  Leaf base tapering 2
2 Leaves with short soft hairs, sometimes confined to the veins on the under surface 3
  Leaves without hairs 5
3 Leaves generally covered with short soft hairs although sometimes sparsely so, or confined to the under surface; pockets of hairs in the axils of the veins minute or absent 4
  Leaves with hairs confined to the veins and with conspicuous pockets of hairs in the axils of the veins on the under surface .... **T. capensis**
4 Flowers solitary, about 2 cm in diameter, creamy-white .... **T. jasminiflora**
  Flowers in dense, white, axillary clusters, small, about 1 to 1,5 cm in diameter, greenish white
  .... **T. angolensis**
5 Fruits crowned with the distinctive collar-like persistent calyx round the apex, almost half as long as the fruit .... **T. nyassae**
  Fruits may have a crowned tip, but not the large collar-like ring 6
6 Occurring in Rhodesia and adjacent areas in Moçambique, not in South Africa; not a coastal species .... **T. congesta**
  Occurring in South Africa and the coastal belt in Moçambique, not in Rhodesia 7
7 Leaves elliptic to lanceolate .... **T. lanceolata**
  Leaves ovate, oblong to broadly elliptic.. **T. sonderana**

Tricalysia allenii (Stapf) Brenan   Illust. 298
[*T. allenii* var. *kirkii* (J. D. Hook.) Brenan; *T. allenii* var. *australis* (Schweick.) Brenan]
S.A. no: Smooth-bark tricalysia
Rhod. no: 1083   Smooth-bark tricalysia

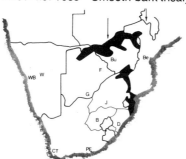

A shrub, occasionally a small tree, 3 to 4 m in height; occurring in riverine thicket, in open woodland often on rocky ridges. **Bark:** light brown, smooth; young branches velvety. **Leaves:** oblong-elliptic to ovate, up to 12 × 6 cm, with soft to scabrid hairs on both surfaces, the veins depressed above making the surface puckered; apex tapering to broadly so; base narrowly rounded to shallowly lobed; margin entire; petiole 1 to 3 mm long. **Flowers:** white often tinged with pink, 19 mm in diameter, corolla shortly bell-shaped, about 5 mm long, with fluffy hairs in the throat, sweetly scented, in axillary clusters (October to December). **Fruit:** ovoid to almost spherical, about 5 to 8 mm long, black when mature, strongly marked with a circular apical scar (December to May).
In Zululand the slender branchlets are used to make fish-traps.

Tricalysia angolensis A. Rich.
S.A. no: —
Rhod. no: 1084   Scaly-bark tricalysia

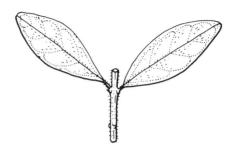

A shrub or small tree, 3 to 4 m in height; occurring in open woodland and among rocks. **Bark:** pale brown, slightly scaling. **Leaves:** oblanceolate, obovate to almost circular, 3 to 7,5 × 1,5 to 3 cm, soft textured, pale green, usually covered with short soft hairs sometimes sparsely so; apex tapering to rounded; base tapering; margin entire; petiole about 2 to 3 mm long. **Flowers:** small, about 1 to 1,5 cm in diameter, greenish-white, in dense tight axillary clusters along the slender branchlets (October to November). **Fruit:** almost spherical, about 5 mm in diameter, white tipped with a minute crown or collar formed by the persistent calyx lobes, with persistent bracts round the base of the fruit (March to April).

Tricalysia capensis (Meissner) T. R. Sim
[*Bunburya capensis* Meissner; *Tricalysia galpinii* Schinz; *T. ligustrina* S. Moore; *T. myrtifolia* S. Moore]
S.A. no: 698   Velvet tricalysia. Boswildekoffie
Rhod. no: 1085   Velvet tricalysia

A shrub or small tree, 2 to 4 m in height; occurring in coastal and dune forest and in medium altitude forest and riverine fringes. **Bark:** light brown, finely longitudinally fissured; young branchlets covered with fine soft hairs. **Leaves:** ovate to lanceolate, 3 to 10 × 1 to 3,5 cm, with hairs confined to the veins, and conspicuous pockets of hairs on the under surface in the axils of the 5 pairs of lateral veins; apex attenuate, forming a drip-tip; base tapering; margin entire, rolled under; petiole about 10 mm long, with rusty hairs. **Flowers:** small, white, 1,5 cm in diameter, sweetly scented; corolla with a cylindric tube about 10 mm long and 6 spreading lobes; calyx hairy; flowers in few-flowered axillary clusters (October to December). **Fruit:** ovoid, about 8 mm long, red and finally black when mature, crowned with the remains of the calyx (February to July).

Tricalysia congesta (Oliver) Hiern
S.A. no: —
Rhod. no: 1086   Mauve tricalysia

A much-branched shrub inclined to scramble, or a small tree up to 10 m in height; occurring in evergreen forest and dense woodland. **Bark:** brown, longitudinally fissured. **Leaves:** ovate to

865

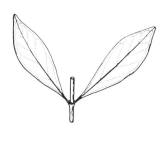

obovate, usually 3,5 to 7,5 × 1,8 to 3,5 cm, but occasionally larger, shiny green, without hairs; apex attenuate; base tapering; margin entire; petiole 1 to 3 mm long. **Flowers:** white to pale mauve, sweetly scented, about 5 mm long × 10 mm in diameter, in few-flowered axillary clusters (October to December). **Fruit:** ellipsoidal, about 3 mm long, red when mature, with a small but distinct crowned tip (April to May).

Tricalysia jasminiflora (Klotzsch) Benth. & J. D. Hook. ex Hiern
[*Neorosea jasminiflora* (Klotzsch) N. Hallé]
S.A. no:—
Rhod. no: 1086/1   Single-flowered tricalysia

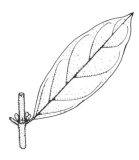

A shrub or small unarmed tree up to 7 m in height; occurring at medium to low altitudes in ever-green forest and in riverine fringes. **Bark:** reddish-brown. **Leaves:** opposite, simple, lanceolate to elliptic, up to 12 × 5 cm, but usually rather smaller, usually with short soft hairs on the under sur-face or with minute pockets of hairs in the axils of the veins; apex and base tapering; margin en-tire; petiole 1 to 3 mm long. **Flowers:** creamy-white, about 2 cm in diameter, with slender corolla lobes; axillary, solitary, either with the leaves or when the tree is bare; corolla 5-lobed bearded; stamens 5 to 7 (May to December). **Fruit:** ovoid, about 10 mm long, bright red when mature, crowned with the small grey velvety remains of the calyx (August to March).

Tricalysia lanceolata (Sonder) Burtt Davy
S.A. no: 699   Common tricalysia. Gewone wildekoffie
Rhod. no: —

A shrub with a tendency to scramble, or a small tree up to 6 m in height; occurring at the margins of evergreen forest, in forest, wooded kloofs, dry woodland, scrub and on hill and mountain slopes; from coastal sand dunes and dune scrub to medium altitude forest. **Bark:** brownish, corky, longitudinally furrowed; branchlets yellow. **Leaves:** elliptic to lanceolate, 2,5 to 10 × 1 to 3 cm, thinly textured, shiny green, entirely without hairs; with 12 or more pairs of lateral veins; apex and base tapering; margin entire, rather wavy; petiole about 5 mm long. **Flowers:** white, sweetly scented, corolla with 5 spreading lobes about 1,3 cm in diameter, the calyx without hairs; in tight axillary clusters (October to November). **Fruit:** spherical, about 5 mm in diameter, red and finally purplish-black when mature,

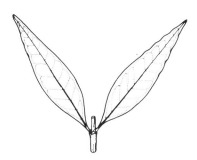

inconspicuously crowned with the remains of the calyx, tightly clustered along the branchlets below the new leaves (December to March and later).

Tricalysia nyassae Hiern
S.A. no: —
Rhod. no: 1088   Crown-fruited tricalysia

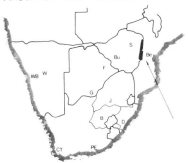
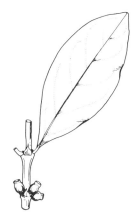

A shrub or small tree, 1 to 8 m in height; occurring at low altitudes always near water, along stream and river banks, in riverine fringe forest and among rocks. **Bark:** grey to brown. **Leaves:** elliptic to oblanceolate, 6 to 17 × 1,3 to 3 cm, but usually about 10 × 2 cm, olive green, without hairs; the midrib prominent below; apex and base tapering; margin entire, finely rolled under; petiole about 2 to 5 mm long. **Flowers:** waxy white occasionally tinged with pink, 8 to 13 mm in diameter, with the corolla tube about 3 mm long and 6 spreading lobes, sweetly scented; in tight axillary clusters along the stem (August to October). **Fruit:** distinctive, ovoid, 3 to 5 mm in length, orange-yellow to bright red when mature, crowned with the conspicuous collar-like persistent calyx round the apex, almost half as long as the fruit itself, with a slight constriction between the fruit and the calyx (November to December).

This species has been divided into two varieties, all the material occurring south of the Zambezi River belonging to var. *angustifolia* Garçia; the typical variety occurs only in countries to the north.

Tricalysia sonderana Hiern
S.A. no: 700   Dune tricalysia. Duinekoffie
Rhod. no: —
A low shrub or small tree up to 6 m in height; occurring in coastal bush, dune forest and open woodland. **Bark:** brown with longitudinal fissures; young branches pale grey. **Leaves:** broadly elliptic, oblong to ovate, 2,5 to 9 × 1,5 to 3 cm, leathery, without hairs; conspicuous veins on both surfaces, particularly the upper surface; apex broadly tapering sometimes finely hair-tipped; base tapering; margin entire, rolled under; petiole thickset, 2 to 4 mm long. The leaves resemble those of *T. lanceolata* but are ovate, oblong to broadly elliptic, thickly leathery in texture, and they are wider, with the apices more broadly tapering. **Flowers:** white or pale pink, about 1,5 cm in diameter, corolla with a short tube, and spreading lobes with a conspicuously bearded throat; in dense axillary clusters (September to December). **Fruit:** spherical, about 7 mm in diameter, black when mature, on slender stalks up to 1,5 cm long, crowned with the short remains of the calyx (December to April).

867

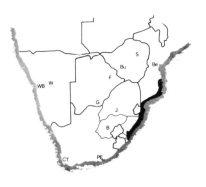

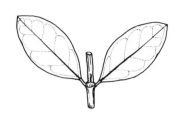

19. KRAUSSIA Harvey

Kraussia floribunda Harvey
S.A. no: 700,1   Kraussia. Wildekornoelie
Rhod. no: —

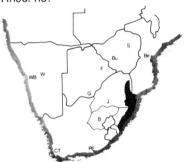

A shrub or small tree up to 6 m in height; occurring in dune scrub, swamp forest and riverine fringing woodland. **Bark:** grey to brownish. **Leaves:** opposite, simple, elliptic, 4 to 9 × 2,5 to 4 cm. upright, glossy dark green, with bacterial nodules forming small pockets at the base of the lateral veins; apex rounded to broadly tapering; base rounded or abruptly decurrent; margin entire, inclined to be wavy; petiole 1 to 5 mm long. Stipules triangular, hairy within, falling early. **Flowers:** creamy-white, about 10 mm in diameter, axillary, in loose, rather few-flowered branched heads, or simple lax bracteolate cymes, with long stalks, not very conspicuous but quite attractive. Bisexual; floral parts in fours to sixes; calyx lobed; corolla with 5 spreading lobes, free almost to the base, hairy within; stamens 5, attached at the mouth of the tube; ovary 2-chambered, the style 10 mm long and prominent (November to January). **Fruit:** almost spherical, about 8 mm in diameter, purplish black when mature, edible with a sweet flavour (February to July).

20. SERICANTHE Robbrecht

Sericanthe andongensis (Hiern) Robbrecht   Illust. 299
[*Neorosea andongensis* (Hiern) N. Hallé; *Tricalysia andongensis* Hiern; *T. pachystigma* K. Schum.]
S.A. no: 697   Sericanthe. Vendakoffie
Rhod. no: 1089   Sericanthe

A shrub or small unarmed tree usually up to 5 m in height, but occasionally rather taller; occurring in wooded hills, along stream banks and among rocks. **Bark:** grey to brownish, smooth. **Leaves:** opposite, simple, obovate to oblanceolate, 3 to 9 × 1 to 5 cm, with short soft hairs on both surfaces when young, losing most of these by maturity, thinly textured; the veins conspicuous below; apex tapering to rounded; base tapering; margin entire; petiole 1 to 3 mm long. **Flowers:** white, sweetly scented, 2 to 3 cm in diameter, with the corolla lobes slender and slightly twisted; the sepals and backs of the corolla lobes with long silky hairs; basal bracts are brownish and hairy; axillary, solitary,

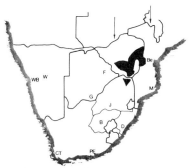 

produced in profusion along the branches (June to October). **Fruit:** spherical, about 8 mm in diameter, shiny orange to scarlet when mature with sparse hairs, the persistent calyx forming a papery funnel-shaped structure at the tip with a distinct constriction between it and the fruit itself (April to June).

This species is sometimes seen in gardens, but it is frost-tender.

21. HEINSIA DC.

Heinsia crinita (Afzel.) G. Taylor
S.A. no: Bastard gardenia. Basterkatjiepiering
Rhod. no: 1091   Small false gardenia

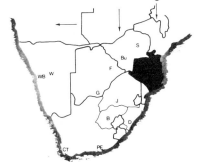 

A shrub to small unarmed tree up to 6 m in height; occurring at low altitudes in riverine fringe forest and thicket. **Bark:** grey to light brown, rather mottled, smooth. **Leaves:** opposite, simple, ovate, 2 to 8 × 1 to 5 cm, light green with few to many harsh hairs on the upper surface, velvety below; apex and base tapering; margin entire; petiole about 2 mm long. Stipules small, falling early. **Flowers:** white, 3 to 4 cm in diameter, with the corolla tube up to 3 cm long with spreading lobes and a bearded throat, with rather sparse hairs on the outside; axillary or terminal, solitary or in few-flowered cymes. Bisexual; floral parts in fives to sixes; calyx tube short; corolla tubular, 5-lobed; stamens attached deep in the tube; ovary 2-chambered (November to February). **Fruit:** ovoid, about 10 mm long, orange when mature, crowned with the conspicuous leaf-like remains of the calyx (January to April).

22. AULACOCALYX J. D. Hook.

Aulacocalyx diervilleoides (K. Schum.) Petit
[*Heinsenia sylvestris* S. Moore]
S.A. no: —
Rhod. no: 1092   Miniature bells

A shrub or small unarmed tree up to 6 m in height; occurring in evergreen forest. **Bark:** dull grey, smooth. **Leaves:** opposite, simple, elliptic to oblanceolate, up to 14 × 5 cm, almost without hairs, the veining prominent below and the veins and petioles reddish; apex narrowly attenuate; base tapering; margin entire; petiole about 3 mm long. Stipules small. **Flowers:** creamy-white, with the throat attractively mottled with pink, and 1,5 to 2 cm in diameter; corolla bell-shaped about 10 mm long with spreading lobes; flowers in axillary, congested many-flowered clusters, or fascicles. Bisexual; all floral parts in fives; calyx short; corolla with silky hairs on the outside; stamens attached in the

869

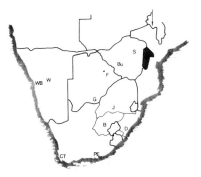

mouth of the tube (July to October). **Fruit:** ellipsoidal, fleshy, about 8 mm long, brown to blackish when mature, finely crowned with remains of the old calyx teeth (December to May).

23. CREMASPORA Benth.

Cremaspora triflora (Thonn.) K. Schum.
S.A. no: —
Rhod. no: 1093   Cremaspora

A shrub or small unarmed tree up to 7 m in height; a constituent of the under-storey in high altitude evergreen forest, often along river banks. **Bark:** light grey to pale brown, finely longitudinally scaling; the lateral branchlets with soft hairs, arising above the axils of the leaves and subtended by large leafy shield-like stipules. **Leaves:** opposite, simple, elliptic to obovate, 3,5 to 15 × 1,5 to 5 cm, deep glossy green, with or without hairs; apex attenuate; base tapering; margin entire, wavy; petiole 2 to 5 mm long. **Flowers:** white, about 10 mm in diameter, heavily scented, in axillary short-stalked clusters. Bisexual; floral parts in fives to sixes; calyx small, with short hairs; corolla funnel-shaped with 5 spreading lobes; stamens attached in the mouth of the tube (October to December). **Fruit:** ellipsoidal, fleshy, about 8 mm long, brown to blackish when mature, finely crowned with remains of the old calyx teeth (December to May).

24. POLYSPHAERIA J. D. Hook.

Polysphaeria lanceolata Hiern
S.A. no: —
Rhod. no: —   Polysphaeria

A shrub or small unarmed tree, 2 to 5 m in height; occurring along streams and in evergreen forest. **Bark:** brown and finely longitudinally fissured; branchlets arising above the axils of the leaves. **Leaves:** opposite, simple, lanceolate to narrowly elliptic, 4,5 to 9 × 2 to 3 cm, thinly leathery, shiny dark green; the midrib prominent below; apex tapering, sharp-tipped; base tapering; margin entire; petiole 1 to 3 mm long. Stipules small, falling very early. **Flowers:** waxy white, about 7 mm in diameter, shortly stalked, in 2- to 9-flowered compact axillary clusters, sometimes as a tight head, or cyme, on a slender stalk. Bisexual; all floral parts in fours; calyx short; corolla 4-lobed, funnel-shaped, with the throat densely bearded; stamens attached in the mouth of the tube (May to

870

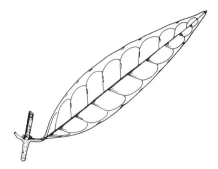

November). **Fruit:** almost spherical, fleshy, about 10 mm in diameter, purple when mature, in short-stalked dense clusters (July to March).

25. ALBERTA E. Meyer

Meyer named this genus *Alberta* in 1838 and in the same year, probably just before this, Schimper gave the name *Albertia* to a genus of fossil plants. These two names are considered too similar and, in 1903, Kuntze published the name *Ernestimeyera* for the South African genus, but this name has never been taken up and the earlier name, *Alberta,* although probably incorrect, is generally used and widely known. However, it now appears that the original description of *Albertia* Schimper stemmed from mixed type material and therefore has never been adopted by palaeontologists, but neither has it been placed in synonymy by them; were this to be done, it is hoped that a strong case could be made out for conserving the name *Alberta* E. Meyer, for the South African tree.

Alberta magna E. Meyer   Illust. 300
S.A. no: 701   Natal flame bush. Breekhout
Rhod. no: —

A medium sized tree up to 13 m in height; occurring in evergreen forest, wooded ravines and bush. **Bark:** pale grey, rather smooth, almost folded, becoming rough with age. **Leaves:** opposite, simple, elliptic, 7 to 13 × 3 to 5 cm, glossy dark green above, paler green below; the midrib and lateral veins yellowish and prominent, particularly on the under surface; apex broadly tapering to rounded; base narrowly tapering; margin entire, rolled under; petiole stout, 2 to 4 mm long. Stipules cup-shaped, bearded, falling early. **Flowers:** striking, brilliant red to crimson, tubular, up to 3 cm long, curved, in dense opposite heads, or terminal panicles with opposite cymose branches. Bisexual; all floral parts in fives; calyx tube short; corolla shortly lobed, with a long, narrowly funnel-shaped tube; stamens attached in the upper part of the tube; ovary 10-ribbed, 2-chambered (January to April). **Fruit:** ovoid, dry, 10-ribbed, about 5 × 3 mm, developing 2 membraneous wings up to 2 × 0,7 cm, the fruit and wings also becoming brilliant red to scarlet, even more spectacular than the flowers, the flowering and fruiting times often overlapping (February to August).

Although spectacular in gardens at the coast, this tree does not thrive inland or under dry conditions. Its germination is very sporadic, but cuttings take quite easily; the tree is usually slow-growing. This is a protected plant in South Africa.

871

RUBIACEAE

26. VANGUERIA Juss.

Shrubs or small trees, often unarmed, the branches opposite, each pair being set at right angles to the next. **Leaves:** opposite, simple. Stipules often broad, joined at the base, hairy within, falling fairly early. **Flowers:** in a many-flowered axillary raceme of cymes. Bisexual; all floral parts in fives; calyx with a saucer-shaped tube and long, very slender and contorted lobes; corolla bell-shaped, hairy in the throat, with ovate lobes as long as the tube; stamens fixed in the mouth of the tube; ovary usually 5-chambered. **Fruit:** ovoid to almost spherical, fleshy, on rather long stalks, the fruit usually crowned with the persistent calyx remains.

Key to the tree species of *Vangueria:*

1 Leaves and branchlets hairy 2
  Leaves and branchlets without hairs 3
2 Leaves large, 5 to 24 cm long, densely hairy; apex tapering to rounded .... **V. infausta**
  Leaves not conspicuously large, 8 to 12 cm long, with short soft hairs; apex attenuate............
  .... **V. esculenta**
3 Calyx lobes conspicuously long and slender, giving a rather tangled appearance to the clusters of
  flowers .... **V. apiculata**
  Calyx lobes not conspicuously long; may be slender and twisted but not tangled 4
4 Flower buds usually with the tip markedly drawn out into a fine hair-like point .... **V. randii**
  Flower buds without a hair-like tip .... **V. esculenta**

Vangueria apiculata K. Schum.

[*V. longicalyx* Robyns]
S.A. no: —
Rhod. no: 1094   Tangle-flowered wild medlar

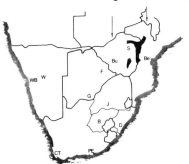

A shrub or small tree up to 9 m in height; occurring in open woodland, mountain grassland and among rocks. **Bark:** dark grey, smooth. **Leaves:** ovate to ovate-elliptic, 6 to 16 × 2,5 to 10 cm, thinly textured, glossy green, without hairs; apex tapering; base broadly tapering, rounded to shallowly lobed; margin entire, wavy; petiole about 5 mm long. **Flowers:** greenish-white, up to 10 mm in diameter, the calyx lobes conspicuously long, narrow and rather tangled, the corolla lobes curved back; in dense, axillary branched rather untidy heads (November to February). **Fruit:** ovoid, 2 to 2,5 cm long, yellow-green when mature (March to May).

Vangueria esculenta S. Moore

[*V. chartacea* Robyns; *V. cyanescens* Robyns; *V. floribunda* Robyns; *V. esculenta* var. *glabra* S. Moore]
S.A. no: 702,1   Forest wild medlar. Blinkblaarmispel
Rhod. no: 1095   Forest wild medlar

A shrub to small tree up to 10 m in height; occurring in evergreen forest, dune forest and at the margins of forest. **Bark:** grey, smooth; branchlets with short hairs. **Leaves:** elliptic to ovate, 8 to 12 × 3 to 5 cm, thinly textured, densely covered with short soft hairs on both surfaces or may be without hairs, paler green below than above; apex attenuate; base tapering; margin entire; petiole about 3 to 6 mm long. **Flowers:** yellow-green, up to 10 mm in diameter, calyx lobes short with the corolla lobes

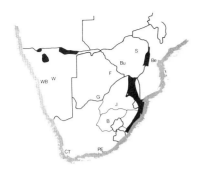

curving back, sweetly scented, in small sparse axillary heads (October). **Fruit:** almost spherical, about 2,5 cm in diameter, yellow-brown when mature, in pendulous clusters (December to February).

Vangueria infausta Burch.   Illust. 301
[*V. tomentosa* Hochst.; *V. lasioclados* K. Schum.; *V. rupicola* Robyns]
S.A. no: 702   Wild medlar. Wildemispel
Rhod. no: 1096   Wild medlar

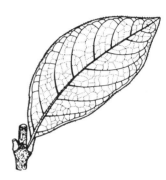

A small tree, 3 to 7 m in height; occurring in wooded grassland, among rocks and on sand dunes. **Bark:** grey, smooth; branchlets covered with short hairs. **Leaves:** elliptic to ovate, 5 to 24 × 3,8 to 15 cm, densely covered with golden to tawny short soft hairs especially when young; net-veining conspicuous below; apex tapering to rounded; base tapering; margin entire; petiole 3 to 10 mm long. **Flowers:** greenish-white to yellowish, about 4 mm long and 6 mm in diameter, the corolla falling early; in small branched groups densely clustered along short lateral branchlets (September to October). **Fruit:** almost spherical, 2,5 to 3,5 cm in diameter, yellowish to brown when mature (January to April).

The specific name of this tree means 'unlucky' and many Africans, believing that it possesses evil powers, will not use the wood, even as a fuel. Nevertheless, the roots are regarded as a remedy for a number of complaints, including malaria and pneumonia. It has long been known that the pulp, when mixed with a little sugar and water, makes a good substitute for apple sauce and today many farmers' wives make use of it in puddings. Small gall-like growths may be noticed on the leaf surfaces: these are caused by a species of fungus which often attacks these trees. The similarity between this species and *Vangueriopsis lanciflora* is discussed under the latter.

Vangueria randii S. Moore
S.A. no: —
Rhod. no: 1097   Ant-heap wild medlar

A shrub or small tree up to 7 m in height; occurring in open woodland, along river banks, at the base of rocky koppies, often associated with termite mounds; nowhere common. **Bark:** grey, smooth. **Leaves:** ovate, up to 9 × 3,5 cm, but usually smaller, thinly textured, dark green above, paler green below, without hairs; apex attenuate sometimes very shortly so; base tapering to rounded; margin entire, wavy; petiole up to 3 mm long. **Flowers:** pale yellow or greenish-yellow, up to 10 mm in

873

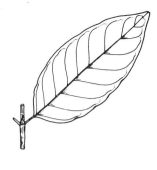

diameter, the flower buds with the tips of the calyx lobes drawn out into conspicuous hair-like points; in small dense axillary heads (November to March). **Fruit:** almost spherical, 2,5 cm in diameter, yellowish-green when mature (February to April).

27. TAPIPHYLLUM Robyns

Herbs springing from a woody rootstock, shrubs or small trees. **Leaves:** opposite or crowded on lateral branchlets, simple. Stipules joined at the base. **Flowers:** axillary in dense clusters, or fascicles, or axillary pedunculate cymes. Bisexual; all floral parts in fives; calyx tube short; corolla tube shortly and broadly tubular, with or without hairs; stamens fixed in the mouth of the tube; ovary usually 4- to 5-chambered. **Fruit:** spherical, fleshy.

Key to the tree species of *Tapiphyllum:*
Leaves usually 1 to 2 cm long, up to 4 × 3 cm; with fine soft hairs on both surfaces; occurring in Natal, the Transvaal, Botswana, South West Africa and Angola .... **T. parvifolium**
Leaves usually about 4 cm long, up to a maximum of about 8 × 7,5 cm; densely covered with thick woolly hairs on both surfaces; occurring in Rhodesia and northwards, not in South Africa or Botswana .... **T. velutinum**

Tapiphyllum parvifolium (Sonder) Robyns ex Good
S.A. no: 703   Small velvet leaf. Bergmispel
Rhod. no: —

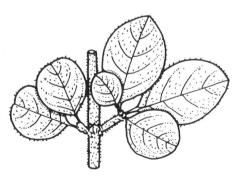

A small strongly branched tree up to 6 m in height; occurring on rocky hills and koppies. **Bark:** light grey, rather smooth to rectangular flaking; the wood is brittle.**Leaves:** frequently crowded on dwarf, knobby, lateral branchlets, broadly elliptic to almost circular, up to 4 × 3 cm, but usually about 1,5 cm long, covered with dense fine soft hairs on both surfaces; the midrib and lateral veins prominent below but net-veining not visible; apex broadly tapering to rounded; base square or lobed; margin entire, slightly wavy; petiole almost absent. **Flowers:** greenish to yellowish-green, about 5 mm in diameter with a short corolla tube; inconspicuous, in dense axillary clusters (October to December). **Fruit:** spherical, up to 1,5 cm in diameter, brown or reddish when mature, rather narrowly and abruptly tapering to the base; calyx lobes persistent; edible (January to March).

874 Africans in Botswana and South West Africa make arrowheads from the wood.

Tapiphyllum velutinum (Hiern) Robyns
[*T. vestitum* Robyns]
S.A. no: —
Rhod. no: 1098   Velvet leaf

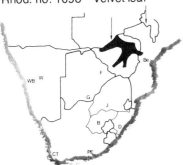
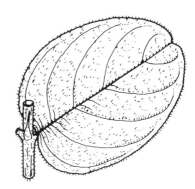

A shrub or small tree, 2 to 4 m in height; occurring in open woodland, often among rocks. **Bark:** brown to reddish-brown or blackish, rough and flaking; young shoots covered with dense woolly hairs. **Leaves:** broadly ovate to almost circular, 2 to 8 × 1,6 to 7,5 cm, but usually about 4 cm long, densely covered with thick woolly hairs and with prominent net-veining on both surfaces, dull green to light green above, whitish to yellowish below; apex rounded, notched; base lobed, almost clasping the stem; margin entire; petiole thickset, 1 to 2 mm in length. **Flowers:** greenish-yellow, pale green, greenish-white to bright yellow, about 6 mm long and 6 mm in diameter, the calyx lobes long and slender, in axillary clusters of 10 to 12 (October to January). **Fruit:** spherical, about 1,5 cm in diameter, tapering towards the base, densely covered with short soft hairs, the persistent calyx lobes long, conspicuously slender; yellow-brown when mature (December to March).

28. RYTIGYNIA Blume

Shrubs or small trees. **Leaves:** opposite, simple. Stipules joined at the base. **Flowers:** axillary, solitary or in few-flowered cymes. Bisexual; all floral parts in fives; calyx tube very short; corolla tube bell-shaped with a bearded throat; stamens fixed in the mouth of the tube. **Fruit:** spherical, fleshy.

Key to the tree species of *Rytigynia:*
Leaves usually about 7 × 2,8 cm, with the petiole 5 to 8 mm long; corolla lobes short and thickset .. .. **R. schumannii**
Leaves usually about 4 × 1,6 cm, with the petiole barely 1 mm long or absent; corolla lobes long and
    slender with a hair-like tip .... **R. sp. no. 1**

Rytigynia schumannii Robyns
S.A. no: —
Rhod. no: 1099   Large-leaved rytigynia

A shrub or small tree, 1 to 4 m in height; occurring in evergreen forest. **Bark:** pale brown, smooth.
Leaves: broadly ovate, usually about 7 × 2,8 cm, dark green to mid-green, without hairs; apex narrowly attenuate forming a slender drip-tip; base tapering; margin entire; petiole slender, 5 to 8 mm

875

long. **Flowers:** cream tinged with green, about 8 mm in diameter, the anthers conspicuously orange to brown; corolla tube narrowly tubular, with short and thickset lobes; the flowers on slender stalks about 10 mm long, axillary, solitary (December). **Fruit:** almost spherical, fleshy, about 10 mm in diameter, green with a brown ring scar on one side, on slender stalks up to 2 cm long, black and soft when mature (December to April).

Rytigynia sp. no. 1
S.A. no: —
Rhod. no: 1100   Small-leaved rytigynia

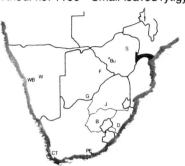

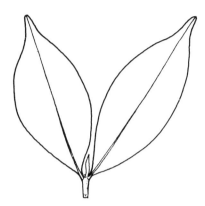

A shrub or small tree up to 4 m in height; occurring at the margins of evergreen forest and in forest. **Bark:** grey to brown. **Leaves:** ovate, usually about 4 × 1,6 cm, light green, thinly textured, with very sparse hairs; apex narrowly attenuate forming a drip-tip; base tapering; margin entire; petiole almost absent. **Flowers:** white to creamy-green up to 10 mm in diameter the corolla lobes narrow ending in a hair-like tip; solitary on a slender stalk (December). **Fruit:** about 10 mm in diameter, dark blackish when mature (December to April).

29. VANGUERIOPSIS Robyns ex Good

Vangueriopsis lanciflora (Hiern) Robyns   Illust. 302
S.A. no: 704   False wild medlar. Valsmispel
Rhod. no: 1101   False wild medlar

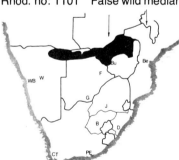

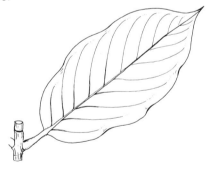

A shrub or small tree up to 7 m in height; occurring in woodland and wooded grassland, often associated with rocky outcrops. **Bark:** grey, fairly smooth, flaking to reveal an orange under-bark; branchlets often russet. **Leaves:** opposite, simple, oblong to oblanceolate, up to 13 × 6 cm, dark green and rather roughly hairy to almost without hairs above, yellowish-white with densely woolly hairs; veining prominent below; apex rounded to broadly tapering; base tapering; margin entire, rather wavy; petiole thickset, up to 10 mm long. Stipules joined at the base. **Flowers:** cream, with a short corolla tube, with slender corolla lobes, up to 2,5 cm long, curving right back, lyre-shaped, and the calyx velvety green to golden-green; flowers in axillary heads or cymes. Bisexual; all floral parts in fives; calyx tube almost absent; corolla broadly tubular and 5-lobed; the stamens fixed in the mouth of the tube; ovary 2-chambered (August to September). **Fruit:** ovoid, asymmetric, about 2,5 × 2 cm, fleshy, yellowish-brown when mature crowned with the persistent calyx; edible (September to January).

This species resembles *Vangueria infausta* but the latter has leaves which are pale green and very hairy on both surfaces and its branches are opposite, arising almost from ground level. Although the branchlets are reddish, they are not as conspicuously russet as those of *Vangueriopsis*. This is one of the trees known as 'live-long' or 'never-die' because posts in the ground usually grow.

Vangueriopsis lanciflora

30. LAGYNIAS E. Meyer ex Robyns

Shrubs or small trees. **Leaves:** opposite, simple. Stipules shortly joined at the base, pointed and hairy. **Flowers:** in axillary Y-branched cymes. Bisexual; all floral parts in fives; calyx tube very short with the lobes almost as long as, or exceeding, the corolla tube; corolla tube cylindric, 5-lobed, with the slender lobes curved back; stamens attached in the mouth of the tube; ovary 5-chambered. **Fruit:** spherical, fleshy.

Key to the tree species of *Lagynias:*
Leaves with dense short soft hairs, up to 4 × 2 cm, but usually smaller; only occurring in Rhodesia, the northern Transvaal and adjoining parts of Moçambique .... **L. dryadum**
Leaves usually almost without hairs, usually longer than 4 cm; only occurring in Natal and the extreme south of Moçambique .... **L. lasiantha**

Lagynias dryadum (S. Moore) Robyns
S.A. no: Lagynias
Rhod. no: 1102   Lagynias

A straggling shrub or small tree up to 4 m in height; occurring in open woodland, along rivers, frequently on koppies sheltered among rocks. **Bark:** pale grey to grey-brown, smooth or very finely fissured; branches long and arching. **Leaves:** narrowly ovate to elliptic, up to 4 × 2 cm, finely and densely covered with soft hairs on both surfaces, yellowish-green to grey-green; apex tapering; base broadly tapering to rounded; margin entire; petiole about 5 mm long. **Flowers:** pale yellow, calyx lobes conspicuous, 7 to 10 mm long; sweetly scented, in clusters on short side shoots (November to December). **Fruit:** spherical, about 2,5 cm in diameter, pendulous on slender velvety stalks about 3 cm long, brown when mature, crowned with the old dry calyx lobes (February to March).

Lagynias lasiantha (Sonder) Bullock
S.A. no: 705   Umtulu. Natalmispel
Rhod. no: —

877

A small tree, 3 to 6 m in height; occurring in and at the margins of evergreen forest, in open woodland and scrub. **Bark:** grey, smooth. **Leaves:** ovate to lanceolate, 2,5 to 10 × 1,5 to 3 cm, glossy green above, dull and paler green to whitish below, generally without hairs, except along the midrib which is prominent on the under surface; apex tapering; base broadly tapering, rounded to shallowly lobed; margin entire, wavy; petiole about 8 mm long. **Flowers:** yellowish-green aging to yellowish-brown, less than 10 mm in diameter, with the corolla lobes curled back, in clusters on short lateral branchlets (November to December). **Fruit:** spherical, 2,5 to 4,5 cm in diameter, yellowish-brown when mature, crowned with the remains of the old calyx; rather pendulous on twisted stalks; edible and said to be pleasantly flavoured (March to April).

31. CANTHIUM Lam.

Shrubs or trees, sometimes scrambling, armed or unarmed. **Leaves:** opposite, simple. Stipules small, awl-shaped, falling early. **Flowers:** in axillary, few- to many-flowered, corymbose cymes. Bisexual; floral parts in fours to fives; calyx saucer-shaped, with very small teeth round the rim; corolla shortly and broadly tubular or urn-shaped, the throat sometimes bearded, with the ovate to oblong lobes varying in length, curved well back, spreading or erect; stamens attached in the mouth of the corolla; ovary usually 2-chambered; stigma 2-lobed, protruding beyond the corolla lobes. **Fruit:** ovoid to almost spherical, often paired, sometimes asymmetric, shiny, fleshy, indehiscent.

Key to the tree species *Canthium:*

1 Branches armed with paired straight spines 2
  Branches without spines 7
2 Leaves usually larger than 3 cm long 3
  Leaves usually less than 3 cm long 4
3 Petiole 8 to 12 mm long; corolla throat bearded .... **C. inerme**
  Petiole 1 to 2 mm long; corolla throat without hairs .... **C. spinosum**
4 Leaves hairy 5
  Leaves without hairs 6
5 Leaf margin fringed with hairs, petiole short but distinct .... **C. ciliatum**
  Leaf margin not hair fringed, but the leaf may be hairy, petiole obscured by the decurrent leaf base
  .... **C. frangula**
6 Leaves fascicled on dwarf side shoots .... **C. frangula**
  Leaves opposite, although they may be crowded on lateral branches .... **C. pauciflorum**
7 Leaves very large, up to 19 × 16 cm, usually about 10 to 11 cm long .... **C. lactescens**
  Leaves usually less than 10 cm long, although some leaves may be larger 8
8 Flowers in few-flowered, shortly stalked heads, or in axillary fascicles 9
  Flowers in larger, longer branched heads 12
9 Large forest trees up to 30 m in height; petiole and midrib may be orange .... **C. vulgare**
  Small to medium sized trees, 3 to 15 m in height; petiole and midrib green 10
10 Fruits up to 1,7 cm long, kidney-shaped .... **C. pauciflorum**
  Fruits up to 0,7 cm long 11
11 Leaves broadly elliptic to almost circular, 4 to 8,5 × 1,8 to 5,5 cm, on short, rigid, peg-like,
  almost spinescent lateral spurs .... **C. martinii**
  Leaves obovate to ovate, usually narrowly so, 1,5 to 5 × 1 to 3 cm, without short rigid spurs .
  .... **C. obovatum**

12 Apex shortly to conspicuously attenuate 13
   Apex tapering, broadly tapering to rounded 19
13 Leaves hairy, rather scabrid 14
   Leaves without hairs or may have minute pockets in lower vein axils or also along the veins or with hairs confined to the veins only 15
14 Leaves ovate, usually 3 cm or less broad .... **C. huillense**
   Leaves ovate to almost circular, more than 3 cm broad .... **C. burttii**
15 Leaves with minute pockets of hairs in axils of veins on under surface **C. pseudoverticillatum**
   Leaves without pockets of hairs below 16
16 Leaf base square to lobed 17
   Leaf base tapering to rounded 18
17 Leaf base distinctly lobed; rough hairs along the veins especially on under surface .. **C. gueinzii**
   Leaf base shallowly lobed to square; smooth appressed hairs along the veins on under surface .. .. **C. venosum**
18 A constituent of evergreen forest; fruits single, ovoid, not 2-lobed, asymmetric   **C. captum**
   Occurring in woodland and thicket, often on Kalahari sand; fruits single, pear-shaped, or 2-lobed, slightly asymmetric .... **C. huillense**
19 Bark markedly corky on main stem and powdery on the branches .... **C. suberosum**
   Bark on the main stem and branches not corky or powdery 20
20 Leaf base tapering and running into the petiole .... **C. locuples**
   Leaf base more or less rounded to shallowly lobed 21
21 Branchlets roughly, or harshly hairy; bases of petioles and stipules not persistent **C. setiflorum**
   Branchlets not roughly hairy; bases of petioles and stipules persistent, producing small, woody, knobby swellings along the branchlets .... **C. mundianum**

Canthium burttii Bullock
S.A. no: —
Rhod. no: 1103   Mottled-bark canthium

A shrub or small tree up to 8 m in height; occurring at low altitudes on rocky hills and in hot dry woodland. **Bark:** grey, often mottled, smooth although sometimes tending to peel and becoming rough with age; without spines. **Leaves:** ovate to almost circular, 5 to 9 × 3 to 6 cm, with fine but rather harsh hairs, the veining darker than the blade; apex narrowly attenuate; base tapering to rounded; margin entire; petiole 5 to 10 mm long. Stipules broad, up to 10 mm long, falling early. **Flowers:** greenish, sweetly scented, in small axillary rounded heads at the ends of common stalks up to 2 cm long (November to December). **Fruit:** ovoid, up to 10 mm long, blackish when mature, in dense clusters (January to February).

Canthium captum Bullock
S.A. no: —
Rhod. no: 1104   Chimanimani canthium

A shrub or small tree up to 4 m in height; occurring at the margins of evergreen forest and as a constituent of the under-storey. **Bark:** pale brownish, smooth; the branches opposite, each pair set at right angles to the next, rather weak and brittle, tending to droop; branchlets green, without spines. **Leaves:** ovate, 3 to 6 × 1,2 to 2,5 cm, shiny pale to dark green, without hairs; apex narrowly

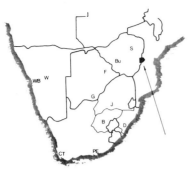

attenuate; base rounded; margin entire; petiole 2 to 4 mm long. Stipules small, inconspicuous. **Flowers:** small greenish-yellow, in rather sparse heads on a stalk 1 to 1,5 cm long (October). **Fruit:** ovoid, asymmetric, about 10 mm long, blackish when mature (April).

Canthium ciliatum (Klotzsch) Kuntze
S.A. no: 705,1   Dwarf turkey-berry. Dwergbokdrol
Rhod. no: —

Usually a shrub, sometimes a small tree 3 to 4 m in height; occurring in evergreen forest and on grassy mountain slopes. **Bark:** dark grey; the branches armed with paired slender spines. **Leaves:** ovate to elliptic, 0,6 to 3 × 0,4 to 1,8 cm, paler green below than above, with short soft hairs; apex tapering to broadly so; base rounded; margin entire, fringed with hairs (the specific name refers to this); petiole about 1 to 3 mm long. Stipules triangular, hairy. **Flowers:** small, cream to greenish, axillary, solitary, or in pairs (October to December). **Fruit:** single or 2-lobed, asymmetric, about 1,3 cm long, dark brown to blackish and slightly wrinkled when mature, resembling goat or sheep droppings (February to May).

The resemblance between this species and *C. frangula* is discussed under the latter.

Canthium frangula S. Moore
S.A. no: Pink-fruited canthium
Rhod. no: 1105   Pink-fruited canthium

A shrub or small tree up to 5 m in height; occurring at low altitudes in hot dry woodland and riverine thicket. **Bark:** grey to brown; branches long, lax, with paired straight spines up to 2 cm long. **Leaves:** crowded on dwarf side shoots; ovate, usually up to 3 × 1,7 cm, with or without hairs; apex tapering; base tapering and running into the petiole; margin entire; petiole obscured by the decurrent leaf base, almost absent, or about 2 mm long. Stipules inconspicuous. **Flowers:** very small, whitish to creamy-green, without a scent, in axillary 3-flowered clusters (November to January). **Fruit:** ellipsoidal, 5 to 10 mm long, pink when mature, on slender stalks (February to March).

This species resembles *C. ciliatum,* but that species has its opposite leaves on slender branches, the leaf margins are fringed with hairs and the petiole, although short, is distinct.

Canthium gueinzii Sonder
S.A. no: 705,2   Climbing canthium. Rankklipels
Rhod. no: 1106   Climbing canthium

A shrub, often scrambling, or a small tree occasionally reaching 10 m in height; occurring in grassland, at the margins of, and in evergreen forest. **Bark:** dark to almost black; branches long and trailing, without spines. **Leaves:** ovate to oblong-lanceolate, up to 11 × 5 cm, glossy dark green, without hairs except for rough hairs along the veins only, especially on the under surface; apex attenuate; base lobed; margin entire; petiole about 5 mm long. Stipules small, yellowish, falling early. **Flowers:** cream to pale yellow, sweetly smelling, in dense axillary branched heads, produced in profusion (September to November, also April to June). **Fruit:** single or 2-lobed, 1 × 1,4 cm, in dense clusters, dark when mature; edible but astringent (July to October).

Canthium huillense Hiern   Illust. 303
[*Plectronia wildii* Suesseng.; *Canthium wildii* (Suesseng.) Codd]
S.A. no: 707   Bushveld canthium. Bosveldklipels
Rhod. no: 1108   Common canthium

A shrub or small tree, 3 to 6 m in height; occurring in woodland and thicket, among rocks and on deep Kalahari sand. **Bark:** pale grey-brown, smooth; the branches horizontal, without spines. **Leaves:** ovate, 2 to 7,5 × 1 to 3,8 cm, bright green to dark green, with or without hairs which are sometimes confined to the veins; apex shortly, sometimes obscurely, attenuate; base tapering to rounded; margin entire; petiole about 5 mm long. Stipules hairy. **Flowers:** creamy-yellow, with the corolla lobes tipped with green and only 1 to 2 mm long; the styles are long, slender and conspicuous; strongly but not very pleasantly scented; flowers in small dense axillary branched heads; quite handsome when in profusion (December). **Fruit:** spherical, ovoid or often 2-lobed, slightly asymmetric; about 7 × 10 mm, brownish to black when mature (February to May).

The trees are sometimes evergreen, in which case they are conspicuous in the veld during the winter when all else is brown and bare. The leaves are browsed on by cattle. The wood is hard, compact and takes a good polish.

Canthium inerme (L.f.) Kuntze   Illust. 304
[*C. ventosum* auct. non *Plectronia ventosa* L.; *C. swynnertonii* S. Moore]
S.A. no: 708   Turkey-berry. Gewone bokdrol
Rhod. no: 1109   Turkey-berry

A shrub or tree up to 10 m in height; occasional in patches of evergreen forest, on coastal dunes, in scrub and in high altitude grassland among rocks. **Bark:** grey, smooth; branches upright; branchlets lenticellate, waxy and longitudinally wrinkled and armed with spines. **Leaves:** elliptic, 2,5 to 7,5 × 1 to 3,8 cm, thinly and softly textured, light green above and markedly paler green below, without hairs; apex and base tapering to rounded; margin entire, finely rolled under; petiole 8 to 12 mm long. Stipules small, falling early. **Flowers:** very small, greenish, slightly scented, the throat of the corolla tube bearded, axillary, in fine many-flowered, well-branched heads, about 1,5 to 3 cm in diameter (September to November). **Fruit:** ovoid, about 1,3 cm long, dark brown when mature, slightly wrinkled and resembling goat droppings, as do the fruits of a number of species of *Canthium;* often remaining on the tree into the next flowering season (November to March).

The similarity between this species and *C. suberosum* is discussed under the latter. The leaves are used to treat stomach ailments. The wood is hard, heavy, tough and, having a marbled grain, finishes well. It is suitable for small fancy articles and furniture if the pieces are large enough.

Canthium lactescens Hiern
[*C. randii* S. Moore]
S.A. no: —
Rhod. no: 1110   Gummy canthium

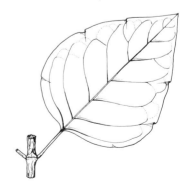

A small unarmed tree up to 5 m in height, with horizontal branches; occurring in deciduous woodland, often protected among rocks. **Bark:** grey to dark grey, smooth, becoming rough with age. **Leaves:** produced on slow-growing lateral spur shoots, one pair of leaves and an internode being added each year; ovate to broadly elliptic, up to 19 × 16 cm, frequently smaller but usually about 10 to 11 cm long, with the smooth feel of soft high quality leather, pale green to dark green, turning yellow in autumn; the main veins are prominent, and the lateral veins arise close together from the base of the leaf; net-veining conspicuous; apex rounded, abruptly and shortly attenuate; base lobed; margin entire; petiole thickset, up to 1,5 cm long, the lower 1 to 2 mm being persistent, becoming woody and giving the branchlets a rough appearance. Stipules large and conspicuous, the short stalks being persistent and woody. **Flowers:** small, whitish to pale yellow, sweetly scented, in lax open-branched axillary sprays, sometimes with a long common stalk, and a more compact head (November to February). **Fruit:** ovoid, asymmetric, 7 to 10 mm long, shortly keeled, sometimes 2-lobed, brown to purple when mature, edible (April to June or later).

The wood is soft, and plentiful light amber gum oozes from the branches when they are broken or damaged.

Canthium locuples (K. Schum.) Codd
S.A. no: 709   Whipstick canthium. Basterkwar
Rhod. no: 1111   Whipstick canthium

A shrub or small unarmed tree up to 5 m in height; occurring in dense bush, scrub and on rocky mountain slopes. **Bark:** pale grey, smooth becoming roughish with age. **Leaves:** ovate to elliptic, up to 5 × 2,5 cm, usually less, shiny green; apex tapering; base tapering and running into the petiole; margin entire; petiole almost absent due to the decurrent leaf base. **Flowers:** very small, greenish, white to creamy-yellow, in small loose axillary branched heads on a common stalk 1 to 1,5 cm long (October to December). **Fruit:** ovoid, 5 × 7 mm, sometimes 2-lobed with a deep cleft between the lobes, black when mature (January to June).

This species resembles *C. obovatum,* but has small flowers, in smaller more lax sprays and the stalks are hairy, the styles long and the fruits smaller.

Canthium martinii Dunkley
S.A. no: —
Rhod. no: 1112   Spurred canthium

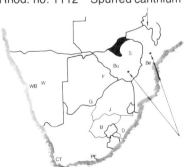

A shrub or a small unarmed tree up to 5 m in height, usually (if not always) many-stemmed; occurring in low altitude woodland and bush, thicket and on rocky hillsides. **Bark:** pale grey, rather smooth; branches long and slender. **Leaves:** broadly elliptic to almost circular, 4 to 8,5 × 1,8 to 5,5 cm, on short rigid peg-like almost spinescent lateral spurs; with or without short soft hairs on both surfaces; apex tapering to rounded; base broadly tapering, rounded to square; margin entire; petiole up to 10 mm long. Stipules falling early. **Flowers:** corolla white, about 6 mm long × 5 mm in diameter,

883

anthers yellow, in dense axillary shortly branched, more or less spherical heads at the ends of short lateral spurs (November to December). **Fruit:** spherical, about 7 mm in diameter, or 2-lobed, 7 × 10 mm, black when mature, on slender stalks (January to March).

Canthium mundianum Cham. & Schlecht.
[*C. gilfillanii* (N. E. Brown) O. B. Miller]
S.A. no: 710   Rock alder. Klipels
Rhod. no: 1113   Rock alder

Shrubs or small armed or unarmed trees up to 5 m in height; occurring from sea level to about 1 500 m, in evergreen forest and at the margins of forest, often associated with termite mounds; also in scrub and on rocky outcrops; a pioneer species in scrub and in mountain grassland. **Bark:** pale grey, smooth. **Leaves:** frequently on dwarf lateral shoots; elliptic, ovate to almost circular, 1,5 to 7 × 1 to 5,5 cm, smaller in the drier localities, light green, greyish-green to deep green with characteristic pockets of hairs in the axils of the prominent veins on the under surface; fine soft hairs are frequently present on both surfaces; apex broadly tapering; base tapering, rounded to shallowly lobed; margin entire, rolled under, inclined to be wavy; petiole 1 to 3 mm long, the base of the petiole and of the stipules persistent forming woody, knobby swellings. **Flowers:** small, about 5 mm in diameter, green to greenish-white or yellowish, faintly scented, in small dense branched heads about 2,5 cm in diameter, on short stalks about 6 mm long (September to November). **Fruit:** ovoid, asymmetric, about 8 × 5 mm, frequently 2-lobed, appearing like 2 fruits apparently stuck together, about 10 × 10 mm, black when mature (November to May, but may remain on the tree for months).
The timber is durable and is said to be untouched by borers or termites; it makes good fencing posts, furniture and implements.

Canthium obovatum Klotzsch
S.A. no: 711   Quar. Kwar
Rhod. no: 1114   Pioneer canthium

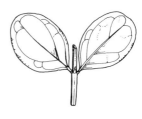

Usually a medium to large unarmed tree up to 17 m in height; occurring in coastal and inland forest, in bush, scrub and on coastal dunes where it is somewhat dwarfed, gnarled and twisted. **Bark:** grey to very dark grey, rather rough; the bole may be fluted in large forest specimens. **Leaves:** obovate to ovate or narrowly so, 1,5 to 5 × 1 to 3 cm, glossy dark green above, paler green below, without hairs; the veins prominent on the under surface, with the lateral veins looping well before the margin and with scattered small glandular pits in their axils; apex broadly tapering to rounded; base tapering;

margin entire; petiole up to 3 mm long. **Flowers:** green to cream, sweetly scented, small, inconspicuous, the corolla lobes narrow, about 6 mm long, curling back, in dense small axillary branched heads, near the ends of the branches (November to April). **Fruit:** ovoid, about 6 mm long, often 2-lobed with a shallow groove between the lobes, black when mature (March to May but may remain on the tree for months).

The wood is yellow or reddish-brown, very hard, heavy, close-grained, tough and slightly aromatic; it provides a useful general purpose timber. The trees are valuable in consolidating sand dunes. This species resembles *C. locuples*.

Canthium pauciflorum (Klotzsch) Kuntze
S.A. no: 712   Kidney-fruited canthium. Waterbokdrol
Rhod. no: 1114/1   Kidney-fruited canthium

 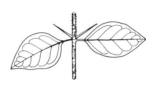

A spreading shrub, often scrambling, or a small tree up to 6 m in height; occurring at high altitudes in evergreen forest, wooded kloofs and in moist places. **Bark:** dark brown, rather smooth; the young branches may be thick, short and knobby, and may have paired straight spines. **Leaves:** opposite, and may be crowded on short branchlets; ovate, 1,3 to 5 × 0,7 to 2,8 cm but usually about 2,5 × 1,5 cm, bluish-green, without hairs; apex broadly tapering to rounded, occasionally notched; base tapering to rounded; margin entire, sometimes wavy particularly near the apex; petiole 2 to 5 mm long. **Flowers:** greenish-cream, inconspicuous, about 5 mm long and 5 mm in diameter, axillary, in few-flowered branched heads of 2 to 4, (sometimes solitary by abortion), on stalks about 5 mm long (October to January). **Fruit:** kidney-shaped, up to 1,7 cm long, or 2-lobed, black when mature (March to September).

Canthium pseudoverticillatum S. Moore
S.A. no: —
Rhod. no: 1115   Manica spurred canthium

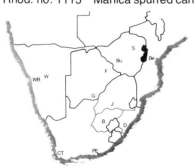 

A shrub or small unarmed tree up to 4 m in height; occurring in riverine forest, often among rocks. **Bark:** grey, fairly smooth. **Leaves:** clustered on short lateral spurs or paired on very abbreviated knobby branchlets; lanceolate to narrowly ovate, 1,5 to 6 × 0,7 to 2,2 cm, without hairs except for pockets in the axils of the veins on the under surface; apex attenuate; base tapering; margin entire;

885

petiole 1 to 3 mm long. **Flowers:** small, greenish-white to yellowish, in few-flowered axillary small branched heads, the common stalk not more than 5 mm long (November to December). **Fruit:** ovoid, 4 to 6 mm long, in very small clusters (February to April).

Canthium setiflorum Hiern
S.A. no: 712,1   Rough-leaved rock alder. Skurweklipels
Rhod. no: 1116   Bristly canthium

A shrub or small tree, 2 to 5 m in height; occurring on deep sand, in riverine fringe forest, often among rocks, or in dune forest. **Bark:** grey, smooth; branches stiff but not spiny, roughly hairy, lenticellate. **Leaves:** on dwarf, knobby lateral branches; small, ovate, 1,2 to 4,5 × 0,5 to 1,2 cm, with or without rough hairs; apex and base broadly tapering to rounded; margin entire; petiole 1 to 2 mm long. Stipules short and broad, with rough hairs. **Flowers:** pale yellow, 2 to 3 mm long, with the calyx roughly hairy (the specific name refers to this), in 5- to 7-flowered branched heads (January to April). **Fruit:** ovoid, about 6 mm long, single or 2-lobed, yellow, brown to blackish when mature (March to December).

Canthium spinosum (Klotzsch) Kuntze
S.A. no: 713   Coastal canthium. Doringklipels
Rhod. no: —

A shrub to medium sized tree up to 10 m in height; occurring in coastal forest and bush often on rocky hill slopes. **Bark:** pale grey; branches upright with hard rigid branchlets and pale straight spines up to 2,5 cm long. **Leaves:** clustered on knobby dwarf lateral shoots which arise above the spines; on young strongly growing shoots these dwarf branchlets are absent and the leaves are opposite, each pair arising immediately below a pair of spines; leaves ovate, 1,5 to 5 × 0,7 to 2,5 cm, but usually 3 to 5 × 1,5 to 2,5 cm, with fine soft hairs when young losing most of these by maturity, paler green below than above; apex broadly tapering; base tapering; margin entire; petiole 1 to 2 mm long. **Flowers:** greenish-white, about 5 mm in diameter, inconspicuous, axillary, in short branched heads, 1 to 2 cm in diameter (May to September). **Fruit:** ovoid, sometimes asymmetric, or shallowly 2-lobed, about 1,3 × 1 cm, bluish-black when mature, edible and pleasantly flavoured (September to November).

Canthium suberosum Codd
S.A. no: 714   Corky-bark canthium. Kurkbokdrol

Rhod. no: —

A shrub or small tree, 3 to 6 m in height; occurring in kloofs, along dry watercourses and on rocky wooded hillsides. **Bark:** grey, corky, powdery on the branchlets; without spines. **Leaves:** elliptic to oblanceolate, 3,5 to 7 × 1,4 to 3,5 cm, leathery, bluish-green; with or without rather sparse short soft hairs; apex rounded; base tapering; margin entire; petiole 2 to 5 mm long. Stipules fall early. **Flowers:** small, creamy-green, about 5 mm in diameter, in shortly stalked, few-flowered axillary heads (September to November). **Fruit:** ovoid to almost spherical, often 2- or even 3-lobed, about 10 mm long, with a circular scar round the apex, black when mature, on slender stalks (December to February).

This species resembles *C. inerme*, but the latter has spinescent branchlets, which are without hairs, waxy and longitudinally wrinkled, not powdery or corky, and the bark on the main trunk never becomes corky; also its leaves are thinly and softly textured, and the flowers are usually in well-branched many-flowered heads.

Canthium venosum (Oliver) Hiern
S.A. no: —
Rhod. no: 1117   Raisin-fruited canthium

An unarmed shrub with a strong tendency to scramble, a liane or a small tree up to 5 m in height; occurring in evergreen forest, at the margins of forest and along streams. **Bark:** greyish to brownish. **Leaves:** elliptic, up to 11 × 5,5 cm, leathery, glossy dark green; without hairs, except for appressed hairs along the veins; apex attenuate; base square to shallowly lobed; margin entire, wavy; petiole 4 to 8 mm long. Stipules broadly based, finely tapering, falling early. **Flowers:** white, small, in very dense almost spherical axillary heads on short common stalks (February to October). **Fruit:** single or 2-lobed, about 10 mm in diameter, blackish-green to brown when mature, raisin-like (August to June).

Canthium vulgare (K. Schum.) Bullock
S.A. no: —
Rhod. no: 1118   Giant canthium

A medium to large unarmed tree up to 30 m in height; occasional in evergreen forest. **Bark:** brown to pale grey, rather rough, longitudinally fissured; the bole fluted to buttressed; branchlets rather sickle-shaped. **Leaves:** ovate to oblong-elliptic, up to 15 × 6 cm, but usually about 7 to 9 × 3 to 3,5 cm, leathery, shiny dark green, without hairs, the petiole and midrib may be orange, especially below; apex shortly attenuate; base broadly tapering; margin entire, wavy; petiole 5 to 10 mm long.

887

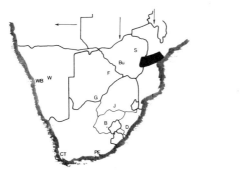

Flowers: small, greenish-white to yellowish, in axillary branched heads, the common stalk 1 to 1,5 cm long (March to April). **Fruit:** spherical, about 10 mm in diameter, black when mature (May to July).

32. PLECTRONIELLA Robyns

Differs from *Canthium* in its bell-shaped corolla and 3-lobed sub-spherical stigmas; *Canthium* has a tubular or urn-shaped corolla and the stigmas are usually 2-lobed.

Plectroniella armata (K. Schum.) Robyns
S.A. no: 715   Bastard turkey-berry. Basterbokdrol
Rhod. no: —

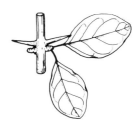

A shrub or small tree up to 8 m in height; occurring from mopane woodland and rocky ridges to mountain slopes. **Bark:** brown, rather smooth; branches armed with straight opposite spines up to 4 cm long. **Leaves:** opposite or fascicled on dwarf, knobby side shoots arising below the spines, simple, obovate, 2 to 5 × 1,5 to 3 cm, shiny dark green above, paler green below, usually without hairs but occasionally with short soft hairs especially on the under surface; apex very broadly tapering to rounded; base broadly tapering; margin entire; petiole slender, up to 1,3 cm long. **Flowers:** white, the corolla lobes about 4 mm long, curling backwards over the short tube, in dense branched axillary heads about 4 cm in diameter on slender stalks, or peduncles, up to 4 cm long; sweetly scented (November to February). **Fruit:** ovoid, fleshy, asymmetric, about 1,2 × 0,8 cm, becoming yellow, orange and finally red when mature, in clusters (February to April).

33. DINOCANTHIUM Bremek

Dinocanthium hystrix Bremek.
S.A. no: 714,3   Porcupine bush. Ystervarkbos
Rhod. no: —

A shrub or small tree up to 4 m in height; occurring at low altitudes in forest and bush. **Bark:** grey, rather smooth; branches opposite, at right angles to the main stem and each pair being set at right angles to the next; branchlets grey, rigid, short, almost spinescent to spiny. **Leaves:** opposite or fascicled on dwarf knobby side branches; simple, obovate, 0,8 to 2,5 × 0,5 to 1,3 cm; apex rounded;

 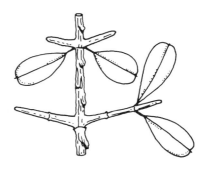

base tapering; margin entire; petiole about 1 mm long. Stipules hairy, falling early. **Flowers:** very small, greenish to greenish-white, with the corolla lobes about 1 to 1,5 mm long, axillary, solitary or fascicled in groups of 2 to 3 on the dwarf branchlets. Bisexual; all floral parts in fours; calyx about equal to the corolla tube in length, with 4 triangular lobes; corolla more or less spherical, densely bearded in the throat, with 4 finely pointed lobes; stamens fixed in the throat of the tube; ovary 2-chambered (December to April). **Fruit:** spherical, fleshy, about 3 to 4 mm in diameter, reddish to brown when mature (March to July).

34. CRATERISPERMUM Benth.

Craterispermum schweinfurthii Hiern

[*C. laurinum* auct. non (Poir.) Benth.]
S.A. no: —
Rhod. no: 1120   Porridge-stick

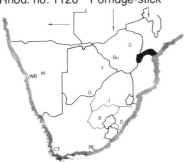 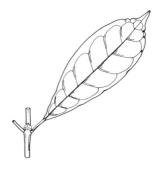

A large shrub to medium sized tree up to 15 m in height; occurring in evergreen forest, riverine fringes and forested ravines. **Bark:** grey-brown, finely fissured and slightly corky. **Leaves:** opposite, simple, oblanceolate to obovate, up to 12,5 × 4,5 cm, leathery, glossy dark green to rather pale green above, slightly paler below; the midrib pale and prominent and net-veining conspicuous on the under surface; apex finally abruptly and narrowly attenuate; base tapering; margin entire, rolled under; petiole about 1 to 1,5 cm long. Stipules joined, persistent. **Flowers:** small, white, about 3 to 4 mm in diameter, inconspicuous, on stalks about 10 mm long, in few-flowered axillary clusters, or fascicles, occasionally solitary. Bisexual; all floral parts in fives; calyx top-shaped; corolla tube short, funnel-shaped, with a bearded throat, and ovate spreading lobes; stamens inserted in the throat of the corolla; ovary 2-chambered (October). **Fruit:** pear-shaped, 6 to 10 mm long, tapering to a blunt tip, purplish-black when mature (December).

35. PACHYSTIGMA Hochst.

Pachystigma macrocalyx (Sonder) Robyns

[*P. bowkeri* Robyns]
S.A. no: 714,1   Crowned false medlar. Bosmispel
Rhod. no: —

A dwarf shrub or a tree up to 13 m in height; occurring in open woodland, bush, on mountain slopes, at the margins of evergreen forest, along streams and also in dry rocky areas, on stony hillsides. **Bark:**   **889**

light grey; the tips of the branchlets often spinescent. **Leaves:** opposite, simple, ovate to elliptic, 3,5 to 14 × 2,5 to 8 cm, but usually about 8 to 11 × 3 to 6 cm, apex broadly tapering to attenuate; base tapering to rounded, often asymmetric; margin entire; petiole up to 10 mm long. Stipules small. The leaves are larger with sparser hairs in the forest specimens and smaller and more densely hairy when growing among rocks in dry areas as a dwarf shrub; both forms often occur in the same locality. **Flowers:** greenish-yellow, 1 to 1,5 cm in diameter, the corolla lobes about 3 mm long, falling early, the flower then dominated by the comparatively large, persistent, hairy calyx lobes, 5 mm long (the specific name refers to these); flowers shortly stalked, in few-flowered to dense axillary clusters. Bisexual; all floral parts in fives; calyx divided almost to the base, with the lobes linear-lanceolate and leaf-like; corolla with a short tube and the 5 lobes curving back; stamens fixed in the mouth of the tube; ovary 4- to 5-chambered; the stigmas thick (November to December). **Fruit:** ovoid, fleshy, about 2 cm long, clearly ridged longitudinally by 3 to 5 lobes, yellow-orange when mature, crowned by the enlarged, now strap-like calyx lobes about 10 mm long; the fruits are said to be edible (January to February).

36. ANCYLANTHOS Desf.

Ancylanthos monteiroi Oliver
S.A. no: 714,2   Dune false medlar. Duinemispel
Rhod. no: —

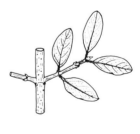

A sprawling shrub or small tree, 3 to 5 m in height; occurring in coastal and dune forest. **Bark:** grey-brown, rather pale, flaking; all the parts covered with long hairs. **Leaves:** opposite or fascicled on dwarf, almost spinescent lateral branches; simple, ovate, up to 3 × 2 cm, but usually smaller, with soft hairs on both surfaces, leathery, rather paler below than above; apex broadly tapering to rounded; base rounded; margin entire; petiole 2 to 3 mm long, softly hairy. Stipules small. **Flowers:** cream or yellowish-green, velvety on the outside, faintly scented, axillary, solitary or in few-flowered groups; corolla with the tube about 2 cm long and the narrow finely pointed lobes 5 to 10 mm long. Bisexual; all floral parts in fives; calyx deeply divided; corolla tube slightly curved; stamens fixed in the throat of the tube; ovary 5-chambered (September to December). **Fruit:** ovoid to almost spherical, fleshy, 1,5 × 1,2 cm, velvety, reddish when mature, crowned with the persistent calyx lobes (November onwards, the old hard fruits sometimes persisting for some time).

37. GUETTARDA L.

Guettarda speciosa L.
S.A. no: Beach false medlar. Strandmispel
Rhod. no:—

A soft wooded shrub or small tree up to 5 m in height; occurring in coastal scrub, often in the spray zone. **Bark:** brown; the branches brittle, with conspicuous lenticels and leaf scars. **Leaves:** opposite, simple, elliptic, up to 17 × 13 cm, the upper surface without hairs or very finely hairy, the lower surface· velvety with rather long golden hairs along the veins; apex rounded; base broadly tapering; margin entire, but so curved under that the whole leaf becomes boat-shaped and the margins may almost touch; petiole about 2 cm long, velvety. Stipules broadly ovate, falling early. **Flowers:** white; corolla with the tube densely velvety, 2 to 3 cm long, and lobes almost 10 mm long; flower stalks up to 4 to 5 cm long; in dense axillary heads, or cymes. Bisexual; floral parts in fours to nines; calyx bell-shaped or almost spherical or truncate; corolla 4- to 9-lobed with a cylindric, rather slender tube which may be thinly bearded at the throat; stamens as many as the corolla lobes, inserted in the tube, without filaments (May to September). **Fruit:** almost spherical, fleshy, about 1,5 cm in diameter, green streaked and spotted with white, becoming reddish-brown when mature (July to December).

38. COFFEA L.

Shrubs or small trees, branches opposite, without hairs, or with pockets of hairs in the axils of the veins. **Leaves:** opposite, simple. Stipules ovate to lanceolate. **Flowers:** solitary or clustered, axillary or terminal, bracteolate. Bisexual; floral parts in fives to eights; calyx tube short; corolla funnel-shaped, 5- to 7-lobed, without hairs at the throat; stamens inserted in the mouth of the corolla, filaments very short; ovary 2-chambered. **Fruit:** ellipsoidal to almost spherical, fleshy.

Key to the tree species of *Coffea:*
1 Petiole of mature leaflets 3 to 10 mm long .... **C. zanguebariae**
  Petiole of mature leaflets up to 3 mm long 2
2 Occurring in low altitude woodland .... **C. racemosa**
  Occurring in evergreen forest .... **C. ligustroides**

Coffea ligustroides S. Moore
S.A. no: —
Rhod. no: 1121   Small-leaved wild coffee

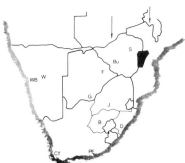

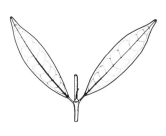

891

RUBIACEAE

A shrub or small tree up to 4 m in height; occurring in forested ravines and as a constituent of the under-storey in evergreen forest. **Bark:** light grey. **Leaves:** elliptic to narrowly ovate, up to 6,5 × 2,5 cm, rather leathery, glossy deep green; the midrib reddish on the under surface; the young leaves rather sticky; apex and base tapering; margin entire, wavy; petiole up to 3 mm long. Stipules slender, about 4 mm long, persisting for some time. **Flowers:** creamy-white, about 1 to 1,5 cm in diameter, with the corolla lobes slender; axillary, solitary, or in few-flowered clusters (October to December). **Fruit:** ovoid, about 9 × 6 mm, waxy, orange when mature (May to August).

Coffea racemosa Lour.
S.A. no: 715,1   Wild coffee. Inheemse koffie
Rhod. no: 1122   Wild coffee

A shrub or rather slender spindly tree up to 5 m in height; occurring at low altitudes in hot dry woodland, on rocky outcrops, along rivers and in dune forest. **Bark:** grey-brown, thinly longitudinally fissured. **Leaves:** elliptic, up to 9 × 4 cm, but usually about 3 to 4 × 1 to 1,5 cm, thinly leathery, dark green; apex and base tapering; margin entire, wavy; petiole 1 to 3 mm long. Stipules very short and broad-based, falling early. **Flowers:** white to pink, up to 2 cm in diameter, with a slender corolla tube about 1,5 cm long and 6 to 8 spreading lobes; axillary, solitary or in few-flowered short racemes, often when the tree is leafless (August to November). **Fruit:** almost spherical, up to 1,4 × 1 cm, purplish when mature (October to January).

The trees are very hardy and resistant to disease. They have been cultivated for many years in Moçambique and the fruits exported, for the seeds, when ground, produce a good and distinctively-flavoured coffee. This is a protected plant in South Africa.

Coffea zanguebariae Lour.
S.A. no: —
Rhod. no: 1123   Large-leaved wild coffee

A small tree up to 5 m in height; occurring in evergreen forest. **Bark:** whitish to brownish, with shallow longitudinal fissures. **Leaves:** elliptic to ovate, up to 14 × 6 cm, thinly textured, glossy green, with pockets of hairs in the axils of the veins on the under surface; apex attenuate; base broadly tapering; margin entire, sometimes wavy; petiole 3 to 10 mm long. Stipules present. **Flowers:** white, about 2,4 cm in diameter, with the corolla tube about 10 mm long, and 6- to 8-lobed; axillary, solitary or in groups of 2 to 3 (June to August). **Fruit:** ovoid, fleshy, 1,4 × 1 cm, green with dull red stripes, red when mature (August to September).

39. PAVETTA L.

Usually shrubs, occasionally small trees. **Leaves:** opposite, whorled or fascicled, simple, often with bacterial nodules. Stipulate. **Flowers:** in axillary or terminal heads, branched and variable in structure. Bisexual; floral parts in fours, very rarely fives; calyx tube short; corolla with a long slender tube and rather short, elliptic-lanceolate lobes sometimes with a bearded throat; stamens fixed in the mouth of the tube; ovary 2-chambered; the styles long and slender, with club-shaped stigmas protruding well beyond the mouths of the flowers, producing the characteristic pin-cushion appearance of this inflorescence. **Fruit:** ovoid to spherical, fleshy.

Key to the tree species of *Pavetta:*

1 Leaves usually less than 6 cm long 2
  Leaves usually more than 6 cm long 6
2 Leaves conspicuously narrow, 3,5 to 11 × 0,5 to 2 cm 3
  Leaves not conspicuously narrow, comparatively broader than the above species 4
3 Growing in coastal and inland evergreen forest .... **P. lanceolata**
  Growing in drier types of woodland, on stony hillsides or rocky outcrops .... **P. zeyheri**
4 Growing inland, in open woodland, among rocks and on granite koppies ... **P. gardeniifolia**
  Growing in coastal belt in forest, dune forest and dune bush 5
5 Leaves leathery, with groups of hairs in axils of veins on under surface; widespread along coast
    from eastern Cape to Moçambique .... **P. revoluta**
  Leaves thinly leathery, without groups of hairs; confined to extreme north-east of Zululand .....
  .... **P. gerstneri**
6 Bark corky, especially on the branches .... **P. edentula**
  Bark not corky 7
7 Leaves usually without hairs and shiny green 8
  Leaves with hairs 9
8 In the east of Rhodesia and adjacent Moçambique only .... **P. umtalensis**
  In eastern Cape and Natal only .... **P. natalensis**
9 Leaves softly velvety .... **P. eylesii**
  Leaves harshly, roughly hairy above, velvety below 10
10 Leaves harshly hairy above, densely velvety below .... **P. schumanniana**
  Leaves harshly hairy above, although sometimes with only sparse hairs, the under surface always
    without hairs 11
11 Calyx and ovary hairy .... **P. johnstonii**
  Calyx and ovary without hairs .... **P. angolensis**

Pavetta angolensis Hiern

[*P. comostyla* S. Moore]
S.A. no: —
Rhod. no: 1124   Rare pavetta

A shrub or small tree usually about 3 m in, height, occasionally reaching 7 m; occurring in moist evergreen forest. **Bark:** brownish-grey. **Leaves:** elliptic, up to 20 × 8 cm, but usually about 9 × 5 cm, thinly textured, harshly hairy above, sometimes with only sparse hairs, always without hairs on the under surface; apex abruptly attenuate; base tapering; margin entire; petiole up to 1,5 cm long.

893

Flowers: white, with a long slender corolla tube and the calyx and ovary without hairs; terminal, in handsome panicles (January). **Fruit:** almost spherical, about 10 mm in diameter, in terminal clusters, black when mature (July to October).

This species is closely related to *P. johnstonii* which has the calyx and ovary covered with hairs.

Pavetta edentula Sonder

S.A. no: 717   Large-leaved bride's bush. Grootblaarbruidsbos
Rhod. no: —

A shrub or small tree usually 3 to 4 m in height, occasionally reaching 5 m; occurring on steep rocky hillsides. **Bark:** creamy-brown to grey with distinctive rather rounded corky segments; branchlets also corky, thick and knobby. **Leaves:** lanceolate, up to 20 × 8 cm, bright green, almost fleshy, without hairs; the midrib very prominent below; the leaves characteristically drooping; apex tapering to rounded; base tapering; margin entire; petiole stout, up to 2,5 cm long. **Flowers:** white, up to 2 × 1 to 1,3 cm, sweetly scented, in rather lax, long stalked heads about 9 cm in diameter (October to January, or later). **Fruit:** almost spherical, about 7 to 9 mm in diameter, blue-black when mature, in rather sparse, long branched clusters (January to April).

Pavetta eylesii S. Moore

S.A. no: 717,1   Broad-leaved bride's bush. Breëblaarbruidsbos
Rhod. no: 1126   Flaky-bark pavetta

A shrub or small tree, 3 to 6 m in height; occurring in mixed sandveld woodland, on rocky koppies and stony hills. **Bark:** light brown, flaking in narrow strips. **Leaves:** obovate, up to 16 × 9 cm, but usually smaller, dark green above, paler green below, the upper surface with or without soft hairs, and the under surface always velvety; veining obscure; usually with conspicuous dark bacterial nodules; apex broadly tapering, usually finally abruptly attenuate; base tapering; margin entire; petiole about 1 to 1,5 cm long. **Flowers:** white, rather small, with very fine styles; in dense axillary heads up to 9 cm in diameter (November to December). **Fruit:** almost spherical, 8 to 10 mm in diameter, purplish-black when mature (February to June).

Pavetta gardeniifolia Hochst. ex A. Rich.   Illust. 305

[*P. assimilis* Sonder; *P. rhodesiaca* Bremek.]
S.A. no: 716 and 716,1   Common bride's bush. Gewone bruidsbos
894   Rhod. no: 1125   Common pavetta

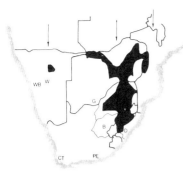

A shrub or small tree up to 4 m in height; occurring among rocks, on granite koppies and in open woodland. **Bark:** grey, smooth or with fine fissures. **Leaves:** opposite or often fascicled on dwarf lateral branchlets, obovate, 2,5 to 6 × 1,5 to 4 cm, shiny light green, harshly hairy on both surfaces, or sometimes without hairs; usually with dark bacterial nodules; apex broadly tapering to rounded; base tapering; margin entire; petiole 1 to 3 mm long. **Flowers:** white to cream about 10 mm long and 10 mm in diameter, heavily scented; the calyx finely toothed; in compact axillary clusters (November to January). **Fruit:** almost spherical, about 5 mm in diameter, black when mature, in dense clusters (February to May).

Pavetta gerstneri Bremek.
S.A. no: 717,3   Zulu bride's bush. Zoeloebruidsbos
Rhod. no: —

A small tree up to 5 m in height; occurring in coastal and dune forest. **Bark:** grey. **Leaves:** elliptic to obovate, 2 to 9 × 1 to 4 cm, but usually about 2 to 5 cm long, thinly leathery, without hairs; apex broadly tapering, sometimes abruptly and shortly attenuate; base tapering; margin entire, rolled under; petiole about 10 mm long. **Flowers:** white, slender, the corolla tube about 10 mm long, the petal lobes spreading, together about 6 mm in diameter, the long slender conspicuous style and stigma protruding well beyond the mouth of the corolla tube, the sepals short and broad; in compact axillary branched heads, 2 to 4 cm in diameter, near the tips of the branches (November to December). **Fruit:** ovoid, about 10 mm long, dark blackish when mature (July).
This species resembles *P. delagoensis* Bremek., but the latter is a small shrub and the sepals are long and narrow.

Pavetta johnstonii Bremek.
[*P. inyangensis* Bremek.]
S.A. no: –
Rhod. no: 1129   Hairy manica pavetta

A shrub or small tree usually about 3 m in height, occasionally taller; occurring in moist evergreen forest.
This species closely resembles *P. angolensis*, but has the calyx and ovary covered with hairs.

895

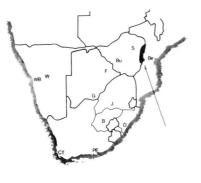

Pavetta kotzei Bremek.

Eve Palmer includes this species, but material of tree size does not appear to have been collected and it is felt likely that this will prove to be conspecific with *P. galpinii* Bremek., which is always a shrub.

Pavetta lanceolata Ecklon
[*P. inandensis* Bremek.; *P. tristis* Bremek.]
S.A. no: 718   Forest bride's bush. Bosbruidsbos
Rhod. no: —

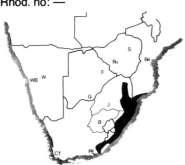

A shrub or small tree up to 7 m in height; occurring in coastal and inland evergreen forest. **Bark:** light brown to grey, smooth becoming finely longitudinally fissured with age. **Leaves:** lanceolate, 3,5 to 11 × 0,5 to 2 cm, but usually 4 to 6 × 1 to 1,5 cm, glossy dark green above, dull green below, with pockets of hairs in the axils of the veins on the under surface; with or without scattered dark bacterial nodules; apex and base tapering; margin entire; petiole 3 to 10 mm long. **Flowers:** white, with conspicuously long styles; axillary and terminal, in dense branched heads 3 to 5 cm in diameter (November to January). **Fruit:** almost spherical, about 8 mm in diameter, black when mature, in dense clusters (March to August).

Pavetta natalensis Sonder
S.A. no: 719   Natal bride's bush. Natalbruidsbos
Rhod. no: —

896

A shrub or small tree, 3 to 4 m in height; occurring as a constituent of the under-storey in evergreen forest. **Bark:** light brown to grey. **Leaves:** elliptic, 5 to 14 × 2 to 4 cm, shiny green, without hairs; usually with conspicuous bacterial nodules; apex tapering to attenuate; base narrowly tapering; margin entire; petiole up to 1,6 cm long. **Flowers:** white, tubular, up to 2 cm long, with the corolla lobes each about 10 × 3 mm; in loose axillary heads, 6 to 11 cm in diameter on stalks up to 10 cm long (December to February). **Fruit:** spherical, about 5 mm in diameter, black when mature; young fruit crowned with the remains of the long slender calyx lobes, but these shrivel and are not conspicuous in the mature fruit (January to August).

Pavetta revoluta Hochst.
S.A. no: 720   Dune bride's bush. Duinebruidsbos
Rhod. no: —

A shrub or small tree up to 6 m in height; occurring in forest and dune bush. **Bark:** greyish-white to light brown, softly flaking making the stems slightly rough. **Leaves:** elliptic to obovate, 2,5 to 8 × 1,8 to 4 cm, glossy green above, dull green below, leathery, with pockets of hairs in the axils of the veins on the under surface; apex broadly tapering to rounded; base tapering; margin entire, tightly rolled under (the specific name refers to this); petiole 5 to 10 mm long. **Flowers:** white, up to 2 cm long and 1,5 cm in diameter; axillary or terminal, in dense heads, 4 to 8 cm in diameter (November to January). **Fruit:** spherical, about 10 mm in diameter, black when mature, with the remains of the old calyx lobes forming 4 small apical projections (January to March, or on to June or July).

Pavetta schumanniana F. Hoffm. ex. K. Schum.
S.A. no: 721   Poison bride's bush. Gifbruidsbos
Rhod. no: 1130   Poison pavetta

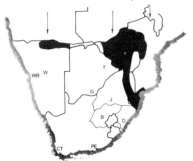
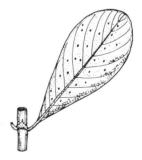

A shrub or small tree up to 7 m in height; occurring over a wide range of altitudes, in open woodland, often among rocks and on termite mounds. **Bark:** light grey to dark brown, furrowed. **Leaves:** opposite, in whorls of 3, or fascicled at the ends of the branches; obovate, 7 to 15 × 2,5 to 7,5 cm, harshly hairy above, densely but softly hairy below where net-veining is conspicuous; irregularly dotted with dark bacterial nodules; apex broadly tapering to rounded, sometimes abruptly attenuate; base tapering; margin entire; petiole up to 1,5 cm long. **Flowers:** white, with a strong sweet scent, in dense axillary heads on long stalks up to 2 cm in length; bracts are present at the base (November to January). **Fruit:** spherical, about 8 mm in diameter, black when mature, in dense clusters (April to June).

RUBIACEAE

The leaves are poisonous, causing *gousiekte* in stock and resulting in heart failure but the toxic principle has not been isolated. The roots are said to be used as a remedy for colds.

Pavetta umtalensis Bremek.
S.A. no: —
Rhod. no: 1131   Shiny manica pavetta

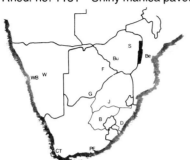

A small tree up to 7 m in height; occurring in mountain evergreen forest. **Bark:** whitish to pale grey, smooth or finely cracked into square segments, not corky. **Leaves:** elliptic, 3,5 to 14 × 1 to 4 cm, rather thinly textured, glossy dark green on both surfaces, without hairs; apex attenuate, sometimes forming a narrow drip-tip; base tapering; margin entire; petiole up to 1,5 cm long. **Flowers:** greenish-white to white, fragrant, attractive, up to 1,6 cm in diameter, in axillary or terminal branched heads (October to December). **Fruit:** spherical, about 10 mm in diameter, black when mature (April to June).

Pavetta zeyheri Sonder
S.A. no: 722   Small-leaved bride's bush. Fynblaarbruidsbos
Rhod. no: —

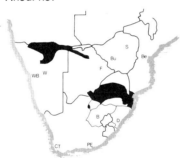

A shrub or small tree up to 3 m in height; occurring in dry woodland, on stony hillsides and rocky ridges. **Bark:** grey, rough; branches smooth. **Leaves:** narrowly lanceolate, 1,5 to 7,5 × 0,5 to 1,2 cm, leathery, dark green, without hairs; bacterial nodules distinct; apex tapering; base narrowly tapering and running into the petiole; margin entire; petiole almost obscured by the decurrent leaf base. **Flowers:** white, faintly scented, slender, about 1 cm long × 1,2 cm in diameter, in dense axillary branched heads (October to January). **Fruit:** spherical, 7 to 9 mm in diameter, black when mature, crowned with the small spike-like remains of the calyx lobes (January to March but may remain for several months).

40. IXORA L.

Ixora narcissodora K. Schum.
[*I. chaseii* Bullock]
S.A. no: —
Rhod. no: 1132   Red trumpets

A small lightly foliaged tree up to 5 m in height; occurring in low altitude high rainfall areas, along river banks and between rocks. **Bark:** brown. **Leaves:** opposite, simple, narrowly elliptic to lanceolate, up to 12 × 3,5 cm, leathery, glossy dark green; apex and base tapering; margin entire, often wavy; petiole 5 to 10 mm long. **Flowers:** pink to brick red, 1,5 cm in diameter, sweetly scented, the corolla 4-lobed with the tube remarkably long and slender, up to 8 cm in length, the tube and the backs of the corolla lobes pink to reddish, the inner surface of the lobes white to cream; in lax terminal, rarely axillary, bracteolate cymes. Bisexual; floral parts in fours, rarely fives; calyx tube short; corolla tube slender, lobes spreading, the throat usually without hairs; stamens attached in the throat or in the mouth of the tube (May to December). **Fruit:** slightly 2-lobed, each lobe pear-shaped, about 7 × 10 mm, reddish-brown to dark brown when mature (July to March).

41. PSYCHOTRIA L.

Shrubs and trees. **Leaves:** opposite or sometimes whorled, simple. Stipules undivided, toothed or cleft. **Flowers:** in terminal or axillary heads, or panicles. Bisexual; floral parts in fives to sixes; calyx small, with a cup-shaped tube; corolla funnel-shaped or cylindric with 5 lobes, the throat usually bearded; stamens equal the corolla lobes in number and are attached in the throat of the tube; ovary 2-chambered. **Fruit:** almost spherical or ovoid, fleshy, with a conspicuous apical ring scar.

Key to the tree species of *Psychotria:*

1 Leaves with 10 to 16 pairs of veins; fruits strongly ribbed; flowers very small, 1 to 2 mm in diameter
.... **P. zombamontana**
   Leaves with up to 10 pairs of veins; fruits smooth; flowers 4 to 6 mm in diameter 2
2 Leaves with 4 to 6 pairs of veins; a shrub or small tree rarely more than 7 m in height .. **P. capensis**
   Leaves with 7 to 10 pairs of veins; usually a medium to large tree up to 20 m in height or more
.... **P. mahonii**

Psychotria capensis (Ecklon) Vatke   Illust. 307
[*Grumilea capensis* (Ecklon) Sonder]
S.A. no: 723   Cream psychotria. Lemoenbos
Rhod. no: 1137   Cream psychotria

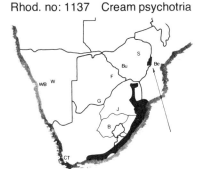 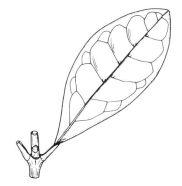

A shrub or small tree up to 7 m in height, only rarely reaching 9 m; occurring from sea level to about 1 500 m, in evergreen forest, riverine fringes, scrub and dune bush. **Bark:** pale grey to creamy brown. **Leaves:** elliptic to obovate, 7 to 15 × 1,5 to 6 cm, leathery, glossy light green to dark green, faintly dotted with bacterial nodules; the midrib and the 4 to 6 pairs of lateral veins pale and conspicuous, with pockets of hairs in their axils on the under surface; apex tapering to almost rounded; base tapering; margin entire, slightly rolled under; petiole up to 1,5 cm long. Stipules fall early. **Flowers:** rich cream or yellow, about 4 to 5 mm in diameter, the throat of the tube densely hairy, in terminal branched heads, about 8 cm in diameter (September to January). **Fruit:** ovoid, about 7 mm long, red when mature, aging to blackish, in dense, rather flat-topped clusters about 10 cm in diameter (April to August).

The wood is yellow to brownish, dense, hard, tough and close-grained; it is a useful general-purpose timber.

Psychotria mahonii C. H. Wright

[*P. megistosticta* (S. Moore) Petit var. *punicea* (S. Moore) Petit; *Grumilea punicea* S. Moore]
S.A. no: —
Rhod. no: 1139   Large psychotria

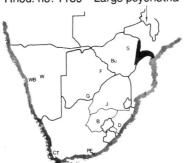

May be small, but usually a medium to large tree, 5 to 20 m in height, usually a constituent of the under-storey in evergreen forest, forested ravines and riverine fringes; also occurring in open grassland, often on termite mounds. **Bark:** grey, rather smooth. **Leaves:** elliptic to obovate, up to 17 × 7 cm, leathery, irregularly dotted with bacterial nodules; the 7 to 10 pairs of lateral veins with pockets of hairs on the under surface; apex and base tapering; margin entire, rolled under; petiole up to 1,5 cm long. Stipules fall early. **Flowers:** greenish-yellow, cream to white, about 5 mm in diameter, faintly scented, with the throat of the corolla tube bearded; in terminal heads about 6 cm in diameter, on a slender stalk up to 6 cm long (December to February). **Fruit:** ovoid, about 5 to 6 mm long, yellow and finally red when mature (March to April).

Psychotria zombamontana (Kuntze) Petit

[*Grumilea kirkii* Hiern]
S.A. no: 723,1   Mountain psychotria. Berglemoenbos
Rhod. no: 1140   Rib-fruited psychotria

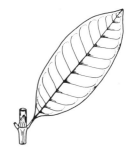

A shrub or small tree, 4 to 8 m in height, rarely reaching 10 m; occurring as a constituent ot the under-storey in closed evergreen forest. **Bark:** grey to brown, rather smooth. **Leaves:** elliptic to oblanceolate, 7,5 to 15 × 1,3 to 6 cm, leathery, shiny dark green, dotted with bacterial nodules; the 10 to 16 pairs of lateral veins without pockets of hairs on the under surface; apex tapering, often

900

slightly attenuate; base tapering; margin entire, slightly rolled under; petiole up to 1,5 cm long. Stipules large, conspicuous, falling early. **Flowers:** greenish-white, 1 to 2 mm in diameter, in rather lax, slender branched terminal heads, 1 to 3 cm long (November to March). **Fruit:** ovoid, about 4 to 5 mm long, pink, yellow-orange to red when mature, conspicuously vertically ribbed (April to October).

42. LASIANTHUS Jack

Lasianthus kilimandscharicus K. Schum.
S.A. no: —
Rhod. no: 1142   Sky-berry

A shrub or small tree up to 7 m in height with drooping branches; occurring in evergreen forest, forested ravines and riverine fringes. **Bark:** light brown, smooth. **Leaves:** opposite or whorled, simple, elliptic, 7 to 14 × 2 to 4 cm, shiny dark green, without hairs on the upper surface, but may be finely hairy below, especially along the veins; apex attenuate; base tapering; margin entire, rolled under; petiole up to 1,5 cm long. Stipules small, ovate to lanceolate, inconspicuous, falling early. **Flowers:** white, about 10 mm long, with the throat of the tube bearded, almost without stalks, in tight axillary clusters of 2 to 4. Bisexual; floral parts in threes to sixes; calyx almost spherical to oblong, 3- to 6-lobed; corolla bell-shaped to funnel-shaped, the throat bearded, 4- to 6-lobed; stamens 4 to 6, attached in the throat (September to February). **Fruit:** spherical, 4 mm in diameter, 3- to 4-lobed, blue when mature, crowned with the remains of the persistent calyx lobes (November to May).

COMPOSITAE *(The daisy and thistle family)*

Key to the tree genera:

1 Fruits succulent and berry-like .... **7. Chrysanthemoides**

  Fruits small nutlets, seed-like 2

2 Flowers in daisy-like heads with ray florets round the margin of the broad, flattened receptacle, or in large, flat, discoid heads, lacking the ray florets, but with conspicuous bracts round, and just below, the margin 3

  Flowers thistle-like, rather narrow, to conical 4

3 In Namaqualand and South West Africa only .... **8. Didelta**

  In Albany district of the Cape only .... **9. Oldenburgia**

  In eastern Rhodesia, adjacent Moçambique and northwards .... **6. Crassocephalum**

4 Stems and leaves rather fleshy .... **4. Lopholaena**

  Stems brittle, woody to semi-woody, leaves not fleshy 5

5 Leaves small, needle-like, ericoid, about 10 mm long .... **5. Metalasia**

  Leaves not small and needle-like 6

901

6 Fruits woolly .... **3. Tarchonanthus**

   Fruits not woolly 7

7 Florets unisexual, plants dioecious; i.e. sexes separate on different trees ..... **2. Brachylaena**

   Florets bisexual; heads with all the florets of the same kind .... **1. Vernonia**

1. VERNONIA Schreber

Herbs, shrubs, climbers or small trees, woody to semi-woody. **Leaves:** alternate, simple. **Flowerheads:** 4- to 40-flowered, solitary, on a long peduncle, or a corymb, or spike, occasionally branched; florets bisexual with all the flowers in the head the same; corolla tube cylindric or tubular; stamens narrow; ovary 1-chambered. **Fruit:** a small, seed-like nutlet, with a conspicuous tuft of hairs, or pappus.

Key to the tree species of *Vernonia:*

1 Leaves less than 2,5 cm long, grey-green, in clusters on dwarf lateral knobby branches ....
   .... **V. cinerascens**
   Leaves more than 2,5 cm long, green, not in clusters 2
2 Leaf margins with pronounced, irregular jagged teeth 3
   Leaf margins entire or finely and obscurely toothed 4
3 Flowers in small spherical heads with a papery appearance, the bracts conspicuous, up to 2 cm
   long, white with pinkish to purple tips .... **V. leucocalyx**
   Flowers in large branched heads, axillary and terminal, the whole inflorescence being 30 to 60 cm
   in diameter; bracts not conspicuous .... **V. stipulacea**
4 Leaves rather small, usually up to 7 × 3,2 cm, the under surface with dense silvery-white matted
   hairs .... **V. bellinghamii**
   Leaves usually larger than 7 × 3,2 cm, the under surface not silvery-white, although frequently
   markedly paler than the upper surface 5
5 Upper surface of the leaves either without hairs or with very sparse hairs, with fine soft hairs below
   and conspicuous net-veining; petiole very short, rarely reaching 1 to 2 cm long; flowers
   creamy-white, sometimes slightly touched with mauve; fruits with minute hairs on the body in
   addition to the pappus .... **V. amygdalina**
   Upper surface of the leaves rather harshly hairy, with dense woolly hairs below rather obscuring the
   net-veining; petiole up to 3 cm long; flowers mauve when young, fading to dull white; fruit with
   a pappus only, the body without hairs .... **V. colorata**

Vernonia amygdalina Delile   Illust. 306
[*V. randii* S. Moore]
S.A. no: 723,3   Tree vernonia. Rivierbloutee
Rhod. no: 1145   Tree vernonia

A bushy shrub or small but well-formed tree up to 7 m in height; occurring from sea level to about 1 700 m, in open woodland, riverine fringes and often associated with termite mounds. **Bark:** light grey or brown, rather rough and longitudinally flaking; branches brittle. **Leaves:** lanceolate to oblong, up to 28 × 10 cm, but usually about 10 to 15 × 4 to 5 cm, leathery, medium to darkish green, with or without very sparse hairs above, with fine soft pale hairs below and conspicuous net-veining; apex and base tapering, base always almost symmetric; margin entire or very finely toothed; petiole usually very short but may be 1 to 2 cm long. **Flowerheads:** thistle-like, small, creamy-white, sometimes slightly touched with mauve, about 10 mm long, grouped in dense heads, axillary and terminal, together forming large flat clusters about 15 cm in diameter but not conspicuous; sweetly scented especially in the evening (May to September). **Fruit:** a small nutlet, with minute glands and hairs on the body and a long tuft of bristly hairs at the top (June to November).

A cold infusion of the root bark, with the inclusion of other plants, is given in daily half-litre doses to treat bilharzia. The bark and root are taken as a tonic by people suffering from fevers; 'chew sticks' from the roots and twigs are regarded as an appetizer as well as a tonic while the leaf, although rather bitter to taste, is eaten as a vegetable.

Vernonia bellinghamii S. Moore
S.A. no: —
Rhod. no: 1146   Rock tree vernonia

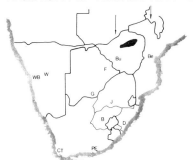 

A shrub or occasionally a small tree up to 4 m in height; occurring on rocky outcrops and stony slopes. **Bark:** dark grey, rough. **Leaves:** ovate to elliptic, up to 7 × 3,2 cm but usually smaller; upper surface densely covered with silvery-grey to white cottony hairs; apex and base tapering to rounded; margin finely toothed; petiole up to 5 mm long. **Flowerheads:** thistle-like, white, occasionally slightly mauve, in small capitula, gathered into dense terminal clusters, 2 to 7 cm in diameter (May to September). **Fruit:** a small nutlet, without hairs except for an apical tuft of long bristles (July to October).

Vernonia cinerascens Schultz Bip.
S.A. no: Small-leaved tree vernonia
Rhod. no: 1149   Small-leaved tree vernonia

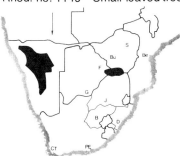 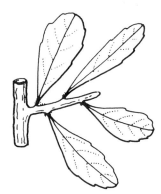

Usually a shrub, or small shrub, but may reach tree proportions up to about 3 m in height; occurring at low altitudes in hot dry woodland. **Bark:** grey; branchlets covered with pale soft hairs. **Leaves:** clustered on dwarf side shoots, ovate, 2,5 cm long or less, grey-green, covered with fine soft pale hairs; apex rounded; base narrowly tapering; margin entire, or very finely toothed; petiole absent. **Flowerheads:** thistle-like, individual flowers purple or deep claret, grouped in small dense heads, in short branched terminal sprays (January to February). **Fruit:** a very small nutlet, conspicuously ridged, tufted with an apical tuft of hairs, or pappus (February to April).

903

COMPOSITAE

Vernonia colorata (Willd.) Drake
S.A. no: 723,4   Lowveld tree vernonia. Laeveldbloutee
Rhod. no: 1150   Star-flowered tree vernonia

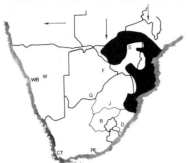

An erect shrub or small tree up to 5 m in height; occurring at low altitudes in open woodland, at the base of koppies, along stream banks, in riverine fringes, and often at the edges of vleis or pans. **Bark:** pale brown, rather rough when old; smaller branches green and dotted with lenticels. **Leaves:** ovate-elliptic, up to 13 × 6,5 cm, dark green, rather harshly hairy above, paler green and covered with long dense woolly hairs below; net-veining obscure; apex tapering; base tapering to rounded; margin entire, or very finely toothed, markedly wavy; petiole up to 3 cm long. **Flowerheads:** thistle-like, individual flowers about 10 mm long, urn-shaped, mauve when young but fading to white or off-white, grouped in small dense heads about 1,5 cm in diameter, rather star-shaped, all joining to form a wide branched panicle. The colour soon fades and the corollas fall, bristly hairs on the fruits rapidly develop and remain conspicuous for a long time, protruding from the involucral bracts (April to June). **Fruit:** a small nutlet, 2 to 3 mm long, slightly ridged, with very small glands, no hairs on the body, but a conspicuous pappus (May to September).
The bark is said to be very bitter. The roots are thought to contain an alkaloid and are used as a tonic, to treat fevers and as a cough remedy. These trees are sometimes grown in gardens where they are attractive, but they are tender to frost.

Vernonia leucocalyx O. Hoffm.   Illust. 308
S.A. no: —
Rhod. no: 1148   Long-flowering tree vernonia

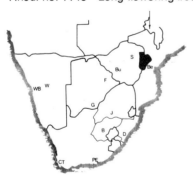

A shrub or small tree up to 4 m in height; occurring in high rainfall areas, at the margins of evergreen forest, along stream banks and in thickets. **Bark:** dark grey, smooth. **Leaves:** ovate to elliptic, up to 17 × 5,5 cm but usually considerably smaller; upper surface puckered and with scattered hairs, and the lower surface with soft hairs; veins and net-veining distinct; apex tapering; base tapering and running into the petiole, or rounded; margin jaggedly and irregularly toothed; petiole obscured by the decurrent leaf-base, or up to 10 mm long. **Flowerheads:** thistle-like, attractive, the bracts up to 2 cm long, white with pink to purple tips, the florets themselves white, mauve or purple, forming almost spherical heads having a rather papery appearance (the plants flower abundantly at most times of the year). **Fruit:** a small brown nutlet, about 3 mm long, with an apical tuft of bristly hairs about 1,3 cm long (at most times of the year).

Vernonia stipulacea Klatt   Illust. 310
[*V. ampla* O. Hoffm.]
S.A. no: 723,2   Poison tree vernonia. Bosbloutee
Rhod. no: 1154   Poison tree vernonia

Usually a lax shrub but may be a small tree up to 8 to 10 m in height; common at the margins of evergreen forest, in open mountain grassland, but also on drier hillsides, often along steam banks and in shady moist places. **Bark:** grey-green, rather smooth becoming roughish with age. **Leaves:** oblong-elliptic, up to 15 × 4 to 10 cm, some reaching 30 × 13 cm in evergreen forest; upper surface roughly hairy when young, losing most of these by maturity, the under surface densely covered with pale green hairs; net-veining is conspicuous; apex tapering; base narrowly rounded and usually markedly asymmetric; margin irregularly and jaggedly toothed, occasionally obscurely so; petiole up to 3 cm long. **Flowerheads:** thistle-like, with individual flowers about 1 to 1,5 cm long, faintly scented, lavender-blue to mauve when young aging to white, with inconspicuous involucral bracts, grouped into small heads on branched stalks, axillary and terminal, all these together forming a large inflorescence, 30 to 60 cm in diameter (August to October). **Fruit:** a small nutlet, 2 to 3 mm long, with a bristly pappus at one end (August onwards).

The leaves are said to be toxic to stock.

2. BRACHYLAENA R. Br.

Shrubs or trees. **Leaves:** alternate, simple. Stipules absent. **Flowers:** in small heads, or capitula, arranged in axillary and terminal sprays, or racemes or panicles. Sexes separate on different trees. Male capitula 1- to 19-flowered; involucre almost spherical, ovoid to oblong, the bracts in 3 to 7 rows; the receptacle slightly convex, honeycombed; the corolla tube cylindric, usually 5-lobed; anthers slender; ovary usually absent, with a pappus of scabrid bristles in one row. Female capitula 1- to 10-flowered; the involucre ovoid or almost so, the bracts in 5 to 9 rows; the receptacle flat, honeycombed; corolla tube cylindric, 5-lobed; 5 staminodes occasionally present; ovary ovoid to oblong, ribbed, hairy or glandular, 1-chambered, with a pappus of scabrid bristles in one row. **Fruit:** a small nutlet, with an apical pappus.

Key to the tree species of *Brachylaena:*
1 Mature leaves without hairs on the under surface (one species occasionally with rusty hairs) 2
  Mature leaves with white or grey, often woolly hairs on the under surface 3
2 Leaves usually slender, 0,5 to 1,8 cm wide .... **B. neriifolia**
  Leaves 1,5 to 5 cm wide .... **B. glabra**
3 Flowers in 1- to 4-flowered heads .... **B. uniflora**
  Flowers in 5- to 50-flowered heads 4
4 Leaf apex with a distinct hair-like tip 5
  Leaf apex without a hair-like tip 6
5 Involucral bracts (i.e. below the flowerhead) densely covered with white woolly hairs ....
  .... **B. huillensis**
  Involucral bracts without white woolly hairs .... **B. ilicifolia**
6 Flowerheads usually less than 10 mm long .... **B. elliptica**
  Flowerheads usually 10 mm or more long (except in *B. discolor* subsp. *transvaalensis*) 7

7 Involucral bracts (i.e. below the flowerhead) in 6 to 7 rows; leaves deciduous, or partially so
.... **B. rotundata**

Involucral bracts in 4 to 10 rows; leaves evergreen .... **B. discolor**

Brachylaena discolor DC.

[*B. transvaalensis* Phillips & Schweick.]
S.A. no: 724 and 731   Wild silver oak. Wildevaalbos
Rhod. no: —

A shrub or small tree usually 4 to 10 m in height, but subsp. *transvaalensis* may reach 30 m; occurring in coastal woodland and bush, littoral scrub and at the margins of evergreen forest. **Bark:** dark grey to brownish-grey, rough. **Leaves:** evergreen, lanceolate to elliptic, up to 11,5 × 4 cm, but usually about 7,5 × 3,5 cm, leathery, dark green above, pale whitish with dense hairs below; apex tapering to almost rounded; base narrowly tapering and running into the petiole; margin almost entire or obscurely to irregularly and jaggedly toothed; petiole 1 to 2 cm long. **Flowerheads:** thistle-form, individual flowers creamy-white, grouped in 7- to 50-flowered heads about 10 × 5 mm, although only 5 × 2 mm in subsp. *transvaalensis,* the heads grouped together giving large terminal panicles; involucral bracts in 4 to 10 rows (July to September). **Fruit:** a small nutlet, with a bristly creamy-brown pappus (August onwards).

This species has been divided into two subspecies and a number of varieties:

Shrub or tree up to 10 m in height; involucral bracts in 5 to 10 rows extending down the stalk ...
.... subsp. *discolor*

A shrub or small tree up to 6 m in height; female involucre 10 to 13 × 6 to 9 mm, bracts up to 7,5 mm long, often woolly, in 7 to 10 rows; male involucre obconic, 5 to 7,5 × 3,5 to 5 mm, bracts in 6 to 8 rows (rarely 9) .... var. *discolor*

A shrub or tree, 3 to 9 m in height; female involucre 5 to 8 × 4 to 6 mm, bracts up to 6 mm long, often woolly, in 6 to 7 rows; male involucre obconic-spherical, 3,5 to 5 × 3 to 3,5 mm, bracts in 5 to 6 rows .... var. *mossambicensis* J. Paiva

A medium to tall tree, 6 to 30 m in height; involucral bracts in 4 to 6 rows, not extending down the stalk .... subsp. *transvaalensis* (Phillips & Schweick.) J. Paiva

These would make good garden subjects, being attractive, hardy and fast growing. The wood provides a useful general-purpose timber.

Brachylaena elliptica (Thunb.) Less.

S.A. no: 725   Bitter-leaf. Bitterblaar
Rhod. no: —

A shrub or small tree up to 4 m in height; occurring in coastal scrub and semi-karroid areas, sometimes at the margins of evergreen forest. **Bark:** light grey to brown becoming rough with age; young branches grooved, with very fine hairs. **Leaves:** lanceolate, elliptic to ovate, 2 to 10 × 0,5 to 3 cm, dark green above, with or without very sparse hairs, the under surface with white felted hairs and prominent veins; apex very broadly tapering to rounded; base narrowly tapering and running into the

906

petiole; margin usually irregularly toothed, often with 2 lobes near the apex giving the end of the leaf a 3-lobed effect; petiole either obscured by the decurrent leaf base or up to 5 mm long. **Flowerheads:** thistle-like, individual flowers creamy-white, small, grouped together forming small capitula less than 10 mm long, in terminal and axillary branched heads (September to October). **Fruit:** a small nutlet with a pappus only 4 mm long (September onwards).

The bitter leaves which are sometimes browsed on by stock, are regarded by the Xhosa and Zulu as a treatment for diabetes, and an infusion of them provides a gargle and mouthwash. The poles are suitable for fencing posts, and sticks were used in the past to make fire by friction.

Brachylaena glabra (L.f.) Druce
S.A. no: 726   Malbaar. Malbaar
Rhod. no: —

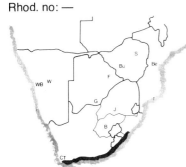

A medium sized tree up to 18 m in height; occurring mainly at the margins of coastal evergreen forest. **Bark:** pale greyish to brownish. **Leaves:** lanceolate to obovate, 3 to 14 × 1,5 to 5 cm, yellowish-green, aromatic; the young leaves covered with rusty hairs but these are lost by maturity; apex broadly tapering to rounded; base tapering; margin entire, or sinuate and toothed, occasionally lobed near the apex; petiole 1 to 2 cm long. **Flowerheads:** thistle-like, individual flowers whitish, grouped together in dense male heads, the female capitula being few-flowered, together forming branched panicles up to 13 cm in diameter, terminal or axillary (April). **Fruit:** a small nutlet, the pappus whitish (May onwards).

Brachylaena huillensis O. Hoffm.
S.A. no: 727   Lowveld silver oak. Laeveldvaalbos
Rhod. no: 1160   Lowveld brachyleana

A small tree usually 3 to 5 m in height, occasionally reaching 8 m; occurring in dry arid areas, in dense scrub, on rocky koppies and stony hillsides. **Bark:** dark grey and rather finely fissured, becoming roughly longitudinally furrowed with age. **Leaves:** obovate to broadly elliptic, 5 to 7 × 2 to 2,5 cm, green, sparsely hairy above, with pale whitish long hairs below; the young leaves covered with dense creamy hairs; apex broadly tapering with a sharp hair-like tip; base tapering; margin entire, rolled under, or obscurely toothed to almost jaggedly toothed; petiole about 1 to 1,5 cm long. **Flowerheads:** thistle-like, individual flowers white, grouped together in 7- to 50-flowered capitula about 10 × 5 mm, the involucral bracts densely covered with white woolly hairs, together forming dense

907

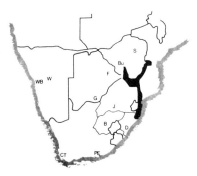

branched terminal heads (October to December). **Fruit:** a slender nutlet, 3 to 5 mm long with a creamy pappus about 6 mm long (October onwards).

Brachylaena ilicifolia (Lam.) Phillips & Schweick.
S.A. no: 728   Small bitter-leaf. Fynbitterblaar
Rhod. no: —

A shrub or small tree, 3 to 4 m in height; occurring in bush, scrub forest and on rocky hillsides. **Bark:** grey to brown. **Leaves:** often on short lateral branches, small, narrowly oblong, lanceolate to ovate, 1 to 4,5 × 0,2 to 1 cm, green and without hairs above, with pale whitish-green hairs below; the young leaves covered with whitish soft hairs; apex rounded with a sharp spine-like tip; base rounded to broadly tapering; margin entire or with very small teeth; petiole about 2 mm long. **Flowerheads:** thistle-like, individual flowers creamy to yellowish, grouped into small 7- to 50-flowered capitula, only a few of which form small branched axillary heads, inconspicuous, rather lost among the leaves; involucral bracts without white hairs. **Fruit:** a small nutlet, with a whitish pappus about 5 mm long. The leaves, which are said to be intensely bitter, are used by Africans to treat diabetes.

Brachylaena neriifolia (L.f.) R. Br.   Illust. 309
S.A. no: 729   Kloof brachyleana. Waterwitels
Rhod. no: —

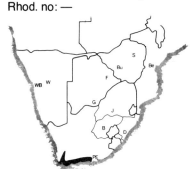

A shrub or small tree up to 6 m in height; occurring along stream banks and in moist mountain forest.
908   **Bark:** dark grey-brown, vertically fissured. **Leaves:** lanceolate, 2 to 11 × 0,5 to 1,8 cm, leathery,

without hairs, resembling those of *Nerium oleander* (the specific name refers to this); the under surface sometimes with rusty hairs; apex tapering; base tapering and running into the petiole; margin entire, rolled under, occasionally with a few small teeth mainly over the upper half; petiole about 1 cm long but largely obscured by the decurrent leaf base. **Flowerheads:** thistle-like, individual flowers whitish fading to brown, grouped together in small capitula, together forming dense axillary and terminal pyramidal heads up to 7 cm long; the stalks covered with rusty brown hairs (December to February). **Fruit:** a small nutlet, the pappus cream, up to 5 mm long (December onwards).

Brachylaena rotundata S. Moore   Illust. 311
[*B. rhodesiana* S. Moore]
S.A. no: 730   Mountain silver oak. Bergvaalbos
Rhod. no: 1161   Yellow brachyleana

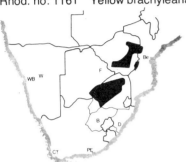

A shrub or small tree, 3 to 8 m in height, often with slender rather drooping branches; occurring in open woodland, frequently among boulders, on rocky koppies and also in riverine fringes. **Bark:** dark brown-grey, longitudinally fissured; young branches grooved and densely covered with white hairs. **Leaves:** at least partially deciduous, elliptic, 2,5 to 10 × 1 to 5,5 cm, with upper surface greyish-green and almost without hairs when mature, and the under surface with paler green to whitish hairs; the young leaves densely covered with pale white hairs; apex broadly tapering; base tapering to almost rounded, sometimes asymmetric; margin roughly and irregularly toothed, sometimes obscurely so; petiole up to 10 mm long. **Flowerheads:** thistle-like, individual flowers rather drab yellow, grouped together in 7- to 50-flowered capitula, about 10 mm long, together forming dense terminal panicles up to 15 cm long, often produced before the leaves; involucral bracts in 6 to 7 rows (August to September). **Fruit:** a small nutlet with a tawny pappus about 5 mm long (August onwards).

Brachylaena uniflora Harvey
S.A. no: 732   Natal silver oak. Natalvaalbos
Rhod. no: —

A small to medium sized tree, 7 to 15 m in height, sometimes larger; occurring in coastal and inland evergreen forest. **Bark:** greyish-brown, vertically fissured. **Leaves:** elliptic to narrowly obovate, 6 to 12 × 1,5 to 4 cm, dark green, without hairs above, with creamy-white hairs below; apex rounded, often abruptly and narrowly attenuate; base tapering; margin entire or finely scalloped to toothed over the upper half; petiole up to 2 cm long. **Flowerheads:** thistle-like, individual flowers whitish, grouped together in inconspicuous 1- to 4-flowered capitula, together forming short axillary panicles **909**

COMPOSITAE

about 7 cm long, rather lost among the leaves (July to August). **Fruit:** a nutlet with an unusually short creamy pappus, up to 3 mm long (July onwards).

3. TARCHONANTHUS L.

Shrubs or trees. **Leaves:** alternate, simple. **Flowerheads:** small, in terminal and/or axillary panicles, the whole inflorescence normally covered with rather long hairs. Sexes separate on different trees; male capitulum several-flowered; the involucre broadly bell-shaped, bracts 5 to 6 in 1 row; receptacle rather convex, honeycombed, usually covered with long silky hairs; corolla tube cylindric, hairy, may be glandular, 5-lobed; anthers slender, with narrow appendages; ovary absent. Female capitulum 1- to 3-flowered; the involucre almost spherical, bracts in 2 rows; receptacle flat; corolla tube short, silky, 4- to 5-lobed; stamens absent; ovary ovoid, silky. **Fruit:** a small nutlet, without a pappus.

Key to the tree species of *Tarchonanthus:*
Leaf apex tapering to narrowly rounded, upper surface glandular but not conspicuously puckered, petiole 1 to 7 mm long; female flowerheads 3- to 5-flowered .... **T. camphoratus**
Leaf apex usually conspicuously 3-lobed, occasionally 5- to 8-toothed, rarely rounded, upper surface without glands but markedly puckered, petiole more than 1,5 cm long; female flowerheads 1-flowered .... **T. trilobus**

Tarchonanthus camphoratus L.   Illust. 312
[*T. minor* Less.]
S.A. no: 733   Camphor bush. Kanferbos
Rhod. no: 1162   Wild camphor bush

A shrub or small tree up to 9 m in height; over its great range this species has adapted to a wide variety of habitats, from sea level to about 1 600 m, from coastal dunes and dune scrub to the fringes of mountain forest, in karroid scrub and semi-desert. **Bark:** brownish-grey, rough; all parts have a strong smell of camphor. **Leaves:** narrowly oblong to elliptic, 1,3 to 15 × 0,8 to 4 cm, but usually about 1,5 to 5 × 0,5 to 1,5 cm, leathery, green to grey-green above, pale greyish-white and velvety below, fine net-veining is visible on both surfaces, the upper surface velvety when young but losing most of these hairs by maturity, glandular; apex tapering to narrowly rounded; base tapering; margin entire to finely toothed; petiole 1 to 7 mm long. **Flowerheads:** thistle-form, individual flowers creamy-white, grouped into 3- to 5-flowered capitula, about 0,8 to 1,2 cm long, in terminal leafy branched sprays up to 9 × 5 cm, more or less covered with white woolly hairs (April to June, but sporadically throughout the year depending upon the locality and conditions). **Fruit:** a small nutlet, covered with white woolly hairs, the heads resembling balls of cotton wool, about 12 × 9 cm (June to September, but may be at almost any time in the year).

The wood is greyish-brown, close-grained, hard and heavy; it polishes well and has been used for musical instruments, cabinet work, fancy articles and boat-building; the poles make very durable fence posts. Splinters are poisonous, causing septic sores which are difficult to heal. It provides good fuel, burning even when green and Zulu women use the leaves to perfume their hair. The seed germinates easily and the species makes an attractive garden tree which is becoming increasingly popular.

Tarchonanthus trilobus DC.   Illust. 313
[*T. galpinii* Hutch. & Phillips; *T. camphoratus* var. *litakunensis* (DC.) Harvey]
S.A. no: 734 and 736   Camphor tree. Kanferboom
Rhod. no: 1163   Broad-leaved wild camphor bush

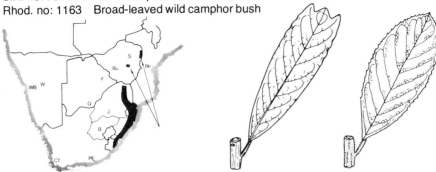

A shrub or small tree up to 8 m in height, occasionally reaching 10 m; occurring in wooded ravines, on hillsides and at the margins of evergreen forest. **Bark:** grey to dark grey, vertically fissured and cracked, flaking in narrow pieces; branchlets with well marked leaf scars. **Leaves:** obovate or narrowly so to oblong-elliptic, 7,5 to 20 × 2 to 9 cm the upper surface dark green to olive green, puckered by the depressed net-veining which is prominent on the under surface but rather obscured by the dense pale creamy-grey hairs; strongly aromatic; apex usually markedly 3-lobed, sometimes 5- to 8-toothed, or rounded to broadly tapering; base tapering; margin entire or toothed, crisped and crinkly; petiole stout, 1,5 to 3 cm long; the petiole and young leaves covered with dense creamy woolly hairs which partially wear away later. **Flowerheads:** thistle-form, individual flowers pale yellowish to cream, the male in small spreading capitula, together forming usually axillary woolly panicles, about 5 to 10 cm long; female flower heads 1-flowered, which is unusual in this family (August to February). **Fruit:** a thinly woolly nutlet, about 5 mm in diameter including the wool, in fluffy heads about 12 × 7 cm (January to October).

The typical variety, var. *trilobus,* has the conspicuous 3-lobed leaf apex and its distribution is more southerly, reaching approximately south and central Natal; var. *galpinii* (Hutch. & Phillips) J. Paiva, has the leaf apex rounded to broadly tapering and its distribution is more northerly, approximately from Zululand to Rhodesia. The wood is brown with yellow graining, hard, durable and aromatic. This would make a good garden subject.

4. LOPHOLAENA DC.

Lopholaena platyphylla Benth.
S.A. no: 736,1   Lopholaena. Breëblaarpluisiesbos
Rhod. no: —

A low-growing semi-woody shrub, 1 to 2 m in height, or a small tree up to 3 m, with rather soft succulent stems; occurring on grassy hillsides. **Leaves:** alternate, simple, broadly elliptic to broadly obovate, 6 to 12 × 3 to 7 cm, rather fleshy; apex rounded; base tapering and running into the petiole; margin entire; petiole thickset and obscured by the decurrent leaf base. **Flowerheads:** thistle-like, individual flowers whitish, the involucre bell-shaped with strap-like bracts in one row at the base of   **911**

a compact capitulum, and subtended by 2 large leaf-like structures. Bisexual; all individual flowers similar in structure, and fertile; receptacle flat, honeycombed; corolla tube cylindric at the base, spreading to bell-shaped near the mouth, 5-lobed; anthers slender; ovary ovoid; capitula solitary, terminal or axillary (May to July). **Fruit:** a small nutlet, grooved, with an apical tuft of silky hairs (with, or just after, the flowers).

5. METALASIA R. Br.

Metalasia muricata (L.) Less.
[*Gnaphalium muricatum* L.]
S.A. no: 736,4   White bristle bush. Witsteekbos
Rhod. no: —

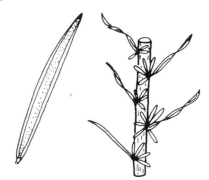

A shrublet, shrub, or occasionally a small tree up to 4 m in height; occurring from coastal dunes to mountain forest, often along streams and in thicket. **Bark:** whitish to pale grey, rather smooth; the branchlets slender, growing vertically. **Leaves:** alternate to scattered, simple, tightly clustered along the branches, ericoid, narrow, rolled under to become needle-like and sharp-tipped, up to 10 × 1 to 2 mm, grey-green, almost without hairs or covered with woolly white hairs; petiole absent. **Flowerheads:** individual flowers white, pink, red or purple, honey-scented; with white involucral bracts, grouped into small capitula about 10 mm long, together forming terminal branched heads, or cymes, 4 to 6 cm in diameter. Bisexual or sterile; involucre narrowly bell-shaped with bracts in 4 to 6 rows; receptacle bare; corolla tube cylindric to rather bell-shaped, 5-lobed; anthers narrow; ovary oblong, ribbed (at most times of the year depending upon the locality). **Fruit:** a small ribbed nutlet, with a pappus of scabrid bristles equalling the corolla tube in length (with or shortly after the flowers). These plants have proved valuable in consolidating sand dunes. They are browsed on by stock in times of food shortage and the dried leaves are reputed to make a good tea.

6. CRASSOCEPHALUM Moench

Crassocephalum mannii (J. D. Hook.) Milne-Redh.
S.A. no: —
Rhod. no: 1171   Canary-creeper tree

A shrub or a lax much-branched, soft-wooded tree up to 7 m in height; occurring at high altitudes on rocky hillsides, in thicket and at the margins of evergreen forest. **Bark:** green to grey-green;

branchlets marked with very conspicuous pale leaf scars. **Leaves:** crowded at the ends of the branches, simple, oblong-elliptic, up to 40 × 12 cm, but usually about 15 to 20 × 3,5 cm, light green, finely velvety; apex and base tapering; margin irregularly and jaggedly toothed; petiole broad based, clasping the stem, up to 2 cm long. **Flowerheads:** daisy-like, individual flowers small, yellow, with a powerful and unpleasant scent in the evening; in about 6-flowered capitula, grouped together in large branched terminal heads, or dense panicled cymes, 30 to 60 cm long (September to October). **Fruit:** a small nutlet, with a conspicuous pappus (about May).

7. CHRYSANTHEMOIDES Medik.

Chrysanthemoides monilifera (L.) Norlindh   Illust. 314
[*Osteospermum moniliferum* L.]
S.A. no: 736,2   Bush-tick berry. Bietou
Rhod. no: 1172   Bush-tick berry

A low shrub or small tree, 1 to 6 m in height; occurring in a wide variety of habitats, from coastal dunes, where it is valuable in consolidating the sand, to rocky hillsides and at the margins of evergreen forest. **Bark:** grey mottled with pale grey or white, smooth. **Leaves:** alternate, simple, ovate to broadly lanceolate, 1,5 to 7,5 × 0,5 to 4 cm, rather leathery, greyish-green; the young leaves covered with cobweb-like hairs which are lost at maturity, the mature leaves being glossy; apex tapering to rounded; base narrowly tapering; margin toothed; petiole 5 to 10 mm long, rarely reaching 1,5 cm. **Flowerheads:** daisy-like, bright yellow, up to 4 cm in diameter, solitary or in small axillary or terminal groups. Bisexual or female only, with the marginal ray florets female or sterile each bearing a single yellow petal; involucre bell-shaped, with or without woolly hairs; corolla tube cylindric, the limb, or petal, on the ray florets, up to 4,5 times longer than the tube, with 3 apical teeth; sterile stamens may be present; ovary oblong; pappus absent. Disc-florets with the corolla tube funnel-shaped, glandular, hairy, 5-lobed; anthers narrow; ovary narrow or oblong (May to October). **Fruit:** ovoid to almost spherical, fleshy, about 6 mm in diameter, purple when mature, arranged round the edge of the receptacle, the specific name meaning 'bearing a necklace' (October onwards).
Over its wide range, six fairly distinct geographical races are apparent and each of these has been given subspecific status:

subsp. *monilifera* – in the south-western Cape.

subsp. *pisifera* (L.) Norlindh – from the south-western Cape eastwards to Transkei (Kentani); also from Namaqualand.

subsp. *subcanescens* (DC.) Norlindh – in and bordering the Karoo.

subsp. *rotundata* (DC.) Norlindh – in the coastal belt from Port Elizabeth to Maputo.

subsp. *canescens* (DC.) Norlindh – mainly along the Drakensberg.

subsp. *septentrionalis* Norlindh – at high altitudes in Rhodesia, Moçambique and northwards.

The fleshy fruits, which are most unusual in this family, are eaten by local Africans and an infusion of the leaves is used as an enema to treat fevers. These trees are sometimes planted as hedges and windbreaks. **913**

COMPOSITAE

8. DIDELTA L'Hérit.

Didelta spinosa (L.f.) Ait.
S.A. no: 736,3   Thorny salad bush. Doringslaaibos
Rhod. no: —

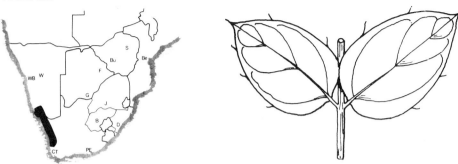

A shrub or dense narrow tree up to 3 m in height; occurring in stony desert areas. **Bark:** pale brown, rough, flaking in longitudinal strips. **Leaves:** opposite, with each pair rising at right angles to the next, simple, broadly elliptic, elliptic to ovate, 2 to 6 × 1,3 to 5 cm, succulent, with or without a dense covering of cobweb-like hairs; net-veining conspicuous on both surfaces; apex broadly tapering to rounded, spine-tipped; base broadly tapering, rounded to lobed, often clasping the stem; margin irregularly toothed, each tooth spine-tipped (the specific name refers to this), occasionally entire; petiole absent. **Flowerheads:** daisy-like, yellow, about 6 cm in diameter, with conspicuous large ovate leaf-like bracts forming a base to the solitary and terminal capitulum. Ray florets sterile, the petalloid limb narrowly oblong, with the apex 4-toothed; disc florets bisexual, with the corolla tube cylindric, widening towards the mouth, with sparse glandular hairs, 5-lobed; anthers narrow; arrow-shaped; ovary cone-shaped, ribbed (August to September). **Fruit:** a small seed-like nutlet, the pappus being a crown of hairy scales (September to October).
The leaves are used in salads and are also heavily grazed on by stock.

9. OLDENBURGIA Less.

Oldenburgia arbuscula DC.
S.A. no: 737   Mountain hunch back. Suurbergse dikblaar
Rhod. no: —

The characteristically gnarled form of Oldenburgia arbuscula.

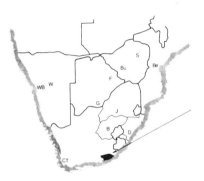 

A bushy shrub or small gnarled tree up to 5 m in height; confined to a small area in mountainous places, always on hard sandstone outcrops. **Bark:** dark, thick, corky. **Leaves:** large, in rosettes at the ends of the branches, simple, oblong to ovate, up to 33 × 15 cm, very stiff and leathery, dark glossy green at maturity; at first all parts covered with pale creamy woolly hairs which persist on the under surface; apex broadly tapering to rounded; base tapering; margin entire, rather widely rolled under; petiole absent. **Flowerheads:** individual flowers, purple, in large flat heads, 10 to 13 cm in diameter; the involucral bracts and stalk below the flowerhead white and woolly, the stalk very thickset and short; the flowerheads solitary and terminal. Involucre almost spherical, with the bracts in several rows, densely woolly, the upper row giving a rather petal-like effect; marginal florets 2-lipped without a petalloid limb, narrow, bisexual; disc-florets female only, with sterile anthers (sporadic throughout the year). **Fruit:** a small brown nutlet, with a pappus formed from one row of stiff bristles (sporadically throughout the year).

The leaves, resembling those of the loquat, *Eriobotrya japonica* Lindl. are said to be poisonous. This attractive and interesting small tree is cultivated occasionally, but the seed is difficult to germinate.

915

Glossary

A. LEAVES

Simple leaves

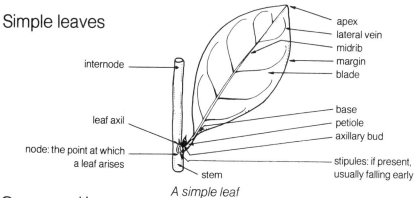

- apex
- lateral vein
- midrib
- margin
- blade

- base
- petiole
- axillary bud

internode

leaf axil

node: the point at which a leaf arises

stipules: if present, usually falling early

stem

A simple leaf

Compound leaves

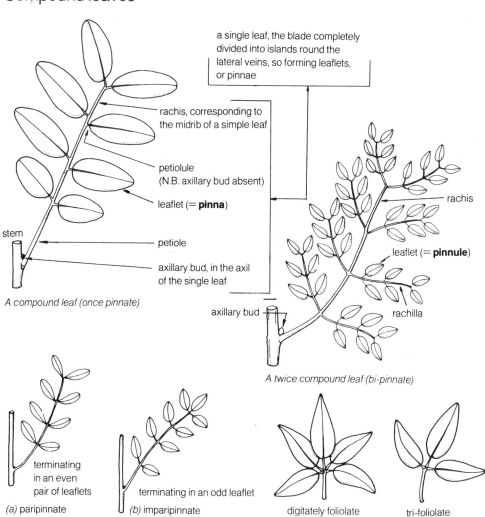

a single leaf, the blade completely divided into islands round the lateral veins, so forming leaflets, or pinnae

rachis, corresponding to the midrib of a simple leaf

petiolule (N.B. axillary bud absent)

leaflet (= **pinna**)

stem

petiole

axillary bud, in the axil of the single leaf

A compound leaf (once pinnate)

rachis

leaflet (= **pinnule**)

axillary bud

rachilla

A twice compound leaf (bi-pinnate)

terminating in an even pair of leaflets

terminating in an odd leaflet

916

(a) paripinnate

(b) imparipinnate

digitately foliolate

tri-foliolate

Arrangements of leaves

(a) alternate

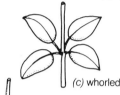

(b) opposite

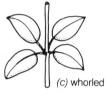

(c) whorled

(d) fascicled or clustered all rising together from almost the same point

Shape of leaves

(a) linear   *(b) lanceolate*

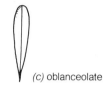

(c) oblanceolate

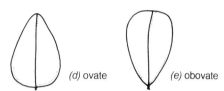

(d) ovate   *(e) obovate*

Apices

 (a) rounded

 (b) notched

 (c) tapering (= acute)

 *(d) attenuate (= acuminate)*

 *(e) square (= truncate)*

 *(f) hair-like tip (= mucronate) or bristle-tipped if hard (= aristate)*

Bases

 (a) rounded

 (b) tapering (= cuneate)

 (c) square (= truncate)

 (d) lobed (= cordate)

 (e) decurrent

 (f) sessile (without a stalk or petiole)

 (g) peltate

  (h) oblique

Margins

 (a) entire

 (b) toothed (= serrate)

 (c) coarsely toothed (= dentate)

 (d) scalloped (= crenate or finely so = crenulate)

 palmately lobed

917

B. FLOWERS

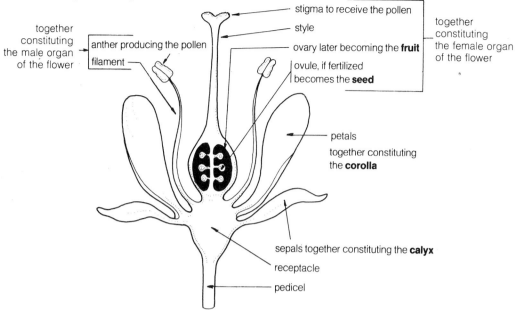

together
constituting
the male organ
of the flower

anther producing the pollen

filament

stigma to receive the pollen

style

ovary later becoming the **fruit**

ovule, if fertilized
becomes the **seed**

together
constituting
the female organ
of the flower

petals

together constituting
the **corolla**

sepals together constituting the **calyx**

receptacle

pedicel

Diagrammatic section through a flower

Inflorescence

A group of flowers together forming a definite structure

Types of inflorescence

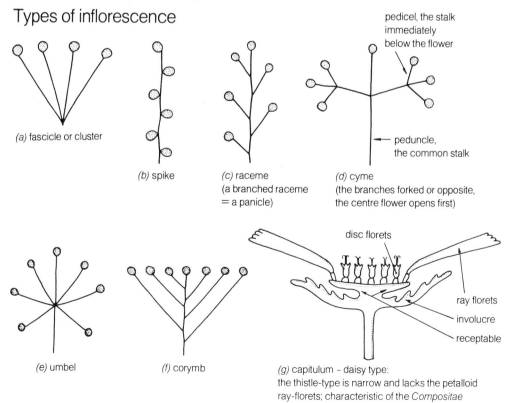

pedicel, the stalk
immediately
below the flower

(a) fascicle or cluster

peduncle,
the common stalk

(b) spike

(c) raceme
(a branched raceme
= a panicle)

(d) cyme
(the branches forked or opposite,
the centre flower opens first)

disc florets

ray florets

involucre

receptable

(e) umbel

(f) corymb

(g) capitulum – daisy type:
the thistle-type is narrow and lacks the petalloid
ray-florets; characteristic of the *Compositae*

Arrangement of flowers

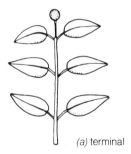

(a) terminal

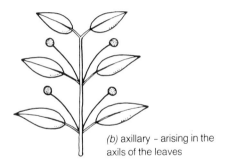

(b) axillary – arising in the axils of the leaves

MISCELLANEOUS TERMS

acarodomatia: small pockets in the leaves, usually in the axils of the veins, which are said to house mites

androphore: a stalk carrying the stamens

gynophore: a stalk carrying the female parts of the flower

androgynophore: a stalk carrying both the stamens and the ovary

aril: an extension, sometimes fleshy, from the placenta at the base of the seed, partially or completely enveloping the seed

arilode: a false aril, actually part of the seed coat and not arising from the placenta, but resembling an aril in appearance

bract: a small often modified leaf associated with the flower or the inflorescence

calycine: as in the genus *Erica* (Ericaceae) which has two forms of flowers; one with the calyx lobes comparatively large and dominating the flower (calycine), the other with the petal lobes (corolla) comparatively large and dominating the flower (corolline)

carpels: one of the sections of an ovary, usually joined together; sometimes the carpels are separate, and one such separate section when developed into the fruit is termed a *mericarp*

ciliate: with hair-like outgrowths

corolline: see under calycine

corymbose: like a corymb, as applied to an inflorescence

cyathium: the peculiar inflorescence found in the genus *Euphorbia* having a cup-shaped involucre with stamens and stalked ovary, each stamen and the ovary being a separate flower

dehiscent: splitting

indehiscent: not splitting

dichasial cyme: a 'double' cyme in which two lateral branches occur at about the same level

dioecious: with the sexes separate in separate flowers on different trees

disc: in the flower, an enlargement of the receptacle, usually ring-, cup- or cushion-shaped, sometimes lobed

dwala: a flat, sloping sheet of granite

fynbos: low-growing, woody scrub characteristic of the Cape; this is a very characteristic community made up of plants mostly small-leaved and drought resistant

gynophore: see under androphore

hispid: with stiff hairs or bristles

hypocotyl: in a plant embryo or very young seedling, that portion of the stem below the first or food leaves, or cotyledons

indehiscent: see under dehiscent

involucre: bracts forming a whorl or whorls and produced at the base of, or below, a very compact, or condensed, flower head

lenticels: corky spots, usually on young bark

medusoid: a head of snake-like structures, or branches

mericarp: see under carpel

mesophyte: plants thriving in a normal temperate climate, avoiding both very wet and very dry conditions

nectary: a gland, usually in flowers, producing nectar

obconic: an inverted cone

oblique: as applied to leaves, when the two sides of the leaf base join the petiole at different levels

pappus: a circle or tuft of bristles or hairs on the apex of a fruit (especially on the small fruits, or nutlets, in Compositae)

pneumatophores: the 'breathing roots' produced by constituents of mangrove swamp forests

pulvinus: a swelling on the petiole just below the blade of a leaf

scabrid: rough to the touch, usually from the presence of fine rough hairs

Scaberulous: finely scabrid

scandent: tending to clamber or climb by means of tendrils

scorpioid: floral branches developing on opposite sides alternately with the flowers strictly 2-ranked, said to resemble a scorpion's tail

staminodes: a sterile or abortive stamen

stipels: two small stipule-like outgrowths from the base of the leaflets of a compound leaf

suffrutex: a shrub, or shrublet, usually producing leafy and flowering shoots each year from a perennial underground woody rootstock

thecae: the pollen-producing bodies in the anther of a stamen

thyrse: a mixed inflorescence with the main axis a raceme and later axes in the form of cymes

whale-backs: great dome-shaped masses of solid granite, forming hills

xerophytes: plants specially adapted to growing under desert conditions or conditions with very little available water

Selected bibliography

JOURNALS CONSULTED
Flora of Southern Africa
Flora of Tropical East Africa
Flora Zambesiaca
Flora of Tropical Africa
Flora of Tropical West Africa
Flora Capensis
Boletim da Sociedade Broteriana
Bothalia
Bulletin du Jardin Botanique de l'Etat, Bruxelles
Kew Bulletin
Kirkia
Journal of the Linnaean Society
Journal of South African Botany
South African Journal of Science
Prodromus einer Flora von Südwestafrika
Rhodesian Agricultural Journal
Flowering Plants of Africa
Flowering Plants of Southern Africa
Trees in South Africa
Rhodesia Science News
Excelsa

BOOKS AND OTHER PUBLICATIONS
ADAMSON, R. S. & SALTER, T. M., *Flora of the Cape Peninsula,* Juta, 1950
BAKER, H. A. & OLIVER, E. G. H., *Ericas in Southern Africa,* Purnell, 1967
BURTT DAVY, J., *A Manual of the Flowering Plants and Ferns of the Transvaal and Swaziland,* 2 Vols., Longmans, Green, 1926 & 1932
COATES PALGRAVE, K., *Trees of Central Africa,* National Publications Trust, 1956
CODD, L. E., *Trees and Shrubs of the Kruger National Park,* Government Printer, Pretoria, 1951
DE WINTER, B., *et al., Sixty-six Trees of the Transvaal,* Botanical Research Institute, Pretoria, 1966
DE WINTER, B. & VAHRMEIJER, J., *The National List of Trees,* van Schaik, 1972
DRUMMOND, R. B. & COATES PALGRAVE, K., *Common Trees of the Highveld,* Longmans, 1973
DYER, R. A., *Genera of Southern African Flowering Plants* – revised Vol. 1, Department of Agricultural and Technical Services, Pretoria, 1975
GILGES, W., *Some African Poisonous Plants and Medicines of Northern Rhodesia,* Occasional Paper No. 11, Rhodes-Livingstone Museum, 1955
HENNESSY, E. F., *South African Erythrinas,* Natal Branch of the Wildlife Protection and Conservation Society of South Africa, 1972
IMMELMAN, W. F. E. *et al., Our Green Heritage,* Tafelberg, 1973
JEPPE, B., *South African Aloes,* Purnell, 1969
LEACH, L. C., various papers in several journals already cited
MOLL, E. J., *Forest Trees of Natal,* Natal Branch of the Wildlife Protection and Conservation Society of South Africa, 1967
PALMER, E. & PITMAN, N., *Trees of Southern Africa,* 3 Vols., Balkema, 1972 & 1973
PHILLIPS, E. P., *Genera of South African Flowering Plants,* Botanical Survey Memoir No. 25, 1951
REYNOLDS, G. W., *The Aloes of South Africa,* Aloes of South Africa Book Fund, 1950
REYNOLDS, G. W., *The Aloes of Tropical Africa and Madagascar,* The Aloes Book Fund, 1966
ROSS, J. H., *Flora of Natal,* Department of Agricultural and Technical Services, Pretoria, 1972
ROSS, J. H., *The Acacia Species of Natal,* Natal Branch of the Wildlife Protection and Conservation Society of South Africa, 1971

ROSS, J. H. & MOLL, E. J., *A List of Natal Trees,* Natal Branch of the Wildlife Protection and Conservation Society of South Africa, 1972

ROURKE, J. P., *Taxonomic Studies on Leucospermum,* Journal of South African Botany, Suppl. Vol. 8, 1972

SIM, T. R., *The Forests and Forest Flora of the Colony of the Cape of Good Hope,* Government of the Cape of Good Hope, 1907

SMITH, C. A., *Common Names of South African Plants,* Botanical Survey Memoir, 1966

SYMON, S. A., *African Medicine in the Mankoya District, Northern Rhodesia,* Rhodes-Livingstone Institute Communication No. 15, 1959

TREE SOCIETY OF SOUTHERN AFRICA, *Trees and Shrubs of the Witwatersrand,* Witwatersrand University Press, 1964

WATT, J. M. & BREYER-BRANDWIJK, M. G., *The Medicinal and Poisonous Plants of Southern and East Africa,* E. & S. Livingstone, 1962

WEST, O., *Field Guide to the Aloes of Rhodesia,* Longmans, 1974

WHITE, DYER & SLOANE, *Succulent Euphorbieae,* 2 Vols., Pasadena, California, 1941

WICHT, H., *The Indigenous Palms of Southern Africa,* Timmins, 1969

WILD, H., *Rhodesian Botanical Dictionary of African and English Plant Names* – revised BIEGEL, H. M. & MAVI, S., Government Printer, Salisbury, 1972

WILLIAMS, I. O. J. M., *A Revision of the Genus Leucodendron,* The Bolus Herbarium, 1972

VAN WYK, P., *Trees of the Kruger National Park,* 2 Vols., Purnell, 1972 & 1974

VON BREITENBACH, F., *Southern Cape Forests and Trees,* Government Printer, Pretoria, 1974

Index

To use this index:
- the main entries are printed in **bold;**
- entries in *italic* refer to synonyms (see page 12);
- all other entries are set in Roman;
- an asterisk * denotes exotics;
- numbers in **bold** refer to the main entries;
- numbers in *italic* refer to the colour illustrations.

923

925

927

933

935

939

943

945

947

953

INDEX